ANALYSIS OF DEVELOPMENT

EDITED BY

BENJAMIN H. WILLIER

Professor of Zoology, Johns Hopkins University, Baltimore, Maryland

PAUL A. WEISS

*Member, Rockefeller Institute for Medical Research, New York, New York;
formerly Professor of Zoology, University of Chicago, Chicago, Illinois*

VIKTOR HAMBURGER

Professor of Zoology, Washington University, St. Louis, Missouri

ILLUSTRATED

W. B. SAUNDERS COMPANY

Philadelphia & London · 1955

CONTRIBUTORS

L. G. BARTH, Ph.D.

Professor of Zoology, Columbia University, New York, New York.

N. J. BERRILL, Ph.D., D.Sc., F.R.S., F.R.S.C.

Strathcona Professor of Zoology, McGill University, Montreal, Quebec.

DIETRICH BODENSTEIN, Ph.D.

Insect Physiologist, Medical Laboratories, Army Medical Center, Maryland.

EDGAR J. BOELL, Ph.D., D.Sc.

Ross Granville Harrison Professor of Experimental Zoology, Yale University, New Haven, Connecticut.

ROBERT KYLE BURNS, Ph.D., D.Sc.

Staff Member, Department of Embryology, Carnegie Institution of Washington; Honorary Professor of Zoology, The Johns Hopkins University, Baltimore, Maryland.

W. M. COPENHAVER, Ph.D.

Professor of Anatomy, College of Physicians and Surgeons, Columbia University, New York, New York.

DONALD P. COSTELLO, Ph.D.

Kenan Professor of Zoology, University of North Carolina, Chapel Hill.

WILLIAM ETKIN, Ph.D.

Associate Professor of Biology, The City College, New York, New York.

GERHARD FANKHAUSER, Ph.D.

Professor of Biology, Princeton University, Princeton, New Jersey.

VIKTOR HAMBURGER, Ph.D.

Professor of Zoology, Washington University, St. Louis, Missouri.

JOHANNES HOLTFRETER, Ph.D.

Professor of Zoology, The University of Rochester, Rochester, New York.

FLORENCE MOOG, Ph.D.

Associate Professor of Zoology, Washington University, St. Louis, Missouri.

J. S. NICHOLAS, Ph.D.

Sterling Professor of Biology, Yale University, New Haven, Connecticut.

JANE M. OPPENHEIMER, Ph.D.

Professor of Biology, Bryn Mawr College, Bryn Mawr, Pennsylvania.

MARY E. RAWLES, Ph.D.

Research Associate (Embryology), Department of Biology, The Johns Hopkins University, Baltimore, Maryland.

HANS RIS, Ph.D.

Professor of Zoology, University of Wisconsin, Madison.

DOROTHEA RUDNICK, Ph.D.

Professor of Biology, Albertus Magnus College, New Haven, Connecticut.

FRANCIS O. SCHMITT, Ph.D., D.Sc.

    Professor of Biology, Massachusetts Institute of Technology, Cambridge.

ISAAC SCHOUR, D.D.S., Ph.D.

    Professor of Histology, University of Illinois, College of Dentistry, Chicago.

H. B. STEINBACH, Ph.D.

    Professor of Zoology, University of Minnesota, Minneapolis.

CURT STERN, Ph.D.

    Professor of Zoology, University of California, Berkeley.

VICTOR C. TWITTY, Ph.D.

    Professor of Biology, Stanford University, Stanford, California.

ALBERT TYLER, Ph.D.

    Professor of Embryology, California Institute of Technology, Pasadena.

RAY L. WATTERSON, Ph.D.

    Associate Professor of Biology, Northwestern University, Evanston, Illinois.

PAUL A. WEISS, Ph.D., M.D. (hon.)

    Member, Rockefeller Institute for Medical Research, New York, New York; formerly Professor of Zoology, University of Chicago.

BENJAMIN H. WILLIER, Ph.D., Sc.D.

    Henry Walters Professor of Zoology, The Johns Hopkins University, Baltimore, Maryland.

C. L. YNTEMA, Ph.D.

    Professor of Anatomy, State University of New York Medical Center at Syracuse.

EDGAR ZWILLING, Ph.D.

    Associate Professor of Animal Genetics, Storrs Agricultural Experiment Station, University of Connecticut, Storrs.

PREFACE

THIS BOOK owes its inception to informal gatherings, seminar fashion, of a small group of embryologists who for several summers (1933–1940) periodically retired from the busy scene of the Marine Biological Laboratory at Woods Hole to the peace and quiet of the sand dunes along the northern coast of Cape Cod near Barnstable. With the sea as background and the sand for a blackboard the "Sandpipers" (a name derived from our alert and ever-searching avian companions on the beach) discussed at length the problems of development and groped for a better understanding of the mechanisms of embryogenesis.

To those who took part in them, these group discussions were a valuable experience. The satisfaction that came from the exchange and conciliation of conflicting views aroused our urgent desire to broaden the experience and share it with a far wider circle of biologists. Jointly the hope was engendered that future accounts of embryological knowledge would emphasize the dynamic and causal aspects of embryogenesis rather than mere description and seriation of developmental stages, a practice still too common in the lecture room and textbook. To transcend descriptive embryology and blend experimental data with "Beobachtung und Reflexion" was clearly set as our goal. Only by such an account could younger students be challenged and influenced in their future research and teaching in this important field. Above all, the need was felt for helping to overcome the trends of overspecialization by encouraging a wider, interdisciplinary perspective and by integrating the ever-growing volume of accumulated information into a broad conceptual framework. The need for a well-balanced account of the developmental process was apparent. But how was such a plan to be translated into action?

It was evident from the start that the subject matter had grown in volume and intricacy to the point where it seemed futile for any one individual to attempt to cope with such a task. The alternative was to call on many specialists for authoritative presentations of their respective subjects. We realized that by this procedure much of the desired unity and integration would be sacrificed, and the present volume bears plainly the stigmata of these imperfections. Yet, despite our hesitations on this score, the three of us, encouraged by the urging of many colleagues, outlined in 1947 a plan for a collaborative work on the analysis of the developmental process.

The original blueprint contained an outline and table of contents of the subject matter to be covered in hierarchical divisions, as well as specifications for their serial order and relative proportions. For this basic pattern the three Editors take full responsibility. Yet, within that general frame, the individual contributors were given no more than a general topical guide that left full scope to their personal preferences in the choice of samples, style, and manner of presentation, the only provision being that they conform to the general spirit and objectives of the undertaking. The guiding aims were expressed to them in the following commentary.

The purpose of this book is to present a modern *synthesis* of our knowledge of the principles and mechanisms of development. In these days of rapidly expanding information, it becomes increasingly difficult to keep perspective. It is urgent, therefore, that this book provide not just another source of information, but that it view the phenomena of development from a common perspective so that the reader may recognize the great main lines and inner coherence of the field above the multiplicity of often unrelated details of which the field seems composed when viewed too closely. There is perhaps need for a comprehensive compilation of all the experimental data that have been amassed in the field of Experimental Embryology in the past. However, this book is *not* intended to fill that need. It is not to be a handbook. It does not aim at a complete and exhaustive review of the field. Each contributor is asked to make a critical and, in a way, subjective selection of the special field to be covered in his article. He should give a clear outline of the general problems, concepts, and lines of investigation of his topic and illustrate them with selected examples from experimental data. Only those experiments should be presented that are crucial and analytically strong and convincing. Repetitiveness should be avoided. Use should be made of tabulations and graphs wherever possible. Since the book addresses itself mainly to active or potential investigators (particularly in the experimental branches of embryology, pathology, histology, endocrinology, and developmental genetics), it would be of value to point out gaps in our knowledge, the lack of critical experimental data in unexplored or controversial fields, and lines of research which would deserve being followed up. In summary, the book has as its major objective the synthesis and evaluation of pertinent material selected from the whole field of animal growth and development, with emphasis upon recognized principles and mechanisms as well as on unsolved and new problems.

With these suggestions we approached twenty-five biologists prominent in the subject areas to be covered in the volume. They readily accepted the invitation to collaborate despite the tribulations and obligations inherent in such undertakings. The Editors are very grateful to all of them not only for their contributions to this book but also for the spirit of cooperation and patience which they exhibited during the years of arduous labor that went into its preparation. As in all concerted creative efforts of this kind, progress in realization was slow and at times faltering. Contrary to the development of an organism, no forces were at work to coordinate the separate creative efforts, and the Editors did not see fit to weld the different contributions into a uniform mold. Each contributor is finally responsible for the organization, scope, and content of his text. The Editors, on the other hand, must bear the responsibility for the plan and the scope of the book, and assume the blame for any defects in its structure.

Whatever its imperfections and limitations, the book represents a first-hand portrayal of present-day views of animal development. As such, we hope it may provide a basis of departure for future endeavors of this kind. The science of embryology, like the embryo, is governed by the principles of progressive differentiation, its present status only a transitory moment between past and future—its full potentialities yet to be realized. It is to the pioneering spirit of those students who hereafter will enter the field of development and growth that this volume is primarily dedicated. In no lesser degree we inscribe these pages to students and investigators in other fields of the biological sciences, including medicine and agriculture, who are constantly confronted with problems of a developmental nature and must deal with them.

The Editors have been fortunate indeed in the cordial relationship which has existed between them and the publishers from the beginning of this undertaking. We are most grateful to them for their unlimited patience, resourcefulness, and splendid cooperation in making a book such as this all that it should be in style and typography.

B. H. Willier
Paul Weiss
Viktor Hamburger

CONTENTS

SECTION VII

SPECIAL VERTEBRATE ORGANOGENESIS 346

Chapter 1. NERVOUS SYSTEM (Neurogenesis) 346

BY PAUL WEISS

Chapter 2. EYE 402

BY VICTOR TWITTY

Chapter 3. EAR AND NOSE 415

BY C. L. YNTEMA

Chapter 4. LIMB AND GIRDLE 429

BY J. S. NICHOLAS

Chapter 5. HEART, BLOOD VESSELS, BLOOD, AND ENTODERMAL DERIVATIVES 440

BY W. M. COPENHAVER

Chaper 6. UROGENITAL SYSTEM 462

BY R. K. BURNS

Chapter 7. TEETH 492

BY ISAAC SCHOUR

Section I

PROBLEMS, CONCEPTS AND THEIR HISTORY

JANE M. OPPENHEIMER*

"Is cell-differentiation inherent or induced?
"A thoughtful and distinguished naturalist tells us that while the differentiation of the cells which arise from the egg is sometimes inherent in the egg, and sometimes induced by the conditions of development, it is more commonly mixed; but may it not be the mind of the embryologist, and not the natural world, that is mixed? Science does not deal in compromises, but in discoveries. When we say the development of the egg is inherent, must we not also say what are the relations with reference to which it is inherent? When we say it is induced, must we not also say what are the relations with reference to which it is induced? Is there any way to find this out except scientific discovery?"

W. K. Brooks ('02, pp. 490–491)

IT IS the self-imposed task of the present compendium to review and evaluate the past and present accomplishments of the science of embryology in order more intelligently to facilitate progress into its future. The separate contributions which make up the main body of the volume must necessarily concentrate on particular fields of investigation. It is the purpose, therefore, of the first two chapters to provide a general background against which these more special subjects may be considered. Out of convenience, rather than from logical necessity, these two chapters will concern themselves first with concepts, and secondly with techniques, though the nature of the scientific method is such that these two aspects of the problem are inextricably interrelated. Arbitrarily, too, the topics chosen for discussion will be selective rather than exhaustive; since it is not possible in a few pages to do justice to even a few of the great contributors of the past, only those have been chosen whose writings are most relevant to the sequel, and

* The writing of Sections I and II was carried out both at the Osborn Zoological Laboratory, Yale University, and at Bryn Mawr College. I owe especial gratitude to the Library of the College of Physicians of Philadelphia for the use of their collections and for generous assistance.

even of these, many can enjoy only the barest mention.

THE EARLY EMBRYOLOGY OF THE GREEKS: ARISTOTLE

Since it was the Greeks who performed the great *tour de force* of freeing science from magic and elevating it into the realms of pure reason, it is sensible to begin by examining a few of their contributions to embryology. They were early to develop an interest in beginnings; their very word for nature ($\phi\acute{u}\sigma\iota\varsigma$, physis) according to some, including Aristotle (*Parts of Animals*, 1945 edition, pp. 74–75), implies growth, genesis or origin ($\phi\acute{u}\epsilon\sigma\theta\alpha\iota$.), and Anaximander, who flourished in the sixth century B.C., spoke of the $\gamma\acute{o}\nu\iota\mu\sigma\nu$, the germ or fetus of the world. They recognized early that change was an essence of existence, as we know from Herakleitos' emphasis on flux, and as is evident from their mythological conception of cosmos evolving from chaos. And from the beginning they compared cosmos to the organism, witness Plato (*Timaeus*, [1944] edition, p. 117):

Its composing artificer constituted it from *all* fire, water, air, and earth; leaving no part of any one of these, nor any power external to the world. For by a reasoning process he concluded that it would thus be a whole animal, in the highest degree perfect from perfect parts.

But more than this, perhaps even because of it, they were able even as early as the time of Anaximander to conceive of the organism as emergent, and indeed of animals as related to man: a fragment concerning the teachings of Anaximander reads that "living creatures arose from the moist element, as it was evaporated by the sun. Man was like another animal, namely, a fish, in the beginning" (Burnet, '30, p. 70).

No attempt can be made here to enumerate the many Greek philosophers to build upon these beginnings, or to evaluate the

1

contributions of those who did. It will have to be sufficient here to name a few, and the interested reader is referred to Balss ('36) for additional details. Suffice it here to comment that theirs was the task of the first early and perhaps random collection of data, which must precede even the primitive classification which many consider to represent the first stage of scientific inquiry.

Of some, we know only from the meager extant fragments, that they recorded what they thought to be observed fact; for instance, from Parmenides a fragment remains implying that males are generated on the right and females on the left. In the case of others, even before Aristotle, it is clear that they believed that around the observed facts they could elaborate theory. Empedokles, for example, believed the fetus to arise partly from male and partly from female semen, the children resembling most the parent who contributed most to the offspring; he spoke of the influence of pictures, statues and so forth in modifying the appearance of the offspring, of twins and triplets as due to "superabundance and division of the semen" (Burnet, '30, p. 244); he knew there was a regular sequence of events in development and spoke of the heart as formed first in development, the nails last, sowing seeds of concepts, which, right or wrong, were destined often to recrudesce in subsequent ages.

A Hippocratic treatise on generation went further in developing theories, formulating an early expression of the doctrine of pangenesis, and, relating to it, what seems to be on *post hoc* reasoning a doctrine of the inheritance of acquired characters. This treatise, before Aristotle, recognized the importance of methodology, and advocated systematic daily observation of chicken eggs: "Take twenty or more eggs and let them be incubated by two or more hens. Then each day from the second to that of hatching remove an egg, break it, and examine it. You will find," continues the writer, illustrating an apparent dependence of concept on method and inferring the great generalization, "exactly as I say, for the nature of the bird can be likened to that of man" (Singer, '22, p. 15).

Aristotle's own accomplishment was none the less impressive, for all he drew on his predecessors and contemporaries. "There was a wealth of natural history before his time; but it belonged to the farmer, the huntsman, and the fisherman—with something over (doubtless) for the schoolboy, the idler and the poet. But Aristotle made it a science,

and won a place for it in Philosophy" (Thompson, '40, p. 47). And in establishing it as scientific, he set its standards higher than hitherto by far.

He followed, in embryology, the method of the Hippocratic writer *On Generation,* to perform and record most of the available observations, many in error but also many correct, thus to constitute a collection of knowledge on the development of the chick which became the foundation on which all embryology was to build; and it has been said, with much justice, of his account that "almost two thousand years were to roll by before it was to be equaled or surpassed" (Adelmann, *ed.,* in Fabricius, 1942 edition, p. 38). He concerned himself not only with the development of the chick but also with the generation of many other forms, and elaborated a kind of classification (though not in the modern sense; cf. Thompson, '40) of animal forms according to their mode of reproduction. By so doing, he both established embryology as an independent science, and he fitted embryological knowledge into a pattern larger than its own, with great clarity of vision and imagination.

On the theoretical side, he followed his predecessors by adopting a modified view of pangenesis, and concurred with them in supporting the doctrine of the inheritance of acquired characters. He broke away from his predecessors, however, in developing a new and erroneous yet highly influential concept of the relative roles of male and female in development, postulating the former as providing the form, at once formal, efficient and final cause, and the latter the substance, the material cause, for the new organism.

By thus undervaluing the egg, he paid embryology the obvious immediate disservice; but in formulating his conception of biological form as inseparable from matter he laid the way open for ultimate progress in biological science. The argument is metaphysical to the taste of the modern scientist; but Aristotle will be found not to be the last embryologist to be so tainted. We concur with his intent, after all, every time we speak of "animal forms" as a euphemism for "animal species." And Aristotle, with the natural historian's innate feeling for natural form, by envisioning form as a part of actuality rather than something above it, brought biological material to be directly investigable by the sense organs.

His theories concerning special developmental phenomena, related to his primary philosophy as they were, are deep in much of the embryological and indeed the wider biological thinking both of the past and the present. His description of the heart as the first organ of the embryo to be formed, both in time and in primacy, tied as it was to the conception of the soul as formal and final cause and of vital heat in the blood as the agent of the soul, dominated the notions not only of the developing but also of the adult circulation, and hence all physiology, through to the nineteenth century and the downfall of the phlogiston theory. His concept of organ as related to final cause epitomizes teleology, and with all the weight of Galen's authority in support still permeates much of the thought of modern biology. Matter with form inseparable from it as opposed to the more material matter postulated by Leucippus' and Democritus' atomic theory, which implied preformation, in a way made possible the whole doctrine of epigenesis, first clearly formulated by Aristotle and still central in all embryological thinking today. Form as inseparable from matter makes possible a conception of pattern emergent, an analogy of development and the *process* of plaiting a net or the *process* of painting a picture; for Plato, the Ideal mesh would have been already woven, the Ideal portrait previously complete. Aristotle (*Generation of Animals*, 1943 edition, pp. 147, 149, 225) could frame the modern question:

How, then, are the other parts formed? Either they are all formed simultaneously—heart, lung, liver, eye, and the rest of them—or successively, as we read in the poems ascribed to Orpheus, where he says that the process by which an animal is formed resembles the plaiting of a net. As for simultaneous formation of the parts, our senses tell us plainly that this does not happen: some of the parts are clearly to be seen present in the embryo while others are not. . . . Since one part, then, comes earlier and another later, is it the case that A fashions B and that it is there on account of B which is next to it, or is it rather the case that B is formed after A? . . .

In the early stages the parts are all traced out in outline; later on they get their various colours and softnesses and hardnesses, for all the world as if a painter were at work on them, the painter being Nature. Painters, as we know, first of all sketch in the figure of the animal in outline, and after that go on to apply the colours.

The metaphor will speak for itself to modern experimental embryologists. Aristotle, however, for all his natural acuity, was strangely double-minded. In his dynamic feeling for form, derived from direct study of living biological material, he was modern, and was to lead eventually straight to the inductive biology of modern times. But his conceptions of the wider Universe, based on pure reason, because statically and structurally interpreted and thus transmitted by medieval commentators, deluded posterity, and it was unfortunately the static Aristotle, the Aristotle of a sterile cosmogony, crystal clear but crystal rigid, who dominated the thought of the Middle Ages. So far as even the embryology was concerned, the Middle Ages transmitted his concepts, and occasionally amplified them, as in the case of Albertus Magnus, but devitalized them and thereby hardly improved them. Appreciation of their dynamic qualities awaited the Renaissance and later ages.

EMBRYOLOGY AND THE RENAISSANCE: FABRICIUS, HARVEY

When the Renaissance came under way it accelerated its course into the new thought by taking strength from the Greek past through all the resources of Humanism; and a "reconstruction of the Greek spirit" (cf. Singer, ['41], p. 166) was an essential part of the rebirth. Even Galileo has been called a "typical Paduan Aristotelian" in method and philosophy at least, if not in physics (Randall, cited by Adelmann, *ed.*, in Fabricius, 1942 edition, p. 55), and Whitehead ('25, p. 17) reminds us that Galileo "owes more to Aristotle than appears on the surface of his *Dialogues:* he owes to him his clear head and his analytic mind." Vesalius' interpretations of his observations were as teleological as those of Galen after which they were modelled (cf. Singer, '44, p. 81, who called him "a disciple of Galen by training, by inclination, and by his whole cast of thought"); his method, however, was also in part that of Aristotle. Copernicus, who was accused by Kepler of interpreting Ptolemy, not nature, at least challenged the Aristotelian cosmogony; Vesalius imitated the method of the Aristotle who is so rarely remembered as having written about an embryological problem (*Generation of Animals*, 1943 edition, pp. 345, 347):

This, then, appears to be the state of affairs . . . so far as theory can take us, supplemented by what are thought to be the facts about their behaviour. But the facts have not been sufficiently ascertained; and if at any future time they are ascertained, then credence must be given to the direct evidence of the senses more than to theories.

The scientist, who customarily characterizes

the Renaissance as a movement for freedom with respect to authority, often neglects to remember that it was in part from "authority" that the inspiration to achieve freedom derived.

It was Fabricius, student of Fallopius, himself a student of Vesalius, who first exhaustively applied the rigorous "new" Vesalian method of direct observation to the study of embryos, though he had many predecessors who had made isolated observations on embryonic material (among them Columbus, Fallopius, Eustachius, Arantius, Aldrovandus, Coiter et al. Cf. Needham, '34, and Adelmann, *ed.*, in Fabricius, 1942 edition, for full discussion; see also Adelmann for full critical treatment of Fabricius himself).

On the observational side, he was the first to publish illustrations based on systematic study of the development of the chick, and this, though he neglected to describe them in detail, was probably his most significant contribution. He made the way easier for the later preformationists by drawing the supposed three and four day chicks much too advanced for their normal chronological age; among his other fallacies, the most notable was his ascription to the chalazae of the role of forming the embryo. Among his improvements to the existing embryological knowledge was his emphasis that the *carina* (whose metaphysics he discussed more completely than its embryological fate) is formed before the heart, controverting Aristotle, and before the liver, taking issue with Galen in both fact and philosophy. He studied the fetal anatomy of various vertebrates, that of many mammals, including man, and presented illustrations of the comparative anatomy of the placenta, showing his special interest in the umbilical and the fetal circulation, though he devoted himself to Galenic principles in his interpretations of these. Even Fabricius, then, as late as the sixteenth century was exemplifying the conflict of the Renaissance between allegiance to authority and confidence in direct personal observations. But though in one sense his position represents an inevitable retreat, even behind the position of Aristotle, in that he emphasized the anatomy of embryos rather than the process of development, yet his work looked forward to the new embryology in the influence it exerted on William Harvey.

Fabricius' name, as Adelmann points out (*op. cit.*, p. 115) begins the first sentence of Harvey's text on generation; and Harvey, too, like his preceptor, looked back to Aristotle in his interpretations, for all that his demonstration of the circulation in method, fact, and conception, was to lead to the whole experimental and analytical biology of the future. Harvey followed Bacon's principle of explaining nature by observation and experiment, and Galileo's of measuring what is measurable and making measurable what is not. Harvey's contemporaries believed, with Fracastorius, that "the motion of the heart was to be understood by God alone" (Harvey, *De motu*, 1931 edition, p. 25). Harvey proved it to be a mechanical function. Yet he could speak of the motion of the blood, after Copernicus, Kepler and Galileo, as "circular in the way that Aristotle says air and rain follow the circular motion of the stars" (*ibid.*, p. 70) and, like a good Aristotelian, he left the vital spirits remaining in the blood. "Whether or not the heart," he wrote, "besides transferring, distributing and giving motion to the blood, adds anything else to it, as heat, spirits, or perfection, may be discussed later and determined on other grounds" (*ibid.*, p. 49). Harvey may have surmised how to treat the organ as a machine, but he was in some ways too Aristotelian to appreciate the implications of his own advanced experiment.

He was not so bound by authority, however, as to be unable to free himself from some of the old embryological errors. He refuted on an observational basis, for instance, the notion that right and left represent maleness and femaleness, and he corrected the idea of Fabricius concerning the role of the chalazae by demonstrating the *cicatricula* (our blastoderm) as the source of the embryo; he corrected, too, various specific observational errors of Aristotle. Most important, he abolished for all time the Aristotelian conception of female as substance and male as form. Galen to be sure had seemed to localize both material and efficient causes in both male and female semen, as had Fabricius after him in a confused sort of way; but it was Harvey, for all his fanciful speculation concerning the significance of fertilization, who finally elevated the egg to its full and ultimate dignity. The processes of development can obviously hardly be investigated before the object that is developing is at least defined as their residence, and Harvey's contribution here was therefore a significant one.

It is abundantly clear, however, that by egg Harvey meant something different than we do. He knew there was necessary for development a double contribution, deriving from both male and female parent:

The *egge* is a certain Conception proceeding from Male and Female, qualified with the power of both: and out of it being One, one *Animal* is constituted. . . . An *egge* can no more be made without the assistance of the *Cock* and *Henne*, then the *fruit* can be made without the *Trees* aid. . . . For without a *Cock* it cannot be *fruitfull*, without a *Henne* it cannot be at all (1653, pp. 136, 157, 155).

Yet even in the case of the chick this is not the egg to Harvey that is the visible entity of the laboratory or kitchen:

And though it be a known thing, subscribed by all, that the *foetus* assumes its original and birth from the Male and Female, and consequently that the *Egge* is produced by the Cock and Henne, and the Chicken out of the Egge: yet neither the Schools of Physitians, nor *Aristotles* discerning Brain, have disclosed the manner, how the Cock and its seed, doth mint and coine the Chicken out of the Egge. . . . But that neither the *Hen* doth emit any Seed in *coition*, nor poure forth any blood at that time into the cavity of the *Uterus*; as also that the egge is not formed after *Aristotles* way; nor yet (as *Physitians* suppose) by the commixture of Seeds, and likewise that the *Cocks* seed doth not penetrate into the hollow of the *womb*, nor yet is attracted thither, is most manifest, from this one Observation, namely, *That after coition there is nothing at all to be found in the* Uterus, *more then there was before* (ibid., pp. 250, 199).

He met the same failure in a vain examination of the uterus of the mammal, and was driven therefore to resolve his dilemma by a poor analogy:

The *Egge* is . . . a kind of an *exposed Womb*, and placed where the *Foetus* is formed: for it executes the office of the *Matrix*, and shelters the *Chicken* till its just time of *Birth*. . . . *Oviparous creatures* are therefore not distinguished from *Viviparous*, in this, that these bring forth their *Foetus* alive, but they do not; . . . but their maine difference consists in the *manner* of *Generation*; namely, in that *Viviparous creatures* continue their *Womb* within them, in which the *Foetus* is fashioned, cherished, and compleated: *but Oviparous expose their Egge or Matrix without:* yet nevertheless they do ripen and cherish it as much by *Incubation*, as if they did reserve it within their *bowels* (ibid., p. 127).

Martin Llewellyn put it more succinctly, if less elegantly, in his poem "To the Incomparable Dr. Harvey, On his Books of the Motion of the Heart and Blood, and of the Generation of Animals," when he wrote (*ibid.*, n.p.):

That both the *Hen* and *Houswife* are so matcht,
That her Son *Born*, is only her Son *Hatcht*.

Harvey began his embryology from an Aristotelian metaphysical preconception:

"All perfect science depends upon the knowledge of all causes: and therefore to the plenary comprehension of Generation, we must ascend from the last and lowest efficient to the very *first* and *most supreme*, and know them all" (*ibid.*, p. 259). Frustrated by the inability of his own senses to find the physical reality he sought, he took solace in a metaphysical conception of his own, at a different level, and envisioned a metaphysical egg:

The Egge . . . seemes to be a kinde of *Medium;* not onely as it is the *Principium*, and the *Finis*, but as it is the Common work or production of both Sexes, and compounded of both. . . . It is also a *Medium*, or thing between an *Animate* and an *Inanimate* creature; being neither absolutely impowered with life, nor absolutely without it. It is a Midway or Passage between the *Parents* and the *Children*; between those that were, and those that are to come. . . . It is the *Terminus à quo*, the Point or Original from which all the *Cocks* and *Hennes* in the world do arise and spring: and it is also the *Terminus ad quem*, the Aim and End proposed by nature, to which they direct themselves all their life long. By which it comes to pass, that all *Individuals*, while to supply their *Species* they beget their Like, do continue and perpetuate their duration. The *Egge* is at were [*sic*] the Period of this Eternity (*ibid.*, p. 137).

But though Harvey necessarily ended as he began in metaphysics, he had shown the embryologists to follow him where to begin their physical investigations. His transmission, therefore, of Aristotle's notions of epigenesis takes on a new meaning, since his epigenesis takes place in an egg which to embryologists succeeding him was the visible egg of reality, the egg which he searched for even though he failed to find it. His description of epigenesis, in which

All . . . parts are not constituted at once, but successively, & in *Order*. . . . *Nature* doth feed and enlarge all the Parts, out of the self same Nutriment, whereof the [*sic*] *first* did frame them . . . and like a *potter*, first she divides her *materials*, and she allots to the *Trunk*, the *Head*, and the *Limbs*, every one their *share* or *cantlin:* as *Painters* do, who first draw the *Lineaments*, and then lay on the *Colours* (*ibid.*, pp. 225, 331),

is a description significant for the modern embryologist in more ways than by the repetition of Aristotle's metaphor.

The fairly common delusion, however, that Harvey championed the cause of epigenesis to the exclusion of others has little basis in fact. Harvey was more cautious than many more modern investigators in emphasizing that "the *principles* of divers *Animals* being also diverse . . . the manner of the generation of *Animals* is diverse likewise" (*ibid.*, p. 384), and while he considered some animals to be "perfected by a *succession* of *parts*" (*ibid.*, p. 344), he knew others to be "made intire at once" (*loc. cit.*), "formed and transfigured, out of *matter* already concocted and grown" (*ibid.*, p. 222). "The form ariseth *ex potentiâ materiae praeexistentis*, out of the power or potentiality of the pre-existent matter; and the *matter* is rather the first cause of the *Generation*, then any *external Efficient*" (*ibid.*, p. 223).

This resounds strongly of preformationism, and indeed in the modern rather than the old-fashioned sense. There are those who claim that Harvey's work on generation was of little historical moment because of its relative obscurity at the time of its publication. Malpighi, however, knew it, and he knew because of it to start his studies with the blastoderm; indeed, Harvey is mentioned on the first page of Malpighi's text, a notation which may bear witness to the fact that the ideas of preformation may themselves have been fostered at least in part by the inadequacies of the early epigenetic postulate.

EMBRYOLOGY AND THE NEW MICROSCOPE: PREFORMATION AND MALPIGHI; EPIGENESIS AND WOLFF

Harvey's failure which drove him back to the metaphysics from which he started we have called a physical one related to the inadequacy of his senses. Malpighi here had the advantage over him, with the use of the microscope as a new tool, and with it he overstepped the old limitations to enter what might seem in some ways a new conceptual realm, namely that of preformationism.

This doctrine of preformation, however, was no clear and strong new reply to an old question by a new science. It was a principle deeply intrenched in ancient philosophy and destined to outlast for many years the validity of the scientific evidence once seeming to favor it. It remained, indeed, a philosophical dogma rather than a scientific principle even after long being discussed on a scientific basis: its most ardent biological champion, Bonnet, was to betray the preponderance of its philosophical over its scientific weight by calling it "one of the greatest triumphs of rational over sensual conviction" (cited by Needham, '34, p. 191).

The concept roots, on the philosophical side, at least as remotely into antiquity as the times of Leucippus and Democritus, whom Aristotle so strongly opposed, and the implications of preformation inherent in the ancient materialistic doctrines were clearly realized by Lucretius (*De rerum natura*, Bk. I, lines 159–214). Seneca wrote as early as the first century (cited by Needham, '34, p. 48):

In the seed are enclosed all the parts of the body of the man that shall be formed. The infant that is borne in his mother's wombe hath the rootes of the beard and hair that he shall weare one day. In this little masse likewise are all the lineaments of the bodie and all that which Posterity shall discover in him.

When the formed element is present *ab initio*, the end and the beginning are the same, and the principle of *emboîtement* becomes difficult to escape. It too was recognized early; a theory of *emboîtement* expressed by Saint Augustine is quoted by Wheeler (1898). Nearer to the time of Malpighi (for the early and intervening development of the concepts see Cole, '30; Meyer, '39; and Needham, '34), Joseph of Aromatari (1625) reiterated an old idea of Empedokles that the plant is present in the ungerminated seed and said that "the chick is formed before the hen broods upon it" (Meyer, '39, p. 63).

It was Malpighi, however, who in 1673 reported the observations which were to endow the theory with new vigor. He studied with the new microscope what he thought to be the unincubated egg, to see in its blastoderm the structures so magnificently portrayed in the familiar plates, and to interpret them to signify that the parts of the animal may pre-exist in the egg. He indulged in less dogmatism in his claims, however, than posterity customarily attributes to him, as is emphasized in analysis of his work by Adelmann currently in progress. Malpighi organized no formal and systematic theory of development; he did not himself use the word preformation, and there is some question, according to Adelmann, as to what he meant by the pre-existence of the animal in the egg. He expressed his notions only tentatively, and he was, in fact, uncertain whether new structures existed before he observed them: "Nam primum ortum non assequuti, emergentem successivè partium manifestionem expectare cogimur" (1685 edition, p. 577). In sum, according to Adelmann's interpretation, he can justly be called a preformationist only with considerable qualification.

As Maître-Jan was to point out and explain in 1722, the egg examined by Malpighi was not what he had considered it—an egg studied after exposure to the heat of the August sun in Bologna is "unincubated" only with reference to the hen—but the work was no less influential than had it been founded on a different premise. Malpighi's primary contribution was his successful presentation for the first time of visible evidence on the detailed constitution of the young embryo. And evidence adduced by one of the new tools was as certain in the seventeenth as in the twentieth century to draw popular enthusiasm.

It was a function of his times that such evidence could be construed as support for embryological theory. What Malpighi saw and figured could be interpreted according to postulates compatible with Descartes' hypothesis of the infinite divisibility of matter; what he figured could be generalized into theories implying the embryo to be the same kind of "earthly machine" as Descartes' adult, and the concepts which were to incorporate his observations into the doctrine of preformation were crystallizing in many minds. Malpighi was no lone prophet of the new embryology. His contemporaries were going far to cry physical facts to fit a philosophical pattern. Croone, at much the same time, was making somewhat similar claims for the pre-existence of the chick in the egg, on the basis of a fantastically egregious error, mistaking a fragment of vitelline membrane for the embryo (Cole, '44). Swammerdam had in 1672 expressed a somewhat comparable concept for the egg of the frog, and Grew an analogous one for plants the same year. Malebranche, on the basis of observations as well as speculation, was expressing similar conclusions and generalizing the doctrine for plants and animals on a strong philosophical foundation (Schrecker, '38). For Leibniz, preformation was not only a metaphysical but also a strictly biological postulate which he related to his concept of the fixity of species. Bonnet, after his discovery of parthenogenesis in aphids, made preformation the basis for all his biological and philosophical speculations; the theory was supported by all the weighty authority of Haller, and even by such advanced experimentalists as Spallanzani and Réaumur.

Vallisnieri's speculations on the possibility that not only the whole human race but also all human parasites were represented in the ovaries of Eve, and Hartsoeker's calculation of the necessary size of a rabbit large enough to enclose all rabbits from the beginning of time; Dalenpatius' absurd claims to have

seen the homunculus in the spermatozoon, and all the foolish arguments between ovists and animalculists exemplified the extremes to which the doctrine was led; and such ridiculous claims served primarily to overburden it until it was close to collapse under its own weight. But it also fell, as it rose, on the basis of more serious philosophical principles; again a philosophical need had created a demand which again an observational embryologist—this time Caspar Friedrich Wolff—was to fulfill.

Wolff started out with a full appreciation of the philosophical limitations to embryological progress implied by the preformation doctrine: "Qui igitur systemata praedelineationis tradunt, generationem non explicant, sed, eam non dari, affirmant" (1759; cited from 1774 edition, p. xii); those who adopt the systems of predelineation do not explain generation but affirm that it does not occur. He was to launch his own attack from two sides, from the philosopher's and the observer's, but he started from the former's position: "Verum explicat generationem, qui ex traditis principiis & legibus partes corporis & modum compositionis deducit. . . . Et absoluit theoriam generationis, qui totum corpus generatum ex principiis & legibus illis eo modo deducit" (*ibid.*, pp. xii, xiii).

Deducing the body from principles and laws is the philosopher's way, not the embryologist's; but Wolff's virtue was that he felt compelled to supplement his abstruse reasoning by examination of his material and he was thus able to substantiate his theory. Aristotle, as a Greek, had experienced no such compulsion; Harvey had had the will but not the way; Wolff had not only the desire, but also the good fortune and the good skill to be both philosophically and observationally accurate within closer limits than his predecessors, and posterity concurs in von Baer's evaluation of some of his work as at that time "die grösste Meisterarbeit, die wir aus dem Felde der beobachtenden Naturwissenschaften kennen" (1837, II, 12).

Starting from highly abstract speculations concerning growth and nourishment in their relation to what we should call differentiation, he took up in particular detail (to be sure, some years before Goethe, but also, well over a millennium later than Theophrastus) the metamorphosis of plants, pointing out that the rudiments of leaves are basically similar to those of the parts of the flower and that the rudiments of both alike are derived from essentially undifferentiated tissue. This was to lead to his fundamental premise that in animals as well as plants development proceeds by gradual differentiation of originally homogeneous material.

There is importance in the fact that he considered the undifferentiated material to be comparable in plants and animals. But though his emphasis on this similarity of construction of material in plant and animal may, as Sachs and Huxley realized though later generations have forgotten, have had effect on the development of the doctrines implying universality of cell and protoplasm, it was primarily his emphasis on its early undifferentiatedness that was of more immediate import.

It has been said of Wolff, as of Harvey, that he was without influence in his own day, his writings neglected and without effect until after their translation into German by Meckel in 1812. This is inaccurate. Haller knew his work, and certainly the biological world was kept plentifully and liberally informed of what Haller was thinking; Kant knew of the concept via Blumenbach (cf. *Critique of Judgment*, §81) and from the beginning Kant had the attention of the scientists. Diderot could affirm with confidence, as early as 1769, when writing about "germes préexistants," that

Cela est contre l'expérience et la raison: contre l'expérience qui chercherait inutilement ces germes dans l'oeuf et dans la plupart des animaux avant un certain âge; contre la raison qui nous apprend que la divisibilité de la matière a un terme dans la nature, quoiqu'elle n'en ait aucun dans l'entendement (*Entretien entre D'Alembert et Diderot*; written 1769, first published 1830; cited from 1875 edition, II, 110).

Diderot was no technical embryologist; while it is possible, it is hardly probable that he had read the *Theoria generationis*. It is far more likely that he was expressing for political reasons an appropriate scientific concept which was already sufficiently widely disseminated to have reached his admittedly universal ear.

May not this be the clue to Wolff's success where Malpighi had failed? The new century had brought new thinking with it, a new thinking in terms of change. Social and political change were soon to grow out of it: revolution and evolution had a common philosophical background; it was eventually, with Hegel, to reach full fruition as the central doctrine of a specific philosophical system. Wolff's work was an early expression of this tendency. It is no accidental

coincidence that the Christian Wolff who taught philosophy to Caspar Friedrich Wolff, the originator of a biology of change, was a popularizer of Leibniz who had invented a calculus as a mathematics of change. Without this background, it is as unlikely that Wolff would have found a homogeneous blastoderm under his microscope as it was inevitable that Malpighi should have denied one a century before.

But Wolff's thinking typified too another kind of thought that was soon to broaden more generally. Wolff was prone to generalize from plant to animal (cf. "a bat is a perfect leaf . . . for the mode of origin of the two is the same"; from *Theorie der Generation*, 1764, §64, unavailable to me; cited by Huxley, 1853b, p. 293). His first proof of epigenesis in the chick came from his demonstration that the blood vessels of the chick blastoderm are not present from the beginning; he was probably led to the investigation by his false and far-fetched analogy between the vessels of the animal and those of the plant whose development he had already studied. Certainly if semantics gives any indication, his preoccupation with plants colored his later interpretations of observation on animal development. When he demonstrated that animal organs—the intestine and probably the central nervous system—are formed by the folding of homogeneous layers into tubes he called them by the name for leaf.

This is a strong hint, as is his "tracing of the body from principles and laws," of the *Naturphilosophie* to come, and it is curious, from his own point of view, that the emphasis laid by history on his accomplishment is centered so strongly on his microscopic discovery of what was not there. In his time, what influence he had probably spoke more positively in the direction of transcendentalism. Upon his concept of epigenesis and change and upon his intimations of layering in the embryo—both concepts to which Wolff was led by his tendencies towards *Naturphilosophie*—embryology was to follow with its whole momentous sequel, but only after a serious delay during which concepts were to arise which in many ways negated the concept of change which Wolff originated, concepts paradoxically enough also derived on a basis of *Naturphilosophie*.

EMBRYOLOGY AND NATURPHILOSOPHIE: GOETHE AND VON BAER

But why now *Naturphilosophie*, whose influence on embryology was to grow so strong that its domination is not yet now completely outworn? It was certainly at least in part the clear and inevitable reaction against Cartesianism and against the instillation of the analytical order and system of seventeenth century mechanics into the study of animate nature. Goethe, one of its warmest partisans, has spoken specifically to this point in his *Geschichte meines botanischen Studiums* (*Gedanken und Aufsätze*, 1944 edition, XII, 314):

Vorläufig . . . will ich bekennen, dass nach *Shakespeare* und *Spinoza* auf mich die grösste Wirkung von *Linné* ausgegangen, und zwar gerade durch den Widerstreit, zu welchem er mich aufforderte. Denn indem ich sein scharfes, geistreiches Absondern, seine treffenden, zweckmässigen, oft aber willkürlichen Gesetze in mich aufzunehmen versuchte, ging in meinem Innern ein Zwiespalt vor: Das, was er mit Gewalt auseinanderzuhalten suchte, musste, nach dem innersten Bedürfnis meines Wesens, zur Vereinigung anstreben.

Goethe is as good an example as any with whom to continue the discussion, not only because he originated the concept of morphology in our modern and dynamic sense, but also especially because he was so vividly articulate in describing what went on in his own mind during the process of it. His own studies on the metamorphosis of plants and on the vertebral constitution of the skull, emphasizing the unity of type, and what he thought was his discovery of the intermaxillary bone in the human fetus, suggesting that the uniformity of anatomical plan is based on the existence of a developmental archetype, typify the new *Naturphilosophie*. Natural phenomena represent modifications of an Idea in the Mind of the Creator: here is a new Idealism, less important in that it revivified Plato than that it again lost sight of Aristotle, with as disastrous delaying consequences as in the Middle Ages: Agassiz, as late as 1857, could still answer with an unequivocal affirmative his self-addressed question as to whether the taxonomic divisions of the animal kingdom have "been instituted by the Divine Intelligence as the categories of his mode of thinking" (1857, p. 8).

This must inevitably appeal, with all of its implications of beauty in nature, to Goethe the poet, who is said to have soothed himself to sleep visualizing a seed growing into a plant. Its mysticism, quite in the neo-Platonic tradition, should have been opprobrious to the scientist; but this was the moment in history when the scientist turned romantic, to his own loss. The Middle Ages,

for all the weaknesses of scholasticism, maintained the firm conviction that the Universe was capable of being understood by human reason; and, as Whitehead ('25) reminds us, it is to medieval scholasticism that we are indebted for our habits of exact thought. The *Naturphilosophen*, at their most emotional extremes, grew away from reason in its best sense, and their thought was hardly precise in the sense of modern science. Whitehead stresses too the high standard of objectivity set by the ancient and medieval worlds, with its obvious advantage for science. Its loss was part of the price paid for the developing individuality emerging from the philosophy of the late eighteenth and early nineteenth centuries, and this was a debt whose payment nearly bankrupted the intellectual economy of the *Naturphilosophen*.

The movement had its philosophical support from Kant, who, like Leibniz before him, laid emphasis on the metaphysical, and who put a premium on transcendentalism; Kant's categories, after all, were given in advance of experience and the *Ding-an-sich* was beyond it. Goethe, however, was independent of Kant. "Meine 'Metamorphose der Pflanzen,'" he told Eckermann, "habe ich geschrieben, ehe ich etwas von Kant wusste, und doch ist sie ganz im Sinne seiner Lehre" (Eckermann, 1905 edition, I, 310). It might have been better if he, and the other *Naturphilosophen*, had known Kant better. Kant, as Rádl ('30, p. 369) has pointed out, "had declared that the Absolute is never known and can never be known; yet his followers," to continue with Rádl, "—the Romantic Philosophers—made this Absolute the basis of their philosophy, the only real thing left in the Universe."

For biology, it was this confusion between the Idea and its representation in the organism, the Absolute and the knowable, that was dangerous. Goethe typifies this, too. He could coolly dictate the rules for observing scientific objectivity (*Gedanken und Aufsätze*, 1944 edition, XII, 93):

Jeder Forscher muss sich durchaus ansehen als einer, der zu einer Jury berufen ist. Er hat nur darauf zu achten, inwiefern der Vortrag vollständig sei und durch klare Belege auseinandergesetzt. Er fasst hiernach seine Ueberzeugung zusammen und gibt seine Stimme, es sei nun, dass seine Meinung mit der des Referenten übereintreffe oder nicht.

"Sobald man in der Wissenschaft einer gewissen beschränkten Konfession angehört," he said to Eckermann, "ist sogleich jede unbefangene treue Auffassung dahin. . . . Es gehört zur Naturbeobachtung eine gewisse ruhige Reinheit des Innern, das von gar nichts gestört und präokkupiert ist" (Eckermann, 1905 edition, II, 218, 220).

He could, however, as sublimely ignore his own precepts. Where was his inner purity without preoccupation, where was his independence of a particular confession, when Eckermann came in to him with news of the July Revolution to have him cry (*ibid.*, II, 473):

Nun ... was denken Sie von dieser grossen Begebenheit? Der Vulkan ist zum Ausbruch gekommen; alles steht in Flammen, und es ist nicht ferner eine Verhandlung bei geschlossenen Thüren,

and heard him reply, when Eckermann spoke of ministers and royal family (*ibid.*, II, 474–475):

Ich rede gar nicht von jenen Leuten; es handelt sich bei mir um ganz andere Dinge. Ich rede von dem in der Akademie zum öffentlichen Ausbruch gekommenen, für die Wissenschaft so höchst bedeutenden Streit zwischen *Cuvier* und *Geoffroy de Saint-Hilaire!* ... Die Sache ist von der höchsten Bedeutung. ... Wir haben jetzt an Geoffroy de Saint Hilaire einen mächtigen Alliierten auf die Dauer. ... Das Beste ... ist, dass die von Geoffroy in Frankreich eingeführte synthetische Behandlungsweise der Natur jetzt nicht mehr rückgängig zu machen ist. ... Von nun an wird auch in Frankreich bei der Naturforschung der Geist herrschen und über die Materie Herr sein. Man wird Blicke in grosse Schöpfungsmaximen thun, in die geheimnisvolle Werkstatt Gottes!—Was ist auch im Grunde aller Verkehr mit der Natur, wenn wir auf analytischem Wege bloss mit einzelnen materiellen Teilen uns zu schaffen machen, und wir nicht das Atmen des Geistes empfinden, der jedem Teile die Richtung vorschreibt und jede Ausschweifung durch ein innewohnendes Gesetz bändigt oder sanktioniert!

Here is the romantic fallacy that lies at the hollow core of *Naturphilosophie:* here it is that the *Naturphilosophen* separate from Kant. Kant did not question the validity of natural science in its own realm; indeed, he justified it. He simply defined the regions in which it could operate, while the *Naturphilosophen* with their zeal for synthesis and their preoccupation with the spirit as the synthesizing element related the real to the transcendent in such a confused way that they could think clearly on neither.

Idealism for the philosopher is one thing: Kant felt that science could be accurate only when mathematically expressed, which is one kind of idealism. Huxley had the same intuition; in a paper on the Mollusca he wrote (1853a, p. 50):

From all that has been stated, I think that it is now possible to form a notion of the archetype of the Cephalous Mollusca, and I beg it to be understood that in using this term, I make no reference to any real or imaginary "ideas" upon which animal forms are modelled. All that I mean is the conception of a form embodying the most general propositions that can be affirmed respecting the Cephalous Mollusca, standing in the same relation to them as the diagram to a geometrical theorem, and like it, at once imaginary and true.

Boyle had presented the problem earlier to the physical scientist. His law was set for the ideal gas, and it became the task of the scientist to check experimentally the behavior of the real gas against that postulated for the ideal. Such a conception lacks meaning to the biologist; no such experiment is possible for him in relating the real to the ideal set up by the *Naturphilosophen*. Neither Boyle's kind of idealism, nor Huxley's, is that of the *Naturphilosophen*, whose weakness was not so much that it left no room for the experiment as that it closed their minds to whole systems of possible interpretations of the observed phenomena which they collected to gain credence for their fancies.

The weakness of the *Naturphilosophen* by and large was that they tried to force a rigid and fixed and obvious structure out of Spinoza's deeper and more fluid and subtle pantheism. Goethe, with more strength and with more sensitivity, could like Herder pass beyond them to be carried away by the dynamic wholeness of nature which to him was alive in the sense of the new morphology which was to follow later. Goethe, too, could grow beyond the romantic in other realms of thought than the scientific; but the professional biologists largely lacked his profundity and maturity and remained at the static phase too long. While Goethe's significance as a prophet for *Naturphilosophie* is hardly to be minimized, there were others who were to bear the responsibility for working out the biological details and who carried the doctrine to the illogical extremes which were so to retard the progress of biology proper: Goethe's friend, Nees von Esenbeck, who considered the entire vegetable world a leaf; Goethe's hero Étienne Geoffroy Saint-Hilaire; and Serres, who said, as Oken was saying too, that the entire animal kingdom was a single organism; Oken was going so far as to compare the parts of a plant to fire, water, earth and air.

Yet it was against this dark background that the students of the natural philosopher Döllinger (cf. Temkin, '50) at **Würzburg** were to begin to build constructively upon Wolff's concepts; and the fact that they could start to do so is related probably to Wolff's own compatibility with *Naturphilosophie*. Wolff's epigenesis had started as conceptual; his concept, and the results of his own microscopic examinations, led those who were to follow him to the material where they could build upon what he had postulated and demonstrate a mechanism of the process of change he had postulated.

The group consisted of Pander, who first demonstrated the existence of the three primary germ layers in the embryo of the chick; of Goethe's friend D'Alton, who acted as artist; and of von Baer, who generalized Pander's germ layers for other animals and who in so doing generalized the science of embryology itself.

Pander's advance was a great one, in a way, in terms of independence of thought; and his achievement, in an environment of overgeneralization, in being able to concentrate on describing specific processes of development in a single form without drawing far-fetched analogies, was considerable. But Pander could not, or did not, carry through, and it was left to von Baer, or rather, von Baer took it upon himself, to broaden the base by the examination of more varied material.

With his inspiration from the romantics, he looked at the diverse material with a question in his mind as to its comparability; and he came away from it with the conviction that the comparability was there, in terms of origin (hence the discovery of the mammalian egg), and in terms of process in the similarity of the formation of the germ layers and in the derivation of similar organs from comparable layers in the different vertebrate forms. He demonstrated development to be at once from homogeneous to heterogeneous, from general to special, in all the forms that he studied. Though his feat was an overwhelmingly intellectual, not technical, achievement, his great advance was the extent to which he based his conclusions on the zealous and accurate and untiringly meticulous microscopic observations on a wide variety of animal material: *Beobachtung* preceded *Reflexion* in his title.

His emphasis on comparability involved, to be sure, as did that of the other *Naturphilosophen*, an emphasis on Type: "Zufrieden würde ich seyn," he wrote, "wenn man es als meinen Antheil betrachtet, nachgewiesen zu haben, dass der Typus der Organisation die Entwickelungsweise bedingt" (1828, I, xxii). But he meant by Type something different than the others:

Vor allen Dingen mache ich darauf aufmerksam, dass man den Grad der Ausbildung des thierischen Körpers und den Typus der Organisation unterscheiden muss. *Der Grad der Ausbildung des thierischen Körpers* besteht in einem grössern oder geringern Maasse der Heterogenität der Elementartheile und der einzelnen Abschnitte eines zusammengesetzten Apparates, mit einem Worte, *in der grössern histologischen und morphologischen Sonderung. . . . Typus* nenne ich das Lagerungsverhältniss der organischen Elemente und der Organe (1828, I, 207–208).

Our persuasion, that the grades of development must be distinguished from the types of organization, is founded upon the following considerations: —We know that all the functions of the perfect animal body contribute to a general result,—to the life of the animal; but also that the general mass manifests the total life (for animal life is always a totality). . . . With a greater separation and more complete independence of these functions is combined a greater differentiation of the body into organic systems, and of these systems again into separate more individualized sections. In this consists the higher development of the animal body.

But the mode in which these organs of the animal body are united together, is a wholly distinct matter. And it is to this manner in which the organic elements are combined that we give the name of *Type.* Every type may be manifested in higher and lower degrees of organization; the type and the grade of development together determine the special forms (1826; cited from 1853 edition, pp. 178–179).

Here there is an implication still of the Type and Archetype of the *Naturphilosophen*, but it is becoming more Type in common with Aristotle's form in the sense of potentiality. While von Baer has adopted a concept from *Naturphilosophie*, he has developed it further; for von Baer, it is the embryo, not the Idea, that is becoming the type. It is irrelevant for our purposes that he considered the primary types to be those of the vertebrate, the annulate, the radiate and the mollusk (the double symmetrical, the longitudinal, the radiate and the spiral; polarity and symmetry were a central idea, both problem and metaphysical reply to it, for the *Naturphilosophen* as for modern biologists). What is significant is that he could regard them, rightly or wrongly, as separate types of extant, visible, dissectable and observable animals perceived by his sense organs. This is phenomenological type, type not in an Idea but present as structure in an adult organism, and if masked there, sometimes discernible in the structure of the embryo; and thereby the relationship of embryology to comparative anatomy becomes fixed for all time.

The extent to which he could emancipate himself from the tendency to overgeneralize of the *Naturphilosophen* is probably nowhere made clearer than in his refusal to accept the "law" of parallelism most clearly expressed before his time by Meckel (for discussion of earlier contributors to the development of this concept see especially Needham, '34, and Meyer, '35; there are those who consider the doctrine to be foreshadowed even by Aristotle and Harvey, an interpretation which Meyer quite justly disputes):

Dass der Embryo höherer Thiere, ehe er seine vollkommne Ausbildung erreicht, mehrere Stufen durchläuft, wurde schon oben bemerkt; hier ist nachzuweisen, dass diese verschiednen Stufen denen entsprechen, auf welchen tiefer stehende Thiere das ganze Leben hindurch gehemmt erscheinen (Meckel, 1821, I, 396–397).

Von Baer, in contrast, with his emphasis on difference in adult type, denies the validity of Meckel's "Law" (1828, I, 220):

Dadurch ist aber nicht erwiesen, dass jeder Embryo einer höhern Thierform allmählig die niedern Thierformen durchlaufe. Vielmehr scheint sich der Typus jedes Thiers gleich anfangs im Embryo zu fixiren und die ganze Entwickelung zu beherrschen . . . *Der Embryo des Wirbelthiers ist schon anfangs ein Wirbelthier. . . . Mithin durchlaufen die Embryonen der Wirbelthiere in ihrer Entwickelung gar keine (bekannten) bleibenden Thierformen.*

Frequent misconceptions have been expressed concerning von Baer's relationship to the formulation of the biogenetic law which have been well clarified by Meyer ('35); misconceptions which have arisen probably at least in part because of Darwin's quotation, in later editions of the *Origin of Species,* of von Baer's passage accentuating, in line with his stress on development from the general to the special, the likeness of young vertebrate embryos:

The embryos of mammalia, of birds, lizards, and snakes, probably also of chelonia are in their earliest states exceedingly like one another, both as a whole and in the mode of development of their parts; so much so, in fact, that we can often distinguish the embryos only by their size. In my possession are two little embryos in spirit, whose names I have omitted to attach, and at present I am quite unable to say to what class they belong (Darwin, 1902 edition, II, 241),

and his stress was exclusively on resemblances between embryos rather than between adults of one group and embryos of another.

Darwin might have made von Baer's position clearer had he cited the delightful passage from the Fifth Scholion (1828, I, 203–204):

Denke man sich nur, die Vögel hätten ihre Entwickelungsgeschichte studirt, und sie wären es, welche nun den Bau des ausgewachsenen Säugethiers und des Menschen untersuchten. Würden nicht ihre physiologischen Lehrbücher Folgendes lehren können? "Jene vier- und zweibeinigen Thiere haben viele Embryonenähnlichkeit, denn ihre Schädelknochen sind getrennt, sie haben keinen Schnabel, wie wir in den fünf oder sechs ersten Tagen der Bebrütung; ihre Extremitäten sind ziemlich gleich unter sich, wie die unsrigen ungefähr eben so lange; nicht eine einzige wahre Feder sitzt auf ihrem Leibe, sondern nur dünne Federschafte, so dass wir schon im Neste weiter sind, als sie jemals kommen, ihre Knochen sind wenig spröde und enthalten, wie die unsrigen in der Jugend gar keine Luft; überhaupt fehlen ihnen die Luftsäcke und die Lungen sind nicht angewachsen, wie die unsrigen in frühester Zeit; ein Kropf fehlt ihnen ganz; Vormagen und Muskelmagen sind mehr oder weniger in Einen [*sic*] Sack verflossen; lauter Verhältnisse, die bei uns rasch vorübergehen, und die Nägel sind bei den meisten so ungeschickt breit, wie bei uns vor dem Auskriechen; an der Fähigkeit zu fliegen haben allein die Fledermäuse, die die vollkommensten scheinen, Theil, die übrigen nicht. Und diese Säugethiere, die so lange nach der Geburt ihr Futter nicht selbst suchen können, nie sich frei vom Erdboden erheben, wollen höher organisirt seyn, als wir?

It must be granted that von Baer himself sometimes indulged in flights of fancy comparable to those of the other *Naturphilosophen.* "Dass nämlich Kiefern und Extremitäten Modificationen eines Grundtypus sind," he wrote, "ist augenscheinlich . . . Die Kiefern aber nähern sich so sehr der Natur der Rippen, dass man von ihnen einen Grund hernehmen kann, auch die Extremität des Rumpfes für verstärkte Rippen anzusehen" (*ibid.,* I, 192). His theories of fertilization, and of the significance of symmetry with regard to type, were as foolish as those of his contemporaries; but his strength in being so frequently able to overcome such temptation was more remarkable than the occasional symptoms of his succumbing to it.

He had on the whole a particularly clear appreciation of his contemporaries' confusion between fact and idea: he stated it explicitly in one of his criticisms of the theory of parallelism: "Man lernte allmählig die verschiedenen Thierformen als aus einander entwickelt sich denken—und schien dann, von einigen Seiten wenigstens, vergessen zu wollen, dass die Metamorphose nur eine Vorstellungsart sey" (*ibid.,* I, 200).

Von Baer's own embryology, for the first time, for all of its emphasis on the relationship of the special to the general, was an embryology in which the metaphysical became subordinate to the biological in the sense of modern embryology, and became an embryology which proceeded from embryological facts and phenomena towards embryological concepts, rather than in the reverse direction; and von Baer, in accomplishing this feat, made one of the greatest advances in all biological history. His force of intellect, his consequent self-mastery and ability to free himself to develop beyond the thought in which he was trained, are unmatched in biological progress. He could emancipate himself from the thinking of his times more than Vesalius, more than Harvey before him; more than Darwin after him, and though perhaps not in an analytical sense, yet in a synthetic sense more than Mendel to follow.

His courage to maintain his own independence of thought may have been fed by his century's new kind of awareness of the individual, with its philosophical background from Leibniz and Kant, developed by Fichte and Schelling and Hegel, and its translation during the eighteenth century into more widespread acceptance than ever before of the significance of freedom of individual action. Von Baer absorbed the concept of independence: "Deswegen ist auch das wesentlichste Resultat der Entwickelung, wenn wir sie im Ganzen übersehen, die *zunehmende Selbstständigkeit* des werdenden Thiers" (*ibid.*, I, 148), he wrote, and he concentrated on the individual. *Wesenheit* was all: "Die Wesenheit des Thiers beherrscht die Ausbildung.... Die Wesenheit ... der zeugenden Thierform beherrscht die Entwickelung der Frucht" (*ibid.*, I, 147–148).

But like Aristotle and Goethe, von Baer was obsessed with the dynamic and functional qualities of the organism as a whole. "We know that all the functions of the perfect animal body contribute to a general result,— to the life of the animal," we have already quoted, "but also that the general mass manifests the total life (for animal life is always a totality)." "Die Entwickelungsgeschichte des Individuums ist die Geschichte der wachsenden Individualität in jeglicher Beziehung" (*ibid.*, I, 263), he wrote too; and he thought of the growing individual too, like Goethe, in respect to a larger whole; to him the palm, "dem es vorbehalten ist, die bildenden Kräfte des thierischen Körpers auf die allgemeinen Kräfte

oder Lebensrichtungen des Weltganzen zurückzuführen" (*ibid.*, I, xxii).

Like Goethe, he could say, and in almost the same figure of speech, that "die *Geschichte der Natur* ist nur *die Geschichte fortschreitender Siege des Geistes über den Stoff*" (1864, pp. 71–72), but he meant it in a different context (1828, I, 263–264):

Hat aber das eben ausgesprochene allgemeinste Resultat Wahrheit und Inhalt, so ist es *Ein* Grundgedanke, der durch alle Formen und Stufen der thierischen Entwickelung geht und alle einzelnen Verhältnisse beherrscht. Derselbe Gedanke ist es, der im Weltraume die vertheilte Masse in Sphären sammelte und diese zu Sonnensystemen verband, derselbe, der den verwitterten Staub an der Oberfläche des metallischen Planeten in lebendigen Formen hervorwachsen liess. Dieser Gedanke ist aber nichts als das Leben selbst, und die Worte und Sylben, in welchen er sich ausspricht, sind die verschiedenen Formen des Lebendigen.

But if von Baer's outlook, like Goethe's, was cosmic in scope, his inspiration was the detailed and specific study of the developing form of the individual living embryo. Like Aristotle, he accepted form as inseparable from the formed. The advantage of refinement bestowed by time to his philosophical and technical method, as compared with Aristotle's, enabled him to concentrate more on the formed, which was biological material, than on form as such and metaphysical; and in so advancing he became the true synthetic genius which Goethe had aspired to be, "der grösste unter uns in Vergangenheit, Gegenwart und weiter Zukunft" (Roux, 1889; cited from Roux, 1895b, II, 25).

EMBRYOLOGY AND EVOLUTION: DARWIN AND HAECKEL

It has been said that all biology since Darwin has been a commentary on the *Origin of Species*. Embryology would be in a more advanced position than its present one if one could claim that all embryology after von Baer represented a commentary on his great treatise. It is true that immediately following his time, even during it, great strides were made in the amplification and refinement of his teachings. Rathke, in particular, whose quality of mind was in many ways like that of von Baer, made particular advances in demonstrating the existence of the germ layers in invertebrates as well as vertebrates and in discovering the presence of gill slits in the mammalian embryo. The universality of the germ layers was given new meaning with the enunciation of the doctrines of universality of protoplasm and of cells when von Kölliker and Remak and others brought together the results of these with the results of the germ layer doctrine. Had these continued as the main trends of embryology, von Baer's synthetic scheme would have been broadened in the fashion it deserved. Instead, a return to the overgeneralization of *Naturphilosophie* once more delayed its progress into the future.

One symptom of this was the continued emphasis, in spite of von Baer's warnings, on the comparability of embryos of "higher" forms to the adults of "lower," and such false analogy was carried over even into the germ layers, von Baer's own territory, thus seeming to be supported by his facts though he had so explicitly denied the concept. Huxley, in 1849 (p. 426), described the Medusae as constructed of two membranes "which appear to bear the same physiological relation to one another as do the serous and mucous layer of the germ," opening the way for the ultimate generalization. When, therefore, shortly after the publication of the *Origin of Species*, Kowalewski found that invertebrate and vertebrate embryos alike formed from a bilaminar sac, that in the most varied material—Psolinus, Amphioxus, Phoronis, Limnaeus, Ophiura, Echinus, Asteracanthion, Sagitta, Ascidia, Escholtzia, Sepiola as well as birds, mammals and turtles—

. . . bei allen von mir hier erwähnten Embryonen geht die Bildung der beiden erwähnten Schichten oder Blätter (der äusseren und inneren) ganz auf dieselbe Weise vor sich. . . . Also wäre die erste Bildung des Embryo für alle diese verschiedenen Thiere ganz übereinstimmend; nur in den weiteren Veränderungen sehen wir die Unterschiede auftreten, welche jeden einzelnen Typus bezeichnen (1867, p. 5),

the decision was sealed. He ended on the same note of caution as von Baer, but his voice too was drowned out by the clamor originating from a new cry of transcendentalism that surpassed anything the earlier *Naturphilosophen* would have dreamed possible. The difference, of course, was that meantime the *Origin of Species* had appeared.

The compulsion to synthesize all of animate nature into a single grandiose scheme which the false analogies of the earlier transcendentalism had formerly satisfied was now to be assuaged by the evolution doctrine, which represented a synthesis on another basis; in the new scheme, common descent replaced the archetype as the primary synthesizing factor.

It has been said that it was Darwin who "dragged [organisms] down from . . . metaphysical regions into daily life, and examined their immediate purpose in relation to the whole environment of the living organism" (Rádl, '30, p. 381). But Darwin in some ways advanced no more abruptly in respect to the descent from metaphysics than had von Baer, and the structure of thought he created was in many ways as metaphysical as that of his predecessors. The influence of the environment alone was no new concept; philosophy had been worrying about this problem at least since the time of Leibniz. The species concept, from which Darwin started, was so highly metaphysical that even now the term defies adequate biological definition. Darwin's system was a metaphysical one, too, in that his concern for the individual organism was subordinate to his interest in the interdependence of organisms; his clue to the nature of their relationships came equally from the organisms themselves and from wider areas of thought: from generalizations invented for the fields of geology and economics, and indeed, in a way from his whole century's mood for "Progress."

One of the primary contributions of Darwin, however—indeed of all those concerned with the new doctrine of evolution: Buffon, Erasmus Darwin, Lamarck, John Hunter, Wallace and the many others—was the refocussing once more of attention on the organism as a whole. The key to evolution had come from consideration of the whole living animal, not its parts; evolution was inferred from natural history, not deduced from the preparations in the cabinets of the anatomists where the evidence had been awaiting for centuries the interpretations which the fixity and the tenacity of the notions of unity of type had excluded from coming into being.

It is one of the more curious ironies of history that while before Darwin, transcendentalism had closed the minds of investigators to the possibility of explanation of resemblances between parts of organisms and between whole organisms on the basis of common descent, yet after him the combination of the doctrines was to lead to extremes of exaggeration that were attained separately by neither. There were many who were to contribute to this: Kleinenberg in Germany and Lankester in England made an early start by relating phylogeny to ontogeny on the basis of comparability of the germ layers (for fuller treatment see

Oppenheimer, '40), but their views were relatively mild compared to those of many who followed them. The culmination was the work of Haeckel, the greatest revisionist of them all.

The most extreme example of his immoderation was perhaps his naming, on the basis of the "similarity, or *homology*, of the gastrula in all classes of compound animals" (concept originally expressed in monograph on the *Kalkschwämme*, 1872; cited here from Haeckel, [1900], p. 61), in the stead of the coelenterates formerly nominated for the position by Kleinenberg, the imaginary gastraea as the progenitor of all multicellular forms. His figuring of a section through an animal that never existed on the same page (1891, p. 161) that illustrates Kowalewski's gastrulae of Sagitta and Amphioxus and Carl Rabl's of Limnaeus, with no comment in the label to signify that the "Gastrula eines einfachsten Pflanzenthieres, einer Gastraeade (*Gastrophysema*, Haeckel)" is any less real than the others—where is there a handsomer example in all biological or scientific history of what Whitehead has called the "Fallacy of Misplaced Concreteness"?

Such a silly invention as the gastraea, that "magere Tiergespenst," as Kleinenberg (1886, p. 2) called it, as an isolated case might probably have proved of little influence; and its significance is as a symptom (a word used advisedly for its pathological connotations) of Haeckel's basic trouble. What was damaging to science was Haeckel's fervency to oversystematize all morphology through his biogenetic law that "die Ontogenie ist eine Recapitulation der Phylogenie" (1891, p. 7).

In formulating it, he returned to the law of parallelism of Tiedemann, Meckel and Serres, quite by-passing von Baer's more temperate statements. He was influenced to do so of course in part by Fritz Müller, who had earlier (*Für Darwin*, 1864) pointed out on the basis of the study of crustacean larvae that individual development provides a clue to ancestral history. But he misinterpreted Müller, as have many more modern readers (cf. Meyer, '35). While Müller was supporting Darwin—indeed, as Meyer says ('35, p. 392), "his main conclusion was that his studies on the development of crustacea confirmed Darwin's idea of evolution"—he yet was formulating no such dogma as Haeckel's concerning the causal relationships between evolution and individual development.

Sir John Lubbock, too, was early considering the relationships of evolution and individual development in support of Darwin; but when he questioned whether insects during the course of metamorphosis pass through their ancestral stages he felt forced to a negative reply in the absence of evidence that a caterpillar ever existed as a fully developed organism. Rádl has commented ('30, p. 140) concerning the biogenetic law that "everything important that has ever been cited against the theory was known when the theory was first put forward; nevertheless it was widely accepted." Lubbock's reservation is an example. But his exception, and all the other exceptions, seemed to lack the dramatic appeal of the false generalization, and the biogenetic law was acclaimed with the same rapt enthusiasm that had greeted the earlier theories of preformation and of unity of type.

Investigators in widely varied fields of interest rapidly carried over the theory into their own territories. Bunge applied it to physiology:

The amount of common salt in the organism corresponds with the amount in the environment. . . . Many plants contain only traces of sodium; those which are rich in it are only the sea-weeds and the plants which grow on the sea-shore, and on the salt-steppes which are dried-up sea-basins. . . .

This is also the case with invertebrate animals; only those which live in the sea, and those nearest allied to them on land, contain much salt. . . .

The land vertebrates are all remarkably rich in salt, in spite of the scanty supply around them. But even these are only apparent exceptions. We need but remember the fact that the first vertebrates on our planet all lived in the sea. Is not the large amount of chlorid of sodium found in the present inhabitants of dry land another proof of the genealogical connection we are forced to accept from morphological facts? . . .

If this interpretation is correct, we should expect that the younger the vertebrates are in their individual development, the more salt they would possess. This is in fact the case. I have convinced myself by numerous experiments that an embryo of a mammal contains more salt than a new-born animal, and that it gradually becomes, after birth, poorer in chlorin and sodium as it develops. Cartilage contains the most sodium of any tissue in our bodies, besides being also the tissue of greatest antiquity. . . . This phenomenon . . . can only be explained by the theory of evolution" ('02, pp. 101–103).

Workers in other fields than biology, too, adopted the theory with as much warmth. Preyer, a colleague of Haeckel's at Jena, formulated his conceptions of child psychology with reference to Haeckel's law; Herbart and Ziller before him had held that the individual repeats in his development the stages of cultural development through which the human race has passed. And in our own times, Jung, following Nietzsche and Freud among others, with all his immeasurable influence on modern psychology and literature, has erected the superstructure of his *Psychology of the Unconscious* on the acceptance of Haeckel's premise as though this were the immutable truth that Haeckel in his own day had hoped it:

All this experience suggests to us that we draw a parallel between the phantastical, mythological thinking of antiquity and the similar thinking of children, between the lower human races and dreams. This train of thought is not a strange one for us, but quite familiar through our knowledge of comparative anatomy and the history of development, which show us how the structure and function of the human body are the results of a series of embryonic changes which correspond to similar changes in the history of the race. Therefore, the supposition is justified that ontogenesis corresponds in psychology to phylogenesis. Consequently, it would be true, as well, that the state of infantile thinking in the child's psychic life, as well as in dreams, is nothing but a re-echo of the prehistoric and the ancient" ('27, pp. 27–28).

But the blind adoption of Haeckel's doctrines by such workers in bordering fields, and their infection with his faith that "development is now the magic word by means of which we shall solve the riddles by which we are surrounded" (cited from Rádl, '30, pp. 126–127), is less reprehensible than their uncritical acceptance by the professional embryologists, who swallowed them with as much gullibility, and who remained utterly unperturbed by the fact that Haeckel himself was never in any sense a professional embryologist. The seduction of embryology by a fanatic who expressed himself even metaphorically in terms of magic represents a darker chapter in its history than any of its earlier or later retreats to mere metaphysics lacking such taint of the mystic.

Deplorably enough, the record of many of our "modern" textbooks is none too pure with respect to the biogenetic law. But there is no space here for a modern critique of the doctrine (for brief statements of the modern position see Shumway, '32, and de Beer, '51); what is relevant here at the moment is not so much Haeckel's rightness or wrongness as the magnitude of his influence. It was considerable, and acted as a delaying rather than an activating force; and it was stifling to immediate progress, since embryologists were for many years after to examine embryos primarily to establish evidence of phy-

logenetic relationship. This was not wholly detrimental, of course; like the earlier transcendentalism this gave a strong incentive for looking at embryos, and many accurate observational data were collected which were later to stand embryology in good stead; but progress in terms of new concepts was necessarily impeded. Balfour specified the task, prescribed the fashion, set the standard (1880, I, 4–5):

To test how far Comparative Embryology brings to light ancestral forms common to the whole of the Metazoa. . . .
How far . . . larval forms may be interpreted as the ancestral type. . . .
How far such forms agree with living or fossil forms in the adult state. . . .
How far organs appear in the embryo or larva which either atrophy or become functionless in the adult state, and which persist permanently in members of some other group or in lower members of the same group. . . .
How far organs pass in the course of their development through a condition permanent in some lower form. . . .

Balfour himself acknowledged another department of embryology concerned with the origin of organs and germ layers and tissues, but to this he devoted only a quarter of his great treatise; many of his contemporaries more fully ignored it, and advance had to wait until the furor over Darwin and recapitulation had subsided. The degree to which evolutionary relationships dominated embryology is nowhere better shown than by the results of the few cases where investigators attempted to pursue other paths, and failed in influence.

Leuckart and Bergmann had, in fact, several years before the publication of the *Origin of Species*, already set the programme for a new embryology (1851; cited from 1855, p. 36):

Ebenso wie man gegenwärtig strebt, die Combination von Wirkungen zu ermitteln, auf welcher eine bestimmte Krystallform oder die Bildung und Umbildung der Zelle beruht, so wird man sich auch Wege zu eröffnen suchen, um die bewirkenden Ursachen der Anordnung der Organe zu ermitteln: man wird *eine Physiologie der Plastik* dereinst anstreben.

But the few who had the originality, during the nineteenth century, to attempt to work out a "physiology of the plastic" were doomed to failure. Lereboullet made an attempt to do so, in France (cf. Oppenheimer, '36), where he could do so in part because of the dominating spirit of Cuvier, who, like von Baer, emphasized animals rather than relationships and their structure rather than their metaphysics. In part because of Cuvier's strength of mind, Darwin never attained the same heights of scientific popularity in France as in Germany and England; and if Lereboullet was not of such intellectual calibre as to take full advantage of this for embryology, French science still benefited from it in the persons of Pasteur and Claude Bernard. In Germany, Wilhelm His in 1874, Goette in 1875, and Rauber in 1880 attempted mechanical explanations of development, working towards a "physiology of the plastic"; they attracted a few strong disciples such as von Kölliker, but on the whole they cried in the wilderness. His' cry was the most explicit, perhaps, certainly one of the most violent against Haeckel; and quite the obverse, in many ways, of what Balfour was later to declaim (1874, pp. 161, 171–172, 174–175):

Gegenstand und Methode der phylogenetischen Forschung . . . sind durchaus andere als diejenigen der von mir bearbeiteten physiologischen Entwicklungsgeschichte des Individuums . . . Das nächste Interesse für uns liegt in der . . . formulirten Frage: in wie weit die phylogenetische Geschichte einer Form zugleich als deren Erklärung gelten darf, und wie sich ihre eventuelle Erklärung verhält zur physiologischen Erklärung? . . .

Ich behaupte nun, die Körperform ist eine unmittelbare Folge des Keimwachsthums, und bei gegebener Anfangsform des Keimes aus dem Gesetze des Wachsthums abzuleiten . . .

Weiterhin ist aber das Keimwachsthum eine Folge der Eigenschaften des eben befruchteten Keimprotoplasmas. Diese sind eine Folge von den Eigenschaften der elterlichen Keimstoffe und der Art ihres Zusammentreffens u.s.w. Wir bekommen somit folgende Reihenfolge zu leistender Erklärungen:

1) Erklärung der Körperform aus dem Wachsthum des Keimes;

2) Erklärung des Keimswachsthums aus den Eigenschaften des befruchteten Keimprotoplasmas und aus den Bedingungen seiner Entwickelung (Temperatur, Ernährungsbedingungen u.s.w.).

3) Erklärung der Eigenschaften des befruchteten Keimprotoplasmas aus den Eigenschaften der elterlichen Keimstoffe und der besonderen Bedingungen ihres Zusammentreffens;

4) Erklärung der Eigenschaften der Keimstoffe aus dem Gange der elterlichen Körperentwickelung;

5) Erklärung der besonderen Bedingungen der Befruchtung aus den Lebensverhältnissen der beiden Erzeuger und so fort.

Erst mit Nr. 5 der obigen Kette beginnt das Gebiet der phylogenetischen Erklärung, und es erstreckt sich von da in periodischer Wiederkehr ins Unermessliche nach rückwärts.

But to no immediate avail did His attempt to remove explanation from the level of the transcendental and ideal, and from the level of metaphysical relationships between organisms, to the level of the embryo itself; Haeckel spoke too strongly in opposition. Haeckel's greatest disservice, after all, was not his simple ignorance of the morphological exceptions to his law as a descriptive statement, but his emphasis on it as an irrefutable explanation of causal relationships. Transcendentalism of Haeckel's variety was as fundamentally incompatible as had been the other kind with any concept of *process*. "Die Phylogenie," he insisted, "ist die mechanische Ursache der Ontogenese" (1891, p. 7), not only distracting to other areas the many who might have otherwise become interested in true mechanical explanations, but refuting, as he thought, irrevocably those who were already involved in developing such interests. He felt His a particular foe, as well he might have; and his polemics against him, since they were inadequate to combat His on his own grounds, descended to ridicule of the most inane sort:

. . . [Es] lässt sich aus dem Studium der ontogenetischen Arbeiten von His bald erkennen, dass in seiner Vorstellung die bildende "Mutter Natur" weiter Nichts als eine geschickte *Kleidermacherin* ist. Durch verschiedenartiges Zuschneiden der Keimblätter, Krümmen und Falten, Zerren und Spalten derselben gelingt es der genialen Schneiderin leicht, alle die mannichfaltigen Formen der Thierarten durch "Entwickelung" (!) zu Stande zu bringen. Vor Allem spielen die Krümmungen und Faltungen in dieser *Schneider-Theorie* die wichstigste Rolle. . . . Am possirlichsten ist, wie die Schneiderin bei Fabrication der zwei Paar Gliedmaassen verfährt . . . . Doch wird diese herrliche "Briefcouvert-Theorie" der Wirbelthier-Beine noch übertroffen durch die "Höllenlappen-Theorie," welche His von der Entstehung der *rudimentären Organe* giebt. . . . Hier wirft also die schneidernde Natur die überflüssigen Gewebslappen hinter den Ofen, in die "Hölle"! (1891, pp. 53–54).

Haeckel, however, can hardly have been expected to accept His' whole cloth. Whitehead has spoken, in connection with his Fallacy of Misplaced Concreteness, and thinking surely of precisely such mentalities as Haeckel's, of those "clear-cut trenchant intellects, immovably encased in a hard shell of abstractions [who] hold you to their abstractions by the sheer grip of personality" ('25, p. 82). But it was not mere personality that won for Haeckel his felicitous reception. His personality may have made him think as he did; but it was the eagerness of his contemporaries for oversystematization, in terms of just such abstractions as his, that was responsible for the success of his doctrine. Its supplanting had therefore to wait until a new period demanded a different kind of thought, and until Wilhelm Roux could succeed where Leuckart and Bergmann and His had apparently failed.

The attempts at mechanical explanations of development begun by His and the others in the 1870's were surely an outgrowth of the whole philosophy of materialism that pervaded the thinking of the 19th century. But the 19th century was also a strongly romantic century in many ways, perhaps again specifically in reaction against materialism. It is a curious paradox that the Haeckelian doctrines, steeped in romantic idealism, emanated from the impersonal and objective doctrines of Darwin. But they did, and in doing so, flourished with sufficient strength to repress the mechanical theories of development really so much more compatible with the doctrines of evolution; and it is ironical that therefore the success of the new embryological theories had to await a waning of interest in Darwinism.

It must be admitted, however, that although evolution had delayed the new movement in one way, it is also true, in another, that it fostered it. The new interest in the new embryology came again from a new attack on the problem of epigenesis versus preformation, and this derived its origin from the absorption of the evolution doctrine into everyday thinking. The process of evolution implies epigenesis, in that change is the essence of both, and a gradual process from step to step. A generation habituated to thinking about change building on change in evolution could more easily than its fathers accept the concept of epigenesis with its causal connotations. Embryologists have been familiar with chain reactions for centuries; the significance of progressive differentiation in ontogeny had been made explicit in the modern sense by Leuckart and Bergmann, and through His, who though his "organbildende Keimbezirke" are usually accredited for heralding neo-preformation, yet inferred the causal relationships implicit in neo-epigenesis (1874, p. 2):

Die Entwicklungsgeschichte ist ihrem Wesen nach eine physiologische Wissenschaft, sie hat den Aufbau jeder einzelnen Form aus dem Ei nach den verschiedenen Phasen nicht allein zu beschreiben, sondern derart abzuleiten, dass jede Entwicklungsstufe mit allen ihren Besonderheiten als nothwendige Folge der unmittelbar vorangegangenen erscheint.

Roux himself, who was a student of Haeckel's, and felt himself his disciple, very definitely acted as intermediator between Darwinism and the new causal analytical embryology. His "Kampf der Theile im Organismen," though written before his great concentration of interest on embryological problems, was consummately important in this respect. By striking an analogy between the struggle for existence among organisms on the one hand, and that between the parts of an organism on the other, Roux pointed up for the first time in a new way the possible significance for differentiation of interrelationships between tissues, and suggested the possibility already in that communication of the "Hervorbildung des chemisch und morphologisch Differenzirteren aus dem Einfacheren ohne differenzirende äussere Einwirkungen," as opposed to the conditions where "andere Gewebe . . . secundär durch Einwirkung seitens der ersteren aus dem embryonalen Blastem differenzirt werden" (1881; cited from Roux, 1895a, I, 332–333). But are not these clearly Haeckel's *innere* and *äussere Bildungstriebe*—words and concepts borrowed by him deliberately from Goethe? And Haeckel, for all his faults, was infected by Goethe with an enthusiasm for the dynamic wholeness of the organism and its environment, which he passed on to Roux who made use of it as Haeckel never could. Spemann was to be moved by it too. He mentioned in his autobiography having known Martin Donndorf who had seen Eckermann, and commented that "man wird nicht mehr leicht jemand begegnen, der in Augen geblickt hat, welche Goethe gesehen haben" (['43], p. 86). His own intellectual distance from Goethe was, like Roux', diminished by the intermediacy of Haeckel:

Im Lager fiel mir das Buch von Wilhelm Preyer über die Seele des Kindes in die Hand; mit schlechtem Gewissen, wie ein Schuljunge mit einem Buch unter der Bank, sass ich damit in einer dunklen Ecke. Das kam aus der Gegend von Ernst Haeckel, der so manchen jungen Mann meiner und der vorhergehenden Generation zur Biologie geführt hatte. Dort begegnete ich auch zum erstenmal, soviel ich mich erinnere, dem Begriff der Biologie als einer umfassenden Wissenschaft vom Leben, mit all ihren aufwühlenden Lehren über seine letzte Tiefe (*ibid.*, p. 116).

But if Roux began his work against the natural philosophical background of Haeckel, from whom he also inherited his predilection for setting up his concepts in a strongly theoretical framework, he was later to grow far beyond Haeckel's romanticism. Haeckel's own strong predilection for monism may have exerted its influence in this respect. But Roux had studied also with Goette. Particularly, also, he was influenced in the direction of the new preformationism by Weismann. For the new embryology, strangely enough, received a strong impetus from the old preformation as this was revived in a new form. Rádl ('30, p. 263) has made the clever comment, and justly so, that "Haeckel silenced von Baer, the embryologist, and returned to the ideas of Meckel. Weismann ignored [von] Baer, the epigeneticist, and went back to the idea of the tedious and insipid Bonnet." Roux derived his parentage from them both; and Weismann himself had been, after all, a student of Leuckart's.

It is always tempting to contrast Roux' mechanistic preformationist tendencies with the vitalistic and epigenetic interpretations of Driesch, and to assume the enthusiasm for the new experimental embryology as arising out of the clear-cut difference between them, and as demanding the collection of new evidence to justify the choice between them. But what was more influential in starting the new experimental embryology on its way was not the opposition of results and interpretations of Roux and Driesch so much as the desire to verify or refute the Roux-Weismann hypothesis that the qualitative distribution of nuclear material is responsible for the mosaic sort of differentiation which Roux thought he could demonstrate; and the attack begun on it by Driesch and Hertwig in 1892 not only represented the beginning of all the active experimentation to follow, but led directly to the constriction experiments of Spemann which were destined to have such momentous results.

In the same measure as Weismann was indirectly responsible for the new embryology to follow, nineteenth century materialism lay behind it. Weismann was no freer than any other from the influence of his times; his idioplasm is a modification of that of Nägeli which was "like a microscopic picture of the macroscopic individual" (cited from Rádl, '30, p. 226). Atomicity, as elucidated by Dalton for chemistry, was implicit in the biological ideas of Mendel and Pasteur, and equally in the determinants postulated by Weismann. Weismann's contribution, like that of so many influential figures in the history of science, was the expression of his doctrine to a century philosophically ripe for its acceptance.

And once more a new tool could be exploited to make visibly manifest concrete evidence of a theory bound to become popular because of its appropriateness to the demands of its times. Now, it was the improved achromatic lens, which brought out the cytological details of nuclear behavior during mitosis and meiosis and fertilization, and which gave new meaning to the relationship between cellular inclusions and cellular differentiation, and thus evoked a new interest in the old preformation. This had its effect not only on Roux among the embryologists. In a way, the work of Whitman and all his disciples who devoted themselves to the study of cell lineage in eggs with determinate cleavage grew out of the same background as Weismann's, and came in a different way to setting up the premises for a new kind of preformation (see especially Whitman, 1894a, 1894b, and Wheeler, 1898, for brilliant expositions of the *fin de siècle* position against the older historical background). It led too to the magnificent work of Boveri, who on a purely embryological basis established as soundly as the geneticists later the role of qualitative and quantitative distribution of the chromosomes.

Weismann, however, and the new materialism and the new preformationism, and Goette and His and Haeckel were not the only influences to culminate in Roux. He had his ideas from the botanists, too, and not only indirectly as in the case of Nägeli's idioplasm adopted by Weismann. Sachs, who was also greatly influenced by Nägeli, had been experimentalizing plant biology as Roux was to do with embryology; with the physiologists' primary interest in irritability he worked out the basis of what was later to culminate with Loeb in the theory of tropisms, a concept which the embryologists adopted as soon as the physiologists, and perhaps with even greater fruit. Roux, in the first paper, after the introduction, published in the new *Archiv* (1895d), took it over in his use of "cytotaxis" and "cytotropism" as explanatory of the relationships of amphibian blastomeres to one another. And Roux was not the only one to employ it: Driesch called in "taktische Reizbarkeit" to explain certain behavior of the mesenchyme cells in the echinoderm embryo. Herbst elaborated it further for embryology, even going so far, in his *Formative Reize in der tierischen Ontogenese,* as to postulate on a theoretical basis the dependence of the development of the vertebrate lens on the optic cup, the very year that Spemann (who had himself learned botany from Sachs) was to perform his first experiment demonstrating it (though independent of Spemann; cf. Spemann, '03, p 566). The ideas of progressive differentiation which had been developing since Aristotle were thus to come to final fruition; Spemann's precision of thought and performance, and his supreme intellectual power, instigated their analysis in a new way, doing more than full justice to the causal analytical motive of Roux.

For if in Roux many influences converge and if from him many new trends begin, and if in embryology after his time as directly before it, it is not always easy to follow a single guiding motive, yet there stems from him the single modern approach, the *experiment*, and this we owe to him alone. It is true, as so often, that before he was to perform the experiment which was to start the new trend, there had been a gradual preparation for its acceptance on the conceptual side: biological science, like physical, had finally become generally experimentalized; it was no accident that Pasteur and Claude Bernard preceded Wilhelm Roux in time. But Chun had previously performed a similar experiment with as striking results if not as momentous influence; and Roux not only performed the experiment but generalized its significance. His ability to mobilize thought around it was due to his own qualities of mind and person.

Driesch, in a different way than Chun, represents the contrast against which the contribution of Roux becomes more capable of evaluation. Roux had the perspicacity to appreciate that the embryo could be grappled with experimentally; Driesch, though he made a great experimental contribution to embryology, lacked it, and was so steeped in metaphysics that he finally made his option for philosophy proper.

The comparison of their interpretations of what they thought a single comparable experiment illustrates the strength and weakness of both. Roux believed he freed one blastomere in the two-celled amphibian egg from the influence of another by killing the latter, and thought he demonstrated thereby the independent differentiation of the surviving cell. Driesch found a single isolated blastomere of the two-cell echinoderm egg able to form a whole embryo and believed he could prove the differentiation of a cell to be dependent on its position with respect to the whole. Both experiments were subject to critical errors, as we now know, and for both eggs both explanations are partially correct and partially inadequate.

But this was not the only issue between them, nor the fundamental one. Roux interpreted the egg for the first time as a mech-

anism mechanically analyzable by outside interference; Driesch envisioned it as ruled by an entelechy as spiritual as any *deus ex machina* must be. This difference was within them, and not dictated by their times. Though the spirit of particular times may facilitate choosing one view or the other, there have been mechanists and vitalists at all ages. But those differences in Roux' and Driesch's interpretations were here determined by their own casts of mind, and the fact is that Roux, by his choice, brought the embryo to become experimentally attackable by exact investigation. Roux set the whole program for experimental embryology, and this is his importance, not the fact that he performed an experiment which by 1910 had been proved to be erroneously conceived and interpreted.

Roux' importance, however, is not only in terms of presenting a method of solving problems, but of setting them, and this is pertinent. He could perform an experiment on an embryo because he could ask a question of the embryo that was experimentally answerable, at least within limits. His opposition of *differentiatio sui* and *differentiatio ex alio* answers the warning raised by Brooks (cf. rubric heading this section) that points of reference must be specified. The choice between them could be made in a limited way by his own method of isolation; the necessity of a more crucial method to certify the choice led to the development of the transplantation technique by Born, Harrison and Spemann. And Roux' experimental program, carried to its logical outcome by the addition of the transplantation methods, in a way implied by it, has led straight to the modern embryology which incorporates the valid features of both epigenetic and preformationistic concepts. Every embryologist, whether concerned with the development of enzyme systems, or the cleavage of so-called determinative eggs, or with fields and gradients in a regulative egg, or whatever, is still concerning himself with the degree to which his material at a particular moment in development is answering to Roux' description of *differentiatio sui* or *differentiatio ex alio*.

Roux' own primary interest was in a theoretical and philosophical problem, that he called the *Causalnexus* of events. But his gift was that he could address his problem in such a way to the embryo that the embryo reacted in what Roux believed an intelligible way to laboratory interference.

The degree of intelligibility of the reaction of the embryo to interference is a problem to which we shall return in the next section. But it may be commented here that Roux, like von Baer, has made a greater advance than Darwin in the descent from metaphysics to the level of the organism; as a result of Roux' program, after all, hypotheses can be tested by exact investigation —and the investigator need only to read any single paper by Spemann or Harrison to know how exact—in an experimental laboratory.

* * * * * *

This section was started, it may be remembered, from the premise that a backward look might give a clue as to how to proceed in the future for the best progress of embryology. The primary trend that emerges from the survey has seemed the gradual transition from the metaphysical to the physical that characterizes the progress of all developing science. What help may we derive, then, from the embryologists who have made the greatest progress in this respect?

The one valid generalization that can be drawn is that the great progressive minds of embryology—those of Aristotle, Wolff, von Baer, and Roux—and in our own times those of Spemann and Harrison—have been those of the investigators who have learned to address the embryo by the right question; and these are the men who have derived their intuitions primarily from the study of the embryo itself. The investigators who have derived their ideas from the philosophical side, and examined their embryos to fit their observations into philosophical patterns already set and rigid—Goethe, St. Hilaire, Haeckel, Driesch—were the minds whose philosophical patterns delayed rather than accelerated the course of embryological progress. Aristotle and Wolff and von Baer and Roux started out too from philosophical and theoretical premises, but in such a way that they relegated the initiative of answering their problems to the embryo itself; they could do so only because it was the embryo that gave them their clues as to how to ask their questions. The others had been more interested in the ideas than the embryos, and had become captured by them to the detriment both of themselves and science.

Examining the problem from another aspect, we may say that the greatest delaying influences on embryology have been first the acceptance of the seventeenth century preformation doctrine, then the doctrines of Unity of Type, later the recapitulation doctrine, all concepts whose philosophical rather than their embryological content insured their success. Are we in the course of undergoing a similar delay? Are we too indulging in too high a degree of metaphysical speculation, pushing back what we cannot understand into concepts of fields and gradients which still have only metaphysical reality and into invisible realms what visible structure only inadequately explains? Is our present emphasis on the biochemical and biophysical constitution of the embryo a reaction against this? It is now again beginning to be admitted (cf. many authors in Parpart, ed., '49) that the new biochemistry is insufficient to answer our fundamental problem of organization. We can not safely underestimate the complexity of the problem we attempt to solve, to borrow phraseology from Wheeler (1898). In biological science, structure is inadequate to explain process. As biologists, we are bound to fail when we use methods applicable only to the study of structure for the analysis of processes functioning in time. The problem of modern embryology as stated above was crudely summed up as the problem of determining the degree to which particular material answers to Roux' description of *differentiatio sui* or *differentiatio ex alio* at any *one moment*. We have no methods as yet to deal with analyzing the transition from one moment to the next. Here the problem is simpler for the classical physiologist, and it is because of this that the progress of the embryologist has followed rather than preceded his.

Another trouble has been, historically speaking, our constant opposition of the metaphysical to the physical; there may be a biological level, too, at which one might work without retreating to the camp of the spiritualists and vitalists, and this is where our imagination has been and still is at its weakest. Roux saw the dilemma, as have so many others (1895c, p. 23):

Für den Forscher auf dem Gebiete der Entwickelungsmechanik gilt in hohem Masse das Wort:

"Incidit in scyllam, qui vult vitare charybdim."

Die zu *einfach mechanische* und die *metaphysische Auffassung* repräsentiren die Scylla und die Charybdis, zwischen welchen dahin zu segeln in der That schwer und bis jetzt nur Wenigen gelungen ist.

Some of the limitations of the too simply

mechanical conception will be entered into further in the section to follow; suffice it to conclude here with a few more words about the metaphysical. Modern science considers respect for it a fault, which in many ways it is. But modern science must remember, as Whitehead reminds us, that all thought is abstract, and that intellectual induction at least presupposes metaphysics. And primary success in dealing with the embryo, because of its complexity, must derive from the inductive rather than the deductive process. No scientific progress has ever been made without reflection and speculation; and it must be remembered that both imply holding a mirror to nature, and that the surfaces must be held true.

Woodger ('48), as a matter of fact, in a most interesting theoretical paper, "Observations on the present state of embryology," presented recently at the Second Growth Symposium in England, has concerned himself with the necessary conditions for immediate embryological progress, to conclude that what we need is to concentrate our attention on a few key data in order to derive the key hypotheses we require to proceed. There is a fallacy here for embryology. The greatest progressive minds of embryology have not searched *for* hypotheses; they have looked *at* embryos. How they have looked, and how they are looking now, is the burden of the section to follow.

REFERENCES

Agassiz, L. 1857 Essay on classification; in Contributions to the Natural History of the United States of America, Vol. I, pp. 1–232. Little, Brown and Company, Boston.

Aristotle 1943 Generation of Animals. With an English translation by A. L. Peck. Harvard University Press, Cambridge, Massachusetts.

———— 1945 Parts of Animals. With an English translation by A. L. Peck and a foreword by F. H. A. Marshall. Movement of Animals. Progression of Animals. With an English translation by E. S. Forster. Harvard University Press, Cambridge, Massachusetts.

Baer, K. E. von 1828, 1837 Ueber Entwickelungsgeschichte der Thiere: Beobachtung und Reflexion. Gebrüder Bornträger, Königsberg.

———— 1853 Fragments relating to philosophical zoology. Selected from the works of K. E. von Baer; In Scientific Memoirs, Selected from the Transactions of Foreign Academies of Science, and from Foreign Journals: Natural History, edited by A. Henfrey and T. H. Huxley, pp. 176–238. Taylor and Francis, London.

———— 1864 Reden gehalten in wissenschaft-

lichen Versammlungen und kleinere Aufsätze vermischten Inhalts, Part I: Reden. H. Schmitzdorff, St. Petersburg.

Balfour, F. M. 1880, 1881 A Treatise on Comparative Embryology. Two vols. Macmillan and Co., London.

Balss, H. 1936 Die Zeugungslehre und Embryologie in der Antike. Quellen u. Studien zur Geschichte der Naturw. u. der Med., 5:193–274.

Beer, G. R. de 1951 Embryos and Ancestors. Clarendon Press, Oxford, England.

Bergmann, C. and Leuckart, R. 1855 Anatomisch-physiologische Uebersicht des Thierreichs. Vergleichende Anatomie und Physiologie. Ein Lehrbuch für den Unterricht und zum Selbststudium. New ed. J. B. Müller, Stuttgart.

Brooks, W. K. 1902 The intellectual conditions for the science of embryology. Science, N.S., 15: 444–454, 481–492.

Bunge, G. 1902 Textbook of Physiological and Pathological Chemistry. 2d English ed. translated from the 4th German ed. by F. A. Starling and edited by E. H. Starling. P. Blakiston's Son & Co., Philadelphia.

Burnet, J. 1930 Early Greek Philosophy. 4th ed. A. & C. Black, Ltd., London.

Cole, F. J. 1930 Early Theories of Sexual Differentiation. Clarendon Press, Oxford, England.

———— 1944 Dr. William Croone on generation; in Studies and Essays in the History of Science and Learning Offered in Homage to George Sarton on the Occasion of his Sixtieth Birthday 31 August 1944, edited by M. F. Ashley Montagu, pp. 113–135. Henry Schuman, New York.

Darwin, C. 1902 The Origin of Species by Means of Natural Selection or the Preservation of Favored Races in the Struggle for Life. With additions and corrections from 6th and last English edition. Two vols. in one. D. Appleton and Company, New York.

Diderot, D. 1875. Entretien entre D'Alembert et Diderot. Rêve de D'Alembert. Suite de l'entretien; in Oeuvres complètes de Diderot, edited by J. Assézat, Vol. II, pp. 101–191. Garnier, Paris.

Eckermann, J. P. 1905 Gespräche mit Goethe in den letzten Jahren seines Lebens, edited by A. Bartels. Two vols. Eugen Diederichs, Jena.

Fabricius, H. 1942 The Embryological Treatises of Hieronymus Fabricius of Aquapendente. The Formation of the Egg and of the Chick (De formatione ovi et pulli). The Formed Fetus (De formato foetu). A facsimile edition, with an introduction, a translation, and a commentary by H. B. Adelmann. Cornell University Press, Ithaca, New York.

Goethe, J. W. von 1944 Gedanken und Aufsätze; in Goethes Werke, edited by E. Merian-Genast, Vol. XII. Birkhäuser, Basel.

Haeckel, E. 1891 Anthropogenie oder Entwickelungsgeschichte des Menschen. Keimes- und Stammes-Geschichte. 4th rev. and enl. ed. Wilhelm Engelmann, Leipzig.

———— [1900] The Riddle of the Universe at the Close of the Nineteenth Century. Translated by J. McCabe. Harper & Brothers, New York.

Harvey, W. 1653 Anatomical Exercitations, Concerning the Generation of Living Creatures: To Which Are Added Particular Discourses, of Births, and of Conceptions, &c. Octavian Pulleyn, London.

———— 1931 Exercitatio anatomica de motu cordis et sanguinis in animalibus. An English translation with annotations by C. D. Leake. Charles C Thomas, Springfield, Illinois.

His, W. 1874 Unsere Körperform und das physiologische Problem ihrer Entstehung. Briefe an einen befreundeten Naturforscher. F. C. W. Vogel, Leipzig.

Huxley, T. H. 1849 On the anatomy and the affinities of the family of the Medusae. Philos. Trans. Roy. Soc. London, 139:413–434.

———— 1853a On the morphology of the Cephalous Mollusca, as illustrated by the anatomy of certain Heteropoda and Pteropoda collected during the voyage of H. M. S. "Rattlesnake" in 1846–50. Philos. Trans. Roy. Soc. London, 143: 29–65.

———— 1853b The cell-theory (Review). British & Foreign Medico-Chirurgical Review, 12:285–314.

Jung, C. G. 1927 Psychology of the Unconscious. A Study of the Transformations and Symbolisms of the Libido. A Contribution to the History of the Evolution of Thought. Authorized translation, with introduction, by B. M. Hinkle. Dodd, Mead and Company, New York.

Kleinenberg, N. 1886 Die Entstehung des Annelids aus der Larve von Lopadorhyncus. Nebst Bemerkungen über die Entwicklung anderer Polychaeten. Wilhelm Engelmann, Leipzig.

Kowalewski, A. 1867 Die Entwickelungsgeschichte des *Amphioxus lanceolatus*. Mém. de l'Acad. de St. Pétersbourg, 7th series, 11, No. 4, pp. 1–17 (page numbers recorded from offprint; original journal not available).

Maître-Jan, A. 1722 Observations sur la formation du poulet, où les divers changemens qui arrivent à l'oeuf à mesure qu'il est couvé, sont exactement expliqués & representés en figures. d'Houry, Paris.

Malpighi, M. 1685 Dissertatio epistolica de formatione pulli in ovo Regiae Societati Londoni ad scientiam naturalem promovendam institutae, dictata; in Bibliotheca anatomica sive recens in anatomia inventorum thesaurus completissimus . . . edited by D. LeClerc and I. I. Magnetus, pp. 575–594. Chovet, Geneva.

Meckel, J. F. 1821–1833 System der vergleichenden Anatomie. 6 pts. in 7 vols. Renger, Halle.

Meyer, A. W. 1935 Some historical aspects of the recapitulation idea. Quart. Rev. Biol., 10:379–396.

———— 1939 The Rise of Embryology. Stanford University Press, Stanford, California.

Needham, J. 1934 A History of Embryology. Cambridge University Press, Cambridge, England.

Oppenheimer, J. M. 1936 Historical introduction to the study of teleostean development. Osiris, 2: 124–148.

———— 1940 The non-specificity of the germ-layers. Quart. Rev. Biol., 15:1–27.

Parpart, A. K. (editor) 1949 The Chemistry and Physiology of Growth. Princeton University Press, Princeton, New Jersey.

Plato [1944] The Timaeus and the Critias or Atlanticus. The Thomas Taylor translation. Pantheon books [New York].

Rádl, E. 1930 The History of Biological Theories. Translated and adapted from the German by E. J. Hatfield. Oxford University Press, Oxford, England.

Roux, W. 1895a Der züchtende Kampf der Theile oder die "Theilauslese" im Organismus. Zugleich eine Theorie der "functionellen Anpassung." Ein Beitrag zur Vervollständigung der Lehre von der mechanischen Entstehung des sogenannten "Zweckmässigen"; in Gesammelte Abhandlungen über Entwickelungsmechanik der Organismen, Vol. I, pp. 135–422. Wilhelm Engelmann, Leipzig.

———— 1895b Die Entwicklungsmechanik der Organismen, eine anatomische Wissenschaft der Zukunft; in Gesammelte Abhandlungen über Entwickelungsmechanik der Organismen, Vol. II, pp. 24–54. Wilhelm Engelmann, Leipzig.

———— 1895c Einleitung. Roux' Arch. Entw.-mech., 1:1–42.

———— 1895d Ueber den "Cytotropismus" der Furchungszellen des Grasfrosches (*Rana fusca*). Roux' Arch. Entw.-mech., 1:43–68, 161–202.

Schrecker, P. 1938 Malebranche et le préformisme biologique. Revue internat. de philos., 1:77–97.

Shumway, W. 1932 The recapitulation theory. Quart. Rev. Biol., 7:93–99.

Singer, C. 1922 Greek Biology & Greek Medicine. Clarendon Press, Oxford, England.

———— [1941] A Short History of Science to the Nineteenth Century. Clarendon Press, Oxford, England.

———— 1944 A word on the philosophical background of Vesalius; in Studies and Essays in the History of Science and Learning Offered in Homage to George Sarton on the Occasion of His Sixtieth Birthday 31 August 1944, edited by M. F. Ashley Montagu, pp. 75–84. Henry Schuman, New York.

Spemann, H. 1903 Entwickelungsphysiologische Studien am Triton-Ei. III. Roux' Arch. Entw.-mech., 16:551–631.

———— [1943] Forschung und Leben. Edited by F. W. Spemann. J. Engelhorns Nachf. Adolf Spemann, Stuttgart.

Temkin, O. 1950 German concepts of ontogeny and history around 1800. Bull. Hist. Med., 24: 227–246.

Thompson, D'A. W. 1940 Science and the Classics. Oxford University Press, Oxford, England.

Wheeler, W. M. 1898 Caspar Friedrich Wolff and the *Theoria generationis*. Biol. Lect. Marine Biol. Lab. Woods Holl, 1898, pp. 265–284.

Whitehead, A. N. 1925 Science and the Modern World. The Macmillan Company, New York.

Whitman, C. O. 1894a Evolution and epigenesis. Biol. Lect. Marine Biol. Lab. Woods Holl, 1894, pp. 205–224.

———— 1894b Bonnet's theory of evolution. Biol. Lect. Marine Biol. Lab. Woods Holl, 1894, pp. 225–240.

Wolff, C. F. 1774 Theoria generationis. New ed., enl. & corr. Hendel, Halle.

Woodger, J. H. 1948 Observations on the present state of embryology; in Growth in Relation to Differentiation and Morphogenesis, Symposia of the Society for Experimental Biology, No. 2, pp. 351–365. Academic Press, New York.

METHODS AND TECHNIQUES

JANE M. OPPENHEIMER

INTRODUCTION: SOME GENERAL CONSIDERATIONS

GREAT ADVANCES, in scientific history, have almost always depended more on intellectual than on technological innovations. No new technique has alone either answered any problem of primary importance or has itself set one. In biological history, specifically, so far as technique is concerned, the work of Harvey and of Darwin and of Mendel could have been performed far earlier than it was: their advances were on the intellectual side, rather than technical in any sense. Harvey's greatest contribution was perhaps the application of the principle of measurement to biological material, and his ability to perform his experiment was an inevitable outcome of his quantitative considerations. There was a certain greater ease for him, who was bred in the halls of Padua a generation after Galileo, than for his predecessors to think quantitatively. But there is no *a priori* reason why such thinking might not have emanated from some Greek mind near Archimedes who in considering specific gravity in physical terms was thinking as quantitatively as Harvey who had only to collect and count a few cups of blood. Darwin was led to the formulation of his doctrine by the consideration of Malthus' economic principles and Lyell's geological ones: but might not a clue to the genetic relationship of man and the ape have come from a comparison of their faces? Indeed had it not already done so in Buffon's concept of the ape as a "degraded" man? And what did Mendel do but separate his generations, keep careful records, count accurately and think clearly? The material of these men was the organism pure and simple; the instruments with which they attacked it were primarily their ideas. To quote Woodger, who emphasizes the same point:

Neither Dalton nor Mendel were afraid to put forward their hypotheses because of the absence of physical apparatus like that provided by X-ray photography. Their hypotheses were devised to explain the generalizations of their day—chemical generalizations about combining proportions in Dalton's case, and generalizations about ratios of kinds of offspring of known parentage in Mendel's case. The apparatus which subsequently provided confirmation of these hypotheses might never have been invented (at least in the case of Dalton) if the hypotheses themselves had not first been invented ('48, p. 360).

In embryology, too, as we have seen, the concept developed before the technique to verify or refute it. It was changes in thinking, not the mechanical tool, that permitted Wolff and von Baer to see more than Malpighi, in seeing less. Thinking in terms of concrete units such as Dalton's atoms, Mendel's unit characters in heredity and Pasteur's germs preceded the discovery and observation of discrete particles in the form of chromosomes and cytoplasmic inclusions by the use of improved achromatic lenses in the masterly cytological studies at the turn into the present century that were to become so important for embryology. Boveri ('07) established the fact of qualitative difference of the chromosomes by an intellectual *tour de force* in his analysis of dispermic echinoderm eggs before the technical methods of genetics were available. Spemann reached his primary premises out of thoughtful consideration of methodologically simple constriction experiments; he was later only to test and confirm, by the application of the technically more involved transplantation methods of Born and Harrison, what he had already suspected.

Indeed, one of the more curious phenomena of embryological history is the great lag in the application of more general biological techniques to the particular problems of embryology. Vesalius' *Fabrica* was published over 75 years before the treatise of Fabricius on the developing chick. Strong magnifying lenses were used fruitfully for a half century on other biological material before Malpighi used the compound microscope to examine the blastoderm of the chick. Alchemy and pharmacology had puzzled over the uses of specific salts, at least since the ninth century, for the adult organism; the modern statement of the fundamental chemical problems of embryology awaited the nineteenth century. If the embryo waited centuries for even such simple quantitative approach as had been devoted to the adult by Sanctorius Sanctorius, it had to wait millennia, from the time surgeons first used their scalpels on biological material to cut off an offending member, for the hot needle of Roux and the discerning eye of Chun (1880) who observed comparable effects of the stormy Mediterranean seas. John Hunter had attempted modern methods of grafting in the adult organism over a century before transplantation techniques were applied to embryological material. There is surely no simple reason to account for these long delays in embryological evolution. But certainly they may be related to the fact that no method or technique developed for other sciences, even within the biological realm, has been adequate to enable the embryologist to come to grips with his fundamental and most inescapable problem, the nature of embryonic organization.

The important progress, then, in the history of embryology, has been in the gradual changes in the cast of thought and clarification, as it seems from our point of view, in the setting of the question to be answered by the embryo. How the question is expressed, at any one moment in history, is of course conditioned by the technical procedures available at the time, as well as by the influence of more general currents of thought; and the problem of the embryologist becomes the problem of asking a question, with whatever means are at his disposal, that the embryo can answer in a manner intelligible to the investigator.

What are the means of investigation available to the embryologist today? How have they developed? To what degree do they permit adequate reply to the problems they purport to attack? What are their limitations and how far can these be overcome? In what measure do they inhibit, as did the late nineteenth century concentration on genealogical research, or in what way do they encourage, as did the happy exploitation of the transplantation method by Spemann and Harrison, the posing of new and searching problems? What does the experience of the past and the present inform us at all usefully as to how the future might best be explored

in terms of new techniques and of new problems? These are questions which the embryologist must answer if he is to review his work in proper perspective with relation to larger fields, and only by so doing can he hope to facilitate his approach to the problems next facing him.

OBSERVATION VS. INTERFERENCE AS AN APPROACH TO EMBRYOLOGICAL PROBLEMS

Modern embryology, since Roux, has tended strongly both in its pedagogical and investigational aspects to contrast the descriptive, or morphological, or observational, approach, with the so-called experimental, an only apparent distinction whose illusion of dichotomy leads to an important paradox to be taken up below. But since the observational method, at least in a crude form, has always been available to the investigator, a few of the difficulties inherent in the interpretation of what seem to be the simplest observations may be pointed out at the beginning of this discussion. Since even the results of experiments must be observed in some fashion, and this is only part of the paradox, these difficulties of interpretation are of significance in a much wider sense and therefore will be discussed also in relation to the broader issues.

In the first place, observation of the embryo can rarely, if ever, remain observation pure and simple. This seems a truism; yet there are certain inferences to be drawn from it which are not so completely obvious as it might seem.

Perhaps the greatest interference with constructive and advancing observation derives from the preconceptions already present in the mind of the observer, and there is no need further to labor the point that modern investigators, like the great minds of the past, like Wolff, like Roux, tend to see in terms of what they are looking for.

It is the what-he-is-looking-for that is so strongly conditioned by the mechanical tools at the disposal of the embryologist, which both expand and limit what is visible to him. In the early days of the microscope the embryologist saw organs, tissues, layers, perhaps cells. With the improvement of the techniques of microtomy and staining and with the perfection of achromatic lenses he could examine parts of the nucleus and what now seem the grosser cytoplasmic inclusions. The technique of modern optics and microscopy enable him to push his frontiers far beyond the old limits, and new instruments will continue to help him in this respect. Many other techniques, biophysical, biochemical, immunological, and so forth, allow the identification and description, if not the actual visualization, of components of the embryonic cell at the molecular and even the submolecular level.

Roux was frankly skeptical of the possibility of reducing embryological problems to the molecular level:

Auch wenn wir von den letzten Ursachen ganz absehen, so ist es doch fraglich, ob wir das von Carl Ernst v. Baer gesteckte Ziel: "Die bildenden Kräfte des thierischen Körpers auf die allgemeinen Kräfte oder Lebensrichtungen des Weltganzen zurückzuführen," je erreichen werden, vorausgesetzt, dass die zu Grunde liegende Auffassung überhaupt vollkommen richtig ist (1889, cited from Ges. Abh. 2:28–29).

He preferred to approach them by investigating, by means of interference with the embryo, what he called the *Causalnexus* of events. Causality is more suspect to the modern scientist, and becomes mere statistical probability, but following Roux, nevertheless, the tendency is fortunately to describe not simple structure but events, and specifically a sequence of events in time. If Roux believed this sequence capable of being subject to causal analysis, he realized also that the results of any such analysis could become significant only in a frame of reference defined by the normal developing embryo, and must have taken for granted that the "control" for an experimentally treated embryo must be an undisturbed one.

If a primary obligation of the embryologist, before he can evaluate an experimental result, is the knowing of the normal condition of the embryo, the fundamental paradox arises that he cannot perhaps adequately know the normal without the benefit of the experiment, whose whole *raison d'être* can surely be only that it elucidates the normal; yet he cannot interpret his experimental result without comparison with the normal control. Leaving aside, however, for the moment this dilemma, the task of the embryologist concerned with "normal" development becomes the task of describing the sequence of events in time as accurately as possible in terms of what he can see with the tools available to him, and to describe the components which are acting and their manner of action in as precise physical and chemical terms as his instruments and techniques will allow, as objectively as is possible in the light of the general biological and broader philosophical tenets of his times.

A first difficulty arises in that it is virtually impossible to observe an embryo under external conditions that do not interfere with it. Fixation, staining and other chemical treatment disturb the "normal" condition of the embryonic cell and alter it. Suffice it to say about the living embryo, without entering into the obvious detail, that the laboratory is not its normal environment. Indeed, is it always possible to define, let alone reproduce, a "normal" environment?

What is the "normal" environment of a developing Bonellia or Crepidula, whose sexual differentiation may be modified by it, in terms of distance from another Bonellia or Crepidula (Herbst, '36, '37; Baltzer, '37; Coe, '48)? What is the "normal" salinity for the development of Artemia whose form depends on the salt concentration of its environment (Abonyi, '15)? To come to the vertebrate, which we are in the habit of considering more conventional and stable embryological material, *Fundulus heteroclitus* embryos raised at constant temperatures reach specific morphological stages after different periods of time when raised at varying salinities (Merriman, unpublished). The adults live and breed both in brackish water and sea water in nature, and the temperatures of the seas and the estuaries are inconstant. What then is the "normal" environment of the developing Fundulus? What are the criteria for determining objectively which set of conditions is "optimum" for the embryo developing in the laboratory, and what biological significance these have for the organism developing in nature?

Comparable problems arise for the chemical embryologist who tries to describe the constituent systems of the embryonic cell in biochemical terms. Unpublished data of Dumm have suggested that the cholinesterase level of Fundulus embryos at particular morphological stages varies according to the temperature at which the embryos have been raised; and Boell (unpublished) also has data suggesting that the course of enzyme development in the amphibian can be altered by varying the temperatures at which the embryos are reared. Weiss ('49) has introduced in another connection a useful concept of "molecular ecology" which may well serve to remind the embryologist of what he already knows but sometimes forgets, namely, that the embryo has an internal as well as an external environment that may well bear more strict definition than it has always hitherto received.

For the embryologist who considers himself primarily concerned with descriptive and morphological questions, the problems arising from these examples, and the countless others that could have been enumerated, may seem of little moment. He can evade them by ignoring them, or more profitably, he can meet them by specifying as strictly as possible the conditions under which he is making his observations. For the investigator, however, who is looking for "normal" controls for experimental material, the situation becomes more critical.

It becomes especially so for the interpretation of certain isolation experiments which will be discussed in more detail below, and it presents very particular problems in the case of some transplantation experiments. The rate of growth of an eye or a limb grafted heteroplastically onto an amphibian host varies according to whether or not the host is maximally or less than maximally fed (Twitty and Schwind, '31); how often does an Amblystoma in nature enjoy a condition of maximum repletion? The growth of an Amblystoma embryo varies according to the organisms constituting the diet it is fed; who can define the "normal" diet of Amblystoma in nature? Members of the same species of Amblystoma reared under similar laboratory conditions develop at different rates of growth when collected in Pennsylvania and New Jersey on the one hand, in Illinois on the other (DuShane and Hutchinson, '44); which is the more "normal" larva, that collected in the East or that which is spawned in the Midwest? This is a more than philosophical problem when experimentalists in Princeton, for instance, are comparing their results with those of investigators working at the University of Chicago in an attempt to work out basic mechanisms of development. And while it is particularly accentuated by the results of the heteroplastic experiments, it touches the heart of each investigation involving the growth of the whole or parts of the developing amphibian.

In the case of more complicated experiments it raises even more complex issues. Haploid tissues developing from the hybrid androgenetic merogons of Hadorn ('34, '37) and Baltzer ('40), for instance, die in the embryos which they constitute but survive in tissue culture or after transplantation to normal diploid hosts of one of the experimental species. Is a favorable tissue culture medium or the tissues of a diploid host to be defined as more "normal" or "abnormal" for these cells than the haploid parent embryo from which they were derived? Under which conditions are the operations of the gene in development more "normal"? In other cases, what seems "optimum" according to the subjective judgment of an investigator concerned with a particular experiment may lack biological significance to the organism. Of what biological significance is it to Lytechinus that its egg can be so treated in the laboratory that it is more readily activated by sperm of a foreign species than by that of its own (Tennent, '25)? Tennent ('10) has found that in reciprocal crosses of Hipponoë × Toxopneustes the larvae were of the Hipponoë type when raised in sea water of higher pH, of the Toxopneustes type when reared in sea water of lower pH, and has suggested that seasonal variations in hybrid echinoderm larvae obtained in other laboratories might be accounted for by seasonal variations in the alkalinity of the seas; who is to say whether autumn or spring is more "normal" for echinoderm hybrids? Under which conditions, and this is the crux of the matter, does the action of the gene, which according to its end-effect varies in the different situations, more closely simulate its norm?

This is not the appropriate place to take up the developmental action of genes, which will be considered in a separate section below; but it is necessary to emphasize here the advantages to the embryologist of working with genetically known and genetically specified material when he is able to do so. Embryos vary. Many of the factors which induce them to vary are difficult to control, as we have seen. The genetic factors are perhaps uncontrollable too when specimens are collected in nature. But when the genetic factors are known, they can be controlled, and thereby great strides into unknown territory can be accomplished (cf. Gluecksohn-Schoenheimer, '49), and, as important, the results can be specified in the best biological sense of the word.

Consideration, in fact, of all the limitations to interpretation discussed above, and of many others like them, leads to the same inescapable necessity for specification of the conditions under which an investigation proceeds. It may often accrue to the advantage of the investigation, rather than otherwise, that observations and experiments carried out in different situations lead to different outcomes as well as different interpretations. Only when investigators specify as closely as possible the conditions against which particular outcomes eventuate will there become available new data and new ideas through which correlations and significances which currently still elude us may eventually be discerned.

Granted that the conditions, intrinsic and extrinsic to the embryo, under which observations are made are specified as accurately as possible, the question arises as to their ideal manner of description once they have been obtained. For embryology, the problem of semantics which faces all scientists arises in a particularly desperate form, perhaps at least partly because embryology, never having formulated its own problems nor having developed its own techniques, has adopted descriptive words from the lingo of other sciences. Spemann, it may be remembered, concluded his great monograph with a confession that he borrowed words to describe embryonic phenomena which point not to physical but to psychical analogies, to emphasize his conviction that

these processes of development, like all vital processes, are comparable, in the way they are connected, to nothing we know in such a degree as to those vital processes of which we have the most intimate knowledge, viz., the psychical ones. It was to express my opinion that, even laying aside all philosophical conclusions, merely for the interest of exact research, we ought not to miss the chance given to us by our position between the two worlds ('38, p. 372).

Investigators more neutral with respect to this issue use the words induction, determination, regulation, organization, and so forth, borrowed, as Spemann would say, from the psychic sphere, partly out of wonderment at the unexplained powers of regulation of the embryo, but largely for lack of more clearcut or appropriate ones. The problem, however, is not so much of word as of concept; and only when the embryologist can more completely emancipate himself from the domination of other sciences and their techniques, and formulate his problems in his own terms, will he be motivated to create and define such terms with requisite precision.

Roux seems to have been the first, and the last, to worry over this problem, sufficiently, at least, to be driven to a specific attempt to solve it. He drew up his *Terminologie der Entwicklungsmechanik,* a discursive text with only the remotest resemblance to our own unfortunate glossaries, with the express aim "das causal-analytische Denken [zu] fördern und auch das vollkommene Verständnis der Autoren untereinander [zu] erleichtern" ('12, p. ix). His recognition of the difficulties

inherent in adapting for *Entwicklungsmechanik* terms borrowed from other sciences is perhaps nowhere made clearer than by the fact that he found it necessary to include in the *Terminologie* two separate definitions in sequence for *Tropismus,* one for zoological material composed by himself, the other for botanical, contributed by Küster, one of the botanical collaborators who assisted in the preparation of the book. No modern attempt to emulate the *Terminologie* has ever been made; no one since Roux has had either the courage or the conceit to try, and modern embryology is still confronted with the old problem of using borrowed terms. Perhaps, however, it is an advantage to the embryologist to be forced to utilize, as a temporizing device, the terminology of physics and chemistry, since in doing so he must also use their methods and resources.

It is indisputably by the application of these resources that the greatest advances are being made at the present time. The results of current investigations of structure and ultrastructure by phase-contrast microscopy and cinemicrography and by electron microscopy; of molecular arrays by polarization optics; of chemical constitution and activity by histochemical and immunological techniques, by microspectrography and microspectrophotometry; of the localization, constitution and kinetics of enzymes and enzyme systems and of other metabolic systems, by microrespirometry, by "biochemical dissection" by antimetabolites and other specific poisons, by modern nutrition studies and by the use of both radioactive and stable isotopes as tracers; of genetic effects of ionizing radiations—all these will be discussed in ensuing chapters of this book.

Continuation and elaboration of such physical and chemical descriptions of the embryo, of its cells and of their components, are a *conditio sine qua non* for further embryological progress. Such description, however, dynamic though it may seem, is essentially structural rather than functional, analytical rather than synthetic, and this new morphology, like the old, is not able to penetrate to the core of the problem of organization. A physical-chemical model of the embryo may ultimately be adequate to represent some phase of what embryonic organization has produced, but as yet there is no assurance that it can reproduce the process by which organization has functioned. Structure, in embryonic material, is not yet adequate to "explain" process.

This may be bound up with the fact that

the embryo has the disadvantage, from the point of view of the investigator, of developing in time. The methods appropriated by embryology from other disciplines, which have a different concern for the time factor, have been invented to describe material at a given moment, not to analyze transition from one moment to the next. Insight into the problems of organization demands new approaches to the physiology of development as such, while as yet we confine our efforts to the descriptive physiology of embryos, which is something different. However, it is possible that the clue to new methods for analyzing organization may well come from a deeper comprehension of structure than we now enjoy; and in any case, any knowledge of process we ever may hope to obtain is certain to become more meaningful in the light of as intimate an understanding as possible of ultimate structure.

One evident superiority of the results of the new morphology over those of the old is that they allow quantitative expression. There is no question but that embryological descriptions must be as quantitatively exact as is appropriate for the material and techniques in question, and there is no greater need to justify the benefits of this for embryology than for any other science. There are, however, certain sources of error in interpretation which may be pointed out which are inherent in some attempts to analyze the significance of certain aspects of growth and differentiation by presenting descriptions of them in quantitative form.

It is well to remember that mathematical abstraction is a particular kind of abstraction which is in itself highly specialized. Any progressive science deals in abstraction as well as in measurement, but it requires always to question the appropriateness of whatever abstraction it utilizes to the particular material with which it deals. There is no more fascinating collection of biological facts than those by which Sir D'Arcy Thompson referred growth and form to certain mathematical relationships, but surely Sir D'Arcy's analogies are provocative rather than explanatory, and he himself hardly claimed more for them.

A curve, for instance, which describes the "growth" of a colony of bacteria is useful in that it designates periods of change at particular moments, and these may be periods with which the investigator may wish to concern himself; but the "growth" of a colony of micro-organisms is something different from that of a multicellular organism, and the growth of one organism may be controlled by different factors than that of another. Weiss' warning of a few years ago is still relevant and will continue to remain so:

A purely formal treatment of growth, as is often attempted through the interpretation of growth curves, is only a valuable guide to and supplement of, but never a substitute for, a precise analysis of the different forms in which growth manifests itself.

There can be no research on growth as such. We can only study growing objects. And different growing objects follow different methods. . . . To know growth we must therefore break down each one of its manifestations into its constituent elementary processes and then study these and describe them in objective terms. This is a long way to go, but there is no short cut ('49, p. 182).

Weiss' admonition holds equally true for other aspects of development: differentiation, determination, or whatever. Exact quantitative description of embryological data is another *conditio sine qua non* for future embryological progress, but only if the embryologist keeps in mind which of his problems quantification cannot solve, as well as those which it can elucidate.

The success of quantitative methods in creating the new morphology has tended to encourage attempts to adapt quantitative methods to the results of the older; and this condition, together with the fact that the journals currently encourage the publication of data in graphic and tabular form, leads to a growing tendency to make material appear quantitative which may not necessarily be so in its own right. An example is the current procedure of using morphological stage numbers from stage series to represent ordinates or abscissae of graphs. This may be useful provided the author works with a footnote, in his thinking if not on his page, calling for caution in interpretation, but it is a question to what extent this reservation is kept in mind. The presence, in the curve of such a graph, of maxima or minima, and whether a line rises or falls is surely significant; not in the same way the slope of the line nor the character of the curve in other respects. A straight line in such a graph is not what it purports to be; "morphological age," as Needham ('42) calls it, is not equivalent to time, which can be quantified. *Stage 5* of an embryo is not something that equals *the sum of stage 2 plus stage 3*, which, unless specifically qualified, is what the conventional graphic representation implies.

There are innumerable cases, too, where

presentation of quantitative data is inadequate and perhaps irrelevant to answer the basic question presented by the material to be analyzed. What is the meaning, for instance, of the "quantitative" results described in percentages of positive differentiation in grafts? Luther ('36), for instance, has concluded that there is a gradient of physiological activity (*Aktivitätszustand*) around the rim of the trout blastoderm on the basis of the fact that differentiation occurs in a decreasing percentage of grafts as the material for grafting is removed from progressively greater distances from the midline of the embryonic shield. If a particular factor, or group of factors, or a certain quantity of such factors necessary for differentiation, characterizes the cells near the embryonic shield should not every graft from that area differentiate if the experiment is adequately performed? What is the meaning, in terms of the functions of the grafted cells, of the fact that only 84% of the grafts removed from a particular region have differentiated? May not the significance of these results be that the grafts have been removed in different ways from zones of transition, or that they have been implanted under differing experimental conditions? In other words, may not the quantitative variations in such results indicate variation in the technique of experimental procedure as well as variation in the activity of the tissue? Too many factors, which need no enumeration here, are varied in even such a simple experiment as the implantation of a graft on the yolk sac, which though in some ways is simple in others is drastic and crude; and the experimental procedure, which is manual and therefore difficult to subject to critical control, is probably differently performed each time.

It can be of the greatest advantage to the investigator to acknowledge that quantitative variation in his results reflects his own uncertainties as well as the accomplishment of his embryonic material, if he wishes to improve his experimental approach both from the technical and the intellectual aspect. The value of statistical treatment and its advantages in connection with the endeavor to attain the maximum precision in analysis are particularly great in the case of embryological material where so bewilderingly many variations are inherent in the material and where so many sources of error confuse the methods of analysis. But statistical results must not be interpreted as final to such a degree that they mask the weaknesses of the technical procedure where these

actually affect the interpretation of results. Embryology has not yet sufficiently matured towards the perfection of its methods that quantification can be its only desideratum, and it may well be that the necessity to improve upon these methods represents the most urgent challenge immediately confronting us.

TECHNIQUES OF INTERFERENCE WITH THE EMBRYO

It was Wilhelm Roux who first had the insight to appreciate the inadequacy of the descriptive method, no matter how precise the terms in which its results are couched, to demonstrate what he called the *Causalnexus* of events, and to formulate a program designed to analyze that causal relationship within sequences of events which had already been so clearly expressed on an inferential basis by His (see quotation on p. 17, Section I). It was the simplicity of Roux' first statement of his problem that enabled him to try to answer his question with an apparently simple experiment:

Fast alle aber führten im Weiterfolgen zu einer und derselben grossen Vorfrage, *zu einer Alternative, von welcher aus die causale Auffassung fast aller Bildungsvorgänge in zwei wesentlich verschiedene Bahnen gelenkt wird.* Dies ist die Frage: *Ist die Entwicklung des ganzen befruchteten Eies resp. einzelner Theile desselben "Selbstdifferenzierung" dieser Gebilde resp. Theile oder das Produkt von "Wechselwirkungen mit ihrer Umgebung?"* Eventuell, *welches ist der Antheil jeder dieser beiden Differenzirungsarten in jeder Entwicklungsphase des ganzen Eies und seiner einzelnen Theile?*
In der Beantwortung dieser Frage liegt meiner Einsicht nach der Schlüssel zur causalen Erkenntnis der embryonalen Entwicklung (1885; cited from Ges. Abh. 2:14).

The question with which he was concerned happened to involve the relationship of the part to the whole, and happened to revive in a new form the old controversy between preformationists and epigeneticists; but this was not its main significance. His great contribution from the methodological point of view was that he saw his problem in terms of a single alternative and in terms of clearcut relationships; relationships so expressed that he could alter them in what was to him a simple experiment. An embryo or an embryonic part depends for its capacity to differentiate on a mutual interaction with its surroundings, or it does not; remove it from its surroundings, and its reply should be unequivocal.

The significance, however, of the behavior of a part removed from its surroundings is lost except in comparison with its behavior in those surroundings, as Roux already knew. In most cases, except where natural pigments are present, the observation of the egg as a whole sheds all too little light on the separate activities of its individual parts, and Roux himself attempted to circumvent this difficulty by inventing a crude marking experiment and by pricking his eggs to produce extra-ovates which might serve as markers. This experiment is open to the obvious criticism that it may alter the status of the part whose normal behavior it purports to elucidate, and it was to obviate this that the technique of local vital staining was developed. It has reached its highest perfection as developed for application to the amphibian egg by Vogt ('25), where its success depends on the fact that inclusions of the egg adsorb the stain from the carrier more rapidly than it diffuses into the solution, and a mark of the utmost sharpness of outline is therefore achieved and maintained.

The data obtained by the local vital staining method are indispensable for the interpretation of experiments in which the activities of particular parts are to be studied by other means, and the dyes currently used (Nile blue sulfate, neutral red and Bismarck brown) are sufficiently nontoxic that the data derived from their use are thoroughly valid. There are conditions, however, under which the method has strong limitations. In some cases the dyes may be transformed to leukobases within the cells. In the case of embryos whose cells lack inclusions with special affinity for the dyes, for instance young stages of chick and teleost, the stains are far more diffuse and ephemeral than in the amphibian, and the results of their use may prove unreliable when checked against results obtained by other methods. The newer method of following morphogenetic movements by the application to the cells of carbon particles (Spratt, '46) has, for instance, produced results for the chick which are incompatible with those previously derived for the same form by vital staining (Pasteels, '37). The use of carbon particles holds great promise for the future, but the introduction of macroscopic particles within the cells raises certain dangers for the interpretation of what are supposed to be unhampered movements; and when the particles are applied to the outer surface of the cell there may always remain some doubt as to whether they may have shifted in position.

So far as the localization and retention of a marker is concerned, the least reproachable method of distinguishing one group of cells from another remains the observation of forms in which natural pigments occur. It may be remembered in this connection that the method of heteroplastic grafting was at its earliest inception used to trace the migration of elements distinguished by natural pigment (Harrison, '03; see Harrison, '35, for later uses of heteroplastic grafting). Grafting, however, as an operative method, introduces new sources of error not inherent in the methods of marking cells in an unoperated embryo. Unfortunately there is still no equivalent of a Geiger counter to report on the migrations of cells in the embryo. The data, however, which have been accumulated by the present techniques as applied by cautious investigators are adequate to serve as a frame of reference against which studies of the parts may be judged.

Since killing a cell is probably the easiest thing that an embryologist can do, it was perhaps inevitable that the study of the behavior of parts of an embryo should have first been examined by defect methods, and it is appropriate next to mention some of the ways in which defects have been produced. Experiments involving the removal or the supposed inactivation of cells or their parts have been carried out by mechanical, chemical, thermal and electrical methods and by combinations of them, and by the use of various sorts of radiations.

A primary and insidious source of error common to all these methods is that in applying them the investigator may alter more factors than he knows. The classical experiment of Roux (1888) was designed by killing a blastomere to eliminate its influence on its neighbor; the fact that its corpse exerted mechanical influence of moment could be appreciated only after McClendon ('10) completely removed a blastomere to demonstrate a different accomplishment by the remaining cell than had been achieved in Roux' experiment. Comparable sources of error may lie hidden in many if not all of the defect experiments subsequently performed.

In dealing with the deletion or inactivation of components of cells, the perils of interpretation may be as great. Boveri ('18) long ago recognized as an inevitable source of error in experiments designed to exclude nuclear influence that nuclear residues might remain undetected in the cytoplasm, which in any case has necessarily been produced under the influence of the nucleus. The centrifuge is a tool which can translocate substances from a particular part whose behavior is to be studied in their absence, but who knows what effects it may have had on the invisible components of the zone?

Nor are the mechanical methods the only ones open to suspicion. It is unthinkable that in anything kinetically as complex as the simplest protoplasm, alteration of its equilibria by chemical or thermal changes could be limited in its effects to a single system alone. Temperature changes probably affect all its constituent systems in some measure, and indeed the laws of thermodynamics are hardly such as to permit such effects to remain local. Methods involving the use of radiations and electricity, in spite of the advantage that the amounts of energy applied may be measured, cannot be construed in most cases as affecting single localizable or identifiable systems within the cell. Exception, however, may be made in the cases where radiations or other agents affect the known gene; the most reliable defect method, perhaps the ideal, is that which excludes identified genes (Poulson, '40, '45). Manipulation of the gene, by man or nature, is probably the most satisfactorily controlled experimental method available to the embryologist to date, and it will become the more useful the more exhaustively the intermediate steps between the primary action of the gene and the end-effects of its activity, as expressed in differentiation, become known.

Despite the reservations enumerated, however, excellent contributions to embryology have been made by the use of all of the defect methods. These methods were the first to demonstrate the high degree of regulability of which the embryo is capable, and thus have led directly to the primary embryological problem of ultimate organization, and the data which they have provided will be indispensible for the final solution of it.

A fact to be kept in mind in this connection is the impossibility of consideration of the defect experiment as separate from the isolation or explantation experiment, which is its corollary as well as its complement. In the ideal situation the embryologist wishes to consider both experiments. In one, the investigator studies what remains after something has been taken away; in the other, he studies the behavior of what he has removed. In this sense, the study of a single blastomere isolated from a two-celled egg may be regarded either as a defect experiment or as an isolation experiment. Roux, as a preformationist, considered it as an isola-

tion experiment. He knew that in the egg one blastomere forms half an embryo, and interpreted the blastomere in his experiment as duplicating its normal action. He concluded that its processes of development were identical in normal and experimental material, and the experiment seemed to him essentially a way to confirm what he had postulated the behavior of the normal part to be.

The questions that are put to the isolated part are now framed by more open minds, but they still deal in the main with the degree to which a cell is dependent for its differentiation on factors impinging upon it from its surroundings. To what degree does a part begin or continue differentiation when isolated from its usual cellular surroundings? Does it differentiate the same structures it was destined to form in the normal embryo? If not, what is the direction of its differentiation and what factors determine this direction? Attempts to isolate these factors involve not only the negative phase of the experiment and determining what factors usually present are lacking when the part is isolated, but also the more positive one of demonstrating the new or different ones to which it is subjected. This was a side of the problem on which Roux did not concentrate, though it is clear that he recognized its importance; and it is this aspect of it which raises some of the most immediate issues facing the present interpreters of isolation or explantation experiments.

Ideally the investigator may express a wish to culture his isolate in a neutral or indifferent medium (cf. Needham, '42, p. 175) which will permit it to continue its own development in its own way. This is essentially what Harrison ('07) did when he isolated the neuroblast in clotted lymph, a medium which did not inhibit the production of the axon yet which excluded the presence of the cells which had been thought by some to manufacture it. If the behavior of a cell is to be studied in the absence of influence from surrounding cells, it is essential that the medium to which it is removed cannot itself alter the chain of reactions to be studied. To what degree can this ideal be achieved?

First and foremost, the emancipation of a cell from influences emanating from its neighbors may now be recognized as more difficult to achieve than formerly was anticipated, in view of Holtfreter's ('44) recent demonstration that some of the cells constituting the very cultures being studied may attain a sublethal state of cytolysis, as a result of reaction to the medium, which may exert hitherto unsuspected effects on other cells nearby in the cultures.

Even in cases, however, where such effects may be discounted in the interpretation of results, many other difficulties arise in attempts to prepare a suitable medium. Cells can never be independent of mechanical factors in their environment, and indeed are notoriously susceptible to their influence, as was so clearly demonstrated by Harrison ('14). In a liquid environment they take quite different shape than when they have access to a solid substrate, and the physical framework of the matrix in which they develop is of paramount importance in determining their form (cf. Weiss, '49). Sometimes hidden mechanical influences quite prejudice the interpretation of investigations designed to analyze the effects of quite different factors; for an example, the reader is referred to Weiss' ('50) critique of Marsh and Beams' ('46) experiments where developing nerve cells were subjected in vitro to apparent modification by the passage of electrical currents. Indeed the demonstration of the degree to which cells are susceptible to influences of external mechanical factors has been one of the most fruitful contributions of the isolation method.

From the point of view of nutritive and chemical effects of the milieu on isolates, the analysis is more highly complex. If a part is isolated in inorganic media of easily reproducible composition, many components of the normal environment are lacking which may be essential to foster the processes of normal differentiation; and even such simple factors as a change in pH (though in view of the widely divergent systems in the cell which this might affect its simplicity is only apparent) can alter the accomplishment of cells in such media (Holtfreter, '45). If the isolate is explanted to parts of another organism, as in implants to the eye cavity, the anterior chamber of the eye, the chorioallantois, or to the various sites employed for the window techniques, or even to culture fluids containing embryonic extract, plasma or other body fluids, it is impossible in our present state of knowledge to ascertain what components are present. While to some the ultimate aim may seem the perfection of synthetic media—and the embryologists proper lag far behind the tissue culture experts and the microbiologists in their progress towards this goal—it is a little soon to divine what all the ingredients of such media might

be, since embryologists have hardly yet exhausted the knowledge of all the biochemical requirements of their material.

A fundamental problem arises as to the criteria by which a neutral or indifferent medium could be recognized as such, granted the validity of the assumption that it exists and granted that it would be capable of preparation. Just as there are various conditions under which cells removed from an embryo behave differently than in the normal embryo, so there are various sets of conditions under which cells removed from the embryo might carry out the same performance as in the embryo; the most striking manifestations of embryonic organization are those regulatory phenomena whereby processes resembling the normal are carried out under a great variety of abnormal conditions.

Devillers ('50), for instance, has found the trout blastoderm incapable of differentiation in triple-strength Holtfreter's solution but able to differentiate in modified White's solution. It is unthinkable that this is the single solution capable of supporting differentiation in this form. Devillers' result demonstrates the fact that triple-strength Holtfreter's solution is unsatisfactory for his particular experiment, but provides no essential information about the blastoderm; the fact that modified White's solution is more favorable furnishes little information about differentiation as such, but signifies primarily that the medium used permits certain embryonic processes to occur. The absence of differentiation of cultures in solutions of particular composition does not necessarily demonstrate that the cells are characterized by the presence or absence of particular potencies, but rather may indicate that the media lack certain factors required as stimuli for the realization of normal potencies, or even that they include agents which may actively inhibit such realization.

Whether or not the cells will differentiate, furthermore, is not the only test of the suitability of the medium; the direction of differentiation and what the factors are which determine it are as important considerations. Using the prospective nervous system of the young urodele gastrula as an example, when isolated in salt solution it will under some conditions form only simple epidermis, under others nervous tissue (Holtfreter, '45). Implanted in vivo, where it is subjected to a wider variety of influences, it is capable of differentiating widely divergent structures (Holtfreter, '29; Bautzmann, '29; Kusche, '29) quite other than those it would have formed in the normal embryo, hence Bautzmann's term *bedeutungsfremde Selbstdifferenzierung.* The occurrence of these and other examples of *bedeutungsfremde Selbstdifferenzierung* signifies that the cells have sufficient plasticity to differentiate in other than their normal direction as a result of change in the conditions with reference to which they are differentiating, but is not adequate to define the changes which have produced an alteration in the direction of differentiation.

It has been postulated that one way, theoretically, to come closer to a definition of conditions essential to differentiation might be the testing of differentiation capacity in the widest possible variety of media. But if the reactions and directions of differentiation should be studied under as many experimental conditions as possible, how is the information to be referred to the cells in action in the normal embryo? Observations would be available as to media satisfactory to elicit all ranges of differentiation; but would not the ascertained data remain knowledge of reactions in an external medium rather than of processes internal to the embryo itself? The comparison of different results in various solutions fails to permit reference of the experimental results to the processes which might have been carried out by the cells *in situ.* What is the way to prove in the isolation experiment whether the cells which have differentiated particular structures are the same which would have done so in the embryo or whether they have used the same method to reach their end?

If, however, the processes studied experimentally cannot be referred without caution back to the normal embryo, it is clear that the processes examined experimentally require rigid definition as to the conditions under which they occur. No medium can be neutral or indifferent with respect to early differentiation; if it were actually either of these, isolates could continue no development at all; a medium can be neutral or indifferent only to a cell that is dead. The failure to come to grips with the problem of relationship between embryo and medium grows partly out of the tendency to emphasize the degree to which cells "self-differentiate." The concept of self-differentiation implies a contradiction in terms; no cell can "self"-differentiate, *bedeutungsfremd* or *bedeutungsgemäss,* insofar as no cell can be separated from its environment.

Roux expressed the problem more cogently when he opposed dependent and independent differentiation, a classification which demands enumeration of the *factors with reference to which* differentiation might be defined as either of these. One of the strong needs of the moment is more specific definition of the conditions with reference to which both normal and abnormal differentiation occur; only this will permit evaluation of the meaning of changes in the differentiating systems proper, since only in this way can embryologists be certain when they are dealing with these systems themselves and not something extraneous to them.

While attempts to invent the medium ideal to support specific types of differentiation may suffer in that the results of the studies lack referability to the normal embryo, the attempts must still be continued, though as a means to an end. Only when knowledge is available concerning the reactions of the cells to the media in which they develop can other experiments be interpreted which are conducted in other ways to answer the more searching questions which remain at the backs of our minds; but the fact must not be lost sight of that these more fundamental questions remain to be asked by other experimental methods.

The remaining one of these methods to be discussed is the transplantation method, which allows the framing of different questions than those methods already discussed, or which perhaps rather allows comparable questions to be asked in a slightly different way.

Strictly speaking, the implantation of cells to such cellular environments as the chorioallantois, the eye chamber and the other sites used for studies in vivo might be considered either as transplantation or as explantation experiments; and perhaps some of the best uses to which the transplantation method has been put have been those in which it has been employed as an isolation method, as in the case of Harrison's ('03) early experiments on the lateral line.

When cells are isolated in culture in some synthetic medium, the direction of their differentiation presumably may be influenced by the reaction of cells to factors in the medium; if they are transplanted to a new cellular environment, it will be conditioned in relationship to factors emanating from neighboring cells, and therefore by mutual interactions between cells of graft and cells of host.

When cells are transplanted to a cellular environment they are transferred, as in many explantation experiments, to a milieu in which many factors are still unknown, and to this extent the transplantation method shares the limitations of many of the isolation methods. In addition, furthermore, it has many of its own incident to the complexity of variables introduced by using a living organism as host; the results in grafting experiments vary according to the species used, according to the size, age and growth rate of the graft and host, according to the site of implantation and so forth. However, in spite of these, indeed perhaps because of them, the method has advantages peculiar to itself, in that it permits, and in fact leads to, the demonstration of interactions at cellular rather than subcellular levels. It thus encourages some analysis, at least, of that *Wechselwirkung* between cell and environment postulated by Roux (cf. quotation on p. 31, this section), and the exploitation of the method by Spemann and Harrison has demonstrated the reality of the progressive quality of differentiation which Roux and His before them had postulated.

The significance, after all, of what a cell can do in isolation can reach its full value only in the light of what the cell does in combination with other cells, and recombination therefore by means of grafting is obligatory to clarify interpretation of the results of the isolation and deletion experiments. Without physical and chemical description of the cells and their components, and without the knowledge of the separate activity of the cells as ascertained by vital staining and defect and isolation experiments, the results of the transplantation experiments themselves might have little meaning. But it is the results of the transplantation experiments which impute final validity to these others, by presenting as a frame of reference not some chance combination of inert substances but the organized living embryo itself.

It is when the embryologist attempts to refer the phenomena which the transplantation experiments demonstrate as occurring at the cellular level to phenomena with which he is familiar at the subcellular level that he meets his greatest difficulty. But though this problem may seem to present itself more acutely at a time when biochemistry is forging the most rapid advances, it is not in any way a new one, nor was it new when Roux found himself confronted with his passage between the Scylla of the overphysical and the Charybdis of the overmetaphysical interpretation of his results (cf. quotation on p. 21, Section I). Nor is it any new solution to claim that between these two levels a

biological plane exists, and to recognize that here, where problems of organization are concerned, all biology works to its least satisfaction. Embryology, as a matter of fact, occupies a more favorable position in this respect than many other fields of biology, because it is so fortunate in having had a Spemann and a Harrison whose special genius lay in their ability to probe more deeply than investigators in other areas into the forbidden territories. Their method, as a synthetic one rather than an analytic, as a method dealing with mutual interactions in terms of cell and cell, rather than simpler reaction of cell to some less organized entity, has the unique merit to come as close to the biological plane of investigation as has yet been approached.

For the knowledge to proceed still further into the investigation of these intercellular phenomena and finally into those obscurer supracellular ones which express themselves as organization, embryology must bide its time, but while awaiting the new insight it is clear what its investigators may do. They may continue to elaborate their physical and chemical descriptions as precisely as possible, though recognizing the limitations of these with respect to the fundamental problem of organization. They may specify, as strictly as possible, the conditions under which work is carried out, in the hope of arriving at possible correlations that may eventually provide new clues. And last, but not least, they will do well to remain as closely preoccupied as possible with the living embryo itself. Spemann, it may be remembered, had the habit of considering the embryo as a *Gesprächspartner* who must be allowed to answer in his own language; as a subject, in this sense, rather than a mere object of investigation (cf. Goerttler, '50). The attitude may seem excessively anthropomorphic, but serves to keep freshly in mind that the embryo, if given the initiative, may have some wise instruction to offer. How intelligibly the embryo can answer the questions directed towards it depends on the questions asked; these must of course be reduced to simple terms, but they must be terms which the embryo can comprehend. Roux accomplished this, in setting up his first simple alternative; Harrison did so when he isolated the neuroblast, and indeed in many of his subsequent experiments. The most formidable task of the embryologist is the intellectual one of restating the problems, not the technical one of physical manipulation. The embryo makes its replies at a supracellular level, and inspiration as how best to address it at this level can come only from the embryo alive, from *Beobachtung und Reflexion* freely expended upon it, in the future as in all the great advances in the past.

REFERENCES

Abonyi, A. 1915 Experimentelle Daten zum Erkennen der Artemia-Gattung. Zeit. wiss. Zool., *114*:95–168.

Baltzer, F. 1937 Analyse des Goldschmidtschen Zeitgesetzes der Intersexualität auf Grund eines Vergleiches der Entwicklung der Bonellia- und Lymantria-Intersexe. Zeitlich gestaffelte Wirkung der Geschlechtsfaktoren (Zeitgesetz) oder Faktorengleichzeitigkeit (Gen-Gleichgewicht). Roux' Arch. Entw.-mech., *136*:1–43.

——— 1940 Ueber erbliche letale Entwicklung und Austauschbarkeit artverschiedener Kerne bei Bastarden. Naturwiss., *28*:177–187.

Bautzmann, H. 1929 Ueber bedeutungsfremde Selbstdifferenzierung aus Teilstücken des Amphibienkeimes. Naturwiss., *17*:818–827.

Boveri, T. 1907 Zellen-Studien. VI. Die Entwicklung dispermer Seeigel-Eier. Ein Beitrag zur Befruchtungslehre und zur Theorie des Kerns. Jena. Zeit. Wiss., *43*:1–292.

——— 1918 Zwei Fehlerquellen bei Merogonieversuchen und die Entwicklungsfähigkeit merogonischer und partiell-merogonischer Seeigelbastarde. Roux' Arch. Entw.-mech., *44*:417–471.

Chun, C. 1880 Die Ctenophoren des Golfes von Neapel; in Fauna und Flora des Golfes von Neapel. Monographie I. W. Engelmann, Leipzig.

Coe, W. R. 1948 Variations in the expression of sexuality in the normally protandric gastropod *Crepidula plana* Say. J. Exp. Zool., *108*:155–169.

Devillers, C. 1949 Explantations en milieu synthétique de blastodermes de Truite (*Salmo irideus*). Journ. Cyto-embryol. belgo-néerland., *1949*: 67–73.

DuShane, G. P., and Hutchinson, C. 1944 Differences in size and developmental rate between eastern and midwestern embryos of *Ambystoma maculatum*. Ecol., *25*:414–423.

Gluecksohn-Schoenheimer, S. 1949 Causal analysis of mouse development by the study of mutational effects. Growth Suppl., *12*:163–176.

Goerttler, K. 1950 Entwicklungsgeschichte des Menschen. Ein Grundriss. Springer-Verlag, Berlin.

Hadorn, E. 1934 Ueber die Entwicklungsleistungen bastardmerogonischer Gewebe von *Triton palmatus* (♀) × *Triton cristatus* ♂ im Ganzkeim und als Explantat in vitro. Roux' Arch. Entw.-mech., *131*:238–284.

——— 1937 Die Entwicklungsphysiologische Auswirkung der disharmonischen Kern-Plasmakombination beim Bastardmerogon *Triton palmatus* (♀) × *Triton cristatus* ♂ . Roux' Arch. Entw.-mech., *136*:400–489.

Harrison, R. G. 1903 Experimentelle Untersuchungen über die Entwicklung der Sinnesorgane der Seitenlinie bei den Amphibien. Arch. mikr. Anat., *63*:35–149.

——— 1907 Observations on the living developing nerve fiber. Anat. Rec., *1*:116–118.

——— 1914 The reaction of embryonic cells to solid structures. J. Exp. Zool., *17*:521–544.

——— 1935 Heteroplastic grafting in embryology. Harvey Lecture for 1933–1934, pp. 116–157.

Herbst, C. 1936 Untersuchungen zur Bestimmung des Geschlechtes. VI. Mitteilung. Neue Gedanken zur Geschlechtsbestimmung bei Tieren. Roux' Arch. Entw.-mech., *135*:178–201.

——— 1937 Untersuchungen zur Bestimmung des Geschlechts. VII. Mitteilung. Ueber die Bedeutung des SO_4-ions für die Weiterentwicklung und geschlechtliche Differenzierung der Bonellia-Larven und über den Einfluss des erhöhten Ca-Gehaltes im SO_4-armen Medium auf diese Prozesse. Roux' Arch. Entw.-mech., *136*:147–168.

Holtfreter, J. 1929 Ueber die Aufzucht isolierter Teile des Amphibienkeimes. I. Methode einer Gewebezüchtung in vivo. Roux' Arch. Entw.-mech., *117*:421–510.

——— 1944 Neural differentiation of ectoderm through exposure to saline solution. J. Exp. Zool., *95*:307–343.

——— 1945 Neuralization and epidermization of gastrula ectoderm. J. Exp. Zool., *98*:161–209.

Hutchinson, C., and Hewitt, D. 1935 A study of larval growth in *Amblystoma punctatum* and *Amblystoma tigrinum*. J. Exp. Zool., *71*:465–481.

Kusche, W. 1929 Interplantation umschriebener Zellbezirke aus der Blastula und der Gastrula von Amphibien. I. Versuche an Urodelen. Roux' Arch. Entw.-mech., *120*:192–271.

Luther, W. 1936 Potenzprüfungen an isolierten Teilstücken der Forellenkeimscheibe. Roux' Arch. Entw.-mech., *135*:359–383.

Marsh, G., and Beams, H. W. 1946 In vitro control of growing chick nerve fibers by applied electric currents. J. Cell. Comp. Physiol., *27*:139–157.

McClendon, J. F. 1910 The development of isolated blastomeres of the frog's egg. Am. J. Anat., *10*:425–430.

Needham, J. 1942 Biochemistry and Morphogenesis. Cambridge University Press, Cambridge, England.

Pasteels, J. 1937 Etudes sur la gastrulation des vertébrés méroblastiques. III. Oiseaux: IV. Conclusions générales. Arch. de Biol., *48*:381–488.

Poulson, D. F. 1940 The effects of certain X-chromosome deficiencies on the embryonic development of *Drosophila melanogaster*. J. Exp. Zool., *83*:271–325.

——— 1945 Chromosomal control of embryogenesis in Drosophila. Am. Nat., *79*:340–363.

Roux, W. 1885 "Einleitung" zu den "Beiträgen zur Entwickelungsmechanik des Embryo." Ges. Abh., *2*:1–23.

——— 1888 Beiträge zur Entwickelungsmechanik des Embryo. V. Ueber die künstliche Hervorbringung "halber" Embryonen durch Zerstörung einer der beiden ersten Furchungszellen, sowie über die Nachentwicklung (Postgeneration) der fehlenden Körperhälfte. Ges. Abh., *2*:419–521.

——— 1889 Die Entwicklungsmechanik der Organismen, eine anatomische Wissenschaft der Zukunft. Ges. Abh., 2:24–54.

———— 1912 Terminologie der Entwicklungsmechanik der Tiere und Pflanzen. Wilhelm Engelmann, Leipzig.

Spemann, H. 1938 Embryonic Development and Induction. Yale University Press, New Haven, Connecticut.

Spratt, N. T. 1946 Formation of the primitive streak in the explanted chick blastoderm marked with carbon particles. J. Exp. Zool., 103:259–304.

Tennent, D. H. 1910 The dominance of maternal or of paternal characters in echinoderm hybrids. Roux' Arch. Entw.-mech., 29:1–14.

———— 1925 Investigations on specificity of fertilization. Carnegie Inst. Wash. Yrbk., 24:240–242.

Twitty, V. C., and Schwind, J. L. 1931 The growth of eyes and limbs transplanted heteroplastically between two species of Amblystoma. J. Exp. Zool., 59:61–86.

Vogt, W. 1925 Gestaltungsanalyse am Amphibienkeim mit örtlicher Vitalfärbung. Vorwort über Wege und Ziele. I. Methodik und Wirkungsweise der örtlichen Vitalfärbung mit Agar als Farbträger. Roux' Arch. Entw.-mech., 106:542–610.

Weiss, P. 1949 Differential growth; in The Chemistry and Physiology of Growth, edited by A. K. Parpart, pp. 135–186. Princeton University Press, Princeton, New Jersey.

———— 1950 The deplantation of fragments of nervous system in amphibians. I. Central reorganization and the formation of nerves. J. Exp. Zool., 113:397–461.

Woodger, J. H. 1948 Observàtions on the present state of embryology; in Growth in Relation to Differentiation and Morphogenesis, Symposia of the Society for Experimental Biology, No. 2, pp. 351–365. Academic Press, New York.

CELLULAR STRUCTURE AND ACTIVITY

CHAPTER 1

Cell Constitution

FRANCIS O. SCHMITT

CLASSICAL cytology was concerned primarily with the elucidation of cell structure by examination, with the light microscope, of living cells and of fixed and stained preparations. In the study of chromosomes, cytology helped provide the foundation of modern genetics by revealing a correlation between chromosome structure and genetic function. Histology has been of immense value in physiology and pathology but in a more limited sense. The limitations are primarily (1) that the fundamental physiological apparatus of the cell has dimensions far below the resolving power of the light microscope, and (2) that little is known concerning the chemical composition and biochemical properties of the cell entities which can be optically resolved.

The development of new optical techniques such as electron microscopy and various cytochemical techniques, particularly the isolation and characterization of cell particulates, has enormously broadened the cytological horizon. One has only to examine current texts on experimental cytology, such as the excellent compilation of Bourne ('51), to see how important the biophysical and biochemical aspects have become. Indeed, an impressive portion of the work in analytical cytology is now being done by general physiologists, biochemists, enzymologists and biophysicists.

This rapid expansion of experimental cytology makes it impossible, within the space of this chapter, to deal with the details of cell constitution. Rather, we shall attempt to outline the more salient features of cell structure as they relate to function, particularly in growth and development. Nuclear structures and nucleus-cytoplasm relations will be considered in another chapter and will therefore not be included in this presentation. Where possible, key references will be cited from which more detailed information may be obtained.

TECHNIQUES OF ANALYTICAL CYTOLOGY

Most of the techniques of analytical cytology are physical or chemical in nature. The investigator in almost any field of modern experimental biology should have a general notion not only of the existence and potentialities of these techniques but of their limitations as well. Those wishing to employ any of the various techniques effectively as a fundamental portion of their research program must understand that is it not enough to learn the mere manipulations necessary to "make the gadget work"; it is essential to gain a good grasp of the physical and chemical principles underlying the techniques.

For the convenience of beginners in this field, the principal techniques are listed, together with references from which an introduction may be obtained.

STRUCTURE ANALYSIS
(DIRECT METHODS)

Ultraviolet and Infrared Microscopy and Microabsorption Spectroscopy. Permit resolution higher than the light microscope. Give information about chemical composition of regions as small as 1 sq. μ in cells. References: Caspersson ('50), Loofbourow ('50), Barer et al. ('50).

Electron Microscopy (EM). Provides resolution to or near the molecular range (15 to 200 A), depending on the resolving power of the instrument and the nature of the specimen. Ultrathin sectioning makes the method applicable to a study of cells and tissues. The necessity that the specimen be dry requires previous fixation or freeze-drying. References: Schmitt ('49), Drummond ('50), Cosslett ('51), Hall ('53).

X-ray Absorption Techniques. Permit determination of the content and location of particular elements in cells and of the mass of small objects within cells. References: Engström ('50), Brattgard and Hyden ('52).

Interference Microscopy. May be used to follow changes in dry weight of undamaged, living cells. Is more sensitive than x-ray absorption technique. References: Barer ('52), Davies, Engström and Lindström ('53).

Autoradiography. Reveals location in cells of elements introduced as radioactive isotopes. Resolution relatively low and only roughly quantitative results so far achieved. References: Glick ('49), Doniach ('53).

Phase Contrast Microscopy. By converting small differences of refractivity into changes of intensity this method permits visualization of objects having refractive index similar to that of the surrounding medium. Continuous (rather than discrete) variation of phase offers promise of detection of very small objects within cells. References: Bennett, Jupnik, Osterberg and Richards ('51).

Fluorescence Microscopy. Reveals the presence of fluorescent substances normally present or introduced into cells. References: Sjöstrand ('44), Hamley and Sheard ('47).

Reflected Light Techniques. Permit study of opaque objects and very thin objects, such as cell membranes, one dimension of which may be submicroscopic. References: Waugh and Schmitt ('40), Pfeiffer ('49).

STRUCTURE ANALYSIS (INDIRECT METHODS)

Polarization Microscopy. Reveals orientation and state of subdivision of molecules and submicroscopic constituents. Provides some information about chemical composition of cellular constituents. Being applicable to living cells it avoids some of the indeterminacies of fixation and is a valuable adjunct to electron microscopy. References: Schmidt ('37), Frey-Wyssling ('48), Schmitt ('50a), Bennett ('50), Seeds ('53). The study of natural and artificial dichroism gives information about the orientation of molecular species which absorb in the ultraviolet (especially

valuable in studying structures, like chromosomes, which contain nucleic acid). Dichroism studies in the infrared have been employed to deduce the orientation of particular bonds, such as peptide and hydrogen bonds, in proteins. Reference: Perutz, Jope and Barer ('50).

X-ray Diffraction. Permits deduction of intra- and intermolecular structure of biological materials, the degree of regularity of structure, orientation and particle size. X-ray diffraction can, under certain conditions, be applied to undried materials, e.g., fibrous tissues, crystalline proteins and the like. Though x-ray studies have been concerned chiefly with small, interatomic separations, small-angle techniques now permit investigating separations as large as 700 to 1000 A (e.g., large axial repeating patterns of fibrous proteins). References: Perutz ('49), Hodgkin ('50).

Electron Diffraction. Electron microscope techniques make it possible to obtain electron diffraction data from particular, small regions located and observed in the electron microscope. Reference: Drummond ('50).

CYTOCHEMISTRY (HISTOCHEMISTRY)

As originally employed, the terms cytochemistry or histochemistry referred to the recognition, localization and quantitation of chemical entities, such as certain enzymes, steroids, polysaccharides, proteins and minerals in cells and tissues. Localization was the chief purpose and this was accomplished by reactions, usually in sections of fixed material, which characterize the pure substance in vitro. Subsequently, many other types of procedures, including isolation of particulates by differential centrifugation of fragmented tissues, were included in the field of histochemistry by some authors. The writer will continue to use the original more restricted definition, reserving the term "analytical cytology" for the more inclusive field.

Perhaps the chief pitfalls are the uncritical assumption that chemical entities react in the complex colloidal systems of protoplasm in the same way they do in simple in vitro systems and the assumption that, during the over-all procedure, the substance in question remains localized exactly as it was in life. The latter point is particularly to be considered in the inevitable application of the electron microscope to the problem of localization. References: Glick ('49), Gomori ('50), Glick, Engström, and Malmström ('51).

FRACTIONATION OF CELL PARTICULATES

The development of the technique originally employed by that pioneer of analytical cytology, Robert R. Bensley, has led to great advance in our knowledge of the constitution and function of subcellular systems. Cells are fragmented in a medium usually containing an indifferent non-electrolyte. By differential centrifugation, particles of varying size, density and composition may be isolated. Particulates so obtained exist in an environment very different from that obtaining in the cell. Biochemical tests show that certain of the properties of the particulates may be retained after isolation. However, much further progress may be expected from further investigation of the effect of the fragmentation medium on the system. The work of Kopac ('50a,b) strongly indicates that mere cytolysis, to say nothing of complete cell fragmentation, produces surface denaturation of cytoplasmic proteins, as indicated by the spontaneous Devaux effect. A truly indifferent "Ringer's solution" for the suspension of cellular constituents has yet to be devised.

The term "particulate" has been used to connote subcellular aggregates of dimensions near or below the resolution of the light microscope. Fractionation and characterization of much smaller particles, such as protein macromolecules and complexes, is a field which is destined to play a very significant role in the next few decades. This will be facilitated by adaptation of ultracentrifuge, electrophoresis and other physical chemical methods to deal with very small amounts of sample. References: Glick ('49), Schneider and Hogeboom ('51).

THE PROBLEM OF FIXATION

The purpose of fixation is to treat cells in a manner such that their structure may be examined in the greatest detail with minimal alteration of the normal state, and also to gain information concerning the chemical properties of cell constituents by interpretation of fixation reactions. The advent of electron microscopy has required a reinvestigation of the mechanism of fixation (see Palade, '52a). The present problem is essentially similar to that which faced cytologists of old. Aside from the fundamental indeterminacy arising from the fact that any treatment must alter the cell, one is faced with the difficulty that, until one knows the structure of the normal living cell, one can only guess whether a given method of preparation preserves that structure unaltered. Except for gross alterations (shrinkage, swelling, etc.), judgment as to the value of a fixative depends upon what the investigator chooses to regard as normal structure. When dealing with a system such as the cytoplasmic "ground substance" where the components are of colloidal dimensions, the electron microscopist's problem is at least as great as that of the histologist working at light microscope resolution. No doubt we may expect in the next few decades description of new "fundamental" protoplasmic structures observed with the electron microscope (EM) in tissues fixed in various ways. The extent to which sound interpretation of such fixation "artifacts" can be made will probably depend upon concurrent advances in the physical and analytical chemistry of protoplasmic systems.

The problem of fixation is amenable to systematic investigation and some preliminary investigations have already been made. It has long been realized that the fixative should be isotonic with the tissue (especially true in the case of solutions of osmium tetroxide, which is un-ionized). The importance of appropriate carbon dioxide tension has not yet been sufficiently realized. The effect of pH, ionic strength, redox potential and the like have been studied (Zeiger, '49), as well as the chemical properties of particular fixatives, such as osmium tetroxide (Hirschler, '43; Schmidt, '47) and Formalin (French and Edsall, '45; Crawford and Barer, '51). Since many structures can be seen in the living cells by phase contrast microscopy, useful comparisons have been made before and after fixation (Buchsbaum, '48; Zollinger, '48a,b). Most cellular objects exist as organized *systems* of components. It is therefore necessary to preserve not only the individual entities but the organization of the various systems with respect to each other as well. It seems improbable that any procedure will be found which will fully meet these requirements. The feeling is growing that it may be better not to try to "fix" the various components chemically but rather merely to remove water by freeze-drying (see Sylvén, '51). This has proven useful to many who work with the EM.

THE COLLOIDAL ORGANIZATION OF PROTOPLASM

The cell consists of a highly aqueous colloidal system, enclosed in a complex limiting envelope, and containing particulates of various sizes and shapes, including a tenuous fibrous system capable of sol-gel reversal. In the microcosm of the living cell the various particulates and subcellular systems have intimate chemical and structural relationship with each other. The properties of the individual components depend on this interrelationship and the normal physiological function of the cell requires an appropriate organization of the system as a whole. It is improbable that we can fully learn the chemical and structural properties of the individual components after their removal from the cell. However, information about such partial systems must be obtained before the types of interaction which provide the emergent organizational properties can be deduced. Much of the discussion in this chapter will necessarily deal with partial systems of various sorts.

For convenience of presentation these systems will be considered according to the geometric form of the components rather than according to chemical composition or supposed function. It is convenient to consider three geometric forms: the one-, two- and three-dimensional arrays. These correspond, respectively, to the fibrous, membranous and globular particles, which will be considered separately, though not in that order. Equally important, of course, is the aqueous milieu with dissolved substances and this will be considered first.

WATER AND DISSOLVED SUBSTANCES

The water content of protoplasm ranges from 80 to about 95 per cent or more. In terms of molecular species, water represents over 98 per cent of the molecules present in the cell. If we were to look at a cell with "molecular spectacles" we should see little besides water molecules.

Water is unique among biological liquids in regard to its physical and chemical properties, owing primarily to its peculiar dipolar structure and the bonding of molecules to each other by means of hydrogen bonds (see Gortner, '49). Similarly, water is bonded to polar groups of organic molecules in cells and this solvation determines many of the colloidal properties of cell structures. Physiological functions, such as contractility, depend importantly upon the reversible alterations of the reactivity of chemical groupings which, in turn, are conditioned by the shell of water molecules coordinated about the groups.

Important for the chemical coordination of cell processes is the high solubility of organic and inorganic substances in water. Dissolved in the cell water are the mineral salts, lyoenzymes, intermediary metabolites and certain hormones. Energy-rich compounds, such as adenosine triphosphate (ATP), presumably diffuse freely in the aqueous phases of protoplasm from their site of synthesis, primarily in the mitochondria, to the molecular effectors where the energy is liberated.

In general the water content of cells is greatest in cells in which chemical metabolism is high. Embryonic cells have a higher water content and a higher metabolism than do the corresponding cells in the adult organism. Osmotic influx of water resulting, for example, from the hydrolysis of large molecules or macromolecules to form a much larger number of smaller molecules may play a role in morphogenesis through change in cell shape (particularly if the water permeability of one surface of a cell layer is different than that of the other surface).

PARTICULATE SYSTEMS

The view that many of the essential reactions of protoplasm occur within, or at the surfaces of, subcellular, macromolecular systems having a high degree of internal organization is not original with modern analytical biologists. It has been inherent in the thinking of great physiologists, morphologists, geneticists and embryologists for over a century.* However, the isolation and analysis of several types of particulate systems has now given valuable clues as to the structures responsible for certain of the major functions of the cell and there is every reason to expect that further important advances will be forthcoming by the use of fractionation techniques.

For purposes of convenience we shall consider in one category the organized particulates, whether they occur as microscopically visible structures in the cell or as submicroscopic aggregates. This is probably justified since in most cases, where such systems have

* To realize how fundamental this concept has been, one has only to recall the numerous terms which were invented over the years for the giant colloidal particles in which "life" was thought to reside: biogens (Buffon, Verworn), physiological units (Spencer), bioplasts (Altmann), gemmules (Darwin), pangens (DeVries), plastidules (Haeckel), biophores (Weismann), idiosomes (Naegeli) and many others. The gene, in its original form, is a descendent of such concepts.

been observed in the EM or have been isolated by fractionation, they have been demonstrated to be aggregates of quite small particles.

It has been found that when fragmented cell material is centrifuged, three easily separable fractions can be obtained: the "large granule" fraction, the "small granule" fraction and the supernate. We shall consider them in that order.

LARGE GRANULE FRACTION

Mitochondria. Observed in intact cells, mitochondria appear as granules, elongated threads or as intermediate forms depending on the type of cell and the conditions obtaining at the time of observation. In size they vary from 0.5 μ to about 1 μ, when granular, to several micra when filamentous. They may manifest active movement, changing from elongated threads to globules, as observed in phase contrast (Hughes and Preston, '49). Filaments may curl into loops, rotating the while. They may also bifurcate and again fuse longitudinally. This incessant movement suggests both that their substance is semi-fluid in nature and that contact between cytoplasmic substrate and enzymes contained in the mitochondria may be facilitated thereby.

According to Claude ('50), mitochondria are probably capable of self-duplication. They grow by elongation but apparently divide transversely. Granules about 0.1μ in diameter were observed within the mitochondria. However, it is not certain that these pre-exist in vivo. EM observations indicate that at least certain mitochondria are enclosed in a formed membrane (Mühlethaler et al., '50; Palade, 52b). This was presumed to be the case from the way in which isolated mitochondria swell or shrink as a function of the osmotic pressure of the suspending medium. In the sarcosomes of insect muscle it is stated that, after osmotic lysis, a residual limiting membrane may be observed analogous to the "ghosts" which remain after lysis of red cells (Williams and Watanabe, '51, '52). These sarcosomes manifest most of the chemical, enzymatic and staining properties of mitochondria. Their presence in abundance in insect muscle is correlated with the need for immediate energy supply to this active tissue.

Birefringence has been observed in mitochondria in living cells by Giroud, Monné and others. The analysis is only fragmentary but may be considered consistent with the view that oriented protein and lipid molecules are present. A more detailed study of mitochondria with improved methods of polarization microscopy may prove rewarding.

The chemical composition and enzymatic properties have been studied in mitochondria isolated by differential centrifugation. Among the constituents are protein (ca. 50 per cent), lipids (25 to 30 per cent, consisting chiefly of phospholipids), nucleotides, flavins, and relatively small amounts of ribose nucleic acid (RNA) (Claude, '49). Mitochondria may account for 15 to 20 per cent of the cell mass and, according to Schneider and Hogeboom ('51), they may represent as much as 26 per cent of the total nitrogen and 33 per cent of the total protein of the mouse liver.

The enzymes demonstrated to be present in the mitochondrial fraction include cytochrome oxidase, succinoxidase, cytochrome c, members of the Krebs cycle, D-amino acid oxidase, diphosphopyridine nucleotide (DPN)–cytochrome c reductase, triphosphopyridine nucleotide (TPN)–cytochrome c reductase, acid phosphatase and ATP-ase. This fairly complete complement of the oxidizing mechanism clearly indicates the respiratory function of mitochondria, and their ability to carry out aerobic phosphorylation and possibly to supply energy for other synthetic processes including peptide and protein synthesis. The mitochondria appear to constitute the "power plant" of the cell. This discovery represents one of the great milestones in modern biochemistry and analytical cytology.

Mitochondria have been studied in some detail with the EM (see Palade, '52b). An internal layered structure, whose perfection depends importantly on the method of preparation, has been observed. Possibly these lipid-protein layers are the locus of the organized enzymes known to be present in mitochondria.

Secretion Granules and Other Members of the "Large Granule" Group. Characteristic particulates are found in the large granule fraction of secreting cells, such as pancreas and liver; they are thought to derive from zymogen and other secretion granules. In the pancreas they may be about as abundant as the mitochondrial components. Claude ('50) suggests that secretion granules may arise by a progressive transformation of mitochondria, a view expressed long ago by classical cytologists on morphological grounds.

Other members of the large granule fraction have been assigned special names on the basis of real or supposed function and composition (see Zollinger, '48a). Among these are: storage granules, starvation granules, degeneration granules, resorption granules, glycogen granules, melanin and perhaps the so-called "biosomes."

Centrioles and Kinetosomes. These highly important granules have not as yet been isolated from fragmented cells. What little we know about them rests mostly on circumstantial evidence based on cytological investigations. Being relatively large macromolecular aggregates they are doubtless very complex chemically. Nothing approaching a fractionation and chemical characterization of these constituents has yet been attempted.

The centrioles and kinetosomes are presumably autonomous entities frequently found in association with fibrous structures (cilia, flagella, sperm tails, mitotic mechanism, trichocysts, etc.), and are thought to be causally concerned with the production and maintenance of the fibrous arrays. In the ciliates much study has been given to these granules, particularly by Lwoff ('50) and Weisz ('51), from which it is concluded that they are pluripotent morphogenetically and essentially equipotential. Caspari ('50) considers them to be "visible plasmagenes"! Though their relation to the genome and cytogenes is far from clear, there seems little doubt that these granules play a significant role in processes of differentiation, particularly of cortical structures of protozoa and possibly of metazoan cells as well. Aside from the problem of their role in differentiation, the biochemical problem is at least as interesting. If they do play a role in the formation of organized protein fibers from cytoplasmic precursors, one may expect that enzymes may be involved. It may not be too much to hope that sufficiently delicate micromethods may be developed by which these structures may be isolated and studied in vitro.

SMALL GRANULE FRACTION (MICROSOMES)

Claude's ('43) redefinition of the term "microsome," which is an old one in cytological literature, would include any particulates that are separable from fragmented cells at relatively high centrifugal force (after removal of the heavier large granule fraction). There is no doubt that this fraction includes many types of particulates, the composition of which may vary with growth,

differentiation and function. Therefore, analyses of the entire fraction cannot characterize any particular species in the particulate population. However, such analyses indicate something of the nature and possibly the function of these components of protoplasm.

According to Claude ('49, '50), microsomes have diameters in the range of 0.06 to 0.25μ. They constitute some 15 to 20 per cent of the dry weight of the cell and have been shown to contain protein, lipid, ribose nucleic acid (as much as 60 per cent of that of the whole cell), some nucleotide and a number of enzymes. It is thought that the basophilic properties of cytoplasm may be due primarily to the microsomes and to the endoplasmic reticulum (which will be discussed below). At least five different subfractions of the microsome fraction have been obtained by differential centrifugation (Chantrenne, '51, '52). The relative amounts of RNA and other constituents vary with the size of the particle, and Brachet ('50) suggests that during embryogenesis the particles start out small but become more complex and richer in RNA as development proceeds, this increasing complexity being an important factor in differentiation.

Several enzymes, including phosphatase, ATP-ase, dipeptidase and cathepsin have been found to be associated with microsomes. Notions as to the functions of microsomes rest chiefly on circumstantial evidence. Brachet ('49, '50) believes they may be concerned with protein synthesis and discusses their relation to plasmagenes and viruses. Claude inclines to the view that they are concerned with anaerobic respiration. Chargaff ('45, '49) isolated particulates 0.08 to 0.12μ in diameter from lung and other tissue which have high thromboplastic activity and he suggests that cell structuration may be influenced by such intracellular enzyme-containing particles (perhaps along the general lines of the clotting process in blood).

Basophilic Components. The basophilic granules and filaments were early grouped together under the term "chromidia" by Hertwig. This term has been revived recently by Monné ('48) and Lehmann and Biss ('49) to denote the "self-duplicating" RNA-containing submicroscopic particles (biosomes) to which have been ascribed most of the vital properties of protoplasm, including respiration, metabolism, irritability and morphogenesis! It is possible that a portion of the chromidial apparatus is actually composed partly of adlineated microsomal particulates, as suggested by Bessis and

Bricka ('49) and partly of the so-called "endoplasmic reticulum" which Porter ('53) and Porter and Kallman ('52) regard as a system of RNA-protein-containing structures which may appear canalicular or reticular and which may be concerned with synthetic processes in the cell. A somewhat different description of the same component has been given by Sjöstrand and Rhodin ('53). This class of cytoplasmic organelles is probably of considerable functional importance and worthy of further detailed study.

SUPERNATE

The supernate which remains after centrifugal removal of the small granule fraction contains chiefly globular proteins (Sorof et al., '51a, b, c; Gjessing et al., '51), organic and inorganic compounds of relatively low molecular weight, "soluble" enzymes, some RNA, nucleotides and the like.

LIPOCHONDRIA (GOLGI SYSTEM)

Despite the enormous literature (over 2000 papers) written during the last half century on the Golgi apparatus, "we know very little and our hypotheses are pure guesses," to quote Bensley ('51). After reviewing the literature, Palade and Claude ('49a, b) conclude that the Golgi system as seen in cytological preparations is an artifact produced by the action of the alcohol in the fixative upon pre-existing highly refringent droplets which stain with Sudan black and have an affinity for neutral red; the more slowly diffusing osmium tetroxide then fixes these artifacts in the form characteristic of the Golgi apparatus. Structures closely resembling Golgi apparatus were produced by the action of fixatives on lipid-containing fractions of cells.

Palade and Claude ignore the evidence that the Golgi material can be seen in the living cell. According to Baker ('49), "the Golgi bodies are the most evident objects in the cell," where they appear as spheroids when viewed with phase contrast. Bensley ('51), Gatenby and Moussa ('51) and others favor the view that the "apparatus" pre-exists in the cell as vesicles and canals similar to the structures seen in fixed preparations.

The evidence seems to the present writer to indicate that the Golgi bodies represent a pleomorphic system which pre-exists in the cytoplasm and whose colloidal organization is sensitive to alterations of the environment, particularly to acids and organic solvents. Although little is really known about their chemical composition (Sosa, '48) there seems little doubt that lipids are an important component and may be primarily responsible for the pleomorphism.

It may be desirable, therefore, to adopt Baker's ('50) suggestion to drop the name Golgi apparatus (since this may indeed be an artifact) and refer to the system as "lipochondria." Adopting this relatively noncommital name may restore respectability to a cellular system which is almost certainly an important protoplasmic constituent and which, because of colloidal sensitivity, has suffered much uncritical abuse.

The evidence in the cytological literature that lipochondria are intimately associated with the process of secretion, though circumstantial, is perhaps as good as that which, in the same literature, associated mitochondria with respiration (which later biochemical evidence proved to be correct). To what extent the lipochondrial system will prove to be multicomponent, with "internal and external" components, remains to be seen. The author leans to the view that a portion of the instability and of the difficulty of obtaining the material as particulates from fragmented cells (see Worley, '51) may be due to the fact that certain of the components exist in the smectic paracrystalline state (a view not inconsistent with the meager polarized light data available). If so, the pleomorphism, ease of solvation and sensitivity to alterations in the chemical environment would be expected.

Fairly substantial evidence points to the possibility that ascorbic acid and phosphatase occur in lipochondria. Gersh ('49), applying the Hotchkiss reaction to frozen-dried material, concluded that the material which reacts positively is a glycoprotein which may provide "a suitable frame-work for the orderly arrangement of enzymes and other activities." This must be regarded as pure speculation at the present time.

The determination of the composition and function of lipochondria has lagged behind that for mitochondria for the reason that the subject is very much more complex and difficult. However, especially if the material is involved in the vital process of secretion, the problem is all the more challenging and worthy of a renewed vigorous attack involving the chemical and enzymatic as well as the morphological approach. Quite possibly progress would be accelerated by the exploitation of the most favorable source of material, whether that may prove to be long known or yet to be discovered.

FIBROUS SYSTEMS OF CYTOPLASM

The linear, fibrous array is geometrically, physically and chemically well adapted to subserve a number of fundamental biological processes. It permits the specific adlineation and segregation of chemical and biological entities, as in chromosomes. It provides mechanical strength and rigidity: the tensile strength of collagen fibers may be as high as 100 kg./cm.^{2} (as high as some metals). Contractility is almost uniquely a property of fibrous material. Most fibers of biological origin, particularly those composed of proteins and their complexes, are capable of contraction when subjected to appropriate chemical environment. To grasp the processes underlying the basic phenomena of growth and differentiation, insofar as they concern the molecular machinery of the cell, the investigator must delve fairly deeply into the physical and chemical mechanisms of contractility. This involves the submicroscopic fibrous lattices responsible for sol-gel transformation as well as the more obvious fibrous systems described in classical cytology.

Most of our detailed knowledge about fibers has been derived from a study of proteins, polysaccharides, nucleic acids and their conjugates which can be purified and subjected to physical chemical analysis. This knowledge has been of great value in studying the intracellular fibrous systems which have not yet been isolated and characterized. Accordingly, it will be useful to discuss a few of the salient features of purified proteins as well as to describe the far less perfectly understood intracellular systems.

POLARIZATION OPTICAL ANALYSIS

Protein fibers usually manifest positive intrinsic and form birefringence. This permits detection, in living cells, of fibrous arrays and their direction of orientation even though the structures are too thin to be resolved by the light microscope. This is made possible by high sensitivity of the polarization optical method (Swann and Mitchison, '50; Inoué, '51).

Application of the Wiener theory of form birefringence led to the deduction that fibrils which show positive form birefringence are composed of still finer fibrous structures whose thickness is small with respect to the wave length of light. This deduction has been verified with the EM in each case so far investigated. Indeed, electron microscopy has shown that the fibrous elements responsible for the form birefringence may occur as filaments of characteristic width, frequently about 100 to 300 A.

When lipid or nucleic acid is associated with fibrous proteins their presence can be deduced from polarized light examination, since the sign of their birefringence is opposite to that of fibrous proteins.

X-RAY DIFFRACTION ANALYSIS

The eventual aim of x-ray diffraction crystallography is to determine not only the major structural features of the molecule but also the exact position of each atom within the molecule. This has not yet been possible with the crystalline, globular proteins which produce hundreds or thousands of diffraction spots in the x-ray pattern. The task is enormously more difficult in the case of the fibrous proteins whose patterns may be relatively poor in diffractions.

The polypeptide chain is the structural unit of fibrous proteins. The diffraction analysis centers around the determination of the configuration of the polypeptide chains, the interchain relationships and the larger structural features which relate to molecular domains or supermolecular patterns.

Configuration of Polypeptide Chains. In certain types of fibrous proteins, such as silk, feather keratin and highly stretched hair and muscle protein, the polypeptide chains are thought to be nearly fully extended (Astbury's *beta* type). Extended chains may form fabrics which Pauling and Corey ('51a) call "pleated sheets" because the two chain bonds of the α carbon atom form a plane which is perpendicular to the plane of the sheet, forming "pleats." However, in most fibrous, and probably globular, proteins the chains have a folded configuration (Astbury's *alpha* type) whose detailed configuration may differ among the various types of proteins.

The precise configuration of the folded chains has not yet been unequivocally demonstrated in any protein. The best evidence at present favors the view that the chains may be helically coiled, the pitch and number of amino acid residues per turn varying with different proteins (Pauling and Corey, '51b,c; Bear, '52; Bull, '52). For a discussion of recent developments in this field see Kendrew ('54) and Edsall ('54).

Large Periods in Protein Fibers. Small-angle x-ray data have shown that some fibrous proteins are characterized by large axial and transverse periods (Table 1). Although it has been suggested in several cases that the axial period represents the length of the molecule, this has not yet been proven. Indeed, in some cases (collagen, paramyosin) it has been possible, by solution and appropriate reconstitution, to produce fibrils which manifest an axial repeat period several times that of the native fibers. It is of course possible that, in the native state, the chains are coiled and that, in passing from the normal length of the period to the "long-spacing" form, the chain molecules become fully extended and then manifest the long-spacing period.

From the x-ray data, it has been possible also to deduce something about the intra-period fine structure. In the case of collagen, Bear ('52) suggests that the neighboring chains form parallel, ordered regions alternating with more poorly ordered regions. These regions have precise position within the main repeat period, giving rise to intra-period bands as seen in the EM. The relative order or disorder is thought to depend upon the length of the side chains and the perfection of packing of these side chains between neighboring polypeptide chains. This would imply that there is a fairly precise sequence of amino acid types, if not of amino acids themselves, along the chain molecules, a view for which there is analytical evidence in the case of globular proteins (Sanger, '52).

It seems possible that characteristic, long axial repeating periods may be discovered in many other fibrous proteins thus far not adequately investigated. This is of considerable importance because such periods provide molecular "fingerprints" by which proteins may be identified in tissues and in various kinds of preparations and give information about molecular structure.

Classification of Fibrous Proteins. Astbury early pointed out that the wide-angle, *alpha*, patterns of certain proteins are closely similar. Keratin, myosin, epidermin and fibrin are grouped together as the "KMEF class." A different large-angle pattern characterizes a group of proteins called by Astbury the "collagen class." The latter group includes the collagens of vertebrates and invertebrates and a number of proteins from forms as low phylogenetically as the Porifera. Astbury suggested that the polypeptide chains of members of the collagen class are not folded

upon themselves as are those of the KMEF class but are essentially fully extended. Recent analyses (Bear, '52) indicates that chains of the members of the collagen class probably have a helical configuration as do members of the KMEF class although the geometry of the helix may differ in detail.

It is interesting to note that, despite striking differences in chemical composition, various members of the collagen class which

TABLE 1. *Large Repeating Periods in Fibrous Proteins*

PROTEIN	REPEATING PERIOD	
	FIBER AXIS PERIOD, A	LATERAL PERIOD, A
β Keratin	95	34
α Keratin	198	82
Collagen "Long Spacing"	640 (∼2100)	— —
Paramyosin "Long Spacing"	720 (∼1400)	261
Muscle (Actomyosin?)	405	86
Fibrin	230	—
Trichocyst Protein	550 (2200)	—

have been carefully studied manifest not only the same large-angle pattern but the same axial long period (about 640 A) as well. Each member of the KMEF class has a different, characteristic axial long period (see Table 1). The meaning of these facts will probably not be fully understood until much more is known about the chemical composition and molecular configuration of these proteins.

ELECTRON MICROSCOPE ANALYSIS

The hierarchies of fiber sizes are well demonstrated in EM studies. It has long been known that macroscopic fibers, such as muscle or tendon, having widths from 10 to 100μ, are composed of thinner fibrils which may be at or below the limit of resolution of the light microscope (Heidenhain). The electron microscope has shown that these *fibrils* (whose presence was deduced from their positive form birefringence) have widths ranging from several hundred to several thousand Angström units. The fibrils, in turn, are composed of still finer arrays which may be called *filaments* and which may be of the order of 100 A in width, or smaller. The ultimate fibrous array is the polypeptide chain. Figure 1, taken from Bear ('52), illustrates this fibrous hierarchy. Long axial repeat periods demonstrated by small-angle x-ray studies have been observed in the EM in the form of cross-striations consisting of

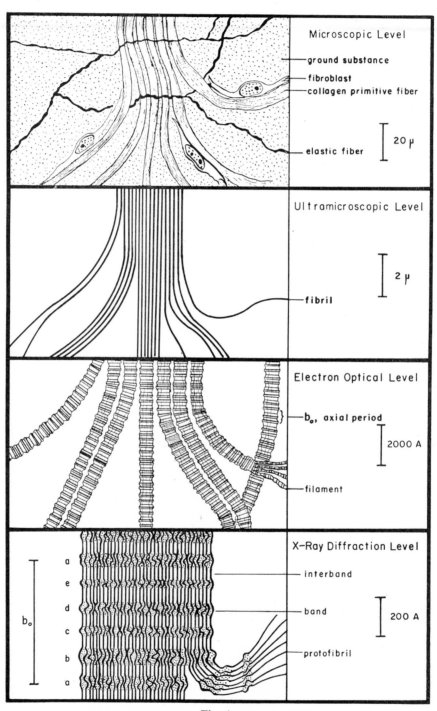

Fig. 1.

bands of varying density, thickness and affinity for stains like phosphotungstic acid. This is true for vertebrate muscle, paramyosin and collagen. Detailed intraperiod structure, in the form of fine bands having characteristic position and density, has been observed in several fibrous proteins. The combination of x-ray and EM data may provide clues as to the physical and chemical meaning of such accurately repeating axial structure. In some cases it is suspected that a globular component may be associated with the fibrous component in forming the periodic structure and in determining the properties of the fiber.

Cilia, Flagella and Sperm Tails. It has long been suspected, on the basis of their positive form birefringence (Schmidt, '37), that these microscopically visible fibrous structures are composed of still finer submicroscopic fibrous components. EM examination has demonstrated that they are, in fact, bundles of fibrils, each fibril being 300 to 600 A in width and running the full length of the cilium, flagellum or sperm tail.

A very interesting point is that the number of these fibrils is relatively constant. In mammalian sperm tails there are usually eleven fibrils, of which two may be thinner than the remainder. According to Fawcett and Porter ('52), molluscan cilia also contain eleven fibrils, two in the center surrounded by nine peripheral filaments. The detailed mechanism of the formation of these fibrils, presumably in association with the centriolar apparatus, constitutes a challenging subject for future EM study.

There is some indication of an axial repeating pattern in such fibrils (Grigg and Hodge, '49; Fawcett and Porter, '52) but thus far no clear-cut proof of such a period has been demonstrated.

Around the sperm tail may be distinguished a sheath composed of one or more helically coiled fibrils. For a good description of the fine structure of plant cilia the reader is referred to Manton ('52).

The structural and chemical basis of the contraction of cilia, flagella and sperm tails has not yet been demonstrated. Unlike muscle, the contraction is not a longitudinal shortening and thickening of the fibers but rather a screw or helical type of beating. It is not clear whether the filaments are themselves contractile or whether they provide chiefly mechanical rigidity as was supposed in older theories.

The flagella of motile bacteria appear to be individual fibrils about 120 A wide protruding from the bacteria rather than bundles of fibrils aggregated to form individual flagella. The flagella may be isolated in relatively pure form and their composition and structure studied. According to Astbury and Weibull ('49) they give the alpha wide-angle diffraction pattern characteristic of the KMEF class. An axial period of about 400 A, similar in magnitude at least to that of vertebrate muscle, has also been found by Astbury (personal communication), who suggests that such flagella may be considered "monomolecular hairs or muscles" (Astbury, '51).

Trichocysts. The Paramecium trichocyst is an elongate, thin-walled tube terminating in a dense, pointed tip. The wall as well as the tip shows birefringence positive with respect to the axis of the trichocyst (Schmidt, '39). In the EM the wall of the tube shows cross-striations with an axial period of 550 A (possibly the main period is four times this) and intraperiod fine structure (Jakus, '47). It would appear that the trichocyst wall is composed of a fibrous protein or conjugated protein of unknown nature, the fiber axis being parallel to that of the trichocyst shaft. It will be interesting from the comparative biostructure view to discover to which class of proteins, in the x-ray diffractionist's terms, this material belongs.

CYTOPLASMIC SUBMICROSCOPIC FIBROUS STRUCTURES

The view that cytoplasm contains, besides the fibers visible in the microscope, a submicroscopic fibrous network or lattice rests not only on the tendency for fixatives to produce fibers but also on a number of physical properties manifested by unfixed protoplasm. When protoplasm is made to flow through a capillary tube the flow is non-Newtonian in nature, e.g., the rate of flow is not proportional to the force applied (Pfeiffer, '40). This is a property of solutions containing elongate, threadlike, rather than spherical, particles. When frog eggs were centrifuged in a centrifuge microscope equipped for observation in polarized light, it was found that birefringence was developed which is positive with respect to the direction of the centrifugal field (Pfeiffer, '42). This indicates the existence in the cytoplasm of elongate, fibrous particles which were aligned by the centrifugal force. The viscosity of cytoplasm can be estimated by a variety of methods (Heilbrunn, '52). Although it is possible to do this only semiquantitatively, the results support the view that cytoplasm contains submicroscopic fibrous particles. The thixotropy sometimes displayed by cytoplasm favors the same conclusion. When cells at rest or in division are subjected to high hydrostatic pressure the phenomena observed (decrease in viscosity, reduction of amoeboid movement and cell division) resemble those observed in certain fibrous systems (Marsland, '51) and are interpreted as due to the breaking of interparticle bonds faster than the rate of their reformation (Eyring, Johnson, and Gensler, '46). When mineral oil is injected into the axoplasm of a squid giant fiber the oil takes on an elongated, rather than a globular, shape (Chambers and Kao, '52), indicating the presence in the axoplasm (a specialized form of cytoplasm) of an oriented submicroscopic fibrous lattice. From studies involving magnetic control of artifically introduced intracellular metallic particles, Crick and Hughes ('49) suggested the presence in cytoplasm of submicroscopic particulates in fibrous arrays.

It is supposed by some that this fibrous submicroscopic lattice—sometimes called the "cytoskeleton" — is an internal molecular framework characteristic of all cells.

Polarized Light Evidence. Tissue cells as such have received relatively little careful study in polarized light as compared with muscle and nerve fibers and other specialized structures which lend themselves well to such study. Fresh nerve cells show birefringence of the type expected if they possessed submicroscopic fibrous arrays with the same orientation as the neurofibrils of fixed and stained preparations (Chinn, '38). Hillarp and Olivecrona ('46) investigated many types of epithelial cells and observed form birefringence positive with respect to the base-apex axis, together with intrinsic birefringence negative with respect to this axis. This was interpreted to indicate the presence of protein (or possibly nucleoprotein) submicroscopic filaments oriented parallel to the base-apex axis with lipid molecules oriented with their paraffin chains perpendicular to the protein filaments. In the fresh marine egg it is possible to demonstrate regions in the cytoplasm which show positive birefringence (Inoué and Dan, '51; Swann, '51a, b; Hughes, '52). In certain instances it has been possible to show that such regions do, in fact, possess a fibrous structure as seen in fixed cells with the electron microscope (McCulloch, '52). In the case of nerve axoplasm a semiquantitative analysis has been made of the form birefringence, which is positive

with respect to the long axis of the fiber (Bear, Schmitt and Young, '37). The conclusion that an oriented fibrous submicroscopic array exists has been confirmed by subsequent EM study (Schmitt, '50b; Fernandez-Moran, '52).

Electron Microscope Evidence. In most of the cell types thus far studied, including fibroblasts, blood, tumor, nerve and liver cells, examination of thin sections has revealed a reticular fibrous system in the cytoplasm. The appearance of the fibrils depends importantly on the fixative used. Acid fixatives usually produce coarse, somewhat irregularly contoured, fibrils probably resulting from the aggregation of finer filaments. Lehmann and Biss ('49) identify the rather coarse fibrous structures which they observed in Tubifex eggs with the chromidial strands of Monné, though they may also be interpreted as cytoplasmic filaments upon which microsomes are attached. In well fixed preparations the fibrous structures may appear as thin filaments or as the system which has been called by Porter "endoplasmic reticulum." The latter may appear tubular or as a linear series of elongate, bladder-like structures. While this structure appears to be rather characteristic of cells generally, the structure in unfixed cytoplasm which corresponds to this picture in fixed cells is difficult to assess.

In a careful EM study of the unfertilized sea urchin egg, McCulloch ('52) observed bundles of nodose fibrils, about 1100 A in thickness, oriented in directions consistent with the positive birefringence which he observed in the living egg cells. McCulloch's failure to observe fibrous structures generally distributed in the cytoplasm may suggest that such fibrous molecules are either too thin to be resolved by the EM under the conditions or that the fixation caused reactions which obscured them.

While the EM evidence to date is not inconsistent with the view that the ground substance of cytoplasm contains a fibrous component, it must be realized that the system is highly complex and that much must be done before the high resolution of the EM will reveal the true molecular basis of the fibrous system in cytoplasm.

Chemical Identification of the Fibrous Constituents. To gain an understanding of the role of the fibrous cytoplasmic constituents in cell functioning it is necessary eventually to isolate these constituents by fractionation procedures and to determine their composition and physical and chemical properties.

The history of muscle physiology reveals that it was only when the fibrous proteins of muscle were isolated (at least with a semblance of purity) that rapid advances were made in our concepts of the mechanism of muscle contraction. We are still far from a full understanding of this process despite the enormous work which has been devoted to its investigation by the most competent biochemists over the past few decades and despite the fact that muscle proteins may be obtained in any desired quantity. The problem of the cytoplasmic fibrous proteins is enormously more difficult because their concentration in cytoplasm is low and there are many other substances present which complicate isolation without significant chemical alteration. Constituents other than the proteins may also occur as fibrous particles in cells (nucleic acids and polysaccharides and their complexes with proteins, lipids and other materials) and this further complicates the problem.

Protein fractionation procedures which proved so effective in isolating the proteins of blood plasma are currently being applied to the fractionation of tissue proteins in various laboratories. However, even granting that this had been successfully achieved, the problem of the localization of components in particular cell types would remain. In fortunate instances the localization problem may be overcome by the use of especially favorable material. Thus the use of the giant nerve fiber of the squid permits the extrusion of axoplasm uncontaminated by nonaxonal material. Already one axonal protein in monodisperse, relatively pure form has been characterized and the existence of several other proteins demonstrated (Maxfield, '51). Studies in the author's laboratories are directed at the isolation and characterization of the protein of the axon filaments (the fibrous constituents of neurofibrils) and some progress has already been made. Perhaps when success has been achieved we shall have a better notion of the role of these proteins in nerve function.

A beginning has also been made in the isolation of proteins from single cells. Mirsky ('36) had suggested that a "myosin-like" protein is present in sea urchin eggs and that the state of aggregation of this macromolecular component varies with physiological state. Monroy ('50) has undertaken to fractionate the macromolecular constituents of the sea urchin egg and to characterize them by electrophoretic and ultracentrifugal methods. Though he has not yet succeeded in isolating individual components in pure form he has obtained evidence for the presence of at least five components and has demonstrated changes which occur in several of the components on fertilization.

The adaptation of physical chemical methods (ultracentrifuge, electrophoresis, streaming birefringence, viscosity, etc.) to very small samples (e.g., from single cells) would greatly facilitate the analysis of cytoplasmic constituents.

Intracellular Fibrogenesis. Fibroblasts are thought to produce a protein which is the precursor of the collagen fibers of connective tissue. Thus far, there is little evidence for the formation of fibrous collagen (identifiable with the EM) inside the fibroblast cells. Porter and Vanamee's ('49) EM studies of collagen formation by fibroblasts in tissue culture suggest that the collagen fibrils are formed at or near the external surface of the cells. It is possible that further detailed studies of this sort may lead to information about the process by which the elongate collagen molecules are formed in the cell. If, as the writer suspects, the intracellular precursor occurs as discrete, probably elongate molecules, the task will require a chemical as well as a morphological approach.

For present purposes we are primarily concerned with the mechanism of formation of the fibrous materials characteristic of the cell itself rather than with the "secretion" of fibrous substances. Fibrous arrays are the chief building stones of cell structure. Yet almost nothing is known about the process by which the constituent molecules are assembled into fibers. Definitive evidence must await chemical isolation and characterization as discussed in the preceding section. Meanwhile background information obtained by indirect methods and by a study of fibrogenesis in vitro will prove useful in guiding our thoughts and in devising direct experiments in cells themselves.

Intracellular fibrogenesis may be thought to occur along two (not mutually exclusive) lines: (a) that which may occur spontaneously without the known action of enzymes, and (b) that known to be controlled enzymatically. The precursor molecules, which become linked by covalent or electrostatic bonds, may themselves be highly elongate or more nearly spherical in shape.

Fibrilization without Enzyme Action. In this type the adlineation of protein molecules, chiefly through electrostatic or hydrogen bonds at opposite ends of molecules, is chiefly involved. Stability of the fiber depends importantly on ionic strength and on linkage through particular types of groups, such as SH groups.

A good example of this type is the muscle protein, actin. In solutions of low ionic strength the viscosity is relatively low and the actin exists as globular particles. Increase in ionic strength increases the viscosity markedly due to the formation of fibers by the adlineation or polymerization of globular actin molecules. Reduction of ionic strength, as by dialysis, reconverts the fibers to globular molecules. This type of reversible process may play an important role in muscle contraction. According to Straub and Feuer ('50) the globular actin contains ATP as a functional group; removal of the terminal phosphate causes the linking of actin molecules, in which process SH and Ca may be involved. However, the process requires no enzyme such as ATP-ase.

Tropomyosin, investigated extensively by Bailey ('48a,b), and thought to be the precursor of myosin, is also capable of reversible globule-fiber transformation depending upon the ionic strength.

Insulin, whose chemical composition and structure have been thoroughly investigated, normally exists in the form of globular molecules but can be converted to the fibrous form by heating in acid solution. The fibrous form, which has no biological activity, can be reconverted to the globular form with full restoration of activity (Waugh, '48). If a minute amount of the fibrous form is added to a solution containing globular insulin, all the insulin comes down in fibrous form. The transformation is quantitative and occurs even in the presence of other proteins and foreign substances (the process has been used by Waugh for in vitro assay of insulin from crude preparations). This suggests the possibility that fibrous proteins may be formed autocatalytically in cells once the fibrous form is produced. Whether a similar type of process plays a role in the differentiation of cellular proteins remains to be determined.

Enzymatically Induced Fibrilization. The classic example of this type is the conversion of elongate fibrinogen molecules into fibrin under the influences of thrombin. Neglecting the complex system of activators and inactivators which control the formation of thrombin from prothrombin, the fibrogenesis may be thus described: Fibrinogen molecules, having dimensions of about 35×600 A, under the influence of thrombin, are converted into fibrils which appear cross-striated in the EM. The axial period is about 230 A (Hawn and Porter, '47). Hall ('49) has demonstrated intraperiod fine structure and suggests that the striations are due to lateral alignment by colloidal forces of components within the fibrinogen molecules. Ferry ('52) has offered additional suggestions concerning the forces and groups involved in the lateral and longitudinal aggregation of fibrinogen molecules to form fibrin. It is possible that fibrogenesis of other proteins may involve a complex system analogous to that of blood clotting.

Underlying the complex, balanced system of activators and inactivators in blood clotting is the requirement that the clotting system be under the strictest biological control; breakdown of this control may lead to death.

The mitotic mechanism, with its elaborate spindle and astral fibrilization, may have similar general properties. Many investigators have suggested a basic similarity between the mitotic mechanism and blood clotting and have suggested that it may be no less complex. Heilbrunn ('52) and his associates have emphasized this view and find that certain anticoagulants (heparin, Dicumarol) prevent formation of the mitotic figure in the marine egg. They believe release of Ca^{++} from the cell cortex is an essential factor in cytoplasmic clotting. However, until the structural proteins and other components are isolated and their mechanism of action elucidated, such analogies must be considered speculative. Chargaff ('45, '49) finds that particles from the large-granule fraction of lung cells have high thromboplastic action. He suggests that such granules may be involved also in intracellular structure formation.

Careful polarization optical studies of dividing cells have been made by Swann and Mitchison ('50), Inoué and Dan ('51) and Swann ('51a,b). The results, well summarized by Hughes ('52), indicate that the spindle and asters contain oriented fibrous protein particles which must be very thin (possibly tens or hundreds of Angström units) and about as highly hydrated as the protoplasm surrounding them. Swann concluded that the chromosomes liberate a "structural agent" which affects the organization of the spindle and astral fibers, decreasing their birefringence. No evidence is yet available as to the nature of such a substance. The experiments demonstrate the great sensitivity of the polarization optical method to detect alterations of protoplasmic ultrastructure.

THE PARACRYSTALLINE (MESOMORPHIC) STATE; TACTOIDS, COACERVATES AND LONG-RANGE FORCES

The crystal is possessed of perfect, non-statistical order. However, symmetry may occur in certain types of materials in one or two dimensions as well as in three dimensions. There are, in fact, various transitions of ordered arrangement between that in a crystal and the lack of order characteristic of a liquid. Hermann showed that there are 18 possible transitional states, which have been called paracrystalline or mesomorphic. Two of these, the nematic and smectic states, are of great importance in the microstructure of protoplasm and will be briefly characterized. The nematic state concerns the fibrous systems discussed in the preceding and following sections. The smectic state concerns more importantly a subsequent section on lamellar, membranous systems. However, for the sake of clarity, both states are considered jointly.

THE NEMATIC STATE

This state is characterized by arrays of thin elongate particles which are constrained to remain oriented parallel to a preferred axial direction. The particles are free to rotate about their axes or be translated laterally or axially. Such systems are birefringent and show evidences of the parallel orientation of the particles in x-ray patterns. The particles may be regularly spaced laterally, the interparticle distance depending on the concentration, the charge distribution on the particles, the ionic strength and the pH of the aqueous medium.

The conditions which determine the state of a nematic system were investigated in some detail in the case of solutions of tobacco mosaic virus (TMV) by Bernal and Fankuchen ('41) and by Oster ('50). This will be discussed below in connection with tactoid theory. EM studies have greatly enhanced our knowledge of such systems.

THE SMECTIC STATE

In smectic systems there is one degree of freedom less than in nematic systems. The elongate molecules, though oriented in a common direction, are constrained to lie in planes perpendicular to the direction of molecular orientation. The system has thus a layered, planar structure. The molecules may have freedom of rotation and of lateral translation but are constrained to remain within their own planes (like people standing on floors of a building but unable to walk between floors).

The lipids compose the chief type of smectic system encountered biologically. In such systems the lipid molecules usually occur as bimolecular layers, the polar ends of the molecules being located at the aqueous surfaces. The distance between double layers depends upon the water content, ionic strength, specific ions and pH. In some cases, e.g., cephalin, lipid double layers may be separated by water layers thicker than the double layers themselves (Palmer and Schmitt, '41). Because such layered lipid and lipid-protein systems are of great importance biologically, as in the nerve myelin and in cell membranes, it is important to gain an understanding of the forces and conditions which determine their stability.

Most cellular lipid double layers are composed of mixed lipids: phospholipids, cerebrosides and steroids. The ability to incorporate water extensively between double layers of mixed lipids is determined primarily by certain of the lipids, notably the cephalins, which present negative charges at the aqueous surfaces. When positively charged ions, particularly multivalent cations such as Ca^{++} or histones and protamines, are added the water is expelled from between the double layers, causing the system to precipitate and lose its characteristic colloidal texture. This illustrates the great sensitivity of such systems to changes in the ionic environment.

Both nematic and smectic systems show birefringence which is positive with respect to the optic axis which parallels the direction of orientation of the molecules. The sign of the birefringence depends upon the nature of the molecules and on the distance between layers (extensive solvate layers may produce lamellar form birefringence which is uni-axially negative).

TACTOIDS AND LONG-RANGE FORCES

Mesomorphic systems, both of the nematic and the smectic types, frequently form tactoids and coacervates (Kruyt, '49) in which phases form spontaneously depending on the concentration of the material and the nature of the environment. The phases may separate microscopically or macroscopically in vitro. These are illustrated in the case of TMV suspensions. The threadlike macromolecules aggregate laterally to form birefringent lens- or spindle-shaped droplets. These are called positive tactoids (Bernal and

Fankuchen, '41). Negative tactoids may also be formed, in which case the dispersed phase is low in protein content. Tactoids may also be formed by smectic systems such as dispersions of certain types of lipids, soaps and certain inorganic materials such as iron oxide and vanadium pentoxide.

The forces involved in the formation and behavior of tactoids have received considerable attention theoretically and experimentally (for recent reviews see Verwey and Overbeek, '48; Oster, '50). The behavior of the system is determined importantly by the shape, size and concentration of the particles (rodlets or platelets), their charge density, the concentration and valence of the ions in solution and, of course, the pH. Determinative is the type and extent of the ion atmosphere about the particles, since the interaction between the particles is primarily electrostatic in nature. Except at the isoelectric point the particles will bear a predominantly negative or positive charge. Since the reaction of most protoplasmic systems is near to neutrality and since most of the proteins have isoelectric points in the acid range, the charge will, in general, be negative (basic proteins such as histones and protamines are of course positive). Assembled about the particles are the ions of opposite sign (counter ions). The thickness of the diffuse double layers, hence the interaction between the particles, is inversely proportional to the square root of the salt concentration. It has been shown that colloidal particles of this sort will, in the presence of their counter ions, repel each other, the equilibrium distance of separation varying with the concentration of ions, the repulsive force between the particles and the potential of the particles. Verwey and Overbeek suggested that van der Waal's attraction between particles of this sort will, in the presence of their counter ions, repel each other, the atmospheres. Van der Waal's forces are very short-range (inversely proportional to the sixth power of the distance in the case of atoms) but, being additive, become important in the case of large particles such as virus particles, fibrous proteins or smectic lipid systems. The intensity of the van der Waal's attraction and of electrostatic repulsion depends upon the conditions obtaining in each particular system and it would be pointless for our purposes to discuss the theoretical aspects further. Suffice it to say that the evidence that long-range attractive forces need be invoked to explain the behavior of

most colloidal systems which have thus far been carefully studied is highly questionable.

Long-range forces have been supposed by some to be important in determining the structure of systems composed of long chain molecules containing alternate single and double bonds. London ('42) has shown that such conjugated double bond chains may attract each other over distances comparable to the lengths of the chains owing to the fact that they behave like oscillators. Such forces may be quite specific. Rothen ('47, '50, '52) has invoked them to explain his experiments in which he finds that films of antigen and antibody may interact with each other even when separated by inert films several hundred Angström units thick. Enzymes were also thought to attack substrate molecules separated by similar distances. Although this finding has given rise to much speculation on the role of long-range forces in protoplasmic systems [even including the attractive forces during the somatic pairing of dipteran chromosomes (Cooper, '48)], Rothen's experiments have been criticized on technical grounds (Iball, '49; Karush and Siegel, '48; Singer, '50) and on theoretical grounds (Pauling, '48; Winter, '52). At the present writing it seems that Rothen's results are susceptible of explanation without reference to long-range forces. However, as pointed out above, each system must be considered as a special case in order effectively to analyze the possible role of long-range forces. Bernal ('49) is convinced that "they must play a very large part in the inner organization of the cell" and that the properties of the mitotic spindle are explicable in terms of a tactoidal organization. The latter view has been strongly criticized (Schrader, '44; Hughes, '52).

SOL-GEL TRANSFORMATIONS, CONTRACTILITY AND THE CELL CORTEX

In a sol the asymmetric colloidal or macromolecular particles have a relatively large average interparticle separation, depending on the concentration of particles, charge on the particles, pH, ionic strength and type of ionic environment, as discussed in the preceding section. When these environmental factors are altered the particle interaction may be greatly increased, causing the sol to be transformed into a gel.

Thus a sol containing elongate macromolecules of nucleic acid dissolved in salt solution may be transformed into a gel by removal of salt by dialysis. An acetic acid solution of collagen containing only 0.1 per cent protein may be converted into a gel by dialysis against water. In this case the collagen filaments are very thin (≤ 50 A) and very long ($\sim$ micra); there are many cross-bonds between particles and a gel is formed although the concentration of protein is very low. When the average particle length is much less, as in gelatin, the concentration necessary for gelling is much higher. Sol-gel transformations of such substances are freely reversible.

Gels may be broken down also by the action of depolymerases which convert the elongate macromolecules into lower polymers or monomers. Ribose and desoxyribose nucleic acid depolymerases and hyaluronidase are examples of such action. About the enzymatic polymerization of such nucleic acid and polysaccharide molecules much less is known.

Much has been learned by a study of sol-gel transformations produced in systems containing purified components. Indeed, only in such systems can we possibly hope to evaluate the physical and chemical factors involved. However, biological systems manifesting sol-gel transformations may be very much more complex, frequently involving a system of enzymes, kinases and antikinases. Although it is useful as a first approximation, and for economy of thought, to visualize protoplasmic sol-gel transformations as obeying a common set of rules, this is by no means necessarily true (see Kopac, '51). Careful distinction must be made between speculations based on the assumption that particular cellular processes behave as do known partial systems and the demonstration that such is, in fact, the case. To really understand a system such as the cortical gel-sol transformation or the formation of the mitotic mechanism there is only one way which, in the end, will suffice: the isolation of the individual components and the analysis of the physical chemical factors involved. This may be a discouraging point of view for the enthusiast who would seek a simpler approach by a study of the system in cells themselves—a field in which much valuable work still remains to be done. However, the problem should not be regarded as insuperable; it will certainly yield when attacked with persistence and patience by modern micromethods of fractionation and physical chemical analysis.

Contractility is a property of most gelled systems of biological materials. The contraction may be isodiametric, as in the syneresis of many gels in which the constituent particles have little or no preferred orientation. Anisodiametric contraction presumes preferential orientation. The precise mechanism of such contractility has not yet been clearly demonstrated even in the much studied case of muscle, in which the proteins may be obtained in kilogram amounts. In recent years emphasis has been placed on the view that the protein polypeptide chains themselves contract to form a configuration more highly folded or helically coiled than is characteristic of the chains in the uncontracted state. However, the alternative view, proposed half a century ago, that the process involves a change in orientation of the particles without change in their internal organization, has received strong support recently (Huxley and Hanson, '54).

Space permits mention of only a few illustrative cases of intracellular sol-gel transformations which are of unquestioned physiological and embryological significance. During mitosis the internal organization of the cytoplasm undergoes striking alterations leading to the formation of the spindle and asters. When tested with a micromanipulator the spindle is found to be a fairly stiff gel capable of being moved about as a semirigid structure (Chambers, '51). The isolation of the gelled mitotic apparatus from fragmented cells recently reported by Mazia and Dan should prove very valuable in work on this subject. Although the fibrous particles composing the spindle are oriented, as shown by their positive birefringence, they must be extremely thin (probably less than 100 A). The robust fibers in electron micrographs of sections shown in certain published work are almost certainly aggregates due to the action of the fixative.

The region of cytoplasm lying immediately below the plasma membrane and having varying thickness (one to several micra depending on the cell type), is usually in a gelled state and is known as the cortex or cortical gel. From birefringence and EM data one may suppose that this region contains very fine threadlike particles, having strong interaction with each other and having orientation predominantly parallel with the surface. Lipid molecules in the cortex are oriented with paraffin chains normal to the surface plane.

Although little is known about the composition of the cortical gel, important properties have been attributed to it. One of these is concerned with the mechanism of ameboid movement and perhaps of cell movement generally.

As DeBruyn ('47) points out, current theories of ameboid movement again stress the contractility of the plasmagel as fundamental to the movement. It is also frequently supposed that protein passes from cortical gel to endoplasm at the "tail" of the ameba and from endoplasm to cortical gel in the advancing pseudopod. It has further been suggested that the cortical gel contains fibrous proteins analogous to the actomyosin system of muscle and that contraction may depend upon the interaction of such proteins with ATP. According to Goldacre and Lorch ('50), injection of ATP into ameba causes contraction and liquefaction of the cortical gel; this liquefied gel is squeezed forward to form more gel on the surface of the advancing pseudopod. Kriszat ('50) found that ATP causes the ameba *Chaos chaos* to contract, presumably because of an increase in the rigidity of the "ground cytoplasm." Lettré ('52) suggested that the stage of contraction of the cortical gel depends on the ATP level and thus on cell metabolism. It is interesting that Loewy ('52) has demonstrated the presence of an actomyosin-like substance in a myxomycete plasmodium.

Goldacre ('52) speculates that the fibrous protein chains of the cortical gel upon contraction fold and remain in this condition in the plasmasol; when these particles reach the front of the advancing pseudopod the chains again unfold to form cortical gel. For such speculations there is as yet little direct evidence.

From the ultrastructural, and possibly from the chemical, viewpoint the process causing ameboid movement may be fundamentally similar to muscle contraction, e.g., localized changes in affinity of fibrous proteins under the influence of ATP, together with changes in configuration or relative positions or orientations of protein particles. In muscle the fibrous proteins are highly oriented, making possible rapid reversible and anisodiametric contraction. In the ameba the fibrous particles are apparently oriented with long axes predominantly in planes parallel with the surface but the structural organization is of low order, making contraction relatively slow and uncoordinated.

Lewis ('47) has invoked the "contractile tension" of the cortical gel to explain changes in cell configuration and movements occurring in embryogenesis. Equatorial constric-

tion resulting in cell division is also attributed to contraction of the cortical gel (Marsland, '51). Many other cases might be cited in which investigators have considered the cortex to be contractile.

Several observations may be pertinent on this matter. Although really very little detailed knowledge exists about the ultrastructure and composition of the cortical gel, the inference that it contains a lattice of very thin protein filaments seems justified. Such a system may well exhibit contractility. However, the contractile phenomena attributed to this gel would seem to require specific orientation of the fibrous components. For this there is little evidence except the polarization optical indication that the anisodiametric protein components may lie predominantly in planes parallel to the cell surface. Finally, direct physical measurements of force generated in the cortex at times when contraction is supposed to occur are either lacking or unconvincing.

This is said not to reflect skepticism about the contractility of the cortex but rather to emphasize the desirability of a direct physical or physical chemical investigation of the properties of this important region of the cell.

Other instances of intracellular contractility for which no mechanism has yet been demonstrated might be mentioned. One thinks, for example, of the movement of pigment granules in melanophores. Under certain physiological conditions the granules move out into the cell processes while under other conditions they move into the center of the cell. The movement in or out may be produced by drugs which cause the contraction or relaxation, respectively, of smooth muscle. A preliminary unpublished investigation in this laboratory by J. B. Finean failed to reveal a fibrous structure resolvable under the conditions with the EM. Similarly the mechanism of cyclosis in plant cells and the rhythmic contraction of slime molds (Seifriz, '43, Loewy, '49) remain challenging subjects for investigation with modern micromethods.

THE CELL MEMBRANE

The limiting envelope or cell membrane, though representing but a very small fraction of the cell volume, is a highly critical structure because so many aspects of cell function depend upon it. Being only relatively few molecules in thickness, contiguous with the cortical cytoplasm on the inner side and the environment on the outer side (which may include connective tissue constituents, "cement" substances and other poorly defined materials), it has been difficult to obtain reliable evidence of a direct nature as to its composition, structure and function. Many of our concepts originated from indirect evidence, chiefly from the lore of permeability studies, from a consideration of the limiting envelope of the mammalian erythrocyte (which may lack important aspects of the membrane of tissue cells) and from a consideration of the properties of thin surface and interfacial films as studied by physical chemists.

For detailed discussions of the literature on the cell membrane see Ponder ('48), Waugh ('50), and Davson ('51). It will be our purpose in this section to draw attention to a few aspects of the subject which may be particularly significant for the student of growth and development and to pose a few problems worthy of further investigation.

First, to what extent is the limiting envelope or cell membrane an entity having characteristic ultrastructure, composition and function and to what extent does it represent merely a non-specific interfacial structure—a repository of all the various materials merely adsorbed upon it from the underlying cytoplasm and external environment? Unfortunately, direct evidence is meagre; one can only present a point of view with the hope that it may stimulate further investigation.

The polarization optical evidence suggests that the ultrastructure of the cell membrane, the nuclear membrane and the membrane surrounding cytoplasmic vacuoles have the common property of being composed of protein layers thin with respect to the wavelength of light. The membranes show negative uni-axial form birefringence with optic axes normal to the plane of the membrane. Estimates of the thickness of the red cell envelope range from 50 A (Hoffman and Hillier, '52) to several hundred Ångström units (Waugh and Schmitt, '40) depending on the method used. Since this includes the lipid components it is obvious that the protein layers must be very thin. The polarization optical evidence gives no clue as to whether the protein or the lipid component is external, whether they are interleafed or arranged in a mosaic. It is consistent with the view that the protein may be a meshwork of very thin filaments lying in the plane of the membrane. Rather ill-defined filaments have been observed with the EM in fixed

preparations of red cell envelopes by some authors, although Latta ('52) found the surface free of discontinuities within the resolution of his preparations (60 A). No significant fine structure has thus far been observed with the EM in the plane of the cell membrane of tissue cells.*

In the red cell envelope and in the cell membrane of several other types of cells which have been studied, the lipid molecules are oriented with paraffin chains normal to the plane of the membrane. The intrinsic birefringence is uniaxially positive with optic axes perpendicular to the plane of the membrane. It seems probable that the lipids occur as bimolecular leaflets of mixed lipids (chiefly phospholipids, galactolipids and steroids). However, there is little direct evidence for or against the view that such lipid bimolecular layers are continuous over the surface of the cell—a matter of considerable importance in permeability theory.

The proteins of the red cell envelope, though still poorly understood, seem characteristic of this type of cell. Chief among these is stromatin, which has not yet been isolated in pure form but which appears to have similar amino acid composition in a variety of mammalian species (see Ponder, '48). Evidence has been presented by Moskowitz et al. ('50, '52) for another protein, "elinin," which is said to be an elongate macromolecule and to contain the Rh antigens. No doubt other proteins, present in relatively small quantities in the red cell envelope, remain to be discovered. However it seems probable that the bulk of the protein moiety is composed of complex molecules which are characteristic of this envelope and which resemble each other in various animal forms (as do the muscle proteins).

Almost nothing is known about the proteins of the membranes of embryonic cells and of various tissue cells. One good reason for this is that, unlike the mammalian erythrocyte, it is very difficult to separate the limiting envelope of tissue cells from the remainder of the cell material. It is therefore impossible to say whether there is a class of proteins or macromolecular complexes which is characteristic of the cell membrane generally. It is also impossible to say whether

* On the other hand, considerable structure has been observed in the nuclear membrane. In the case of the amphibian egg, Callan and Tomlin ('50) found that the nuclear membrane consists of an outer porous layer and continuous inner layer. The pores in the outer layer have a diameter of 400 A and are regularly arranged.

the protein complex of the membrane responds dynamically to changes in chemical environment, for example to the presence of ATP. This possibility may repay inquiry, for a dynamic system of this sort might well be capable of altering permeability (through change in state of aggregation of the protein fabric of the membrane) in response to physiological changes in the cytoplasm. In such considerations, it is of course difficult to rule out the possible role of the cortical cytoplasm immediately underlying the membrane, for it too contains macromolecular protein complexes which are known to be responsive to changes in the environment.

That the membrane is indeed highly reactive is shown by the fact that the permeability for sodium ions, which must depend in some way on the molecular lattice of the membrane, may be increased several hundred fold in a ten-thousandth of a second in response to the passage of current. This has been clearly demonstrated in the membrane of nerve and muscle fibers; it might also be demonstrable, with different time constants, in other types of cells if adequate techniques were available.

The surface membrane is intimately concerned with the establishment of the characteristic electrolyte pattern and with bioelectric phenomena which occur at this discontinuity. The facts in this area of physiology bear importantly on the concept of the surface membrane as a structure in dynamic relationship with metabolic reactions in the underlying cytoplasm. For example, certain ions, such as Na^+, are present in much lower concentration inside the cell than outside. This concentration gradient is maintained by an ion "pump" capable of moving Na^+, which enters the cell at a low rate, back across the membrane into intracellular space (see Steinbach and Moog in this volume, Section III, Chapter 2).

The energy necessary for this osmotic work derives from metabolic reactions but the coupling of the reactions with membrane structure is not known. One possibility is that the "pump" may be located in the membrane itself, the ability of a carrier molecule to combine with or release Na^+ being determined by its reaction with molecules involved in intermediary metabolism. A redox carrier mechanism proposed by Conway ('51) encounters certain theoretical difficulties but serves to illustrate the idea (see also Ussing, '49; Rosenberg and Wilbrandt, '52). Bioelectric phenomena depend upon such ion regulatory mechanisms, as do ion secretory processes such as the secretion of hydrochloric acid, Cl^-, etc.

The phenomena which occur at or near the surface of the egg cell when activation (natural or artificial fertilization) occurs are very complex (see Runnström, '49). In a not too literal sense they resemble the activation of the irritable membrane in nerve and muscle though of course the structural and chemical impedimenta of this cytoplasmic system differ markedly from those of nerve and muscle.

Enzymes form an important part of the chemical complement of the surface membrane. Cholinesterase, catalase and several other enzymes occur in the red cell envelope. Alkaline phosphatase has been demonstrated in the surface of the cells of the intestinal epithelium and of the proximal convoluted tubules of the kidney. A variety of hydrolytic enzymes concerned with phosphate and sugar metabolism (phosphatase, invertase, lactase, sucrase, trehalase and ATP-ase) are thought to be located at the surface of yeast cells; enzymic phosphorylation of sugar is generally believed to be necessary for entrance of the sugar into the cell (cf. Rothstein, Meier, and Hurwitz, '51; Brown, '52; Rosenberg and Wilbrandt, '52).

Living cells are usually resistant to the action of tryptic enzymes. This may be due in part to the presence in the cell surface of certain polysaccharides which are powerful tryptic inhibitors (Runnström, '49).

Some difference of opinion exists as to whether the cell membrane is in fact an organized, complex molecular lattice as indicated in the above discussion or whether it is merely surface film which forms by adsorption of solutes from the underlying cytoplasm. It has long been known that when the cell wall is ruptured, a film forms very quickly over the naked protoplasm and this film may have some of the semipermeable characteristics of the normal membrane (Naegeli). Chambers points out that Ca^{++} is necessary for this reaction. However, proponents of this view must demonstrate that such a spontaneously formed interfacial film has more of the properties of the normal cell membrane than mere water immiscibility and impermeability to certain colloidal dyes.

On the other hand, too much preoccupation with the "fixed" lattice of the membrane at the expense of study of the dynamic aspects is also undesirable. We have stressed certain of these dynamic aspects above. Another aspect of the molecular ecology (to borrow a phrase from Paul Weiss) of the cell membrane is the incorporation into the film of molecules which have diffused from the cytoplasm to the region of the surface film. Experiments with monofilms show that molecules from the subsolution may readily penetrate the film, increasing the film pressure. Since the tension at the surface of the cell is very low, sensibly zero, penetration from the subsolution may increase the surface area and possibly the shape of the cell. This was shown in model systems by Langmuir and Waugh ('38). Conversely, molecules in the surface film may be ejected either by increase in surface pressure or by a decrease in their affinity for film molecules. The degree to which forces in the surface film may determine the shape of cells, especially free cells, cannot yet be accurately assessed. The matter will be considered more in a subsequent section.

An important factor not thus far mentioned is the surface charge of the cell membrane. Electrophoretic measurements show that the net charge is negative on the surface of most cells. The red cell membrane is negative over the entire range in which the cell is stable (down to pH 4). This negativity may be due in part to ionization of phosphoric acid groups in phospholipids (chiefly cephalin), although proteins and possibly also acid polysaccharides may also be involved.

Dan ('47) has made electrophoretic studies of the sea urchin egg treated in various ways. The surface charge is negative even at pH's as low as 2. Fertilization is said to reduce the negativity. Dan also studied the effect of Ca^{++}, Ce^{+++} and other ions on the electrokinetic potential and the role of this potential in surface adhesiveness and agglutination phenomena. Such quantitative studies, relatively rare in the literature, are to be encouraged. They give information of the net charge, but not of the particular types of ionized groups in the exterior surface of the cell. While the electrokinetic potential is of importance in determining cell to cell interaction, the entire constellation of charges and ion atmosphere must also be considered.

SOME PHYSICAL CHEMICAL CONSIDERATIONS OF MORPHOGENETIC PROCESSES

STRUCTURAL PATTERNS AT VARIOUS LEVELS OF ORGANIZATION

Chemical analytical and crystallographic data, as well as biological properties, support the view that there is very precise regularity of structure in protein molecules, reaching to the atoms themselves. To understand this regularity of pattern, it is necessary to suppose that each native protein molecule is composed of a specific number of amino acid residues arranged in a specific sequence of residues or residue types and that the specific configuration of the polypeptide chains is that which has maximum stability under any particular conditions.

We are still far from an understanding of the mechanisms by which protein molecules are formed. Much work is currently being done on the biosynthesis of peptides utilizing energy-coupling reactions revealed in recent years. However, the process by which the specific sequences of amino acid residues are joined and the chains characteristically folded remains a matter of speculation.

Precise patterns of organization exist also at the level of the giant macromolecular complexes. Illustrative are the fibrous proteins (Table 1) which manifest axial periodic structure so regularly repeating as to give dozens of orders of x-ray diffraction. This regularity depends in turn upon a precise sequence of amino acid types along the chains, giving rise to alternating regions of relative order and disorder in the adjacent chains which form the fibrils. These regions are thought to correspond to the bands, or cross-striations, seen in the EM.

Important light on the processes by which such fibrous patterns are formed is thrown by experiments made some years ago by Nageotte and Fauré-Fremiet, in which it was demonstrated that collagen fibers may be dissolved in dilute acid and reconstituted by neutralization or addition of salt. The reconstituted fibrils have the same period (ca. 650 A) and fine structure as the native fibrils, as seen in the EM (Schmitt, Hall and Jakus, '42). Appropriate adjustment of ionic strength and pH causes the dispersed, solvated chains to aggregate again in perfect register with respect to the axial discontinuities. When serum acid glycoprotein or certain other substances are added to the acid solution of collagen, dialysis yields fibrils with a new axial period (Highberger, Gross and Schmitt, '51) several times greater (2000 to 3000 A) than that of native collagen. Apparently the added substance combines with the collagen chains to produce a new pattern of structure. Bizarre two-dimensional patterns have been observed in which grids were formed by the intersection of long-spacing fibrils radially directed from several centers.

An equally striking reconstitution of a new fibrous repeating pattern has recently been accomplished by Hodge ('52). The fibrous protein, paramyosin, of the adductor muscles of the clam has an axial repeat pattern of 145 A with a main period five times this value, or 725 A (Hall, Jakus and Schmitt, '45). The paramyosin fibrils dissolve in dilute acetic acid. Reconstitution of the native-type structure has not yet been accomplished. However, upon increase in ionic strength, a new fibrous form was obtained by Hodge which has a repeating period of about 1400 A. This pattern, never observed in nature, has intraperiod band structure strikingly similar to that of skeletal striated muscle; the counterparts of the A, I, Z, M, H and N bands are all represented. However, the axial repeating period is only one-twentieth to one-thirtieth that of striated muscle. Whether this similarity is merely coincidental remains to be determined.

It is possible that systems which form such highly ordered structural patterns in vitro are, in fact, multicomponent systems in which small amounts of non-fibrous material are required to integrate the protein chains in particular structural arrays. At any rate, the systems are chemically complex and little is as yet known about the conditions required to produce the patterns. Two new patterns have already been obtained (collagen and paramyosin) and it may be expected that more will be found when reconstitution studies are made of other fibrous proteins.

The results described above suggest a point of view regarding the mechanism by which fibrous and possibly other types of structural patterns are formed in cells. This may be illustrated in the case of muscle. In the premorphological stages of differentiation the proteins and other components are synthesized by the cell but have not yet been fashioned into the form characteristic of the differentiated cells. The presence of myosin and actin in predifferentiation stages of muscle has been demonstrated by Hermann and Nicholas ('48). When the physical chemical environment of the cell is favorable, the components of the fibrous pattern may "crystallize" out spontaneously in a manner similar qualitatively to that observed in in vitro experiments. The pattern may form in several stages. Thus in muscle the first stage of morphological differentiation is the formation of unstriated fibers which show positive birefringence. It is not known whether, at this stage, the fibers have an axial perio-

dicity of 400 A, as do fully differentiated fibers, or whether the characteristic ratios and geometric relations of myosin and actin have already been achieved. Formation of the banded structure (Z, A, I, M and other bands) follows in a sequence and manner which is not yet fully understood. The finally differentiated structure shows a high degree of regularity of axial repeating pattern. As many as four orders of diffraction, representing the sarcomere length included between Z bands, have been observed with visible light (Buchthal and Knappeis, '40). How can such linear repeating patterns, having periods as large as 3 to 15μ and in a few cases very much larger, be produced? It seems probable that the pattern-forming potentialities reside in the fibrous system itself and that the process is spontaneous as in the in vitro cases. Any other explanation would require that some kind of equivalent regular structural discontinuities which direct the process preexist in the cell; we would then be required to explain the origin of this intrinsic precursor pattern.

The longest axial period thus far observed by reconstituting fully dispersed fibrous proteins is about 0.3μ (3000 A)—the so-called collagen long-spacing. It seems reasonable to expect that when the system contains many more constituents (several fibrous proteins in muscle and an undetermined number of other participating compounds), the emerging pattern may have much larger dimensions and be more complex. It is interesting to note in passing that the pattern of axial structure in striated muscle, as manifested by band characteristics, is the same whether the repeating sarcomere period is $2\ \mu$ or $15\ \mu$ [in the proventriculus muscles of certain marine annelids (cf. Schmidt, '36), the period may be as much as $100\ \mu$]. It seems improbable that the myosin and actin molecules in the different species vary so markedly in properties. It is more likely that the differences depend on other pattern-modulating substances and circumstances.

It is difficult enough to attempt to interpret the phenomena which occur when fibrous proteins as well known chemically as collagen are reconstituted in vitro. Experiments with more complicated systems such as skeletal muscle would be very empirical indeed. However, it will be many years before the chemistry of muscle constituents is fully known. Meanwhile, stimulating new discoveries and ideas may come from empirical attempts at reconstitution of muscle structure which may throw light not only on muscle structure itself but also on the general conditions which determine the formation of complex structural patterns in cells, tissues and organisms generally. Thus far only structureless or *periodic* fibers have been reconstituted in vitro. To reconstitute fibers with *aperiodic* axial structure, such as chromosomes, would seem much more difficult because matching points along the chains do not occur periodically but are presumably unique for each point. Nevertheless, conditions may be found which would permit even so improbable a process to occur.

It is not our intention to attempt to force all biological pattern formation into relatively simple concepts such as those discussed above. The value of such suggestions has an inverse relation to the complexity of the system. One might, for example, suggest that cells themselves may be able to "crystallize" into structural patterns or tissues when the chemical environment is appropriate. The experiment, using certain types of free cells, or cells liberated from tissues or embryonic masses by the use of trypsin, seems quite feasible and may be a rewarding exercise, particularly in the analysis of factors concerned in cell-to-cell interaction. It is conceivable that an important new concept may emerge from such experiments. However, they should in no way distract attention from the straightforward analytical approach to the complex problems of morphogenetic fields and the genesis of patterns of organization.

FACTORS INVOLVED IN CELL-TO-CELL AND CELL-TO-SUBSTRATE INTERACTION

For purposes of simplification let us consider a somewhat idealized free cell, neglecting any surface coats or other organic matrix surrounding the cell. The surface will bear electric charges depending upon the dissociation of groups in the molecules composing the surface envelope. Depending on the ultrastructure and composition of the surface molecules the charges will have configurational arrays and will be both positive and negative. As indicated in the previous section, the negative charges will, in general, exceed the positive charges considerably so that the net charge will be negative.

Surrounding the cell there will be an ion atmosphere consisting of ions of sign opposite to those of the fixed charges on the surface molecules. These counter ions will be predominantly positive and their density will grade out from the surface, forming a diffuse double layer, as exists around charged colloidal particles. The density and extent of the ion atmosphere will depend upon the density of fixed charges on the membrane and upon the ionic strength of the medium surrounding the cell. The ionic strength of the medium in vertebrate cells being rather high (between 0.1 and 0.2), the ion atmosphere will not extend far out into the medium. The ion atmosphere exists in an aqueous medium or water shell which forms a part of the fixed environment of the cell.

At least so far as our idealized cell is concerned, cell-to-cell interaction will be governed by the same laws which govern the interaction of colloidal particles. Like cells will have a similar ion atmosphere. Neglecting long-range forces (which may actually exist between such giant macromolecular systems), there will be little interaction between cells until they approach within distances equal to their ion atmosphere. There would then be a repulsion (because they bear the same net charge) unless the distribution of positive and negative charges is such as to permit a "matching," in which case the cells would form stable aggregates. It should be pointed out that, particularly in processes of growth and development, the probability that an appreciable fraction of the cells would have the "ideal" properties assumed above is very small.

Adhesion of cells to other cells and to substrates probably depends most importantly upon the formation of electrostatic bonds between groups of opposite sign and also to hydrogen bonds; there is little clear evidence for covalent bonds.

The force necessary to separate a cell from another cell or from a substrate (hence the stability of the cohesion) depends upon the number and types of linkages between the surfaces. Cells, such as mammalian erythrocytes, may adhere strongly to a hydrophilic surface such as glass covered with thorium-conditioned stearate layers. This is a nonspecific adhesion due to the presence of a large number of attractive groups per unit area in the substrate. When there is steric conformity between the molecular configurations in the opposing surfaces the probability of strong adhesion is greatly increased. Thus, if the surfaces of two cells contain a fabric of the same fibrous protein (presumably not combined at the surface with other substances, thus saturating outwardly directed bonds), these proteins might combine to form patches in the interface which would represent a true union between the cells. In such highly localized regions, it would be impossible to tell which part of the surface belongs to which cells.*

A possibly analogous situation may exist when cells behave "as though they knew their own kind." An example is the recombination or self-sorting of coelenterates, hydroids and sponges with cells of their own kind to the exclusion of heterologous combinations (Brøndsted, '36). Immunologically specific cell aggregation or agglutination involves both steric matching and the resultant formation of stable bonds between surface molecules. Phenomena of this kind may be partially analyzed by studying the adhesion of cells containing an antibody upon a slide coated with a film of antigen suitably prepared. The possibility of intercellular adhesion by antigen-antibody like surface bonds was long ago pointed out by Weiss ('41), who has developed the idea in a series of papers (see particularly Weiss, '47, '50).

In actual biological situations, materials in the intercellular medium play a significant, sometimes dominating role. The presence of Ca^{++} and other multivalent cations is particularly significant (see the reviews of Robertson, '41, and Reid, '43). Such ions may cause cell aggregation in the same manner in which they cause precipitation or coacervation of colloids. They may actually bond surface molecules of adjacent cells by combination with negative charges in the apposing surfaces (as they do in built-up layers of fatty acids). Organic cations, such as histones and protamines, may form very stable bonds between negatively charged cell surfaces, such as those of mammalian erythrocytes (Schmitt, '41). Rouleaux of red cells, presumably involving bonding by certain poorly identified hydrophilic substances, represent a similar example. In both cases the bonding is so firm that considerable mechanical force is required to separate the cohering cells.

Valuable analyses of the factors promoting cohesion of epithelial cells are those of Hermann and Hickman ('48), in which it was possible to estimate the force necessary to separate the epithelium from the underlying stroma and to separate individual epi-

* This possibility might be susceptible of experimental test if a type of free cell were found capable of being coated with a dispersed fibrous protein such as collagen. By appropriate manipulation of the ionic environment, it might then be possible to cause the cells to aggregate owing to the affinity of the coating collagen filaments for each other.

thelial cells from each other. Cohesion is decreased by proteolytic enzymes, anionic detergents and high pH (> 9). It was impossible to arrive at a common primary cohesive mechanism for cells generally; there is great variability in tissues of different types.

Connective tissue, the chief components of which have low if any antigenicity, may serve to separate cell types in embryological development, thus permitting strongly interacting cells to form tissue anlagen without interference from contact attractions from other adjacent cell types (Weiss, '41).

Surface interactions between cells may have an important influence on cell shape. Since the tension at the surface of cells is very low (near zero), surface interaction with other cells or with substrate may profoundly alter cell shape (assuming that cell volume does not change appreciably during the process). Strong intercellular bonding, causing cells to share surfaces to a maximal extent, may be expected to lead to the formation of tall, columnar epithelia while low interaction leads to flat, cuboidal epithelia (Schmitt, '41). Where cells are free to migrate, as in tissue cultures, the configuration of the substrate molecules or macromolecules may determine the shape of the cells (Weiss, '49; Weiss and Garber, '52). When the cell-to-substrate interaction is low the shape and movements of the cell are determined primarily by properties inherent in the protoplasm, especially in the cortex, favoring ameboid movement (Holtfreter, '46, '47). High cell-to-substrate interaction would cause the cells to flatten and round up when the substrate has an isodiametric molecular organization. When the substrate has an anisodiametric molecular organization the cells may form elongate processes because of strong interaction with elongate substrate particles having preferred orientation. Such processes lead also to directional migration of cells, depending upon the orientation of substrate particles. Apparent attractions between cells over large distances may be explained by such cell-to-oriented-substrate interactions (Weiss, '52). Some evidence indicates that cells may liberate organic materials which influence not only their own contact relations but also directions of migration along macromolecular pathways having preferred orientations (Weiss, '45). Possibly optical and electron optical investigation of these phenomena would throw light on the mechanism of such effects.

In the preceding section, it was suggested that the surface envelope, or plasma membrane, of "typical" tissue cells may be the seat of very dynamic processes involving energy coupling with metabolic processes and possibly alterations in the configurations and interactions of the macromolecular constituents which form the fabric of the membrane. Such processes may be expected to be particularly significant in stages of embryological development and growth. The synthesis or activation of enzyme systems (Spiegelman and Steinbach, '45; Boell, '48) and of new proteins and macromolecular constituents exposes the surface membrane to possible penetration by such substances. If the penetration is not readily reversible and ephemeral, these substances will play a role in surface interactions of cells.

MORPHOGENETIC FIELDS AND THEIR REGULATION

It is not in the competence of this writer to evaluate, at the biological level, the various factors involved in the genesis and regulation of morphogenetic fields which lead to the orderly development of the embryo. However, it may be useful to suggest a point of view regarding the analysis of such complex phenomena and to offer a few suggestions as to methods which might prove fruitful.

First it is necessary to state some of the limiting conditions defining the problem. It seems clear that intimate contact between cells is a necessary condition for induction (see Weiss, '47; McKeehan, '51). To obtain a normal induction for a particular locus the appropriate cells must be in apposition. This is made possible by the orderly movement of cells, bringing acting and reacting cells together at the proper time. What occurs between cells at this time is not known, but induction involves the specific structural and chemical properties of both the acting and reacting cells. The idea that a few hypothetical diffusible substances, perhaps occurring in gradients of concentration, may trigger off the complex field and regulatory processes seems to have been abandoned as fruitless. Variation in the chemical environment, as by the addition of lithium, ammonia and assorted other inorganic and organic substances, affects the differentiation of inductors or the properties of reacting systems but these results seem to be purely empirical; there is no coherent body of chemical facts which explain the effects.

All this leaves us with respect for the specificity of structure and composition of

cells in close contact and for the complexity of the problem, but with no detailed analytical facts from which to proceed.

Useful in filling this factual vacuum are speculations and working hypotheses based primarily on observed and inferred surface interactions of cells (see particularly Weiss, '50). It seems probable that various types of cell-to-cell and cell-to-substrate interactions, some of which have been discussed in the present chapter, play a significant role in the aggregation of cells into specific tissue or tissue anlagen (see also Loeb, '45; Tyler, '47). However, the complexity of the situation is seen by the necessity of invoking subsidiary hypotheses about the dynamic interaction of surface membrane constituents with the cytoplasm and with solutes in the environment. Almost no direct analytical physical or chemical data are at hand concerning these surfaces with properties which are, or can be made, specific with respect to developmental processes.

The failure of the enthusiastic chemical attack of some years ago is voiced by Holtfreter ('51): ". . . until more adequate biochemical methods of investigation are found, the burden of elucidating the problems of induction rests more upon the shoulders of the analytically minded morphologist than upon those of the biochemist." But what would constitute more adequate biochemical and biophysical methods? How can one devise methods unless the problem to be solved is clearly focussed? It seems clear that answers are to be sought chiefly at the molecular level of organization.* At this level the distinctions between morphology and chemistry largely vanish. But what techniques will provide the "molecular spectacles" with which to discern the critical phenomena involved in embryonic fields and their regulation?

The direct frontal attack on cell ultrastructure has been greatly implemented by modern techniques of electron microscopy. Important new facts may be expected to result from a systematic EM examination of embryological material in thin sections. However, even EM techniques require considerable development before it will be possible to

* Many valuable investigations have been made of the relation of biochemical processes, such as high energy phosphate bond transfer (Barth and Barth, '51) and respiratory metabolism (Barth and Sze, '51), to embryonic development. However, these do not lead directly to clues to the mechanism of induction and the regulation of morphogenetic fields.

resolve the detailed fine structure of the cell membrane, to say nothing of transient molecular constituents within the membrane, which appear or disappear as development proceeds. And the indeterminacies of fixation are always with us!

There is of course no substitute for the slow, painstaking structural and chemical analysis of embryonic cells by ever improving techniques. However, pending the accumulation of such data, useful new data and concepts may result from consideration of partial systems along lines briefly outlined below.

Let us regard embryogenesis as a process of "crystallization" in which the constituent parts are themselves highly diverse, changing in composition and position as development proceeds. Induction of a particular structure corresponds to a crystallization of a pattern within the larger complex of the spatially and temporally integrated complex of patterns. How would such a view lead to fruitful experimentation?

Recalling the results on the in vitro crystallization of fibrous macromolecular patterns described above, we discern certain similarities to induction at a very much lower level of organization. From an acid solution of collagen may be formed not only typical collagen fibrils but also fibrils having one-third the normal period, fibrils with no axial period, or long-spacing fibrils, depending on the conditions. The specificity and morphogenetic potentiality resides in the fibrous, dissolved collagen; various substances when added to the system may "evoke" one or another of the patterns previously described (Gross, Highberger and Schmitt, '52; Schmitt et al., '53). What forms depends upon the concentration of collagen and of non-collagenous organic material, upon the ionic strength, and upon pH and other factors which can be controlled. The reconstitution of paramyosin affords similar challenging opportunities for studying the way in which the protein molecules can interact despite the fact that almost nothing is known about the composition of paramyosin.

May it not be possible similarly to study the ability of embryonic partial systems, possibly of in vitro suspensions of individual cells or groups of cells, to form specific tissue-like aggregates under conditions in which the chemical environment of the cells is subject to reasonably strict control? Such experiments may involve development of special techniques and preparation of material on a rather heroic scale in order to make possible

all types of combinations and to permit a statistically significant evaluation of the results. Under such controlled conditions (assuming that the viability of the cells is not damaged too much) it may be possible to introduce materials—or even cells—suspected of having inductive or regulatory significance. To obtain even a single type of cellular system which is amenable to such manipulation may require considerable effort. However, once obtained, it may yield information about factors involved in the formation of cell patterns obtainable in no obvious way from a study of the whole embryo or of parts transplanted into embryos, because under these conditions there are too many variables to permit drawing any simple conclusions directly.

REFERENCES

Astbury, W. T. 1951 Flagella. Sci. Amer., *184:* 21–24.

———, and Weibull, C. 1949 X-ray diffraction study of the structure of bacterial flagella. Nature, *163:*280–281.

Bailey, K. 1948a Tropomyosin: A new asymmetric protein component of the muscle fibril. Biochem. J., *43:*271–279.

——— 1948b Molecular weight of tropomyosin from rabbit muscle. Biochem. J., *43:*279–281.

Baker, J. R. 1949 Further remarks on the Golgi element. Quart. J. Mic. Sci., *9:*293–307.

——— 1950 Morphology and fine structure of organisms. Nature, *165:*585–586.

Barer, R. 1952 Interference microscopy. Nature, *170:*29.

———, Holiday, E. R., and Jope, E. M. 1950 The technique of ultraviolet absorption spectroscopy with the Burch reflecting microscope. Biochim. Biophys. Acta, *6:*123–134.

Barth, L. G., and Barth, L. J. 1951 The relation of adenosine triphosphate to yolk utilization in the frog's egg. J. Exp. Zool., *116:*99–121.

———, and Sze, L. C. 1951 The organizer and respiration in *Rana pipiens*. Exp. Cell Res., *2:*608–614.

Bear, R. S. 1952 The structure of collagen fibrils. Adv. Protein Chem., *7:*69–154.

———, Schmitt, F. O., and Young, J. Z. 1937 The ultrastructure of nerve axoplasm. Proc. Roy. Soc., (London) B, *123:*505–519.

Bennett, A. H., Jupnik, H., Osterberg, H., and Richards, O. W. 1951 Phase Microscopy. John Wiley & Sons, Inc., New York.

Bennett, H. S. 1950 Microscopical investigations of biological materials with polarized light; in McClung's Handbook of Microscopical Technique, pp. 591–677. Paul B. Hoeber, Inc., New York.

Bensley, R. R. 1951 Facts versus artifacts in cytology: The Golgi apparatus. Exp. Cell Res., *2:* 1–9.

Bernal, J. D. 1949 The structure and interactions of protein molecules. Exp. Cell Res., Suppl., 1:15–23.

———, and Fankuchen, I. 1941 X-ray and crystallographic studies of plant virus preparations. J. Gen. Physiol., 25:111–165.

Bessis, M., and Bricka, M. 1949 Nouvelles études sur les cellules sanguines au microscope électronique avec une étude particulière de leur ultrastructure. Arch. Anat. mic. Morph. exp., 38: 190–215.

Boell, E. J. 1948 Biochemical differentiations during amphibian development. Ann. N. Y. Acad. Sci., 49:773–800.

Booth, F. 1953 Recent work on the application of the theory of the ionic double layer to colloidal systems. Progress in Biophysics and Biophysical Chemistry, 3:131–194.

Bourne, G. H. 1951 Cytology and Cell Physiology. 2d ed. Oxford University Press, Oxford, England.

Brachet, J. 1949 L'hypothèse des plasmagenes dans le dévelopment et la différenciation. Publ. Staz. Zool. Napoli Suppl., 21:77–105.

——— 1950 The localization and the role of ribonucleic acid in the cell. Ann. N. Y. Acad. Sci., 50:861–869.

Brattgard, S. O., and Hyden, H. 1952 Mass, lipids, pentose nucleoproteins and proteins determined in nerve cells by x-ray microradiography. Acta Radiologica Supp., 94:1–48.

Brøndsted, H. V. 1936 Entwicklungsphysiologische Studien über Spongilla locustris. Acta Zool., 17:75–172.

Brown, R. 1952 Protoplast surface enzymes and absorption of sugar. Intern. Rev. Cytology, 1:107–118.

Buchsbaum, R. U. 1948 Individual cells under phase microscopy before and after fixation. Anat. Rec., 102:19–35.

Buchthal, F., and Knappeis, G. G. 1940 Diffraction spectra and minute structure of the cross-striated muscle fibre. Skand. Arch. Physiol., 83: 281–307.

Bull, H. B. 1952 The chemistry of amino acids and proteins. Am. Rev. Biochem., 21:197–208.

Buschke, W. 1949 Studies on intercellular cohesion in corneal epithelium. J. Cell Comp. Physiol., 33:145–175.

Callan, H. G., and Tomlin, S. G. 1950 Experimental studies on amphibian oocyte nuclei. I. Investigation of the structure of the nuclear membrane by means of the electron microscope. Proc. Roy. Soc., B, 137:367–378.

Caspari, E. 1950 Visible plasmagenes. Evolution, 4:362–363.

Caspersson, T. 1950 Cell Growth and Cell Function. W. W. Norton & Co., Inc., New York.

Chambers, R. 1951 Micrurgical studies on the kinetic aspects of cell division. Ann. N. Y. Acad. Sci., 51:1311–1326.

———, and Kao, C. Y. 1952 The effect of electrolytes on the physical state of the nerve axon of the squid and of stentor, a protozoon. Exp. Cell Res., 3:564–573.

Chantrenne, H. 1951 Recherches sur le mécanisme de la synthèse des proteines. Pubblicazioni della Stazione Zoologica di Napoli, 23:70–86.

——— 1952 Acides ribonucleiques et biogenèse des proteines. Symposium on the Biogenesis of Proteins, 2nd Int. Cong. of Biochem. (Paris), pp. 85–95.

Chargaff, E. 1945 Cell structure and the problem of blood coagulation. J. Biol. Chem., 160: 351–359.

——— 1949 Recent studies on cellular lipoproteins. Trans. Faraday Soc., No. 6, pp. 118–124.

Chinn, P., 1938 Polarization optical studies of the structure of nerve cells. J. Cell. Comp. Physiol., 12:1–16.

Claude, A. 1943 The constitution of protoplasm. Science, 97:451–456.

——— 1949 Discussion in symposium on lipoproteins. Trans. Faraday Soc., No. 6, pp. 125–129.

——— 1950 Studies on cell morphology and functions: methods and results. Ann. N. Y. Acad. Sci., 50:854–860.

Conway, E. J. 1951 The biological performance of osmotic work. A redox pump. Science, 113: 270–273.

Cooper, K. W. 1948 The evidence for long range specific attractive forces during the somatic pairing of dipteran chromosomes. J. Exp. Zool., 108: 327–335.

Cosslett, V. E. 1951 Practical Electron Microscopy. Butterworths Scientific Publications, London.

Crawford, G. N. C., and Barer, R. 1951 The action of formaldehyde on living cells as studied by phase-contrast microscopy. Quart. J. Mic. Sci., 92:403–452.

Crick, F. H., and Hughes, A. F. W. 1949 The physical properties of cytoplasm. Exp. Cell. Res., 1:37–80.

Dan, K. 1947 Electrokinetic studies of marine ova. V. Effect of pH-changes on the surface potentials of sea-urchin eggs. Biol. Bull., 93:259–266.

Davies, H. G., Engström, A., and Lindström, B. 1953 A comparison between the x-ray absorption and optical interference methods for the mass determination of biological structures. Nature, 172:1041.

———, and Wilkins, M. H. F. 1952 Interference microscopy and mass determination. Nature, 169: 541.

Davson, H. 1951 A Textbook of General Physiology. The Blakiston Company, Philadelphia.

DeBruyn, P. P. H. 1947 Theories of amoeboid movement. Quart. Rev. Biol., 22:1–24.

Doniach, A. H. 1953 Autoradiography. Progress in Biophysics and Biophysical Chemistry, 3:1–26.

Drummond, D. G. 1950 The practice of electron microscopy. J. Roy. Mic. Soc., 70:1–141.

Edsall, J. T. 1954 Pasadena conference on the structure of proteins. Science, 119:302–305.

Engström, A. 1950 Use of soft x-rays in the assay of biological material. Progress in Biophysics, 1:164–196.

———, and Lindstrom, B. 1950 A method for the determination of the mass of extremely small biological objects. Biochim. et Biophys. Acta, 4: 351–373.

Eyring, H., Johnson, F. H., and Gensler, R. L. 1946 Pressure and reactivity of proteins, with particular reference to invertase. J. Phys. Chem., 50:453–464.

Fawcett, Don W., and Porter, Keith, R. 1952 A study of the fine structure of ciliated epithelial cells with the electron microscope. Anat. Rec., 113:33.

Fernandez-Moran, H. 1952 The submicroscopic organization of vertebrate nerve fibres. Exp. Cell Res., 3:1–83.

Ferry, John D. 1952 The mechanism of polymerization of fibrinogen. Proc. Nat. Acad. Sci., 38:566–569.

French, D., and Edsall, J. T. 1945 The reactions of formaldehyde with amino acids and proteins. Adv. Protein Chem., 2:278–336.

Frey-Wyssling, A. 1948 Submicroscopic Morphology of Protoplasm and Its Derivatives. Elsevier Publishing Co., New York.

Gatenby, J. Bronte, and Moussa, T. A. A. 1951 The nature of the Golgi apparatus. The liver cell and the Palade-Claude mash cytology. La Cellule, 54:49–64.

Gersh, I. 1949 A protein component of the Golgi apparatus. Arch. Pathol., 47:99–109.

Gjessing, E. C., Floyd, C. S., and Chanutin, A. 1951 Studies on the proteins of the particulate-free cytoplasm of rat liver cells. J. Biol. Chem., 188:155–165.

Glick, D. 1949 Techniques of Histo- and Cytochemistry. Interscience Publishers, New York.

———, Engström, A., and Malmström, B. G. 1951 A critical evaluation of quantitative histo- and cytochemical microscopic techniques. Science, 114:253–258.

Goldacre, R. J., 1952 The folding and unfolding of protein molecules as a basis of osmotic work. Int. Rev. Cytol., 1:135–164.

———, and Lorch, I. J. 1950 Folding and unfolding of protein molecules in relation to cytoplasmic streaming, ameboid movement and osmotic work. Nature, 166:497–500.

Gomori, G. 1950 Pitfalls in histochemistry. Ann. N. Y. Acad. Sci., 50:968–981.

Gortner, R. A. 1949 Outlines of Biochemistry. John Wiley & Sons, New York.

Grigg, G., and Hodge, A. 1949 Electron microscopic studies of spermatozoa. Australian J. Sci. Res., 2:271–286.

Gross, J., Highberger, J. H., and Schmitt, F. O. 1952 Some factors involved in the fibrogenesis of collagen in vitro. Proc. Soc. Exp. Biol. Med., 80:462–465.

Hall, C. E. 1949 Electron microscopy of fibrinogen and fibrin. J. Biol. Chem., 179:857–864.

——— 1953 Introduction to Electron Microscopy. McGraw-Hill Book Co., Inc. New York.

———, Jakus, M. A., and Schmitt, F. O. 1945 The structure of certain muscle fibrils as revealed by the use of electron stains. J. App. Phys., 16:459–465.

Hamley, D. H., and Sheard, C. 1947 Factors in fluorescence microscopy. J. Opt. Soc. Amer., 37:316–320.

Hawn, C. V. Z., and Porter, K. R. 1947 The fine structure of clots formed from purified bovine fibrinogen and thrombin: A study with electron microscope. J. Exp. Med., 86:285–292.

Heilbrunn, L. V. 1952 The physiology of cell division; in Modern Trends in Physiology and Biochemistry, edited by E. S. Barron, pp. 123–134. Academic Press, Inc., New York.

Hermann, H., and Hickman, F. H. 1948 The adhesion of epithelium to stroma in the cornea. Bull. Johns Hopkins Hosp., 82:182–207.

———, and Nicholas, J. S. 1948 Quantitative changes in muscle protein fractions during rat development. J. Exp. Zool., 107:165–176.

Highberger, J. H., Gross, J., and Schmitt, F. O. 1951 The interaction of mucoprotein with soluble collagen; an electron microscope study. Proc. Nat. Acad. Sci., 37:286–291.

Hillarp, N., and Olivecrona, H. 1946 Structural proteins and oriented lipoids in the cytoplasm of secreting and resorbing epithelial cells. Acta Anat., 2:119–141.

Hirschler, J. 1943 Grundsätzliches über Osmiumfixierung und Osmiumfärbung. Z. wiss. Mik., 59:113–130.

Hodge, A. 1952 A new type of periodic structure obtained by reconstitution of paramyosin from acid solutions. Proc. Nat. Acad. Sci., 38:850–855.

Hodgkin, D. C. 1950 X-ray analysis and protein structure. Cold Spring Harbor Symp. Quant. Biol., 14:65–78.

Hoffman, J. F., and Hillier, J. 1952 Ultrastructure of the plasma membrane. Federation Proc., 2:71–72.

Holtfreter, J. 1946 Structure, motility and locomotion in isolated embryonic amphibian cells. J. Morph., 79:27–62.

——— 1947 Observations on the migration, aggregation and phagocytosis of embryonic cells. J. Morph., 80:25–56.

——— 1949 Phenomena relating to the cell membrane in embryonic processes. Exp. Cell Res. Suppl., 1:497–510.

——— 1951 Some aspects of embryonic induction. Growth Suppl., 15:117–152.

Hughes, A. 1952 The Mitotic Cycle. Academic Press, New York.

Hughes, A. F. W., and Preston, M. M. E. 1949 Mitosis in living cells of amphibian tissue cultures. J. Roy. Mic. Soc., 69:121–131.

Huxley, H., and Hanson, J. 1954 Changes in the cross-striations of muscle during contraction and stretch and their structural interpretation. Nature, 173:973–976.

Iball, J. 1949 Antigen films and long-range forces. Science, 109:18.

Inoué, S. 1951 A method for measuring small retardations of structures in living cells. Exp. Cell Res., 2:513–517.

———, and Dan, K. 1951 Birefringence of the dividing cell. J. Morph., 89:423–456.

Jakus, M. A. 1947 The structure and properties of the trichocysts of paramecium. J. Exp. Zool., 100:457–476.

Johnson, F., and Eyring, H. 1948 The fundamental action of pressure, temperature and drugs on enzymes as revealed by bacterial luminescence. Ann. N. Y. Acad. Sci., 49:376–396.

Karush, F., and Siegel, B. M. 1948 The structure of antigen films and long-range forces. Science, 108:107–108.

Kendrew, J. C. 1954 Structure of proteins. Nature, 173:57.

Kopac, M. J. 1950a The surface chemical properties of cytoplasmic proteins. Ann. N. Y. Acad. Sci., 50:870–909.

———— 1950b Physical properties of protoplasm. Ann. Rev. Physiol., 12:7–26.

———— 1951 Probable ultrastructures involved in cell division. Ann. N. Y. Acad. Sci., 51:1541–1546.

Kriszat, G. 1950 Die Wirkung von Adenosinetriphosphate und Calcium auf Amöben (Chaos chaos). Arch. f. Zool., 2:477–490.

Kruyt, H. R. 1949 Colloid Science, Vol. 2: Reversible Systems. Elsevier Publishing Co., New York.

Kurbatov, J. D., and Poole, M. L. 1943 Radioactive isotopes for the study of trace elements in living organisms. Chem. Rev., 32:231–248.

Langmuir, I., and Waugh, D. F. 1938 The adsorption of proteins at oil-water interfaces and artificial protein-lipoid membranes. J. Gen. Physiol., 21:745–750.

Latta, H. 1952 The surface of the mammalian erythrocyte. An electron microscope study of the effect of lipid solvents, fixatives, hypotonicity and hemolysin (amboceptor) and complement. Blood, 7:508–521.

Lehmann, F. E. 1947 Über die plasmatische Organisation tierischer Eizellen und die Rolle vitaler Strukturelemente, der Biosomen. Rev. suisse Zool., 54:246–251.

———— 1950 Die Morphogenese in ihrer Abhängigkeit von elementaren biologischen Konstituenten des Plasmas. Rev. suisse Zool., 57:141–156.

————, and Biss, R. 1949 Elektronenoptische Untersuchungen an Plasmastrukturen des Tubifex-Eies. Rev. suisse Zool., 56:264–269.

Lettré, H. 1952 Some Investigations on Cell Behavior under Various Conditions: A review. Cancer Research, 12:847–860.

Lewis, W. H. 1947 Mechanics of invagination. Anat. Rec., 97:139–156.

Loeb, L. 1945 The Biological Basis of Individuality. Charles C Thomas, Springfield, Illinois.

Loewy, A. G. 1949 A theory of protoplasmic streaming. Proc. Amer. Phil. Soc., 93:326–329.

———— 1952 An actomyosin-like substance from the plasmodium of a myxomycete. J. Cell. Comp. Physiol., 40:127–156.

London, F. 1942 On centers of van der Waals attraction. J. Phys. Chem., 46:305–316.

Loofbourow, J. R. 1950 Microspectroscopy. J. Opt. Soc. Amer., 40:317–325.

Lwoff, A. 1950 Problems of Morphogenesis in Ciliates. John Wiley & Sons, Inc., New York.

Manton, J. 1952 The fine structure of plant cilia. Symp. Soc. Exp. Biol., No. 6, pp. 306–319.

Marsland, D. 1951 Action of hydrostatic pressure on cell division. Ann. N. Y. Acad. Sci., 51:1327–1335.

Maxfield, M. 1951 Studies of nerve proteins. Isolation and physicochemical characterization of a protein from lobster nerve. J. Gen. Physiol., 34:853–863.

McCulloch, D. 1952 Fibrous structures in the ground cytoplasm of the arbacia egg. J. Exp. Zool., 119:47–63.

McKeehan, M. S. 1951 Cytological aspects of embryonic lens induction in the chick. J. Exp. Zool., 117:31–64.

Mirsky, A. E. 1936 Protein coagulation as a result of fertilization. Science, 84:333–334.

Monné, L. 1948 Functioning of the cytoplasm. Adv. Enzymol., 8:1–69.

Monroy, A. 1950 A preliminary electrophoretic analysis of proteins and protein fractions in sea urchin eggs and their changes on fertilization. Exp. Cell Res., 1:92–104.

Moskowitz, M., and Calvin, M. 1952 On the components and structure of the human red cell membrane. Exp. Cell Res., 3:33–46.

————, Dandliker, W. B., Calvin, M., and Evans, R. S. 1950 Studies on the antigens of human red cells. I. The separation from human erythrocytes of a water-soluble fraction containing the Rh, A and B factors. J. Immunol., 65:383.

Mühlethaler, F., Müller, A. F., and Zollinger, H. U. 1950 Zur Morphologie der Mitochondrien. Experientia, 6:16–17.

Oster, G. 1950 Two-phase formation in solutions of tobacco mosaic virus and the problem of long-range forces. J. Gen. Physiol., 33:445–473.

Palade, G. E. 1952a A study of fixation for electron microscopy. J. Exp. Med., 95:285–298.

———— 1952b Fine structure of mitochondria. Anat. Rec., 113:33.

————, and Claude, A. 1949a The nature of the Golgi apparatus. I. Parallelism between intracellular myelin figures and Golgi apparatus in somatic cells. J. Morph., 85:35–70.

————, and Claude, A. 1949b The nature of the Golgi apparatus. II. Identification of the Golgi apparatus with a complex of myelin figures. J. Morph., 85:71–112.

Palmer, K. J., and Schmitt, F. O. 1941 X-ray diffraction studies of lipide emulsions. J. Cell. Comp. Physiol., 17:385–394.

Pauling, L. 1948 Nature of forces between large molecules of biological interest. Nature, 161:707–709.

————, and Corey, R. B. 1951a The pleated sheet, a new layer configuration of polypeptide chains. Proc. Nat. Acad. Sci., 37:251–256.

————, and Corey, R. B. 1951b Atomic coordinates and structure factors for two helical configurations of polypeptide chains. Proc. Nat. Acad. Sci., 37:235–240.

————, and Corey, R. B. 1951c Configuration of polypeptide chains. Nature, 168:550–551.

————, and Corey, R. B. 1951d The structure of hair, muscle, and related proteins. Proc. Nat. Acad. Sci., 37:261–271.

Perutz, M. F. 1949 X-ray studies of crystalline proteins. Research, 2:52–61.

——, Jope, E. M., and Barer, R. 1950 Observations of proteins in polarized ultraviolet light. Disc. Faraday Soc., No. 9, pp. 423–427.

Pfeiffer, H. H. 1940 Rheologische, polarisationsoptische und beugungspolarisatorische Untersuchungen an Protoplasmatropfen einigen Modellsubstanzen. Protoplasma, 34:347–352.

—— 1942 Ueber die Abhängigkeit der Doppelbrechung von der Orientierung protoplasmatischer Leptonen durch Zentrifugieren. Koll. Z., 100:254–263.

—— 1949 Auflichtmikroskopische Messungen der anisotropie-Parameter zur quantitativen Erfassung der Dicke des Plasmalemmas roter Blutzellen. Koll. Z., 113:6–10.

Ponder, E. 1948 Hemolysis and Related Phenomena. Grune and Stratton, New York.

Porter, K. R. 1953 Observations on a submicroscopic basophilic component of cytoplasm. J. Exp. Med., 97:727–750.

——, and Kallman, F. L. 1952 Significance of cell particulates as seen by electron microscopy. Ann. N. Y. Acad. Sci., 54:882–891.

——, and Vanamee, P. 1949 Observations on the formation of connective tissue fibers. Proc. Soc. Exp. Biol. Med., 71:513–516.

Reid, M. E. 1943 Interrelationships of calcium and ascorbic acid to cell surfaces and intercellular substances and to physiological action. Physiol. Rev., 23:79–99.

Ries, E. 1940 Der submikroskopische Bau der Pankreaszelle. Z. Zellforsch. mik. Anat., 456–466.

Robertson, J. D. 1941 The function and metabolism of calcium in the invertebrata. Biol. Rev., 16:106–133.

Rosenberg, T., and Wilbrandt, W. 1952 Enzymatic processes in cell membrane penetration. Intern. Rev. Cytol., 1:65–92.

Rothen, A. 1947 Films of protein in biological processes. Adv. Protein Chem., 3:123–137.

—— 1950 III Interaction de films d'antigène avec des anticorps homologues et des enzymes. Helv. Chim. Acta, 33:834–849.

—— 1952 La nature de l'interaction des enzymes proteolytiques avec des films de proteine. Symposium on the Biogenesis of Proteins, 2nd Int. Cong. Bioch., Paris, pp. 96–99.

Rothstein, A., Meier, R., and Hurwitz. L. 1951 The relationship of the cell surface to metabolism. V. The role of uranium-complexing loci of yeast in metabolism. J. Cell. Comp. Physiol., 37:57–81.

Runnström, J. 1949 The mechanism of fertilization in metazoa. Adv. Enzymol., 9:241–327.

——, and Kriszat, G. 1952 The cortical propagation of the activation impulse in the sea urchin egg. Exp. Cell Res., 3:419–426.

Sanger, R. F. 1952 The arrangement of amino acids in proteins. Adv. Protein Chem., 7:1–67.

Schmidt, W. J. 1936 Die Doppelbrechung der quergestreiften Muskelzellen im Proventriculus von Eusyllis blomstrandi. Z. Zellforsch. mik. Anat., 24:525–539.

—— 1937 Die Doppelbrechung von Karyoplasma, Zytoplasma, und Metaplasma. Berlin, Geb. Borntraeger.

—— 1939 Über die Doppelbrechung der Trichocysten von Paramecium. Arch. Protistenk, 92:527–536.

—— 1947 Der Wandel der optischen Anisotropie bei topochemischen Reaktionen histologischer Strukturen. Ber. Oberhess. Ges. Naturheilk. Giessen. N. F. Naturwiss. Abt., 23:56–85.

Schmitt, F. O. 1941 Some protein patterns in cells. Growth, 5:1–20.

—— 1949 Some commentaries on electron microscopy as applied in biology. Federation Proc., 8:530–535.

—— 1950a Tissue structure: polarization optical analysis; in O. Glasser's Medical Physics, vol. 2, pp. 1128–1132. Yearbook Publishers, Chicago.

—— 1950b The structure of the axon filaments of the giant nerve fibers of Loligo and Myxicola. J. Exp. Zool., 113:499–512.

——, Gross, J., and Highberger, J. H. 1953 A new particle type in certain connective tissue extracts. Proc. Nat. Acad. Sci., 39:459–470.

——, Hall, C. E., and Jakus, M. A. 1942 Electron microscope studies of the structure of collagen. J. Cell. & Comp. Physiol., 20:11–33.

Schneider, W. C., and Hogeboom, G. H. 1951 Cytochemical studies of mammalian tissues: The isolation of cell components by differential centrifugation: A review. Cancer Res., 11:1–22.

Schrader, F. 1944 Mitosis. Columbia University Press, New York.

Seeds, W. E. 1953 Polarized ultraviolet microspectrography and molecular structure. Progress in Biophysics and Biophysical Chemistry, 3:27–46.

Seifriz, W. 1943 Protoplasmic streaming. Bot. Rev., 9:49–123.

Singer, S. J. 1950 On the unlikelihood of specific long range forces in immunologic and enzymatic reactions. J. Biol. Chem., 182:189–211.

Sjöstrand, F. 1944 Über die Eigenfluoreszenz tierischer Gewebe mit besonderer Berücksichtigung der Säugetiere. Anat. Suppl., 1:1–163.

——, and Rhodin, J. 1953 The ultrastructure of the proximal convoluted tubules of the mouse kidney as revealed by high resolution electron microscopy. Exp. Cell Res., 4:426–456.

Sorof, S., Claus, B., and Cohen, P. P. 1951a Effect of regeneration and inanition on the electrophoretic properties of soluble rat liver proteins. Cancer Res., 11:873–876.

——, and Cohen, P. P. 1951b Electrophoretic and ultracentrifugal studies on the soluble proteins of various tumors and of livers of rats fed 4-dimethylamino azobenzene. Cancer Res., 11:376–382.

——, Cohen, P. P., Miller, E. C., and Mileer, J. A. 1951c Electrophoretic studies on the soluble proteins from livers of rats fed amino ozodyls. Cancer Res., 11:383–387.

Sosa, J. M. 1948 On the morphological, chemical and physicochemical significance of the Golgi apparatus. Rev. Sudamericana de Morfologia, 6:115–133.

Spiegelman, S., and Steinbach, H. B. 1945 Substrate-enzyme orientation during embryonic development. Biol. Bull., *88:*254–268.

Straub, F. B., and Feuer, G. 1950 Adenosinetriphosphate the functional group of actin. Biochim. et Biophys. Acta, *4:*455–470.

Swann, M. M. 1951a Protoplasmic structure and mitosis. I. The birefringence of the metaphase spindle and asters of the living sea-urchin egg. J. Exp. Biol., *28:*417–433.

———— 1951b Protoplasmic structure and mitosis. The nature and cause of birefringence changes in the sea-urchin egg at anaphase. J. Exp. Biol., *28:*434–444.

———— 1952 Structural agents in mitosis. Intern. Rev. Cytol., *1:*195–210.

————, and Mitchison, J. M. 1950 Refinements of polarized light microscopy. J. Exp. Biol., *27:*227–237.

Sylvén, B. 1951 On the advantage of freeze-vacuum dehydration of tissues in morphological and cytochemical research. Extrait de Acta Union Intern. contre le Cancer, *7:*708–712.

Tyler, A. 1947 An auto-antibody concept of cell structure, growth and differentiation. Growth, *10* (Suppl.):7–19.

Ussing, H. H. 1949 Transport of ions across cellular membranes. Physiol. Rev., *29:*127–155.

Verwey, E. J. W., and Overbeek, J. T. G. 1948 The Theory of the Stability of Lyophobic Colloids. Elsevier Publishing Co., New York.

Waugh, D. F. 1948 Regeneration of insulin from insulin fibrils by the action of alkali. J. Amer. Chem. Soc., *70:*1850–1851.

———— 1950 The ultrastructure of the envelope of mammalian erythrocytes. Ann. N. Y. Acad. Sci., *50:*835–853.

————, and Schmitt, F. O. 1940 Investigations of the thickness and ultrastructure of cellular membranes by the analytical leptoscope. Cold Spring Harbor Symposia, Quant. Biol., *8:*233–241.

Weiss, P. 1941 Nerve patterns: The mechanics of nerve growth. Growth, Third Growth Symp., *5:*163–203.

———— 1945 Experiments on cell and axon orientation in vitro: The role of colloidal exudates in tissue organization. J. Exp. Zool., *100:*353–386.

———— 1947 The problem of specificity in growth and development. Yale J. Biol. & Med., *19:*235–278.

———— 1949 Differential growth; in Chemistry and Physiology of Growth, pp. 135–186. Princeton University Press, Princeton, New Jersey.

———— 1950 Perspectives in the field of morphogenesis. Quart. Rev. Biol., *25:*177–198.

———— 1952 Attraction fields between growing tissue cultures. Science. *115:*293–295.

————, and Garber, B. 1952 Shape and movement of mesenchyme cells as functions of the physical structure of the medium. Contributions to a quantitative morphology. Proc. Nat. Acad. Sci., *38:*264–280.

Weisz, P. B. 1951 A general mechanism of differentiation based on morphogenetic studies in ciliates. Amer. Naturalist, *85:*293–311.

Wilkins, M. H. F. 1951 I. Ultraviolet dichroism and molecular structure in living cells. II. Electron microscopy of nuclear membranes. Pubblicazioni della Stazione Zoologica di Napoli, *23:*104–114.

Williams, C. M., and Watanabe, M. I. 1951 Mitochondria in the flight muscles of insects. J. Gen. Physiol., *34:*675–689.

————, and Watanabe, M. I. 1952 The giant mitochondria of insects. Science, *115:*488.

Winter, J. 1952 Sur les actions à distance en biologie. Symposium on the biogenesis of proteins, 2nd Int. Cong. of Bioch., Paris, pp. 100–107.

Worley, L. G. 1951 Recovery of the Golgi apparatus from homogenates of normal mammalian liver. Exp. Cell Res., *2:*684–687.

Zeiger, K. 1949 Haftpunkttheorie und histologische Fixation. Z. Zellforsh, mik. Anat., *34:*230–256.

Zollinger, H. U. 1948a Cytologic studies with the phase microscope. II. The mitochondria and other cytoplasmic constituents under various experimental conditions. Amer. J. Path., *24:*569–589.

———— 1948b Cytologic studies with the phase microscope. III. Alterations in the nuclei of "resting" and dividing cells induced by means of fixatives, anisotonic solutions, acids, and alkali. Amer. J. Path., *24:*797–806.

———— 1950 Zum qualitativen Nucleoprotein-Gehalt und zur Morphologie der Mitochondrien. Experientia, *6:*14–16.

CHAPTER 2

Cellular Metabolism

H. B. STEINBACH AND F. MOOG

In the life of a cell, morphological arrangements and chemical processes bear a quite different relationship to the integrity of the unit. Parts of cells, or structures within cells, may be shifted around, in many cases without marked changes in the life of the whole. But slight alterations in any one of the many chemical events that make up the total metabolism usually call forth severe, and often fatal, effects. Traces of drugs, vitamins, and poisons may alter the entire course of a cellular unit or, properly applied, may momentarily and reversibly block some special function.

Not only individual cells, but also organizations of cells, are thus dependent on the maintenance of their normal metabolic constitution. The development of embryos particularly illustrates this dependency. Experimental morphogenesis has amply demonstrated that an embryo may go on developing in spite of radical alterations in the numbers and orientations of its parts. Chemical interference with the metabolism of the embryo, on the other hand, readily leads to serious abnormalities or death.

Since the classic studies of Lavoisier, the gross similarity between the chemical activities of a living substance and of a burning candle has occupied the attention of many workers. Only in recent years has the consequent emphasis on the respiratory aspects of cellular metabolism begun to give way to study of those aspects of cell metabolism of most interest to the general biologist, i.e., mechanisms for utilizing the energy of the burning foodstuffs and the linkage of these mechanisms with oxidative processes. Much careful work has shown us a great deal about the nature of the burning process; the outlines of how energy evolved is used by the cell, however, have by the present time been only vaguely sketched in.

Our knowledge of special details of metabolism is voluminous, and it would be futile to attempt a comprehensive factual coverage of the subject in one chapter. On the other hand, a few general mechanisms (which may be regarded as models for a variety of metabolic processes) are emerging from the welter of biochemical investigations. The attempt to use such principles as have been established should be made only against a background of special knowledge. While a general treatment may be a useful intellectual guide, the planning and execution of specific experiments on cellular metabolism requires critical application of specific knowledge, hard work, and considerable familiarity with experimental techniques (and their limitations!).

In general terms, cellular metabolism may be diagrammed as shown in Figure 2. Reduced carbon chains represent the available fuel burned by cells and, in terms of heat content or, more accurately, free energy, are first encountered by animal cells at a relatively high energy level. By a series of steps, electrons* are removed, leaving CO_2 (oxidized carbon) as ultimate residue. The electrons are combined finally with electron acceptors, usually oxygen molecules, in which case water is formed by union with protons. As electrons progress stepwise towards a terminal state, other cellular processes are proceeding whereby carbon chains are built up and degraded, units are fixed into cellular structures, and energy is made available for movements of various kinds, for production of electricity, for syntheses and for other types of utilization of energy. The oxidative trail releases energy, the synthetic trail requires energy.

Frequently the energy-releasing side of the picture is termed catabolism, the synthetic side anabolism. This distinction is no longer of use since all cellular processes are known to be closely linked. However, it is still fruitful to consider oxidation

---

* Hydrogen may be regarded as composed of a proton and an electron. In normal combination with other elements, the electron serves as a binding agent. With the electron removed, H^+ results, which is free to react with the buffers always present in protoplasm. Thus all instances of hydrogen transfer can also be regarded as electron transfers.

and synthesis separately. They apparently may be dissociated in cells by such agents as dinitrophenol, and off-on switching devices between the two phases of metabolism may well be operative in normal physiological control.

There is abundant evidence that at temperatures in the physiological range, the downhill release of energy to be used by the uphill synthetic paths cannot involve a simple transfer of heat such as one finds in the usual heat expansion type of machine. Rather, it has become obvious that chemical forms of linkage energy must be made available. These chemical links must be such that they can be formed by the oxidative pathways and then enter into reactions with the synthetic pathways, giving up their high energy content for purposes of chemical synthesis, transport of materials, gross movements and so forth (cf. Johnson, in Lardy, '50).* A good rule-of-thumb to keep in mind is that, in order for an energy-yielding (exergonic) reaction to drive an energy-using (endergonic) reaction, the two reactions must have a common component.

It is apparent that the whole study of cellular metabolism involves a number of aspects. Starting with the outside of the animal cell and working inward we may list the following:

1. The exchange of foods and waste products between cell and environment. Under this heading are frequently listed such subjects as permeability, secretion, and excretion. Although of obvious importance, these subjects will be treated only incidentally here.

2. The oxidative breakdown of the reduced carbon chains of the foods taken in.

3. Formation of energy linkage compounds. It is here that the coenzyme systems become of greatest importance. Three systems will be invoked frequently (cf. Meyerhof, '49): the coenzyme I and II systems (nicotinamide coenzymes) concerned with hydrogen (electron) transfer; the adenylic acid systems (ATP and ADP) concerned with phosphate bond energy transfer; and the cocarboxylase system (thiamine pyrophosphate) relating to decarboxylation and carbon dioxide formation.

4. The synthetic mechanisms themselves, or perhaps better, the transducer mechanisms whereby one form of energy is converted to another. Of the biochemical syn-

* Frequent reference will be made to the provocative review by Barron ('43) and to the volume "Respiratory Enzymes," edited by Lardy. In many instances, rather than referring to original papers, citations will be given by name of the author of the appropriate chapter in "Respiratory Enzymes." Thus, citations given in this way do not necessarily mean that the author cited is the originator of the work mentioned.

thetic systems, the formation of polysaccharide is best adapted to serve as a model system (cf. Hassid and Doudoroff, '50); for other types of processes, perhaps the best model is found in Szent-Györgyi's muscle protein preparations (cf. Szent-Györgyi, '51).

Finally, an aspect of cell metabolism that is perhaps the most intriguing and mysterious of all must be treated: that of the control of the reactions in the protoplasmic substance. It is at this point, as well as with item number four in our list, that cytology and general physiology come closest together, since certainly a large proportion of the trans-

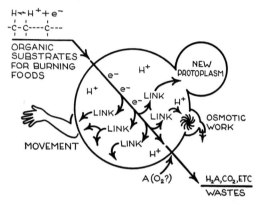

Fig. 2. Schematic model to illustrate some general principles of cellular metabolism. Organic substrates (foods or products of assimilation) at a high energy level are represented as reduced carbon chains. These chains are oxidized stepwise, each step potentially an energy-transferring link to physiological functions.

ducer and controlling mechanisms must reside in the formed elements of the protoplasm.

This preliminary general outline could fit almost all types of cells, with, of course, special modifications. The cells of green plants have the photosynthetic mechanism added to the scheme outlined; for these living units energy is taken directly from the environment as radiant energy so that reduced carbon chains are built up. Presumably from here on their metabolism is similar, in general outline, to that of animal cells. Similarly, some microorganisms can obtain the energy for chemical energy storage from the oxidation of simple, sometimes elementary, substances.

GLYCOLYTIC AND OXIDATIVE MECHANISMS

The most common, but by no means exclusive, fuel for cells appears to be carbo-

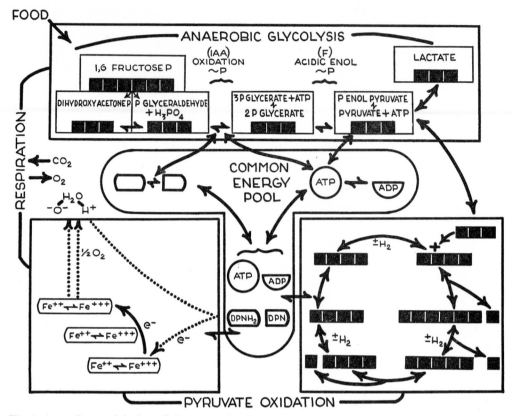

Fig. 3. An outline model of a cellular system having anaerobic and aerobic mechanisms for carbohydrate oxidation. Glycolysis (top section), Krebs–Szent-Györgyi cycle (bottom right) and oxidase systems (lower left) are diagrammed separately since they may well be separate morphological entities in cells. Each major unit is linked by (1) raw materials and (2) coenzymes of the common energy pool. Synthetic and other energy-using reactions should also be keyed in to the common energy pool. Within each unit process, individual reactions are also linked together by raw materials and coenzymes.

hydrate. In any case, the schemes built up for the oxidative degradation of carbohydrate provide such generalized models that they serve well to illustrate pathways which may be available in any given type of living system. It should, of course, be clearly understood that some of the most interesting physiological variations may be concerned with additional systems not yet discovered, and that there may also be both ontogenetic and phylogenetic stages yet to be outlined* (cf. Barron, '43).

In Figure 3 is presented a simplified diagram of pathways traversed by the elements of a common hexose sugar, after a preliminary treatment in-

* While the number of specific chemical reactions taking place in cells in general is probably finite, reporting on all of them would hardly be a fruitful undertaking for the student of cellular metabolism. The "Annual Review of Biochemistry" serves as an excellent device for following details, as also does "Chemical Abstracts." In this chapter, examples which serve as models are deliberately chosen in order to illustrate principles involved.

volving phosphorylation, leading to the final formation of carbon dioxide and water (or, in glycolysis, to lactic acid). Further details are given in Figure 4. The over-all reaction for the oxidative process is:

$$C_6H_{12}O_6 + 6 O_2 \longrightarrow$$
$$6 CO_2 + 6 H_2O + 683,000 \text{ calories}$$
(at normal physiological concentrations)
(cf. Johnson, in Lardy, '50)

For lactic acid fermentation the reaction is:

$$C_6H_{12}O_6 \longrightarrow 2 C_3H_6O_3 + 50,000 \text{ calories}$$

The gas exchange resulting from oxidation is called respiration; the process is mediated by a series of enzymatically catalyzed steps so arranged that the energy of oxidation is delivered in a series of small "packets" (cf. Szent-Györgyi, '39). To oversimplify the case, any single step might be pictured as follows:

Reduced substrate + cofactor $\longrightarrow$
  (with energy
    packet)

                Oxidized substrate + reduced cofactor
                                      (with energy
                                        packet)

Sugar, to feed the mechanism, may enter from the environment or from endogenous stores such as glycogen. In either instance, stages to be discussed

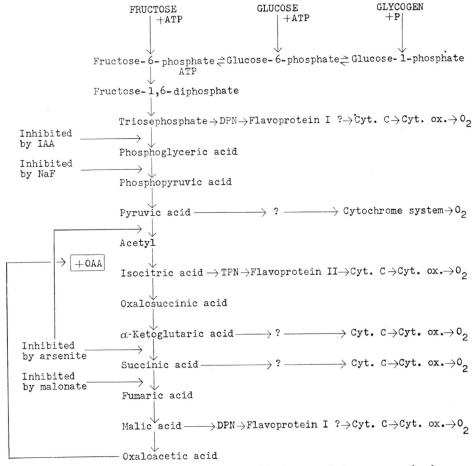

Fig. 4. Intermediate catalysts involved in the transfer of hydrogen and electrons to molecular oxygen in the stepwise oxidation of carbohydrate in muscle. Abbreviations: *IAA*, iodoacetic acid; *OAA*, oxaloacetic acid; *Cyt. C*, cytochrome c; *Cyt. ox.*, cytochrome oxidase.

The factor of Lockhart and Potter, and Altschul et al. is referred to as Flavoprotein I with a question mark. This factor is specific for DPN. Flavoprotein II, specific for TPN, is the cytochrome reductase of Haas, Horecker, and Hogness. Whether cytochromes *a* and *b* are involved in any of the steps is not definitely known. The important discovery has recently been made that the phosphorylation of glucose by ATP to glucose-6-phosphate, catalyzed by the enzyme hexokinase, is under the dual control of hormones from the anterior pituitary and adrenal cortex on one side, and insulin on the other. (From Ochoa, '47.)

later give the sugar a preliminary working over to result in the phosphorylated form shown. Direct oxidation without preliminary phosphorylation possibly may also occur (cf. Barron, '43), but its physiological role is still to be established. The usual hexose for the scheme shown would be glucose. There is evidence that other sugars may also enter the system provided the appropriate enzymes are present (cf. Lardy, '50).

A preliminary splitting of the 1,6-fructose diphosphate leads to the formation of two triose monophosphates, which, in the presence of triose isomerase, are interconvertible. The phosphoglyceraldehyde formed, in the presence of phosphate and a phosphate acceptor (ADP), is then oxidized by phosphoglyceraldehyde oxidase to yield phosphoglyceric acid and ATP.

At this important step, two ubiquitous coenzyme

systems are introduced: the pyridine nucleotide* coenzymes (cf. LePage, in Lardy, '50) concerned with hydrogen transport, and the adenylic acid system† (ATP and ADP) concerned with energy packet storage and transport. For the reaction to be

* The diphosphopyridine nucleotide is best known and will be referred to as oxidized (DPN) or reduced (DPNH$_2$) coenzyme. This is the coenzyme I of Warburg.

† Adenylic acid is a nucleotide containing one phosphate group per molecule. This form (adenosine monophosphate, or AMP) can add phosphate by energy-rich bonds (cf. Lipmann, '41) to form adenosine diphosphate (ADP) or adenosine triphosphate (ATP). In most of the discussion that will follow, only the change ADP + P $\rightleftharpoons$ ATP will be considered, although the other forms may also be concerned.

carried out successfully, all components—phosphate, triose, oxidized DPN, ADP and the appropriate enzymes—must be present. In the absence of DPN the oxidation will not take place; in the absence of phosphate and phosphate acceptor, on the other hand, or in the presence of a competing substance for phosphate, such as arsenate, the oxidation

After rearrangement and addition of water, phosphoenolpyruvic acid is formed from phosphoglyceric acid. Phosphoenolpyruvic acid contains a high energy phosphate linkage. In the presence of ADP, transphosphorylation occurs to yield pyruvic acid and ATP. Enolase, the enzyme leading to the formation of the enol form, is especially sensitive to fluor-

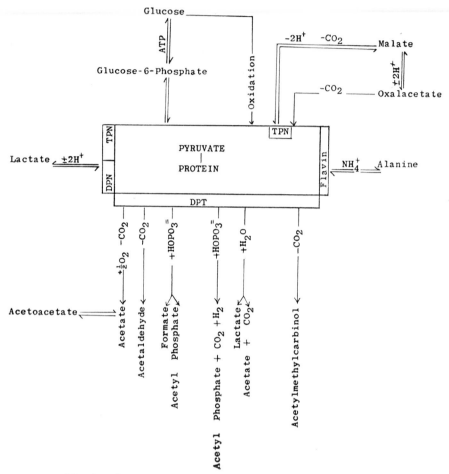

Fig. 5. Pathways in the metabolism of pyruvate. (From Barron.)

takes place without the formation of a utilizable energy packet. Phosphoglyceraldehyde oxidase is highly sensitive to iodoacetic acid (IAA) and related compounds—hence the special virtue of IAA in preventing glycolysis. This type of interplay of enzymes, cofactors, and substrates is found repeatedly throughout oxidation of foodstuffs, and usually the same coenzyme systems are present. It is a remarkable fact that adenylic acid systems (DPN contains ADP in its molecule) are so widely spread throughout living matter (cf. Barron, '43). The nitrogenous base coenzymes, diffusible and labile, are nucleotide systems containing phosphate, nitrogenous base and pentose sugar. In their role as cofactors for enzyme proteins, these complexes must bear a rather interesting relationship to the nucleoproteins.

ide ion, the fluoride forming a complex with phosphate and with magnesium, an essential part of the active enzyme. Thus, from the addition of fluoride, the formation of two molecules of pyruvate from one molecule of hexose diphosphate is accompanied by the formation of four ATP energy-rich phosphate bonds together with the reduction of two molecules of DPN. [Cf. a discussion by McShan in Lardy ('50) on the roles of DPN and TPN.] To start with simple nonphosphorylated hexose, the preliminary phosphorylation would require the utilization of two molecules of ATP phosphorus, giving a net gain of two rather than four energy-rich bonds. With glycogen as an original substrate, having glucosidic linkages already established, only one labile phosphate is required to convert each glucose residue to hexose diphosphate. Hence the

the initial linkage. A series of "trans" enzymes have been described (cf. Cohen, in Lardy, '50) in addition to the transphosphorylases already mentioned. Transaminase, transiminase, transulfurase, transmethylase have all been studied with considerable precision. The dehydrogenase enzymes are essentially transhydrogenases and, with the DPN coenzyme system, function in a fashion perfectly analogous to the transphosphorylases working with the adenylic acid coenzyme system.

While mechanisms of protein and fat synthesis are not clearly understood as the carbohydrate models, essentially similar systems have been postulated on the basis of very suggestive data (cf. Ratner, '49; Lipmann, '49; Borsook et al., '49).* Fruton ('50), in an interesting paper, suggests that cellular peptidase may act in building up polypeptides and proteins by transferring peptides to already existing peptide chains, the process being in many respects similar to the reactions noted for the formation of polysaccharide by transferring a monosaccharide from a disaccharide to an existing chain of sugar residues.

THE CONTROL OF CELLULAR METABOLISM†

A living cell at work must depend upon the precise integration of a complex mosaic of active units. The examples chosen from the glycolytic and oxidative cycles illustrate both the multiplicity of the parts involved and their interdependence. In addition, it

* The discussion by Borsook is especially illuminating with respect to the general nature of the problems considered and the careful speculations about cellular mechanisms that may be concerned with amino acid incorporation into tissues.

† In this section, as in the preceding one on glycolytic and oxidative mechanisms, we shall discuss examples rather than attempt a complete coverage of all experiments designed to elucidate control of metabolism. Much good work has been done in an attempt to analyze the relationship of physiological processes and chemical reactions, mainly by defining enzyme systems in tissue breis and by determining the effects of added inhibitors on functions, or the effects of addition or depletion of substrate. No single formula is yet available that will ensure that such studies are meaningful in terms of the life of the cell. The interpretation of studies which involve upsetting the metabolic machinery must always be made cautiously against the background of the material so well set forth by Heilbrunn in his "Outline of General Physiology," as well as the details of our knowledge of enzyme systems.

must be remembered that there are many special pathways associated with special cellular functions. The existence of multi-unit systems that function in an orderly manner implies also the existence of precise controlling mechanisms. Probably the most challenging problem confronting the general physiologist today is that of piecing together our knowledge of fragments of the active framework of the living cell in such a fashion that not only will the energy balances hold true, but the orderliness of life will also follow.

If the components of the glycolytic and oxidative systems are mixed together in a test tube, some orderly controlled reactions will take place by virtue of the sharing of reactants and reaction products of unit processes of the system. For example, in the fermentation of sugar by cell-free extracts of yeast, the rate of carbon dioxide production can be controlled by the concentration of such components as sugar, phosphate, ATP and so forth. If the enzymes hydrolyzing ATP are blocked, phosphate tends to disappear as new ATP is formed; thus further phosphorylation of sugars is inhibited and hexose monophosphate accumulates. Thus a "control" of sugar phosphorylation can be effected by controlling ATP dephosphorylation. This type of control, however, would have distinct limitations and, in particular, it is difficult to visualize regulation of the many rather fast "off-on" shifts in metabolism in this fashion. Fortunately, there is good evidence that the components of the reactions are not free to mix as in the test tube, but are highly and precisely localized within the structure of the cell. Evidence for intracellular localization of enzymes has been accumulating over a period of years and need not be detailed here (cf. Schneider, in Lardy, '50). Ever since the work of Warburg, it has been recognized that the metal-containing oxidases are associated with insoluble cell fragments in a suspension of fragmented tissue. Cytochrome c appears to be reasonably soluble but the other cytochromes and the oxidase are put into solution only with great difficulty. Similarly, the cytochrome-linked dehydrogenases are separated from insoluble cell particles only with difficulty (cf. McShan, in Lardy, '50). Green (in Lardy, '50) discusses evidence that the enzymes of the citric acid cycle are always associated with the insoluble residue of tissue homogenates; partly on this basis he names the system cyclophorase. The enzymes primarily associated with glycolysis appear, on the other hand, to be more soluble* than those associated with decarboxylation and oxidation (cf. Dixon, '49).

In addition to enzymes, many small-molecule substances such as ATP and acetylcholine have been considered to be at least in part bound in the normal living cell (cf. Caspersson and Thorell, '42).

In a general fashion, it may be fruitful for the cell physiologist to regard those enzyme systems which are fixed to insoluble units of cell homogenates as being of primary importance in the regulatory activities of cells. A notable exception to this generalization would be the apparent local activity of phosphorylating mechanisms at the cell surface (Rothstein and Meier, '48).

Thus a discussion of the control of cellular metabolism should not be limited to test tube factors, but must also include factors relating to the discrete structural organization of enzyme systems. Basically it might be said that variations in metabolic intensity are due to differences either in molar enzyme concentration or in enzyme activity. But molar enzyme concentrations are rarely known and, under the heading of enzyme activity, it will obviously be necessary to consider spatial orientations as well as material supply and availability of cofactors.

DIFFERENCES IN ENZYME CONCENTRATION

The rate at which an enzymatic reaction proceeds may be limited either by the chemical reactants in the usual sense, or by the catalytic system. This fact was first clearly established by Michaelis and Menten ('13) in studies on the inversion of cane sugar. Recent work has shown that the rate of oxygen uptake may be regulated by the concentra-

tion of electron donor (cytochrome c), the concentration of electron acceptor (oxygen), or the concentration of enzyme (cytochrome oxidase).† In this section we shall consider the possibility of variations in activity resulting from variations in the molar concentration of a given enzyme—necessarily assuming that substrates and cofactors are not limiting *in the cell* or *at localized regions* in the cell. Unfortunately, this assumption is not supported by clear-cut evidence at the present time.

Assays of enzyme content of cells are carried out routinely by homogenizing the tissue to break down the cell structure, adding appropriate amounts of substrate and cofactors, and then measuring the rate of the reaction in question. Under these conditions one expects that *total* enzyme content will be determined, any control by cell structure having presumably been abolished by the homogenization procedure.

Large numbers of studies made with this technique have shown that adult tissues possess distinctive enzyme patterns, differing markedly in amounts of various enzymes per unit of tissue. In many cases the differences are plainly correlated with the function of the tissue—for example, high cholinesterase activity in nerve tissue, high apyrase activity in muscle, high phosphatase activity in kidney. Under pathological conditions enzyme patterns are significantly altered (cf. Greenstein, '47).

The activity of enzymes as determined in test tube assays is obviously less meaningful than activity as deduced from metabolic studies on whole cells. Technical difficulties have prevented such comparisons from being frequently made, but where they have been made (particularly in the field of oxygen uptake), wide discrepancies have been revealed. The work of Spiegelman and Steinbach ('45), showing a large increase in cytochrome oxidase activity on homogenization in frogs' eggs, is an example of this. As a matter of fact, it seems reasonable to assume that most cells of adult organisms ordinarily

---

* The word *solution* is poorly defined in the biochemical literature. Due to the lack of precise usage of words by enzymologists, it is difficult to decide whether an "extract," for example, means a solution of the substance in question or whether it is a suspension of granules. Enzymes are here designated as soluble if they have been prepared and crystallized by relatively mild methods. It should be understood that the so-called soluble enzyme may be loosely associated with structures insoluble in the cell or, on the other hand, enzymes difficult to separate from insoluble material may, under certain conditions, be floating freely. Greenstein et al. ('49) record an interesting example of a change of type of enzyme, more liver glutaminase appearing in insoluble fraction with the onset of cancerization while the activity of the soluble enzyme diminishes.

† Activity of an enzyme is usually expressed as rate of substrate change per unit; but the appropriate unit basis on which to calculate activity is a difficult matter to decide. Some authors use a standard number of cells, some dry weight, some nitrogen content. Since enzymes are probably localized within cells, it is probable that any base unit is valid only in the most general sense, the most specifically valid being the cellular unit, if it can be clearly defined (cf. Davidson and Leslie, '50).

carry an inactive reserve of enzymes to be used only in periods of unusual stress. This is self-evident in tissues like muscle, in which there is a clear-cut difference between resting and activity metabolism; but it is probably true for many other tissues also. Cells of embryonic tissues, however, may well operate with virtually no safety factors in enzyme concentration. Such cells presumably are never "resting" in the sense that adult muscle fibers or gland cells rest, and accordingly enzyme systems might be expected to function continuously at near maximum activity.

A second element of uncertainty in the homogenate technique is the influence on activity of association of enzyme with structural components of the cell. Although grinding tissue may destroy all the coarser elements of cell structure, it is well known, as we have pointed out before, that different enzymes show varying affinities for particulate matter in breis. Since enzyme activity must certainly depend in large part on precise steric configurations, such as may be involved in the antigen-antibody situation (cf. Pauling, '48), it would not be surprising if a given number of enzyme molecules bound onto particles would exhibit a different activity from the same number of molecules in free solution (Mazia and Blumenthal, '50).

That such variations do occur is indicated by several studies in which different homogenization media were used. In the case of muscle apyrase, for example, a water homogenate has high activity but is insensitive to Ca^{++}, whereas extraction with strong potassium chloride produces a soluble enzyme preparation of low activity which is strongly activated by Ca^{++} (Steinbach, '49). Similar effects have been noted with apyrase in the granules of chick embryo breis (Steinbach and Moog, '45). In neither case is there any assurance that only one enzyme is being dealt with, but the results are consistent with the view that association of enzymes with insoluble material alters their activity. The same interpretation can be placed on the report of Tyler ('50) that respiration is inhibited by dinitrophenol in tissue breis prepared as water homogenates, but is activated by dinitrophenol when the brei is prepared by homogenizing in Ringer's solution with glucose added.

The same enzyme might possibly vary in its structural relations from tissue to tissue. For this reason the differences in enzyme patterns previously cited may only partly reflect differences in actual concentration of enzymes.

Enzyme patterns have also been studied by the methods of chemical genetics. Here enzyme activity is measured in terms of activities of intact cells, the assumption being made (but rarely tested) that other factors are not limiting. An excellent summary of these studies has been published by Tatum ('49).

DIFFERENCES IN ENZYME ACTIVITY

Given a fixed number of enzyme molecules in a cell, their in vivo activity will depend

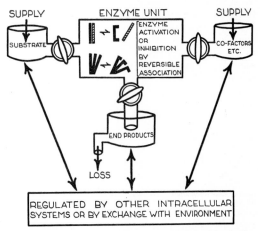

Fig. 8. Diagram to illustrate some possible methods by which unit enzyme systems might be controlled. The enzyme unit (its protoplasmic analog might be a mitochondrion) is pictured as connected to the rest of the living system by (1) substrate supply, (2) waste or product removal and (3) diffusible co-factor supply. Control of activity might be accomplished by control of rate of flow of any of these factors.

In addition, the state of the enzyme within the unit could be altered by (1) reversible association with inhibitors or (2) reversible change of activity by association or dissociation of enzymes into structures. From our present knowledge of enzymatic content of particulate units it can be deduced that all these factors, and possibly more, might enter into the delicate control of cellular metabolism.

on the quantity of the substrate available, on the adequacy of the cofactor supply, and on geometrical relations tending to inhibit or promote the reaction in which the enzyme participates. The term "activity," applied to enzyme systems, bears an obvious relationship to the same term used in orthodox chemistry, i.e., a fudge-factor introduced to account for the differences between observed rates of actions and those calculated on the basis of known molar concentrations. In the case of enzyme activity, neither molar concentrations nor causes of activity variations are usually known. In this section we shall consider enzyme activity* in terms of variations in molar concentrations and in activities. The diagram in Figure 8 may help to illustrate some of the variety of factors that might be operative in controlling the rate of an over-all reaction catalyzed by a given enzyme system.

Supply of Substrate and Cofactors. A general illustration of this type of control involving the cofactor ATP has been developed with special acuity by Potter ('44). The way in which ATP and DPN aid in regulating phosphorylations and fermentations should be kept in mind here, for the general reasoning used in these cases probably applies to other substances both in the entire cell and in localized areas within the cell. Interesting modifications in patterns of activity must arise when any single substance or cofactor serving several enzyme systems is in short supply. Under such conditions competition for the limiting factor might even result in the complete exclusion of one reaction in favor of another.

Exogenous substrate supply may be called a controlling factor of the second order, since it appears to be itself under the control of selective mechanisms in the outer layers of the cell. Phosphate and sugar, for example, appear to enter yeast cells only during active metabolism (Spiegelman and Kamen, '47), and even simple elements such as potassium have selective exchange systems related to the production of specific organic acids (Rothstein and Meier, '48). The clearest examples of active regulation of movement of material in a living system are contained in the studies on sugar resorption in the kidneys (Pitts and Alexander, '44); and these findings and interpretations are useful in considering the penetration of foodstuffs into cellular systems. The more orthodox aspects of permeability do not seem to shed much light on the problems of transfer of material in living cells (cf. material in the monograph by Davson and Danielli, '43).

An interesting aspect of surface control is the finding of Rothstein and Meier ('48) that numerous esterases and other enzymes localized on the outer layers of yeast cells will break down various tested intermediates of the glycolytic and oxidative cycles, and release the hydrolytic products quantitatively into the medium. Thus they may guard the

* See preceding footnote.

orderly train of events going on within the cell by preventing the entrance of unplanned-for intermediates. We might, for example, infer that glucose, in order to be properly channeled into cell metabolism, must originally enter into the metabolic reactions of the cell by being phosphorylated in the initial stages; previously formed glucose phosphate appears to be excluded.

The Structural Orientation of Enzymes. The tendency of many enzymes to be associated with insoluble particulates after cellular disruption has already been pointed out. At the present time a tentative understanding of many significant intracellular phenomena can be arrived at by assuming that such associations exist within the cell, and that they control activity both by keeping enzyme and substrate apart or bringing them together, and also by bringing enzyme into contact with activators or inhibitors. Such geometrical arrangements are probably at the basis of very rapid changes in activity—for example, the rise in respiration in muscle and nerve that can be detected within milliseconds after the onset of electrical activity. This rise is probably due to the "switching in" of enzymes previously immobilized, to act on substrates previously held in reserve. That the system switched in may be at least in part different from the resting system is indicated by studies like those of Stannard ('39), who showed that azide does not affect resting muscle respiration, but abolishes the increase of respiration upon activation.

In comparing enzyme reactions in tissue under different physiological states, *time* is an important criterion in determining whether observed increases are due to alterations in activity of pre-existing enzyme molecules, or to synthesis of new molecules. A short time change is of more diagnostic value because it most likely indicates enzyme activation or inhibition. A change occurring over a long time, on the other hand, might indicate either enzyme activation or enzyme formation.

There are numerous cases suggesting, but not proving, that enzyme localizations may serve as isolating mechanisms. All the studies showing enzyme binding to cytoplasmic particles might be cited here, subject, of course, to confirmatory studies showing evidence of controlled change during activity. Chantrenne's ('43) examination of the effects of moving the cytochrome oxidase-rich granules of intact Amphiuma liver cells by centrifugation is especially interesting. In these large cells the granules can be seen packed into the centrifugal region. Concomitantly the Qo_2 is depressed, apparently because the enzyme has been concentrated to a point where the uniformly distributed substrate becomes limiting, even though the total amounts of both substrate and enzyme per cell are unchanged. Similar observations and conclusions have been reported for silk worm eggs (Wolsky, '50).

The methods of cytochemistry have revealed many suggestive localizations of enzymes in cells (cf. Bradfield, '50). The Gomori technique for alkaline phosphatase particularly has been examined with sufficient thoroughness that we can rely on some, at least, of the intracellular localizations it has revealed; but again, correlated studies are needed to show how these localizations aid in controlling the functions of the cell. One instance apparently demonstrating functional change in location is the reported movement of ATP of striated muscle from the A bands, where it occurs during rest, to the I bands during activity (cf. Caspersson and Thorell, '42).

To explain the very fast off-on effects that occur in response to stimulation, it may be necessary to seek out something more precise than simple isolation between enzyme and substrate, which would apparently require diffusion of substance over a finite distance. Minor structural alterations, converting an inhibited to an activated unit or vice versa, might be a faster mechanism. Among the few studies that appear to demonstrate a possible mechanism for such a type of control is that of Zamenhof and Chargaff ('49) who found that DNase activity in cell-free yeast preparations is increased with age. The increase was shown to be due to the destruction of an inhibitor which is bound to the enzyme in fresh preparations. Probably the same association of enzyme and inhibitor in the intact cell controls the rate of breakdown of the cellular DNA. In the same category we may perhaps place the report of Barron and his associates ('48) that the fixed sulfhydryl-containing enzymes in cells are poised at a given state of oxidation, and thus of activity, by the influence of other sulfhydryl groups freely diffused in the cytoplasm.

One more possibility that should be mentioned in this section is that the activity of an enzyme might be controlled simply by being bound or not bound to structural units. The evidence that the association of enzyme molecules into formed structures influences their activity has already been considered.

THE REGULATION OF METABOLISM IN DEVELOPMENT

That growth and differentiation must involve enzyme production is axiomatic. Recognition of this fact brings into sharp focus the problems concerned with the mechanisms by which the newly produced enzymes are integrated into the orderly scheme of developmental events. In this section we shall attempt to determine to what extent the integrations of the embryonic period may be explained in the same terms as have proved useful in dealing with controlling mechanisms in adult cells. No attempt will be made to discuss the general energetics of development, since this topic is covered in Section VIII.

It is necessary in this context first to distinguish between metabolism as an aspect of development, and metabolism as a "cause" of development. Failure to make this distinction has led to considerable confusion in the past. The melange of events that make up the life of the embryo is biochemical and functional as well as structural. That the chemogenetic events in some instances are causally related to the morphogenetic events is reasonable to assume; but attempts to establish the causality are largely premature in the present state of our knowledge. It seems to us that studies of regulating mechanisms in general embryonic biochemistry may provide the most fruitful clues to the nature of the linkages between the chemistry and the morphology of embryos.

Three special precautions must be kept in mind in dealing with researches on enzymes in embryos. First, the assumption that enzyme, cofactor, or substrate is not limiting where one of the three is being dealt with is less acceptable than in adult tissue, for obvious reasons. Second, the small quantities of embryonic tissue generally available, and its relative instability, make negative results more than usually suspect. The reported demonstration that the chick embryo does not have phosphorylative glycolysis, for example, was completely refuted by the more careful studies of Novikoff, Potter and LePage ('48). Third, it must never be forgotten that an embryo is in a continual state of differentiation. Any circumstances or conditions established for one stage, therefore, cannot be assumed to hold for any other stage unless specifically shown to do so.

ENZYME CONCENTRATION IN EMBRYONIC LIFE

The most straightforward way in which embryonic metabolism is altered is through changes in relative concentrations of different enzymes. Among the few studies clearly bearing on this problem are a sufficient number on one form, the chick embryo,* to enable us to state with assurance that embryonic tissue at every stage is enzymatically individual, rather than being merely a simplified or diluted version of any adult type (cf. Moog, '52). During the first few days of development, the tissue of the embryonic chick is relatively poor in phosphatases (Moog and Steinbach, '46; Moog, '46); relatively rich in various peptidases (Levy and Palmer, '43); and very rich in cytochrome oxidase and succinoxidase [this fact is calculated in part from the data of Albaum et al. ('46) who, however, reported their findings only in terms of total quantity per embryo]. Interestingly enough, the period of intensive histogenetic activity beginning at the end of the first week of incubation is preceded by a slackening in rate of production of all enzymes so far studied.

Finding a differential increase in enzyme activity per unit of embryo by the homogenate method may, of course, mean only that a given tissue rich in the enzyme in question is increasing faster than other tissues. Undoubtedly this is the explanation for numerous cases of enzyme increase per unit of whole organism. But it has by now been amply demonstrated that differential changes in enzyme concentrations also occur in isolated tissues; in the brain of the honey bee, in fact, cholinesterase rises while cell number declines (cf. Rockstein, '50). Studies like those of Sawyer ('43a, '43b) on cholinesterase in muscle and nerve, Hermann and Nicholas ('48) on apyrase in muscle, and

* This section will be largely, but not wholly, confined to the chick embryo. By reason of easy availability and relative purity of cytoplasm, the chick embryo seems better adapted to the type of research we are dealing with here than any other form. The enzymology of amphibian embryos has been much studied, but in these the difficulty of separating inert yolk from active cytoplasm, or of determining how fast one is converted into the other, has meant that there has been no satisfactory unit basis to which enzyme activity could be referred. Gregg and Løvtrup ('50) have, however, recently proposed a method for determining non-yolk nitrogen in salamander eggs. At the present time, no form has been explored fully enough to serve as the sole basis of even a brief résumé of embryonic metabolism.

Moog ('50, '51) on phosphatase in intestine, seem to be establishing as a fact the repeated finding that in advanced stages of development an enzyme accumulates only in correlation with the function it subserves—either in parallel with the function, or in slight forward reference to it.

If this view is correct, it will serve as a valuable guide in examining the poorly explored enzymology of the early stages of development. It is in these early stages (roughly the first six days in the life of the chick, for example) that we can with approximate correctness speak of "embryonic tissues" as a type, in contrast to the partly or fully differentiated tissues of later stages. Finding that enzymes do not behave independently of their correlated function may justify our concluding that some, at least, of the enzymes of very young embryonic tissue are actively related to the proper function of such tissue, i.e., development.

With embryonic material just as with adult, values for enzyme activity obtained for homogenates or extracts cannot be uncritically accepted as reflecting the state of affairs in vivo. Quite possibly, however, the enzyme activities obtained with embryonic homogenates are generally closer to the activities in intact tissue than is the case with adult material. As pointed out before, the embryonic cell might be expected not to store a large reserve of enzymes for emergency use, since the orderly nature of embryonic life is itself a guarantee against the stresses that the adult must face.

ENZYME ACTIVITY IN EMBRYONIC LIFE

The Influence of Substrate and Cofactor Concentration. That the activity engaged in by a given number of enzyme molecules may be limited by availability of substrate or of cofactors has already been pointed out. It might be supposed, then, that the rate at which raw materials are supplied, by the yolk sac or placenta or other commissary agency, would control the rate at which biochemical reactions go forward within the embryonic body. At the present time, however, no good evidence bears on this problem. One might call to mind the old observation reported by Needham ('31), that the tendency of the chick embryo to use its energy sources in succession—carbohydrate first, then protein, then fat—is not altered by the injection of large amounts of glucose at the period when protein is in principal use. But in this case it was not clear that the injected material was actually carried into the embryo at an enhanced rate.

There are no unequivocal cases, either, to show that differentiated enzymes are inhibited by lack of necessary cofactors. In a very thorough study, Novikoff et al. ('48) demonstrated that even at three days, the earliest stage investigated, the chick embryo contains ATP, DPN and phosphocreatine in amounts falling within the same range as in various mature rat tissues. They also found that numerous intermediates of the phosphorylating glycolytic system are present in substantial quantities, indicating that this system proceeds with about equal intensity in embryonic and mature tissues. The finding of Potter and DuBois ('42) that cytochrome c is present only in traces in the six-day chick embryo is, on the other hand, an example of the difficulty of accepting negative evidence in this field. For we know that during the first three days the intact embryo takes up oxygen freely (Philips, '40), that it gives a strong Nadi reaction that is inhibited by azide (Moog, '43), and that homogenates contain abundant cytochrome oxidase (Albaum et al., '46); the latter authors make the rather equivocal statement that in young embryos "autoxidation" of added substrate in the absence of added cytochrome c represents a large fraction of the observed oxygen uptake.

But perhaps it is naive to assume that the embryo differentiates or accumulates some elements of its biochemical machinery in anticipation of others. The lack of evidence demonstrating this type of control may in itself be evidence that the various factors are produced only as they are needed, and in correlation with other necessary factors. This view is in harmony with the previously mentioned parallelism between enzyme accumulation and function.

Recent studies on the formation of the so-called adaptive enzymes may provide a more subtle approach to the problem of enzyme regulation by material supply. The important discussion by Spiegelman ('48) suggests a mechanism by which substrate availability may direct the actual formation of enzymes, and thus control the processes of growth and morphogenesis dependent on the enzymes formed. In essence the hypothesis of long-term regulation of enzyme patterns in cells, whether embryonic or adult, by adaptive formation of enzymes, rests upon three postulates, which we will consider here. Each of these postulates, it should be noted, is a demonstrated fact in itself; the extent to which these three processes actually cooperate in regulating cell metabolism, however, remains to be studied in detail.

1. The amount of enzyme normally present in a cell represents a balance between synthesis and destruction.

2. Enzymes tend to be stabilized (i.e., destruction is retarded?) when combined with suitable substrate (cf. Bayliss, '19). According to more recent evidence, substances other than normal substrate can promote the formation of adaptive enzymes (Spiegelman, '48).

3. Most, perhaps all, of the protein of a living cell is potential material for the formation of enzymes. Thus synthesis of special enzymes must involve competitive interactions. In yeast, under conditions of starvation, even an enzyme regarded as constitutive (glycozymase) can be depleted during the formation of a clearly adaptive enzyme, galactozymase (Spiegelman and Dunn, '47).

A plausible, though not yet demonstrated, integration of these three facts into a single regulatory mechanism is shown in Figure 9. This figure illustrates how, in the normal steady state, with raw materials supplied and breakdown products removed, the relative amount of activity of enzymes A and B will depend on availability of substrate, among other factors. With low supply of substrate for B, for example, the total amount of B would diminish; but increase of substrate for B would raise the activity only as fast as new B could be formed. Presence of a stabilizing (inhibiting) substance (B') would, however, save the enzyme from destruction and allow immediate increase of activity of B if normal substrate were added in excess, the excess substrate then outcompeting the inhibitor.

Although enzyme patterns have been altered by supplying excess substrate in yeasts and bacteria, it should be noted that such treatment does not *necessarily* affect enzyme concentration. For example, the substrate might be present in excess to begin with, or an enzyme might be held in large quantities as a form of storage protein. Some seeds contain tremendous quantities of urease, which falls sharply during development (Williams, '50). Assuming that the urease-synthesizing system is a good competitor, one might interpret the observation to mean that the seed uses urease as a means of storing protein out of reach of other enzyme systems, which might otherwise get out of hand.

Hypothetically, at least, the scheme of competitive interaction is applicable to the problem of embryonic differentiation. Since no egg is completely homogeneous in the distribution of its chemical constituents, a way is immediately open for the differential

bryos is alterable by addition of succinate (Boell, '49), but in this case normal development is possible over only a narrow range of enzyme enhancement. Probably a more favorable type of material for experiments on adaptation is made available in the important experiments of Spratt ('49), who has shown that explanted chick blastoderms

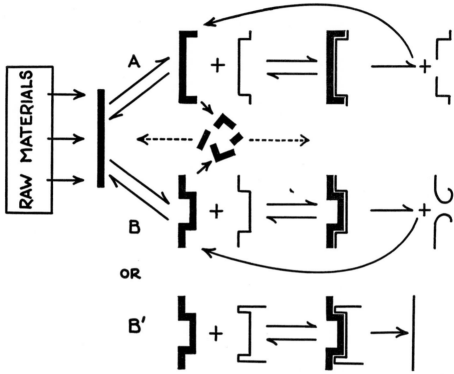

Fig. 9. Diagram to illustrate some of the principles pertinent when two or more enzymes, subject to degradation, are competing for a common stock of enzyme precursor. Raw materials, presumably from endogenous synthetic mechanisms, supply precursor. Enzymes, once formed, are stabilized by (A and B) combination with substrate or (B') combination with inhibitor or structural analog of normal substrate. If precursor is limiting, A or B enzyme systems might dominate depending on (1) the effectiveness of the synthetic system for A or B and (2) the relative stabilization by substrate. Thus starvation might have highly differential effects.

production of various enzymes in different regions. As the enzymes so produced must themselves affect their surroundings, continued differentiation becomes self-perpetuating. How amenable this scheme is to experimental verification is, however, another matter. Work with great numbers of inhibitory agencies has taught us little except how easy it is to upset fatally the delicate balance of developmental events. Will excess substrates merely add themselves to the list of inhibitors, if they have any effect at all? One preliminary report does indicate that succinic dehydrogenase in amphibian em-

can use a variety of six-carbon sugars as exogenous energy sources.

The Influence of Structural Orientation. Embryology provides us with many instances of systems held in an inhibited state. The dormant seed of a green plant, the orthopteran egg in diapause, the winter egg of rotifers, the unfertilized egg of marine invertebrates, the prolonged blastocyst of the deer, the unincubated cicatrix of the hen's egg, are examples of such restraint. In many cases the system can be released suddenly, indicating that structural factors were responsible for the blockage. Experimentally the low rate of oxygen uptake of frogs' eggs can be raised merely by homogenizing (Spiegelman and Steinbach, '45).

The most thoroughly explored case of sudden activation in normal development is that of the fertilization of sea urchin eggs. In this field we owe most of our knowledge to the laboratory of Professor Runnström, who has recently reviewed the work (cf. Runnström, '49). We have no room here to do more than point out some of the major evidences that the first few minutes following sperm entrance involve simultaneous and no doubt correlated changes in enzymatic activity and structural characteristics. During this period the rate of oxygen uptake is raised or at least stabilized (Borei, '48), with the previously immobilized cytochrome system coming into action; there is a rapid breakdown of high molecular weight carbohydrates (Örström and Lindberg, '40); and nonprotein nitrogen increases rapidly (Örström, '41). At the same time calcium is liberated, apparently from a proteinate (Mazia, '37); an increasing amount of protein becomes insoluble in molar potassium chloride (Mirsky, '36); and cephalin changes to an ether-insoluble form (Öhman, '44). The egg surface is strongly affected, the thin jelly-coated vitelline membrane giving way to the tough, birefringent fertilization membrane. Of course the practical outcome of all this postfertilization activity is the lifting of the block to development and the initiation of cleavage. In this whole system, it would seem, we have the most favorable material now available* for showing on the one hand the relationship between protein structure and enzyme activity, and on the other the nature of the linkage between the structure-controlled activity and the events of development.

Sudden alterations of activity are, however, probably a minor aspect of the life of the embryo. The proper business of an embryo is differentiation, and one would expect that the enzymatic orientations of the embryo differentiate in the same sense as does the body structure itself. In a few cases we have evidence that biochemical elaboration of formed elements does occur.

* The much-studied diapause state of the orthopteran egg has previously seemed to be an equally useful case of inhibition of development paralleled by immobilization of enzyme systems. The recent finding that the respiratory intensity of diapause homogenates is lower than that of homogenates from active stages (Bodine, '50) indicates, however, that the situation is more complex than previously supposed.

The granular structure of embryonic cytoplasm is the one problem in this field that has been studied with any degree of thoroughness. The real existence of granules in intact embryonic cells has recently been shown by experiments in which P^{32} was injected at unspecified stages into hen's eggs or gravid mice (Jeener, '49). In embryos homogenized two hours after the injection, the specific activity of radiophosphate was found to be differentially distributed among the nucleic acids of granules isolated at 13,000 g. and at 60,000 g., and of the final supernate. Since the differences are too great to be accounted for merely by the exchange rate, it appears that the granules are not merely artifacts accumulated during the homogenization process, but occur as real entities in the intact cells.

In the chick embryo from seven to eleven days of incubation, centrifugable granules accumulate an increasingly large portion of the total nitrogen, and at the same time become relatively richer in apyrase and alkaline phosphatase activity (Steinbach and Moog, '45; Moog and Steinbach, '46). The granules of amphibian eggs gradually bind all of the nucleoprotein, which is entirely free at the beginning of development, and they also become associated with catalase, dipeptidase, ribonuclease, and alkaline phosphatase, although they are, surprisingly, said to be poor in respiratory enzymes (Brachet and Chantrenne, '42); it is unfortunate that these fascinating results have never been well documented. In sea urchin eggs a number of enzymes are bound to granules, but others are dispersed in the hyaloplasm (cf. Holter, '49). It is not known, however, if the enzymatic character of the granules changes during development.

Among the few other instances of biochemical elaboration of structure during development, the most interesting is the finding that in the muscles of the rat, just before and after birth, apyrase accumulates at a faster rate than myosin (Herrmann and Nicholas, '48). The enzyme activity, it appears, is added to the protein structure as warranted by the needs of the whole organism. A similar, though less clear, case is the shift in calcium activability of apyrase in homogenates of chick liver. Under the same conditions of preparation, the enzyme is slightly inhibited by calcium before hatching, but strongly stimulated after hatching (Moog, '47); as pointed out earlier, a difference in structural association could account for such an effect. A recent study correlating quantitative and histochemical results has shown that the tremendous quantities of alkaline phosphatase which accumulate in the chick intestine at hatching are largely restricted to the presumable functional localization in the striated border (Moog, '50, '51). If this is a general situation—and other cytochemical studies indicate that it is—one may be justified in concluding that differentiating cells control the activity of newly synthesized enzymes by placing them immediately in the positions in which their activity can be directed and used.

Thus the middle of the twentieth century finds us with but a rudimentary understanding of the field of metabolic regulations during development. Plainly we do not have the answers to either of the two aspects of the problem as stated at the beginning of this section. Before we can hope to understand either the way in which the differentiating threads of the total metabolism are woven together into a unified whole, or the way in which morphogenesis emerges from the controlled metabolism, further developments along two lines are necessary. First, our knowledge of the control of embryonic enzymology can move forward only as fast as our general knowledge of the ultrastructure of protoplasm advances. In this realm undoubtedly lie many explanations that we can only hint at now. Second, within the field of embryology itself, more study of isolated tissues is indicated. Although what has been called the actuarial approach to embryonic enzymology has yielded some valuable information on the enzymatic characteristics of differentiating tissue, the validity of such a method is obviously limited. It is with the aid of the methods of histochemistry and cytochemistry that we may expect biochemical embryology to make its next steps forward.

REFERENCES

Albaum, H., Novikoff, A., and Ogur, M. 1946 The development of the cytochrome oxidase and succinoxidase systems in the chick embryo. J. Biol. Chem., *165:*125.

Barron, E. S. G. 1943 Mechanisms of carbohydrate metabolism. Adv. Enzymol., *3:*149.

———— 1952 The oxidation pathways of carbohydrate metabolism; in Trends in Physiology and Biochemistry. Academic Press, New York.

————, Nelson, L. and Ardao, M. A. 1948 Regulatory mechanisms of cellular respiration. II. The role of soluble sulfhydryl groups. J. Gen. Physiol., *32:*179.

Bayliss, W. M. 1919 The Nature of Enzyme Action. Longmans, London.

Bodine, J. H. 1950 To what extent is O_2 uptake of the intact embryo related to that of its homogenate? Science, *112:*110.

Boell, E. J. 1949 The effect of sodium succinate on the development of succinic dehydrogenase in *Amblystoma punctatum*. Anat. Rec., *105:*120.

Borei, H. 1948 Respiration of oocytes, unfertilized eggs, and fertilized eggs from Psammechinus and Asterias. Biol. Bull., *95:*124.

Borsook, H., Deasy, C. L., Haagen-Smit, A. J., Keighly, G., and Lowy, P. H. 1949 Uptake of labelled amino acids by tissue proteins in vitro. Fed. Proc., *8:*597.

Brachet, J., and Chantrenne, H. 1942 Nucleoproteides libres et combinés sous forme de granules chez l'oeuf d'Amphibiens. Acta biol. belg., *4:*451.

Bradfield, J. R. G. 1950 The localization of enzymes in cells. Biol. Rev., *25:*113.

Caspersson, T., and Thorell, B. 1942 The localization of the adenylic acids in striated muscle fibers. Acta Physiol. Scand., *4:*97.

Chantrenne, H. 1943 Association de la cytochrome-oxydase à des complexes sedimentables dans le cytoplasme vivant. Acta biol. belg., *3:*99.

Clark, W. M. 1949 Topics in Physical Chemistry. Williams & Wilkins Co., Baltimore.

Davidson, J. N., and Leslie, I. 1950 A new approach in the biochemistry of growth and development. Nature, *165:*49.

Davson, H., and Danielli, J. F. 1943 The Permeability of Natural Membranes. The Macmillan Co., New York.

Dixon, M. 1949 Multi-enzyme Systems. Cambridge University Press, Cambridge, England.

Fruton, J. S. 1950 Role of proteolytic enzymes in biosynthesis of peptide bonds. Yale J. Biol. & Med., *22:*263–271.

Goldinger, J. M., and Barron, E. S. G. 1946 The pyruvate metabolism of sea-urchin eggs during the process of cell division. J. Gen. Physiol., *30:*73.

Greenstein, J. P. 1947 Biochemistry of Cancer. Academic Press, New York.

————, Fodor, P. J., and Leuthardt, F. M. 1949 The neoplastic transformation as a biological fractionation of related enzyme systems. J. Nat. Cancer Inst., *10:*271.

Gregg, J. R., and Løvtrup, S. 1950 Biochemical gradients in the axolotl gastrula. Compt. rend. Trav. Lab. Carlsberg., 27 (No. 12): 307.

Hassid, W. Z., and Doudoroff, M. 1950 Enzymatic synthesis of sucrose and other disaccharides. Adv. Carbo. Chem., *5:*29.

Heilbrunn, L. V. 1943 An Outline of General Physiology. W. B. Saunders Co., Philadelphia.

Herrmann, H., and Nicholas, J. S. 1948 Enzymatic liberation of inorganic phosphate from adenosine triphosphate in developing rat muscle. J. Exp. Zool., *107:*177.

Holter, H. 1949 Problems of enzyme localization in development. Publ. Staz. Zool. Nap., 21 (suppl.):60.

Jeener, R. 1949 Distribution of ribonucleic acid in the cytoplasm of growing cells studied with P[32]. Nature, *163*:837.

Kalckar, H. 1945 Enzymatic synthesis of nucleosides. Fed. Proc., *4*:248.

Krebs, H. A. 1943 The intermediary stages in the biological oxidation of carbohydrates. Adv. Enzymol., *3*:191.

Lardy, H. A. (editor) 1950 Respiratory Enzymes. Burgess Publishing Co., Minneapolis.

LaValle, J. E., and Goddard, D. E. 1948 The mechanism of enzymatic oxidations and reductions. Quart. Rev. Biol., *23*:197.

Levy, M., and Palmer, A. J. 1943 Chemistry of the chick embryo. IV. Aminopeptidase. J. Biol. Chem., *150*:271.

Lipmann, F. 1941 Metabolic generation and utilization of phosphate bond energy. Adv. Enzymol., *1*:99.

——— 1949 Mechanism of peptide bond formation. Fed. Proc., *8*:597.

Lundegårdh, H. 1945 Absorption, transport and exudation of inorganic ions by the roots. Arch. Botanik, *32A* (No. 12): 1–139.

Mazia, D. 1937 The release of calcium in Arbacia eggs on fertilization. J. Cell. Comp. Physiol., *10*:291.

———, and Blumenthal, G. 1950 Inactivation of enzyme substrate films by small doses of x-ray. J. Cell. Comp. Physiol., *35:* Suppl. 1, 171.

Meyerhof, O. 1949 Glycolysis of animal tissue extracts compared with the cell-free fermentation of yeast. Wallerstein Comm., *38*:255.

Michaelis, L., and Menten, M. L. 1913 Die Kinetik der Invertinwirkung. Biochem. Z., *49*:333.

Mirksy, A. E. 1936 Protein coagulation as a result of fertilization. Science, *84*:333.

Moog, F. 1943 Cytochrome oxidase in early chick embryos. J. Cell. Comp. Physiol., *22*:223.

——— 1946 Alkaline and acid phosphomonoesterase activity in chick embryos. J. Cell. Comp. Physiol., *28*:197.

——— 1947 Adenylpyrophosphatase in brain, liver, heart, and muscle of chick embryos and hatched chicks. J. Exp. Zool., *105*:209.

——— 1950 The functional differentiation of the small intestine. I. The accumulation of alkaline phosphatase in the duodenum of the chick. J. Exp. Zool., *115*:109.

——— 1951 The functional differentiation of the small intestine. II. The differentiation of alkaline phosphatase in the duodenum of the mouse. J. Exp. Zool., *118*:187.

——— 1952 Enzymes in the development of the chick embryo. Ann. N. Y. Acad. Sci., *55*:57.

———, and Steinbach, H. B. 1946 Localization of acid and alkaline phosphomonoesterases in cytoplasmic granules. J. Cell. Comp. Physiol., *28:* 209.

Needham, J. 1931 Chemical Embryology. Cambridge University Press, Cambridge, England, Vol. II, p. 997.

Novikoff, A. B., Potter, V. R., and LePage, C. A. 1948 Phosphorylating glycolysis in the early chick embryo. J. Biol. Chem., *173*:239.

Ochoa, S. 1947 Chemical process of oxidative recovery. Ann. N. Y. Acad. Sci., *47*:835.

———, and Stern, J. R. 1952 Carbohydrate metabolism. Ann. Rev. Biochem., *21*:547.

Öhman, L. 1944 On the lipids of the sea-urchin egg. Ark. Zool., *36A* (No. 7):1.

Örström, Å. 1941 Über die chemischen Vorgänge inbesondere den Ammoniakstoffwechsel bei der Entwicklungserregung des Seeigeleis. Z. physiol. Chem., *271*:1.

———, and Lindberg, O. 1940 Über den Kohlehydratstoffwechsel bei der Befruchtung des Seeigeleies. Enzymol., *8*:376.

Pauling, L. 1948 Antibodies and specific biological forces. Endeavour, 7 (No. 26):43.

Philips, F. S. 1940 The oxygen consumption of the early chick embryo at various stages of development. J. Exp. Zool., *86*:257.

Pitts, R. F., and Alexander, R. S. 1944 The renal reabsorption of inorganic phosphate in the normal dog. Fed. Proc., *3*:37.

Potter, V. R. 1944 Biological energy transformations and the cancer problem. Adv. Enzymol., *4:* 201.

———, and DuBois, K. P. 1942 The quantitative determination of cytochrome. J. Biol. Chem., *142*:417.

Ratner, S. 1949 Mechanism of urea synthesis. Fed. Proc., *8*:603.

Rockstein, M. 1950 The relation of cholinesterase activity to change in cell number with age in the brain of the adult worker honeybee. J. Cell. Comp. Physiol., *35*:11.

Rothstein, A., and Meier, R. 1948 The relationship of the cell surface to metabolism. I. Phosphatases in the cell surface of living yeast cells. J. Cell. Comp. Physiol., *32*:77.

Runnström, J. 1949 Some results and views concerning the mechanism of activation of the sea-urchin egg. Pub. Staz. Zool. Nap., 21 (suppl.):9.

Sawyer, C. H. 1943a Cholinesterase and the behavior problem in Amblystoma. I. The relationship between development of the enzyme and early motility. J. Exp. Zool., *92*:1.

——— 1943b Cholinesterase and the behavior problem in Amblystoma. III. The distribution of cholinesterase in nerve and muscle throughout development. J. Exp. Zool., *94*:1.

Spiegelman, S. 1948 Differentiation as the controlled production of unique enzymatic patterns. Symp. Soc. Exp. Biol., *2*:286.

———, and Dunn, R. 1947 Interactions between enzyme-forming systems during adaptation. J. Gen. Physiol., *31*:153.

———, and Kamen, M. D. 1947 Some basic problems in the relation of nucleic acid turnover to protein synthesis. Cold Spring Harbor Symp., *12*:211.

———, and Reiner, J. 1942 A kinetic analysis of potassium accumulation and sodium exclusion. Growth, *6*:367.

———, and Steinbach, H. B. 1945 Substrate-enzyme orientation during embryonic development. Biol. Bull., *88*:254.

Spratt, N. T., Jr. 1949 Nutritional requirements

of the early chick embryo. I. The utilization of carbohydrate substrates. J. Exp. Zool., *110:*273.

Stannard, J. N. 1939 The mechanisms involved in the transfer of oxygen in frog muscle. Cold Spring Harbor Symp., *7:*394.

Steinbach, H. B. 1949 Calcium and apyrase system of muscle. Arch. Biochem., *22:*328.

———, and Moog, F. 1945 Localization of adenylpyrophosphatase in cytoplasmic granules. J. Cell. Comp. Physiol., *26:*175.

Szent-Györgyi, A. 1939 On Oxidation, Fermentation, Vitamins, Health and Disease. Williams & Wilkins Co., Baltimore.

——— 1951 Muscular Contraction. Academic Press, New York.

Tatum, E. L. 1949 Amino acid metabolism in mutant strains of microorganisms. Fed. Proc., *8:*511.

Tyler, D. B. 1950 Rate of oxygen uptake of differently prepared brain suspensions in the presence of 2,4-dinitrophenol. Arch. Biochem., *25:*221.

Werkman, C. H., and Wood, H. G. 1942 Heterotrophic assimilation of CO_2. Adv. Enzymol., *2:*135.

Williams, W. T. 1950 Function of urease in Citrullus seeds. Nature, *165:*79.

Wolsky, A. 1950 Changes in the response of silkworm eggs to rotational force during cleavage. Nature, *165:*119.

Zamenhof, S., and Chargaff, E. 1949 Studies on the desoxypentose nuclease of yeast and its specific cellular regulation. J. Biol. Chem., *180:*727.

CHAPTER 3

Cell Division

HANS RIS

INTRODUCTION

GROWTH usually is connected with the formation of new cells. The ways in which new cells originate have been intensively investigated and much debated ever since the cellular nature of organisms was realized. Though Trembley had already illustrated binary fission of a diatom in 1748, the significance of this process was first realized by von Mohl in 1837 (Baker, '51). Yet not until the middle of the century did it become generally accepted that cells originate only through division of pre-existing cells, mainly because of the influence of Schleiden and Schwann who vigorously fought for their theory of free cell formation. With the introduction of fixatives and stains, the paraffin sectioning technique and improved microscopes, more detailed study became possible. The first suggestion of the complexity of nuclear division appeared in a paper by Schneider in 1873 who noticed the formation of chromosomes and their separation into two groups which formed the daughter nuclei. In a few exciting years following this the essential features of cell division in plants and animals were discovered through the work of Flemming and Strasburger, van Beneden, Fol and Bütschli, O. and R. Hertwig and Boveri.

In 1879 Flemming described the longitudinal division of the chromosomes and the separation of the halves into the two daughter cells. The appearance of these basophilic threads in the nucleus and their exact longitudinal division was the most striking aspect of cell division and Flemming therefore called it "mitosis" (*mitos* = thread). The direct simple fission of nucleus and cytoplasm was thought to be another mode of cell proliferation and named "amitosis." With the establishment of the chromosome theory of inheritance at the turn of the century the complexity of nuclear organization was realized and the significance of the beautiful

precision of mitosis became clear. More gradually we have become aware of the complexity of cytoplasmic organization because it is more subtle and more varied. Today the cell appears as a complex system, a kind of hierarchy of more or less autonomous components. In the chromosomes we have the highest concentration of the factors that are responsible for specificity in the cell, and their irreplaceability is expressed in the extreme care taken in their exact duplication and distribution during the reproduction of the cell. It is not surprising that the mechanisms by which the cell accomplishes this have been in the center of interest so far. There exist in the cytoplasm, however, systems of at least partial autonomy and the ways of their reproduction and distribution must be more intensively investigated. For the student of development and differentiation particularly they may prove of even greater interest than the behavior of the chromosomes.

The division of the nucleus, however, is the central process around which cell reproduction is organized and it is better known than the reproduction of the cytoplasmic systems. The following discussion will, therefore, be organized mainly around nuclear behavior. No attempt will be made to review the large literature in the field. The discussion may be regarded as rather a personal and therefore somewhat biased essay on some of the essential problems of cellular reproduction.

DESCRIPTION OF MITOSIS IN THE WHITEFISH BLASTULA

From algae to orchids and amoeba to man the essential processes of cell division are remarkably similar. We can describe, therefore, the division of one cell and thereby illustrate the fundamental strategy in all. Only bacteria and blue-green algae still

91

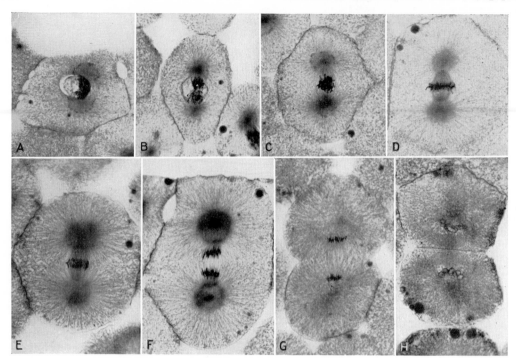

Fig. 10. Mitosis in the whitefish blastula (from Turtox slides).

seem to fall outside of the general picture (but cf. DeLamater and Mudd, '51).

The divisions of the blastomeres in the whitefish blastula are useful to describe the morphological aspects of mitosis in an animal cell (Fig. 10). Following Strasburger the process is subdivided into four phases: During *prophase* the centrosome divides (Fig.

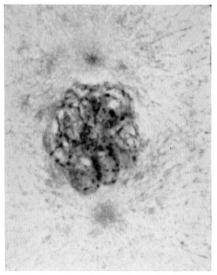

Fig. 11. Prophase in blastomere of whitefish, stained with iron-hematoxylin to show centriole.

10*A*); the centrioles are not visible in these preparations but can be demonstrated in slides stained with iron-hematoxylin (Fig. 11). The chromosomes now appear embedded in eosinophilic material that later forms the spindle (Figs. 10*A* and *B*) and finally the nuclear membrane breaks down (Fig. 10*C*). While the spindle takes shape the chromosomes become oriented in the equatorial plane (Fig. 10*D*): *metaphase*. During *anaphase* the chromosomes move toward the spindle poles and the spindle elongates (Figs. 10*E*, *F*, *G*). Finally, in *telophase* the nuclear membrane reappears, in this case around each chomosome separately, so that karyomeres are formed which later may fuse into a single nucleus. The cytoplasm is subdivided by the cleavage furrow (Fig. 10*H*).

This account of mitosis in the whitefish blastomere has been pieced together from various stages in fixed and stained cells. Is it possible to follow the process in the living cell as it divides? If we place the blastula of a whitefish egg during cleavage in calcium-free Ringer's solution and gently squeeze it in a rotocompressor,* the cells separate and a single layer of cells can be obtained. For some time the blastomeres continue to divide

* Obtained from Biological Institute, Philadelphia.

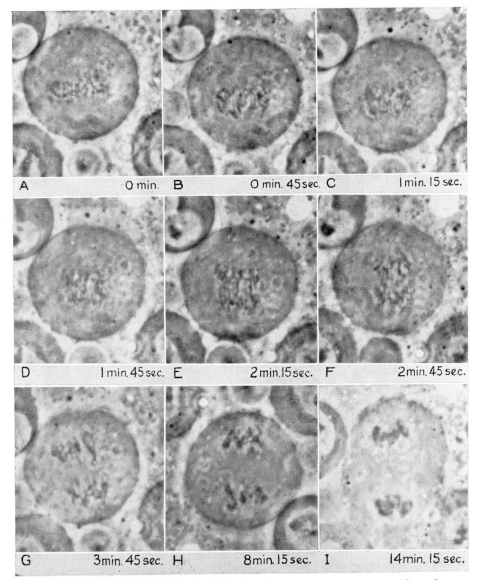

Fig. 12. Mitosis in a living blastomere of the whitefish *Leucichthys artidi* (Spencer Phase Contrast, dark medium).

and the process can be followed in the phase microscope. The anaphase in such a cell is shown in Fig. 12. In addition to chromosomes the outline of the spindle is clearly visible in the living cell, and sometimes even details such as the centrioles, chromosomal fibers and aster-rays (Fig. 12C).

Many other cells of plants and animals have been used to study mitosis in the living cell. With the phase microscope many structures are now visible in life that before were known only from fixed and stained preparations. Photographs of a variety of living cells in division have been published (Table 2).

ANALYSIS OF MITOSIS

After this brief description of a cell in division we shall now look at some aspects of mitosis in more detail. We can recognize two main events: The division of the nucleus (karyokinesis) and the division of the cytoplasm (cytokinesis). The nuclear division normally involves duplication of the chromosome units, the splitting of the chromosome into two equivalent halves (chromatids), their condensation into compact bodies, and a series of chromosome movements resulting in the distribution of the chromosome halves

TABLE 2. *Illustrations of Living Cells in Mitosis*

MATERIAL	AUTHOR
Amblystoma heart tissue culture	Wang, '52
Grasshopper sperma-tocytes	Bělař, '29; Michel, '50
Frog fibroblast tissue culture	Hughes and Preston, '49
Chick embryo osteoblast tissue culture	Hughes and Swann, '48
Mouse spleen tissue culture	Fell and Hughes, '49

into the daughter cells. Cytokinesis divides the cytoplasm more or less equally around the daughter nuclei. Cytoplasmic components are generally segregated at random but may become differentially distributed in certain cells.

KARYOKINESIS

THE CHROMOSOME CYCLE

One of the most striking aspects of mitosis is the cyclical change in the chromosomes.

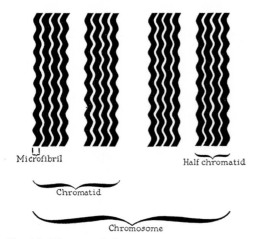

Fig. 13. Diagram of the subunits in a completely uncoiled chromosome.

This involves chromosome reproduction, changes in structure (spiralization cycle) and chemical and physiological changes.

Structural Changes in Chromosomes. It is generally agreed today that chromosomes consist of a bundle of threads that undergo a cycle of coiling and uncoiling. The exact number of units (chromonemata) has been much debated. There is good evidence that

in many cases the daughter chromosomes at anaphase contain at least two and sometimes even four microscopically visible units. Recent studies with the electron microscope in this laboratory, however, have shown that the elementary longitudinal unit is submicroscopic and in several animals and a plant was found to be of the same thickness (about 500 A). The number of longitudinal subunits in a chromosome therefore must be determined with the electron microscope. We have found evidence that the number of these *elementary microfibrils* is not the same in comparable chromosomes of different organisms (Ris and Kleinfeld, '52). The microfibrils and the larger units they compose may be either closely appressed or separate from each other laterally. This fact and the submicroscopic size of the structural unit are probably responsible for most disagreements and uncertainties of chromosome structure. The unit of reproduction in the chromosome must therefore be sought in the elementary microfibril. Since chromosomes contain more than one microfibril it is, however, not the unit of division during mitosis. This unit is the chromatid, that itself may be visibly separated into two or more bundles of microfibrils (half-chromatids and quarter-chromosomes) (Fig. 13).

In early prophase chromosomes show a large number of small gyres. These increase in width through a process of "despiralization." While the number of gyres decreases, through this process of "gyre elimination" the chromosomes become shorter and thicker and gain their typical metaphase form (Sparrow, Swanson, Ris; for references see Manton, '50).

In prophase of meiosis the chromosomes usually condense more than in somatic cells. This is connected with the formation of a double spiral (minor and major coil). The number of gyres in a metaphase chromosome seems to be remarkably constant for one type of cell under similar conditions, but may vary considerably in different types of cells (somatic mitosis, first and second division of meiosis, for instance). In telophase the process of gyre elimination continues so that only a general waviness remains in the interphase nucleus (relic spiral).

A few workers have attempted to calculate the length of the chromonemata during the coiling cycle. In the fern Osmunda (Manton) and in Trillium (Sparrow, Wilson and Huskins) considerable variation in the length of the chromonema was found during prophase of meiosis (see Manton, '50). Whether such changes take place generally during mitosis is not known.

What causes the spiralization of chromosomes? So far we have no satisfactory explanation. Much more needs to be known about the chemical changes during coiling and the submicroscopic structure of the chromosome before we can begin to understand the mechanism of coiling.

During prophase the chromosomes are said to become surrounded by a membrane (pellicle) and a matrix in which the coiled chromonemata are embedded or which surround each individual chromonema (cf. Kaufmann, '48), but there is no good evidence for this contention.

Chemical Changes in the Chromosome. In recent years much progress has been made in our knowledge of chromosome chemistry since it has become possible to isolate nuclei and chromosomes for chemical analysis and with the development of appropriate cytochemical techniques. (For a review see Davidson, '50; Mirsky, '51; Mazia, '52.) Chromosomes consist mainly of nucleoprotein. The bulk of the nucleic acid is of the desoxypentose type (DNA), which normally occurs only in chromosomes. Variable amounts of pentose nucleic acid (PNA) have been detected cytochemically and in isolated chromosomes. The basic proteins of chromosomes, the histones and protamines of certain sperm nuclei, have been known for a long time. The presence of more complex, non-histone type proteins was first demonstrated by the Stedmans ('43) and by Mirsky and Ris ('47). These four groups of compounds are the major components of chromosomes. Lipids and carbohydrates may be present in nuclei, but have not been localized in the chromosomes themselves. Of inorganic constituents besides the phosphorus of nucleic acids, magnesium and especially calcium have been found in chromosomes (Scott, '43). Quantitative determinations on isolated nuclei and cytochemical studies have revealed the remarkable fact that the amount of DNA is constant per chromosome set (Boivin, Vendrely and Vendrely; Mirsky and Ris, Swift; for references see Swift, '53). The absolute amount of DNA in a diploid nucleus is characteristic for an animal and varies considerably from one taxonomic group to another (Mirsky and Ris, '51). In contrast to the DNA, the amounts of non-histone protein and PNA seem to vary a great deal with physiological conditions and from one tissue to another (Mirsky and Ris, '49).

Changes in the composition of chromosomes during the mitotic cycle have been studied so far only cytochemically. Quantitative determinations by histospectrophotometry have been hampered by the uneven and changing distribution of the absorbing material. The recently developed methods of Ornstein ('52) and of Pätau ('52), however, have overcome this difficulty and accurate determinations of DNA (with the Feulgen reaction) are now possible through the mitotic cycle. Thus Pätau and Swift ('53) have demonstrated that the amount of DNA in the chromosomes does not change from earliest prophase up to metaphase. If the quantity of DNA per chromosome is constant, any increase in this substance would have to be associated with the reproduction of chromosomes. How cytochemical determination of DNA can be used to determine the time of chromosome duplication will be shown later. Changes in PNA content of chromosomes during mitosis were reported by Schultz ('41), Brachet ('42), Kaufmann ('48), Turchini ('49), Battaglia and Omodeo ('49), and Jacobson and Webb ('52). These investigators found marked changes in the staining of chromosomes with certain basic dyes before and after digestion with ribonuclease, especially in metaphase and anaphase, and concluded that there was an increase in PNA in chromosomes in late prophase followed by a decrease in telophase. According to Jacobson and Webb ('52) the loss of ribonucleoprotein from anaphase chromosomes is accompanied by an increase of this material in the spindle area between the separating chromosomes, suggesting that chromosomes give off ribonucleoprotein during anaphase movement. The findings are supported by the photographs of chick fibroblasts in anaphase taken by ultraviolet light (at 2650 A), which show increased absorption at this wave length between the separating chromosomes (Davies, '52). The "chromatin elimination" at anaphase of the first meiotic division in eggs of Lepidoptera (Seiler, '14) and some other insects (Cooper, '39) involves shedding of nucleoprotein material from chromosomes in discrete bodies that remain in the equatorial plane of the spindle and later disintegrate (Ris and Kleinfeld, '52). It remains to be seen whether the loss of ribonucleoprotein from anaphase chromosomes is a general phenomenon and what physiological significance it may have.

Changes in the proteins of chromosomes during mitosis were first described by Caspersson ('40) on the basis of ultraviolet spectrophotometry of spermatocytes from a grasshopper (as a cell in division) and salivary gland chromosomes of Drosophila (as a resting cell). Unfortunately the quantitative determination of different types of proteins in chromosomes by this method is highly questionable. Until confirmed by other methods and by analysis of individual chromosomes through the mitotic cycle (instead of comparing prophase or resting nuclei with metaphase chromosomes), Caspersson's scheme remains an interesting speculation. A decrease in protein content of chromosomes from interphase to metaphase was also suggested by Pollister ('51) on the basis of comparison of Millon-stained interphase nuclei and metaphase chromosomes. So far our information on the chemical composition of chromosomes during mitosis is thus very fragmentary. Certainly we are not justified in generalizing from one type of cell. It has long been known that metaphase chromosomes may vary in size in different tissues of the same animal (cf. Geitler, '38; Biesele, '46), under different physiological conditions (tissue culture, e.g., Hance, '26) and in tumors (Biesele, '47). The most striking example is the decrease in the size of metaphase chromosomes during cleavage of many forms (Erdmann, '08). If we are correct in assuming that the amount of DNA is constant, the variations in volume must be due mainly to proteins. The protein content of metaphase chromosomes may thus be just as variable as it was found to be in interphase chromosomes. A number of cytologists have inferred chemical changes in mitotic chromosomes from their visual appearance after staining and have constructed ambitious theories on such information (Darlington, '42; Serra, '47). The recent quantitative cytochemical studies have shown the dangers of overextended deductive reasoning that has been so common in cytology. To be productive, inventive speculation needs reliable empirical data as a basis.

Chromosome Reproduction. The duplication of the chromosomes is perhaps the fundamental process of mitosis and one of the most interesting problems of biology. In what stage of the mitotic cycle does it take place? At a time when the chromosome was considered to be a single fiber that divided longitudinally during mitosis it was appropriate to speak of the time of chromosome splitting and this was often identified with the time of gene reproduction. It appears now that we must distinguish several processes that may be quite independent: (1) Syn-

thesis of the essential chemical components of the chromosome; (2) duplication of the submicroscopic elementary microfibrils. These two processes together shall be called "chromosome reproduction"; (3) subdivision of the bundle of microfibrils into the units that separate at anaphase, or that behave independently with regard to x-ray breakage or genetical exchange (crossing over) or become resolved in the UV or light microscope. We might call this splitting of the chromosome into chromatids, half- or quarter-chromatids, etc. (cf. Fig. 13). While the first one involves chemical synthesis and is presumably irreversible, the second process is often reversible.

In the past the time of chromosome splitting has mainly been discussed. But this is clearly of secondary interest and the fundamental process is chromosome reproduction. With the discovery of DNA constancy in chromosomes a study of this question became at least partially possible. Chromosome reproduction must involve DNA synthesis and the time in the mitotic cycle when this happens can be determined (for a review see Swift, '53). Ultraviolet spectrophotometry has been used (Caspersson, '39; Walker and Yates, '52) but since this is not specific for DNA the results are not decisive. The most reliable information comes from absorption measurements on Feulgen stained chromosomes. Extensive measurements on animal and plant cells by Swift, Alfert, and Pätau and Swift have established that the increase in DNA takes place in interphase, before visible changes in the nucleus occur; earlier measurements by Ris ('47) must now be considered in error (for references see Swift, '53). Unfortunately there are no good criteria to subdivide interphase into the different physiological phases which we know must exist.

In a diploid tissue with dividing cells there are generally two classes of nuclei. One contains twice as much DNA as the other, in preparation for mitosis. The doubling in DNA content, however, may also be associated with endomitosis resulting in polyteny or polysomaty. The doubling of DNA in interphase just before mitosis was demonstrated in a very different way by Price and Laird ('50) in an analysis of liver regeneration after hepatectomy. The DNA content was determined chemically and from the number of nuclei in the homogenate the amount per average nucleus was calculated. In the first 12 to 24 hours the DNA per average nucleus approximately doubled. After that mitoses appeared and the average amount of DNA per nucleus returned to the value of normal liver.

Another interesting property of DNA suggested an independent approach to the problem. Experiments with radioactive phosphorus (P^{32}) had shown an extremely low turnover of the phosphate of DNA in tissues with no or few dividing cells (e.g., Hevesy, '48). Apparently P^{32} is incorporated into DNA only when this is synthesized during chromosome reproduction. Howard and Pelc ('51a) using an ingenious radioautographic technique of high resolution studied the uptake of P^{32} into the DNA of chromosomes during mitosis in the root tips of Vicia. Their results are in complete agreement with the cytochemical and chemical studies. P^{32} is incorporated into chromosomes only during interphase before mitosis, not during mitosis proper or in interphase of differentiated non-dividing cells.

In disagreement with the work discussed so far is the view held by Lison and Pasteels (see Swift, '53), who made absorption measurements on Feulgen-stained nuclei of the rat, chicken and sea urchin embryo. They claim that DNA doubling takes place in telophase immediately after formation of the nuclear membrane. This may be true in some rapidly dividing cells, but the evidence so far is against this being the general situation. In the sea urchin, for instance, Mc-Master (see Swift, '53) found that DNA doubling takes place early in interphase during the first cleavage divisions. Later on the DNA synthesis occurs during interphase at rates that vary among different blastomeres. The DNA content of interphases in different cells thus differs but is intermediate between the telophase and metaphase value.

With regard to the synthesis of other components of chromosomes we are much less fortunate. Is there a specific protein in chromosomes that is synthesized only at the time of chromosome reproduction? Is it made at the same time as DNA? From experiments of Howard and Pelc ('51b) on incorporation of radioactive sulphur (S^{35}) into chromosomal proteins it looks as if S^{35} is taken up into proteins mainly by dividing nuclei and at about the same time as P^{32}. But no general conclusions can be drawn from these preliminary results.

The most interesting aspect of mitosis is, no doubt, the question of how the cell produces an exact copy of the infinitely complex and specific organization of the chromosomal fiber. This involves not only the synthesis of specific proteins and nucleic acids, but also the weaving together of the proper components into the right patterns. The synthesis of nucleic acids and proteins is today intensively investigated by the biochemist, who may soon give us a better understanding of what goes on during this stage in the life of the chromosome. Models of chromosome duplication were suggested by Friedrich-Freksa ('40), Bernal ('40) and Delbrück ('41). The precursors of the new DNA generally appear to be small molecules. However, in the frog's egg Zeuthen and Hoff-Jørgensen ('52) found that the cytoplasm contains considerable amounts of desoxyribosides. Apparently they are stored in the egg cytoplasm to be used during the rapid chromosome synthesis of early cleavage. The total content in desoxyribosides of the egg remains constant until the late gastrula stage.

The Chromosomes in the Interphase Nucleus. During telophase the chromosomes swell into optically homogeneous vesicles (cf. Lewis, '47). If these are widely spaced on the spindle each chromosome vesicle may form its own nuclear membrane and as a result a large number of small nuclei appear (karyomeres). This is common in cleavage divisions (Fig. 10H). Karyomeres may contain one or several chromosomes. In general, however, the chromosomes are so close together at telophase that a single nucleus is formed. The nuclear membrane originates at the interphase between chromosome and cytoplasm and has a complicated structure (Monné, '42; Schmidt, '39). In the electron microscope two layers can be distinguished (Callan and Tomlin, '50; Bairati and Lehmann, '52; Harris and James, '52). One is mainly lipoid in nature and contains regular perforations. The other has a uniform structure and consists apparently of lamellae of fibrous proteins. The porous layer may be on the outside (amphibian oocyte, Callan and Tomlin, '50) or inside (Amoeba, Harris and James, '52).

The changes taking place in the chromosomes are imperfectly understood. In part a despiralization of the chromonemata takes place. Probably there is also a change in chemical composition, especially an increase in chromosomal proteins. Furthermore, a change in the physical state of chromosomes can be demonstrated. Chromosomes are organized nucleoprotein gels which can swell and contract. In the living interphase nucleus they are in the extended state and usually fill the nucleus completely so that no boundaries between chromosomes or chromonemata are visible. In such nuclei only nucleoli and sometimes heterochromatin are visible (Ris and Mirsky, '49). This compact nucleus is found in many animal and plant tissues. The granular fixation image is due to the shrinking of the chromosome gel in most fixatives.

In some cells the chromonemata appear to be less closely packed and may become visible in the phase microscope (tissue culture of mouse kidney, spleen, heart: Fell and Hughes, '49). Such nuclei may contain in addition to the extended chromosomes some other material (karyolymph or nuclear sap). The extreme development in this direction is found in the germinal vesicle of many eggs (for instance, Amphibia) where the chromosomes finally make up only a small fraction of the nuclear volume. The content of such nuclei may have a viscosity little different from that of water (Gray, '27a).

At present the following points appear to be established: (1) Chromosomes persist as individuals in the resting nucleus. (2) They have a relatively loose structure: except in the heterochromatin the chromonemata are uncoiled and chromatids and half-chromatids are often less closely appressed (see Marquardt, '41). (3) The chromosome material (nucleoprotein gel) is in an extended state and in many nuclei fills the entire nuclear space outside of the nucleoli. (4) Extra-chromosomal material (nuclear sap) may be present in the interstices of the swollen chromosome gel, where the chromosomes fill the entire nucleus. In other cells it may separate the chromosomes that now come visible in the living cell (phase microscope) or in rare cases it may increase to make up the bulk of the nucleus (germinal vesicle).

THE NUCLEOLUS

The nucleolus is an organelle of the resting cell. Chemical and morphological changes indicate that it is involved in cell metabolism but nothing definite is known about its function. During karyokinesis the nucleolus degenerates and is re-formed at telophase in association with a definite region on one or several chromosomes ("nucleolar organizer"). Exchange of material between chromosomes and nucleolus has been suggested, but there is no direct evidence for it. The time of dissolution varies from mid-prophase to anaphase or later. If it gets into the spindle it may become divided or moved to one or the other side and finally into the cytoplasm. In rapidly dividing cells, for instance in early cleavage, no nucleolus is generally formed in the interphase nucleus.

CHROMOSOME MOVEMENTS

Following chromosome reproduction and chromosome splitting normal karyokinesis involves a series of chromosome movements in the course of which the chromosome halves are separated into the daughter nuclei.

Movements inside the Nuclear Membrane. During interphase little movement of the chromosomes occurs. Often they appear in prophase in typical telophase orientation, with the kinetochores of all chromosomes close together (Rabl orientation). In prophase, as they become more compact and the amount of extra chromosomal material increases they begin to show some changes in position. In late prophase they often become evenly spaced, preferably on the nuclear membrane. Where the chromosomes are small and compact this spacing is especially clear. We therefore find the best examples in late meiotic prophase.

Another type of movement of chromosomes within the nuclear membrane appears to be due to a mysterious relationship between chromosomes (especially chromosome ends) and the centrosome. Some beautiful examples are found in spermatocytes of many insects. In early prophase (leptotene) the ends of all chromosomes come together at one spot opposite the centrosome to form the so-called bouquet stage (cf. Schrader, '53). Later in prophase as the daughter centrosomes move apart, the chromosome ends (or, in case of small chromosomes, entire chromosomes) follow along inside the nuclear membrane. The chromosomes are thus separated into two random groups near the centrosome (cf. Hughes-Schrader, '43a). The same occurs in some somatic cells (whitefish cleavage, Fig. 12; mouse spleen in tissue culture: Fell and Hughes, '49, Fig. 16).

Movements on the Spindle. After the nuclear membrane breaks down the spindle takes shape in the former nuclear area and the further movements of chromosomes are in relation to this cell structure. First the chromosomes are moved into the equatorial plane of the spindle where they become spaced in a regular fashion (metakinesis), then after a certain length of time their halves are moved apart toward opposite spindle poles (anaphase movement).

The precise and orderly movements of chromosomes during metakinesis and anaphase have long fascinated cytologists. Many physicochemical explanations have been suggested (for a critical discussion see Schrader, '53). Unfortunately they were more often based on artificial models rather than the cell. Before we can attempt to understand what is going on in physical and chemical terms, it is necessary to know just what happens in cytological terms. What are the special cell structures concerned with the movement of chromosomes? What is their history during the mitotic cycle and how do they interact to assure the orderly disjunction of daughter chromosomes? Once these mitotic organelles are recognized they can be investigated with regard to their chemical composition, their submicroscopic structure and their function in biochemical terms.

We can recognize the following structures as mitotic organelles: cell center (centro-

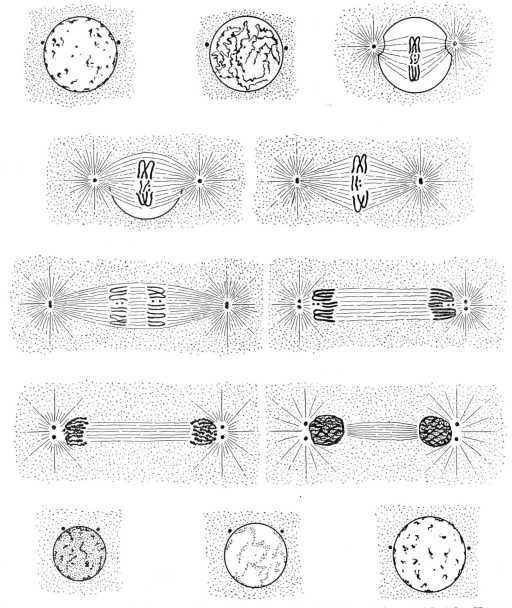

Fig. 14. Mitosis during early cleavage of Drosophila, illustrating the history of the centriole (after Huettner, '33).

some, centriole and aster), spindle, kinetochore, and chromosomal fibers.

CENTROSOME. The cells of animals and
lower plants contain a self-duplicating cytoplasmic structure, the centrosome. During
mitosis it organizes the aster and plays a part
in the polarization of the spindle. In certain
cells it also acts as blepharoplast organizing
the flagellum of flagellated cells and the axial

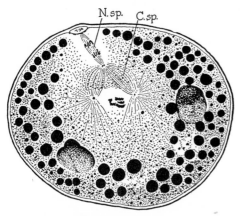

Fig. 15. Fertilization in Nereis. Amphiaster and
spindle of sperm and second maturation spindle of
egg. Note the difference between the central spindles (*C.sp.*) and the nuclear spindles (*N.sp.*). (After
Lillie, '12.)

filament of spermatozoa. It is probably related to the basal body of cilia in ciliated
cells (Renyi, '24) and the kinetosomes of the
Ciliata (Lwoff, '50).

The centrosome usually consists of a small
granule (centriole) that is either round, rod-
shaped or V-shaped (for examples see Johnson, '31) and is surrounded by a spherical,
homogeneous or finely granular area of cytoplasm. Its history during the mitotic cycle is
illustrated in Figure 14, which represents
the nuclear division during early cleavage in
Drosophila (Huettner, '33). The centriole
divides during mitosis and persists during
interphase as a double body (diplosome)
(for examples in amphibian tissues see Pollister, '33). The centrosome divides in prophase. Each half contains a centriole and
forms an aster. Under favorable conditions
the centrosomes and centrioles are visible in
the living cell both during mitosis (Fig. 12c)
and in the non-dividing cell. The size of
centrioles is usually near the limit of resolution of the light microscope (about 0.2 micron) but the rod-shaped centrioles of some
insects may be more than 1 micron long (see
for instance Johnson, '31). Changes in size
and stainability during the mitotic cycle (for

instance Jörgensen, '13; Johnson, '31; Chickering, '27) in tissue culture and in tumor
cells (Ludford, '25) have been reported. The
chemical composition of the centriole is unknown. During prophase the aster develops
around the centriole. The aster rays are positively birefringent gel fibers (cf. Inoué and
Dan, '51) and are anchored in the cortical
gel. They can be moved around and bent
with the microdissection needle (Chambers,
'17). Often they are visible in the living cell,
especially where the cytoplasm contains
many granular inclusions that contrast with
the clear aster rays, or where filamentous
mitochondria become oriented between the
aster rays (Fell and Hughes, '49). According
to Chambers, aster rays are hollow canals
but this has not been confirmed by other investigators. More likely the observed flow of
less viscous cytoplasm occurs between the
aster rays. The area around the centriole is
usually free of cytoplasmic inclusions and
increases in size from prophase to anaphase.
Aster-like structures are sometimes present
also in the cytoplasm of non-dividing cells
such as leukocytes, mesenchyme cells and
other cells in which the centriole is near the
center of the cell. Accumulation of hyaloplasm around the centriole in such cells was
observed by Lewis ('20).

Apparently the centriole influences structure and orientation in the cytoplasm not
only during division but also in the resting
cell, possibly by setting up diffusion currents
as Pollister ('41) has suggested.

The rays between two asters usually connect so that a spindle-like structure is formed
(amphiaster). This purely cytoplasmic structure has been called the "central spindle,"
but is entirely different from the real mitotic
spindle in which chromosome movement
takes place. The "central spindle" is a system
of aster rays, and cytoplasmic inclusions are
free to move through it between the rays
(Fig. 15).

Chemically the asters contain, in addition
to protein, pentose nucleic acids (Brachet,
'42; Pollister and Ris, '47; Stich, '51a) and
polysaccharides (Monné and Slautterback,
'50; Stich, '51b).

Supernumerary asters (cytasters) appear
in the cytoplasm of some invertebrate eggs
after certain experimental treatments (cf.
Wilson, '28). This fact has sometimes been
used as evidence for a de novo origin of
centrioles. However, it has not been established that cytasters contain centrioles and
the possibility thus exists that asters may
arise independently of real centrioles.

SPINDLE. Regular movements of chromosomes are possible only in the presence of a spindle. This interesting structure originates from the prophase nucleus. In most cells the entire non-chromosomal material of the nucleus seems to transform into the spindle, in others only part of the nuclear material is used (Fig. 10A and B, whitefish blastomere). Cytochemical evidence indicates that spindle material appears in the nuclear sap during interphase in cells that are preparing for division (Stich, '51a, b). The size of the

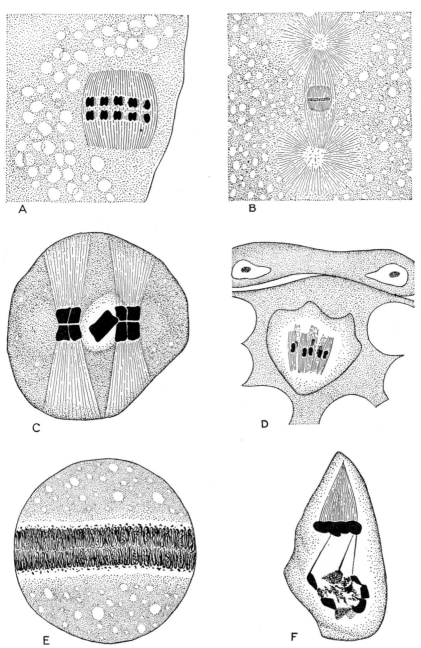

Fig. 16. Types of mitotic spindles. A, First maturation metaphase in egg of Artemia (after Gross, '35). B, Cleavage of Artemia (after Gross, '35). C, First spermatocyte metaphase in a coccid, Llaveia bouvari (after Hughes-Schrader, '31). D, Oogenesis of Acroschismus (after Hughes-Schrader, '24). E, Early anaphase spindle in the radiolarian Aulacantha (after Borgert, '00). F, Second spermatocyte division of Gossyparia (after Schrader, '29).

spindle is commonly proportional to the volume of the nucleus from which it originates. This is especially clear during cleavage of many organisms (Conklin, '12) where nuclei and spindles are large in early divisions and get smaller in late ones. In Pediculopsis the spindle volume decreases from the first to the tenth cleavage about 200 fold (Cooper, '39). Other good illustrations are the large and small spermatocytes of Arvelius (Schrader, '47). Where more than one nucleus is present within a cell, each forms its own spindle. During early cleavage sperm and

to all spindles is the bipolar organization. This bipolarity is independent of centriole and aster as demonstrated by the cases where centrioles are naturally inactive (for instance in oogenesis of Ascaris) or experimentally inhibited (Bataillon and Tchou Su, '30).

In the living cell the spindle is a gelatinous semi-solid body that can be moved about in the cell or even dissected out with the micromanipulator (Chambers, '24; Carlson, '52). Cytoplasmic granules never penetrate the spindle (which differentiates the true

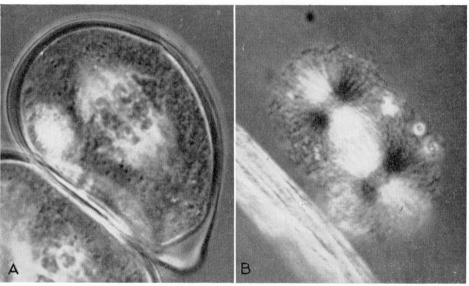

Fig. 17. The birefringence of the spindle. *A*, Pollen mother cell of *Lilium longiflorum* (phot. Inoué). *B*, Amphiaster and spindle isolated from the blastomere of a sea urchin (phot. Inoué, see Mazia and Dan, '52).

egg chromosomes often remain separate and each group forms its own spindle (gonomery). Such independent spindles may fuse into one or remain separate through anaphase (Hughes-Schrader, '24). The spindle may become organized inside the nuclear membrane or only after the membrane has dissolved. In some cells the membrane does not disappear until anaphase or even persists throughout mitosis (intranuclear spindles; cf. Drosophila cleavage, Fig. 14). The form of the spindle is very variable; it may be shaped like a disc, a barrel or a spindle, or may be flared at either end, or it may be asymmetrical (Fig. 16). Where a centriole is present the spindle is usually pointed at the ends and terminates at the centriole unless the asters are very large compared to the spindle (Fig. 16*B*). In animal cells where the centriole is inactive the spindle is usually barrel-shaped (Fig. 16*A*). But common

mitotic spindle from the amphiaster or central spindle, Fig. 15) and in living cells they can be seen bouncing off the spindle (Ris, '43). At metaphase the spindle is firmly anchored to the asters and the whole spindle apparatus (achromatic figure) can be moved about or even isolated from the cell (Mazia and Dan, '52 (Fig. 17*B*). After fixation the spindle generally has a fibrous structure (continuous fibers). In the living spindle this is only rarely visible (Cooper, '41), but Lewis ('23) has shown long ago that a change in *p*H can make it appear reversibly. Recently Inoué ('52) has demonstrated continuous fibers in living spindles with an improved polarizing microscope. Even where spindle fibers are not visible in life they can no longer be regarded as artifacts; they are an expression of the basic organization of the spindle. In the polarizing microscope the spindle shows a positive birefringence with regard to its long axis (Schmidt, '39; Swann, '51; Inoué, '52). This indicates that it consists of elongated submicroscopic units, macromolecules or micelles, that are oriented parallel to the spindle axis (Figs. 17A and B). The similarity of the spindle to the tactoids formed in suspensions of elongated macromolecules (for instance, tobacco mosaic virus) has suggested that the spindle also is a tactoid (Freundlich; Bernal; see Swann, '52). There are, however, fundamental differences between tactoids and the spindle and they were rightly emphasized by Swann ('52). In a tactoid the particles are oriented and held together by long-range ionic forces and the antagonizing action of these with surface tension causes their spindle shape. In the mitotic spindle, however, the micelles must be held together also by chemical bonds or else the spindle could not be fixed or isolated intact from the living cell. The presence of S—S linkages is suggested by the observations of Mazia and Dan ('52).

Ferry ('48) has recently reviewed various types of protein gels and the forces involved in their formation. Perhaps the spindle has properties in common with both tactoids and gels of denatured proteins. Electrostatic forces would be mainly involved in the orientation of the micelle into a bipolar structure, while chemical bonding at certain points would give it the observed rigidity.

The appearance of the spindle in the electron microscope depends on fixation (Rosza and Wyckoff, '51; Beams et al., '50a,b; Sedar and Wilson, '51). After Formalin fixation the spindle looks quite homogeneous, but if acid fixatives are used definite fibers become visible. This suggests that the structural units in the spindle are submicroscopic and less than a few hundred A thick, but that they have the property to bunch together, possibly depending on the degree of hydration, and thus form fibers that are visible in the light microscope.

The behavior of the spindle under increased hydrostatic pressure indicates that it is similar to other protoplasmic gels and myosin, with endothermic gelation reaction and increase in volume upon gelation. It is destroyed by a short exposure to hydrostatic pressure of 5000 to 6000 lbs. per square inch (Pease, '41, '46; Marsland, '51).

Rather little is known about the chemical composition of the spindle. The most promising advance is the recent development of methods to isolate large cleavage spindles in quantity for chemical study (Mazia and

Dan, '52). The bulk of the isolated cleavage spindles and asters of sea urchin eggs was found to consist of a protein that formed a single boundary in the analytical ultracentrifuge. The molecular weight of the particle was calculated to be approximately 45,000. In addition to protein, cytochemical studies indicate the presence of PNA (Brachet, '42; Pollister and Ris, '47; Stich, '51a) and vari-

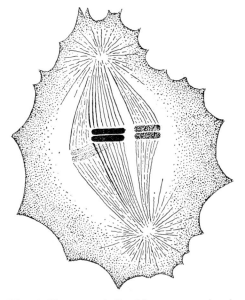

Fig. 18. Cleavage spindle of Steatococcus, showing diffuse kinetochore. One of the two chromosomes has been broken in two by x-rays. (After Hughes-Schrader and Ris, '41.)

able amounts of polysaccharides (Monné and Slautterback, '50; Stich, '51b) in some but not all spindles. The finding of Brachet that nuclear sap, spindle and aster of amphibian eggs and insect testes contain proteins rich in —SH groups is of special interest in view of Rapkine's theory on the role of —SH groups and reversible denaturization of proteins in the formation of gel structures during mitosis (reviewed in Brachet, '50).

KINETOCHORE (centromere, spindle attachment). Chromosomes do not move in the spindle unless they are attached to it by chromosomal fibers (traction fibers). In most organisms these fibers originate in connection with a specialized region of the chromosome, the *localized kinetochore*. In certain animals and plants chromosomal fibers attach along the entire length of the chromosome (*diffuse kinetochore*, see Fig. 18). Where the kinetochore is localized, chromosome fragments lacking this organelle fail to form chromosomal fibers and do not move on the spindle (akinetic fragments, Carlson, '38). In the case of the diffuse kinetochore any piece of the chromosome becomes attached to the spindle and moves normally (Hughes-Schrader and Ris, '41). The diffuse kinetochore is found in certain insects—the

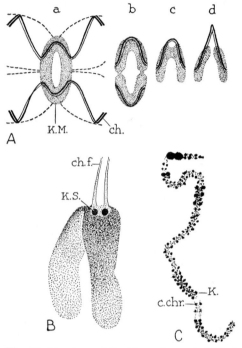

Fig. 19. Structure of the kinetochore. *A*, Meiotic chromosomes of Trillium (after Matsuura, '41); *ch.* = chromonemata, *K.M.* = kinetochore matrix, *a* = metaphase, *b–d* = early anaphase. *B*, Meiotic chromosome of Amphiuma (after Schrader, '39); *ch.f.* = chromosomal fiber, *K.S.* = kinetochore spherule. *C*, Pachytene chromosome of rye (after Lima-de-Faria, '49); *K.* = kinetochore, *c.chr.* = centromeric chromomeres.

Hemiptera, Homoptera and probably also Odonata (Oksala, '43) and Lepidoptera (Suomalainen, '53) in a myriapod (Ogawa, '49), a few scorpions (Rhoades and Kerr, '49), and in a group of plants (Malheiros, de Castro and Camara, '47). The kinetochore in Ascaris, often described as multiple, probably also falls into this category.

New insight into the nature of kinetochores may come from a further study of the accessory kinetochores (neocentric regions) that turned up in some strains of rye and maize (reviewed by Rhoades, '52). During meiotic divisions secondary chromosomal fibers develop in some of the chromosomes in addition to those formed by the

regular kinetochores and prematurely pull the chromosome ends to the poles. Especially interesting is the observation that in maize these neocentric regions form chromosomal fibers only if they are in physical connection with the primary kinetochore (Rhoades, '52).

The microscopic structure of the kinetochore is still imperfectly understood. The clearest photographs are those of the kinetochore in Trillium, published by Matsuura ('41). It appears to be a section of the chromonema that remains uncoiled. On the spindle it is surrounded by a hyaline material (kinetochore matrix) that divides in early anaphase (Fig. 19*A*). In chromosomes of rye, onion and other plants the kinetochore was shown to be an uncoiled region of the chromonema with a pair of "centromeric chromomeres." It has been suggested that the doubleness is due to an inverse repeat (Fig. 19*C*) (see Lima-de-Faria, '49, '50).

It is probable that such special "chromomeres" or heterochromatic knobs of the kinetochore region in the chromonema are identical with the "spindle spherule" which has been described in chromosomes of several plants and animals (Fig. 19*B*, cf. Schrader, '39). Normally the kinetochore divides lengthwise like the rest of the chromonema. A number of cases are known, however, where it divides transversely (misdivision), giving rise to isochromosomes (for instance, Müntzing, '44). The kinetochore may occasionally be broken into two functional fragments (McClintock, '32). Such terminal kinetochores, however, are usually not stable (Rhoades, '40).

CHROMOSOMAL FIBERS. Of all the mitotic organelles, chromosomal fibers are most directly involved in chromosome movement. They develop between the kinetochore and the centrosome or spindle pole. In some instances they may form in the absence of an organized spindle (Peters, '46; Rhoades, '52; Scott, '36; Pease, '41). Under favorable conditions they are visible in the phase microscope in living cells (whitefish, Fig. 12*C*) (Fell and Hughes, '49; Tahmisian, '51). After fixation they appear as a bundle or a sheet of fibers thicker near the kinetochore and tapering toward the poles. They stand out distinctly in the polarizing microscope, also in the living cell (Inoué, '52), owing to their strong birefringence that is positive with respect to their long axis (Fig. 17*A*). Like the spindle body they have been regarded as either positive or negative tactoids (Bernal, '40; Östergren, '49). Just as in the spindle, however, we must assume some chemical bonding between the micelles even though these bonds are weak enough to be easily broken and reformed, so that a chromosome or a microdissection needle can move through a chromosomal fiber without de-

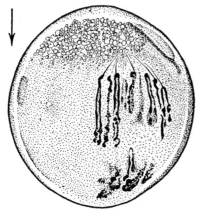

Fig. 20. Pollen mother cell of Lilium, centrifuged (arrow indicates direction of centrifugal force) (after Shimamura, '40). The chromosomal fibers anchor the chromosomes to the spindle in the upper pole. The chromosomes are uncoiled by the centrifugal force.

stroying it permanently (cf. Östergren, '49). The centrifuge experiments of Shimamura ('40) are impressive evidence for the strength of the chromosomal fibers (Fig. 20). Still too many questions remain completely unanswered. What is the material forming these fibers? What is its origin, and what is the role of the kinetochore? What forces cause their orientation to opposite spindle poles? How are they anchored on the chromosome and on the spindle? How do they function as they move the chromosomes? At present it seems most plausible to consider them as a contractile, fibrous gel reversibly liquefied with hydrostatic pressure (Pease, '46).

Some investigators have considered chromosomal fibers to be a liquid material secreted by the chromosomes and adsorbed on the continuous fibers of the spindle. They are thought to pull the chromosomes along the spindle by means of surface forces (Bělař and Huth, '33; Kupka and Seelich, '48). However, surface forces could hardly keep the chromosomes attached to the spindle with the centrifugal forces used (Beams and King, '36) or against the pull of the microdissection needle (Carlson, '52).

After this discussion of the mitotic organelles we must now see how they effect the congression of the chromosomes into the metaphase plate and the anaphase movement to the spindle poles.

Metakinesis. The chromosome movements of metakinesis result in a regular arrangement of chromosomes in the equatorial plane of the spindle (metaphase plate). To accomplish this the following conditions must be fulfilled: (1) a bipolar spindle must be present; (2) the chromosomes (mitosis) or chromosome pairs (meiosis) must be attached to opposite spindle poles through chromosomal fibers.

If the centrosome fails to divide in prophase a single large aster may appear (monaster). In Urechis, Bělař and Huth ('33) found that chromosomes orient in the aster and form chromosomal fibers toward and away from the center. But no metaphase plate is formed. In microspore mother cells of certain hybrids or haploids in plants the univalents usually do not form chromosomal fibers and do not congress on the metaphase plate. In Fig. 21A we see the spindle in a pollen mother cell of haploid Datura. No chromosomal fibers are present and the univalents are scattered over the spindle. In the diploid the bivalents produce oriented chromosomal fibers and a metaphase plate is present (Fig. 21B). Where chromosomal fibers point to one pole only no metaphase plate is formed, as in Sciara (Metz, '33) and Micromalthus (Scott, '36). In spermatocytes of many insects (e.g., grasshopper) the univalent X-chromosome is attached to one pole only and does not go on the metaphase

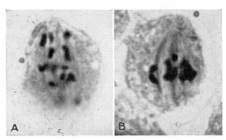

Fig. 21. First meiotic division in microspore mother cell of Datura. A, Haploid Datura; continuous fibers, but no chromosomal fibers are present; no metaphase plate is formed. B, Diploid Datura, chromosomal fibers present; chromosomes have moved into the metaphase plate. (From slide of Dr. Satina.)

plate. In tetraploid spermatocytes of the mantid, Callimantis, the X-chromosomes lie on the metaphase plate if they are paired and have chromosomal fibers to opposite poles. Where pairing is absent, each univalent has a single chromosomal fiber to one pole and remains outside the metaphase plate (Hughes-Schrader, '43b). Congression into the metaphase plate thus seems to be accomplished by the chromosomal fibers. Through them the chromosome or bivalent becomes attached to opposite poles of the spindle and the tension on the chromosomal fibers moves the chromosomes until equilibrium is reached in the metaphase plate (cf. Schrader, '47). In living cells such a movement of chromosomes back and forth in the long axis of the spindle has often been described and is easily seen in most films of dividing cells. The pre-metaphase stretch observed in spermatocytes of several insects

pulsive forces can produce similar patterns, but tell us nothing about the forces involved in the spindle. Most likely a complex interaction of chromosomal fibers, electrostatic charges on chromosomes, and intermolecular attraction between spindle micelles, tending to crowd out foreign bodies (Östergren, '51), is responsible for the metaphase arrangement.

Anaphase Movement. Of all the various aspects of mitosis hardly any has attracted the attention of cytologists more than the strikingly regular movement of chromosomes at anaphase. For years it has been the subject of much speculation and some experi-

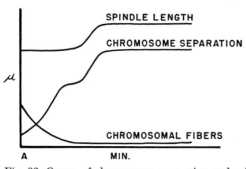 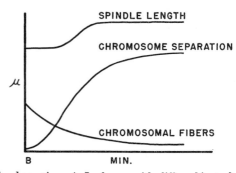

Fig. 22. Curves of chromosome separation and spindle elongation. *A,* In forms with diffuse kinetochore (Hemiptera and Homoptera; after Ris, '43. *B,* In forms with localized kinetochore (grasshopper spermatocytes, Ris, '49; chicken fibroblasts, Hughes and Swann, '48; Hughes and Preston, '49).

(Hughes-Schrader, '43a) and the metaphase position of multivalents give further support to this hypothesis (Östergren, '51). The details and mechanisms of this process, however, are completely unknown. What causes orientation of the kinetochores in the spindle and assures that chromosomal fibers attach to opposite poles? How can we explain the different behavior of kinetochores in mitosis and meiosis? (For a stimulating and interesting discussion of these problems see Östergren, '51.) Another interesting aspect of metakinesis is the spacing of chromosomes in the metaphase plate. The chromosomes are either all on the periphery of the spindle, the arms of long chromosomes directed radially away from the spindle, or they are evenly spaced in the equatorial plane. Even then the radial arrangement of chromosome arms is often striking. Large chromosomes are usually near the periphery, smaller ones in the center. In different cells even of the same organism this metaphase arrangement shows often striking variations and may show a constant pattern characteristic for the type of cell (Wilson, '32).

Model experiments with floating magnets show that a balance of attractive and re-

mental analysis. (For a critical discussion of the various hypotheses, see Schrader, '53.)

The initial separation of the chromatids takes place also in colchicine-treated cells and is therefore independent of the spindle apparatus (Levan, '38) and may be due to a swelling and dissolution of some material that holds the chromatids together at metaphase (cf. Carlson, '52). For the movement to the poles, however, spindle and chromosomal fibers are indispensable. Analysis of chromosome movement in living cells has shown that two factors are involved. The pole-ward movement is correlated with a shortening of the chromosomal fiber. Just how this occurs is not known but probably some kind of contraction of the organelles is involved (see review by Cornman, '44). The second factor is the lengthening of the spindle. The spindle suddenly swells in the equator and then stretches in its long axis. Since the chromosomes are attached to the spindle poles they are thus further moved apart. These two components in the anaphase movement are sometimes separated in time (Fig. 22*A*)—so far this has been found only in animals with diffuse kinetochore (Ris, '43)—but they usually occur simultaneously (Fig. 22B) (Ris, '49; Hughes and Swann, '48; Hughes and Preston, '49). In this case, it is possible to inhibit spindle stretching without affecting the chromosomal fibers, demonstrating the relative independence of the two components also where they act simultaneously (Ris, '49).

In some cells spindle stretching may be absent (the common situation in somatic zonal" fibers. Little is known about their origin, but it is possible that their appearance is related to the shedding of ribonucleoprotein from anaphase chromosomes that was mentioned above (Ris and Kleinfeld, '52).

The future study of anaphase movement will have to be directed mainly toward an experimental analysis of the mechanisms of

TABLE 3. *Maximum Rates of Chromosome Movement and Spindle Elongation during Anaphase*

CELL	TEMPERATURE, ° C.	CHROMOSOME MOVEMENT[*] MICRA/MINUTE	SPINDLE ELONGATION MICRA/MINUTE	AUTHOR
Tamalia				
Embryonic cell	26	0.7–2	0.3–1.1	Ris, '43
Spermatocyte I	26	—[†]	0.3	
Spermatocyte II	26	0.9–1.2	0.4–1.1	
Protenor				
Spermatogonia	26	1.3–1.6	0.3–0.5	Ris, '43
Spermatocyte I	26	0.9	0.7	
Thelia				
Spermatocyte I	26	0.4	0.5	Ris, '43
Chortophaga				
Spermatocyte I	30	1.5	3	Ris, '49
Spermatocyte II	17	0.4	1.4	
	23	1.2	2.4	
	30	2.5	3.6	
Triton fibroblasts, tissue culture	26	5.8[‡]		Hughes and Preston, '49
Rana fibroblasts, tissue culture	26	4.5[‡]		
Xenopus fibroblasts, tissue culture	26	2.1[‡]		
Gallus osteoblasts, tissue culture	40	4	2	Hughes and Swann, '48

[*] Due to contraction of chromosomal fibers only.
[†] Chromosomal fibers do not contract here.
[‡] Combined rate not analyzed into contribution of chromosomal fibers and spindle elongation.

cells of plants); in others the chromosomal fibers do not contract and anaphase movement is due to spindle stretching alone (Ris, '43). Usually the chromosomes all move simultaneously, but cases of autonomous movements of chromosomes are known. This independent behavior of chromosomes is based on the autonomy of the kinetochore and chromosomal fibers.

As the chromosomes approach the poles the region of the spindle in between may remain a semisolid structure (for instance, grasshopper spermatocytes) or it may solate and disappear. This is demonstrated by a decrease in viscosity (Carlson, '46), by the penetration of cytoplasmic granules into this space (Ris, '43), and by the disappearance of birefringence (Swann, '51). Chromosomes at anaphase are often connected by "inter-

chromosomal fiber contraction and spindle elongation. The presence in the spindle of phosphatases that split ATP (Biesele, '49) suggests a possible role of high energy phosphate bonds and a certain similarity to the contractile processes in muscle and myosin gels (cf. Brachet, '50; Hayashi, '52).

The velocity of chromosome movement as determined in living cells is largest in the early part and gradually decreases. The maximum rates of chromosome movement and spindle elongation in a number of cells are given in Table 3.

CYTOKINESIS

Following the separation of the chromosome halves the cytoplasm subdivides to complete mitosis (for a general review see

Mühldorf, '51). In animal cells this is commonly accomplished by the cleavage furrow, a circular groove in the cell surface that gradually deepens and cuts the cell in two. What determines the formation of this furrow and its position in the cell, and how is the formation accomplished? The experimental analysis so far indicates clearly that several factors are involved and that different ones predominate in different cells.

Elongation of the Spindle. As a general rule cleavage depends on the elongation of the cell (mitotic elongation, cf. Churney, '36), and the furrow is formed at a right angle to this elongation. In most tissue cells where asters are relatively small this elongation is dependent on the stretching of the spindle. Elongation by itself does not assure a cleavage furrow, but where it is suppressed the cell does not divide. If the spindle is prevented from stretching in its long axis, for instance through sticking of chromosomes, it may spread out laterally and stretch the cell at a right angle to the normal axis. In this case a furrow appears vertically to the new direction of elongation and splits off an anuclear bud (Ris, '49). Cell elongation may be accomplished independent of the spindle by centrifugation. Irrespective of the orientation of the cell the cleavage furrow again cuts through the narrow region (Harvey, '35).

Function of the Amphiaster. In cells with large asters, such as blastomeres of many eggs, mitotic elongation and cleavage may occur in the absence of a spindle (Fankhauser, '34; Harvey, '36; Briggs et al., '51). In such cells the growing amphiaster is probably responsible for mitotic elongation (Gray, '27b). The role of the aster for the initiation of the cleavage furrow was stressed by Dan ('48). By studying movements of the cell surface with kaolin particles he found that the surface gradually stretches during cleavage except in the region of the furrow, where it first contracts and then expands. He explains this by assuming that aster rays are anchored in the cell cortex and cross in the equatorial region. As the asters move apart in anaphase, owing to spindle elongation, the aster rays pull in the surface of the equatorial ring, thus initiating the furrow. The increased birefringence during anaphase of the aster rays crossing in the equator lends support to this hypothesis (Inoué and Dan, '51).

Function of the Cell Cortex. Certain observations indicate that the cleavage furrow may be formed independently of both spindle and aster and thus suggest a definite autonomy of this structure. Painter ('18) found that in sea urchin eggs treated with phenyl urethane cleavage occurs in the absence of asters. Harvey ('35) displaced the amphiaster to one side by centrifugation and Carlson ('52) did the same by micromanipulation, without affecting the position of the cleavage furrow. According to Marsland ('51) the cell cortex increases in viscosity before cleavage and the cleavage furrow is part of the cell cortex that is particularly thick and more solidified. The study of plasmolysis in the sea-urchin egg by Monroy and Montalenti ('47) also indicates that the viscosity of the cortex is low in metaphase and high before cytokinesis. Like other cytoplasmic gels the cortex can be solated by increased hydrostatic pressure which thus inhibits cleavage or reverses it, if in progress. Wilson ('51), on the other hand, claims that in Chaetopterus the cell cortex decreases in viscosity during division. The gel nature of the cleavage furrow was demonstrated dramatically by Chambers ('38), who destroyed one half of the dividing egg and found the furrow remaining intact. He also showed that only egg fragments containing cortical material can divide. In the amphibian egg Schechtman ('37) has studied the cleavage furrow in detail and concluded that it originates as a localized growth of the cortex toward the egg interior. His view is supported by Waddington's experiments on the frog egg ('52). Here the furrow can grow and deepen even if it is isolated from the egg interior by a cellophane strip.

Changes in the cell cortex are also indicated by the "bubbling" so evident in many films of dividing cells. It is most pronounced near the spindle poles and may be due to a thinning of the cortex in that region. The progress of the cleavage furrow is accompanied by actual contraction of the ring of cortical gel (Lewis, '51). Such contraction has also been observed in the furrow of the sea urchin (Scott, '46).

The Cleavage Substance. Cornman and Cornman ('51) have suggested that as the membrane dissolves a substance is released from the nucleus that spreads to the cortex and initiates the furrow. Similar ideas have been expressed by others, for instance Dalcq, Costello, Beams, and Conklin (for references see Cornman and Cornman, '51). The observation that cytasters develop only after breakdown of the germinal vesicle (Yatsu, '05), and the fact that asters are necessary for division of anucleate cells, suggest that nuclear material somehow enhances gelation in the aster forming material and in the cortex. The whole question of what is released by the germinal vesicle into the cytoplasm needs further investigation. A particulate fraction that facilitates cleavage has been demonstrated in the egg of the Dendraster (Moore, '38), in the sea urchin (Harvey, '36), and in the ascidian egg (Reverberi, '40).

These are the major factors that determine cytokinesis. The development of the furrow is a property of the cortical gel, influenced by mitotic elongation, aster rays and perhaps some nuclear substance. The site of the furrow is mainly determined by the dividing nucleus. If the spindle is in the center and the asters of equal size, cytokinesis is equal. Where the asters are of different size (Conklin, '17) or the spindle is placed asymmetrically in the cell, cytokinesis is unequal. What the detailed mechanisms are by which the cell insures that both daughter cells receive a nucleus whether the spindle is in the middle of the cell or near the surface to one side, we hardly can surmise today.

Differential Mitosis. The significance of mitosis is often sought in the formation of two equivalent cells. Yet the problem whether mitosis can produce two fundamentally different daughter cells may be of equal if not greater interest to the student of development. Is cell division a mechanism for cellular differentiation? Many examples are known where the two offspring of a mitosis have an entirely different and distinctive fate. Often morphogenesis and differentiation are associated with a specific and constant number of cell divisions which give rise to a determined number of cells, each with its own specific fate. This is well illustrated in the development of the various cells of the lepidopteran wing (Henke, '47; Henke and Pohley, '52). Other examples are found in the determinate cleavage of annelids and molluscs. Such cell divisions associated with differentiation are often called *differential mitoses.* However only in few cases has it been demonstrated that differentiation took place at cell division and not through some environmental factors afterwards. A cell division should be called differential only if it can be shown that it leads to a *qualitatively* unequal distribution of nuclear or cytoplasmic elements and that this is responsible for the different development of the daughter cells. Differential division of the nucleus in somatic cells occurs as an accident (e.g., nondisjunction) or a special adaptation (chromatin-elimination in Ascaris and some Diptera) but has been discounted as a general mechanism of differentiation. During meiosis the chromosomes are of course segregated differentially, generally in a random fashion. (For a recent discussion of preferential segregation, see Rhoades, '52.) Differential distribution of cytoplasmic material, on the other hand, has been described in a number of cases, for instance in the determinative cleavage of annelids, molluscs and ascidians. The segregation of cytoplasmic constituents must, however, occur before division, and spindle orientation has to be specific. Nothing is known about the mechanisms involved. The recent emphasis on autonomous cytoplasmic units (plasmagenes) has revived the idea of differentiative mitosis (cf. Ephrussi, '51). A decrease in the relative rate of reproduction of autonomous cytoplasmic units may result in a loss of these from the cell and can thus alter the characteristics of the cell (Lwoff and Dusi, '35; Sonneborn, '46; Ephrussi, '51; Spiegelman, Delorenzo and Campbell, '51). A similar process has been suggested as a possible origin of tumors (Potter et al., '50). Where identical plasmagenes or their precursors exist in large numbers the random separation during cytokinesis assures their distribution to both cells. They may reproduce either in the interphase or during mitosis. If a specific plasmagene occurs in small numbers its reproduction has to be synchronized closely with cell division in order not to get lost (plastids in lower plants).

CYTOPLASMIC CHANGES DURING MITOSIS

Marked physical and chemical changes have been observed in the cytoplasm during mitosis. Rhythmic changes in viscosity were demonstrated in many types of cells by different techniques through the work of Heilbrunn on eggs, Carlson in grasshopper neuroblasts, Zimmermann and Kostoff in plant cells (references in Heilbrunn, '52a). There is general agreement that the viscosity is high in prophase (in eggs it increases after activation: mitotic gelation of Heilbrunn). It then decreases to a minimum in metaphase and anaphase, to increase again before cytokinesis. Related to the changes in viscosity is the rounding off observed in elongated epithelial cells and in irregularly shaped cells such as fibroblasts. According to Lettré ('51) this is the result of the lowered level of ATP in dividing cells and can be produced experimentally with respiratory poisons. In the irregularly shaped cell the cortical proteins are in a state of chronic contraction that needs a high level of ATP. With less ATP irregular amoeboid movements result and the cell takes on a spherical shape.

Cytoplasmic streaming is often pronounced during mitosis. Especially during anaphase and cytokinesis vortical currents are visible in many cells (cf. Bělař, '29). Often these currents carry along pigment granules, yolk platelets, mitochondria and other inclusions that accumulate in the equatorial plane or along the spindle surface (e.g., Nussbaum, '02). Considering these changes in the physical state of the protoplasm and the mixing up through cytoplasmic currents we can understand that mitosis is generally antagonistic to cytoplasmic differentiation and specific functioning of the cell. Not only is there interruption in nuclear functions, but also more or less severe changes in cytoplasmic organization. Cytoplasmic organelles such as cilia, brushborder, and ergastoplasm often disappear and specific function is interrupted (cf. Berrill and Huskins, '36; Peter, '40). Some cells divide, however, without visible simplification in cytoplasmic organization (Dawson, '40), and many highly differentiated cells are able to divide mitotically. Differentiation is usually accompanied by a decrease in the rate of mitosis, yet the factors responsible for cessation of cellular proliferation are independent of differentiation as such.

An interesting change in the cytoplasm is the marked decrease in PNA in late prophase and metaphase (Brachet, '42; Montalenti et al., '50; Battaglia and Omodeo, '49). This may be related to an interruption in nuclear function during division in view of the report of Brachet ('50b) that RNA in the cytoplasm decreased in enucleated halves of amoebae. According to Mazia and Hirshfield ('50), incorporation of P^{32} into the cytoplasmic RNA is under nuclear control and it would be interesting to study how this is affected during mitosis.

MITOSIS AND METABOLISM

In the past the study of the metabolic characteristics of the dividing cell has lagged behind the analysis of the mechanisms of mitosis. Only in recent years have some significant advances been made in the understanding of the metabolic processes associated with cell reproduction. The various aspects of the recent work have been summarized by Brachet ('50a), Krahl ('50), Zeuthen ('51) and Bullough ('52). Much of the older work on the metabolism of mitosis is quite meaningless because mitosis was treated as a unitary process. Mitosis is a chain of individual processes that are quite different in character, and metabolic studies of cell division will make sense only when they are related to the various components of cellular reproduction. We shall want to know, for instance, what changes in metabolism are associated with the initiation of mitosis; are there metabolic pathways specific for dividing cells? What processes furnish the energy for chromosome synthesis, for spindle formation and chromosome movements, for cytokinesis and synthesis of cytoplasmic components? How do the metabolic processes during the various phases of mitosis differ in different types of cells?

Eggs during cleavage have been a favorite material for metabolic studies, especially those of echinoderms (Krahl, '50). In these eggs division occurs only in the presence of oxygen. Inhibition of respiration to less than 30 per cent of normal blocks mitosis. A cyanide-sensitive system containing an iron-porphyrin catalyst (probably cytochrome c) is involved. Mitosis is also blocked by interfering with generation and transfer of energy-rich phosphates. The substrate oxidized during cleavage has not been conclusively characterized. In some eggs, however, oxygen is not necessary for cleavage. For instance in the frog, the toad, Fundulus and Ilyanassa (references in Bullough, '52; Brachet, '50a), cleavage may continue in the absence of respiration.

Several investigators have measured the rate of respiration during cell division. The most careful and extensive determinations have been made by Zeuthen ('51), both on single eggs and on large numbers of eggs dividing synchronously. In the eggs of the frog, Urechis and several echinoderms a definite increase in respiration was demonstrated with each mitosis. Zeuthen, furthermore, showed that the rise in respiration occurred during interphase and not during the actual division in Psammechinus eggs (Fig. 23) and in the ciliate Tetrahymena gelei. This agrees with observations of Förster and Örstrom and Bataillon (references in Brachet, '50a) that respiration is necessary only in the first part of mitosis, before metaphase. In the presence of colchicine, chromosome movements and cytokinesis are suppressed, yet the rhythmic change in respiration associated with rhythmic disappearance and regeneration of the nuclear membrane persists (Zeuthen, '51). The increase in respiration is therefore not associated with chromosome movement or cytokinesis but with some process occurring before visible prophase.

If eggs have the advantage of being easily available in large numbers in the same stage, they have the considerable drawback of being full of storage material and equipped to go on largely independently of the environment. Because of this they are not very useful for the study of the metabolic requirements of mitosis.

A few years ago Medawar and Bullough and Johnson (cf. Bullough, '52) found an excellent material for physiological studies on dividing cells in adult mammalian epidermis, a tissue that can be cultured quite easily. In a series of beautiful studies Bullough has analyzed the metabolic conditions for mitosis. He showed that in the epidermis mitosis is directly proportional to the concentration of glucose and the oxygen tension. Glucose is metabolized through the citric acid cycle. The inhibition of mitosis by 2,4-dinitrophenol suggests that oxidative phosphorylation is involved in the reactions providing the energy for division. Any agent that interferes with the citric acid cycle and oxidative phosphorylation prevents mitosis. These metabolic inhibitors affect the cell only during the part of interphase preceding mitosis, a stage which Bullough named *antephase*. Once the cell has passed this stage it can go on in the absence of respiration.

In other tissues mitosis occurs also in the absence of respiration. Embryonic cells, for instance, either in vivo or in vitro, can divide without oxygen and are not inhibited by respiratory poisons (Parker, Pomerat and Willmer). These cells therefore may depend on glycolysis alone for mitosis (Laser; O'Connor). They are inhibited by fluoride and iodoacetate (Hughes). (References in Bullough, '52.)

The observations on cultured epidermis are corroborated by studies on intact mice (Bullough, '52). The diurnal rhythm of mitosis in several tissues of mice was shown to be related to the deposition of glycogen in the cells during rest. When the animals are active the amount of carbohydrates available is decreased and the number of mitoses goes down. Injection of carbohydrates and phosphate raises the number of mitoses to a maximum. Inhibition of phosphorylation by

phloridzin, on the other hand, blocks division completely.

Though the biochemical analysis of mitosis is still in its beginning, some generalizations are already possible. In order to divide, the cell requires energy. This energy is derived from breakdown of carbohydrates, through glycolysis in some cells and respiration in others. Oxidation of other foodstuffs may also occur, especially in eggs. The energy is then trapped in high-energy phosphate bonds. All this takes place in the antephase, before any visible changes occur

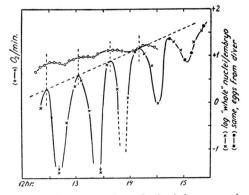

Fig. 23. Oxygen uptake and mitosis in consecutive cleavages of Psammechinus. "Whole" nuclei indicate interphase and prophase, "open" nuclei metaphase and anaphase. The increase in oxygen uptake occurs before each division when the nuclei are "whole." (After Zeuthen, '51.)

in the cell. During this phase the "batteries" of the cell are charged up and from then on mitosis proceeds without further energy uptake from the environment and only direct interference with mitotic organelles, or death of the cell, can block division. Further work will have to show how these metabolic processes of antephase are related to chromosome reproduction, how the energy is stored and made available for the various reactions during actual division.

MITOGENESIS

What are the conditions, both internal and external, that cause a cell to divide? And what conditions are responsible for the cessation of cell reproduction? A free living cell such as an amoeba grows until it reaches a certain size and then it divides. A similar relationship between size and mitosis is found in other protozoans, the rate of division under optimal conditions being characteristic of a species. If the size of an amoeba is kept small by cutting off a piece every day the cell may survive for months without ever dividing (Hartmann, '26). We can consider this situation the simplest and most primitive relationship between growth (cytoplasmic synthesis) and cell division. R. Hertwig ('03) based his theory of mitosis on it. He believed that the change in nuclear-cytoplasmic ratio due to cell growth was the primary stimulus to cell division. It soon became evident, however, that cytoplasmic growth and division are not necessarily connected; the stimulus for division therefore must be sought outside of a simple quantitative relationship between nucleus and cytoplasm. In certain algae division can be suppressed while growth continues, and giant cells are formed. Release of the inhibition is followed by a series of rapid divisions until the usual size is restored again. Under different circumstances several divisions follow each other without interphasic growth and dwarf cells are produced (Hartmann, '33). By exchanging nuclei between amoebae that had just divided and cells entering mitosis, Commandon and de Fonbrune ('42) analyzed the function of cytoplasmic and nuclear growth in mitosis. They found that the nuclear-cytoplasmic volume ratio is not important, but that both the nucleus and cytoplasm have to be in a special state of maturity for mitosis to occur.

Eggs have often been used to study mitogenesis, either through fertilization or artificial parthenogenesis. Some physiologists expected to find a common factor in mitotic stimulation and the stimulation of nerve and muscle. According to Lillie increased permeability of the cell membrane was such a factor. Heilbrunn substituted the increased cytoplasmic viscosity as a common factor and suggested that the mitotic gelation was the primary stimulus to division (see Heilbrunn, '52b). This hypothesis, however, is hardly more satisfactory as a theory of mitosis than the previous ones. It deals with certain phenomena that accompany the division of the cell but not with the fundamental process leading to the complex chain reaction from chromosome synthesis to formation of mitotic organelles, chromosome movements and division of the cell.

In recent years more emphasis has been placed on biochemical changes in the cell during mitogenesis. The cytologist has failed so far in the understanding of mitogenesis because the essential changes in the cell take place before any microscopically visible manifestations appear. A better understanding of mitogenesis has to be based on a study of the shifts in enzyme systems, metabolic pathways and synthetic mechanisms during antephase following the mitotic stimulus.

A cell about to enter mitosis needs energy that is obtained mainly from a breakdown of carbohydrates through glycolysis or respiration. Any factor that increases the amount of substrate available to the cell therefore increases the number of cells in division. Daily rhythms in the number of dividing cells are explained by the variable amounts of carbohydrate available to the cells (Blumenthal, '50; Bullough, '52). Changes in vascularization are responsible for waves of mitoses and certain hormones (estrogen, testosterone) stimulate mitosis, apparently by increasing the carbohydrate supply to the cells affected (cf. Bullough, '52). It has long been known that starvation suppresses cell division. With renewed feeding there is commonly a great increase in the number of divisions, followed by a new minimum. Apparently, in dividing tissues, energy sources affect the length of antephase, but not the entrance into a "ready state." Starvation thus leads to a piling up of "ready" cells and when feeding starts again all these cells go through mitosis at once until all the "ready" cells are exhausted (cf. Kornfeld, '22).

It was shown above that DNA is synthesized during antephase. Continuation of mitosis depends, therefore, also on the availability of precursors, enzymes and coenzymes involved in nucleic acid synthesis. Addition of such factors stimulates cell division (cf. Norris, '49).

The relationship of thiols to cell division seems to be well established through the work of Hammett, Voegtlin, Chalkley and especially Rapkine. The pertinent literature has been reviewed by Brachet ('50a). Sulfhydryl compounds stimulate cell division in plants and in animals, in tissue culture and in vivo. Compounds combining with —SH, on the other hand, inhibit mitosis reversibly. Rapidly growing tissues are especially rich in —SH. An attractive hypothesis of the role of —SH has been suggested by Rapkine and expanded by Brachet ('50a). The changes in —SH in the cell are related to a reversible denaturation of proteins. Denaturation of proteins and associated conversion of globular into fibrous proteins is thought to occur during the formation of asters, spindles and other mitotic gels. The —SH groups freed upon denaturation would then reduce oxidized glutathione in the cell. This could account for the observed increase in free

—SH in dividing cells. S—S linkages, on the other hand, are thought to play a role in the formation of the protein gels of mitotic organelles. Indeed, Brachet has found that asters, spindle and the nuclear sap from which it is formed are especially rich in —SH after denaturation. Since —SH groups are also essential to the functioning of many enzymes (cf. Barron, '51), the effect of thiols on mitosis may be quite diverse.

As mentioned above, the original state of affairs may be illustrated by the amoeba that grows to a certain size and then divides. Cells of metazoa no longer behave that way; they are dependent on checks and balances originating in the tissue, organ or organism as a whole. Single cells in tissue culture are said to be unable to divide except under special conditions (Likely et al., '52); usually there is a minimal number of cells below which growth does not occur (Fischer, '46). In the developing embryo, during regeneration, in buds of asexually reproducing animals this control of cellular proliferation has been demonstrated many times. Cell division in an organ stops when the proper relative size is reached and only where continuous replacement is necessary, as in the intestinal mucosa or in the skin, do we find mitoses. If the balance is upset by removal of tissues or by other injuries to the cells, proliferation sets in again until the normal functional balance is restored.

What factors are responsible for the control of proliferation and what causes renewed mitotic activity?

With the introduction of tissue culture techniques it became possible to study the factors responsible for initiation of mitosis directly and under controlled conditions. The mitosis-stimulating effect of embryo extracts and adult tissue extracts was discovered and the search was on for the nature and mode of action of "growth factors." Much interesting information has been collected in the years since (see Fischer, '46), but it still remains unknown how these extracts act on the cells of the explant and how they stimulate mitosis. The facts indicate that substances released by injured cells and tissue extracts contain a whole spectrum of factors, substrates, coenzymes, building blocks and possibly self-reproducing enzyme systems (cytoplasmic particulates; Shaver, '53). It remains for future work to separate these factors and study their specific mode of action on the cell.

The mitosis-stimulating effect of injury substances and tissue extracts has been studied not only in explants but also in the intact animal. Tissue extracts accelerate the healing of wounds (Auerbach and Doljanski, '45). Tumor extracts increase the growth of tumors (Annau, Manginelli and Roth, '51) and other tissues. Even more interesting is the organ-specific action of tissue extracts. Injury of a certain tissue was shown to release factors that stimulate mitosis in homologous tissues, but not in others. These factors are carried in the blood stream (Teir, '52). Similar results were obtained by Weiss ('52) in embryos. Homologous tissue extracts delay differentiation and stimulate cell proliferation. These experiments so far support Weiss' hypothesis of self-regulation of organ growth by diffusible products. According to Weiss a cell produces "templates" involved in the production of new specific cytoplasm and diffusible units that move into the humoral pool. If these reach a certain concentration further proliferation of the particular cells is inhibited, since the diffusible units combine with and inactivate the "templates." By injecting tissue extracts the concentration of the homologous humoral units is reduced and this leads to renewed proliferation in the particular tissue.

Superimposed on the self-regulation of organs is the activity of hormones. Bullough ('52) has recently reviewed the effect of hormones on mitotic activity in vertebrates. Both androgens and estrogens stimulate mitosis, except in nerve cells and striated muscle. Adrenal hormones, on the other hand, depress mitotic activity. This hormonal control of mitosis apparently operates by influencing the availability of carbohydrate to the cell.

Another kind of tissue interaction was discovered by Carrel ('22). Fibroblasts can grow in serum alone in the presence of leukocytes. He called the substance liberated by leukocytes "trephones." The role of such trephocytes has been investigated recently, especially by Liebman ('47). The nature of trephones is unknown; they may be nutrients, vitamins or enzymes. Bacteria in tissue culture or even in vivo may act as trephocytes (Lasfargues and Delaunay, '49). Wooley ('53) has shown that tumors may act similarly. Mouse embryos deficient in B_{12} could grow if the mother carried certain tumors. These tumors synthesized B_{12} which then became available to the embryonic tissues, enabling them to grow. In this connection it is of interest that certain tumors can grow in serum alone, while normal tissues need special growth factors in addition. It appears that some cells retain or regain the ability to synthesize specific compounds that are essential for mitosis, while other tissues remain unable to do so.

Sometimes differentiation is connected with a permanent loss of mitotic activity. In vertebrates this applies to nerve cells and striated muscle. In some invertebrates the development of the entire organism or of certain organs is a closed system involving a specific and constant number of cell divisions. When morphogenesis is complete all cells have lost the ability to divide.

An important aspect of mitogenesis is the "latent period." Whether in tissue culture or in vivo, no matter what the stimulus, there is invariably a period of many hours between application of the stimulus and appearance of the first mitosis. In tissue culture it lasts from 20 to 24 hours (Fischer, '46). It depends to some extent on the type of medium (Jacoby, '49). In explants of liver it is not the same in different types of cells (Abercrombie and Harkness, '51). It is generally longer than the interphase under optimal conditions. Growth factors act during this time and once mitosis is under way they are no longer required until the next antephase (Jacoby, '37). No doubt mitotic stimulation produces some essential changes in the cytoplasm, as is borne out by the many observations of synchronous division of nuclei in the same cell or in cells connected by cytoplasmic bridges. Whatever the nature of this change it does not go beyond the cell membrane.

In other cells synchronous divisions are most likely the result of an inherent rhythm of mitosis with a fixed length of the various phases characterizing the particular type of cell (spermatocytes of insects, early cleavage).

The rate at which the number of cells increases in a tissue depends on the time for mitosis, the length of the interphase and the rate of removal of cells from the proliferating population by death or differentiation. The sum of *mitotic time* and *interphase* has been called *generation time*. Mitotic time and length of interphase for some cells can be determined directly by observation (eggs, tissue culture). In the intact animal the time for mitosis has been determined for several tissues by making use of the fact that moderate doses of x-rays inhibit the antephase so that no new cells enter mitosis, but those in division continue normally (Knowlton and Widner, '50; Widner et al., '51). From the mitotic index (number of dividing

cells/number of interphases) and the mitotic time the average length of interphase can be calculated (Table 4).

The shortest generation time is found in early cleavage. Probably the shortest on record was reported for early cleavage of Drosophila (Huettner, '33). A short interphase is characteristic also for certain embryonic cells such as the neuroblasts in the grasshopper (Carlson and Hollaender, '48).

In vertebrates the average mitotic time is remarkably similar from one tissue to another. Even in embryonic cells in tissue culture and in various tumors the time for mitosis is about the same. The average length of interphase, however, is very variable. As shown in tissue culture it differs even in daughter cells (Jacoby, '49; Fell and Hughes, '49). In other cells, for instance in spermatocytes (Ris, '49) or in cleaving eggs, mitotic time and interphase may be remarkably constant under the same conditions.

The generation time is determined by intrinsic factors and by external conditions. In the eggs of sea urchins (Moore, '33), amphibians (Porter, '42) and fishes (Moenkhaus, '04), the rate of cleavage is specific for a species and is determined by the cytoplasm. In later cleavage blastomeres may have different rates, specific for each cell and independent of the size of the cells (Chen and Pai, '49).

Both mitotic time and interphase are influenced by environmental factors, for instance, temperature (Barber, '39), pH, concentration of embryo extract in tissue culture (Jacoby, '37), tonicity of the medium (Cornman, '43), and the presence of certain ions (Moellendorff, '38) and hormones (Bullough, '52). The mitotic index has often been used as a measure for the proliferative activity of a tissue. To draw any conclusion, however, more than just the index must be known. The relationship of mitotic time and interphase to the mitotic index under various conditions was discussed by Hoffmann ('49).

We may conclude that many factors influence in one way or another the number of cells in division or change the mitotic time or length of interphase and in a few cases we have some information on the mechanisms of these effects. Other factors are known that are truly mitogenetic, that induce cells to enter mitosis that would not normally divide, even though energy sources and building blocks may be available. So far little is known of how this change in cells is brought about.

TABLE 4. *Some Examples of Mitotic Time and Length of Interphase in Animal Cells*

CELL	TEMPERATURE, °C.	MITOTIC TIME, MINUTES	INTERPHASE, HOURS	AUTHOR
		DIRECT DETERMINATIONS		
Chick heart fibroblasts tissue culture	40	25 (longer in old cultures)	10 or more	Willmer, '33
Chick macrophages tissue culture	40	28–39		Jacoby, '49
Chick embryo tissue culture	40	34–52		Hughes, '49
Chick embryo tissue culture	40		20	Olivo and Slavich, '30
Chick myocardium tissue culture	40		7–21	Olivo and Delorenzi, '33
Mouse spleen tissue culture	40	43–90	8–18	Fell and Hughes, '49
Frog fibroblast tissue culture	26	90		Hughes and Preston, '49
Newt fibroblast	26	120		Hughes and Preston, '49
Chortophaga neuroblast	38	181	27 min.!	Carlson and Hollaender, '48
Rat cornea		70	200	Friedenwald, '50
Rabbit cleavage		9–10	8–9	Pincus, '39
Drosophila cleavage	23	10 min.		Huettner, '33
Echinus miliaris cleavage	17	33–36 min.		Gray, '27b
Psammechinus micro-tuberculatus cleavage	13	33–39 min.		Callan, '49
Sphaerechinus granularis cleavage	13	52–59 min.		Callan, '49
		INDIRECT DETERMINATIONS*		
Mouse, female epidermis, castrate		150		Bullough and van Oordt, '50
with estrogen		45		
Rat tissues jejunum		27.5	33.5	Widner et al., '51
myelotic series marrow		25.7	32.4	
nucleated red cells		24.6	61.0	
Walker rat carcinoma		24.8	11.4	
Jensen rat sarcoma		26.6	12.3	
Mouse tissues myelotic series		35.3	155	Knowlton and Widner, '50
jejunum		23.9	43	
erythrocytic series		29.5	99	
lymph node		23.2	100	
epidermis		30.2	670	
adrenal		14.4	1090	

* Values for mitotic time by indirect determinations are averages.

INHIBITION OF MITOSIS

Many physical and chemical agents inhibit cell division without killing the cell. They have been called "mitotic poisons." Besides being useful tools for dissecting mitosis into its component processes and for the biochemical characterization of these components, they have great practical interest as potential inhibitors of pathological growth. Some inhibitors were discovered empirically to block various phases of mitosis (x-rays, colchicine, nitrogen mustards, etc.). The specific ways in which they affect the cell are now studied in many laboratories. Other inhibitors are well known tools of the biochemist, specific inhibitors of certain enzymes or antimetabolites that block metabolic processes at definite points. They have revealed some of the enzymatic reactions that play a role in cellular reproduction. Reviews of the more recent work on mitotic inhibitors have been published by Lettré ('51, '52) and Lehmann ('51).

Two phases in the course of cell division are especially sensitive to external influences. One is the antephase, the time when energy is produced and stored for mitosis and when chromosome reproduction takes place. The second is characterized by the formation of oriented gels, of which the swelling and contraction play a role in chromosome movement and cytokinesis.

Antephase inhibitors prevent cells from entering prophase, but do not affect those already in division. They include factors that interfere with glycolysis or respiration and with the formation of high-energy phosphates (Bullough, '52; Krahl, '50), and those that inhibit chromosome reproduction. Of special interest in this second group are the inhibitors of DNA synthesis. DNA is generally restricted to chromosomes and its synthesis to chromosome reproduction. Synthesis of DNA may be accomplished by different pathways in different cells, tissues or organisms, and in normal cells and tumor cells; hence the hope for cell specific inhibitors. The better known inhibitors of chromosome reproduction are x-rays (Hevesy, '48; Skipper, '51), nitrogen mustard (Bodenstein and Kondritzer, '48; Friedenwald and Sigelman, '53; Goldthwait, '52), folic acid antagonists such as aminopterin and amethopterin (cf. Petering, '52) and certain purines and pyrimidines (Lettré, '51).

Cells arrested in antephase are extremely labile and easily undergo degeneration. In rapidly proliferating tissues the majority of cells can be accumulated in this phase and then destroyed (Gillette and Bodenstein, '46; Friedenwald, '51). Chemical agents that interfere with chromosome reproduction have cytological effects that are similar to those of ionizing radiations, and therefore have been called radiomimetic (cf. Loveless and Revell, '49). In addition to the antephase block they produce chromosome clumping and chromosome breaks.

Another group of "chromosome poisons" that inhibit antephase and also later stages are acridine derivatives (trypaflavin, proflavin), investigated especially by Bauch ('47) and Lettré ('51). They seem to act by forming complexes with nucleic acids, interfering mainly with polymerization of nucleic acid.

The movements of chromosomes and cell cleavage are dependent on nuclear and cytoplasmic gels (asters, spindle, cortical gel of cleavage furrow). Beginning with metakinesis, mitosis can be blocked by agents that interfere with gelation of these organelles, or with contraction of chromosomal fibers and cortical gel. The relative sensitivity of these structures is often somewhat different so that cleavage, for instance, can be suppressed without halting chromosome movements, or spindle stretching may be inhibited without affecting the contraction of chromosomal fibers (Ris, '49). Complete inhibition of these organelles is produced by certain anticoagulants, for instance, heparin (Heilbrunn, '52a), by hydrostatic pressure (Marsland, '51), by high or low temperature, and by hypotonic media (Lewis, '34).

The best known specific poison of the spindle is colchicine. In the presence of this alkaloid the spindle does not form, or, if it is present, is destroyed together with asters and the cleavage furrow. Chromosome reproduction, spiralization and breakdown of nuclear membrane and the initial parallel separation of chromatids are not affected and nuclei may undergo several cycles of reproduction in colchicine (Zeuthen, '51). Often the chromosomes clump, or are scattered, giving rise to micronuclei with variable numbers of chromosomes.

Inoué ('52) has used an improved polarizing microscope to study the effect of colchicine on the structure of the spindle. He found that colchicine primarily destroys the orientation of the spindle micelles. The spindle material may become scattered or remain in the cell as a spherical mass (Gaulden and Carlson, '51), depending on the colchicine concentration and the type of cell.

Lettré ('51, '52) has studied a great num-

ber of colchicine derivatives and other alkaloids in search for the molecular structure
responsible for the colchicine effect. He
found that the stilbylamine group is essential, though the type of substitution too
is important. It is not yet clear how colchicine acts on the spindle micelles. Lettré
suggested that it interferes with the utilization of ATP for spindle contraction, since
ATP counteracts colchicine. However, there
is more to it than inhibition of contraction,
since the structure of the spindle and asters
is actually destroyed.

Östergren ('44) made a comparative study
of many chemically unrelated substances
that have a colchicine-like action. He called
attention to the fact that the more lipoid-
soluble the substance the lower the threshold
concentration for colchicine-like effect (C-
mitosis). He proposed a protein chain folding
theory according to which the active molecule attracts the lipoid side chains of the
proteins, causing a folding up which would
explain the breakdown of the cytoplasmic
gels and spindle and perhaps also the more
than normal shortening of the chromosomes
typical of colchicine-mitosis.

Colchicine destroys the spindle almost
universally in both animals and plants. It is
very interesting that there are cells and
organisms that are resistant to it. In the
hamster colchicine is without effect (Orsini
and Pansky, '52) and Lettré ('52) has found
a strain of ascites tumor in the mouse that
is resistant.

Another group of spindle poisons have in
common that they combine specifically with
—SH groups. Quinones were discovered by
Lehmann ('51) to affect specifically spindle
and cytokinesis. Organometallic compounds
were studied by Klages and Lettré (for references see Lettré, '51). Their action is reversed by cysteine and other —SH compounds. Chloroacetophenone, another —SH
poison, blocks metaphase in vitro (Hughes,
'50) and in vivo (Beatty, '51). Sulfhydryl
poisons can block mitosis in two ways, either
by inhibition of —SH enzymes (Barron, '51)
or by combining with —SH groups of the
proteins in spindle and asters and thus interfering with the formation and function
of these gel structures. It is interesting that
some —SH poisons are spindle poisons in
low concentrations and inhibitors of antephase in higher concentration, possibly by
interfering with carbohydrate metabolism
(Meier and Allgöwer, '45; Hughes, '50).

Folic acid, as mentioned above, is essential
in antephase and aminopterin prevents cells
from entering prophase. Hughes ('50) and
Jacobson ('51) found that aminopterin and
amethopterin block mitosis also at metaphase.
Folic acid is thus necessary also for anaphase movements of chromosomes, but nothing is known about how it functions here.

MODIFICATION OF MITOSIS

The division of cells involves a complex
series of events that normally follow each
other in a definite order. It can be interrupted experimentally by a variety of inhibitors that affect one or several links in
the chain. Often it is modified in connection
with specializations in the growth and function of tissues or in the life cycle of the
organism. Thus the mitotic chain may be
broken at one point or the other, or the normal sequence of events is changed, or one
of the components is altered in some way.

Completion of cytoplasmic division is most
easily affected and so we find many examples of division without cytokinesis. In mammalian tissues, for instance, binucleate cells
are common, and they are the result of such
failure of cytoplasmic division (Beams and
King, '42). In spermatogenesis of coccids cell
division is omitted regularly in the second
meiotic division (Hughes-Schrader, '48). If
mitosis is interrupted at an earlier point chromosome movements and therefore nuclear
division are absent. Reproduction of nuclear
elements that is not followed by chromosome movements and cytoplasmic division
has been called "endomitosis" (cf. Geitler,
'48). Endomitosis may occur with a typical
prophase, including increase in nuclear volume and chromosome spiralization. The nuclear membrane, however, persists and the
cell becomes polyploid (somatic tissues of
Hemiptera and many other insects). Polyploid cells may later again divide by regular mitosis. In other cases prophase is
suppressed too, only antephase is left, and
there is no visible change in the structure
of the interphase nucleus. Where chromosome reproduction is not followed by chromosome splitting and separation of chromatids, endomitosis does not change the number of chromosomes but increases the number
of units in each chromosome, giving rise to
polytene chromosomes. They are best known
from larval tissues of Diptera, where through
many consecutive endomitoses the number of
chromonemata per chromosome may increase
a hundredfold.

The volumes of polytene and polyploid
nuclei are usually multiples of the original

size, and the amount of DNA per nucleus increases by a factor of two with each endomitosis. The doubling in nuclear size is followed by an increase in cytoplasm.

Endomitosis is a major factor in the growth of many differentiated tissues. Apparently it interferes less with the functioning of differentiated cells than does a complete mitosis. Although the number of cells remains the same, it accomplishes an increase in the functional elements of the cell from chromosomes and nucleolus to the various cytoplasmic elements, and therefore augments the functional capacity of the tissue as a whole. The relationship of endomitosis and polysomaty (polyploidy of tissue cells in a diploid organism) to differentiation has been discussed in detail by Geitler ('41) and by Huskins ('47).

In mammalian tissues polyploid cells originate not only through endomitosis but also through fusion of spindles during mitosis of binucleate cells (Beams and King, '42; Fell and Hughes, '49). Excellent discussions of polysomaty in mammals in connection with the problem of nuclear size classes have been published by Teir ('44) and Helweg-Larsen ('52). Mitosis may be modified also by a change in the sequence of mitotic processes. An interesting example was described by Berger ('38) and by Grell ('46) in the midgut of the mosquito. In these cells several cycles of chromosome reproduction occur in the larva and polytene chromosomes are formed. During metamorphosis these cells then divide repeatedly without chromosome reproduction until the chromatids produced by endomitosis in the larva are divided up into the newly formed cells and the diploid condition is restored. Chromosome reproduction thus takes place in the larva, chromosome separation and cell division in the pupa.

More commonly karyokinesis is separated in time from the division of the cytoplasm. Repeated nuclear divisions give rise to a multinucleated cell which is subdivided later simultaneously into the appropriate number of uninucleated cells (insect cleavage; other examples in Mühldorf, '51).

The cytological literature is rich in descriptions of interesting modifications in the behavior of mitotic organelles. The elimination of certain chromosomes during cleavage in some dipterans, for instance, is accomplished through failure of the chromosomal fibers of the eliminated chromosomes to contract during anaphase. These chromosomes are therefore left behind and are not included in the daughter nuclei. Thus somatic cells with a reduced chromosome number are formed (DuBois, '33; Reitberger, '40; White, '46).

Then there is the puzzling behavior of the chromosomes in the primary spermatocytes of Sciara (Metz, '33). The chromosomes having failed to synapse in prophase, all form chromosomal fibers toward the single aster (monocentric mitosis). No metaphase plate is formed. At anaphase the maternal chromosomes move toward the active center while the paternal chromosomes move away from it, and backward too, since they are still attached to the center by chromosomal fibers that appear to be under tension and attenuate the chromosomes. How can we account for this unorthodox chromosome movement? I think it is unnecessary to introduce any special mechanisms, since it can be understood on the basis of slight modifications in the behavior of the known mitotic organelles. First, the chromosomal fibers contract only in the maternal chromosomes, pulling them to the poles. Secondly, the spindle elongates and carries the paternal chromosomes along passively away from the single aster. The presence of a spindle is indicated by the distribution of the mitochondria and spindle stretching is suggested by the elongation of the cell precisely in the direction in which the paternal chromosomes move. The observation that low temperature, which is known to destroy the spindle, inhibits the backward movements of the chromosomes and also the elongation of the cell supports our interpretation.

The most general and most important modifications of mitosis are found in the meiotic divisions during gametogenesis. In the first division the most significant modification is the pairing of homologous chromosomes during prophase. So far there is no satisfactory explanation of this phenomenon. Theories involving changes in timing (the precocity theory of Darlington, for instance) have no factual basis since Swift and Kleinfeld ('53) have shown that chromosome reproduction (DNA doubling) takes place before prophase as in somatic mitoses. Since the association of homologous chromosomes continues into metaphase, either because of chiasmata or owing to a localized or general persistence of the "pairing force," homologous kinetochores are co-oriented in metakinesis instead of kinetochores of sister chromatids. As a result this division segregates homologous kinetochores and, depending on the degree of crossing over, certain segments of the homologous chromosomes. The second division proceeds without chromosome reproduction. The kinetochores orienting on the spindle are therefore the sister kinetochores of the first division. The fundamental features of meiosis are thus pairing in the first division followed by a separation of the four chromatids in each chromosome pair by two karyokineses without any further chromosome reproduction. The four nuclei resulting from these divisions are therefore haploid.

A somewhat different way in distributing the four chromatids of each bivalent during the two meiotic divisions has been described in some insects with diffuse kinetochore. It was discussed by Ris ('42), Oksala ('43) and Hughes-Schrader ('48).

AMITOSIS

According to Remak the nucleus divides by simple constriction. After the discovery of mitosis many cytologists continued to believe that such direct division, or "amitosis" as Flemming called it, was an alternate method for nuclear and cell reproduction. With the establishment of the chromosome theory of inheritance it became very improbable that cells could proliferate by amitosis. A critical study of most cases of amitosis disclosed that they were either modified or abnormal mitoses (pseudo-amitoses, cf. Politzer, '34) or based on faulty observations. There remained, however, a number of observations of constriction and fragmentation of nuclei into two or more parts, especially in certain highly specialized tissues that no longer divide mitotically. Only very rarely is nuclear fragmentation followed by division of the cytoplasm (Schrader, '45), and then there is no evidence that these cells persist or are able to multiply. Nuclear fragmentation is especially common in cells that have become polyploid through endomitosis (Heidenhain, '19) or inhibited mitosis (Pfuhl, '39; Bucher, '47). It is, however, never followed by cell division.

Direct division of the nucleus, or "amitosis," is not a method of cellular proliferation but of nuclear fragmentation, generally in polyploid cells that are no longer able to divide. As suggested already by Flemming, it appears to be related to increased physiological activity of a cell. Especially in large polyploid cells it would result in a better distribution of nuclear material throughout the cytoplasm.

The term "amitosis" is misleading, since it suggests an alternative to mitosis. Reproduction of cells can take place only through mitosis. Reproduction of nuclear material within a cell may occur through mitosis or endomitosis. The endomitotically enlarged nucleus may remain single or break up into two or more fragments. I would suggest that this process be called "nuclear fragmentation" and that the term "amitosis" be eliminated.

REFERENCES

Abercrombie, M., and Harkness, R. D. 1951 The growth of cell population and the properties in tissue culture of regenerating liver of the rat. Proc. Roy. Soc. London. *B138*:544–561.

Annau, E., Manginelli, A., and Roth, A. 1951 Increased weight and mitotic activity in the liver of tumor bearing rats and mice. Cancer Res., *11*: 304–306.

Auerbach, E., and Doljanski, L. 1945 Effect of cell growth activating tissue extracts, parenterally applied, on experimental skin wounds. Proc. Soc. Exp. Biol. & Med., *58*:111–114.

Bairati, A., and Lehmann, F. E. 1952 Ueber die submikroskopische Struktur der Kernmembran bei *Amoeba proteus*. Experientia, 8:60–61.

Baker, J. 1951 Remarks on the discovery of cell-division. Isis, *42*:285–287.

Barber, H. N. 1939 The rate of movement of chromosomes on the spindle. Chromosoma, *1*:33–50.

Barron, E. S. G. 1951 Thiol groups of biological importance. Advances Enzymol., *11*:201–266.

Bataillon, E., and Tchou Su 1930 Etudes analytiques et experimentales sur les rythmes cinétiques dans l'oeuf. Arch. de Biol., *40*:441–540.

Battaglia, B., and Omodeo, P. 1949 Ricerche istochimiche sugli acidi nucleinici nella spermatogenesi dei Lumbricidi. Caryologia, 2:1–12.

Bauch, R. 1947 Trypaflavin als Typus der Chromosomengifte. Naturwiss., *34*:346–347.

Beams, H. W., Evans, T. C., Baker, W. W., and van Breemen, V. 1950a Electron micrographs of the amphiaster in the whitefish blastula (*Coregonus cluperformis*). Anat. Rec., *107*:329–346.

——, Evans, T. C., van Breemen, V., and Baker, W. W. 1950b Electron microscope studies on structure of mitotic figure. Proc. Soc. Exp. Biol. & Med., *74*:717–720.

——, and King, R. L. 1936 The effect of ultracentrifuging upon chick embryonic cells, with special reference to the "resting" nucleus and the mitotic spindle. Biol. Bull., *71*:188–198.

——, and King, R. L. 1942 The origin of binucleate and large mononucleate cells in the liver of the rat. Anat. Rec., *83*:281–297.

Beatty, R. A. 1951 Effects of chloracetophenone and di-isopropylfluorophosphonate on amphibian eggs. Proc. Roy. Soc. London, *B138*:575–599.

Bělař, K. 1929 Beiträge zur Kausalanalyse der Mitose. II. Roux' Arch. Entw.-mech., *118*:359–484.

Bělař, K., and Huth, W. 1933 Zur Teilungsautonomie der Chromosomen. Z. Zellf., *17:*51–66.

Berger, C. A. 1938 Multiplication and reduction of somatic chromosome groups as a regular developmental process in the mosquito, *Culex pipiens.* Contrib. to Embryol. No. 167, Carnegie Institution of Washington, pp. 211–232.

Bernal, J. D. 1940 Structural units in cellular physiology; in the Cell and Protoplasm, edited by F. R. Moulton. AAAS Pub. No. 14, Washington, D. C., pp. 199–205.

Berrill, N. J., and Huskins, C. L. 1936 The "resting" nucleus. Am. Nat., *70:*257–260.

Biesele, J. J. 1946 The size of somatic chromosomes at different ages in the rat. J. Gerontol., *1:* 433–440.

———— 1947 Chromosomes in lymphatic leukemia of C58 mice. Cancer Res., *7:*70–77.

———— 1949 Phosphatases of the mitotic apparatus in cultured normal and malignant mouse cells; in Proceedings of the First National Cancer Conference, pp. 34–41. American Cancer Society, Washington, D. C.

Blumenthal, H. T. 1950 The nature of cycle variations in mitotic activity: the relation of alimentation and nutrition to this phenomenon. Growth, *14:*231–249.

Bodenstein, D., and Kondritzer, A. A. 1948 The effect of nitrogen mustard on nucleic acids during embryonic amphibian development. J. Exp. Zool., *107:*109–121.

Borgert, A.,1900 Untersuchungen über die Fortpflanzung der tripyleen Radiolarien, speziell von *Aulacantha scolymantha,* H. Zool. Jahrb., Anatomie, *14:*203–276.

Brachet, J. 1942 La localization des acides pentosenucléiques dans les tissus animaux et les oeufs d'amphibiens en voie de développement. Arch. de Biol., *53:*207–257.

———— 1950a Chemical Embryology. Interscience Publishers, New York.

———— 1950b Une étude cytochimique des fragments nucléés et énucléés d'amibes. Experientia, *6:*294–295.

————, and Shaver, J. R. 1950 The injection of embryonic microsomes into early amphibian embryos. Experientia, *5:*204–205.

Briggs, R., Green, E. U., and King, T. S. 1951 An investigation of the capacity for cleavage and differentiation in *Rana pipiens* eggs lacking "functional" chromosomes. J. Exp. Zool., *116:* 455–500.

Bucher, O. 1947 Division nucléaire amitotique dans des cultures de fibrocytes après administration de colchicine. Acta Anat., *4:*60–67.

Bullough, W. S. 1952 Energy relations of mitotic activity. Biol. Rev., *27:*133–168.

————, and van Oordt, G. J. 1950 The mitogenic actions of testosterone propionate and of oestrone on the epidermis of the adult male mouse. Acta Endocrin., *4:*291–305.

Callan, H. G. 1949 Cleavage rate, oxygen consumption and ribose nucleic acid content of seaurchin eggs. Biochim. Biophys. Acta, *3:*92–102.

————, and Tomlin, S. G. 1950 Experimental studies on amphibian oocyte nuclei. I. Investigation of the structure of the nuclear membrane by means of the electron microscope. Proc. Roy. Soc. London, *B137:*367–378.

Carlson, J. G. 1938 Mitotic behavior of induced chromosomal fragments lacking spindle attachments in the neuroblasts of the grasshopper. Proc. Nat. Acad. Sci., *24:*500–507.

———— 1946 Protoplasmic viscosity changes in different regions of the grasshopper neuroblast during mitosis. Biol. Bull., *90:*109–121.

———— 1952 Microdissection studies of the dividing neuroblast of the grasshopper, *Chortophaga viridifasciata* (de Geer). Chromosoma, *5:*199–220.

————, and Hollaender, A. 1948 Mitotic effects of ultraviolet radiation of the 2250 A region with special reference to the spindle and cleavage. J. Cell. Comp. Physiol., *31:*149–174.

Carrel, A. 1922 Growth promoting function of leucocytes. J. Exp. Med., *36:*395–392.

Caspersson, T. 1939 Ueber die Rolle der Desoxyribosenukleinsäure bei der Zellteilung. Chromosoma, *1:*147–156.

———— 1940 Ueber Eiweiss-stoffe im Chromosomengerüst. Naturwiss., *28:*514–515.

Chambers, R. 1917 Microdissection studies, II. J. Exp. Zool., *23:*483–505.

———— 1924 The physical structure of protoplasm as determined by microdissection and injection; in General Cytology, edited by E. V. Cowdry. University of Chicago Press, Chicago, pp. 269–276.

———— 1938 Structural and kinetic aspects of cell division. J. Cell. Comp. Physiol., *12:*149–165.

Chen, C. L., and Pai, S. 1949 Furchungsgeschwindigkeit und Furchungsrhythmus bei *Brachionus pala* und *Polyarthra platyptera.* Exp. Cell Res., Suppl., *1:*540–541.

Chickering, A. M. 1927 Spermatogenesis in the Belastomatidae, II. J. Morph., *44:*541–607.

Churney, L. 1936 The quantitative determination of mitotic elongation. Biol. Bull., *70:*400–407.

Commandon, J., and de Fonbrune, P. 1942 Influence des stades évolutifs du cytoplasme et du noyau greffé d'Amoeba sphaeronucléus sur leurs volumes respectifs et sur le déclenchement de la caryocinèse. Compt. rend. Soc. Biol., *136:*763–764.

Conklin, E. G. 1912 Cell size and nuclear size. J. Exp. Zool., *12:*1–98.

———— 1917 Effects of centrifugal force on the structure and development of the egg of Crepidula. J. Exp. Zool., *22:*311–420.

Cooper, K. W. 1939 The nuclear cytology of the grass mite, *Pediculopsis graminum* (Reut.) with special reference to karyomerokinesis. Chromosoma, *1:*51–103.

———— 1941 Visibility of the primary spindle fibers and the course of mitosis in the living blastomeres of the mite, *Pediculopsis graminum,* Reut. Proc. Nat. Acad. Sci., *27:*480–483.

Cornman, I. 1943 Acceleration of cleavage of Arbacia eggs by hypotonic sea water. Biol. Bull., *84:*244–251.

———— 1944 A summary of evidence in favor of the traction fiber in mitosis. Am. Nat., *78:*410–422.

Cornman, I., and Cornman, M. E. 1951 The action of podophyllin and its fractions on marine eggs. Ann. N.Y. Acad. Sci., 51:1443–1488.

Dan, J. K. 1948 On the mechanism of astral cleavage. Physiol. Zool., 21:191–218.

Darlington, D. C. 1942 Chromosome chemistry and gene action. Nature, 149:66–69.

Davidson, J. N. 1950 Biochemistry of Nucleic Acids. Methuen & Co., London.

Davies, H. G. 1952 The ultra-violet absorption of living chick fibroblasts during mitosis. Exp. Cell. Res., 3:453–461.

Dawson, A. B. 1940 Cell division in relation to differentiation. Growth Suppl., 2:91–106.

DeLamater, E. D., and Mudd, S. 1951 The occurrence of mitosis in the vegetative phase of Bacillus megatherium. Exp. Cell. Res., 2:499–512.

Delbrück, M. 1941 A theory of autocatalytic synthesis of polypeptides and its application to the problem of chromosome reproduction. Cold Spring Harbor Symp. Quant. Biol., 9:122–126.

DuBois, A. M. 1933 Chromosome behavior during cleavage in the egg of Sciara coprophila (Diptera) in relation to the problem of sex determination. Z. Zellf., 19:595–614.

Ephrussi, B. 1951 Remarks on cell heredity; in Genetics in the 20th Century, edited by L. C. Dunn. The Macmillan Co., New York, pp. 241–262.

Erdmann, R. 1908 Experimentelle Untersuchungen über Massenverhältnisse von Plasma, Kern und Chromosomen in dem sich entwickelnden Seeigelei. Arch. f. Zellf., 2:76–136.

Fankhauser, G. 1934 Cytological studies on egg fragments of Triton. IV. J. Exp. Zool., 67:349–395.

Fell, H. B., and Hughes, A. F. 1949 Mitosis in the mouse: a study of living and fixed cells in tissue culture. Quart. J. Micr. Sci., 90:355–380.

Ferry, J. D. 1948 Protein gels. Advances Protein Chem., 4:2–79.

Fischer, A. 1946 Biology of Tissue Cells. Cambridge University Press, Cambridge, England.

Friedenwald, J. S. 1950 Recent studies on corneal metabolism and growth: a review. Cancer Res., 10:461–466.

——— 1951 The action of nitrogen mustards and related substances on cell division. Ann. N. Y. Acad. Sci., 51:1432–1442.

———, and Sigelman, S. 1953 The influence of ionizing radiation on mitotic activity in the rat's corneal epithelium. Exp. Cell. Res., 4:1–31.

Friedrich-Freksa, H. 1940 Bei der Chromosomenkonjugation wirksame Kräfte und ihre Bedeutung für die identische Verdoppelung von Nucleoproteinen. Naturwiss., 28:376–379.

Gaulden, M. E., and Carlson, J. G. 1951 Cytological effects of colchicine on the grasshopper neuroblast in vitro with special reference to the origin of the spindle. Exp. Cell. Res., 2:416–433.

Geitler, L. 1938 Chromosomenbau. Protoplasmamonographien No. 14.

——— 1941 Das Wachstum des Zellkerns in tierischen und pflanzlichen Geweben. Erg. Biol., 18:1–54.

——— 1948 Ergebnisse und Probleme der Endomitoseforschung. Oesterr. Bot. Zeitschr., 95:277–299.

Gillette, R., and Bodenstein, D. 1946 Specific developmental inhibitions produced in amphibian embryos by a nitrogen mustard compound. J. Exp. Zool., 103:1–32.

Goldthwait, D. A. 1952 Effect of nitrogen mustard on nucleic acid metabolism. Proc. Soc. Exp. Biol. & Med., 80:503–504.

Gray, J. 1927a The mechanism of cell-division, IV. The effect of gravity on the eggs of Echinus. Brit. J. Exp. Biol., 5:102–111.

——— 1927b The mechanism of cell division, III. The relationship between cell division and growth in segmenting eggs. Brit. J. Exp. Biol., 4:313–321.

Grell, S. M. 1946 Cytological studies in Culex. I. Somatic reduction divisions. Genetics, 31:60–76.

Gross, F. 1935 Die Reifungs-und Furchungsteilungen von Artemia salina im Zusamenhang mit dem Problem des Kernteilungsmechanismus. Z. Zellf., 23:522–566.

Hance, R. T. 1926 A comparison of mitosis in chick tissue cultures and in sectioned embryos. Biol. Bull., 50:155–159.

Harris, P., and James, T. W. 1952 Electron microscope study of the nuclear membrane of Amoeba proteus in thin sections. Experientia, 8:384–385.

Hartmann, M. 1926 Ueber experimentelle Unsterblichkeit von Protozoen Individuen. Naturwiss., 14:433–435.

——— 1933 Allgemeine Biologie. Springer, Berlin.

Harvey, E. B. 1935 The mitotic figure and cleavage plane in the egg of Parechinus microtuberculatus as influenced by centrifugal force. Biol. Bull., 69:287–297.

——— 1936 Parthenogenetic merogony or cleavage without nuclei in Arbacia punctata. Biol. Bull., 71:10–121.

Hayashi, T. 1952 Contractile properties of compressed monolayers of actomyosin. J. Gen. Physiol., 36:139–152.

Heidenhain, M. 1919 Über die Noniusfelder der Muskelfaser. Anatom. Hefte, 56:321–402.

Heilbrunn, L. V. 1952a An Outline of General Physiology, 3d ed. W. B. Saunders Co., Philadelphia.

——— 1952b The physiology of cell division; in Modern Trends in Physiology and Biochemistry, edited by E. S. G. Barron. Academic Press, New York.

Helweg-Larsen, H. F. 1952 Nuclear class series. Contr. Univ. Institute f. Human Genetics, Copenhagen, 27:1–139.

Henke, K. 1947 Einfache Grundvorgänge in der tierischen Entwicklung. Naturwiss., 34:149–157, 1947.

———, and Pohley, H. J. 1952 Differentielle Zellteilungen und Polyploidie der Schuppenbildung der Mehlmotte Ephestia kühniella Z. A.f. Naturforsch., 7b:65–79.

Hertwig, R. 1903 Ueber Korrelation von Zell und Kerngrösse und ihre Bedeutung für die geschlechtliche Differenzierung und die Teilung der Zelle. Biol. Centralbl., *23:*49–62.

Hevesy, G. 1948 Nucleic acid metabolism; in Advances Biol. Med. Physics, *1:*409–454.

Hoffman, J. G. 1949 Theory of the mitotic index and its application to tissue growth measurement. Bull. math. Biophys., *11:*139–144.

Howard, A., and Pelc, S. R. 1951a Nuclear incorporation of P[32] as demonstrated by autoradiographs. Exp. Cell. Res., *2:*178–187.

———, and Pelc, S. R. 1951b Synthesis of nucleoprotein in bean root cells. Nature, *167:*599–600.

Huettner, A. F. 1933 Continuity of the centrioles in *Drosophila melanogaster.* Z. Zellf., *19:*119–134

Hughes, A. F. W. 1949 The effect of iodoacetamide upon cell division in tissue cultures on the chick embryo. J. Roy. Micr. Soc., *69:*215–224.

——— 1950 The effect of inhibitor substances on cell division. Quart. J. Micr. Sci., *91:*251–278.

——— 1952 The Mitotic Cycle. Academic Press, New York.

———, and Preston, M. M. E. 1949 Mitosis in living cell of amphibian tissue cultures. J. Roy. Micr. Soc., *69:*121–131.

———, and Swann, M. M. 1948 Anaphase movements in the living cell. J. Exp. Biol., *25:* 45–70.

Hughes-Schrader, S. 1924 Reproduction in Acroschismus. J. Morph. *39:*157–207, 1924.

——— 1931 A study of the chromosome cycle and the meiotic-division figure in *Llaveia bouvari* —a primitive coccid. Z. Zellf., *13:*742–769.

——— 1943a Polarization, kinetochore movements, and bivalent structure in the meiotic chromosomes of male mantids. Biol. Bull., *85:*265–300.

——— 1943b Meiosis without chiasmata—in diploid and tetrapoid spermatocytes of the mantid *Callimantis antillarum* Saussure. J. Morph., *73:* 111–140.

——— 1948 Cytology of coccids. Advances Genetics, *2:*127–203.

———, and Ris, H. 1941 The diffuse spindle attachment of coccids, verified by the mitotic behavior of induced chromosome fragments. J. Exp. Zool., *87:*429–451.

Huskins, C. L. 1947 The subdivision of the chromosomes and their multiplication in nondividing tissues: possible interpretations in terms of gene structure and gene action. Am. Nat., *81:*401–434.

Inoué, S. 1952 The effect of colchicine on the microscopic and submicroscopic structure of the mitotic spindle. Exp. Cell. Res. Suppl., *2:*305–314.

———, and Dan, K. 1951 Birefringence of the dividing cell. J. Morph., *89:*423–456.

Jacobson, W. 1951 Biology of mitosis; in Transactions of the 13th Conference on Problems of Ageing, edited by N. W. Shock. Josiah Macy, Jr. Foundation, New York.

———, and Webb, M. 1952 The two types of nucleoproteins during mitosis. Exp. Cell. Res., *3:* 163–183.

Jacoby, F. 1949 A quantitative analysis of the growth of pure populations of fowl macrophages in vitro. Exp. Cell. Res. Suppl., *1:*454–455.

———, Trowell, O. A., and Willmer, E. N. 1937 Studies on the growth of tissues in vitro. J. Exp. Biol., *14:*255–266.

Jörgensen, M. 1913 Zellenstudien II. Die Ei- und Nährzellen von Piscicola. Arch. Zellf., *10:* 127–160.

Johnson, H. H. 1931 Centrioles and other cytoplasmic components of the male germ cells of the Gryllidae. Z. wiss. Zool., *140:*115–166.

Kaufmann, B. P. 1948 Chromosome structure in relation to the chromosome cycle. Bot. Rev., *14,* 57–126.

———, McDonald, M., and Gay, H. 1948 Enzymatic degradation of ribonucleoproteins of chromosomes, nucleoli and cytoplasm. Nature, *162:*814.

Knowlton, N. P., and Widner, W. R. 1950 The use of x-rays to determine the mitotic and intermitotic time of various mouse tissues. Cancer Res., *10:*59–63.

Kornfeld, W. 1922 Ueber den Zellteilungsrhythmus und seine Regelung. Roux' Arch. Entw.-mech., *50:*526–592.

Krahl, M. E. 1950 Metabolic activities and cleavage of eggs of the sea-urchin, *Arbacia punctulata.* Biol. Bull., *98:*175–217.

Kupka, E., and Seelich, F. 1948 Die anaphasische Chromosomenbewegung. Chromosoma, *3:*302–327.

Lasfargues, E., and Delaunay, A. 1949 Sur les trephones d'origine microbienne. Exp. Cell. Res. Suppl., *1:*452–453.

Lehmann, F. E. 1951 Der Kernapparat tierischer Zellen und seine Erforschung mit Hilfe von Antimitotica. Schweiz. Zeitschr. f. Allg. Path. Bakt., *14:*487–508.

Lettré, H. 1951 Zellstoffwechsel und Zellteilung. Naturwiss., *38:*490–496.

——— 1952 Some investigations on cell behavior under various conditions: a review. Cancer Res., *12:*847–860.

Levan, A. 1938 The effect of colchicine on root mitosis in Allium. Hereditas, *24:*471–486.

Lewis, M. R. 1923 Reversible gelation in living cells. Bull. Johns Hopkins Hosp., *34:*373–379.

——— 1934 Reversible solation of the mitotic spindle of living chick embryo cells studied in vitro. Arch. Exp. Zellf., *16:*159–160.

Lewis, W. H. 1920 Giant centrospheres in degenerating mesenchyme cells of tissue cultures. J. Exp. Med., *31:*275–292.

——— 1947 Interphase (resting) nuclei, chromosomal vesicles and amitosis. Anat. Rec., *97:* 433–446.

——— 1951 Cell division with special reference to cells in tissue culture. Ann. N. Y. Acad. Sci., *51:*1287–1294.

Liebman, E. 1947 The trephocytes and their function. Experientia, *3:*442–451.

Likely, G. D., Sanford, K. K., and Earle, W. R. 1952 Further studies on the proliferation in vitro of single isolated tissue cells. J. Nat. Cancer Inst., *13:*177–184.

Lillie, F. R. 1912 Studies of fertilization in Nereis. J. Exp. Zool., *12:*413–476.

Lima-de-Faria, A.   1949   The structure of the centromere of the chromosomes of rye. Hereditas, *35:* 77–85.

——— 1950   The Feulgen test applied to centromeric chromosomes. Hereditas, *36:*60–74.

Loveless, A., and Revell, S.   1949   New evidence on the mode of action of "mitotic poisons." Nature, *164:*938–944.

Ludford, R. J.   1925   The general and experimental cytology of cancer. J. Roy. Micro. Soc., *45:*249–292.

Lwoff, A.   1950   Problems of Morphogenesis in Ciliates. John Wiley & Sons, New York.

———, and Dusi, H.   1935   La suppression expérimentale des chloroplastes chez *Euglena mesnili*. Compt. rend. Soc. Biol., *119:*1092–1095.

Malheiros, N., de Castro, D., and Câmara, A.   1947   Chromosomas sem centromero localizado. O case da *Luzula purpurea* Link. Agron. Lusitana, *9:* 51–71.

Manton, I.   1950   The spiral structure of chromosomes. Biol. Rev., *25:*486–508.

Marquardt, H.   1941   Untersuchungen über den Formwechsel der Chromosomen im generativen Kern des Pollens und Pollenschlauchs von Allium und Lilium. Planta, *31:*670–725.

Marsland, D.   1951   The action of hydrostatic pressure on cell division. Ann. N. Y. Acad. Sci., *51:*1327–1335.

Matsuura, H.   1941   The structure and behavior of the kinetochore. Cytologia, *11:*369-379.

Mazia, D.   1952   Physiology of the cell nucleus; in Modern Trends in Physiology and Biochemistry, edited by E. S. G. Barron. Academic Press, New York.

———, and Dan, K.   1952   The isolation and biochemical characterization of the mitotic apparatus of dividing cells. Proc. Nat. Acad. Sci., *38:*826–838.

———, and Hirshfield, H. I.   1950   The nucleus-dependence of P^{32} uptake by the cell. Science, *112:*297–299.

McClintock, B.   1932   A correlation of ring-shaped chromosomes with variegation in *Zea mays*. Proc. Nat. Acad. Sci., *18:*677–681.

Meier, R., and Allgöwer, M.   1945   Zur Characterisierung zellteilungswirksamer Substanzen an der Gewebekultur. Experientia, *1:*57–61.

Metz, C. W.   1933   Monocentric mitosis with segregation of chromosomes in Sciara and its bearing on the mechanism of mitosis. Biol. Bull., *64:* 333–347.

Michel, K.   1950   Das Phasenkontrastverfahren und seine Eignung für zytologische Untersuchungen. Naturwiss., *37:*52–57.

Mirsky, A. E.   1951   Some chemical aspects of the cell nucleus; in Genetics in the 20th Century, edited by L. C. Dunn. The Macmillan Co., New York, pp. 127–154.

———, and Ris, H.   1947   The chemical composition of isolated Chromosomes. J. Gen. Physiol., *31:*7–18.

———, and Ris, H.   1949   Variable and constant components of chromosomes. Nature, *163:*666–667.

———, and Ris, H.   1951   The desoxyribonucleic acid content of animal cells and its evolutionary significance. J. Gen. Physiol., *34:*451–462.

Moellendorff, V. W.   1938   Ueber regulierbare Einwirkungen auf die Zahl und den Ablauf der Mitosen. Arch. Exp. Zellf., *21:*1–66.

Moenkhaus, W. J.   1904   The development of the hybrids between *Fundulus heteroclitus* and *Menidia notata* with especial reference to the behavior of the maternal and paternal chromatin. Am. J. Anat., *3:*29–65.

Monné, L.   1942   Ueber die Doppelbrechung der Kernhüllen. Ark. f. Zool., *34B*, No. 2:1–81.

———, and Slautterback, D. B.   1950   Differential staining of various polysaccharides in sea-urchin eggs. Exp. Cell. Res., *1:*477–491.

Monroy, A., and Montalenti, G.   1947   Variations of the submicroscopic structure of the cortical layers of fertilized and parthenogenetic sea-urchin eggs. Biol. Bull., *92:*151–160.

Montalenti, G., Vitagliano, G., and de Nicola, M.   1950   The supply of ribonucleic acid to the male germ cells during meiosis in *Asellus aquaticus*. Heredity, *4:*75–87.

Moore, A. R.   1933   Is cleavage rate a function of the cytoplasm or of the nucleus? J. Exp. Biol., *10:* 230–236.

——— 1938   Segregation of "cleavage substance" in the unfertilized egg of *Dendraster excentricus*. Proc. Soc. Exp. Biol. & Med., *38:*162–163.

Mühldorff, A.   1951   Die Zellteilung als Plasmateilung. Springer, Berlin.

Müntzing, A.   1944   Cytological studies of extra fragment chromosomes in rye. I. Iso-fragments produced by misdivision. Hereditas, *30:*231-248.

Norris, E. R., and Majnarich, J. J.   1949   Vitamin B_{14} and cell proliferation. Science, *109:*32–33.

Nussbaum, M.   1902   Ueber Kern-und Zellteilung. Arch. Mikrosk. Anat., *57:*637–684.

Östergren, G.   1944   Colchicine mitosis, chromosome contraction, narcosis and protein chain folding. Hereditas, *30:*429–467.

——— 1949   Luzula and the mechanism of chromosome movements. Hereditas, *35:*445–468.

——— 1951   The mechanism of co-orientation in bivalents and multivalents. Hereditas, *37:*85–156.

Ogawa, K.   1949   Chromosome studies in the Myriapoda. Report 1. The chromosomes of *Thereuonema hilgendorfi* Verhoeff (Chilopoda), with special regard to the post-reductional separation of the sex chromosomes. Jap. J. Genet., *25:*106–111.

Oksala, T.   1943   Zytologische Studien an Odonaten. Ann. Acad. Scient. Fenn., *4*(ser. A. IV):1–64, 1943.

Olivo, O. M., and Delorenzi, E.   1933   Ricerchi sulla velocita di accrescimento delle cellule e degli organi. Arch. Exp. Zellf., *13:*221–257.

———, and Slavich, E.   1930   Ricerche sulla velocita dell'accrescimento delle cellule e degli organi. Roux' Arch. f. Entw-mech., *121:*96–110, 408–429.

Ornstein, L.   1952   The distributional error in microspectrophotometry. Labor. Invest., *1:*250–262.

Orsini, M. W., and Pansky, B. 1952 The natural resistance of the golden hamster to colchicine. Science, 115:88–89.

Pätau, K. 1952 Absorption microphotometry of irregular-shaped objects. Chromosoma, 5:341–362.

——, and Swift, H. 1953 The DNA content (Feulgen) of nuclei during mitosis in a root tip of onion. Chromosoma, 6:149-169.

Painter, T. 1918 Contributions to the study of cell mechanics, II. J. Exp. Zool., 24:445–498.

Pease, D. C. 1941 Hydrostatic pressure effects upon the spindle figure and chromosome movement, I. J. Morph., 69:405–434.

—— 1946 Hydrostatic pressure effects upon the spindle figure and chromosome movement, II. Biol. Bull., 91:145–169.

Peter, K. 1940 Die indirecte Teilung der Zelle in ihren Beziehungen zu Tätigkeit, Differenzierung und Wachstum. Z. f. Zellf., 30:721–750.

Petering, H. G. 1952 Folic acid antagonists. Physiol. Rev., 32:197-213.

Peters, J. J. 1946 A cytological study of mitosis in the cornea of Triturus viridescens during recovery after colchicine treatment. J. Exp. Zool., 103:33–60.

Pfuhl, W. 1939 Die mitotischen Teilungen der Leberzellen im Zusammenhang mit den allgemeinen Fragen über Mitose und Amitose. Z. f. Anat., 109:99–133.

Pincus, G. 1939 The comparative behavior of mammalian eggs in vivo and in vitro, IV. J. Exp. Zool., 82:85–130.

Politzer, G. 1934 Pathologie der Mitose. Protoplasma-monographien, vol. 7. Borntraeger, Berlin.

Pollister, A. W. 1933 Notes on the centrioles of amphibian tissue cells. Biol. Bull., 65:529–545.

—— 1941 Mitochondrial orientations and molecular patterns. Physiol. Zool., 14:268-279.

—— 1951 Nucleoproteins of the nucleus. Exp. Cell. Res. Suppl., 2:59–70.

——, and Ris, H. 1947 Nucleoprotein determination in cytological preparations. Cold Spring Harbor Symp. Quant. Biol., 12:147–157.

Pomerat, C. M., and Willmer, E. N. 1939 Studies on the growth of tissues in vitro. J. Exp. Biol., 16:232–249.

Porter, K. 1942 Developmental variations resulting from various associations of frog cytoplasms and nuclei. Trans. N. Y. Acad. Sci., 4, ser. II:213–217.

Potter, V., Price, J. M., Miller, E. C., and Miller, J. A. 1950 Studies on the intracellular composition of livers from rats fed various aminoazo dyes. Cancer Res., 10:28–35.

Price, J. M., and Laird, A. K. 1950 A comparison of the intracellular composition of regenerating liver and induced liver tumors. Cancer Res., 10:650-658.

Rabinowitz, M. 1941 Studies on the cytology and early embryology of the egg of Drosophila melanogaster. J. Morph., 69:1–50.

Reitberger, A. 1940 Die Cytologie des pädogenetischen Entwicklungszyklus der Gallmücke Oligarces paradoxus Mem. Chromosoma, 1:391–473.

Renyi, G. 1942 Untersuchungen über Flimmerzellen. Z. f. Anat., 73:338–357.

Reverberi, G. 1940 Lo sviluppo dei frammenti dell'uove centrifugato delle Ascidie. Publ. Staz. Zool. Napoli, 18:129–139.

Rhoades, M. M. 1940 Studies of a telocentric chromosome in maize with reference to the stability of its centromere. Genetics, 25:483–521.

—— 1952 Preferential segregation in maize; in Heterosis, edited by J. W. Gowan. Iowa State College Press, Ames, Iowa, pp. 66–80.

——, and Kerr, W. E. 1949 A note on centromere organization. Proc. Nat. Acad. Sci., 35:129–132.

Ris, H. 1942 A cytological and experimental analysis of the meiotic behavior of the univalent X chromosome in the bearberry aphid Tamalia (=Phyllaphis) coweni (Ckll.) J. Exp. Zool., 90:267-330.

—— 1943 A quantitative study of anaphase movement in the aphid Tamalia. Biol. Bull., 85:164–178.

—— 1949 The anaphase movement of chromosomes in the spermatocytes of the grasshopper. Biol. Bull., 96:90–106.

—— 1952 The sub-microscopic structure of chromosomes. Genetics, 37:619.

——, and Kleinfeld, R. 1952 Cytochemical studies on the chromatin elimination in Solenobia (Lepidoptera). Chromosoma, 5:363–371.

——, and Mirsky, A. E. 1949 The state of the chromosomes in the interphase nucleus. J. Gen. Physiol., 32:489–502.

Rosza, G., and Wyckoff, R. W. G. 1951 The electron microscopy of onion root tip cells. Exp. Cell. Res., 2:630–641.

Schechtman, A. M. 1937 Localized cortical growth as the immediate cause of cell division. Science, 85:222–223.

Schmidt, W. J. 1939 Ueber Doppelbrechung und Feinbau der Kernmembran. Protoplasma, 32:193–198.

—— 1939 Doppelbrechung der Kernspindel und Zugfasertheorie der Chromosomenbewegung. Chromosoma, 1:253–264.

Schrader, F. 1929 Experimental and cytological investigations of the life-cycle of Gossyparia spuria (Coccidae) and their bearing on the problem of haploidy in males. Z. wiss. Zool., 134:149–179.

—— 1939 The structure of the kinetochore at meiosis. Chromosoma, 1:230–237.

—— 1945 The cytology of regular heteroploidy in the genus Loxa (Pentatomidae, Hemiptera). J. Morph., 76:157–175.

—— 1947 Data contributing to an analysis of metaphase mechanics. Chromosoma, 3:22–47.

—— 1953 Mitosis, 2nd ed. Columbia University Press, New York.

Schultz, J. 1941 The evidence of the nucleoprotein nature of the gene. Cold Spring Harbor Symp. Quant. Biol., 9:55–65.

Scott, A. C. 1936 Haploidy and aberrant spermatogenesis in a coleopteran, Micromalthus debilis, Le Conte. J. Morph., 59:485–515.

—— 1946 The effect of low temperature and

of hypotonicity of the morphology of the cleavage furrow in Arbacia eggs. Biol. Bull., *91:*272–287.

Scott, G. H. 1943 Mineral distribution in the cytoplasm. Biol. Symp., *10:*277–290.

Sedar, A. W., and Wilson, D. F. 1951 Electron microscope studies on the normal and colchicinized mitotic figure of the onion root tip (*Allium cepa*). Biol. Bull., *100:*107–115.

Seiler, J. 1914 Das Verhalten der Geschlechtschromosomen bei Lepidopteren. Arch. Zellf., *13:*159–269.

Serra, J. A. 1947 Composition of chromonemata and matrix and the role of nucleoproteins in mitosis and meiosis. Cold Spring Harbor Symp. Quant. Biol., *12:*192–210.

Shaver, J. R. 1953 Studies on the initiation of cleavage in the frog egg. J. Exp. Zool., *122:*169–192.

Shimamura, T. 1940 Studies on the effect of the centrifugal force upon nuclear division. Cytologia, *11:*186–216.

Skipper, H. E., and Mitchell, J. 1951 Effect of roentgen-ray radiation on the synthesis of nucleic acids and nucleic acid purines, Cancer, *4:*363–366.

Sonneborn, T. 1946 Experimental control of the concentration of cytoplasmic genetic factors in Paramecium. Cold Spring Harbor Symp. Quant. Biol., *11:*236–266.

Sparrow, A. H. 1942 The structure and development of the chromosome spirals in microspores of Trillium. Canad. J. Res., *20:*257–266.

Spiegelman, S., Delorenzo, W. F., and Campbell, A. M. 1951 A single cell analysis of the transmission of enzyme-forming capacity in yeast. Proc. Nat. Acad. Sci., *37:*513–524.

Stedman, E., and Stedman, E. 1943 Chromosomin, a protein constituent of chromosomes. Nature, *152:*267–269.

Stich, H. 1951a Das Vorkomen von Ribonukleinsäure im Kernsaft und Spindel sich teilender Kerne von *Cyclops strenuus*. Z. f. Naturf., *6b:*259–261.

—— 1951b Das Vorkommen von Kohlehydraten im Ruhekern und während der Mitose. Chromosoma, *4:*429–438.

Suomalainen, E. 1953 The kinetochore and bivalent structure in the Lepidoptera. Hereditas, *39:*88–96.

Swann, M. M. 1951a Protoplasmic structure and mitosis, I. J. Exp. Biol., *28:*417–433.

—— 1951b Protoplasmic structure and mitosis, II. J Exp. Biol., *28:*434–444.

—— 1952 The spindle; in The Mitotic Cycle, by A. Hughes. Academic Press, New York.

Swanson, C. P. 1943 The behavior of meiotic prophase chromosome as revealed through the use of high temperatures. Am. J. Bot., *30:*422–428.

Swift, H. 1953 Quantitative aspects of nuclear nucleoproteins. Internat. Rev. Cytol., *2:*1-76.

——, and Kleinfeld, R. 1953 DNA in grasshopper spermatogenesis, oogenesis, and cleavage. Physiol. Zool., *26:*301-311.

Tahmisian, T. N. 1951 Mechanics of cell division, I. Proc. Soc. Exp. Biol. & Med., *78:*444–447.

Tier, H. 1944 Ueber Zellteilung und Kernklassenbildung in der glandula orbitalis externa der Ratte. Acta Path. microbiol. Scand. Suppl., *51:*1–185.

—— 1952 Observations on the chemical and biological properties of the mitosis stimulating agent in homologous tissue extracts. Growth, *16:*85–108.

Turchini, J. 1949 La détection cytochimique des constituents hydrocarbones provenant de l'hydrolyse des acid nucléiques cellulaires. Exp. Cell. Res. Suppl., *1:*105–110.

Waddington, C. H. 1952 Preliminary observations on the mechanism of cleavage in the amphibian egg. J. Exp. Biol., *29:*484–489.

Walker, P. M. B., and Yates, H. B. 1952 Ultraviolet absorption of living cell nuclei during growth and division. Symp. Soc. Exp. Biol., *6:*265–276.

Wang, L. 1952 In Textbook of Histology, 6th ed., by A. A. Maximow and W. Bloom. W. B. Saunders Co., Philadelphia, p. 2.

Weiss, P., Self-regulation of organ growth by its own products, Science *115:*487–488, 1952.

White, M. J. D. 1946 The cytology of the Cecidomyidae, II. J. Morph., *79:*323–370.

Widner, W. R., Storer, J. B., and Lushbaugh, C. C. 1951 The use of x-ray and nitrogen mustard to determine the mitotic and intermitotic times in normal and malignant rat tissues. Cancer Res., *11:*877–884.

Willmer, E. N. 1933 Studies on the growth of tissues in vitro, II. J. Exp. Biol., *10:*323–339.

Wilson, E. B. 1928 The Cell in Development and Heredity. The Macmillan Co., New York.

—— 1932 Polyploidy and metaphase patterns. J. Morph., *53:*443–471.

Wilson, W. L. 1951 The rigidity of the cell cortex during cell division. J. Cell. Comp. Physiol., *38:*409–415.

Woolley, D. W. 1953 Evidence for the synthesis of vitamin B_{12} by spontaneous tumors. Proc. Nat. Acad. Sci., *39:*6–18.

Yatsu, N. 1905 The formation of the centrosome in enucleate egg fragments. J. Exp. Zool., *2:*287–313.

Zeuthen, E. 1951 Segmentation, nuclear growth and cytoplasmic storage in eggs of echinoderms and amphibia. Publ. Staz. Zool. Napoli, Suppl. *23:*47–69.

——, and Hoff-Jørgensen, E. 1952 Evidence of cytoplasmic deoxyribosides in the frog's egg. Nature, *169:*245–246.

Section IV

THE NUCLEUS AND CYTOPLASM IN DEVELOPMENT

CHAPTER 1

The Role of Nucleus and Cytoplasm

G. FANKHAUSER

INTRODUCTION

ONE OF THE important tasks of experimental embryology is to trace the origin of the organization of the embryo back to fertilization, the earliest stage of development at which the egg becomes available for extensive experimentation. It is at this stage that the most favorable conditions obtain for an analysis of the roles played in early development by the two main components of the egg cell, the cytoplasm and nucleus, one deceptively simple in its visible structure, the other known to be highly complex and orderly in its organization. Although the first attempts to investigate this problem date back to the earliest days of developmental mechanics, our knowledge, even now, is far from complete (cf. Needham, '42, pp. 351–364). Some of the old experiments are in need of completion or re-examination with the aid of new, or at least more refined, techniques. The manifold possibilities of attack and the main results obtained thus far will be outlined briefly in this chapter.

While it is possible in any one experiment to concentrate the attack only on the nucleus or on the cytoplasm, interrelations between the two components are ever present (cf. Fankhauser, '52). The existence of complex interactions from the very beginning of development is evidenced by the study of the processes of fertilization itself and of its various experimental modifications. Witness the frequent disengagement of the nuclear and cytoplasmic (centrosomal) cycles of mitosis under experimental conditions, producing abnormal types of mitosis; the

peculiar behavior of the spermatozoa in immature eggs of echinoderms and amphibians; the inhibition of the division of the accessory sperm nuclei in the normally polyspermic eggs of salamanders and insects (cf. Fankhauser, '48); and the disturbances of the nuclear phenomena of fertilization and of mitosis in various hybrid combinations among species of echinoderms and amphibians (Fig. 36).

Even in the most drastic experiment, in which all nuclear material is removed from an egg and the developmental potentialities of the egg cytoplasm are tested in isolation, we cannot eliminate the egg cytoplasm's history. This includes the long period of development of the oocyte in the ovary during which there was intensive activity of the nucleus taking part in the elaboration of cytoplasmic materials. Although the interest has recently been focused anew on the ovarian egg (cf. Brachet, '44, '47), much descriptive and even more experimental work remains to be done.

QUANTITATIVE CHANGES IN CYTOPLASM OR NUCLEUS

CYTOPLASM

Demonstration of Early Localization of Cytoplasmic Factors of Development. Eggs of many species may be divided into two or more parts by cutting, shaking, or centrifuging, before or after fertilization. The part that contains the egg nucleus as well as a spermatozoon usually completes fertilization in normal fashion and thus begins its development with the double complement of chromosomes ("diploid merogony"). If the resulting embryo or larva shows typical abnormalities or defects, it may be concluded that certain cytoplasmic materials necessary for normal development were lacking in this particular fragment; this implies the more general conclusion that, even at fertilization,

Among vertebrates, so far, the eggs of various species of newts alone have lent themselves to fragmentation before the first cleavage, by means of constriction with a loop of fine hair (Spemann, '14, '28). In these eggs it is possible, furthermore, to have both halves of one egg develop with the

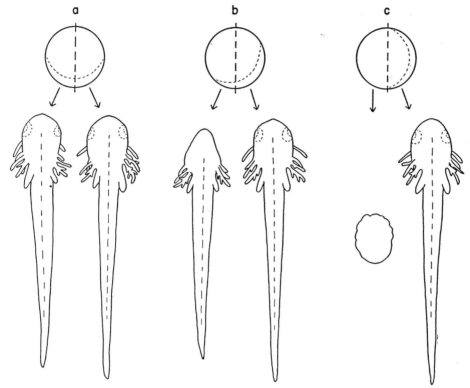

Fig. 24. Diagram to illustrate the origin of different types of twin embryos following constriction of the unsegmented egg in different planes relative to the median plane.

a, Constriction in the median plane, dividing the area of the future dorsal lip evenly. "Left" and "right" twin larvae are produced showing slight deficiencies in the development of eye, balancer, gills and forelimb bud on the "inner" side, facing the partner.

b, Constriction in an oblique plane dividing the dorsal lip area unequally. The left half, with a small lateral portion of the "organization center," develops into a microcephalic larva. The co-twin is normal.

c, Constriction in the frontal plane isolating the dorsal and ventral halves of the egg. The ventral half is unable to form axial organs but may survive for several days. The dorsal half develops normally.

certain areas of the egg cytoplasm differ from others in their organization.

The classic experiments on eggs of various marine invertebrates (see Section VI, Chapter 3) demonstrated that in many species factors necessary for the formation of embryonic or larval structures are localized early. In some cases, particularly in Cerebratulus, this localization was shown to progress during maturation and fertilization of the egg, by the steadily increasing percentage of defective larvae produced by dividing the egg at successively later stages.

normal, diploid complement of chromosomes, by constricting the egg at first partially into a dumbbell shape. Cleavage begins in the half that contains the egg as well as a sperm nucleus. However, following two or more cleavage divisions (depending on the thickness of the bridge connecting the two parts of the egg), the nucleus located nearest the bridge enters it. During telophase of the following mitosis, one of the daughter nuclei moves into the hitherto non-nucleated part and initiates a delayed but normal cleavage. Soon after this "delayed nucleation" has taken place, the cytoplasmic bridge may be severed so that the two halves of the egg will develop independently.

This experiment produces pairs of embryos or larvae of various types (Fig. 24); (1) normal twins, frequently showing slight unilateral defects of the eye, balancer, gills, and forelimb bud on the "inner" side facing the partner; (2) one normal and one microcephalic or acephalic larva; (3) one normal larva and a "ventral embryo" unable to gastrulate normally or to form any axial

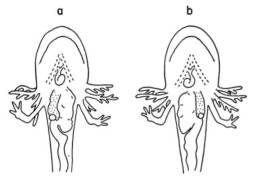

Fig. 25. Ventral view of an older pair of lateral twin larvae obtained by constriction of the egg shortly after fertilization. *a*, The "left" larva shows normal position of the aortic trunk and of stomach, liver (stippled) and gall bladder. *b*, The "right" larva exhibits complete situs inversus of the heart and viscera.

organs. These types of defective embryos correspond to those obtained by constriction of cleavage, blastula and early gastrula stages (Spemann, '01, '02; Spemann and Falkenberg, '19). Their origin may be explained by assuming that the plane of constriction, which always includes the animal-vegetal axis or runs parallel to it, may form any angle with the invisible plane of bilateral symmetry of the egg. This plane in turn is determined by an early localization of the area of the future dorsal lip of the blastopore, i.e., of the center of organization, which is instrumental in the establishment of the embryonic axis. The fate of each egg fragment would depend on what share of this important region it obtains (Fig. 24). Recent experiments of Dollander ('50) on newt eggs with visible symmetry produced more variable results, including the formation of a complete embryo from a ventral blastomere at the two-cell stage, under certain conditions.

It should be noted that it has not been possible as yet to demonstrate any progress in the localization of cytoplasmic factors of

development in the salamander egg between the time of fertilization and the beginning of the first cleavage. A series of constrictions performed from 10 to 50 minutes after insemination, before completion of the second maturation division, gave essentially the same results as a second series in which the eggs were divided between three and four hours from insemination. The future center of organization must be localized on the dorsal side of the egg shortly after fertilization. Since the gray crescent, which marks this area in the eggs of other species of amphibians, does not appear until about one and one-half hours from fertilization, this redistribution of the superficial pigment is no more than a secondary expression of a more fundamental though invisible organization of the egg which may date back to prefertilization stages (Fankhauser, '30, '48).

In addition to a definite differentiation between the dorsal and ventral sides of the egg, the newt egg also shows signs of an early establishment of the bilateral asymmetry of the vertebrate body. The "left" twin of a pair as shown in Figure 24a always has the normal situs of the heart and viscera (Fig. 25a), while about 50 per cent of the "right" twins exhibit situs inversus (Fig. 25b). Again, constriction of the egg shortly after fertilization and at various later stages up to the early gastrula gives the same results. The possible basis of the early origin of this asymmetry has been discussed in detail by Spemann and Falkenberg ('19) and should be investigated further.

Relation of Initial Mass of Cytoplasm to Final Body Size. The relations between egg size and body size have been studied in a number of species which include large and small races. Generally there is no correlation between the two; different breeds of rabbits have eggs of the same size (Painter, '28; Castle and Gregory, '29; Gregory and Castle, '31); in selected large and small lines of *Drosophila funebris*, the size of the eggs varies independently of the body size; i.e., genetically small races may have large eggs (Zarapkin, '34).

Experimental reduction of the size of the egg through fragmentation at an early stage of development produces proportionately smaller embryos and young larvae, made up of a reduced number of cells of normal size. However, if such dwarf larvae from isolated egg fragments or blastomeres of a newt are allowed to develop in the presence of an ample supply of food, they will attain approximately normal size before metamor-

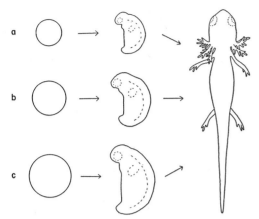

Fig. 26. Diagram to illustrate the independence of final body size from initial mass of cytoplasm of egg. A half-egg of a salamander produces an embryo of half normal size; during later stages the larva grows to approximately the same size as a larva from a whole egg (*b*). A large egg produced by a polyploid female (*c*) gives rise to a large embryo; slower growth during later feeding stages reduces final size to normal.

phosis, at the age of about three months (Fig. 26; Spemann and Falkenberg, '19, Fig. 1, Pl. 1; Fankhauser, '45a). Similarly, tadpoles developing from large and small eggs spawned by the same female frog (*Rana pipiens*), with a volume ratio of 1.73 to 1, reached approximately equal sizes after 53 days of larval growth (Briggs, '49). Furthermore, larvae raised from the large eggs produced by older triploid and tetraploid axolotls, regardless of the number of chromosomes which they contain, are at first conspicuously larger than the controls but will grow more slowly later on (Fankhauser and Humphrey, '50). Final body size is clearly independent of the initial mass of cytoplasm of the egg.

NUCLEUS

Development without Nucleus. Various methods have been applied to induce development of eggs in the complete absence of functional nuclear material (Fig. 27, Table 5). Essentially similar results have been obtained with eggs of both sea urchins and amphibians. Cleavage may proceed more or less regularly, usually in the presence of cytasters or of sperm asters not associated with functional sperm nuclei, but sometimes in the complete absence of an achromatic mitotic apparatus. Development comes to an end at various stages but may proceed to the formation of a blastula without blasto-

coele (sea urchin), a partial blastula with unsegmented areas in the vegetal region (frog), or an apparently normal blastula (axolotl). Although such blastulae may survive for days, in no instance has even an attempt at gastrulation been observed. This is true also of blastulae of newts that contain both nucleated and non-nucleated areas. There is no doubt that some fundamental process or processes beginning at gastrulation cannot take place except in the presence of nuclei in all, or at least a majority of, the cells.

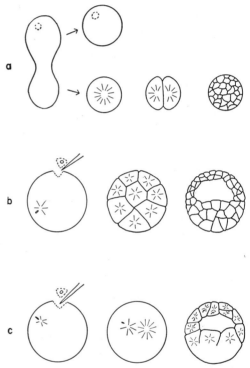

Fig. 27. Development of non-nucleated eggs and egg fragments (see Table 5).

a, Unfertilized egg of sea urchin (Arbacia) is fragmented by centrifuging. Lower non-nucleated half stimulated to parthenogenetic development. Cleavage with cystasters to blastula without blastocoel (after Harvey, '36).

b, Removal of egg nucleus from fertilized egg of axolotl by puncture to produce haploid development (androgenesis). In a single case, the sperm nucleus degenerated, but the sperm aster functioned in cleavage producing a normal, advanced blastula (after Stauffer, '45).

c, Fertilization of egg of *Rana pipiens* with sperm of *R. catesbiana*, previously exposed to heavy dose of x-rays, followed by removal of egg nucleus. The sperm nucleus remains inert, the sperm aster functions in cleavage leading to formation of partial blastula. Remnants of degenerated sperm chromatin visible in some cells (after Briggs, Green and King, '51).

Haploidy. The effects on development of the presence of a single set of chromosomes, either the maternal or the paternal, have been investigated extensively. Haploid embryos may be obtained in various types of experiments which are all designed to circumvent the reconstitution of the normal axolotls, haploid white embryos have appeared spontaneously among offspring from reciprocal combinations, white ♀ × black ♂, and black ♀ × white ♂. This demonstrates that either the egg nucleus or the sperm nucleus may be functioning and contribute the haploid set of chromosomes, al-

TABLE 5. *Development of non-nucleated eggs or egg fragments**

SPECIES	METHOD	CLEAVAGE AND FINAL STAGE REACHED	AUTHOR
Asterias forbesii	Removal of maturation spindle from unfertilized egg, treatment with CO_2 to induce parthenogenesis (formation of cytasters)	Irregular cleavage to "morula"	McClendon, '08
Arbacia punctulata	Fragmentation of unfertilized egg by centrifuging, hypertonic treatment of non-nucleated halves or quarters to induce parthenogenesis (formation of cytasters)	More or less regular cleavage to blastula without blastocoele (up to 500 cells), Fig. 27a	Harvey, '36, '40
Arbacia pustulosa	Same	16 cells	Harvey, '38
Parechinus microtuberculatus	Same	Irregular cleavage or fragmentation to blastula-like structure	
Paracentrotus lividus	Same	Same	
Sphaerechinus granularis	Same	Eggs fragment irregularly	
Chaetopterus pergamentaceus	Same	2 cells	Harvey, '39
Amblystoma mexicanum (axolotl)	Removal of maturation spindle by puncture of egg, spontaneous degeneration of single sperm nucleus; sperm aster probably functioned in cleavage	Advanced, normal blastula with blastocoele (single case), Fig. 27b	Stauffer, '45
Rana pipiens	Eggs inseminated with heavily x-rayed sperm of *R. catesbiana*, maturation spindle removed by puncture; sperm nucleus damaged, did not take part in development, sperm aster probably functioned	Partial blastulae, some cells with degenerated remnants of paternal chromatin, Fig. 27c	Briggs, Green and King, '51
Triturus palmatus, T. viridescens	Polyspermy and removal of maturation spindle by division or puncture of egg, abnormal mitotic figures and cytasters appear frequently, both sperm asters and cytasters may function in cleavage	Advanced blastulae with large areas of non-nucleated cells	Fankhauser, '29, '34; Fankhauser and Moore, '41

* See Figure 27.

diploid chromosome complement during fertilization (Fig. 28, Table 6). Whether the unfertilized egg is stimulated to parthenogenetic development by artificial activation, or the fusion of the egg and sperm nuclei is prevented in the fertilized egg (gynogenesis, androgenesis) seems to have little influence on the results. Recently it has been shown that haploid embryos may develop spontaneously from untreated eggs of various species of salamanders, with a frequency of between one or two in a thousand. In crosses between recessive white and dominant black though the egg nucleus seems to be involved in the majority of cases (Humphrey and Fankhauser, unpublished).

While haploid embryos have often been obtained from eggs of echinoderms, annelids, mollusks, and ascidians, their development has not been followed beyond early larval stages. The analysis of the later manifestations of haploidy has been largely confined to various species of amphibians. Regardless of the method used to induce haploidy, the development of the haploid embryos is usually retarded and abnormal from an early

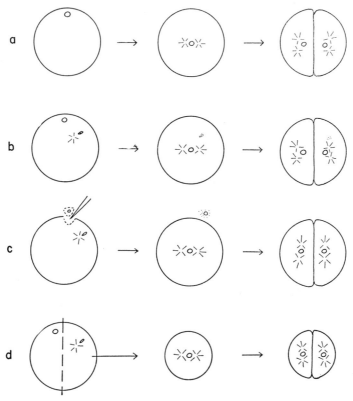

Fig. 28. Diagrammatic representation of the four types of experiments producing haploid embryos (see Table 6).

a, Parthenogenesis. Unfertilized egg is activated by artificial means and develops with haploid chromosome set of egg nucleus.

b. Gynogenesis. Fertilized egg develops with egg nucleus alone; sperm nucleus degenerates but sperm aster usually functions as division center.

c, Androgenesis. Egg nucleus is removed from fertilized egg; haploid sperm nucleus alone takes part in development.

d, Andro-merogony. Fertilized egg is divided into two parts; right-hand half develops with sperm nucleus; left-hand half with egg nucleus rarely cleaves normally because of lack of active division center ("*gynomerogony*").

stage on. In many cases the development of the archenteron is subnormal, leading to various degrees of microcephaly. The body remains short and broad, blood circulation is usually deficient, edema and ascites are common, and motility and general reactivity are reduced. The great majority of embryos die before they reach the feeding stage. However, there is evidence of specific differences in the tolerance of haploidy (Fig. 29). On the whole, embryos of various species of newts are less affected than those of the axolotl and of frogs and toads.

Occasionally, haploid larvae appear that are almost free from the usual symptoms and begin to feed. The most advanced haploid animals obtained so far were a *Triturus taeniatus* developed from an egg fragment (Baltzer, '22; Fankhauser, '37, '38a) which

died at the end of metamorphosis at the age of 100 days; a *Triturus alpestris* developed from a refrigerated whole egg (Fischberg, '44, '47a) which lived longer (290 days) but was more retarded and died at the beginning of metamorphosis; and, from refrigerated eggs of *Triturus granulosus*, two larvae which never metamorphosed and were fixed in vigorous condition at 139 and 146 days of age, respectively (Costello and Holmquist, unpub.). A detailed study of the microscopical anatomy of the first-mentioned haploid showed that the complex transformation from the larva to the terrestrial salamander with most of the characteristics of the adult had taken place normally. In most organs, the reduction of the size of the individual cells to about one-half of the normal diploid size was only in part compensated by an

Table 6. *Methods for Production of Haploid Embryos*

TYPE OF EXPERIMENT	PROCEDURES	ORIGIN OF MITOTIC APPARATUS ASSURING NORMAL CLEAVAGE
Parthenogenesis (activation of unfertilized egg by an agent other than sperm)	Hyper- and hypotonic solutions; puncture with needle; high or low temperatures; etc.	New division center (centrosome) arises in egg cytoplasm
Gynogenesis (development of a fertilized egg with maternal chromosomes alone)	Hybridization; radiation of sperm fluid with x-rays, etc.; treatment of sperm fluid with chemicals such as acriflavine, or toluidine blue; low or high temperature acting during fertilization; also occurs spontaneously	Division center contributed by sperm as in normal fertilization
Gyno-merogony (development of fragment of fertilized egg containing egg nucleus alone)	Fragmentation of fertilized egg isolating egg nucleus in one half	New division center may arise in cytoplasm
Androgenesis (development of fertilized egg with sperm nucleus alone)	Radiation of egg before fertilization; mechanical removal of egg nucleus; low or high temperature acting during fertilization; also occurs spontaneously	Division center contributed by sperm as in normal fertilization
Andro-merogony (development of an egg fragment with the sperm nucleus alone)	Fragmentation of unfertilized egg and fertilization of non-nucleated half, or division of fertilized egg isolating sperm nucleus in one half	Same

increase in cell number. In some glands, however, almost normal size was obtained either through an increase in the size of the individual tubules, as in the lacrymal glands, or through an increase in the number of units, as in the thyroid.

The fact that the most normal haploid amphibian produced so far developed from an egg fragment suggested that the reduction of the initial amount of cytoplasm and yolk, resulting in a more normal nucleoplasmic ratio at the beginning of development, may have a beneficial effect. Recent observations of Briggs ('49) on haploid frog embryos developed from large and small eggs (volume ratio 1.73 to 1) support this view. Those from large eggs showed the symptoms typical for anuran haploids: the heart was

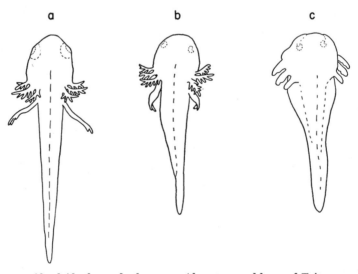

Fig. 29. Three types of haploid salamander larvae. *a*, Almost normal larva of *Triturus pyrrhogaster*, from a heat-treated egg. *b*, Another larva of the same species, also from heat-treated egg, showing typical symptoms of haploidy (stunted growth, microcephaly, edema). *c*, More abnormal larva of axolotl, from cold-treated egg, with extreme edema and poorly developed gills.

poorly formed, the circulation was blocked at various points, and the gut retained its main mass of yolk. All became edematous and ascitic and died without feeding within twelve to eighteen days from fertilization. The majority of the haploids from small eggs showed a more nearly normal circulation and

loid newt larvae developed from whole eggs. Various hypotheses have been proposed to account for the poor viability of experimentally produced haploids (see the reviews in Fankhauser, '37, '45a). One of the most tempting is the suggestion that lethal or at least viability-reducing genes may be pres-

TABLE 7. *Spontaneous and Experimentally Induced Polyploidy in Amphibians*

SPECIES	SPONTANEOUS POLYPLOIDS	EXPERIMENTALLY INDUCED POLYPLOIDS	AUTHOR
Triturus viridescens	Triploid Tetraploid Pentaploid	Triploid (cold) Triploid (heat)	Fankhauser, '38b, '45a; Fankhauser and Griffiths, '39; Fankhauser and Watson, '42
T. pyrrhogaster	Triploid Pentaploid	Triploid (cold) Triploid (heat) Tetraploid (cold)	Kawamura, '41a; Fankhauser, Crotta and Perrot, '42; Sanada, '51
T. taeniatus	Triploid	Triploid (cold)	Böök, '41, '45
T. palmatus		Triploid (cold)	Fischberg, '47b
T. alpestris		Triploid (cold) Tetraploid (cold)	Fischberg, '44, '47a
T. cristatus		Triploid (cold)	Fischberg, '47b
T. granulosus	Pentaploid	Triploid (cold) Tetraploid (cold)	Costello, '42; Costello and Holmquist, unpub.
Pleurodeles waltlii		Triploid	Gallien and Muguard, '50
Amblystoma mexicanum (axolotl)	Triploid Tetraploid Pentaploid	Triploid (cold) Tetraploid* Pentaploid* Hexaploid* Heptaploid*	Fankhauser and Humphrey, '42, '50, and unpublished
Eurycea bislineata	Triploid Tetraploid		Fankhauser, '39
Rana esculenta	Triploid		G. and P. Hertwig, '20
R. temporaria	Triploid	Triploid, tetraploid, pentaploid (colchicine, sulfanilamide)	Jahn, '52
R. pipiens		Triploid (heat) Triploid (parthenogenesis)	Briggs, '47 Parmenter, '33
R. nigromaculata		Triploid (cold) Triploid ⎫ among partheno- Tetraploid ⎬ genetic larvae Hexaploid ⎭	Kawamura, '41b Kawamura, '39

* Among offspring of triploid females mated with diploid males.

a normal utilization of the yolk supply in the gut. Two-thirds of the total were able to feed and did not show edema or ascites; they survived for periods up to nine months, without undergoing metamorphosis. The reduction of the initial amount of yolk may have facilitated the differentiation of the gut in a purely mechanical way, and, at the same time, in the presence of a relatively normal circulation, created the conditions necessary for a more rapid and complete utilization of the yolk material.

That this yolk factor is not alone responsible for the poor development of haploid embryos in general is shown by the frequently normal gut differentiation in hap-

ent in most of the haploid chromosome sets and exert their effect at various early stages of development, unchecked by the normal dominant alleles usually contained in the second set of chromosomes in a diploid. The existence of a recessive lethal factor which kills one-quarter of the offspring of heterozygous parents has recently been demonstrated in the axolotl (Humphrey, '48). It is of the greatest interest that this factor causes a fluid imbalance which appears very early in development, and causes a marked enlargement of the head and suprabranchial region, which may extend later on to the body. The effect is readily distinguishable from the edema of the usual haploid syndrome which appears later and does not affect the head region primarily.

Other possible factors reducing the viability of haploids may be a deficiency in the synthesis of ribose nucleoprotein (Brachet, '44, '47) or of various enzymes, as is suggested by the increased sensitivity of haploid frog embryos to hexenolactone (Briggs, '46). Whether these disturbances in

twice the normal size, e.g., the number of primary mesenchyme cells was reduced from about 43 to 23. Such gastrulae did not develop beyond the early pluteus stage and were usually abnormal. The presence of some larvae with as few as 9 to 13 mesenchyme cells of particularly large size suggested that occasionally a second monaster cycle followed upon the first, producing octoploid embryos.

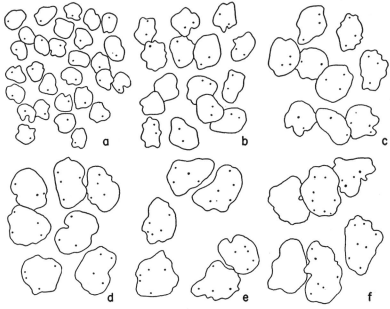

Fig. 30. Drawings of nuclei from epidermis cells of axolotl larvae to show increase in size with increase in chromosome number. The maximum number of nucleoli in each group of nuclei corresponds to the number of chromosome sets present; smaller numbers are caused by fusion of nucleoli. *a*, Haploid; *b*, diploid; *c*, triploid; *d*, tetraploid; *e*, pentaploid; *f*, heptaploid.

the biochemistry of haploid cells are connected with the reduction in the total mass of nuclear material, perhaps the heterochromatin in particular, or with an upset of gene dosage remains to be investigated.

Polyploidy. The first observations on the effect of an increase in chromosome number on development were made by Boveri ('05) on eggs of the sea urchin, *Paracentrotus lividus*, in which the division of the aster during the first cleavage mitosis was suppressed by shaking. In the course of the resulting monocentric mitosis the chromosomes divided normally but, in the absence of a mechanism to separate the daughter chromosomes, they were all incorporated into a single nucleus during telophase. Since the aster often divided normally at the following mitosis, cleavage began with a delay and produced a tetraploid gastrula containing about half the usual number of cells of

A more detailed analysis of the development of polyploid embryos became possible in various species of amphibians through the discovery that triploid and, more rarely, tetraploid and pentaploid individuals appear spontaneously among normal larvae raised in the laboratory (Table 7). These exceptional individuals may be easily identified soon after hatching by means of chromosome counts in stained preparations of the amputated tip of the tail. Very probably they owe their origin to accidents at meiosis, usually nonreduction of the chromosome number during maturation of the egg. Triploid embryos may be produced on a larger scale by treatment of freshly fertilized eggs with extreme temperatures. Refrigeration for several hours, or exposure to +36° C. for ten minutes, frequently suppresses the formation of the second polar body which normally is not given off until about one hour after fertilization.

Two haploid sets of maternal chromosomes are thus left in the egg which combine with the haploid set brought in by the sperm to form a triploid zygote.* In the axolotl, a considerable number of tetraploids and, very rarely, hexaploids and heptaploids, with six or seven sets of chromosomes, respectively, are found among the offspring of triploid females (Table 7).

and, in *R. pipiens,* in the pattern of deeply and lightly pigmented epidermis cells in the young embryo, making an early tentative identification of the polyploid individuals possible.

The early development of most triploid, tetraploid, and pentaploid embryos is normal in appearance and rate, as far as the observations go. Gastrulation, neurulation, and or-

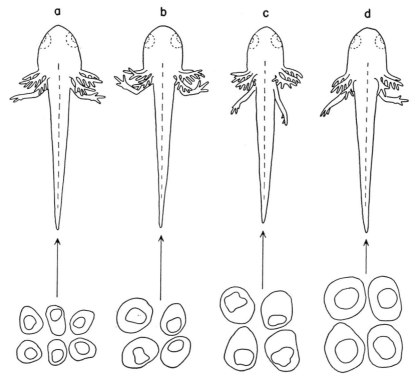

Fig. 31. Absence of gigantism in polyploid salamander larvae (*Triturus viridescens*), in spite of increase in cell size. From left to right: diploid, triploid, tetraploid, pentaploid. Below each larva are groups of gland cells ("Leydig cells") from epidermis of tailfin.

In polyploid embryos the size of the nuclei and cells increases approximately in proportion to the number of chromosomes, up to about the pentaploid level, but changes more slowly from there on (Fig. 30). In the axolotl, a more reliable measure of the degree of polyploidy is to be found in the number of nucleoli per nucleus, the maximum number of which always corresponds to the number of chromosome sets present, since each nucleolus is formed at a particular point of a certain chromosome of each haploid set. In the intact living larva the larger cell size expresses itself in the pattern of melanophores

gan formation are thus surprisingly independent of the size of the cells which, in pentaploids, are about two and one-half times as large as in the diploids. The two heptaploid axolotl embryos recorded to date were abnormal when first observed but continued development to the time of hatching; the upper limit of tolerance for increased chromosome number and cell size, while not known definitely, has probably been reached or surpassed at this level.

The body size of the young larvae at the time of hatching is remarkably constant regardless of chromosome number and cell size (Fig. 31). The increase in the size of the cells is compensated, at each level, by a corresponding decrease in their number. This

* Treatment of frog's eggs with mitotic inhibitors such as colchicine and sulfanilamide produces embryos that are partly polyploid, partly diploid.

is in striking contrast to the gigantism of many polyploid plants and some polyploid invertebrates, for instance, tetraploid brine shrimp embryos (Artemia), triploid isopods (Trichoniscus) and bagworm moths (Solenobia). Triploid and tetraploid silkworms, on the other hand, show the same neutralization of larger cell size by smaller cell number as polyploid amphibian larvae (for a detailed discussion of the literature see Fankhauser, '41, '45a, and '52).*

In later stages of development triploid larvae, as a rule, grow normally, while the growth of tetraploids and pentaploids is usu-

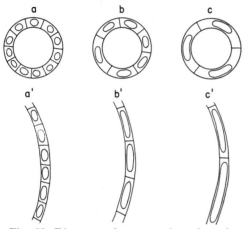

Fig. 32. Diagrams of cross sections through a pronephric tubule (above) and the lens epithelium (below) in (a) a haploid larva, (b) a diploid, (c) a pentaploid (*Triturus viridescens*). Normal size and structure are maintained with cells of different sizes by adjustment of number and shape of individual cells.

ally retarded. Following metamorphosis, triploid *T. alpestris* continue to grow at the normal pace for three and more years (Fischberg, '47a). In the axolotl, adult and sexually mature triploids are of approximately the same size as diploids, while tetraploids are on the average smaller; pentaploids, at one year, lag considerably behind the tetraploids. The final body size of the adult salamander is definitely not determined by the size of the cells present in the individual. It appears, rather, that the total mass of body substance produced is more or less fixed by the genetic constitution of the species and will be reached under favorable conditions irrespective of the initial mass of the egg or of the size of the cells.

* More or less pronounced gigantism has recently been observed in partially polyploid frog tadpoles obtained by colchicine or sulfanilamide treatment of eggs (Jahn, '52).

The reduction in cell number shown by polyploid amphibian larvae produces interesting effects in the structure of the nervous system and sense organs, for which earlier investigators had claimed an approximate "cell constancy." For instance, in the eye of a tetraploid, the structure of the retina is profoundly affected in all layers and shows fewer but conspicuously large rods and cones. Adjustment in cell number becomes impossible in the case of Mauthner's cells, a single pair of giant ganglion cells in the medulla at the point of entrance of the seventh and eighth nerve roots. Tetraploid larvae, like the diploid, still possess two Mauthner's cells which are about twice normal size. A haploid larva, on the other hand, which has a larger number of cells than the diploid, although not nearly twice as many, may form two Mauthner's cells of half normal size on either side (Fankhauser, '52, Pl. 1).

Special conditions are also offered by tubular organs, such as the pronephric tubules and ducts, and by flat epithelia like the epidermis or the epithelium of the lens (Fig. 32). In haploid and polyploid larvae the normal structure of such organs can be maintained only if there is an adjustment both in the number and in the shape of the individual cells. In haploids, the cells are more numerous and more nearly cuboidal; in polyploids, the cells are fewer in number and much more flattened than in the diploid. The thickness of the wall of the tubule or of the epithelium remains approximately the same at all levels of cell size (Fankhauser, '45b).

The normal character of the development and organization of polyploid embryos and larvae indicates that it makes little or no difference whether the genes are present in double, triple, or even in quintuple dose as long as all genes are multiplied to the same degree. In this respect, genes located on the sex chromosomes occupy a special position since polyploids may possess various combinations of sex chromosomes that cannot be realized in diploids. In particular, if sex determination should depend on a balance between "male-determining" and "female-determining" genes that are spread over both sex chromosomes and autosomes, as is the case in Drosophila, this balance might be completely upset.

At the very beginning of the investigations on sex differentiation in triploid *T. viridescens* before and after metamorphosis, it became apparent that the development of the ovaries is much more affected than that of the testes. While the latter show normal size and structure, the former almost always remain small and are characterized by the complete absence of growing oocytes or "auxocytes" (Fankhauser, '41; Fankhauser and Watson, '49). At the age of three years, triploid females of *T. alpestris* still are completely sterile; auxocytes are rarely seen in the ovaries, while triploid males produce mature spermatozoa, although in relatively small numbers (Fischberg, '47a). In triploid axolotls, the young ovaries also show a large-scale degeneration of very young oocytes in early diplotene stages of meiosis and a deficiency of auxocytes. Later on, however, a varying number of oocytes enter the growth phase and eventually develop into mature eggs that are spawned normally.

The complete or partial inhibition of the development of the ovaries in triploid salamanders appeared to find a simple explanation when Humphrey ('45) demonstrated, by a study of the sex ratio among the offspring of female axolotls experimentally converted into males, that the female sex is heterogametic, with the sex chromosome formula WZ. Since the male sex is homogametic (ZZ), triploid males have the corresponding formula ZZZ and might be expected to be normal. Triploid females, obtained by refrigeration of eggs, are two types, WZZ and WWZ, neither of which would have the same ratio of W chromosomes to Z chromosomes or to autosomes as the diploid. A disturbance of the balance of sex-determining genes might thus account for the abnormal development of the ovaries. However, when it became possible, through the use of sex-reversed females and their offspring, to obtain still another type of triploid females, of the constitution WWW, it was discovered that such females exhibited exactly the same deficiency of ovarian development as the other two types, in spite of the fact that their sex chromosome balance was the same as in WW diploids which are normal females (Humphrey and Fankhauser, '46). It appears that the primary process of sex determination may not be involved at all but that the later differentiation of the ovaries, which may be controlled by other genes located on the autosomes, is adversely affected by the triploid constitution of the cells, possibly by a disturbance of gene dosage.

The depression of the growth rate and viability of higher polyploids suggests that some basic metabolic processes may be affected directly by the multiple gene complex, or, indirectly, by the larger size of the nuclei and cells. Measurements of the rate of oxygen consumption and of enzyme activity, which are still in a preliminary stage, should offer valuable information on fundamental problems of cell physiology.

Recently the study of polyploidy has been extended to other vertebrates. Makino and Ozima ('43) found that cold treatment of eggs of the carp inhibits the formation of the second polar body; it is very probable that treated eggs would give rise to triploid embryos. In mammals, the occurrence of polyploidy was demonstrated for the first time by Beatty and Fischberg ('49). Chromosome counts in pre-implantation embryos of the mouse, about three and one-half days after copulation, showed that triploid and, more rarely, tetraploid embryos occur without treatment. The incidence of spontaneous heteroploidy varied with the strain of mice used; a certain silver strain exhibited a particularly high percentage of triploids (3.8 per cent). In this strain, triploid embryos could be identified as late as mid-term (nine and one-half days). A heat shock (45° C. for 5 to 10 minutes), applied to tubal eggs at the estimated time of fertilization, produced 16.5 per cent heteroploid embryos, mostly triploid, as identified at three and one-half days; treatment during the first cleavage mitosis gave 29 per cent tetraploid embryos (cf. Beatty, '51, for review and list of other references).

In the rabbit, insemination of females with sperm suspended in colchicine solution produced two individuals that were complex chromosomal mosaics, partly diploid, partly polyploid or aneuploid (Häggquist and Bane, '50a and b; Melander, '50). Corresponding experiments with pigs produced one heteroploid individual (Häggquist and Bane, '51; Melander, '51). The interpretation of this case is complicated by the fact that the normal, diploid chromosome number seems to vary between different races of pigs. It is interesting that the heteroploid rabbits and pig were reported to be larger than the controls.

Aneuploidy (Unbalanced Chromosome Complements). Hyperdiploid embryos with from one to four extra chromosomes occur spontaneously with very low frequency in various species of amphibians. They can now be obtained on a large scale in the axolotl by breeding triploid females with diploid males (Fankhauser and Humphrey, '50). At the first meiotic division of the triploid eggs, the third set of chromosomes is distributed at random between the poles of the spindle. Eggs are produced with chromosome numbers ranging from the haploid (14) to almost the diploid (28). This is shown by the chromosome numbers found in the tailtips of the resulting embryos, which range from 28 to 41, with a maximum frequency at 33. In about 4 per cent of the triploid eggs, one of

gills, liver, and other organs, accompanied or followed by accumulation of fluid under the skin, in the heart or branchial regions, and in the body cavity. This syndrome is in most aspects typically different from that shown by haploid embryos. Chromosomal imbalance, regardless of the exact number of chromosomes added, seems to have a gen-

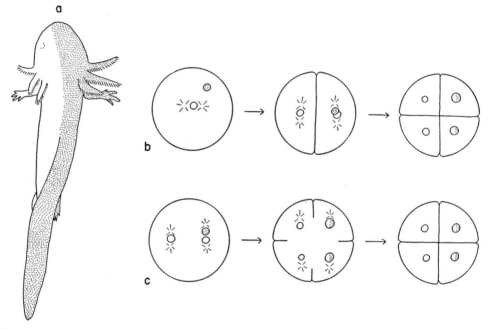

Fig. 33. *a*, A haploid/diploid, white/dark mosaic axolotl from a cross between a white (recessive) female and a heterozygous dark male, at age of six months. Eye, gills, and limbs are smaller on haploid side (after Humphrey and Fankhauser, '43).

b and *c*, Two possible explanations of origin of this mosaic. *b*, "Partial fertilization"; egg nucleus carrying factor for white first divided alone; left-hand cell produced haploid, white side of body; in right-hand cell, the other descendant of the egg nucleus fused with a sperm nucleus carrying the gene for dark and gave rise to the diploid, dark side.

c, *Dispermy*; one sperm nucleus carrying gene for white divided independently and furnished the nuclei for the haploid, white side of the body; a second sperm nucleus with gene for dark fused with the egg nucleus giving rise to the diploid nuclei of the right, dark side.

the meiotic divisions is suppressed so that tetraploid embryos are produced.

In contrast to most balanced polyploids, aneuploids have a greatly reduced viability and are usually abnormal in appearance. The addition of as few as one or two chromosomes to the diploid complement disturbs the genic balance sufficiently to make normal development a rare event. Of 377 embryos with known aneuploid chromosome number only thirteen lived for periods of three months or more. The great majority showed typical abnormalities at an early stage. Most commonly the circulation was either not established at all or remained subnormal, with frequent stasis and hemorrhages in the

eral effect on the development and maintenance of the circulation which in turn creates the fluid imbalance. As might be expected, hypertriploid or near-tetraploid larvae are more viable and normal, since the unbalance created by the addition of single chromosomes to a multiple complement is less severe.

None of the more viable hyperdiploids have reached sexual maturity so far. However, offspring have been obtained from nonviable embryos by transplantation of gonad preprimordia to normal diploid embryos in the tail-bud stage.

Chromosome Mosaics. In most of the species of amphibians investigated, embryos appear, either spontaneously or in various experiments (polyspermy, parthenogenesis, cold or heat treatment of eggs), which exhibit two or sometimes three different chromosome numbers in different regions which may vary in extent from a few cells to one-half of the body. Most frequent are haploid/diploid and haploid/triploid embryos, but several other combinations have been observed.

The haploid side of a mosaic generally shows a much more normal development than may be seen in completely haploid animals (compare Fig. 33a with Fig. 29c). Since mosaics possess a normal circulation, with both hapoid and diploid blood cells circulating through the haploid organs, the better performance of the latter may possibly be explained on this basis. However, parabio-

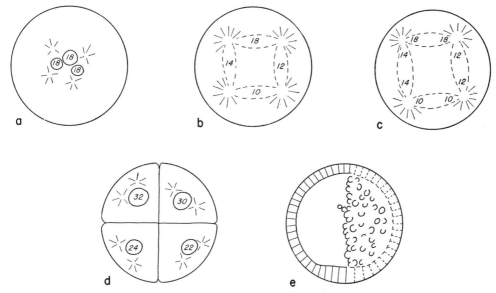

Fig. 34. Development of dispermic sea urchin egg. a, Fusion of both sperm nuclei with egg nucleus, each containing a haploid set of 18 chromosomes; both sperm asters have divided. b, Random distribution of 54 chromosomes among spindles connecting the four poles of the mitotic figure. c, Anaphase; chromosomes from two adjacent spindles move toward each pole. d, Telophase; division of egg into four cells with different numbers of chromosomes. e, "Stereoblastula," final stage of development. Cells of right-hand half disintegrating. (After Boveri, '07.)

Haploid/diploid mosaics are easily discovered among the offspring of crosses between white and dark axolotls, if the haploid area is derived from the white (recessive) parent. Figure 33a shows an unusually regular lateral mosaic of this type with a sharp line of demarkation almost exactly in the median plane. The organs on the haploid (left) side are smaller than those on the right. Dissection of the animal at the age of eight months further revealed that this individual started out as a gynandromorph, with a testis on the left and an ovary on the right side. However, at the time of the autopsy the ovary had been almost completely transformed into a testis under the influence of the male sex hormone produced by the testis on the haploid side. The origin of this lateral mosaic may be explained in either one of two ways which are described in Figures 33b and c.

sis between haploid and diploid embryos of T. pyrrhogaster, which also accomplishes a joint circulation, did not result in the expected improvement of the haploid partner, aside from a reduction of the edema (Kaylor, '40). The presence of a partly diploid nervous system may be another factor favoring normal functioning of the haploid side of the body. Finally, the proximity of normal diploid tissues may have a stimulating influence on adjacent haploid tissues, as has been shown by Hadorn ('35, '37) in chimaeras composed of halves of diploid and haploid embryos.

The Effects of Irregular Distribution of Chromosomes in Multipolar Mitosis. In sea urchin eggs that are fertilized by two spermatozoa, both sperm nuclei fuse with the egg nucleus (Fig. 34a) so that three sets of chromosomes are present at the first division of the egg. In the majority of such eggs, both sperm asters divide to form a mitotic figure with four poles connected by spindles among which the chromosomes are distributed at random (Fig. 34b). During anaphase, the four poles thus receive different numbers of chromosomes which are incorporated into four nuclei (Figs. 34c and d). Since these nuclei divide normally in subsequent mi-

tity of chromosome material that causes the standstill of development, but the presence of abnormal combinations of individual chromosomes in one or more quarters of the blastula or pluteus. Normal development beyond the gastrula stage requires the presence of nuclei containing at least one complete set of chromosomes.

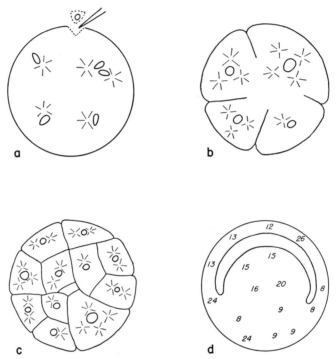

Fig. 35. Diagram of development of polyspermic eggs of the newt, following removal of egg nucleus; frequent disengagement of nuclear and centrosomal cycles producing abnormal mitoses. a, Five sperm nuclei present, two of which are about to fuse. b, First mitotic cycle; tetrapolar mitosis at upper right, two tripolar mitoses at left, monaster at lower right. c, Second mitotic cycle; several cells again contain abnormal mitotic figures. d, Section through final stage of development reached; blastula with wide variety of chromosome numbers in different areas.

toses, the abnormal chromosome sets are reproduced and handed on to all the cells descended from each of the first four blastomeres. A blastula results which consists of four areas differing in chromosome number as is shown by differences in the size of the nuclei; the individual cells are too small to allow actual chromosome counts at this stage. Some of these eggs never develop beyond a "stereo-blastula" in which one or more quarters disintegrate, causing the death of the whole embryo (Fig. 34e). Others may form abnormal plutei in which again a regional breakdown of the cells takes place. Boveri ('02, '07), in a masterly analysis of the development of dispermic eggs, showed that it is not a deficiency in the mere quan-

In polyspermic eggs and egg fragments of newts from which the egg nucleus has been removed, multipolar and other abnormal mitoses occur frequently. Because of the large size of the eggs, several mitotic figures may be present in the same egg and cause the formation of multiple cleavage furrows (Figs. 35a and b). The cytological picture is complicated still further by the fact that multipolar or monocentric mitoses may again occur in individual blastomeres during the second or a subsequent mitotic cycle (Fig. 35c). Counts of chromosomes in the blastula reveal a highly complex pattern of abnormal, mostly aneuploid, chromosome numbers (Fig. 35d). Since, in Triturus, most of the 12 chromosomes of the haploid set may be recognized individually by differences in size and shape, it is possible to analyze the abnormal chromosome complements in detail (Fankhauser, '34) and to demonstrate directly their random composition and extreme unbalance. As would be expected, all of these eggs die in the blastula stage.

Recently Morgenthaler ('48) transplanted pieces from androgenetic Triturus blastulae, of constitution presumably similar to that shown in Fig. 35d, to the flank of normal neurulae. Sections of the host embryos fixed in an early tail-bud stage showed the presence of mitotic figures in the graft, some of which contained fewer than twelve chromosomes. This indicates that subhaploid cells may continue to divide and survive for some time in the normal environment of a diploid embryo.

QUALITATIVE CHANGES: EXPERIMENTS INVOLVING HYBRIDIZATION BETWEEN TWO SPECIES

The introduction of a nucleus of one species into the egg cytoplasm of another offers an opportunity to study the effects of the combination of two components that presumably differ in a qualitative way. A variety of unusual modifications of the processes of development are produced that have been analyzed most intensively in echinoderms and amphibians.

DIPLOID HYBRIDS

Echinoderms. The development of most echinoderm hybrids has not been followed beyond the pluteus stage. The internal phenomena of fertilization may be completely normal, as in the cross Echinus esculentus ♀ × Echinus (Psammechinus) miliaris ♂. In the reciprocal cross a small percentage of the eggs develop and a large proportion of these show elimination of one or a few chromosomes in the first cleavage mitosis (Doncaster and Gray, '13). In the combination Paracentrotus (Strongylocentrotus) lividus ♀ (N = 18) × Sphaerechinus granularis ♂ (N = 20) about sixteen chromosomes lag in the equator of the spindle during the first cleavage mitosis. The paternal origin of these chromosomes was demonstrated by isolation of a Sphaerechinus sperm nucleus in a fragment of a Paracentrotus egg; for at the late anaphase of the first cleavage mitosis about four normal chromosomes could be counted at each pole, while the remaining chromosomes were left behind in the spindle. In all crosses with sperm from Arbacia (N = 20),

chromosome behavior during early cleavages was normal; but a sudden crisis occurred at the blastula or gastrula stage when about half of the chromosomes, presumably the paternal ones, were eliminated in each cell and the embryos became abnormal (Baltzer, '10). The incompatibility between most or all of the sperm chromosomes and the egg cytoplasm may thus be expressed in visible disturbances of mitosis in early or late cleavage stages, and development may stop or become abnormal at gastrulation. Although hybrid plutei have been obtained from reciprocal crosses between species that differ in the characteristics of the larval skeleton in order to study the possible influence of the maternal cytoplasm, the interpretation of the observations is difficult because of the variability of the appearance of the plutei in different series of experiments and the possible influence of external factors such as temperature (cf. Morgan, '27, Chapter 25; P. Hertwig, '36).

Eggs of sea urchins may be activated by sperm of mollusks (Mytilus) and produce typically maternal plutei. Development is gynogenetic since the sperm head is resorbed without forming a sperm nucleus while the sperm centrosome apparently functions as the division center (Kupelwieser, '09).

Amphibians. A wealth of interesting observations has accumulated on the results of hybridization between various species of frogs, toads, and salamanders (cf. the review by P. Hertwig, '36, and the more recent papers by J. A. Moore, '41–'48, Blair, '41, and Baltzer, '52). The following lines of investigation are of particular importance for the analysis of our problem:

Cytology of fertilization in relation to development of hybrid eggs (Bataillon and Tchou-Su, '29; Tchou-Su, '31). Figure 36 illustrates the variety of fertilization phenomena, which range from mere activation of the egg without penetration by the sperm, to completely normal fertilization. In the latter case, development may come to an end at the beginning of gastrulation, sometimes with visible disturbances of mitosis in the blastula, as in the cross T. palmatus ♀ × Salamandra maculosa ♂ (Schoenmann, '38), or normal hybrid larvae and adults may be produced.

Analysis of early arrest of development. The factors involved in the arrest of development at gastrulation in many crosses have been analyzed in different types of experiments. Transplantation of pieces from hybrid blastulae (T. palmatus ♀ × S. ma-

culosa ♂) to normal Triturus embryos has shown that grafted hybrid tissues may survive indefinitely and take part normally in the formation of a variety of organs. It is probable that the "lethal" effect of the Salamandra chromosomes which expresses itself in the blastula is overcome or neutralized in some unknown way by the surrounding tissues of the normal host embryo (Luethi, '38; Baltzer, '40). (See Baltzer, '52, for an alternative explanation involving "partial lethality" of the hybrid tissues.)

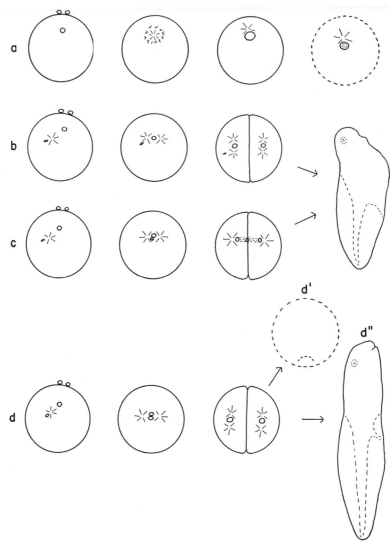

Fig. 36. Cytology of fertilization in crosses between different species of frogs and toads (after Tchou-Su, '31).

a, Rana ♀ × *Hyla* ♂ . Spermatozoon activates the egg on contact with egg surface but fails to penetrate. Second polar body is given off, new egg aster appears but is unable to divide; one or more monaster cycles multiply the chromosomes but do not induce cleavage.

b, Hyla ♀ × *Pelobates* ♂ . Sperm penetrates, sperm aster associates with egg nucleus to produce a bipolar, haploid mitotic figure. Sperm head fails to develop into a nucleus and degenerates; gynogenetic development to haploid tadpole ("false hybrid").

c, Hyla ♀ × *Bufo* ♂ . Sperm head transforms into small sperm nucleus which fuses with egg nucleus; sperm chromosomes are eliminated during telophase of first cleavage mitosis; gynogenesis as in *b.*

d, Normal fertilization and cleavage; no elimination of paternal chromosomes. *d', Bufo* ♀ × *Rana* ♂ . Hybrid dies in gastrula stage because of incompatibility between sperm chromosomes and egg cytoplasm. *d", Bufo vulgaris* ♀ × *B. viridis* ♂ . Normal development to viable diploid species hybrid.

J. A. Moore ('47b, '48) transplanted pieces of ectoderm from nonviable gastrulae of *R. pipiens* ♀ × *R. sylvatica* ♂ to normal neurulae of *R. palustris* or *Amblystoma maculatum* and found that formation of neural tissue and sense organs may be induced in the graft; however, the competence of the hybrid ectoderm to form these structures is definitely reduced. On the other hand, grafts of pieces of dorsal lip from hybrid gastrulae to normal ones induce poorly differentiated secondary embryos in a limited number of cases. Moore proposed the interesting hypothesis that the foreign genes of *R. sylvatica* lower both the competence and the inductive power of the hybrid tissue by competing with the *R. pipiens* genes for a substrate present in limited amount and forming an "analog" that cannot take the place of the substance formed by the normal pipiens cells.

Studies of the metabolism of arrested hybrid gastrulae (Barth and Jaeger, '47; Gregg, '48) have shown a marked reduction in respiration and glycolysis which indicates that one of the effects of the *R. sylvatica* chromosomes in a *R. pipiens* egg is the partial blockage of at least one step in the glycolytic chain. In the *R. esculenta* ♀ × *R. temporaria* ♂ hybrid, synthesis of cytoplasmic RNA is sharply decreased, while an excess of RNA seems to accumulate in the nucleus (cf. Brachet, '52).

Development of viable reciprocal hybrids. As a rule, the rate of cleavage and gastrulation of hybrid eggs is maternal. In the reciprocal crosses *R. pipiens* × *R. palustris*, an effect of the sperm has been detected as early as neurulation, producing an intermediate rate of development from this stage on (J. A. Moore, '41). The hybrids between *T. taeniatus* (or *T. palmatus*) and *T. cristatus* are completely maternal in appearance as far as the limb bud stage, with the possible exception of the size of the optic vesicle. The first effect of paternal genes is visible in the total length of the embryo and in the pigmentation of the tail fin (Hamburger, '36). Hybrids between the three species of California newts show an intermediate condition in the development of the pigmentation, balancers and dorsal fin (Twitty, '36).

Malformations of the hindlimbs are typical for all hybrids between *T. taeniatus* or *T. palmatus* ♀ and *T. cristatus* ♂ but are absent in the reciprocal combinations, possibly because of a difference in the egg cytoplasm of the two species (Hamburger, '35). In the same combination, as well as in hybrids between *T. taeniatus* and *T. alpestris,* Pariser ('32, '36) noted an abnormal sex ratio (over 98 per cent females) and a subnormal development of the ovaries, with a deficiency of growing oocytes. These investigations should be continued since they offer a new line of attack on the complex problem of sex determination in amphibians.

Inviability of hybrids between different geographical forms of Rana pipiens. While *R. pipiens* from most localities produce viable hybrids with *R. palustris,* crosses between northern and southern forms within the species give rise to abnormal and frequently nonviable embryos. Eggs of a northern race (e.g., Vermont) fertilized with sperm from a southern race (e.g., Florida) show retardation of development, extreme head enlargement and defects in the circulatory system. The reciprocal combination produces reduction in head size, frequent fusion of olfactory pits and eyes and absence of mouth. The cross Vermont ♀ × Mexico ♂ results in frequent exogastrulation and beginning of cytolysis in the gastrula and neurula (J. A. Moore, '47a). The existence of differences in the egg cytoplasm, which is suggested by these opposite effects produced in reciprocal diploid hybrids, was also demonstrated by Porter ('41, '46), who removed the egg nucleus from cross-fertilized eggs. The haploid androgenetic "hybrids" showed a more extreme effect of the cytoplasmic factors but also an early activity of the "foreign" sperm nucleus.

HAPLOID, ANDROGENETIC HYBRIDS

The crucial experiment, combination of a sperm nucleus of one species with the egg cytoplasm of another in the absence of the egg nucleus, was first carried out by Boveri (1896, '18) by cross-fertilizing fragments of sea urchin eggs. Table 8 shows that of the several combinations obtained by him and other investigators only two gave rise to plutei. Paracentrotus cytoplasm with Psammechinus nucleus produced a larval skeleton with typically paternal characteristics; and the reciprocal combination showed certain maternal characteristics which may have been due to the effect of the Psammechinus cytoplasm or, possibly, to the influence of unfavorable environmental conditions (Hoerstadius, '36). The importance of the nucleus was also demonstrated by combining the skeleton-forming micromeres of an androgenetic hybrid with the presumptive ecto-

TABLE 8. *Summary of Results of Experiments on Hybrid Androgenesis (Diploid Hybrids Normal Unless Otherwise Noted)*

COMBINATION		STAGE OF DEVELOPMENT REACHED	AUTHOR
CYTOPLASM	NUCLEUS		
1. SEA URCHINS			
Psammechinus (Parechinus) microtub.	Paracentrotus liv.	Pluteus	Boveri, '18 Hoerstadius, '36
Psammechinus (Parechinus) microtub.	Sphaerechinus gran.	Early blastula	Hoerstadius, '36
Paracentrotus liv.	Psammechinus (Parechinus) microtub.	Pluteus	Hoerstadius, '36
Paracentrotus liv.	Sphaerechinus gran.	Early blastula	Hoerstadius, '36
Sphaerechinus gran.	Paracentrotus liv.	Gastrula with short archenteron and small spicules	Boveri, '18 Hoerstadius, '36
Sphaerechinus gran.	Paracentrotus liv.	Pluteus	Harvey, '33; v. Ubisch, '53
Sphaerechinus gran.	Psammechinus (Parechinus) microtub.	Gastrula as above; 2 blastulae; rare plutei	Boveri, '18; Hoerstadius, '36; v. Ubisch, '53
Psammechinus (Parechinus) miliaris	Paracentrotus liv.	Abnormal plutei	Hoerstadius, '36
Psammechinus (Parechinus) miliaris	Echinus esculentus	Blastula or early gastrula	Hoerstadius, '36
Echinarachnius parma	Arbacia punctulata	Blastula	Fry, '27
Toxopneustes	Tripneustes	Blastula	Tennent and Taylor, '24
2. URODELES			
Triton taeniatus	T. palmatus	Embryo with balancers, branching gills and pigment cells	Baltzer, '20, '33; P. Hertwig, '23
Triton taeniatus	T. alpestris	Embryo with gill mounds and early lens formation	Baltzer, '20, '33; P. Hertwig '23
Triton taeniatus	T. cristatus	Embryo with neural tube and eye vesicles	Baltzer, '20, '30b; P. Hertwig, '23
Triton palmatus	T. alpestris	Embryo with eye and ear vesicles	Baltzer, '30a, '33
Triton palmatus	T. cristatus	Embryo with neural tube and eye vesicles	Baltzer, '30a, '33; Hadorn, '34, '36, '37
Triton alpestris	T. palmatus	Embryo with neural tube and indication of eye vesicles	Baltzer, '33; de Roche, '37
Triton alpestris	T. cristatus	Same	Baltzer, '33; Curry, '36
Triton palmatus	Salamandra maculosa,* S. atra	Late blastula	Boehringer '38; Baltzer and Schönmann, '51
Triturus torosus	T. granulosus	Gastrula, few with irregular neural folds	Dalton, '40, '46
Triturus torosus	T. rivularis	Same	Dalton, '40, '46
Triturus granulosus	T. torosus	Embryo with pigment	Dalton, '40, '46
Triturus granulosus	T. rivularis	Embryo dies before pigment formation	Dalton, '40, '46
Triturus rivularis	T. granulosus	Neural folds	Dalton, '40, '46
Triturus rivularis	T. torosus	Tailbud	Dalton, '40, '46
3. ANURANS			
Rana arvalis	R. temporaria	Early gastrula †	P. Hertwig, '23
Bufo communis	B. viridis	Same †	P. Hertwig, '23
Bufo viridis	B. communis ‡	Same †	P. Hertwig, '23
Bufo communis	B. calamita ‡	Same †	P. Hertwig, '23
Bufo communis	R. temporaria §	Blastula	G. Hertwig, '13
Rana pipiens	R. palustris	Early neural folds	B. C. Moore, '41, '50
Rana pipiens	R. areolata	Embryo with small gill filaments	B. C. Moore, '41, '50
Rana palustris	R. pipiens	Semicircular blastopore and short neural folds, rarely to neural tube and eye vesicles	B. C. Moore, '41, '50
Rana palustris	R. areolata	Semicircular blastopore	B. C. Moore, '41, '50

* Diploid hybrid dies at beginning of gastrulation.

† Egg nucleus destroyed by radium treatment of egg before fertilization, which may have harmful effect on egg cytoplasm (cf. Dalcq and Simon, '31).

‡ Diploid hybrid dies as gastrula or embryo.

§ Diploid hybrid dies in blastula stage.

derm and entoderm of a normal egg of the maternal species. The resulting plutei always showed the skeletal characteristics of the species which furnished the nucleus of the micromeres.

The numerous experiments on hybrid androgenesis in amphibians show that development proceeds to more advanced stages in

of *T. palmatus* or *T. alpestris* showed that various tissues with *T. taeniatus* or *T. palmatus* cytoplasm and *T. cristatus* nucleus may survive and differentiate normally. Of particular interest is Hadorn's experiment ('36) illustrated in Figure 37, in which a large graft of androgenetic hybrid skin on an alpestris host survived beyond metamorpho-

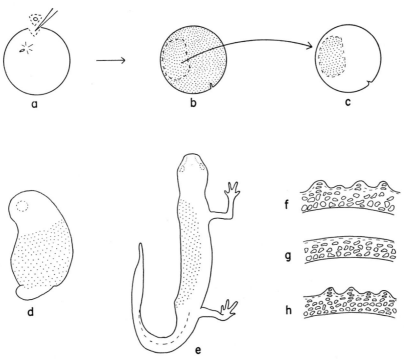

Fig. 37. Demonstration of effect of egg cytoplasm on development of skin characteristics appearing after metamorphosis (after Hadorn, '36). *a*, Fertilization of egg of *Triturus palmatus* with sperm of *T. cristatus* followed by removal of egg chromosomes. *b* and *c*, A large piece of presumptive epidermis from androgenetic hybrid gastrula, stained with nile-blue sulfate, is transplanted to diploid gastrula of a third species, *T. alpestris*. *d*, Transplant survives and covers large part of left flank of host embryo. *e*, Same animal after metamorphosis; skin removed from transplant has taken part normally in transformation. *f*, Diagrammatic section through epidermis of metamorphosed *T. palmatus* showing typical projections formed by series of flattened epidermis cells. *g*, Section through epidermis of metamorphosed *T. cristatus* with smooth surface. *h*, Section through epidermis formed by transplant (cells contain *T. palmatus* cytoplasm and haploid *T. cristatus* nuclei); typical protuberances are present as in *T. palmatus* epidermis.

combinations between more closely related species than in "distant" combinations; however, none of the androgenetic hybrids reach a stage in which differential characteristics of the two species appear (Table 8). A detailed analysis of the combination *T. taeniatus* (or *T. palmatus*) cytoplasm with *T. cristatus* nucleus by Baltzer ('30b, '33, '40) and Hadorn ('30 to '37) revealed that the early death is caused by the disintegration of the head mesenchyme. Cultivation of other regions of the young gastrula in vitro and, particularly, transplantation to normal embryos

sis and developed the epidermal protuberances that are typical for *T. taeniatus* which contributed the cytoplasm, but absent in *T. cristatus*, the donor of the nucleus. This result is probably to be explained as a maternal effect, due to the early activity of the *T. taeniatus* genome in the growing oocyte, before fertilization, although the characteristic does not appear until several months later (cf. Baltzer, '40). Normal histological differentiation of various organs has also been obtained in transplants from gastrulae of the combination *T. alpestris* cytoplasm and *T. palmatus* nucleus (de Roche, '37). Transplantation of neural crest containing *T. rivularis* cytoplasm and *T. torosus* nucleus to diploid *T. torosus* hosts produced a pigment pattern essentially like that of *T. torosus;* however, an influence of the cytoplasm of the donor species *T. rivularis* was manifested in the rate of melanization of the pigment cells (Dalton, '46).

POLYPLOID SPECIES HYBRIDS

A few observations have been made on the combined effects of polyploidy and hybridization ("allo-polyploidy" of the plant geneticists), an experiment which offers interesting possibilities. Eggs of sea urchins activated by carbon dioxide or ammonia pass through one or more monaster cycles, doubling or quadrupling the haploid chromosome number of the egg. Following fertilization with sperm of another species, triploid (and possibly pentaploid) species hybrids are produced which show a preponderance of maternal characteristics (Herbst, '12; Hinderer, '14; Landauer, '22). Triploid species hybrids have also been produced by mating triploid *Drosophila melanogaster* with diploid *D. simulans* for a study of interspecific sterility (Schultz and Dobzhansky, '33). In amphibians triploid hybrids with two sets of maternal chromosomes may be produced easily by refrigeration of eggs, which suppresses the formation of the second polar body (*T. rivularis* ♀ × *T. torosus* ♂, Costello, '42; *T. palmatus* ♀ × *T. alpestris* ♂, Fischberg, '48). In the latter experiment, the hybrid larvae with two sets of *T. palmatus* and one set of *T. alpestris* chromosomes exhibited a predominantly *T. palmatus* pigment pattern, in contrast to the diploid hybrids which showed a preponderance of *T. alpestris* characteristics. Closer resemblance to the maternal species was also found in triploid hybrids *T. pyrrhogaster* × *T. ensicauda* and *Rana japonica* × *R. temporaria ornativentris* (Kawamura, '52a,b).

OTHER EXPERIMENTAL APPROACHES
NUCLEO-CYTOPLASMIC INTERACTION IN THE OVARIAN OOCYTE

During the long period of growth of the amphibian oocyte intensive nucleo-cytoplasmic interactions must take place, as is indicated by the profound structural changes undergone by the chromosomes and the nucleolar apparatus during this time. Recently, Humphrey ('52) has found conclusive evidence for an effect produced by an abnormal, mutated gene, the recessive lethal factor for "fluid imbalance" described on page 133. A single larva showing the trait and thus presumably homozygous for the gene (*ff*) survived to sexual maturity. When this survivor, a female, was mated to a male heterozygous for the gene (*Ff*), it produced offspring half of which developed the fluid imbalance in a more severe form than ordinary *ff* embryos. Moreover, the remaining offspring (*Ff*) developed a less severe imbalance from which the majority recovered. These observations can be explained most easily by assuming that the *ff* genes of the mother produced an effect on the cytoplasm of the oocyte that expressed itself (1) in a more severe condition in the *ff* offspring, and (2) in a temporary early imbalance of the *Ff* offspring neutralized in later development by the dominant *F* gene brought in by the sperm.

TRANSPLANTATION OF NUCLEI

Extending the earlier experiments of Commandon and de Fonbrune ('39), Lorch and Danielli ('50) used the de Fonbrune micromanipulator to enucleate amoebae and to transplant nuclei from one amoeba to another. Cells with a grafted nucleus return to normal activity and may divide normally. If a nucleus is transferred between two different species, e.g., from *A. proteus* to *A. discoides*, reactivation occurs readily while nuclear and cell division are less frequent. Observations on cells consisting of cytoplasm of one species and nucleus of another show that the form assumed by the amoeba in movement is intermediate between the forms typical for the two species, i.e., it is influenced both by the constitution of the nucleus and by that of the cytoplasm.

More recently, Briggs and King ('52) have developed a method for transplanting nuclei from advanced blastula cells into enucleated eggs of the frog, *R. pipiens*. When the nucleus is from the same species as the egg cytoplasm, the egg cleaves normally and can develop into a normal embryo. When a nucleus from a blastula of *R. catesbeiana* is transplanted to an enucleated egg of *R. pipiens*, the egg cleaves but is arrested in the blastula stage, as are normally produced hybrids between these two species. This technique of nuclear transfer from more advanced stages of development to the unsegmented egg should prove of great value in the analysis of nucleo-cytoplasmic relationships and, particularly, of the problem of nuclear differentiation during development.

King and Briggs ('53) obtained normal development of enucleated eggs with nuclei from cells of presumptive chorda and neural plate of the late gastrula.

REFERENCES

Baltzer, F. 1910 Ueber die Beziehung zwischen dem Chromatin und der Entwicklung und Vererbungsrichtung bei Echinodermen-Bastarden. Arch. f. Zellforschg., 5:497–621.

———— 1920 Ueber die experimentelle Erzeugung und die Entwicklung von Triton-Bastarden ohne mütterliches Kernmaterial. Verh. Schweiz. Naturf. Ges. Neuenburg, 101:217–220.

———— 1922 Ueber die Herstellung und Aufzucht eines haploiden Triton taeniatus. Verh. Schweiz. Naturf. Ges., Bern, 103:248–249.

———— 1930a Die Zusammenarbeit von Plasma und Kern in der tierischen Entwicklung. Mitt. Naturf. Ges., Bern, pp. 10–12.

———— 1930b Ueber die Entwicklung des Tritonmerogons *Triton taeniatus* (♀) × *cristatus* (♂). Rev. Suisse Zool., 37:325–332.

———— 1933 Ueber die Entwicklung von Triton-Bastarden ohne Eikern. Verh. Deutsch. Zool. Ges., 1933:119–126.

———— 1940 Ueber erbliche letale Entwicklung und Austauschbarkeit artverschiedener Kerne bei Bastarden. Naturwiss., 28:177–187, 196–206.

———— 1952 The behaviour of nuclei and cytoplasm in amphibian interspecific crosses. Symp. Soc. Exp. Biol., 6:230-242.

————, and Schönmann, W. 1951 Ueber die Letalität des Bastards *Triton palmatus* ♀ × *Salamandra atra* ♂ . Rev. Suisse Zool., 58:495–501.

Barth, L. G., and Jaeger, L. 1947 Phosphorylation in the frog's egg. Physiol. Zool., 20:117–125.

Bataillon, E., and Tchou-Su 1929 Analyse de la fécondation par l'hybridation et la polyspermie physiologique. Roux' Arch. Entw.-mech., 115:770–824.

Beatty, R. A. 1951 Heteroploidy in mammals. Animal Breeding Abstracts, 19:283–292.

————, and Fischberg, M. 1949 Spontaneous and induced triploidy in pre-implantation mouse eggs. Nature, 163:807.

Blair, A. P. 1941 Variation, isolation mechanisms, and hybridization in certain toads. Genetics, 26:398–410.

Boehringer, F. 1938 Ueber die Kernverhaeltnisse und die Entwicklung der merogonischen Amphibienbastarde Triton (♀) × Salamandra ♂ . Roux' Arch. Entw.-mech. 138:376–422.

Böök, J. A. 1940 Triploidy in *Triton taeniatus* Laur. Hereditas, 26:107–114.

———— 1941 Induction of haploidy in a cold treatment experiment with egg-cells of the salamander *Triton taeniatus*. Kungl. Fysiografiska Sallskapets i Lund Forhandlingar, 11:1–16.

———— 1945 Cytological studies in Triton. Hereditas, 31:177–220.

Boveri, Th. 1896 Ueber die Befruchtungs- und Entwicklungsfaehigkeit kernloser Seeigeleier und ueber die Moeglichkeit ihrer Bastardierung. Roux' Arch. Entw.-mech., 2:394–443.

———— 1902 Ueber mehrpolige Mitosen als Mittel zur Analyse des Zellkernes. Verh. phys. med. Ges., Würzburg, N. F., 35:67–90.

———— 1905 Zellenstudien. V. Ueber die Abhängigkeit der Kerngrösse und Zellenzahl der Seeigel-Larven von der Chromosomenzahl der Ausgangszellen. Jena Zeitschr. Naturw., 39 (N. F. 32):445–524.

———— 1907 Zellenstudien. VI. Die Entwicklung dispermer Seeigeleier. Ein Beitrag zur Befruchtungslehre und zur Theorie des Kernes. Jena Zeitschr. Naturwiss., 43:1–292.

———— 1918 Zwei Fehlerquellen bei Merogonieversuchen und die Entwicklungsfaehigkeit merogonischer und partiellmerogonischer Seeigelbastarde. Roux' Arch. Entw.-mech., 44:417–471.

Brachet, J. 1944 Embryologie Chimique. Masson, Paris.

———— 1947 Biochemical and physiological interrelations between nucleus and cytoplasm. Growth, 11:309–324.

———— 1952 The role of the nucleus and the cytoplasm in synthesis and morphogenesis. Symp. Soc. Exp. Biol., 6:173–200.

Briggs, R. 1946 Effects of the growth inhibitor, hexenolactone, on frog embryos. Growth, 10:45–73.

———— 1947 The experimental production and development of triploid frog embryos. J. Exp. Zool., 106:237–266.

———— 1949 The influence of egg volume on the development of haploid and diploid embryos of the frog, *Rana pipiens*. J. Exp. Zool., 111:255–294.

————, Green, E. U., and King, T. J. 1951 An investigation of the capacity for cleavage and differentiation in *Rana pipiens* eggs lacking "functional" chromosomes. J. Exp. Zool., 116:455–499.

————, and King, T. J. 1952 Transplantation of living nuclei from blastula cells into enucleated frogs' eggs. Proc. Nat. Acad. Sci., 38:455–463.

Castle, W., and Gregory, P. W. 1929 The embryological basis of size inheritance. J. Morph., 48:81–104.

Commandon, J., and de Fonbrune, P. 1939 Greffe nucléaire total, simple ou multiple, chez une amibe. Compt. rend. Soc. Biol. Paris, 130:744–748.

Costello, D. P. 1942 Induced haploidy and triploidy in California Triturus. Anat. Rec., 84, No. 4: 60.

Curry, H. A. 1936 Ueber die Entkernung des Tritoneies durch Absaugen des Eifleckes und die Entwicklung des Tritonmerogons *Triton alpestris* (♀) × *Triton cristatus* (♂). Roux' Arch. Entw.-mech., 134:694–715.

Dalcq, A., and Simon, S. 1931 Contribution a l'analyse des fonctions nucléaires dans l'ontogénèse de la grenouille. III. Etude statistique et cytologique des effets de l'irradiation d'un des gamètes sur la gastrulation chez *Rana fusca*. Arch. Biol., 42:107–165.

Dalton, H. C. 1940 Experiments on the nucleus-plasma problem. Anat. Rec., 78: suppl., 53.

———— 1946 The role of nucleus and cytoplasm in development of pigment patterns in Triturus. J. Exp. Zool., 103:169–199.

de Roche, V. 1937 Differenzierung von Geweben und ganzen Organen in Transplantaten der bastardmerogonischen Kombination *Triton alpestris* (♀) × *Triton palmatus* (♂). Roux' Arch. Entw-mech., *135:*620–663.

Dollander, A. 1950 Étude des phénomènes de régulation consécutifs à la séparation des deux premières blastomères de l'oeuf de Triton. Arch. Biol., *61:*1-110.

Doncaster, L., and Gray, J. 1913 Cytological observations on the early stages of segmentation of Echinus hybrids. Quart. J. Micr. Sci., *58:*483–510.

Fankhauser, G. 1929 Ueber die Beteiligung kernloser Strahlungen (Cytaster) an der Furchung geschnuerter Triton-Eier. Rev. Suisse Zool., *36:*179–187.

———— 1930 Die Entwicklungspotenzen diploidkerniger Haelften des ungefurchten Tritoneies. Roux' Archiv. Entw.-mech., *122:*671–735.

———— 1934 Cytological studies on egg fragments of the salamander Triton. V. Chromosome number and chromosome individuality in the cleavage mitoses of merogonic fragments. J. Exp. Zool., *68:*1–57.

———— 1937 The production and development of haploid salamander larvae. J. Hered., *28:*1–15.

———— 1938a The microscopical anatomy of metamorphosis in a haploid salamander, *Triton taeniatus* Laur. J. Morph., *62:*393–413.

———— 1938b Triploidy in the newt, *Triturus viridescens*. Proc. Am. Philos. Soc., *79:*715–739.

———— 1939 Polyploidy in the salamander, *Eurycea bislineata*. J. Hered., *30:*379–388.

———— 1941 Cell size, organ and body size in triploid newts (*Triturus viridescens*). J. Morph., *68:*161–177.

———— 1945a The effects of changes in chromosome number on amphibian development. Quart. Rev. Biol., *20:*20–78.

———— 1945b Maintenance of normal structure in heteroploid salamander larvae, through compensation of changes in cell size by adjustment in cell number and cell shape. J. Exp. Zool., *100:*445–455.

———— 1948 The organization of the amphibian egg during fertilization and cleavage. Ann. N. Y. Acad. Sci., *49:*684–708.

———— 1952 Nucleo-cytoplasmic relations in amphibian development. Internat. Rev. Cytol., *1:*165-193.

————, Crotta, R., and Perrot, M. 1942 Spontaneous and cold-induced triploidy in the Japanese newt, *Triturus pyrrhogaster*. J. Exp. Zool., *89:*167–181.

————, and Griffiths, R. B. 1939 Induction of triploidy and haploidy in the newt, *Triturus viridescens*, by cold-treatment of unsegmented eggs. Proc. Nat. Acad. Sci., *25:*233–238.

————, and Humphrey, R. R. 1942 Induction of triploidy and haploidy in axolotl eggs by cold treatment. Biol Bull., *83:*367–374.

————, and Humphrey, R. R. 1943 The relation between number of nucleoli and number of chromosome sets in animal cells. Proc. Nat. Acad. Sci., *29:*344–350.

————, and Humphrey, R. R. 1950 Chromosome number and development of progenies of triploid axolotl females mated with diploid males. J. Exp. Zool., *115:*207–250.

————, and Moore, C. 1941 Cytological and experimental studies of polyspermy in the newt, *Triturus viridescens*. II. The behavior of the sperm nuclei in androgenetic eggs (in the absence of the egg nucleus). J. Morph., *68:*387–423.

————, and Watson, R. C. 1942 Heat-induced triploidy in the newt, *Triturus viridescens*. Proc. Nat. Acad. Sci., *28:*436–440.

————, and Watson, R. C. 1949 The effects of pituitary implants on diploid and triploid larvae of the newt, *Triturus viridescens*, with particular reference to the gonads. J. Exp. Zool., *111:*349–391.

Fischberg, M. 1944 Veraenderungen der Chromosomenzahl bei *Triton alpestris* nach Kaeltebehandlung der Eier. Rev. Suisse Zool., *51:*430–436.

———— 1947a Experimentelle Ausloesung von Heteroploidie durch Kaeltebehandlung der Eier von *Triton alpestris* aus verschiedenen Populationen. Genetica, *24:*1–117.

———— 1947b. Experimentelle Ausloesung von Heteroploidie bei einheimischen Urodelen. Rev. Suisse Zool., *54:*290–294.

———— 1948 Bestehen in der Ausbildung der Artmerkmale Unterschiede zwischen den diploiden und triploiden Bastarden von *Triton palmatus* ♀ und *Triton alpestris* ♂ ? Rev. Suisse Zool., *55:*304–310.

Fry, J. J. 1927 The cross fertilization of enucleated Echinarachnius eggs by Arbacia sperm. Biol. Bull., *53:*173–178.

Gallien, L., and Muguard, H. 1950 Application de la technique des imprégnations argentiques pour l'appréciation de l'hétéroploidie chez *Pleurodeles waltlii* Michah. Compt. rend. Soc. Biol. Paris, *144:*657–659.

Gregg, J. R. 1948 Carbohydrate metabolism of normal and of hybrid amphibian embryos. J. Exp. Zool., *109:*113–134.

Gregory, P. W., and Castle, W. 1931 Further studies on the embryological basis of size inheritance in the rabbit. J. Exp. Zool., *59:*199–212.

Hadorn, E. 1930 Ueber die Organentwicklung in bastardmerogonischen Transplantaten bei Triton. Rev. Suisse Zool., *37:*333–341.

———— 1932 Ueber Organentwicklung und histologische Differenzierung in transplantierten merogonischen Bastardgeweben. Roux' Arch. Entw.-mech., *125:*495–565.

———— 1934 Ueber die Entwicklungsleistungen bastardmerogonischer Gewebe von *Triton palmatus* (♀) × *Triton cristatus* ♂ im Ganzkeim und als Explantat in vitro. Roux' Arch. Entw.-mech., *131:*238–284.

———— 1935 Chimärische Tritonlarven mit bastardmerogonischen und normalkernigen Teilstücken. Rev. Suisse Zool., *42:*417–426.

———— 1936 Uebertragung von Artmerkmalen durch das entkernte Eiplasma beim merogonischen Tritonbastard, *palmatus* Plasma × *cristatus* Kern. Verh. Deutsch. Zool. Ges., Freiburg, pp. 97–104.

———— 1937 Die entwicklungsphysiologische

Auswirkung der disharmonischen Kern-Plasma-kombination beim Bastardmerogon *Triton palmatus* (♀) ✕ *Triton cristatus* ♂ . Roux' Arch. Entw.-mech., *136*:400–489.

Häggqvist, G., and Bane, A. 1950a Chemical induction of polyploid breeds of mammals. Kungl. Svenska Vetensk. Handl., *1:*(10):1–12.

——— 1950b Studies in triploid rabbits produced by colchicine. Hereditas, *36:*329–334.

——— 1951 Kolchizininduzierte Heteroploidie beim Schwein. Kungl. Svenska Vetensk. Handl., *3*(2):1–14.

Hamburger, V. 1935 Malformations of hind limbs in species hybrids of *Triton taeniatus* (and *palmatus*) ♀ ✕ *Triton cristatus* ♂ . J. Exp. Zool., *70:*43–84.

——— 1936 The larval development of reciprocal hybrids of *Triton taeniatus*, Leyd. (and *T. palmatus*, Duges) ✕ *Triton cristatus*, Laur. J. Exp. Zool., *73:*319–373.

Harvey, E. B. 1933 Development of the parts of sea-urchin eggs separated by centrifugal force. Biol. Bull., *64:*125–148.

——— 1936 Parthenogenetic merogony or cleavage without nuclei in *Arbacia punctulata*. Biol. Bull., *71:*101–121.

——— 1938 Parthenogenetic merogony or development without nuclei of the eggs of sea urchins from Naples. Biol. Bull., *75:*170–178.

———1939 Development of half-eggs of *Chaetopterus pergamentaceus* with special reference to parthenogenetic merogony. Biol. Bull., *76:*384–404.

——— 1940 A comparison of the development of nucleate and non-nucleate eggs of *Arbacia punctulata*. Biol. Bull., *79:*166–187.

Herbst, F. 1912 Vererbungsstudien. VII. Die cytologischen Grundlagen der Verschiebung der Vererbungsrichtung nach der mütterlichen Seite. Roux' Arch. Entw.-mech., *34:*1–89.

Hertwig, G. 1913 Parthenogenese bei Wirbeltieren, hervorgerufen durch artfremden, radiumbestrahlten Samen. Arch. mikr. Anat., *81*, II:87–127.

———, and Hertwig, P. 1920 Triploide Froschlarven. Arch. mikr. Anat., *94:*34–54.

Hertwig, O. 1913 Versuche an Tritoneiern über die Einwirkung bestrahlter Samenfäden auf die tierische Entwicklung. Arch. mikr. Anat., *82*, II:1–63.

Hertwig, P. 1923 Bastardierungsversuche mit entkernten Amphibieneiern. Roux' Arch. Entw.-mech., *100:*41–60.

——— 1936 Artbastarde bei Tieren; in Handbuch der Vererbungswissenschaften, vol. 2,B, pp. 1–140. Borntraeger, Berlin.

Hinderer, Th. 1914 Ueber die Verschiebung der Vererbungsrichtung unter dem Einfluss der Kohlensaeure. Roux' Arch. Entw.-mech., *38:*187–209, 364–401.

Hoerstadius, S. 1936 Studien ueber heterosperme Seeigelmerogone nebst Bemerkungen ueber einige Keimblattchimaeren. Mem. Musée Royal d'Hist. Nat. Belgique, (2d series) *3:*801–880.

Humphrey, R. R. 1945 Sex determination in am-

bystomid salamanders: a study of the progeny of females experimentally converted into males. Am. J. Anat., *76:*33–66.

——— 1948 A lethal fluid imbalance in the Mexican axolotl. J. Hered., *39:*255–261.

——— 1952 Modification of a lethal trait in the Mexican axolotl through influence of its genes upon the developing ovum. Anat. Rec., *112* (2): 114–115.

———, and Fankhauser, G. 1943 Two unusual haploid-diploid mosaics of mixed *Amblystoma mexicanum* and *Amblystoma tigrinum* ancestry. Anat. Rec., *87*, No. 4:23.

———, and Fankhauser, G. 1946 The development, structure, and functional capacity of the ovaries in triploid ambystomid salamanders. J. Morph., *79:*467–510.

Jahn, Ursula 1952 Induktion verschiedener Polyploidie-Grade bei *Rana temporaria* mit Hilfe von Kolchizin und Sulfanilamid. Z. mikr. anat. Forschg., *58:*36–99.

Kawamura, T. 1939 Artificial parthenogenesis in the frog. I. Chromosome numbers and their relation to cleavage histories. J. Sci. Hirosima Univ., Ser. B, Div. 1, *6:*115–218.

——— 1941a Polyploidy in the Japanese newt, *Triturus pyrrhogaster*. Zool. Mag. (Tokyo), *53:* 550–552.

——— 1941b Triploid frogs developed from fertilized eggs. Proc. Imp. Acad. Tokyo, *17:*523–526.

——— 1952a Triploid hybrids of *Triturus pyrrhogaster* and *T. ensicauda*. Annot. Zool. Jap., *25:*218–224.

——— 1952b Triploid hybrids of *Rana japonica* Guenther ♀ ✕ *Rana temporaria ornativentris* Werner ♂ . J. Sci. Hiroshima Univ., Ser. B., Div. 1, *13:*122–138.

Kaylor, C. T. 1940 Experiments on the parabiotic union of haploid and diploid larvae of *Triturus pyrrhogaster*. Anat. Rec., *78*, suppl.:52–53.

King, T. J., and Briggs, R. 1953 The transplantation of living nuclei from late gastrulae into enucleated eggs (*R. pipiens*). Anat. Rec., *117:*556.

Kupelwieser, H. 1909 Entwicklungserregung bei Seeigeleiern durch Molluskensperma. Roux' Arch. Entw.-mech., *27:*434–462.

Landauer, W. 1922 Untersuchungen ueber die Verschiebung der Vererbungsrichtung bei Echinodermenbastardlarven unter dem Einfluss von Ammoniak. Roux' Arch. Entw.-mech., *52* (*97*): 1–94.

Lorch, I. J., and Danielli, J. F. 1950 Transplantation of nuclei from cell to cell. Nature, *166:*329–330.

Luethi, H. R. 1938 Die Differenzierungsleistungen von Transplantaten der letalen Bastardkombination Triton ♀ ✕ Salamandra ♂ . Roux' Arch. Entw-mech., *138:*423–450.

Makino, S., and Ozima, Y. 1943 Formation of the diploid egg nucleus due to suppression of the second maturation division, induced by refrigeration of fertilized eggs of the carp, *Cyprinus carpio*. Cytologia, *13:*55–60.

McClendon, J. F. 1908 The segmentation of eggs of *Asterias forbesii* deprived of chromatin. Roux' Arch. Entw.-mech., *26:*662–668.

Melander, Y. 1950 Chromosome behavior of a

triploid adult rabbit as produced by Häggqvist and Bane after colchicine treatment. Hereditas, 36:335–341.

———— 1951 Polyploidy after colchicine treatment of pigs. Hereditas, 37:288–289.

Moore, Betty C. 1941 Androgenetic frog hybrids. Anat. Rec., 81, No. 4, suppl.:83–84.

———— 1950 The development of reciprocal androgenetic frog hybrids. Biol. Bull., 99:88–111.

Moore, J. A. 1941 Developmental rate of hybrid frogs. J. Exp. Zool., 86:405–422.

———— 1946a Incipient intraspecific isolating mechanisms in Rana pipiens. Genetics, 31:304–326.

———— 1946b Studies in the development of frog hybrids. I. Embryonic development in the cross Rana pipiens ♀ × Rana sylvatica ♂. J. Exp. Zool., 101:173–220.

———— 1947a Hybridization between Rana pipiens from Vermont and Eastern Mexico. Proc. Nat. Acad. Sci., 33:72–75.

———— 1947b Studies in the development of frog hybrids. II. Competence of the gastrula ectoderm of Rana pipiens ♀ × Rana sylvatica ♂ hybrids. J. Exp. Zool., 105:349–370.

———— 1948 Studies in the development of frog hybrids. III. Inductive ability of the dorsal lip region of Rana pipiens ♀ × Rana sylvatica ♂ hybrids. J. Exp. Zool., 108:127–154.

Morgan, T. H. 1927 Experimental Embryology. Columbia University Press, New York.

Morgenthaler, H. 1948 Ueber subhaploide Zellen in Triton-Transplantaten. Rev. Suisse Zool., 55:310–314.

Needham, J. 1942 Biochemistry and Morphogenesis. Cambridge University Press, Cambridge, England.

Painter, T. S. 1928 Cell size and body size in rabbits. J. Exp. Zool., 50:441–454.

Pariser, K. 1932 Verschiebung des Geschlechtsverhaeltnisses bei kuenstlich erzeugten Tritonbastarden (Vorl. Mitt.). Biol. Zentralbl., 52:654–659.

———— 1936 El desarolla y la relacion numerica entre los sexos en les hibridos interspecificos obtenidos por fecundacion artificial en el genero Triton (Molge). Rev. Espan. Biol., 5:11–93.

Parmenter, C. L. 1933 Haploid, diploid, triploid, and tetraploid chromosome numbers and their origin in parthenogenetically developed larvae and frogs of Rana pipiens and Rana palustris. J. Exp. Zool., 66:409–453.

———— 1940 Chromosome numbers in Rana fusca parthenogenetically developed from eggs

with known polar body and cleavage history. J. Morph., 66:241–260.

Porter, K. R. 1941 Diploid and androgenetic haploid hybridization between two forms of Rana pipiens, Schreber. Biol. Bull., 80:238–264.

———— 1946 The inheritance of nuclear properties which find expression in the first 72 hours of development of Rana pipiens, Schreber. Anat. Rec., 94, No. 3:61.

Sanada, M. 1951 The occurrence of tetraploidy in the Japanese newt, Triturus pyrrhogaster, by cold treatment of fertilized eggs. J. Sci. Hiroshima Univ., Ser. B., Div. 1, 12:35–37.

Schoenmann, W. 1938 Der diploide Bastard Triton palmatus ♀ × Salamandra ♂. Roux' Arch. Entw.-mech., 138:345–375.

Schultz, J., and Dobzhansky, Th. 1933 Triploid hybrids between Drosophila melanogaster and Dros. simulans. J. Exp. Zool., 65:73–82.

Spemann, H. 1901 Entwicklungsphysiologische Studien am Triton-Ei. Roux' Arch. Entw.-mech., 12:224–264.

———— 1902 Entwicklungsphysiologische Studien am Triton-Ei. II. Roux' Arch. Entw.-mech., 15:447–534.

———— 1914 Ueber verzoegerte Kernversorgung von Keimteilen. Verh. Deutsche Zool. Ges., 1914:16–221.

———— 1928 Die Entwicklung seitlicher und dorso-ventraler Keimhaelften bei verzoegerter Kernversorgung. Zeitschr. wiss. Zool., 132:105–134.

————, and Falkenberg, H. 1919 Ueber asymmetrische Entwicklung und Situs inversus viscerum bei Zwillingen und Doppelbildungen. Roux' Arch. Entw.-mech., 45:371–422.

Stauffer, E. 1945 Versuche zur experimentellen Herstellung haploider Axolotl-Merogone. Rev. Suisse Zool., 52:231–327.

Tchou-Su, M. 1931 Étude cytologique sur l'hybridation chez les anoures. Arch. d'anat. micr., 27:1–105.

Tennent, D. H., and Taylor, C. V. 1924 Preliminary report on the development of egg fragments. Carnegie Inst. Yearbook, 23:201–206.

Twitty, V. C. 1936 Correlated genetic and embryological experiments on Triturus. I and II. J. Exp. Zool., 74:239–382.

Ubisch, L. von 1953 Ueber Seeigelmerogone. Experientia, 9:294–295.

Zarapkin, S. R. 1934 Analyse der genotypisch und durch Aussenfaktoren bedingten Groessenunterschiede bei Drosophila funebris. II. Verhaeltnis zwischen Koerpergroesse und Zellenzahl. Zeitschr. ind. Abst. Ver.-lehre, 68:163–171.

CHAPTER 2

Gene Action

CURT STERN

THE NEED OF GENIC MATERIAL FOR DEVELOPMENT

THE NECESSITY of a nucleus for the functioning and survival of cells is, of course, a long established fact. For an egg cell, this implies that development cannot occur without presence of a nucleus. The few observations of developmental phenomena in enucleated systems do not contradict this statement. The partial cleavage of Amblystoma eggs whose maternal nucleus had been removed experimentally and whose paternal nucleus underwent degeneration (Jollos and Peterfi, '23), or the cleavage of experimentally activated, enucleated egg fragments of sea urchins (Harvey, '40) can be interpreted as a residual activity initiated while the nucleated egg was formed in the ovary.

This interpretation is supported by the analysis of development of fruiting bodies in the unicellular marine green alga *Acetabularia mediterranea* and related species (order Siphonocladiales) (Hämmerling, '34, '46). In the juvenile state these forms consist of a rhizoid containing a single, large nucleus and a stalk up to 7 cm. in length. On reaching maturity the anterior end of the stalk develops a complicated umbrella-like fruiting body. Early removal of the nucleus, by excision of the rhizoid, inhibits completely the development of the umbrella. Late removal of the nucleus is compatible, in many cases, with qualitatively complete though quantitatively diminished development of the complex morphological features of the umbrella, but more frequently no or only incomplete morphogenesis results. Reintroduction of a nucleus into the enucleated system completely restores the developmental capacity. Clearly, some nucleus-dependent substance or substances are instrumental in these developmental processes. The cytoplasm of the giant cell can store these substances and use them for partial morphogenesis but it is ultimately dependent on the nucleus for their production.

The first step in the analysis of the significance of nuclear constituents for development was made by Boveri ('02, '07). The causes of abnormal development of dispermic sea-urchin eggs were traced to the presence of nuclei in which certain chromosomes were lacking, and different types of abnormal development were linked with absence of different chromosomes. The nature of the experimental material—the 18 chromosomes of the haploid set of the sea urchins were not distinguished individually—did not permit that specific developmental assignments could be made to specific chromosomes.

In *Drosophila melanogaster* the necessity of having each of the four kinds of chromosomes represented in the fertilized egg in order to produce successful development has been proven by the use of genetic techniques which involve the "marking" of each kind of chromosome with specific genes (Li, '27, and earlier indirect evidence: Morgan, Bridges, and Sturtevant, '25, p. 135). An embryological study of the effect of the absence of the X-chromosome showed early abnormalities in the distribution of the cleavage nuclei (Poulson, '40, '45). No blastoderm is formed and neither morphogenetic changes nor differentiation occurs. Cleavage and cell divisions proceed for several hours before degeneration sets in.

We have no similar observations on Drosophila eggs lacking autosomes, and we can only assume but not prove that the breakdown of development would be different in type from that caused by lack of the X-chromosome if another chromosome were absent. That this assumption is probably correct can be judged by studies of eggs in which either one of two complementary sections of the X-chromosome are absent (Poulson, '40). When somewhat more than the proximal half of the X-chromosome is lacking there is, again, disturbed distribution of cleavage nuclei, but an incomplete blastoderm is formed. When somewhat less than the distal half of the X-chromosome is absent, a typical blastoderm develops but gastrulation and separation of the germ layers fail.

Studies of still finer subdivisions of the nuclear material and of the effect of their absence on development have shown that even very short chromosomal deficiencies, when homozygous, are lethal to the developing egg. When the "white" locus in the X-chromosome is lacking, morphogenesis proceeds well into formation and differentiation of the germ layers. Organs of ectodermal origin appear to be more or less normal but those of entodermal and mesodermal nature show malformations. The sac-like midgut fails to differentiate into a convoluted tube, while aorta, fat body and musculature either degenerate after an initial appearance, or fail to be formed completely. When the "facet" locus, a close neighbor of "white," is absent other abnormalities of development are observed (Poulson, '45). The nervous system hypertrophies excessively and, while showing considerable differentiation, possesses deranged patterns of ganglia and fiber tracts. The development of the mesodermal and entodermal derivatives shows specific deficiencies.

These studies prove the necessity of the presence even of minute sections of the genic material if development is to proceed successfully. There are a few exceptions known where complete absence of small chromosome sections is compatible with full development although greatly weakened constitution. On the other hand, for many deficiencies the evidence goes beyond the recognition of the necessity of the presence of the specific chromosomal section for development as a whole. Demerec ('34, '36) has investigated homozygous deficiencies whose lethal nature in the development of the egg was known, in regard to their effect on single hypodermal cells in normally developing individuals of Drosophila (unless specified otherwise, "Drosophila" refers to the species melanogaster). The experiments consisted in raising flies heterozygous for the deficiencies and watching for the appearance of cells which, in consequence of occasional abnormal mitotic distribution of chromosome parts, had become homozygous for the deficiencies. Many of the homozygous deficiencies proved to be "cell-lethal," that is, no cells survived after having received the completely deficient constitution. These cell-lethal deficiencies are thus not only incompatible with development as a whole but even with the carrying out of minor processes of cellular differentiation or of the relatively stationary processes of cellular metabolism.

In other cases, homozygous deficiencies, while unable to support embryonic development, are compatible with survival, division, and differentiation of somatic cells. However, it is not known whether the chromosomal section concerned is actually not required for cellular metabolism, or whether the breakdown of the cells is prevented by diffusion of necessary substances into the deficient cells from the neighboring nondeficient tissues of the developing individual.

The smallest genetically separable sections of chromosomes are called genes. The experiments reported in the preceding paragraphs establish the fact that genes are necessary for development. These experiments made use of the alternative: "presence" versus "absence" of genes. In addition, the geneticist can provide the student of development with other genetic variables as tools for a study of the role of genes in development. These tools consist of variations in the quantity of genes, and in their quality.

QUANTITATIVE VARIABILITY OF GENIC CONTENT

It is possible to obtain quantitative series in which the whole genic content of developing eggs is multiplied from one member of the series to the next: haploid, diploid, triploid, etc. The effects of such differences in plants have been studied extensively (Wettstein, '40), and some important results have also been obtained in animals (see the preceding chapter by Fankhauser in this volume). Usually no strikingly different effects on the phenotype are produced by the simultaneous multiplication of all genes. The developmentally "balanced" system of genic action within a diploid organism retains its proportionate effects in the various polyploids. There are, however, limits to the maintenance of balance. In the various members of the series, the relations between nuclear and cytoplasmic volume and surface are changed. These changes result in differences in the total numbers of cells which make up specific organs, and in differences in both absolute and relative growth.

Furthermore, equal increases in quantity of different genes do not necessarily produce proportional effects on the different reactions which lead to gene-dependent products.

The developmental effects of *partial* quantitative changes in genic content are usually much more striking than those in polyploidy. The most important case of this nature is, of course, the quantitative change in the number of X-chromosomes in bisexual organisms. The change from one X-chromosome to two, with the autosomal genes kept constant in diploid quantity, results in the development of the other sex characterized by striking differences in morphology and physiology. Changes in the quantity of the autosomes likewise upset the developmental balance, resulting in intersexual differentiation (Standfuss, '14; Bridges, '22; reviews in Goldschmidt, '31, and Fankhauser, this volume), or in other morphological changes (Sinnott, Houghtaling, and Blakeslee, '34; Bridges, '22).

Changes in the quantity of small chromosomal sections or of individual genes sometimes have no, or hardly observable, effects, but at other times produce striking results. In Drosophila deficiencies at many loci, in heterozygous condition, lead to the appearance of normal individuals. On the contrary, a heterozygous deficiency at the facet locus results in abnormal, notched wings, and heterozygous deficiencies in various chromosome regions result in "Minute" slender bristled flies with greatly prolonged development (see Bridges and Brehme, '44; Brehme, '41). In these latter cases a single quantity of a normal allele is incapable of maintaining the normal process of development ("haplo-insufficiency") (Mohr, '32). Increase beyond the diploid quantity of normal alleles, by use of duplications of chromosomal sections, is usually of less effect than decrease. This may partially be due to the fact that the relative change in developmental balance is more severe when the quantity of a gene is reduced from 2 to 1, than if it is increased from 2 to 3. In part, the lack of effect of increase in the quantity of a gene from the diploid to the triploid seems to depend on a situation in which the diploid effect involves a threshold of activity which cannot be surpassed. The cause of the existence of such thresholds must be searched for in limiting factors imposed by other genic or non-genic components of the cells or of the developing systems.

QUALITATIVE VARIABILITY OF GENIC CONTENT

Many genes are known to occur in different states, their allelic forms. Any allele has high stability, but rare mutations may transform one allele into another. While in some cases actual absences (deficiencies) of the gene in the chromosome may simulate the effect of an allele, the regular existence of multiple alleles at most, if not all, loci suggests that alleles are qualitatively different representatives of the genic material at each locus.

The different alleles of a gene are recognized as such by their different action. Most studies of genic action in development consist in the description of the effects of *substitution* of one allele for another. If, for example, the effect of the creeper allele in the fowl is being investigated, the direct object of inquiry is the difference between the development of an egg that contains this allele and another that contains, instead, the "normal" non-creeper allele.

Gene action in development may be studied from different aspects. The geneticist may desire to trace the developmental chain of events back to the primary agents, the genes, in the hope of learning about their immediate action and their elementary constitution. The student of development may use the different alleles as differentiating tools by means of which he can introduce internal variables into the course of development in order to gain insight into its processes. The two modes of inquiry are, of course, closely related and have been jointly subsumed under such designations as physiological and developmental genetics (Goldschmidt, '20, '27, '38; Stern, '40; Wright, '16, '34, '41, '45a, b), or in regard to more delimited fields, biochemical genetics (Beadle, '45) and immunogenetics (Irwin, '47).

The chain of events which leads from genes to phenotypic properties must vary in length from case to case. By and large, intracellular biochemical properties will be connected with the genes by fewer links than morphological properties of organs or organ systems. In no case do we yet know with certainty that only a single step intervenes between a gene and a recognizable gene-dependent product. It has, however, been suggested with plausibility that some cellular antigens owe their specificity to direct genic action (Haldane, '37). There exists a one-to-one correspondence between the presence of alleles such as those responsible for the human iso-agglutinogens A and B and the antigens themselves, as shown by the facts that whenever the relevant allele is present the antigen appears in every genetic background, and that in heterozygotes for the alleles I^A and I^B both antigens A and B are produced simultaneously.

It has also been assumed that enzymes, which control a variety of biochemical re-

different rates of gene-controlled, qualitatively identical reactions and has shown how such a rate concept fits a great variety of phenomena in developmental genetics. In some cases, different rates of production of pigments or of growth, controlled by different alleles, have been demonstrated by direct observation (Fig. 38A and B). These different rates have been reported by Goldschmidt ('27) for larval pigmentation in *Lymantria*

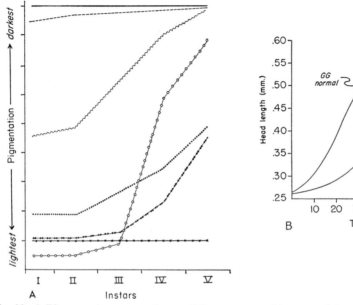
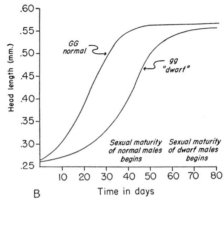

Fig. 38. *A*, Pigmentation curves of seven different geographic races of the gypsy-moth *Lymantria dispar* (after Goldschmidt, '27). *B*, Growth curves for a normal (*GG*) and a "dwarf" (*gg*) strain of *Gammarus chevreuxi* (after Ford and Huxley, '29).

actions in the bread mold Neurospora, are under immediate gene control in the sense that specific alleles impress enzymatic specificity on cellular constituents (Beadle, '45; Bonner, '48; Horowitz, '50). Attempts to prove this hypothesis have met with great difficulties (Emerson, '50).

The examples of gene-controlled antigens and enzymes indicate that the primary products of the action of different alleles may be qualitatively different. There are other examples which suggest quantitative difference in allelic action. A series of multiple alleles of a given gene usually affects the same phenotypic trait, in a graded manner. In Drosophila, for instance, different alleles of the vestigial locus control the appearance of a fully formed wing, of a slightly nicked wing, a deeper notched one, a short vestigial wing stump, and a wingless condition (Mohr, '32). Goldschmidt ('38) has given an interpretation of these cases in terms of

dispar, and by Ford and Huxley ('29) for rate of growth in *Gammarus chevreuxi*.

Different rates of apparently identical processes do not need to depend on different rates of identical primary genic reactions. Different alleles may control the production of qualitatively different primary products which in turn may influence identical reactions in quantitatively graded fashion (Wright, '45a; Stern, '48).

The theory that different alleles of a gene cause their different developmental effects by influencing the rate of gene-controlled reactions has led Goldschmidt to the prediction that the different phenotypes can be produced purely environmentally in developing animals of identical genotype. External agents, particularly temperature, should change differentially the many gene-controlled reactions and thus act, at appropriate stages, essentially like shifts in reactions due to different alleles. This expectation has been verified over a wide range of phenotypes in various organisms, e.g., Lepidoptera (Kühn and Henke, '29–'36), Drosophila (Goldschmidt, '35a,b, '37; Henke, v. Fink, and Ma, '41), chickens (review by Landauer, '48) and mice (Russell and Russell, '48). In Drosophila, for instance, heavy shock of short duration with high temperatures, or less striking temperature increases for longer periods, produce modifications, in genetically normal individuals, of wings and halteres, eyes and aristae, legs and body wall, and bristles. The modifications are of numerous

that the interference with development by an external agent may well occur at the same time, and perhaps in the same manner, as the developmental shift under the influence of the mutant which is phenocopied. In other instances, it has been demonstrated that the sensitive period during which a phenocopy may be induced is later than the phase at which the mutant first shows its developmental effect. Obviously in these latter cases the phenocopy does not actually imitate the course of events initiated by the mutant allele whose effects it simulates.

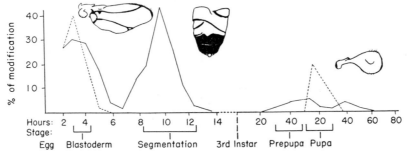

Fig. 39. Sensitive periods of production of developmental anomalies in *Drosophila melanogaster*: tetraptera-like wing modification of the halteres; abnormal abdomen; abnormal bristle growth on halteres (after Henke and Maas, '46).

types, as in the case of wings, where they affect shape and size, venation and distribution of bristles.

Specific relations have been demonstrated between the stage in development of the egg, larva, or pupa, and the production of the various modifications (see Fig. 39). Thus, a period sensitive to moderate temperature effects occurs between two and four hours after fertilization—before completion of the blastoderm—resulting in the later morphogenesis of the metathoracic segment approaching that typical for the mesothorax. Shortly later an embryonic sensitive period may be used to initiate processes leading to abnormal abdominal segmentation. Modifications of imaginal bristles may be induced in newly hatched larvae, of wing shape in larvae of the second instar, and of the eye surface in those of the third instar. Likewise, all these may be induced by treatment of prepupae and pupae (Henke and Maas, '46).

Goldschmidt introduced the name *phenocopy* for these modifications, since they seem to imitate in genetically normal strains the phenotypes known to be caused by mutant allelic substitutions. Comparisons between the development of mutant phenotypes and of phenocopies have shown in some cases

There is, however, an arbitrariness in choosing a single specific mutant and comparing it with a given phenotypic modification. It is known that many different mutant loci may cause the development of similar or identical final phenotypes and it seems possible that every environmentally induced developmental modification may have its true genetic counterpart in one of the various known, or not yet discovered, mutants.

While it is necessary to be aware of the usually somewhat arbitrary nature of designating a modification as the phenocopy of a given mutant, it seems likely that a phenocopy will be found for each mutant, and a mutant for each phenotypic modification. Therefore, the terms "true" and "false" phenocopies, which suggest that an environmentally induced phenotype either corresponds in its developmental origin to a mutant phenotype ("true"), or only simulates it ("false"), have only limited validity.

TIME OF GENIC ACTION

Gene-controlled events are known to occur at various stages of development. One of the earliest evidences for genic action are "size genes" brought into the egg by the sperm in crosses between large and small races of rabbits (Gregory and Castle, '31). The rate of cleavage of eggs, which is correlated with adult body size, is increased under the influence of paternal genes as early as at the third or fourth cell division. Slightly later effects of genes are known in the early embryology of Drosophila (Poulson, '40, '45), in the morphology of sea urchin larvae derived

much earlier, invisibly preparing a situation which is a prerequisite for later effects. There is evidence for both types of activity, the immediate and the distant. Examples of the latter, in purest form, are presented by the so-called maternal effects, in which genes present in the cells of a female, including her immature, premeiotic egg cells, cause developmental effects in her offspring even

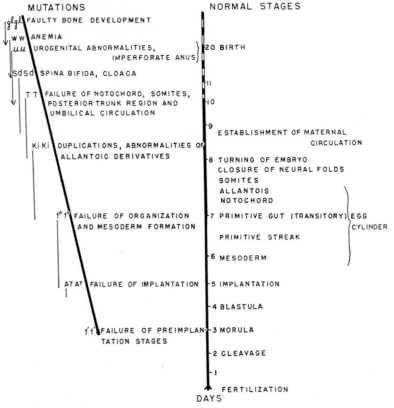

Fig. 40. Some of the lethal mutations affecting embryonic processes in mice (from Dunn, '49).

from species crosses (Moore, '43), at the morula stage of mice homozygous for certain tailless alleles (Dunn, '49; see Fig. 40), and at the blastocyst stage of mice homozygous for the yellow-lethal gene (Robertson, '42). Figure 40 illustrates other embryonic processes in mice affected by lethal mutations.

While it is obvious in these examples that genic action occurs within a short initial period, namely that preceding the time of an observable effect, it is more difficult to make statements when observable effects occur late in development. Here, genic action may have immediately preceded the observable event or it may have taken place

though these genes may not have been included in the zygotic nuclei. This is the well known explanation for the inheritance of dextrality and sinistrality in the snail Limnaea (Boycott, Diver, and Garstang, '30; Sturtevant, '23). The type of configuration which an individual will attain is determined by a pair of alleles, but not by those present in his own genotype. Rather, the genotype of the maternal tissue in which the oocyte is formed fixes the fate of the next generation. This is accomplished by imparting to the cytoplasm of the egg the property, unknown in its essence, of initiating the sequence of its spiral cleavages in either a clockwise or a counterclockwise direction.

suchungen zum Artbildungsproblem, II. Zur Frage der Polyploidie als Artbildungsfaktor. Ber. Deutsch. Bot. Ges., *58:*374–388.

Whiting, A. 1934 Eye colors in the parasitic wasp Habrobracon and their behavior in multiple recessives and in mosaics. J. Genet., *29:*99–107.

Whiting, P. W. 1940 Multiple alleles in sex determination of Habrobracon. J. Morph., *66:*323–355.

———, Greb, J., and Speicher, B. R. 1934 A new type of sex intergrade. Biol. Bull., *66:*152–165.

Winge, O., and Laustsen, O. 1939 On 14 new yeast types, produced by hybridization. Compt. rend. Trav. Lab. Carlsberg, Serie Physiol., *22:* 337–351.

Wright, S. 1916 An intensive study of the inheritance of color and of other coat characters in guinea pigs with especial reference to graded variation. Carnegie Inst. Washington Publ. No. 241, pp. 59–160.

——— 1934 Physiological and evolutionary theories of dominance. Amer. Nat., *68:*24–53.

——— 1941 The physiology of the gene. Physiol. Rev., *21:*487–527.

——— 1945a Physiological aspects of genetics. Ann. Rev. Physiol., *7:*75–106.

——— 1945b Genes as physiological agents: general considerations. Amer. Nat., *79:*289–303.

Section V

EMBRYOGENESIS: PREPARATORY PHASES

CHAPTER 1

Gametogenesis, Fertilization and Parthenogenesis

ALBERT TYLER

GAMETOGENESIS
ORIGIN OF THE GERM CELLS

AN UNDERSTANDING of the factors that endow egg and spermatozoon with the ability to unite and produce a new individual may be expected to depend largely on knowledge of the manner of origin and formation of the gametes. While such knowledge is very far from complete there is a considerable body of descriptive and experimental information relating to it. To illustrate the nature of this information and some of the problems involved certain of the pertinent investigations will be briefly reviewed here. Questions concerning the determination of the gonad are discussed in another chapter of this book.

Much of the stimulus for work on the origin of the germ cells was undoubtedly provided by Weismann's (1883, 1893) views concerning the continuity and segregation of the germ plasm. His concept of a distinct germ plasm is sufficiently familiar, even to beginning biologists, so that it does not require detailed presentation here. A critical review of the original basis of the concept has been published recently by Berrill and Liu ('48).

In many species of animals the primordial germ cells may be recognized at an early stage of development and, particularly among the invertebrates, there are cases in which a "germ-line" is manifest from the start of cleavage (see Wilson, '25, and Bounoure, '39, for references and brief accounts). In these the identification of the primordial germ cells is based on certain distinguishing features of the nucleus or the cytoplasm. We shall consider some examples briefly here.

Chromatin Diminution in Ascaris. The classic case is that of *Ascaris megalocephala* (*Parascaris equorum*) in which Boveri (1887–1910) described a process, termed chromatin diminution (Herla, 1895), occurring during cleavage in the cells that are to form somatic tissue but not in those that are to form the germ cells. In this process the mid-portion of each of the chromosomes (two in *A. megalocephala univalens*) breaks up into a number of small fragments (about 10 per chromosome according to Fogg, '30), leaving two large terminal pieces. The smaller fragments reconstitute the daughter nuclei and continue regular mitotic division but the terminal pieces remain in the cytoplasm and slowly disappear. The ability of the small fragments to continue mitotic division is evidently due to the fact that each possesses a centromere, the original chromosomes being polycentric, as Schrader ('35) and White ('36) have pointed out. It is now well known that chromosomal fragments devoid of a centromere fail to attach to the spindle and to divide.

The diminution phenomenon starts at the second or the third division of the egg. In the former case it occurs in the dorsal, somatic cell (S_1) and not in the ventral, stem cell (P_1), as illustrated in Figure 45. In the latter case it occurs in three cells at once but not in the stem cell P_2. In both cases P_2 divides into a somatic cell which undergoes diminution (at its next division) and another stem cell, P_3. The latter again divides (without diminution) into a somatic cell (that undergoes diminution at its next division) and the definitive primordial germ cell, P_4.

(Boveri, '10a; Hogue, '10). The centrifugation experiments provided the more direct evidence. In many of the centrifuged eggs (as high as 36 per cent in some experiments) it

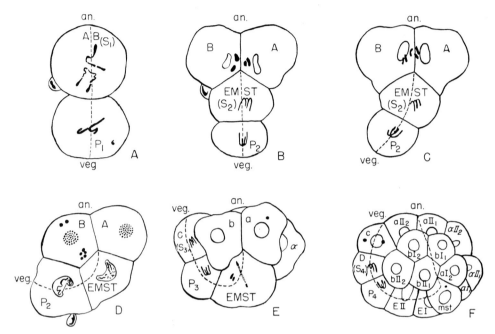

Fig. 45. Cleavage of *Ascaris megalocephala* (*Parascaris equorum*), illustrating location of the stem cells (P_1–P_4) which do not undergo chromatin diminution and from which the germ cells are derived. Note bending of the original egg axis as a result of the shifting of the blastomeres in the 4-cell stage. *A*, 2-cell stage; *B, C, D*, 4-cell stage; *E*, 7-cell stage; *F*, 24-cell stage; *an.*, animal pole; *veg.*, vegetal pole. (From von Ubisch, '43, after Boveri, '99.)

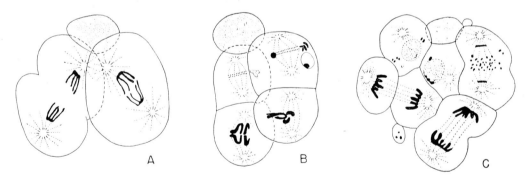

Fig. 46. Second (*A*) and third (*B* and *C*) cleavages of Ascaris eggs that had been centrifuged before the first cleavage; showing (in *B* and *C*) chromatin diminution in the upper cells but not in the two lower cells (from Hogue, '10).

Boveri surmised that differences in the cytoplasm of different regions of the egg were responsible for the occurrence or non-occurrence of the diminution process and, at the same time, for the determination of the germ cells. This view was supported by the results of studies on polyspermic eggs (Boveri, '04, '10b) and on centrifuged eggs

was found that two stem cells formed instead of the single one that normally occurs. Figure 46 illustrates such eggs at the second and third cleavages. Diminution is seen in the upper two blastomeres (adjacent to an extruded ball of cytoplasmic material) but not in the two lower cells. This effect is interpreted as being due to a shift in direction of the first cleavage plane of the centrifuged egg so that the first two blastomeres have essentially the same cytoplasmic constitution with regard to factors inducing or preventing diminution. The next division, then, is differential with regard to these factors in each blastomere.

More recently King and Beams ('38) have subjected Ascaris eggs to high speed (150,000 g.) centrifugation whereby cytoplasmic division was suppressed while nuclear division continued. They noted that, in such eggs, diminution usually occurs in all of the nuclei

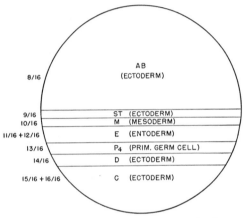

Fig. 47. Diagram illustrating location, in the uncleaved Ascaris egg, of the material for the primordial germ cell (P₄) (after von Ubisch, '43).

at the second or the third mitosis. This led them to interpret diminution on the basis of a "diminisher" substance D, that is produced from some cytoplasmic constituent, An, which is concentrated in the animal region of the egg and grades off to zero at the vegetal pole. Normally, D reaches sufficient concentration to cause diminution in the polar cell or cells at the second or third cleavage, and in the somatic cells derived from the stem cells at succeeding divisions. In the absence of cell boundaries, in the centrifuged egg, D is assumed to be free to diffuse and, upon reaching sufficient concentration, causes diminution to occur in all of the nuclei. This view has been criticized by von Ubisch ('43), who points out that the region of the uncleaved egg that is to be incorporated into the primordial germ cell (P₄) does not comprise the most vegetal material but is located about halfway between the equator and the vegetal pole (see Fig. 47). This fact was evident in the original cell-lineage studies of Boveri (1899) but has been overlooked in most accounts of the

work on Ascaris. However, it seems to the present author that the essential feature of the interpretation of King and Beams remains valid. That feature is the localized production of some substance (either inducing or preventing diminution) during early cleavage. It seems simplest to regard this in terms of the production of materials essential for the continued reproduction of those parts (the ends and possibly the substance in the regions of fracture) of the chromosomes that are eliminated in the cells that undergo diminution. The site of production would be that region of the cytoplasm halfway between the equator and the vegetal pole of the uncleaved egg, and the formation of cell boundaries would presumably prevent diffusion of the material to other cells.

Chromosome Elimination in Sciara. Another remarkable example of differential behavior of the chromosomes in germ cells and somatic cells occurs in the fungus fly Sciara, studied extensively by C. W. Metz and his co-workers (see Metz, '38, for review, and Berry, '41, for some later details). The zygote starts development with three pairs of autosomes, three X-chromosomes and, in twelve of fourteen species examined, one, two or three large chromosomes called "limited" chromosomes (Fig. 48). At the sixth division (sometimes the fifth) of the zygote the "limited" chromosomes are eliminated from all of the somatic nuclei. At this stage the nuclei have migrated from the middle of the egg, where the zygote nucleus is originally located, nearly to the periphery. One or two of the nuclei at the posterior pole of the egg form the primordial germ cells, which retain for some time the full complement of chromosomes present in the zygote.

Another elimination of chromosomes occurs in the somatic cells at the seventh or eighth division. At this time the somatic nuclei of the female-producing eggs eliminate one of the three X-chromosomes and the male-producing eggs eliminate two X-chromosomes. In these elimination divisions the "limited" chromosomes and X-chromosomes that are to be discarded fail to divide, or divide incompletely. They are, then, left on the middle of the spindle in anaphase and do not become incorporated in the daughter nuclei, but slowly break up and disappear in the later embryo. In Sciara an elimination also occurs later in the germ cells after they have migrated to the site of formation of the gonads, one of the X-chromosomes (one of the two paternal X's) being extruded from each nucleus in both male and female larvae. This elimination is described (Berry, '41) as occurring in a resting nucleus, the chromosome being expelled through the nuclear membrane into the cytoplasm. Presumably there is also an elimination of one or more "limited" chromosomes from the germ cells

bud while the maternal chromosomes and the "limited" chromosomes all move to the pole and are incorporated in the single second spermatocyte. The latter forms a bipolar spindle, and the sister chromatids of each chromosome except the X separate to opposite poles. Both chromatids of the X

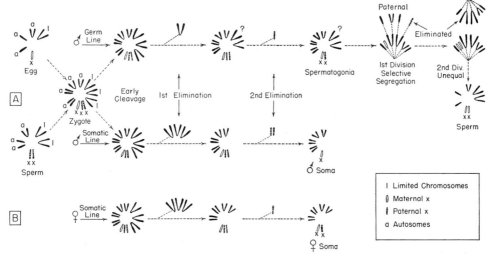

Fig. 48. Diagram of behavior of the chromosomes in *Sciara coprophila*, illustrating difference between somatic and germ line cells in regard to elimination of chromosomes. The female germ line (not illustrated) would be the same as in diagram *A* except that the meiotic divisions do not involve the cytological peculiarities exhibited in spermatogenesis. See text for further description. (From Metz, '38.)

in some cases, but this has not, as yet, been described.

Since the germ cells of Sciara have the same chromosome set in the male as in the female the determination of whether they are to produce spermatozoa or eggs is evidently effected by the somatic cells which, as a result of the elimination of one or two X's at the seventh (or eighth) division, have the typical XO constitution in the male and XX in the female. This, in turn, is evidently determined in the female parent which, as a rule, produces unisexual families. The genetic evidence accumulated by Metz and his co-workers shows that the two X-chromosomes are alike (XX) in the male-producers but differ genetically (XX') in the female producers. The results of fertilization in these two types are diagrammed in Figure 49.

The unusual chromosome constitution of the zygote in Sciara results from peculiarities in spermatogenesis. In the first spermatocyte a monocentric spindle is formed and the chromosomes are separated without pairing, in such a way that all the paternal chromosomes except the "limited" chromosomes are extruded in a small cytoplasmic

go to one pole and are incorporated in the single spermatid that forms, while the chromosomes at the other pole are included in a small bud that later degenerates. All of the spermatozoa that form are, then, alike

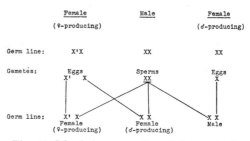

Fig. 49. Metz's interpretation of the production of "unisexual" families in *Sciara coprophila* on the basis of genetically different (X and X') sex chromosomes (from Metz, '38).

and contain a haploid set of autosomes, the "limited" chromosomes and two X-chromosomes. Oogenesis, on the other hand, is regular with random segregation of chromosomes.

Chromosome Elimination in Other Animals. Even more extensive elimination of chromosomes from somatic cells has been described in the gall midges (Cecidomyidae), which have been studied most recently by White ('46, '47a, b, '48). In Miastor, for example, there are 48 chromosomes in the zygote but 36 of these are eliminated from the somatic nuclei of the female and of the pedogenetic larvae at the third and fourth cleavage divisions, while 42 are eliminated in the males. The full complement is retained by the germ cells, which are set aside at the posterior pole of the egg at this time.

Chromosome- or chromatin-diminution also occurs in various animals without rela-

of the germ cells, have been described in several species of animals among the scyphozoans (Equorea), chaetognaths (Sagitta), rotifers (Asplanchna), insects (Chironomus, Calliphora, Calligrapha, Lepintotarsa, Copidosoma, Trichograma, Apanteles), crustaceans (Cyclops, Diaptomus, Polyphemus, Moina) and amphibians (Rana) (see Hegner, '14; Wilson, '25; Bounoure, '39). According to the accounts the cells that receive these granules ultimately become germ cells. However, there is, as yet, no direct experimental evidence, such as might be derived

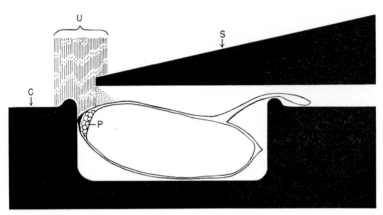

Fig. 50. Geigy's method for exposing the posterior pole of the egg of Drosophila to ultraviolet radiation. C, wax trough; U, ultraviolet beam; S, brass screen; E, egg; P, pole cells. (After Geigy, '31.)

tion to germ-cell determination (see Berry, '41, for references). For example, it occurs in the polar body divisions of several species of Lepidoptera. Here, however, the eliminated chromatin is Feulgen-negative whereas in Ascaris, Sciara, etc., it is Feulgen-positive (Bauer, '32, '33). One of the most striking examples has been described in the grass mite, *Pediculopsis graminum* (Cooper, '39, '41). Feulgen-negative "chromatin" bodies that correspond in number and position to the metaphase chromosomes are left at the equator of the spindle at both polar body divisions and at each of the first nine cleavage divisions, but not in the succeeding mitoses of the embryo or of the oogonia.

Such cases do not, however, rule out the possibility that. where elimination occurs in connection with germ-cell determination, the chromatin that is eliminated from the somatic cells may contain genes that are of importance for the development of the gametes.

Localized Cytoplasmic Factors in Germ-Cell Determination. Special cytoplasmic granules (termed germ-cell determinants), that are considered to be important for the formation

from centrifugation experiments, to show that the particular granules are causative agents in germ-cell determinations.

Apart from the questions of particular granules and of chromatin diminution, the importance of localized cytoplasmic factors in germ-cell determination is very well illustrated in the experiments of Geigy ('31), Aboim ('45), and Geigy and Aboim ('44) on Drosophila. Geigy ('31) succeeded in inhibiting the formation of germ cells by subjecting the posterior pole of the egg to ultraviolet irradiation. The method of localized irradiation is shown in Figure 50. After irradiation the cleavage nuclei that wander into the damaged pole plasm degenerate and the formation of pole cells is partially or completely suppressed. However, even in cases of complete suppression, adult flies are obtained which appear completely normal and have gonads of normal structure although of reduced size. This work not only strikingly confirms the earlier indications that factors essential for germ-cell formation are localized in the posterior cytoplasm of the egg, but also furnishes further convincing evidence that the mesodermal parts of the gonad can develop normally in the absence of the germ cells.

Somewhat similar experiments have been performed in frogs by Bounoure ('35a, b, '37a, b, c). He irradiated the vegetal pole of the egg and obtained a great reduction in the number of germ cells of the larvae that developed. While none of the larvae were completely agamic, at least two cases were obtained in which one gonad was entirely devoid of germ cells. Here, too, the

upon the occurrence of a migration of primordial germ cells to the genital ridge from some other region of the embryo or from extra-embryonic areas, such as described by Allen ('07) in frogs and by Swift ('14) in birds. For a recent example of such studies reference may be made to the work of Witschi ('48) on human embryos, in which migration of the germ cells from the yolk sac to the genital folds is convincingly described.

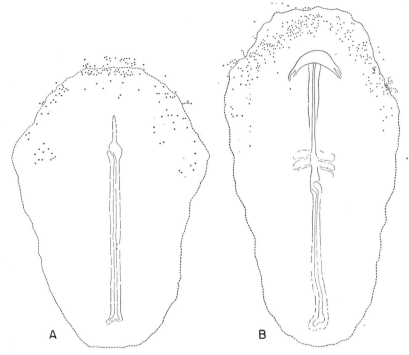

Fig. 51. Maps showing distribution of germ cells in chick blastoderms. *A*, head-process stage; *B*, 3-somite stage. (From Willier, '37.)

somatic constituents of the agamic gonad appeared normal.

Other Experiments Concerning the Origin of the Germ Cells in Vertebrates. The question of the origin of the germ cells in vertebrates has been the subject of much controversy centering primarily upon whether or not they may be formed from "differentiated" somatic cells in various stages of embryonic development and in the adult. The subject has been frequently and extensively reviewed (Willier, '39; Bounoure, '39; Dantschakoff, '41; Everett, '45; Nieuwkoop, '46). The present discussion will restrict itself mainly to some of the more recent experimental work.

There is now fairly general agreement

In many respects birds have provided the more favorable experimental material in attempts to deprive the embryo of germ cells, and several workers have reported success upon subjecting the area of Swift's germinal crescent (see Fig. 51) to extirpation (Reagan, '16; Willier, '33, '37), ultraviolet irradiation (Benoit, '30), and cauterization (Dantschakoff et al., '31). In Willier's ('37) experiments on chorio-allantoic grafting of portions of chick blastoderms, it has been demonstrated that a gonad free of germ cells may develop and claims (e.g., Dantschakoff et al., '31) of the necessity of the presence of germ cells for differentiation of the gonad are refuted. Willier cautions against interpreting the results of his experiments, and those of others, as definitive proof of the extragonadal origin of all of the germ cells in the chick. He points to three somewhat anomalous results: (1) Sterile gonads may be obtained from grafts that contain the germinal crescent as well as from those in which that area has been excluded. (2) Sterile gonads may also form from grafts of the gonad-forming area taken at a stage when it contains germ cells. (3) Germ cells

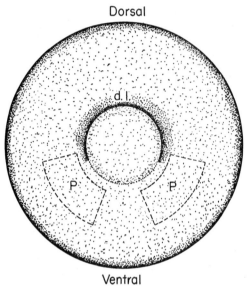

Fig. 52. Diagram illustrating the location of the presumptive primordial germ cells in urodeles at the early yolk plug stage according to experiments of Nieuwkoop ('46). *d.l.*, Dorsal lip of blastopore; *P*, area of presumptive lateral plate and nephrogenous cord mesoderm containing the presumptive primordial germ cells.

may appear in grafts of Hensen's node taken at the head process stage. Willier suggests that results 1 and 2 may be attributed to lack of development of a germ-cell transporting mechanism (blood vascular system) in the graft and to lack of some condition in the graft that is essential for proper growth of the gonad. Result 3 may be interpreted on the basis of observations that show the presence of some primordial germ cells in regions posterior to the antero-lateral crescentic zone of the area pellucida that had previously been considered to be their locus. While the experiments are not presented as definitive proof of the extragonadal origin of the primordial germ cells in birds, they offer strong support for that view.

Evidence that the mature sex cells are

derived from the primordial germ cells rather than secondary germ cells is provided by experiments on removal of the left ovary of young chicks. As is well known, the rudimentary right ovary then tends to develop into a testis. Normally the primordial germ cells of the rudimentary right gonad disappear after the third week. If removal of the left ovary is performed prior to this disappearance the right gonad may form a testis with mature spermatozoa, whereas upon later removal no spermatozoa are produced in the testis that develops (Domm, '29).

Anurans and urodeles apparently differ in regard to the site in which cells that have the appearance of primordial germ cells are first found. In the former it is the entoderm of the gut wall; in the latter it is the lateral plate mesoderm. The results of experiments in these two groups seem, on the whole, to be consistent with the observed differences in location of such cells. Thus, in the anuran Discoglossus, Monroy ('39) obtained germ cell–free embryos when the ventral part of the entoderm was removed from caudal halves of early neurulae, while removal of the dorsal entoderm did not alter the number and location of the germ cells. However, Monroy's experiments do not exclude the interpretation, proposed by Nieuwkoop ('46) for salamanders, that the ventral entoderm acts as an inductor on "predisposed" primordial germ cells that originate elsewhere.

In urodeles the most extensive experiments appear to be those of Humphrey ('27, '28, '29, '33) and Nieuwkoop ('46). By means of a large variety of extirpation and transplantation experiments Nieuwkoop has confirmed Humphrey's view that the germ cells originate in the presumptive lateral plate mesoderm which, in the gastrula, is represented by the ventral and ventrolateral lips of the blastopore. In the uncleaved egg this material would be located equatorially opposite the grey crescent rather than at the vegetal pole that Bounoure regards as its position in anurans. Nieuwkoop was able to distinguish germ cells of different species by differences in their content of pigment granules. So heteroplastic transplantation could be used to demonstrate that the presumptive lateral plate mesoderm is the only source of germ cells (see Fig. 52). However, when the presumptive dorsocaudal entoderm is removed at the gastrula stage, or the whole entoderm at the neurula stage, there is a considerable reduction in the number of germ cells. These and related experiments are interpreted to mean that the dorsocaudal entoderm has a germ cell–inducing influence on certain predisposed cells of the presumptive lateral plate mesoderm, with which it comes in contact at the end of gastrulation and during neurulation. On the basis of early determination and segregation this implies that the germ cells are at first simply endowed with the capacity (competence) to react to such inductive stimulus. The inductive stimulus is apparently not provided by other organs such as the notochord and Wolffian duct. That the reactive cells are not simply ordinary lateral plate cells is illustrated by the absence of germ cells in embryos in which the lateral plate was partially reformed (after removal of its presumptive material) by regulation from more dorsal mesoderm. Nieuwkoop also finds, as Humphrey had demonstrated earlier, that the germ cells do not cross over from one side of the embryo to the other. Concerning the formation of a second generation of germ cells in the genital ridge, Nieuwkoop finds no indication of this in any of the experimental animals in which the presumptive germ-cell material was removed. This is very well shown, too, in his heteroplastic transplantations in which the host germ ridge may contain exclusively donor germ cells. So the possibility that the presence of primary primordial germ cells may induce genital ridge cells to form secondary germ cells is also ruled out.

GROWTH OF THE OOCYTE

Cytological Investigations. There has been a considerable amount of cytological investigation into the manner of yolk formation, centering primarily upon the possible role of various cytoplasmic and nuclear structures, such as the mitochondria, Golgi bodies, chromidia, nucleoli and hyaloplasm. Various workers have implicated one or another, or some combination, of these structures in the process and there is considerable difference of opinion even when the same material is studied. (See, for example Harvey, '29, for references to four investigations, and four different interpretations, of yolk formation in the centipede Lithobius.) The earlier work has been reviewed by Wilson ('25) and MacBride and Hewer ('31). For some of the more recent work reference may be made to the studies of Subramaniam and Aiyar ('36) on sea urchins, of Narain ('37) and Singh and Boyle ('38) on fish, of Beams and King ('38) on the guinea pig, of Worley ('44, '46) on mussels and of Bretschneider ('46) on snails. No general conclusion concerning the mechanism of yolk formation appears to be, as yet, firmly established. The only point on which there seems to be fair agreement among various workers is that the fatty yolk is formed in association with Golgi bodies (see Worley, '44; Bretschneider, '46). Two techniques that hold promise of effective use in further research in this field are centrifugation, employed by Beams and King ('38) and Singh and Boyle ('38), and vital staining, employed by Worley ('44).

TABLE 9. *Relative Radiophosphorus* (P^{32}) *Content of the Phosphatide-Phosphorus Extracted from Various Organs of a Laying Hen 5 Hours after a Subcutaneous Injection of 10 mg. of Labelled Sodium Phosphate (from Hevesy and Hahn, '38)*

ORGAN	P^{32} CONTENT PER MG. P RELATIVE TO THE P^{32} PER MG. INORGANIC P OF THE PLASMA TAKEN AS 100
Liver	54
Plasma	43
Ovary	3.9
Yolk	3.5
Intestine	11
Spleen	0.1
Yolk of freshly laid egg	0

Chemical Investigations. In addition to the more strictly cytological investigations there have also been many contributions of a histochemical type on the changes that occur during oogenesis. Extensive accounts of these are given by Needham ('31, '42), Marza ('38), and Brachet ('47), along with summaries of work done by direct chemical methods. In some of the recent work in this field, as in others, the use of radioactive tracers has provided valuable information. In particular this technique has contributed information concerning the question whether various constituents of the yolk are synthesized within the oocyte or in some other tissue of the body. A brief account of the pertinent experiments is presented in the following section.

Tracer Experiments. The experiments relating to this have been done with radioactive phosphorus (P^{32}) as a tracer for the formation of phosphatides (lecithin and cephalin) and phosphoprotein (vitellin) in eggs of the hen by Hevesy and Hahn ('38),

Entenman et al. ('38), Chargaff ('42) and Lorenz et al. ('43) (see also Hevesy, '47). It is known, in the first place (see Needham, '31), that these compounds are formed by hens when the diet contains phosphorus in inorganic form. The organic phosphorus compounds are evidently synthesized by the hen. It is also known that the serum of laying birds, as well as of reptiles and fish, contains larger amounts of phosphatides and phosphoproteins than are present in the serum of the males or nonlaying females (Roepke and Bushnell, '36; Laskowski, '38; Landauer et al., '39; Zondek and Marx, '39; Riddle, '42; Chaikoff and Entenman, '46).

in the albumin and shell. Other experiments show that active phosphatides are only found in laid eggs that had been in the ovary at the time of injection, and tests up to $6\frac{1}{2}$ days after injection show a progressive increase in the activity of this fraction. Another control, soaking eggs for one day in a solution of labelled inorganic phosphate, showed no incorporation of P^{32} in the phosphatides extracted from the yolk, although active inorganic phosphate had penetrated it.

In the experiments of Entenman et al. ('38) determinations were also made of the relative amounts of P^{32} incorporated in the

TABLE 10. *Relative Radiophospholipid of Tissues of Laying and Nonlaying Birds at 6 and 12 Hours after Injection of 50 mg. of Phosphorus as Na_2HPO_4 Containing 10^6 Radioactive Units (1 Radioactive Unit = 2×10^{-12} curie) (from Entenman et al., '38)*

	LAYING		NONLAYING	
	6 HRS.	12 HRS.	6 HRS.	12 HRS.
Total radiophospholipid of bird as per cent administered P^{32}	3.62	4.55	3.25	4.57
Per cent of total radiophospholipid found in:				
gastrointestinal tract	10	10	23	15
muscle + bone + blood	32	36	27	35
reproductive system (ovary, oviducts, and yolks)	11	20	0.4	0.2
liver	44	29	47	44

This suggests that these substances might be synthesized in some other organ than the ovary. Hevesy and Hahn ('38) determined the content of radioactive phosphorus in inorganic and organic form in the plasma, liver, intestinal mucosa, ovary, yolks and eggs of hens at various times after the subcutaneous injection of labelled sodium phosphate. Table 9 gives the results of a set of analyses performed 5 hours after the injection. The labelled phosphorus content of the phosphatide-phosporus is found to be relatively low in the ovary and the yolk of an ovarian egg at this time. It is much higher in the plasma and highest in the liver. Since the oocytes are growing rather rapidly, in contrast to the liver, the experiment gives strong indication that the phosphatides are synthesized in the liver and transported through the plasma to the ovary. Various controls were run in these experiments. No labelled phosphorus was found in the phosphatides of the yolk of an egg laid at 5 hours after the injection, although active inorganic phosphate is found in it as well as

phosphatides of various parts of the laying and nonlaying hen. The results of one of their experiments, given in Table 10, show that about half of the P^{32}-containing phosphatide of the bird is present in the liver although this organ contains only about 5 per cent of the total phosphatides of the bird. In other experiments from Chaikoff's laboratory the incorporation of P^{32} in phosphatides and other compounds of the yolk was shown to be expressable as a function of the rate of growth of the yolk and the amount of P^{32}-phosphatide present in the plasma at the time (Lorenz et al., '43). These workers and others have also shown a high rate of labelled phosphatide formation by liver slices of male birds, which could be increased significantly by injection of estrogenic hormone (diethylstilbestrol) (see Taurog et al., '44).

The incorporation of P^{32} into the vitellin as well as in the free phosphatide and lipovitellin (a complex containing about half of the total phosphatide of the yolk) of the growing oocyte has been investigated by

Chargaff ('42). He finds equal rates of formation of free and bound phosphatide and somewhat higher initial formation of vitellin.

The results of the various experiments strongly support the view that these compounds are formed elsewhere in the body and transported through the plasma to the growing oocyte. In the case of the phosphatides the main site of synthesis appears to be the liver.

To what extent this situation may hold for the various substances that the oocyte

and estimate that the nuclei are 512-ploid when they have reached full size. On the basis of this and other considerations Painter ('40, '45a, b) proposes that one of the chief functions of the nurse cells is to supply large quantities of nucleoprotein material to the egg so that it may be readily available for the formation of chromosomes in the period of rapid division that follows fertilization. For those species of animals whose oocytes are not associated with nurse cells Painter suggests that the large germinal vesicle assumes this function. He

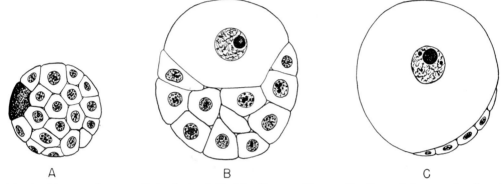

A   B   C

Fig. 53. Oocyte and nurse cells in the leech Pisciola. Groups of four or five "oogonia" are set free into the lumen of the ovary and divide into a mass of about 50 cells (A) of which only one, as a rule, becomes an oocyte (B), while the remainder function as nurse cells, contributing to the growth of the oocyte (C) and finally degenerating. (From Jörgensen, '13.)

accumulates is not known. However, it would not be too surprising if the oocyte were found to be incapable of synthesizing many or most of its stored materials. Presumably the same enzymes that function in synthesis also operate in dissociation, so the lack or inactivation of various enzymes in the oocyte may permit it to perform its storage function more efficiently.

Nurse Cells and Nucleoprotein Absorption. Another example of an important constituent of the yolk that appears to be largely supplied to the oocyte in rather complete form is nucleoprotein. This is illustrated in oocytes of various species of animals that are associated during their growth with large nurse cells. The nurse cells at first increase in size and then, as the oocyte approaches full size, the contents of the nurse cells are absorbed by the egg (see Fig. 53). During the early stages the nuclei of the nurse cells increase considerably in volume. Painter and Reindorp ('39) have described a series of endomitotic cycles occurring during the growth phase of the nurse cell nuclei of *Drosophila melanogaster*

infers that endomitosis also occurs in the germinal vesicle and upon breakdown of the latter at the time of the first maturation division a considerable amount of nucleoprotein is set free in the cytoplasm. This view is opposed by Ris ('45), who interprets the "lampbrush" chromosomes of the germinal vesicle as typical diplotene chromosomes in which there is a great longitudinal growth of the chromonemata and in which the apparent side branches do not represent additional chromosomal material but simply major coils of laterally separated strands. It is, however, of interest to note that the oocyte nucleus remains relatively small in species that have nurse cells, whereas it forms the relatively large germinal vesicle in species that are not provided with such cells.

Along with their general studies of the nucleic acid metabolism of various kinds of cells, Caspersson and Schultz ('38, '40), Schultz ('41), and Brachet ('47) have contributed some interesting observations and experiments relating to the formation of nucleoproteins during oogenesis. Caspersson and Schultz ('40) determined the ultraviolet absorption spectra of different regions within the nucleus and cytoplasm of a sea urchin oocyte. Their results are shown in Fig. 54. The curve for the nucleolus shows an absorption maximum at 2600 A typical of nucleic acid and a small rise at 2800 A indicative of proteins containing aromatic amino acids such as tyrosine and trypto-

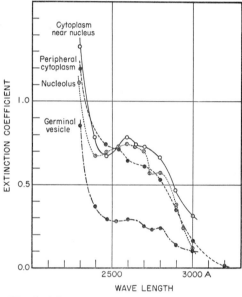

Fig. 54. Ultraviolet absorption spectra of different parts of an ovarian egg of the sea urchin *Psammechinus miliaris* (from Caspersson and Schultz, '40).

phan. The cytoplasm adjacent to the nucleus shows a similar type of curve with somewhat more protein indicated. The more peripheral cytoplasm gives a rather different curve indicative of considerably less nucleic acid. The nuclear sap appears to contain relatively little nucleic acid. This distribution of nucleic acid, which is in accordance with cytochemical observations of Brachet ('47), suggests diffusion of nucleic acid formed in the nucleus out to the cytoplasm or diffusion from the nucleus of some agent active in this synthesis, or synthesis at the nuclear membrane.

MATURATION DIVISIONS

The details of meiosis are beyond the scope of the present work and have been presented in several texts (Wilson, '25; Darlington, '37; Geitler, '38; Sharp, '43). A few words may, however, be said here concerning possible causative factors. One striking feature of the phenomenon is that it is essentially similar in cells that are so radically different in appearance as spermatocytes and oocytes. However, it is well known that preparations for the meiotic divisions are made at an early stage, shortly after the last gonial division, when the germ cells of the two sexes are more nearly alike in appearance. These preparations involve the intimate pairing (synapsis) of homologous chromosomes, a phenomenon that does not occur in the prophase of division of somatic cells except in the Diptera.

Among various suggestions as to the factors responsible for synapsis, the appeal to antigen-antibody type of interaction first made by Lindegren and Bridges ('38) seems to be particularly cogent. Friedrich-Freksa ('40) has interpreted the gene by gene specificity of pairing as due primarily to their arrangement in similar order in the homologous chromosomes, which synapse by the operation of nonspecific forces. However, the preciseness with which the homologous genes adhere, even when translocated or inverted, would seem to require the intervention of forces having the high degree of specificity that is exhibited in antigen-antibody reactions. Lindegren and Bridges suggest that the union is effected by the presence of agglutinins that are specific for each chrommomere of the chromosome. No suggestions are made concerning such important details as to where and when these antibodies are formed, or what reverses the reaction in order to permit the chromosomes to separate.

Another interesting hypothesis to account for homologus chromosome pairing has been offered by Fabergé ('42). This assumes the operation of a hydrodynamical phenomenon known as the Guyot-Bjerknes effect, in which two spheres that pulsate in phase move towards one another as a result of the Bernoulli principle. The pairing units of the chromosomes are considered to have the properties of such pulsating spheres, each with a characteristic frequency so that it can attract its homologue but not nonhomologous units having other frequencies. Fabergé points out that the force is a long range force such as seems to be required to achieve synapsis between homologous chromosomes that may be separated initially by a distance of several micra in the nucleus. Evidence for the operation of such long range forces has been presented recently by Hinton ('46) in a study of pairing of translocation-bearing chromosomes of Drosophila. However, Cooper ('48) has effectively disputed the significance of this evidence and concludes that there is, as yet, no necessity for the assumption of long range forces.

A view of meiosis that has gained both widespread acceptance and controversy is the "precocity theory" of Darlington ('31, '37). According to this view the prophase begins relatively earlier in meiosis than in mitosis, so that the leptotene chromosomes are single rather than split. Synapsis then results from a "universal mitotic affinity of half-chromosomes for one another in pairs." It is further assumed that this relationship is upset by the division of the chromosomes (at pachytene) but that chiasmata resulting from crossing over hold the original pairs together until metaphase, so that normal segregation may occur. It has, however, been shown by a number of workers (see Cooper '44, '49, for references and convincing evidence) that in many species of animals crossing over and the resultant chiasmata are not necessary for metaphase pairing and orderly segregation. So, that part of Darlington's hypothesis cannot be considered to have general validity. Also, there is considerable evidence (Schrader, '44; Mickey, '46, '47) that the leptotene threads are already split, as are the prophase chromosomes in ordinary mitosis. A view that seems to be more consistent with the known features of meiosis is the "retardation theory" proposed by Sax and Sax ('35). According to this view the spiral form of the chromonemata of mitotic chromosomes prevents (because a sufficient number of identical loci cannot come in contact) intimate association of homologous chromosomes. In the prolonged prophase of meiosis the chromonemata are greatly extended and uncoiled, or have only very loose remnant coils, so that homologous chromosomes can adhere intimately. Upon the occurrence of a new split in each chromatid at late pachytene, coiling and separation of homologues begins. This view is consistent with the fact that the chromosomes are considerably longer in meiotic prophase than in ordinary mitotic prophase and with such apparently unusual cases as the dipteran giant salivary chromosomes in which the greatly extended polytene homologues remain permanently synapsed.

Undoubtedly the analysis of meiosis would be greatly helped by its experimental induction in somatic tissue. It is interesting to note, then, that Huskins ('48) has reported the occurrence of chromosome segregation and reduction in onion root tips grown in a solution of sodium nucleate. However, as Huskins points out, further work will be required to determine the relationship of this "somatic meiosis" to the gonocytic meiosis.

FERTILIZATION

One may define fertilization as the series of processes by which the spermatozoon initiates and participates in the development of the egg. As such it includes all steps from the approach of the spermatozoon to the fusion of the pronuclei within the egg. In this chapter we shall consider briefly some of the factors that may be operative in various phases of this series of processes.

APPROACH OF THE SPERMATOZOON

In most species of animals the meeting of egg and spermatozoon is facilitated by virtue of the fact that the latter is a motile cell. Also, the large numbers that are ordinarily available in both external and internal insemination contribute to the likelihood of contact being made with the eggs. For example, Farris ('49) reports that fertile men supply semen samples with a total of 83 million or more motile sperm, whereas a lower total active sperm count is correlated with infertility. However, the question has been raised by many investigators whether or not the spermatozoa are attracted in some way to the egg when their random movements have brought them within a certain distance of the latter. The early investigations concerning chemotaxis has been reviewed by Morgan ('27), who concluded that there is no critical evidence demonstrating its existence. Such evidence, as well as more recent work along this line (Cornman, '41; Hartmann, '40; Vasseur and Hagström, '46), rests on demonstrating a local accumulation of sperm within tubes or other devices containing eggs or certain materials derived from the eggs. However, it is not readily feasible to distinguish between an attractive influence and a trap action effect such as was described many years ago by Jennings ('06). In ferns and mosses there is good evidence for chemotaxis but it has not, as yet, been adequately demonstrated for animal spermatozoa (cf. Rothschild, '51a, b, '52).

On the other hand an increase in the motility of spermatozoa under the influence of material emanating from the egg has been noted in some species of animals. This increase does not generally occur when the spermatozoa are in a highly active condition (see Lillie, '19; Gray, '28). Along with increasing the activity of the spermatozoa the egg water may also increase the rate of oxygen uptake. For example, Gray ('28) found increases ranging from 212 to 425 per cent in the sea urchin *Echinus esculentus*, and similar increases have been found by Tyler ('48a) in the keyhole limpet *Megathura crenulata*. Hartmann et al. ('39) reported that the agent responsible for the activation of the spermatozoa in *Arbacia pustulosa* is the pigment echinochrome which is present in the eggs of this species of sea urchin. However, attempts to confirm this were unsuccessful both in a species of sea urchin whose eggs do not contain echinochrome and in one whose eggs are so pigmented (Tyler, '39b; Cornman, '41). Tyler and Fox ('39, '40) found the activating agent in the egg waters of Strongylocentrotus and of Megathura to remain associated, after dialysis and precipitation, with the large molecular substance that has agglutinating action (see below) on the sperm. While such association has also been reported by Cornman ('41), Kuhn and Wallenfels ('40), and Vasseur and Hagström ('46), these workers find the activating agent to be at least partially dialyzable. Many years ago Clowes and Bachman ('21) found that distillates of Arbacia egg water would activate the sperm and this was confirmed more recently by Cornman ('41). It would appear, then, that the activating agent in egg water is normally bound to the agglutinating agent, from which it may be split off as a relatively small molecular substance, but its exact chemical nature has not, as yet, been determined.

LIFE SPAN OF THE GAMETES

The conditions of insemination in most animals require that the gametes remain in a fertilizable state for a period of time following release from the gonads. It is of interest, then, to inquire into the factors involved in the aging of the gametes.

Senescence of Spermatozoa. In some species of animals, such as the bat, the honeybee and certain terrestrial isopods (Vandel, '41) the sperm may survive for periods of several months to several years in the female genital tract. Apart from such special cases the usual life span of shed sperm is of the order of several hours to a few days (see Hartman, '39). An important factor that is known to affect markedly the functional life span of sperm is dilution. Many workers have shown

(see Morgan, '27; Gray, '28; Rothschild, '48a, b, c) that the duration of life varies directly with the concentration of the suspension. The relative or complete lack of motility of sperm in undiluted semen of sea urchins and other animals has frequently been attributed to a relatively high tension of carbon dioxide. Rothschild ('48b) has shown, however, that lowering the carbon dioxide tension does not induce motility, whereas increasing the oxygen tension activates the spermatozoa. By exposing the semen alternately to nitrogen and oxygen the spermatozoa could be made alternately inactive and active. Hartmann, Schartau and Wallenfels ('40) had proposed that immobility in semen, as well as subsequent senescence of sea urchin sperm, was due to a substance, termed androgamone I, that is liberated by the spermatozoa. This view stood in contradiction to observations of Gray ('28) and Hayashi ('45) showing that sea urchin sperm were as motile when diluted with seminal plasma as with sea water. Rothschild ('48c) showed in addition that the supernatant of a dense two-hour sperm suspension, which is supposed to contain androgamone I, had no inhibitory effect on respiration. These and other experiments show that senescence is not attributable to substances, such as the hypothetical androgamone I, diffusing into the medium from the sperm and that the "dilution effect" cannot be explained on the basis of a dilution of such inhibitor.

More recently it has been shown (Tyler and Atkinson, '50) that the life span of sea urchin sperm can be considerably extended by addition of any one of a number of amino acids to the suspension. Similar results have been obtained in birds and mammals (Lorenz and Tyler, '51; Tyler and Tanabe, '52). It was shown (Tyler and Rothschild, '51) that the amino acid is not utilized metabolically, although it has effects on the respiratory metabolism of the sperm and even enables sea urchin sperm to remain motile anaerobically, whereas they ordinarily die promptly in absence of oxygen. The results suggested that the amino acids act by binding certain trace metals present in the sea water. Tests with other kinds of metal-chelating agents such as ethylenediaminetetraacetic acid (Versene*), diethyldithiocarbamic acid, 8-hydroxyquinoline, and α-benzoinoxime have given similar prolongation of the life span of the sea urchin spermatozoa (Tyler, '53).

* Trade name of Bersworth Chemical Co., Framingham, Mass.

These findings can account in large part for the "dilution effect." The proteins of the seminal plasma can also bind heavy metals. Since such protein would be present in higher concentration the less the semen is diluted, the spermatozoa in denser suspensions would be protected from the toxic action of the trace metals. This is consistent with the favorable action of seminal plasma found by Gray ('28) and Hayashi ('45).

Another interesting effect of the amino acids and other metal-chelating agents is

fluid. Motility is maintained under anaerobic conditions in the presence of glycolyzable substrates. Mann ('46, '49) has recently identified the normal substrate in seminal fluid as fructose. The work of Mann ('45a, b, '49), Lardy and Philips ('41–'45), MacLeod ('39–'46) and others has shown that the glycolysis in sperm is essentially the same as in other animal tissues and in yeast (phosphorylation of the sugar by adenosine triphosphate in the presence of hexokinase to hexosemonophosphate, then hexose di-

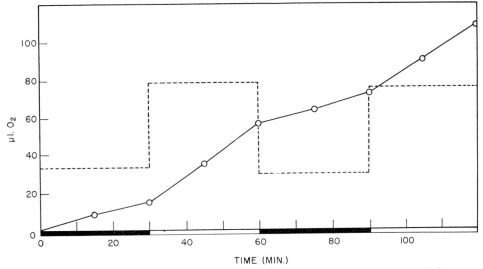

Fig. 55. Photo-reversible inhibition by carbon monoxide of the respiration of sperm of the sea urchin *Echinus esculentus*. Gas mixture, 90% CO and 10% O_2; dark periods, 0 to 30 and 60 to 90 minutes; light periods (700 watt lamp), 30 to 60 and 90 to 120 minutes; temperature, 15:1° C.; sperm suspension, 4.4 × 10^8 per ml. Broken line shows average rate of O_2 consumption per hour. (From Rothschild, '48a.)

their ability to enable the sperm to induce a good fertilization-reaction under conditions in which the sperm, diluted and aged in ordinary sea water, call forth poor membrane elevation (Tyler and Atkinson, '50; Tyler, '53). The results demonstrate that the type of response given by the egg can be determined by the vitality of the inseminating sperm. The spermatozoon evidently does not act simply in "all or none" manner in the sense of operating a trigger mechanism in the egg.

Investigation of the substrate that is normally utilized by the sperm and the enzymatic pathways through which it is metabolized has been confined mainly to mammalian spermatozoa. It is now well established that mammalian sperm have a predominantly glycolytic metabolism even under aerobic conditions and that the substrate is a reducing sugar present in the seminal

phosphate, and breakdown through triosephosphate, phosphoglyceric acid and pyruvic acid to lactic acid; with resynthesis of ATP by transfer of phosphate from phosphoglyceric acid to adenylic acid or reaction between inorganic phosphate and adenylic acid catalyzed by cozymase). Aerobically in the absence of external glycolyzable substrate the spermatozoa apparently oxidize phospholipid. The mammalian sperm have been found to contain all the enzymes involved in the Krebs' cycle, as well as the cytochromes *a*, *b*, and *c* and cytochrome oxidase. However, under aerobic conditions motility is relatively quickly lost even in the presence of glycolyzable substrate. This has been attributed by MacLeod ('46a) to the production of hydrogen peroxide, which he believes may reach sufficient concentration to kill the sperm. Addition of substances containing catalase was found to retard the aerobic loss of motility. These experiments of Mac-Leod on human spermatozoa have been confirmed and extended by Tosic and Walton ('46) and Tosic ('47) with bull spermatozoa.

In contrast to mammalian sperm, that of sea urchins becomes rapidly immotile under anaerobic conditions, as Harvey ('30) demonstrated. Rothschild ('48a, b, c) and Spikes ('48, '49b) have shown that glycolysis does not occur to any very appreciable extent aerobically or anaerobically in presence or absence of glycolyzable sugar. Spikes presents evidence to show that oxidation proceeds through the usual fructose diphosphate, triosephosphate and Krebs cycle pathway. From the spectroscopic identification of cytochromes a, a_3, b, c, and COa_3 (Ball and Meyerhof, '40; Rothschild, '48a) and the demonstration (Rothschild, '48a, c) of photoreversible CO-inhibition (Fig. 55), it is concluded that the respiration of the sea urchin sperm is under control of the cytochrome system. Rothschild ('48c) has also shown that oxidizable substrates and their dehydrogenases are still present in sea urchin sperm that have aged to the point of no motility and respiration. Recent evidence (Rothschild and Cleland, '52) points to phospholipid as the principal endogenous source of energy for motility. From the experiments on prolonging the duration of motility and fertilizing capacity by means of amino acids and other metal-chelating agents (Tyler, '53) it is also clear that death of the spermatozoa upon dilution in ordinary sea water is not due to exhaustion of their food supply. These agents, evidently by binding toxic trace metals, enable the sperm to utilize their endogenous substrate more fully.

Senescence of Eggs. The unfertilized egg likewise has a relatively limited life-span under ordinary conditions, both in animals with external fertilization and in those with internal fertilization. In certain cases, as in many fish and Amphibia, fertilizability is lost within a few seconds or minutes after deposition in water. In these, marked visible changes, involving elevation of a membrane, are generally noted upon contact with the new medium and these are very likely involved in the loss of fertilizability. A rapid loss of fertilizability may, however, occur without such visible changes, as in the case of Platynereis described by Just ('15b, c). In most animals loss of fertilizability and cytolysis of the egg occur in a period of several hours to one or two days under ordinary conditions. This relatively rapid senescence cannot be attributed to depletion of endog-

enous nutrient since, if fertilized, the eggs can survive considerably longer without any added nutrient. For example, fertilized sea urchin eggs will survive for about two weeks without any external source of food, while respiring at a rate that is at least ten times that of the unfertilized egg. The latter might, then, be expected to survive over twenty weeks instead of the two days obtained under ordinary conditions.

Experiments by Whitaker ('37), Tyler, Ricci, and Horowitz ('38), Tyler and Dessel ('39), Schechter ('37, '41) and others have shown that various agents such as weak alcohol, slight acidity, and low calcium content of the medium can prolong the fertilizable life of eggs of marine animals to some extent. It has also been shown (Tyler et al., '38) that sterile conditions extend the survival time of sea urchin eggs by five-fold or more. The deleterious effect of bacteria does not manifest itself until after a certain immune period, since freshly shed eggs can survive in dense bacterial suspensions almost as long as in ordinary sea water. Corresponding with the onset of the susceptible period the surface of the egg undergoes some disintegrative changes which are manifest by the formation of a tight membrane or no membrane upon fertilization. In the absence of bacteria the eggs remain viable and fertilizable for a considerable time after these changes have begun. The agents mentioned above that prolong the functional life of the egg in nonsterile conditions evidently operate by delaying the onset of these autolytic changes.

Runnström ('49) has described in some detail the changes that unfertilized eggs of sea urchins undergo upon aging. Alterations in the surface are detectable by various sorts of tests, such as the hypertonicity test in which, as the eggs shrink, the formation of wrinkles is followed. Ripe unfertilized eggs, shrinking in hypertonic solution, form numerous wrinkles on the surface (indicative of a semisolid state), which later smooth out. Eggs which have aged, so that they form low membranes or no membranes upon fertilization, shrink with a smooth surface, indicative of a liquefied state of the surface.

It seems reasonable to assume that energy is required to prevent the breakdown of the surface that occurs upon aging. It is of considerable interest, then, that adenosine triphosphate, at low concentrations (0.002 to 0.001 M) has been found (Wicklund, '49, reported by Runnström, '49) to be effective in prolonging fertilizable life and even capable of restoring normal membrane-forming capacity to aged eggs. This may mean that the rapid senescence of the unfertilized eggs is due to loss (failure of resynthesis or unavailability) of some such energy-transporting agent.

ATTACHMENT AND PENETRATION

The specificity of fertilization is manifested in the initial steps of the union of the gametes. In general spermatozoa will not adhere to, or penetrate, eggs of other species or other tissues of the same species. Some exceptions to this are known. Thus sperm of the nemertean worm Cerebratulus penetrate eggs of the sand dollar Echinarachnius (Chambers, '33). The sperm remain in the cortex without activating the egg, which can subsequently develop normally upon fertilization with the species sperm. Instances of penetration of sperm into tissue cells have been less frequently reported (see Terni and Maleci, '37). In view of the marked specificity and the superficial resemblance to phagocytosis it is not surprising that the first detailed modern theory of fertilization, namely that of F. R. Lillie ('19), should be based on immunological analogies. This was undoubtedly favored, too, by the discovery (Lillie, '12, '13a, b) that spermatozoa of certain marine animals can be made to agglutinate by the addition of some egg water (supernatant of a suspension of eggs) of the same species. The agglutinating substance in the egg water was termed fertilizin and Lillie assigned it a central role in his theory of fertilization. The early work in this field has been reviewed by Lillie ('19), Lillie and Just ('24), Morgan ('27), Dalcq ('28b) and Just ('30). The present discussion will be based mainly on the more recent work, which has been reviewed in some detail by Tyler ('48a, '49), Bielig and Medem ('49), and Runnström ('49).

We shall consider four groups of interacting substances that have been obtained from eggs and sperm and which are termed fertilizins, antifertilizins from sperm, antifertilizins from eggs, and lytic agents from sperm. The terms gynogamone and androgamone were introduced by Hartmann ('40) to designate the substances derived from eggs and sperm, but this terminology does not seem to be any less prejudicial than that of Lillie, nor sufficiently advantageous to warrant its adoption.

Fertilizins. Agglutination of sperm by homologous egg water has been reported in many species of animals among the echinoderms, annelids, mollusks, tunicates and vertebrates (see Tyler, '48a, and Bielig and Medem, '49, for references). The reaction in strong egg water is usually visible within a few seconds. In sea urchins the clumping is ordinarily head to head (Lillie, '19; Elster, '35). Tail to tail and head to tail, along with head to head unions have been reported in certain mollusks and may occur also in aged sea urchin sperm (Sampson, '22; Tyler, '40a). Figures 56 to 58 illustrate the agglutination reaction of sperm of the keyhole limpet *Megathura crenulata*. The reaction is similar in appearance to that exhibited by sperm that are agglutinated by an immune serum (compare figures of Henle et al., '38). The reaction also exhibits such serological features as the zone phenomenon (Tyler, '40a; Spikes, '49a). Lillie ('19) used the term fertilizin to designate the agent or agents in egg water that were responsible for agglutinating, activating and possibly chemotactic and other effects. At present it seems best to restrict the use of this term to the agglutinin.

A unique feature of the reaction in sea urchins is its spontaneous reversal after a period of time ranging from a few seconds in dilute egg water to many minutes in concentrated egg water, whereas in other groups of animals the agglutination is essentially permanent or long-lasting. Following spontaneous reversal, in the sea urchin, the spermatozoa are incapable of being reagglutinated by the addition of fresh egg water and have lost their fertilizing capacity, although they are fully motile (Lillie, '19; Tyler, '41). An interesting analogy to this is found in the Hirst ('42) reaction of agglutination of vertebrate red blood cells by influenza, and other viruses. This reaction also reverses spontaneously and the red cells are incapable of re-agglutination. In the case of the sea urchin the reversal has been interpreted (Tyler, '41) as due to a splitting of the individual fertilizin molecules that bind the spermatozoa to one another. This interpretation presumes that the now generally accepted mutual multivalence theory of antigen-antibody reactions (Heidelberger, '38, '39; Marrack, '38; Pauling, '40) holds for the agglutination of sperm by fertilizin. According to this theory both antigen and antibody must be multivalent with respect to their combining groups in order for their interaction to result in precipitation or agglutination. In other words, an agglutinin molecule must possess two or more combin-

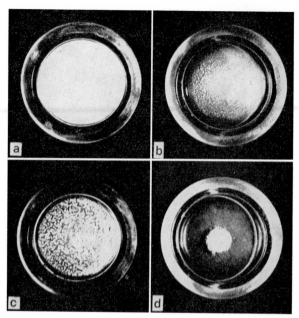

Fig. 56. Macroscopic appearance of agglutination reaction in the keyhole limpet *Megathura crenulata*. Photographed in Syracuse dishes, $\times$ ½. *a*, Untreated sperm suspension (ca. 2 per cent); *b*, *c*, and *d*, 15 seconds, 30 seconds and 10 minutes, respectively, after addition of solution of fertilizin. (After Tyler, '40a.)

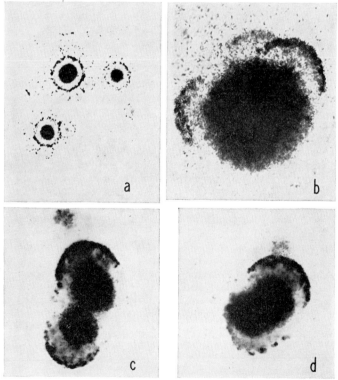

Fig. 57. Photomicrographs of agglutinated sperm of the keyhole limpet *Megathura crenulata*. *a*, Three agglutinates formed in a moderately strong solution of fertilizin, showing spherical shell of sperm heads surrounding central mass of sperm; $\times$ 50. *b*, An agglutinate formed in a strong solution of fertilizin, showing incomplete shells of sperm heads attached to main mass by the ends of the tails; $\times$ 170. *c* and *d*, Fusion of two agglutinates; *d* was photographed 15 seconds after *c*; $\times$ 85. (From Tyler, '40a.)

ing groups available to unite separate cells. Univalent molecules would combine with the separate cells and be incapable of tying them together.

Some support for the above interpretation of the spontaneous reversal of agglutination in sea urchins is obtained from experiments apparent absence of fertilizin in many species of animals. It is known that the egg waters of many species of animals, such as the abalone and Cumingia (Sampson, '22), Urechis (Tyler, '41), some starfish (Metz, '45) and even certain sea urchins (Vasseur and Hagström, '46) fail to agglutinate the

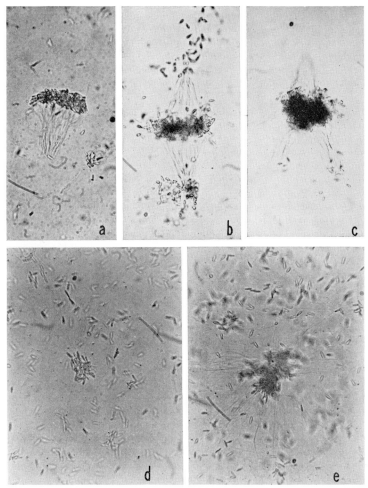

Fig. 58. Photomicrographs of sperm of *Megathura crenulata*, × 260. *a, b,* and *c,* Show union by heads and by end pieces of tails in strong, moderate and weak fertilizin solutions, respectively. *d* and *e,* Show head aggregates originally present in sperm suspension. (From Tyler, '40a.)

in which the ordinary agglutinin is converted into a nonagglutinating (univalent) form by the action of heat, proteolytic enzymes, ultraviolet or x-radiation (Tyler, '41, '42; Metz, '42a, b). Treatment of the sperm with such univalent fertilizin inhibits their agglutination by ordinary fertilizin and also renders them nonfertilizing, without impairing their motility.

The concept of univalent antigen or antibody also provides an interpretation for the homologous spermatozoa. Such failure to demonstrate fertilizin in all species of animals has been used as an argument against considering fertilizin to have any general significance for fertilization. However, that the egg water of such nonagglutinating species might contain a fertilizin-like substance was indicated in experiments of Tyler ('41) and clearly established by Metz ('45). The latter worker was able to cause specific agglutination of sperm, in species of starfish that normally do not give an agglutination reaction, by the addition of a nonspecific adjuvant (from hen's egg white and other sources) along with the egg water. The adjuvant alone has no agglutinating action on the sperm. Thus the failure of agglutination to occur ordinarily in certain species of animals is not necessarily indicative of the absence of fertilizin in the egg water but can be interpreted on the basis of a uni-

TABLE 11. *Method of Preparation of Sea Urchin Fertilizin (from Tyler, '48a)*

1. Extract 20% suspension of washed eggs in sea water at pH 3.5.
2. Decant supernatant (agglutination titer = ca. 1000), centrifuge or filter.
3. Add 40 ml. N/1 NaOH per liter of supernatant (fertilizin precipitates with the Ca and Mg salts of sea water).
4. Suspend precipitate in 3.3% NaCl, neutralize, dialyze.
5. Remove insoluble particles and precipitate with $1\frac{1}{4}$ to $1\frac{1}{2}$ volumes 95% alcohol.
6. Wash with alcohol and dry (re-precipitate with alcohol or saturated $(NH_4)_2SO_4$). (Yield = ca. 250 mg./liter)

valent condition of either the fertilizin or the sperm.

A parallel to univalent fertilizin can be found in the field of immunology in recent studies on Rh antibodies. In most cases these antibodies are found to occur in a nonagglutinating, univalent form (Wiener, '44; Race, '44; Fisk and Morrow, '45; Levine and Walker, '46). Here, too, the addition of an adjuvant (such as serum albumin) enables the antibodies to agglutinate the Rh-positive cells (Wiener, '45a, b; Wiener and Gordon, '48; Diamond and Denton, '45; de Burgh et al., '46). Corresponding to the experimental conversion of fertilizin into a univalent form, immune antibodies have been similarly altered by treatment with various agents, such as heat, diazo compounds, formaldehyde and photo-oxidation (see Tyler, '45a, for references). The alteration appears to involve not simply a splitting of the antibody molecule but also a reassociation of the univalent fragments with fragmented non-antibody protein of the antiserum. Specificity is retained by such univalent antibodies and, in the case of an antitoxin, protective properties persist. The treated antisera are found to have lowered antigenicity and may, therefore, offer a means of avoiding serum sickness (Tyler, '45a, b;

Tyler and Swingle, '45). In connection with fertilization, further use has been made of univalent antibodies in experiments with sea urchin sperm (see below).

A fair amount of information is now available concerning the chemical nature of fertilizin. Lillie ('19) showed that the gelatinous coat of the sea urchin egg contained large amounts of fertilizin but believed that it was being continuously secreted by the ripe unfertilized egg throughout its functional life. However, more recent experiments (Tyler and Fox, '39, '40; Tyler, '40a, '41) have demonstrated that it is identical with material of the gelatinous coat itself and not obtainable from denuded eggs. This has been corroborated by several other workers (Evans et al., '41; Hartmann, '40; Vasseur and Hagström, '46; Runnström and Lindvall, '46). The presence of fertilizin in ordinary egg water results, then, from the slow dissolution of the coat. For chemical purposes sea urchin fertilizin can be obtained in high titer by dissolving the coat

TABLE 12. *Analysis of Electrophoretically Homogeneous Preparations of Fertilizin of the Sea Urchin* Strongylocentrotus purpuratus *(from Tyler, '49, and unpublished)*

Nitrogen	5.6 — 5.8 %
Carbon	33.3 %
Hydrogen	5.5 %
Sulfate	23 %
Phosphate	0.06%
Reducing sugar	>25 %
Amino acids	>20 %
Galactose	+
Methylpentose (fucose)	+
Glucuronic acid	—
Probable amino acids (by paper chromatography and microbiological assay)	Glycine, alanine, serine, threonine, valine, leucine, isoleucine, aspartic, glutamic, arginine, lysine, phenylalanine, tyrosine, tryptophan, proline
Molecular weight	ca. 300,000

with dilute acid, without damage to the rest of the egg. With such preparations Tyler and Fox ('39, '40) obtained evidence for the protein nature of fertilizin of the sea urchin and of the keyhole limpet, on the basis of such properties as non-dialyzability, salting out, common color tests and inactivation with proteolytic enzymes. However, the low values (ca. 5 per cent) obtained for the nitrogen content indicated that the material was not a simple protein.

Carbohydrate was later found in purified fertilizin (Tyler, '42) and in electrophoretically homogeneous gelatinous coat (Runnström et al., '42) of sea urchins. From this and later work (Tyler, '48a,b, '49; Krauss, '49; Vasseur, '48a,b, '49) it has become clear that fertilizin is a complex of amino acids and sugars that may be termed a glycoprotein.

A procedure for the preparation of electrophoretically homogeneous sea urchin fertilizin is outlined in Table 11. Some of the analytical data obtained (Tyler, '48a,b, '49) on such preparations of fertilizin of the sea

Upon electrophoresis the fertilizins of *E. cordatum* (Runnström et al., '42) and of *S. purpuratus* (Tyler, '48a, '49) migrate towards the anode at pH values as low as pH 2. This highly acidic character is probably correlated with the high content (ca. 25 per cent) of sulfate found by Vasseur ('47) in *E. esculentus* and confirmed by Tyler ('48b) in *S. purpuratus*. Upon ultracentrifugation of a jelly coat solution of Psammechinus, Runnström et al. ('42) found a main component with a sedimentation constant of 2.9×10^{-13} varying with con-

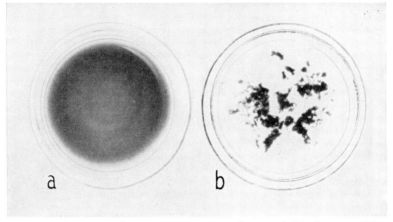

Fig. 59. Eggs of the sea urchin *Strongylocentrotus purpuratus*, photographed in Syracuse dishes, $\times$ $\frac{7}{10}$. *a*, Untreated egg-suspension. *b*, 15 minutes after addition of a solution of antifertilizin. (From Tyler, '40b.)

urchin *Strongylocentrotus purpuratus* are given in Table 12. The values given there for amino acids and reducing sugars are probably low, since some of these very likely contribute to the humin residue that forms upon acid hydrolysis. By means of paper chromatography Vasseur and Immers ('49) find differences in the sugar components of the hydrolyzed jelly coat of different species of sea urchins; namely galactose in *Echinus esculentus*, fucose in *Echinocardium cordatum*, fucose and galactose in *Strongylocentrotus droebachiensis*, fucose and glucose in *Paracentrotus lividus*. The amino acids have also been investigated by microbiological methods, but there is as yet insufficient evidence to indicate whether or not different species differ in this respect too. It is premature to conclude that specificity of the fertilizins is dependent upon differences in particular sugar or amino acid constituents. Even when the constituents are the same, differences in configuration of the molecule may determine specificity of action, as appears to be the situation with immune antibodies.

centration in the manner indicative of nonspherical molecules. With active fertilizin of *S. purpuratus* a sedimentation constant of 6.3×10^{-13} has been obtained (Tyler, '49). The molecular weight is evidently, then, greater than 82,000, which would be the value for spherical shape.

Antifertilizins from Sperm. The substance on the surface of the sperm with which fertilizin reacts has been termed antifertilizin. Frank ('39) and Tyler ('39a) were able to extract such a substance from the sperm of sea urchins and the keyhole limpet, by means of brief heating or freezing and thawing. It is also extractable (Tyler and O'Melveny, '41) by slight acidification of the suspension. It can be assayed by its ability to neutralize the agglutinating action of fertilizin on sperm. Another manifestation of its activity is its ability to agglutinate a suspension of eggs (Fig. 59). In so doing it causes a precipitation membrane to form on the surface of the gelatinous coat of the egg (Fig. 60). With strong solutions this membrane thickens and contracts within a short time to the surface of the egg and is then no longer readily visible. It has been claimed (Hartmann et al., '40) that the jelly coat dissolves under the influence of such extracts. However, shown it to be an acidic protein, isoelectric at pH 3, and containing about 16 per cent nitrogen. Hultin ('47a, b) considers the active principle to be a basic protein. This

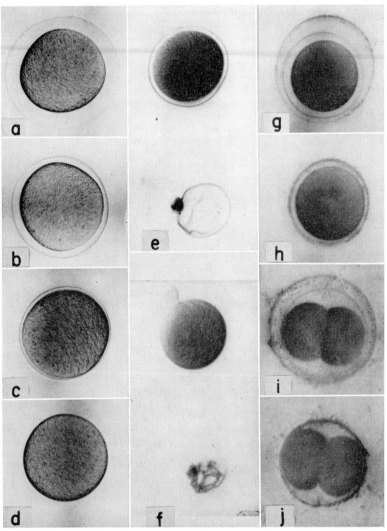

Fig. 60. Eggs of the sea urchin *Lytechinus pictus. a, b, c,* and *d,* Successive pictures of the same egg at about ½ minute intervals after addition of a solution of antifertilizin, showing formation of the precipitation membrane and its contraction to the surface of the egg; × 400. *e* and *f,* Successive pictures of the same egg and an adjacent isolated jelly-hull at 1 minute and 20 minutes, respectively, after addition of antifertilizin, showing the persistence of the material of the isolated jelly-hull at the time when the precipitation membrane has contracted to the egg's surface and has become indistinguishable from it; × 350. *g* and *h,* Successive pictures of the same fertilized egg at 1 minute and 3 minutes after addition of antifertilizin. *i* and *j,* Successive pictures of the same fertilized egg in 2-cell stage at 1 minute and 4 minutes after addition of antifertilizin; × 350. (From Tyler, '49.)

tests with isolated jelly hulls (see Fig. 60*e, f*) show that the precipitation membrane persists long after it has reached the surface in the control eggs.

Chemical studies on antifertilizin (Tyler, '39a, '40b, '48a; Runnström et al., '42) have contention is refuted by Metz ('49) who had earlier ('42a) found that basic proteins from sea urchin sperm have antifertilizin-like effects, but, in contrast to the above antifertilizin preparations, they also agglutinate sperm.

Upon extraction of antifertilizin by acidified sea water the head of the spermatozoon is found to round up and the surface to become diffuse in the region between the acrosome and midpiece, while the latter of this agent are similar to those described for the antifertilizin from sperm. In other words, antifertilizin from within the egg can react with fertilizin on the surface of the same egg. The active agent appears to

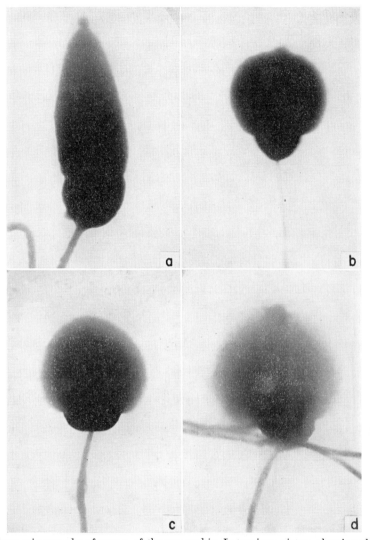

Fig. 61. Electron micrographs of sperm of the sea urchin *Lytecyinus pictus*, showing changes upon extraction of antifertilizin; × 30,000. *a*, Control, unextracted sperm. *b*, Extracted at *p*H 3.5. *c*, Extracted at *p*H 3.0. *d*, Extracted at *p*H 2.8. (From Tyler, '49.)

structures and tail are not visibly affected (Fig. 61). Antifertilizin is, then, considered to be located on the lateral surface of the head between the acrosome and midpiece.

Antifertilizin from Eggs. Lillie ('14) had postulated the presence of an antifertilizin within the egg and Tyler ('40b) was able to obtain such an agent by extraction of sea urchin eggs that had been previously divested of their gelatinous coat. The effects

be a protein (Tyler, '40b, '48a). Injection of the extracts into rabbits induces the production of antibodies that not only precipitate the homologous antigen but also agglutinate sperm of the same species, indicating antigenic similarity to the antifertilizin of sperm.

Consideration of the finding that substances capable of interacting in antigen-antibody–like manner can be obtained from the same cell, along with other evidence from the literature of immunology, has suggested an auto-antibody concept of cell structure, growth and differentiation, the details of which are presented elsewhere (Tyler, '40b, '42, '46b, '47).

Lytic Agents. Sperm extracts of various species of vertebrates and invertebrates have been found to possess the property of break-

(Tyler '39a, '48a; Krauss, '49). Evidence has been obtained that its activity is dependent upon the presence of sulfhydryl groups in the molecule.

Considerable attention has been paid in recent years to the lytic agent in the sperm extracts of mammals (see reviews by Duran-Reynals, '42; Meyer, '47; Meyer and Rapport, '52). This agent causes dispersal of

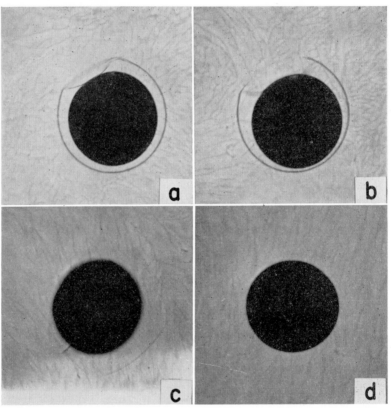

Fig. 62. Photomicrograph of an egg of *Megathura crenulata* at: *a*, 1 minute; *b*, 1¾ minutes; *c*, 2½ minutes; *d*, 3¼ minutes after addition of a sperm extract containing the egg-membrane lysin. × 200. (From Tyler, '39a.)

ing down the membrane or viscous coat that normally surrounds the unfertilized egg in these species (see Hibbard, '28; Wintrebert, '29, '33; Yamane, '30, '35; Pincus, '30, '36; Tyler, '39a; Medem, '42). Figure 62 illustrates the action of such an agent on eggs of the keyhole limpet. The dissolution of the membrane (which can withstand hours of treatment in concentrated acid) can occur in less than a minute in concentrated sperm extracts containing the lytic agent. The active agent has protein properties, is highly heat-labile (about 1 minute half-life at 50° C.), and separable from the antifertilizin present in keyhole limpet sperm extracts

the follicle cells that normally surround the unfertilized tubal egg, by dissolving the cementing material between them. McClean and Rowlands ('42) and Fekete and Duran-Reynals ('43) showed that this was evidently the same agent that was earlier shown to have a dissolving action on the intercellular cementing material of skin and that had been designated hyaluronidase because of its ability to break down the mucopolysaccharide known as hyaluronic acid. Hyaluronidase is also a heat-labile protein and it has, as yet, been only partially purified (see Meyer, '47; Meyer and Rapport, '52). The occurrence of this agent in various invasive bacteria has served to emphasize the relation of the processes of fertilization to those of infection.

Another type of lytic agent has been obtained by Runnström et al. ('42–'46) in methanol extracts of sea urchin sperm. This agent has a liquefying action on the vitelline membrane of the unfertilized egg, an effect which can be duplicated by certain detergents. Present evidence (Runnström, '49) indicates that it is an unsaturated, eighteen-carbon, fatty acid.

motility) is also impaired when they are treated with specific antisera that are prepared by injection of rabbits with antifertilizin and that have been rendered nonagglutinating (univalent) so as to avoid the complications that would be introduced by agglutination (Tyler, '46a).

Studies of the specificity of the reaction have provided some further information concerning the role of these substances. Lillie's ('19) demonstration that fertilizin was not obtained from other tissues than the

TABLE 13. *Comparison of Cross-fertilization with Cross-agglutination among Echinoids (from Tyler, '49)**

EGGS OR FERTILIZIN OF	SPERMATOZOA OF			
	S. purp.	S. fran.	L. pictus	D. excent.
S. purpuratus	3000	3	1	5
	512	8	64	4
S. franciscanus	1	600	1	2½
	0	512	4	0
L. pictus	2	4	850	2½
	64	32	64	8
D. excentricus	1½	40	2	4400
	4	2	1	128

* The upper figures of each pair of rows represent the number of times the sperm suspension is diluted in giving the end point value (2 per cent) of fertilization under certain standard conditions. The lower figures are the agglutination titers in terms of the highest dilution of fertilizin solution that gives visible agglutination.

Role in Fertilization. Various experiments have been performed to attempt to elucidate the function of fertilizin and antifertilizin in fertilization (see Tyler, '48a; Runnström, '49). When sea urchin eggs are deprived of their gelatinous coat they are still fertilizable, but require a higher concentration of sperm to effect fertilization. Whether or not, in addition to facilitating fertilization, the presence of fertilizin is essential for the process cannot, as yet, be readily decided since upon removal of the gelatinous coat the surface of the egg still evidently possesses a thin layer of fertilizin that cannot be removed without damage to the egg. The presence of excess fertilizin in solution around the eggs tends to inhibit rather than promote fertilization. The sperm that have reacted with fertilizin at some distance from the egg are apparently incapable of adhering to the egg, presumably because their combining sites are already occupied by fertilizin. When sperm are partially depleted of antifertilizin by treatment that does not markedly impair their respiratory activity there is considerable lowering of their fertilizing capacity (Tyler and O'Melveny, '41). The fertilizing capacity of sperm (but not their

eggs has been amply confirmed and implicates this agent as furnishing the basis for the tissue-specificity of fertilization. That the action of fertilizin is predominantly species-specific has also been demonstrated by many workers (see Lillie, '19; Just, '30; Elster, '35; Tyler, '48a, 49), and in several investigations comparison has been made between the degree of cross-agglutination and that of cross-fertilization of various species of animals. The data of Table 13 illustrate some of the results that have been obtained in experiments of this type performed with four different species of echinoids. Other species of animals among the asteroids, annelids, and mollusks (not included in the table) that do not crossagglutinate with the echinoids, do not give cross-fertilization.

In general the results show that the degree of cross-agglutination is greater than that of cross-fertilization among the various species. On the other hand, in combinations where cross-reaction of fertilizin and sperm is lacking fertilization does not generally occur. There are apparent exceptions to this, such as may be noted in Table 13, where *S. franciscanus* fertilizin fails to agglutinate

S. purpuratus and *D. excentricus* sperm. In these, interaction can nevertheless be shown by the fact that the sperm of the latter species can absorb *S. franciscanus* fertilizin.

It may be concluded, then, that the specificity of fertilization is based partly on the specificity of the fertilizin-antifertilizin reaction. Since a number of other interactions are undoubtedly involved in the various steps in fertilization it is not surprising to find that specificity is not entirely determined by one of these. On the basis of the present evidence the fertilizin-antifertilizin reaction is concerned in the initial attachment of the spermatozoon to the egg. A scheme for the mechanism of such attachment that has been recently proposed (Tyler, '48a) assumes the same type of interaction that is manifest in antigen-antibody reactions and relates it to the general problem of the mutual adherence of the cells of the various tissues and organs of a multicellular organism.

Lillie ('19) proposed that fertilizin was also involved in other steps including establishment of the block to polyspermy and activation of the egg through interaction with antifertilizin within the egg. Although the presence of an antifertilizin within the egg has been demonstrated, experimental evidence concerning its function is lacking.

The role of the lytic agents, such as the egg membrane lysin and hyaluronidase, is manifestly to enable the sperm to penetrate the membrane barriers that surround the unfertilized egg. In this action the hyaluronidase of mammals shows a rather broad species-specificity while that of the egg-membrane lysin of mollusks is relatively narrow. No evidence is as yet available to indicate whether or not these agents are involved in the further penetration of the surface of the egg proper. For the egg-surface lysin Runnström ('49) suggests a role in the establishment of the block to polyspermy. While this is in harmony with its fertilization inhibiting properties, the availability of this agent under physiological conditions needs to be demonstrated.

The work on hyaluronidase stimulated many attempts to apply this agent clinically to overcome sterility in humans. Although there were some early claims of success, recent controlled experiments (Chang, '47; Leonard et al., '47) with rabbits and rats have shown that the addition of hyaluronidase to inseminates does not enhance fertilization and that fertilization can be effected without visible dispersal of the follicle cells. These results do not refute the above assigned role but rather show that the individual spermatozoon carries sufficient enzyme to make a path for itself through the follicle coat of the egg.

REACTION OF THE EGG

Cortical Change and Block to Polyspermy. The visible changes that occur at the surface of the egg have been investigated extensively, especially in sea urchins, and most of the recent work is discussed in the review by Runnström ('49). Mention may be made here of newer work by Rothschild and Swann ('49), who have examined the question of whether or not the rate of propagation of the visible cortical change is sufficient to account for the block to polyspermy. These workers followed cinematographically the darkfield brightening of the surface of the egg that spreads out from the point of contact of the spermatozoon and constitutes the first visible cortical change. They find that the time required for this change to progress to the opposite side of the egg averages 20 seconds at 18° C. in *Echinus esculentus*. To decide whether or not this is rapid enough to account for the block to polyspermy, estimates are made of the chance of a second sperm striking an unaltered part of the surface. For these calculations measurements are made of the translatory speed of swimming of the spermatozoa. The frequency of collision with an egg is then calculated from the kinetic equation, $N = \pi a^2 n \bar{c}$, in which a is the radius of the egg (50 microns), n is the density of sperm suspension and $\bar{c}$ is the mean translatory speed of the spermatozoa (200 microns per second). For sperm densities of 10^5, 10^6 and 10^7 per milliliter the number of collisions per second would be 0.16, 1.6 and 16, respectively. Since a density of 10^7 per milliliter does not give any appreciable polyspermy in sea urchin eggs that are in good condition it is concluded either that the block to polyspermy is established much more rapidly than the observed surface change or that only a small fraction (about $\frac{1}{160}$) of collisions result in fertilization. Further experiments with oocytes, that respond to insemination by formation of papillae, each of which is associated with a spermatozoon, show the number of papillae to be considerably less than the number of sperm-oocyte collisions. On the basis of this and other considerations, Rothschild and Swann favor the view that the observed cortical change may represent the block to polyspermy and that many of the collisions are ineffective owing to such factors as "muzzling" of the spermatozoa by fertilizin in solution, necessity for particular orientation of sperm head to egg surface, etc. While this analysis involves several assumptions, of which the authors are well aware, it represents an excellent approach to the solution of this perplexing problem. The present author, too, is inclined to favor the view that the block to polyspermy may be established much more slowly than is generally assumed. Experiments on the so-called

enters, in others a hyaline process persists for some time—for example, as long as 15 minutes in Urechis (Tyler, '31). Of special interest is the formation (Fig. 63), by starfish eggs, of a long filament originally described by Fol (1877, 1879) and more recently by Chambers ('30) and Hörstadius ('39). The filaments extend from the surface of the egg to spermatozoa in the outer part of the gelatinous coat and their contraction brings the sperm to the surface. According to Hörstadius ('39) the filament has the

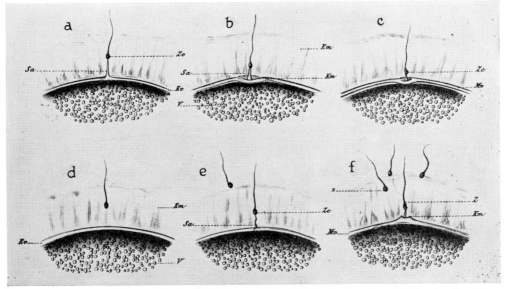

Fig. 63. Reproduction of some of Fol's ('79) figures of fertilization in *Asterias glacialis*, showing filament connecting the spermatozoon with the surface of the egg. Three successive stages for one egg are illustrated in *a*, *b*, and *c*, and for another egg in *d*, *e*, and *f*.

reversal of fertilization in Urechis (Tyler and Schultz, '32), in which treatment of the eggs with weak acid within as much as two or three minutes after insemination stops development and permits subsequent refertilization, accord with this view.

Fertilization Cones. It is well known that the fertilizing spermatozoon becomes motionless upon attachment to the surface of the egg. Penetration is, then, not effected by mechanical activity of the sperm. In many species of animals the egg elevates, at the point of sperm contact, a cone-shaped process that engulfs the sperm. Examples of various types of entrance cone formation may be found in studies by Chambers ('30, '33) and these, perhaps, suffice to emphasize that the process differs so markedly in different species that the common element in each is difficult to discern. While in some species the elevation may disappear as the sperm

form of a hollow cylinder, and Tyler ('48a) interprets it as a precipitate resulting from fertilizin-antifertilizin interaction.

Membrane Elevation. While the elevation of a membrane upon fertilization is not characteristic of fertilization in all groups of animals, its occurrence is a manifestation of important surface changes that occur upon fertilization. Recent studies of this process have been largely confined to echinoderms and are reviewed by Runnström ('49) who, with his co-workers, has contributed extensively to the subject. According to these workers the fertilization membrane of the sea urchin egg forms as a result of the cortical granules of the unfertilized egg merging with the vitelline membrane (Fig. 64). Its elevation is attributed to the osmotic pressure of colloids below it.

Since the fertilization membrane can be removed shortly after fertilization without affecting subsequent development it evidently has no special significance for the later events. Even when its elevation is inhibited, normal development can ensue (Tyler, '37; Tyler and Scheer, '37). If the unfertilized eggs are treated with such agents as isotonic urea or trypsin, that presumably dissolve the vitelline membrane, fertilization and cleavage can occur without membrane formation (Moore, '30a,b, '32, '49). Of particular interest in this connection is the report by Hultin ('48a,b) that such treatment renders

changes in volume of the egg upon fertilization. There are, however, conspicuous changes in shape in many species. Where such changes occur it is invariably in the direction of greater sphericity. Thus many species of echinoids have ellipsoidal, somewhat irregular, eggs that become spherical upon fertilization. Such changes undoubtedly reflect changes in the rigidity of the surface and the viscosity of the egg contents (see Tyler, '32 and Runnström, '49, for further discussion).

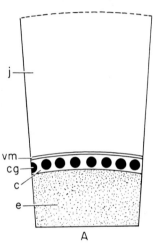
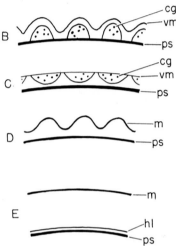

Fig. 64. Diagrams of part of surface of the sea urchin egg, illustrating (A) the different layers of the unfertilized egg and (B to E) steps in the formation of the fertilization membrane, according to the views of Runnström ('49). j, Gelatinous coat; vm, vitelline membrane; cg, cortical granules; c, cortex; e, endoplasm; ps, plasma surface; m, fertilization membrane; hl, hyaline layer. (From Runnström, '49.)

the eggs more susceptible to cross-fertilization. The result implies that specificity is, at least, partly controlled by the vitelline membrane.

In another species of animal, namely the annelid Nereis, in which experiments on removal of the vitelline membrane have been performed, the denuded eggs do not fertilize (Costello, '45, '49). In this species the vitelline membrane is a thick conspicuous structure through which a large amount of gelatinous material is exuded after fertilization. When the unfertilized eggs are placed in an alkaline saline solution the jelly swells but does not pass through the membrane, which thereupon stretches and bursts. If the treatment is delayed until shortly after fertilization the membrane can be removed without preventing the attached sperm from entering the egg and without interfering with normal development.

Changes in Shape and Volume. In most species of animals there are no marked

Changes in Viscosity and Protein Solubility. Along with work on viscosity changes in various kinds of cells, Heilbrunn ('28, '43) and his students have supplied some data concerning fertilization. In general fertilization results in a marked increase, which Heilbrunn interprets on the basis of his calcium-release, protoplasmic gelation, theory of activation. Mirsky ('36) reported that the amount of protein that is soluble in 1 M potassium chloride decreases upon fertilization in sea urchins. This potassium chloride–soluble protein forms highly viscous solutions which show double refraction of flow and has, therefore, been considered a structural protein like myosin. Connors and Scheer ('47) find it to be electrophoretically homogeneous, but, unlike myosin preparations, it possesses no adenosine triphosphatase activity. It is not, as yet, clear how the change in solubility of this material may be correlated with viscosity changes of the intact egg or with the decrease in viscosity upon fertilization reported by Ruffo and Monroy ('45) for egg brei.

Changes in Permeability. In addition to the early demonstration that fertilization results in an increased permeability to water (R. S. Lillie, '16) and such nonelectrolytes as ethylene glycol (Stewart and Jacobs, '32), recent tracer experiments (Abelson, '47; Brooks and Chambers, '48; Lindberg, '48) show a great increase in permeability to phosphate. The fate of the phosphate that is incorporated into the fertilized egg will be discussed further below.

Changes in Electrical Properties. Activation of eggs has often been considered analogous to stimulation of nerves. However, attempts (Peterfi and Rothschild, '35; Rothschild, '38, '46) to detect the propagation of an action potential over the egg surface upon fertilization in sea urchins and frogs have been unsuccessful. In fact, no potential difference was found across the surface of the sea urchin egg. While this might be attributable to short-circuiting between the electrodes, the fact that eggs can be fertilized after insertion of the electrode indicates that the fertilization reaction does not depend upon there being a potential difference across the egg surface. Also, the membrane resistance is apparently unchanged upon fertilization in sea urchins and frogs (Cole, '35; Cole and Spencer, '38; Cole and Guttman, '42). Membrane capacitance is approximately doubled upon fertilization in sea urchins, indicative of change in dielectric constant, but no change is obtained in eggs of Cumingia, Chaetopterus or the frog (Cole and Curtis, '38; Cole and Guttman, '42).

Changes in Metabolism. Detailed surveys of the metabolic changes that occur upon fertilization have been presented by Needham ('42) and Brachet ('47). The newer outlook in this field is largely due to the work of Whitaker ('31a,b,c, '33a,b), who refuted the idea that fertilization was invariably accompanied by a rapid rise in rate of oxidation. In fact a decrease was found to occur in some species, such as the annelid Chaetopterus and the mollusk Cumingia, while in other animals such as the starfish and the annelid Nereis there is no very marked change. In a single species of animal, too, there may be an increase, decrease or no change depending upon the condition of the unfertilized egg, as Tyler and Humason ('37) have shown in Urechis. Even in sea urchins, the classic rise, first described by Warburg ('08), does not occur if the eggs are fertilized very soon after removal from

the ovary, since, as Borei ('48, '49) has shown, the freshly shed unfertilized egg has a respiratory rate as high as that of the fertilized egg. Theories of activation that are dependent upon an increased rate of oxidation are evidently no longer tenable.

It has also been held that the oxidative processes differ qualitatively in the fertilized and unfertilized egg. For example, Rubenstein and Gerard ('34) and Korr ('37) have reported large differences in the temperature coefficient of the rate of oxygen uptake of fertilized and unfertilized eggs of sea urchins. On the other hand, Tyler and Humason ('37) found no significant differences in sea urchins and other species of animals, and Borei and Lybing ('49) confirm this with sea urchins. This is consistent, too, with the newer findings concerning sensitivity to cyanide and carbon monoxide. Runnström ('28, '30a) and Korr ('37) had reported that these agents do not inhibit the respiration of unfertilized sea urchin eggs. Along with the initial failure of many investigators to detect cytochrome spectroscopically in sea urchin eggs, this led to the view (Korr, '37) that before fertilization the respiration is mediated by a nonferrous autoxidizable ferment, such as a flavoprotein, while upon fertilization the previously unavailable cytochrome is thrown into circulation. However, Robbie ('46) has shown that if precautions are taken to avoid absorption of the hydrogen cyanide by the alkali well of the respiration vessel, the oxygen uptake of the unfertilized egg can be almost completely inhibited. Also, photo-reversible inhibition of oxygen uptake by carbon monoxide has now been demonstrated by Rothschild ('49a), who accounts for the earlier misinterpretations on the basis of a simultaneously occurring light-inhibition of respiration and stimulation of oxygen uptake by carbon monoxide (probably by oxidation of the carbon monoxide). On the basis of these experiments, the demonstration of the presence of a cytochrome oxidase (Krahl et al., '41) and the spectroscopic identification of cytochromes (Rothschild, '49a), it may now be concluded that respiration is mediated by the cytochrome system before as well as after fertilization.

In regard to the dehydrogenase part of the respiratory system Runnström ('30a) and Örström ('32) found no change in rate of methylene blue reduction upon fertilization in sea urchins, whereas Ballentine ('40), using ferricyanide as the electron acceptor, found an increase. This contradiction still needs to be resolved. Concerning the pathway of carbohydrate breakdown in the sea urchin egg, it has been suggested (Lindberg and Ernster, '48) that this is through the mechanism known as the hexose monophosphate shunt (Dickens, '38), but more reent evidence (Ycas, '50; Cleland and Rothschild, '52) shows the presence and operation of the conventional glycolytic mechanisms.

Sea urchin eggs are known to contain diphosphopyridine nucleotide (Runnström, '33; Jandorf and Krahl, '42) but no change

is inhibited by cyanide. This might operate by interference with the resynthesis of ATP. While there is evidently no over-all change in content of ATP (or other acid-soluble phosphorus compounds) upon fertilization in sea urchins (Runnström, '33; Örström and Lindberg, '40; Lindberg, '43; Whiteley, '49), this does not, of course exclude it as an important agent in the activation of the egg. There is evidence (Harvey, '30; Runnström, '30b; Barron, '32; Kitching and Moser, '40) that sea urchin eggs can be fertilized or

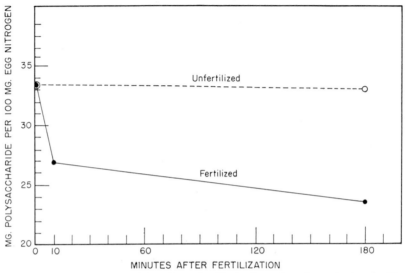

Fig. 65. Change in content of a glycogen-like polysaccharide (estimated as glucose) after fertilization in eggs of the sea urchin *Paracentrotus lividus* (from data of Örström and Lindberg, '40).

in the content of this coenzyme is found upon fertilization. Sea urchin eggs also contain an adenosinetriphosphatase (Runnström, '33) and its activity has been found (Connors and Scheer, '47) to be over twice as high in homogenates prepared from fertilized eggs as in those from unfertilized eggs. Since the ATPase activity is increased by calcium this difference might be correlated with the release of bound calcium (Heilbrunn, '43) upon fertilization. The tracer experiments to which reference was made above have also shown that, as the labelled phosphate is taken up by the fertilized egg, increasing radioactivity is found in the adenosinetriphosphate (ATP) that is prepared from the eggs. Studies of the distribution of the labelled phosphate (Abelson, '48; Chambers et al., '48; Whiteley, '49) have shown that 96 to 97 per cent is in the trichloroacetic acid–soluble fraction (about a third of which is probably ATP and ADP). It is of further interest that the uptake of labelled phosphate

artificially activated under anaerobic conditions. It would be of interest to learn whether or not ATP and other possible energy-yielding agents decrease under such conditions.

Fertilization in sea urchins also results in the temporary (15 to 20 minutes) production of an as yet unknown acid (Runnström, '30b, '33; Örström, '35; Borei, '33; Laser and Rothschild, '39) and in a temporary (10 minutes) increased production of ammonia (Örström, '41). The exact significance of this for fertilization is unknown. Örström has also reported that fertilized eggs can produce glutamine when ammonia and glumatic acid are added, whereas unfertilized eggs lack this ability. This is interpreted as reflecting a general lack of synthetic ability on the part of the unfertilized, in contrast to the fertilized, egg.

From the work of Örström and Lindberg ('40) there appears to be a considerable breakdown of a polysaccharide (that they designate as, but which may not be, glycogen) upon fertilization in the sea urchin *Paracentrotus lividus.* Expressed as glucose the breakdown in the first 10 minutes after fertilization averages 4.7 mg. per 100 mg. of egg nitrogen (= 2.8 cc. of eggs = 5×10^6 eggs = 0.7 gm. dry weight of eggs), whereas during the next 3 hours it is less than 3 per cent of that value (see Fig. 65). If completely oxidized this breakdown would be more than ample to account for the oxygen uptake following fertilization. The available data on

FUSION OF PRONUCLEI

Very little is known concerning the factors responsible for the union of the pronuclei within the egg. Here again attractive influences have been proposed. However, it is known that the egg nucleus in artificially activated eggs can migrate in the same manner as if it were fertilized. Similarly, upon fertilization of non-nucleated eggs the sperm nucleus attains a normal position for

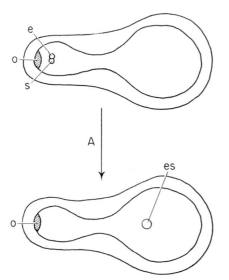 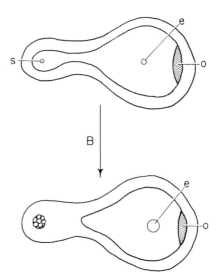

Fig. 66. Behavior of pronuclei in centrifuged eggs of the sand dollar Dendraster. *A*, Two successive stages (at interval of ½ hour) of an egg in which a sperm entered at centripetal end, fused with egg pronucleus and the fusion nucleus moved into large centrifugal part of the egg. *B*, Two successive stages (at interval of 2 hours) of an egg in which a sperm entered at the centrifugal end, failed to unite with egg pronucleus and proceeded to segment the centrifugal end. *e*, Egg pronucleus; *s*, sperm pronucleus; *es*, fusion nucleus; *o*, oil cap. (After Moore, '37.)

the respiratory quotients, however, show a decrease from about unity in the unfertilized sea urchin egg (Borei, '33) to values variously reported as ranging from 0.64 to 0.85 (Ephrussi, '33; Borei, '33; Laser and Rothschild, '39; Öhman, '40) after fertilization. From analyses of lipids Öhman ('44) suggests that these represent the chief energy source, whereas from analysis of ammonia liberation Hutchens et al. ('42) suggest oxidation of protein. These various investigations have evidently all been carefully performed, but it is evidently still necesary to determine to what extent the divergent results are due to technical difficulties and to species differences. Most investigators, however, are in accord with the view that different substrates are utilized before and after fertilization (see Brachet, '47, for further details).

cleavage of the cell. The fact that egg and sperm pronuclei may meet at some distance from the ultimate position of the fusion nucleus does not imply attraction, since it has not been shown that they are diverted from the path that they would take independently. Wilson ('25) and Morgan ('27) have reviewed the early work on this subject and little has been added since that time.

Moore ('37) has studied the movements of the pronuclei in echinoid eggs that had been drawn out into flask-shaped form as a result of high speed centrifugation. He found that when the sperm entered the end of the egg containing the egg nucleus it fused with the latter and the fusion nucleus moved through the "neck" into the larger mass of cytoplasm (Fig. 66*A*). When the sperm entered the opposite end (Fig. 66*B*) it remained there and proceeded to segment that end of the egg while the part with the egg nucleus remained undivided (as is to be expected from the early experiments of Ziegler and others showing that fragments of fertilized eggs containing the egg nucleus

and that cannot operate normally when the pronuclei are separated by too great a distance within the egg. However, in the absence of demonstration of such contractile processes many alternative interpretations

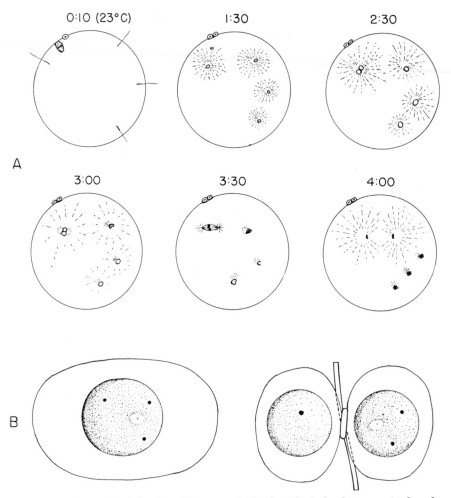

Fig. 67. *A*, Diagrams illustrating behavior of the pronuclei in physiological polyspermy in the salamander Triton. Sequence is indicated by time (hours and minutes) after insemination. All four sperm that enter develop normally until 2:30, at which time the accessory asters attain their maximum size, and one sperm nucleus makes contact with the egg nucleus. At 3:00, when sperm and egg nuclei fuse, the accessory sperm nucleus nearest the fusion nucleus shows signs of degeneration. At 3:30 to 4:00 all of the accessory sperm nuclei progressively degenerate and the one in the animal hemisphere is pushed out of that region by the cleavage amphiaster. (From Fankhauser, '48.)

B, Diagrams illustrating constriction of a salamander egg by means of a hair loop. The unpigmented area represents the location of the second polar spindle. The three darkly pigmented spots mark the entrance points of the spermatozoa. In the constricted egg both fragments can develop into embryos, although normally the spermatozoon in the left fragment, upon failure to fuse with the egg nucleus, would degenerate. (From Fankhauser, '34.)

fail to divide while those with the sperm nucleus do). Moore interprets the results of these and similar experiments on the basis of contractile processes that pull the separate and the fused nuclei to their proper positions

may be suggested. For example, the developing sperm aster could well be responsible for failure of the sperm pronucleus to traverse the narrow neck of the centrifuged egg.

Studies of physiological polyspermy in

urodeles, that have been undertaken principally by Fankhauser (see '48 for references and review), have contributed important information concerning the factors that influence pronuclear behavior. In urodeles all of the sperm that enter undergo the normal pronuclear changes during the first few hours. However, after one of the sperm pronuclei has fused with the egg pronucleus the remainder begin to degenerate, those nearest the fusion nucleus regressing first (Fig. 67A). If the egg is constricted after fertilization so that one fragment contains a sperm pronucleus (see Fig. 67B), this can proceed to form a spindle, and the fragment can undergo cleavage and normal development, as earlier work had also shown. However, if the constriction leaves a rather broad connecting neck between the two parts, the development of the accessory sperm pronucleus is inhibited. These and other observations establish that some inhibitory influence emanates from the fusion nucleus. This could involve either the production of an inhibitory agent or the removal of some agent essential for the division of the accessory cytaster and the nuclear transformations. It could also involve mechanical factors, since the enlarging amphiaster displaces the accessory sperm pronuclei towards regions of the egg where conditions may not be proper for their further development.

ARTIFICIAL PARTHENOGENESIS

Relatively little work in this field has appeared since the last general review of the subject (Tyler, '41). Detailed accounts of earlier work are available in texts by Loeb ('13), Lillie ('19), Morgan ('27) and Dalcq ('28b). Summaries of methods employed in the artificial activation of eggs of various animals have been given by Harvey ('10) and Runnström ('28). In this section a brief summary is presented of some of the features of artificial parthenogenesis previously discussed (Tyler, '41), along with a short account of recent views on the problem of activation.

SUMMARY OF SOME GENERAL FEATURES OF ARTIFICIAL PARTHENOGENESIS

Advanced Stages. It has been established that artificially activated eggs of many animals (sea urchins, starfish, moths, fish, frogs, rabbits) can be reared to the adult condition and sexual maturity. Normal early development is obtainable in practically all the major groups of animals and it is clear that when normal embryos are produced, obtaining the adults is mainly a matter of appropriate culture methods.

Frequency of Normal Development. There have been only occasional reports of experiments in which all of the eggs respond with normal development to a particular activating treatment. In general the percentage of normal development is quite low even when a particular treatment initiates development in all of the eggs in a manner indistinguishable from that induced by the sperm. This is attributable to various factors, such as irregularities in distribution of chromosomes, haploidy, lack of a proper division mechanism (normally supplied by the central body of the sperm) and, in some instances, to failure to establish a plane of bilateral symmetry (determined in some species by the entrance point of the sperm).

Origin of Cleavage Amphiaster. In sea urchins cleavage amphiasters are evidently derived from cytasters that are induced by the artificial treatment. In various annelids and mollusks cytasters are not in general formed. Here the amphiaster arises as a result of suppressed polar body divisions and continued cleavage involves a renewal of the capacity for division on the part of the central bodies of the egg and polar bodies. In polar body suppression, (a) the presumptive polar body spindle may be converted into a cleavage spindle, (b) submerged polar divisions (without cytoplasmic division) may occur followed by fusion of nuclei and association of central bodies. In the latter type of suppression an amphiaster, triaster or tetraster may form depending upon whether only the first, the first and one of the second, or the first and both second polar divisions are submerged, and the first cleavage then correspondingly results in two, three or four cells (see Fig. 68).

Activation of Non-nucleate Egg Fragments. The formation of cytasters capable of multiplication can be induced in non-nucleate fragments of sea urchin eggs. Such fragments may undergo repeated cleavages. This important work of E. B. Harvey acquires further interest in that it may indicate the possibility of *de novo* formation of self-duplicating bodies in the cytoplasm.

Chromosome Numbers. Artificially activated eggs do not invariably develop as haploids. In fact those that have been reared to advanced stages have the diploid chromosome number, whereas the haploids generally die in an embryonic stage. Regulation to diploidy is found to occur in a number of ways depending on the species of animal, the stage of maturation division of the egg at the time of treatment, and the method of treatment. Known methods of regulation include fusion of haploid nuclei at the first or a later cleavage, fusion of egg nucleus with a polar body nucleus, and utilization of a polar spindle for cleavage.

by different methods it is not known to what extent these represent differences in effectiveness rather than failure to find the proper exposure. Eggs of different groups of animals frequently differ in respect to the kind of agent to which they will best respond. As yet no single generally effective method of treatment has been described, nor have any correlations been found between the effective treatments for eggs of various species and

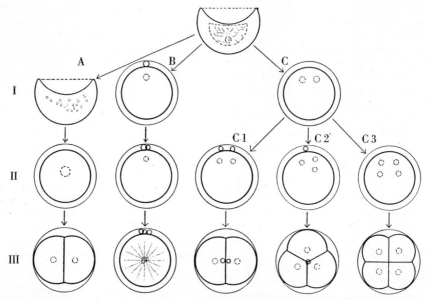

Fig. 68. Diagram of the various types of behavior of the polar divisions and cleavage in Urechis eggs activated with ammoniacal sea water. Upper figure represents the unfertilized egg. *A, B, C1, C2* and *C3* represent the types obtained with increasing time of treatment (e.g., with 0.01 N NH₃ at 20° C., ¼-1 min. → type A; 1-10 min. → type B; 10-20 min. → types *C1, C2* and *C3*). Row *I* shows condition of egg at time when normally fertilized egg has extruded first polar body; row *II*, after time of second polar division; row *III*, after first cleavage time. The small broken circles represent nuclei within the egg; the other circles represent extruded polar bodies. Eggs *IIIC1, IIIC2* and *IIIC3* are figured in polar view, the others in side view.

The type *B* egg, in which polar body formation is normal, fails to undergo cleavage. The other types continue to cleave and can develop into embryos of which many are normal. (After Tyler, '41.)

Sex. In parthenogenetic frogs, silkworms and rabbits the sex is found to accord, in general, with the expectations on the basis of whether the species is male or female digametic and on the method of regulation to diploidy.

Methods of Activation. It is now well known that a large variety of chemical and physical agents may be used to activate eggs of various animals. Even in a single species of animals (e.g., the sea urchin Arbacia) the eggs can respond to hypertonicity, hypotonicity, acids, bases, neutral salt solutions, certain alkaloids, fat solvents, heat, cold, puncture with a fine needle, ultraviolet radiation and radium emanations. Although there are differences in the results obtained

properties or characteristics of the eggs. As a result of the early discovery of the diversity of methods that may be employed to activate the egg the problem of activation has come to be regarded as part of the general problem of cell stimulation. Theories of activation have, then, centered about attempts to find the common factor in the action of various parthenogenetic agents.

CURRENT THEORIES OF ACTIVATION

The basis for Loeb's ('13) concept, that activation resulted from the operation of a cytolytic and a "corrective" factor, was largely removed by Just's ('22, '30) demonstration that the "corrective" hypertonic solution alone is effective. Also, Whitaker's ('33) demonstration that activation could occur with a decrease in respiratory rate removed any general validity from that aspect of Loeb's theory that involved the stimulation of oxidative processes. No newer investigations offer support for Loeb's views or any recognizable modification thereof.

R. S. Lillie ('41) proposed what may be termed a bimolecular theory of activation in which it is assumed that an activating substance (A) is formed from the union of two substances (B and S) that may be initially present in low concentration in the egg. Substance B is considered to be a product of hydrolytic processes in the egg and its formation to be stimulated by the action of such agents as acids and heat, which can act under anaerobic conditions. Substance S is considered to be formed from synthetic processes that may be stimulated by agents such as hypertonicity acting only in aerobic conditions. Since some of each is initially present the threshold concentration of A can be reached by increase in either B or S. This theory provides a consistent formal interpretation of a great mass of data that Lillie has accumulated, mainly on starfish eggs. Thus it accounts for additive and for sensitizing effects when such agents as heat, acids, hypertonicity and anaerobiosis are employed in various combinations. In its general form it is consistent, too, with other views, such as the proposal that release of calcium is an important factor in activation.

The significance of calcium in activation has been emphasized in two rather independently developed theories, namely the "sensitization to calcium" theory of Dalcq, Pasteels and Brachet ('36; see also Brachet, '47; Pasteels, '38a,b, '41; Pasteels and Fautrez, '47) and the "calcium release–protoplasmic clotting" theory of Heilbrunn ('30–'43). These are based on experiments showing that isotonic calcium chloride solutions or calcium-rich solutions are effective activators in many species of animals, that activation by other agents is dependent upon the presence of calcium, and that depriving eggs of calcium will sensitize them to the subsequent action of calcium solutions. Further support for the general view may be found in experiments by Scheer and Scheer ('47) and by Runnström and Monné ('45a, b). Heilbrunn's theory was developed for the phenomenon of stimulation of cells in general. In somewhat specific form it proposes that the stimulating agent releases calcium, from a calcium proteinate in the cell cortex,

and the free calcium initiates a protoplasmic clotting somewhat like blood clotting. It is of interest in this connection that the fertilizin-antifertilizin interaction has been shown to be largely dependent upon the presence of calcium (Loeb, '13; Vasseur, '49) and that fertilizin possesses some heparin-like activity (Immers, '49). However, there is, as yet, no direct evidence indicating that fertilizin is concerned in the activation steps in the processes of fertilization. There seems to be no question that calcium is intimately involved in the activation process and one might speculate on its role on the basis of its action on various enzymes, such as ATPase. However, the details of the picture are still vague. There are very likely a large number of substances concerned in the initial changes of activation and it is not known which constitute the primary reactants or whether activation might be initiated by various pathways.

While the discovery of artificial parthenogenesis did not bring the realization of the early hopes that problems of fertilization would be readily solved, it has provided important information concerning various aspects of the problem. It has, also, greatly enlarged the scope of the attack on the problem of activation by substituting relatively simple chemical and physical agents for the spermatozoon. Further, since activation of the egg involves changes in the activity of various enzyme systems, artificial parthenogenesis may come to be a useful tool for the general problem of the factors responsible for regulation of the enzymatic activities of cells.

REFERENCES

Abelson, P. H. 1947 Permeability of eggs of *Arbacia punctulata* to radioactive phosphorus. Biol. Bull., *93*:203.

——— 1948 Studies of the chemical form of P^{32} after entry into the Arbacia egg. Biol. Bull., *95*: 262.

Aboïm, A. N. 1945 Développement embryonnaire et post-embryonnaire des gonades normales et agamétiques de *Drosophila melanogaster*. Rev. Suisse Zool., *52*:53–154.

Allen, B. M. 1907 An important period in the history of the sex-cells of *Rana pipiens*. Anat. Anz., *31*:339–347.

Ball, E. G., and Meyerhof, B. 1940 On the occurrence of iron-porphyrin compounds and succinic dehydrogenase in marine organisms possessing the copper blood pigment hemocyanin. J. Biol. Chem., *134*:483–493.

Ballentine, R. 1940 Analysis of the changes in respiratory activity accompanying the fertilization of marine eggs. J. Cell. Comp. Physiol., *15:* 217–232.

Barron, E. S. G. 1932 The effect of anaërobiosis on the eggs and sperm of sea urchin, starfish and Nereis and fertilization under anaërobic conditions. Biol. Bull., *62:*46–53.

Bauer, H. 1932 Die Feulgensche Nuklealfärbung in ihrer Anwendung auf cytologische Untersuchungen. Z. Zellforsch. u. mikroskop. Anat., *15:*225–247.

―――― 1933 Die wachsenden Oocytenkerne einiger Insekten in ihrem Verhalten zur Nuklealfärbung. Z. Zellforsch. u. mikroskop. Anat., *18:* 254–298.

Beams, H. W., and King, R. L. 1938 A study of the cytoplasmic components and inclusions of the developing guinea pig egg. Cytologia, *8:*353–367.

Benoit, J. 1930 Contribution à l'étude de la lignée germinale chez le Poulet. Destruction précoce des gonocytes primaires par les rayons ultraviolets. Compt. rend. soc. biol., *104:*1329–1331.

Berrill, N. J., and Liu, C. K. 1948 Germplasm, Weismann and hydrozoa. Quart. Rev. Biol., *23:* 124–132.

Berry, R. O. 1941 Chromosome behavior in the germ cells and development of the gonads in *Sciara ocellaris.* J. Morphol., *68:*547–583.

Bielig, H. J., and Medem, F. 1949 Wirkstoffe der tierischen Befruchtung. Experientia, *5:*11–30.

Borei, H. 1933 Beiträge zur Kenntnis der Vorgänge bei der Befruchtung des Echinodermeneies. Z. vergleich. Physiol., *20:*258–266.

―――― 1948 Respiration of oocytes, unfertilized eggs and fertilized eggs from Psammechinus and Asterias. Biol. Bull., *95:*124–150.

―――― 1949 Independence of post-fertilization respiration in the sea urchin egg from the level of respiration before fertilization. Biol. Bull., *96:* 117–122.

―――― , and Lybing, S. 1949 Temperature coefficients of respiration in Psammechinus eggs. Biol. Bull., *96:*107–116.

Bounoure, L. 1935a Une preuve expérimentale du rôle du déterminant germinal chez la Grenouille rousse. Compt. rend. acad. sci., *201:*1223–1225.

―――― 1935b Sur la possibilité de réaliser une castration dans l'oeuf chez la Grenouille rousse; résultats anatomiques (avec projections). Compt. rend. soc. biol., *120:*1316–1319.

―――― 1937a Le sort de la lignée germinale chez la Grenouille rousse après l'action des rayons ultraviolets sur le pôle inférieur de l'oeuf. Compt. rend. acad. sci., *204:*1837–1839.

―――― 1937b La constitution des glandes génitales chez la Grenouille rousse après destruction de la lignée germinale par l'action des rayons ultraviolets sur l'oeuf. Compt. rend. acad. sci., *204:* 1957–1959.

―――― 1937c Le déterminant germinal est-il bien en cause dans l'atrophie des gonades consécutive à l'action des rayons ultraviolets sur le pôle inférieur de l'oeuf de Grenouille? Compt. rend. soc. biol., *125:*895–897.

―――― 1939 L'Origine des Cellules Reproductrices et le Problème de la Lignée Germinale. Gauthier-Villars, Paris.

Boveri, T. 1887 Ueber Differenzierung der Zellkerne während der Furchung des Eies von *Ascaris megalocephala.* Anat. Anz., *2:*688–693.

―――― 1899 Die Entwickelung von *Ascaris megalocephala* mit besonderer Rücksicht auf die Kernverhältnisse. Gustav Fischer, Jena.

―――― 1904 Protoplasmadifferenzierung als auslösender Faktor für Kernverschiedenheit. Sitzungs-Berichte der Physikalisch-Medicinischen Gesellschaft zu Würzburg, pp. 1–5.

―――― 1910a Ueber die Teilung centrifugierter Eier von *Ascaris megalocephala.* Roux' Arch. Entw.-mech. *30:*101–125.

―――― 1910b Die Potenzen der Ascaris-Blastomeren bei abgeänderter Furchung, zugleich ein Beitrag zur Frage qualitativ ungleicher Chromosomen-Teilung. Festschrift zum sechzigsten Geburgstag Richard Hertwigs, *3:*131–214.

Brachet, J. 1947 Embryologie Chimique. Masson et Cie., Paris.

Bretschneider, L. H. 1946 Oögenesis; in Experimental Embryology in the Netherlands, 1940–1945 (Woerdeman and Raven, editors). Elsevier, Amsterdam.

Brooks, S. C., and Chambers, E. L. 1948 Penetration of radioactive phosphate into the eggs of *Strongylocentrotus purpuratus, S. franciscanus* and *Urechis caupo.* Biol. Bull., *95:*262–263.

Caspersson, T., and Schultz, J. 1938 Nucleic acid metabolism of the chromosomes in relation to gene reproduction. Nature, *142:*294–295.

―――― , and Schultz, J. 1940 Ribonucleic acids in both nucleus and cytoplasm, and the function of the nucleolus. Proc. Nat. Acad. Sci., *20:*507–515.

Chaikoff, I. L., and Entenman, C. 1946 The lipids of blood, liver and egg yolk of the turtle. J. Biol. Chem., *166:*683–689.

Chambers, E. L., Whiteley, A., Chambers, R., and Brooks, S. C. 1948 Distribution of radioactive phosphate in the eggs of the sea urchin, *Lytechinus pictus.* Biol. Bull., *95:*263.

Chambers, R. 1930 The manner of sperm entry in the starfish egg. Biol. Bull., *58:*344–369.

―――― 1933 The manner of sperm entry in various marine ova. J. Exp. Biol., *10:*130–141.

Chang, M. C. 1947 Effects of testis hyaluronidase and seminal fluids on the fertilizing capacity of rabbit spermatozoa. Proc. Soc. Exp. Biol. & Med., *66:*51–54.

Chargaff, E. 1942 The formation of the phosphorus compounds in egg yolk. J. Biol. Chem., *142:*505–512.

Cleland, K. W., and Rothschild, Lord 1952 The metabolism of the sea-urchin egg. J. Exp. Biol., *29:*285–294.

Clowes, G. H. A., and Bachman, E. 1921 A volatile sperm-stimulating substance derived from marine eggs. Proc. Soc. Exp. Biol. & Med., *18:* 120–121.

Cole, K. S. 1935 Electric impedance of Hipponoë eggs. J. Gen. Physiol., *18:*877–887.

―――― , and Curtis, H. J. 1938 Electric impedance of single marine eggs. J. Gen. Physiol., *21:* 591–599.

Cole, K. S., and Guttman, R. M. 1942 Electric impedance of the frog egg. J. Gen. Physiol., *25:765–* 775.

———, and Spencer, J. M. 1938 Electric impedance of fertilized Arbacia egg suspensions. J. Gen. Physiol., *21:*583–590.

Connors, W. M., and Scheer, B. T. 1947 Adenosinetriphosphatase in the sea urchin egg. J. Cell. & Comp. Physiol., *30:*271–284.

Cooper, K. W. 1939 The nuclear cytology of the grass mite, *Pediculopsis graminum* (Reut.), with special reference to karyomerokinesis. Chromosoma, *1:*51–103.

——— 1941 Visibility of the primary spindle fibres and the course of mitosis in the living blastomeres of the mite, *Pediculopsis graminum* (Reut.). Proc. Nat. Acad. Sci., *27:*480–483.

——— 1944 Analysis of meiotic pairing in Olfersia and consideration of the reciprocal chiasmata hypothesis of sex chromosome conjunction in male Drosophila. Genetics, *29:*537–568.

——— 1948 The evidence for long range specific attractive forces during the somatic pairing of dipteran chromosomes. J. Exp. Zool., *108:*327–336.

——— 1949 The cytogenetics of meiosis in Drosophila: mitotic and meiotic autosomal chiasmata without crossing over in the male. J. Morph., *84:* 81–122.

Cornman, I. 1941 Sperm activation by Arbacia egg extracts, with special relation to echinochrome. Biol. Bull., *80:*202–207.

Costello, D. P. 1945 Experimental studies of germinal localization in Nereis. I. The development of isolated blastomeres. J. Exp. Zool., *100:* 19–66.

——— 1949 The relations of the plasma membrane, vitelline membrane and jelly in the egg of *Nereis limbata.* J. Gen. Physiol., *32:*351–366.

Dalcq, A. 1928a Le rôle du calcium et du potassium dans l'entrée en maturation de l'oeuf de pholade (*Barnea candida*). Protoplasma, *4:*18–44.

——— 1928b Les Bases Physiologiques de la Fécondation et de la Parthénogénèse. Presses Universitaires, Paris.

———, Pasteels, J., and Brachet, J. 1936 Données nouvelles (*Asterias glacialis, Phascolion strombi, Rana fusca*), et considérations théoriques sur l'inertie de l'oeuf vierge. Mém. Mus. Hist. nat. Belg., 2 Série, *3:*881–912.

Dantschakoff, V. 1941 Der Aufbau des Geschlechts beim Höheren Wirbeltier. Gustav Fischer, Jena.

Dantschakoff, W., Dantschakoff, W., Jr., and Bereskina, L. 1931 Keimzelle und Gonade. I A. Identität der Urkeimzellen und der entodermalen Wanderzellen; experimentelle Beweise. Z. Zellforsch. u. mikroskop. Anat., *14:*323–375.

Darlington, C. D. 1931 Meiosis. Biol. Rev., *6:* 221–264.

——— 1937 Recent Advances in Cytology. 2d ed. P. Blakiston's Son and Co., Inc., Philadelphia.

de Burgh, P. M., Sanger, R. A., and Walsh, R. J. 1946 Some aspects of the immunology of the Rh

factor. Australian J. Exp. Biol. & Med., *24:*293–300.

Diamond, L. K., and Denton, R. L. 1945 Rh agglutination in various media with particular reference to value of albumin. J. Lab. & Clin. Med., *30:*821–830.

Dickens, F. 1938a Oxidation of phosphohexonate and pentose phosphoric acids by yeast enzymes. Biochem. J., *32:*1626–44.

——— 1938b Yeast fermentation of pentose phosphoric acids. Biochem. J., *32:*1645–53.

Domm, L. V. 1929 Spermatogenesis following early ovariotomy in the brown leghorn fowl. Roux' Arch. Entw.-mech., *119:*171–187.

Duran-Reynals, F. 1942 Tissue permeability and the spreading factors in injection. Bact. Rev., *6:* 197–252.

Elster, H. J. 1935 Experimentelle Beiträge zur Kenntnis der Physiologie der Befruchtung bei Echinoideen. Roux' Arch. Entw.-mech., *133:*1–87.

Entenman, C., Ruben, S., Perlman, I., Lorenz, F. W., and Chaikoff, I. L. 1938 Radioactive phosphorus as an indicator of phospholipid metabolism. III. The conversion of phosphate to lipoid phosphorus by the tissues of the laying and non-laying bird. J. Biol. Chem., *124:*795–802.

Ephrussi, B. 1933 Contribution a l'analyse des premiers stades du développement de l'oeuf: action de la température. Arch. biol., *44:*1–147.

Evans, T. C., Beams, H. W., and Smith, M. E. 1941 Effects of roentgen radiation on the jelly of the Arbacia egg. Biol. Bull., *80:*363–370.

Everett, N. B. 1945 The present status of the germ-cell problem in vertebrates. Biol. Rev. 20: 45–55.

Fabergé, A. C. 1942 Homologous chromosome pairing: the physical problem. J. Genetics, *43:* 121–144.

Fankhauser, G. 1934 Cytological studies on the egg fragments of the salamander Triton. III. The early development of the sperm nuclei in egg fragments without the egg nucleus. J. Exp. Zool., *67:*159–215.

——— 1948 The organization of the amphibian egg during fertilization and cleavage. Ann. New York Acad. Sci., *49:*684–708.

Farris, E. J. 1949 The number of motile spermatozoa as an index of fertility in man: a study of 406 semen specimens. J. Urology, *61:*1099–1104.

Fekete, E., and Duran-Reynals, F. 1943 Hyaluronidase in the fertilization of mammalian ova. Proc. Soc. Exp. Biol. & Med., *52:*119–121.

Fisk, R. T., and Morrow, P. 1945 The occurrence of anti-Rh$_0$ blocking antibodies in anti-Rh' serums. Proc. Soc. Exp. Biol. & Med., *58:*72–73.

Fogg, L. C. 1930 A study of chromatin diminution in Ascaris and Ephestia. J. Morph., *50:*413–451.

Fol, H. 1877 Sur le premier développement d'une étoile de mer. Compt. rend. acad. sci., *84:* 357–360.

——— 1879 Recherches sur la fécondation et la commencement de l'hénogénie chez divers animaux. Mém. Soc. Phys. et d'hist. nat. Genève, *26:* 89–397.

Frank, J. A. 1939 Some properties of sperm extracts and their relationship to the fertilization reaction in *Arbacia punctulata*. Biol. Bull., *76:* 190–216.

Friedrich-Freksa, H. 1940 Bei der Chromosomenkonjugation wirksame Kräfte und ihre Bedeutung für die identische Verdoppelung von Nukleoproteinen. Naturwiss., *28:*376–379.

Geigy, R. 1931 Action de l'ultraviolet sur le pôle germinal dans l'oeuf de *Drosophila melanogaster* (Castration et Mutabilité). Rev. suisse zool., *38:* 187–288.

———, and Aboïm, A. N. 1944 Gonadenentwicklung bei Drosophila nach frühembryonaler Ausschaltung der Geschlechtszellen. Rev. suisse zool., *51:*410–417.

Geitler, L. 1938 Chromosomenbau. (Protoplasma-Monographien 14.) Borntraeger, Berlin.

Gray, J. 1928 The effect of egg secretions on spermatozoa. Brit. J. Exp. Biol., *5:*362–365.

Hartman, C. G. 1939 Ovulation, fertilization and the transport and viability of eggs and spermatozoa; in Sex and Internal Secretions. 2d ed. Williams & Wilkins Co., Baltimore, pp. 630–719.

Hartmann, M. 1940 Die stofflichen Grundlagen der Befruchtung und Sexualität im Pflanzen- und Tierreich. I. Die Befruchtungsstoffe (Gamone) der Seeigel. Naturwiss., *28:*807–813.

———, Kuhn, R., Schartau, O., and Wallenfels, K. 1939 Über die Sexualstoffe der Seeigel. Naturwiss., *27:*433.

———, Kuhn, R., Schartau, O., and Wallenfels, K. 1940 Über die Wechselwirkung von Gyno- und Andro-Gamonen bei der Befruchtung der Eier des Seeigels. Naturwiss., *28:*144.

———, Schartau, O., and Wallenfels, K. 1940 Untersuchungen über die Befruchtungsstoffe der Seeigel, II. Biol. Zentr., *60:*398–423.

Harvey, E. B. 1930 The effect of lack of oxygen on the sperm and unfertilized eggs of *Arbacia punctulata*, and on fertilization. Biol. Bull., *58:* 288–292.

Harvey, E. N. 1910 Methods of artificial parthenogenesis. Biol. Bull., *18:*269–280.

Harvey, L. A. 1929 The oögenesis of *Carcinus moenas* Penn with special reference to yolk formation. Trans. Roy. Soc. Edinburgh, *56:*157–174.

Hayashi, T. 1945 Dilution medium and survival of the spermatozoa of *Arbacia punctulata*. I. Effect of the medium on fertilizing power. Biol. Bull., *89:*162–179.

Hegner, R. W. 1914 The Germ Cell Cycle in Animals. The Macmillan Co., New York.

Heidelberger, M. 1938 The Chemistry of the Amino Acids and Proteins. Charles C Thomas, Springfield, Illinois, pp. 953–974.

——— 1939 Chemical aspects of precipitin and agglutinin reactions. Chem. Rev., *24:*323–343.

Heilbrunn, L. V. 1928 The Colloid Chemistry of Protoplasm. (Protoplasma-Monographien, Vol. I.) Borntraeger, Berlin.

——— 1943 Outline of General Physiology. 2d ed. W. B. Saunders Co., Philadelphia.

———, and Wilbur, K. M. 1937 Stimulation and nuclear breakdown in the Nereis egg. Biol. Bull., *73:*557–564.

———, and Young, R. A. 1930 The action of ultra-violet rays on Arbacia egg protoplasm. Physiol. Zool., *3:*330–341.

Henle, W., Henle, G., and Chambers, L. A. 1938 Studies on the antigenic structure of some mammalian spermatozoa. J. Exp. Med., *68:*335–352.

Herla, V. 1895 Étude des variations de la mitose chez l'Ascaride mégalocéphale. Arch. Biol., *13:* 423–520.

Hevesy, G. 1947 Some applications of radioactive indicators in turnover studies. Advances in Enzymol., *7:*111–214.

———, and Hahn, L. 1938 Origin of phosphorus compounds in hens' eggs. Kgl. Danske Videnskabernes Selskab. Biol. Medd., *14*(2):3–39.

Hibbard, H. 1928 Contribution a l'étude de l'ovogénèse, de la fécondation et de l'histogénèse chez *Discoglossus pictus* Otth. Arch. biol., *38:*251–326.

Hinton, T. 1946 The physical forces involved in somatic pairing in the Diptera. J. Exp. Zool., *102:* 237–251.

Hirst, G. K. 1942 The quantitative determination of influenza virus and antibodies by means of red cell agglutination. J. Exp. Med., *75:*49-64.

Hogue, M. J. 1910 Über die Wirkung der Centrifugalkraft auf die Eier von *Ascaris megalocephala*. Roux' Arch. Entw.-mech., *29:*109–145.

Hörstadius, S. 1939 Über die Entwicklung von *Astropecten araneiacus* L. Pubbl. Staz. Zool. Napoli, *17:*221–312.

Hultin, T. 1947a Some physiological effects of basic sperm proteins. Ark. Kemi, Mineral., Geol., *24B*, No. 12.

——— 1947b On the question of sperm antifertilizin. Estratto Pubbl. Staz. Zool. Napoli, *21:*153-163.

——— 1948a Species specificity in fertilization reaction. I. The role of the vitelline membrane of sea urchin eggs in species specificity. Ark. Zool., *40A*, No. 12.

——— 1948b Species specificity in fertilization reaction. II. Influence of certain factors on the cross-fertilization capacity of *Arbacia lixula* (L.). Ark. Zool., *40*, No. 20.

Humphrey, R. R. 1927 Extirpation of the primordial germ cells of Amblystoma: its effect upon the development of the gonad. J. Exp. Zool., *49:* 363–399.

——— 1928 The developmental potencies of the intermediate mesoderm of Amblystoma when transplanted into ventrolateral sites in other embryos: the primordial germ cells of such grafts and their role in the development of a gonad. Anat. Rec., *40:*67–90.

——— 1929 The early history of the primordial germ cells in the Urodeles: evidence from experimental studies. Anat. Rec., *42:*301–303.

——— 1933 The development and sex differentiation of the gonad in the wood frog (*Rana sylvatica*) following extirpation or orthotopic implantation of the intermediate segment and adjacent mesoderm. J. Exp. Zool., *65:*243–264.

Huskins, C. L. 1948 Segregation and reduction in somatic tissues: initial observations on *Allium cepa*. J. Heredity, *39:*310–325.

Hutchens, J. O., Keltch, A. K., Krahl, M. E., and Clowes, G. H. A. 1942 Studies on cell metabolism and cell division. VI. J. Gen. Physiol., 25: 717–731.

Immers, J. 1949 On the heparin-like effect of fertilizin from sea urchin eggs on blood coagulation and the modifying action of basic proteins and cephalin on the effect. Ark. Zool., 42A, No. 6.

Jandorf, B. J., and Krahl, M. E. 1942 Studies on cell metabolism and cell division. VIII. The diphosphopyridine nucleotide (cozymase) content of eggs of Arbacia punctulata. J. Gen. Physiol., 25:749–754.

Jennings, H. S. 1906 Behavior of the Lower Organisms. Columbia University Press, New York.

Jörgensen, M. 1913 Zellenstudien I. Morphologische Beiträge zum Problem des Eiwachstums. Arch. Zellforsch., 10:1–126.

Just, E. E. 1915a Initiation of development in Nereis. Biol. Bull., 28:1–17.

——— 1915b The experimental analysis of fertilization in Platynereis megalops. Biol. Bull., 28: 93–114.

——— 1915c The morphology of normal fertilization in Platynereis megalops. J. Morph., 26: 217–232.

——— 1922 Initiation of development in the egg of Arbacia. I. Effect of hypertonic sea water in producing membrane separation, cleavage and top-swimming plutei. Biol. Bull., 43:383–400.

——— 1930 The present status of the fertilizin theory of fertilization. Protoplasma, 10:300–342.

King, R. L., and Beams, H. W. 1938 An experimental study of chromatin diminution in Ascaris. J. Exp. Zool., 77:425–443.

Kitching, J. A., and Moser, F. 1940 Studies on a cortical layer response to stimulating agents in the Arbacia egg. Biol. Bull., 78:80–91.

Korr, I. M. 1937 Respiratory mechanisms in the unfertilized and fertilized sea urchin egg: a temperature analysis. J. Cell. Comp. Physiol., 10: 461–485.

Krahl, M. E., Keltch, A. K., Neubeck, C. E., and Clowes, G. H. A. 1941 Studies on cell metabolism and cell division. V. Cytochrome oxidase activity in the eggs of Arbacia punctulata. J. Gen. Physiol., 24:597–617.

Krauss, M. 1949 A mucin clot reaction with sea urchin fertilizin. Biol. Bull., 96:74–89.

Kuhn, R., and Wallenfels, K. 1940 Echinochrome als prosthetische Gruppen hochmolekularer Symplexe in den Eiern von Arbacia pustulosa. Ber. deut. chem. Ges., 73:458–464.

Landauer, W., Pfeiffer, C. A., Gardner, W. U., and Man, E. B. 1939 Hypercalcification, calcemia and lipemia in chickens following administration of estrogens. Proc. Soc. Exp. Biol. & Med., 41:80–82.

Lardy, H. A., and Philips, P. H. 1941a The interrelation of oxidative and glycolytic processes as sources of energy for bull spermatozoa. Am. J. Physiol., 133:602–609.

———, and Philips, P. H. 1941b Phospholipids as a source of energy for motility of bull spermatozoa. Am. J. Physiol., 134:542–548.

———, and Philips, P. H. 1941a The effect of certain inhibitors and activators on sperm metabolism. J. Biol. Chem., 138:195–202.

———, and Philips, P. H. 1943a Effect of pH and certain electrolytes on the metabolism of ejaculated spermatozoa. Am. J. Physiol., 138:741–746.

———, and Philips, P. H. 1943b Inhibition of sperm respiration and reversibility of the effects of metabolic inhibitors. J. Biol. Chem., 148:333–341.

———, and Philips, P. H. 1943c Inhibition of sperm glycolysis and reversibilty of the effects of metabolic inhibitors. J. Biol. Chem., 148:343–347.

———, and Philips, P. H. 1943d The effect of thyroxine and dinitrophenol on sperm metabolism. J. Biol. Chem., 149:177–182.

———, and Philips, P. H. 1944 Acetate utilization for maintenance of motility of bull spermatozoa. Nature, 153:168–169.

———, and Philips, P. H. 1945 Studies of fat and carbohydrate oxidation in mammalian spermatozoa. Arch. Biochem., 6:53–61.

Laser, H., and Rothschild, Lord 1939 The metabolism of the eggs of Psammechinus miliaris during the fertilization reaction. Proc. Roy. Soc. London, 126:539–557.

Laskowski, M. 1938 The gonadotropic hormone and the level of blood phosphorus in the hen. Biochem. J., 32:1176–1180.

Leonard, S. L., Perlman, P. L., and Kurzrok, R. 1947 Relation between time of fertilization and follicle cell dispersal in rat ova. Proc. Soc. Exp. Biol. & Med., 66:517–518.

Levine, P., and Walker, R. K. 1946 On blocking antibody and zone phenomenon in human anti-Rh sera. Science, 103:389–391.

Lillie, F. R. 1912 The production of sperm iso-agglutinins by ova. Science, 36:527–530.

——— 1913a Studies of fertilization. V. The behavior of the spermatozoa of Nereis and Arbacia with special reference to egg extractives. J. Exp. Zool., 14:515–574.

——— 1913b The mechanism of fertilization. Science, 38:524–528.

——— 1914 Studies of fertilization. VI. The mechanism of fertilization in Arbacia. J. Exp. Zool., 16:523–590.

——— 1919 Problems of Fertilization. University of Chicago Press, Chicago.

———, and Just, E. E. 1924 Cowdry's General Cytology. University of Chicago Press, Chicago, pp. 481–536.

Lillie, R. S. 1916 Increase of permeability to water following normal and artificial activation in sea urchin eggs. Am. J. Physiol., 40:249–266.

——— 1941 Further experiments on artificial parthenogenesis in starfish eggs, with a review. Physiol. Zool., 14:239–267.

Lindberg, O. 1943 Studien über das Problem des Kohlehydratabbaus und der Säurebildung bei der Befruchtung des Seeigeleis. Ark. Kemi, Mineral., Geol., 16A, No. 15.

——— 1948 On the turnover of adenosine triphosphate in the sea urchin egg. Ark. Kemi, Mineral., Geol., 26B, No. 13.

———, and Ernster, L. 1948 On carbohydrate

metabolism in homogenized sea-urchin eggs. Biochim. Biophys. Acta, *2:*471–7.

Lindegren, C. C., and Bridges, C. B. 1938 Is agglutination an explanation for the occurrence and for the chromomere-to-chromomere specificity of synapsis? Science, *87:*510–511.

Loeb, J. 1913 Artificial Parthenogenesis and Fertilization. University of Chicago Press, Chicago.

Lorenz, F. W., Perlman, I., and Chaikoff, I. L. 1943 Phosphorus deposition in the egg as measured with radioactive phosphorus. Am. J. Physiol., *138:*318–327.

———, and Tyler, A. 1951 Extension of motile life span of spermatozoa of the domestic fowl by amino acids and proteins. Proc. Soc. Exp. Biol. & Med., *78:*57–62.

MacBride, E. W., and Hewer, H. R. 1931 Zoology; in Recent Advances in Microscopy (Piney, ed.). The Blakiston Co., Philadelphia, pp. 88–123, 140–154.

MacLeod, J. 1939 The metabolism of human spermatozoa. Proc. Soc. Exp. Biol. & Med., *42:*153–155.

——— 1941 The metabolism of human spermatozoa. Am. J. Physiol., *132:*193–201.

——— 1943a The role of oxygen in the metabolism and motility of human spermatozoa. Am. J. Physiol., *138:*512–518.

——— 1943b The physiology of mammalian semen. Ann. Rev. Physiol., *5:*399–412.

——— 1946a Metabolism and motility of human spermatozoa; in The Problem of Fertility (E. T. Engle, ed.). Princeton University Press, Princeton, N. J., pp. 154–168.

——— 1946b The semen specimen: laboratory examination; in Diagnosis in Sterility (E. T. Engle, ed.). Charles C Thomas, Springfield, Illinois, p. 3.

Mann, T. 1945a Studies on the metabolism of semen. Biochem. J., *39:*451–458.

——— 1945b Anaerobic metabolism of spermatozoa. Nature, *156:*80–81.

——— 1946 Fructose, a constituent of semen. Nature, *157:*79.

——— 1949 Metabolism of semen. Advances in Enzymol., *9:*329–390.

Marrack, J. R. 1938 The Chemistry of Antigens and Antibodies. Special Report, Series No. 230, Medical Research Council, London.

Marza, V. D. 1938 Histophysiologie de l'Ovogenèse. Actualités Scientifiques et Industrielles, No. 751. Hermann et Cie., Paris.

McClean, D., and Rowlands, I. W. 1942 Role of hyaluronidase in fertilization. Nature, *150:*627–628.

Medem, F. G. von 1942 Beiträge zur Frage der Befruchtungsstoffe bei marinen Mollusken. Biol. Zentr., *62:*431–446.

Metz, C. B. 1942a Egg and sperm agglutination in invertebrates. Doctorate thesis, California Institute of Technology.

——— 1942b The inactivation by fertilizin and its conversion to the "univalent" form by x-rays and ultraviolet light. Biol. Bull., *82:*446–454.

——— 1945 The agglutination of starfish sperm by fertilizin. Biol. Bull., *89:*84–94.

——— 1949 Agglutination of sea urchin eggs and sperm by basic proteins. Proc. Soc. Exp. Biol. & Med., *70:*422–424.

Metz, C. W. 1931 Chromosomal differences between germ cells and soma in Sciara. Biol. Zentr., *51:*119–124.

——— 1938 Chromosome behavior, inheritance and sex determination in Sciara. Amer. Nat., *72:*485–520.

Meyer, K. 1947 The biological significance of hyaluronic acid and hyaluronidase. Physiol. Rev., *27:*335–359.

———, and Rapport, M. M. 1952 Hyaluronidases. Advances in Enzymol., *13:*199–236.

Mickey, G. H. 1946 The presence of multiple strands in chromosomes of Romalea (Orthoptera). Amer. Nat., *80:*446–452.

——— 1947 Division cycle in grasshopper chromosomes. Proc. Louisiana Acad. Sci., *10:*49–66.

Mirsky, A. E. 1936 Protein coagulation as a result of fertilization. Science, *84:*333–334.

Monroy, A. 1939 Sulla localizzazione delle cellule genitali primordiali in fasi precoci di sviluppo. Ricerche sperimentali in anfibi anuri. Arch. ital. Anat. Embriol., *41:*368–389.

Moore, A. R. 1930a Fertilization and development without membrane formation in the egg of the sea urchin, *Strongylocentrotus purpuratus.* Protoplasma, *9:*9–17.

——— 1930b Fertilization and development without the fertilization membrane in the egg of *Dendraster excentricus.* Protoplasma, *9:*18–24.

——— 1932 The dependence of cytoplasmic structures in the egg of the sea urchin on the ionic balance of the environment. J. Cell. Comp. Physiol., *2:*41–51.

——— 1937 On the centering of the nuclei in centrifuged eggs as a result of fertilization and artificial membrane formation. Protoplasma, *27:*544–551.

——— 1949 The relation of ions to the appearance and persistence of fertilization and hyaline membranes in eggs of the sea urchin. Amer. Nat., *83:*233–247.

Morgan, T. H. 1927 Experimental Embryology. Columbia University Press, New York.

Narain, D. 1937 Cytoplasmic inclusions in the oogenesis of *Sacchobranchus fossiles, Calarias batrachus* and *Anabas scandens.* Z. Zellforsch., *26:*625–640.

Needham, J. 1931 Chemical Embryology. Cambridge University Press, Cambridge, England, Vol. III, App. II, pp. 1679–1684.

——— 1942 Biochemistry and Morphogenesis. Cambridge University Press, Cambridge, England.

Nieuwkoop, P. D. 1946 Experimental investigations on the origin and determination of the germ cells, and on the development of the lateral plates and germ ridges in urodeles. Arch. Néerland. Zool., *8:*1–205.

Öhman, L. O. 1940 Über die Veränderung des respiratorischen Quotienten während der Frühentwicklung des Seeigeleies. Ark. Zool., *32A*, No. 15.

Öhman, L. O. 1944 On the lipids of the sea urchin egg. Ark. Zool., *36A*, No. 7.

Örström, A. 1932 Zur Analyse der Atmungssteigerung bei der Befruchtung des Seeigeleis. Auf der Grundlage von Versuchen über Oxydation und Reduktion von Dimethylparaphenylendiamin in der Eizelle. Protoplasma, *15*:566–589.

——— 1935 Über Ammoniakbildung bei der Entwicklungserregung des Seeigeleies. Ark. Zool., *28B*, No. 6.

——— 1941 Über die chemischen Vorgänge insbesondere den Ammoniakstoffwechsel, bei der Entwicklungserregung des Seeigeleies. Z. Physiol. Chem., *271*:1–176.

———, and Lindberg, O. 1940 Über den Kohlenhydratstoffwechsel bei der Befruchtung des Seeigeleies. Enzymologia, *8*:367–384.

Painter, T. S. 1940 On the synthesis of cleavage chromosomes. Proc. Nat. Acad. Sci., *26*:95–100.

——— 1945a Nuclear phenomena associated with secretion in certain gland cells with especial reference to the origin of cytoplasmic nucleic acid. J. Exp. Zool., *100*:523–541.

——— 1945b Chromatin diminution. Trans. Conn. Acad. Arts Sci., *36*:443–448.

———, and Reindorp, E. 1939 Endomitosis in the nurse cells of the ovary of Drosophila melanogaster. Chromosoma, *1*:276–283.

Pasteels, J. 1938a Le rôle du calcium dans l'activation de l'oeuf de Pholade. Trav. Stat. Zool. Wimereux, *13*:515–530.

——— 1938b Sensibilisateurs et réalisateurs dans l'activation de l'oeuf de Barnea candida. Bull. Acad. Belg. Cl. Sci., *24*:721–731.

——— 1941 Sur quelques particularités de l'activation de l'oeuf d'oursin (Psammechinus miliaris). Bull. Cl. Sci. Acad. Roy. Belg., *27*:123–129.

———, and Fautrez, J. 1947 Remarques sur les effets de la rupture de la balance des sels sur le cytoplasme ovulaire. (À propos d'observations faites sur Hydroides uncinatus et Ascidiella aspersa). Arch. Portugaies Sci. Biol., *9*:42–58.

Pauling, L. 1940 The theory of the structure and process of formation of antibodies. J. Am. Chem. Soc., *62*:2643–2657.

Peterfi, T., and Rothschild, V. 1935 Bio-electric transients during fertilization. Nature, *135*:874–875.

Pincus, G. 1930 Observations on the living eggs of the rabbit. Proc. Royal Soc., *107*:132–167.

——— 1936 The Eggs of Mammals. The Macmillan Co., New York.

Race, R. R. 1944 "Incomplete" antibody in human serum. Nature, *153*:771–772.

Reagan, F. P. 1916 Some results and possibilities of early embryonic castration. Anat. Rec., *11*:489–491.

Riddle, O. 1942 Cyclic changes in the blood calcium, phosphorus and fat in relation to egg laying and estrogen production. Endocrinology, *31*:498–506.

Ris, H. 1945 The structure of meiotic chromo-

somes in the grasshopper and its bearing on the nature of "chromomeres" and "lamp-brush chromosomes." Biol. Bull., *89*:242–257.

Robbie, W. A. 1946 The effect of cyanide on the oxygen consumption and cleavage of the sea urchin egg. J. Cell. Comp. Physiol., *28*:305–324.

Roepke, R. R., and Bushnell, L. D. 1936 A serological comparison of the phosphoprotein of the serum of the laying hen and the vitellin of the egg yolk. J. Immunol., *30*:109–113.

Rothschild, Lord 1938 The biophysics of the egg surface of Echinus esculentus during fertilization and cytolysis. J. Exp. Biol., *15*:209–216.

——— 1946 Physiology of fertilization. Nature, *157*:720–722.

——— 1948a The physiology of Echinus esculentus spermatozoa. J. Exp. Biol., *25*:15–21.

——— 1948b The physiology of sea urchin spermatozoa: lack of movement in semen. J. Exp. Biol., *25*:344–352.

——— 1948c The physiology of sea urchin spermatozoa: senescence and the dilution effect. J. Exp. Biol., *25*:353–368.

——— 1949a The metabolism of fertilized and unfertilized sea urchin eggs: the action of light and carbon monoxide. J. Exp. Biol., *26*:100–111.

——— 1949b The fertilization reaction in the sea urchin egg: a note on diffusion considerations. J. Exp. Biol., *26*:177–181.

——— 1951a Sea-urchin spermatozoa. Biol. Rev., *26*:1–27.

——— 1951b Sperm-egg interacting substances and metabolic changes associated with fertilization. Biochem. Soc. Symposia, *7*:40–51.

——— 1952 Spermatozoa. Sci. Progress, *60*:1–10.

———, and Cleland, K. W. 1952 The physiology of sea-urchin spermatozoa: the nature and location of the endogenous substrate. J. Exp. Biol., *29*:66–71.

———, and Swann, M. M. 1949 The fertilization reaction in the sea urchin egg: a propagated response to sperm attachment. J. Exp. Biol., *26*:164–176.

Rubenstein, B. B., and Gerard, R. W. 1934 Fertilization and the temperature coefficients of oxygen consumption in eggs of Arbacia punctulata. J. Gen. Physiol., *17*:677–686.

Ruffo, A., and Monroy, A. 1945 Variazioni di viscosità delle uova di riccio di mare durante la fecondazione. Boll. soc. ital. biol. sper., *20*:6–7.

Runnström, J. 1928 Struktur und Atmung bei der Entwicklungserregung des Seeigeleies. Acta Zool., *9*:445–499.

——— 1930a Atmungsmechanismus und Entwicklungserregung bei dem Seeigelei. Protoplasma, *10*:106–173.

——— 1930b Spaltung und Atmung bei der Entwicklungserregung des Seeigeleies. Ark. Zool., *21B*, No. 8.

——— 1933 Zur Kenntnis der Stoffwechselvorgänge bei der Entwicklungserregung des Seeigeleies. Biochem. Z., *258*:257–279.

——— 1944 Notes on the formation of the fertilization membrane and some other features of the early development of the Asterias egg. Acta Zool., *25:*159–167.

Runnström, J. 1949 The mechanism of fertilization in metazoa. Advances in Enzymol., *9:*241–327.

———, and Lindvall, S. 1946 The effect of some agents upon the reaction of Echinocardium spermatozoa towards egg water. Ark. Zool., *38A,* No. 10.

———, Lindvall, S., and Tiselius, A. 1944 Gamones from the sperm of sea urchin and salmon. Nature, *153:*285–286.

———, and Monné, L. 1945a On some properties of the surface layers of immature and mature sea urchin eggs, especially the changes accompanying nuclear and cytoplasmic maturation. Ark. Zool., *36A,* No. 18.

———, and Monné, L. 1945b On changes in the properties of the surface layers of the sea urchin egg due to varying external conditions. Ark. Zool., *36A,* No. 20.

——— Monné, L., and Broman, L. 1943 On some properties of the surface layers in the sea urchin egg and their changes upon activation. Ark. Zool., *35A,* No. 3.

———, Tiselius, A., and Lindvall, S. 1945 The action of Androgamone III on the sea urchin egg. Ark. Zoologi, *36A,* No. 22.

———, Tiselius, A., and Vasseur, E. 1942 Zur Kenntnis der Gamonwirkungen bei *Psammechinus miliaris* und *Echinocardium cordatum.* Ark. Kemi, Mineral., Geol., *15A,* No. 16.

Sampson, M. M. 1922 Iso-agglutination and hetero-agglutination of spermatozoa. Biol. Bull., *43:*267–284.

Sax, H. J., and Sax, K. 1935 Chromosome structure and behavior in mitosis and meiosis. J. Arnold Arboretum, *16:*423–439. ,

Scheer, B. T., and Scheer, M. A. R. 1947 Some interrelations of drug and ion actions in the artificial activation of marine eggs. Physiol. Zool., *20:*15–32.

Schechter, V. 1937 Calcium reduction and the prolongation of life in the egg cells of *Arbacia punctulata.* Biol. Bull., *72:*366–376.

——— 1941 Experimental studies upon the egg cells of the clam, *Mactra solidissima,* with special reference to longevity. J. Exp. Zool., *86:*461–478.

Schrader, F. 1935 Notes on the mitotic behaviour of long chromosomes. Cytologia, *6:*422–430.

——— 1944 Mitosis: The Movements of Chromosomes in Cell Division. Columbia University Press, New York.

Schultz, J. 1941 The evidence of the nucleoprotein nature of the gene. Cold Spring Harbor Symposia on Quant. Biol., *9:*55–65.

Sharp, L. W. 1943 Fundamentals of Cytology. McGraw-Hill Book Co., New York.

Singh, B. N., and Boyle, W. 1938 The vitellogenesis of *Gasterosteus aculeatus* (the stickleback) investigated by the ultra-centrifuge. Quart. J. Micr. Sci., *81:*81–106.

Spikes, J. D. 1948 Experiments on fertilization and cleavage. Doctorate thesis for California Institute of Technology.

——— 1949a The prezone phenomenon in sperm agglutination. Biol. Bull., *97:*95–99.

——— 1949b Metabolism of sea urchin sperm. Amer. Nat., *83:*285–301.

Stewart, D., and Jacobs, M. H. 1932 The effect of fertilization on the permeability of the eggs of Arbacia and Asterias to ethylene glycol. J. Cell. Comp. Physiol., *1:*83–92.

Subramaniam, M. K., and Aiyar, G. 1936 Secretion of fatty and albuminous yolk by Golgi bodies in *Stomopneustes variolaris* Lamarck. Z. Zellforsch. u. mikroskop. Anat., *24:*576–584.

Swift, C. H. 1914 Origin and early history of the primordial germ cells in the chick. Am. J. Anat., *15:*483–516.

Taurog, A., Lorenz, F. W., Entenman, C., and Chaikoff, I. L. 1944 The effect of diethylstilbestrol on the in vitro formation of phospholipids in the liver as measured with radioactive phosphorus. Endocrinology, *35:*483–487.

Terni, T., and Maleci, O. 1937 Sulla penetrazione di spermatozoi dentro cellule somatiche coltivate in vitro. Monitore Zool. Ital., *47* (suppl.): 72–79.

Tosic, J. 1947 Mechanism of hydrogen peroxide formation by spermatozoa and the role of amino acids in sperm motility. Nature, *159:*544.

Tosic, J., and Walton, A. 1946 Formation of hydrogen peroxide by spermatozoa and its inhibitory effect on respiration. Nature, *158:*485.

Tyler, A. 1931 The production of normal embryos by artificial parthenogenesis in the echiuroid, Urechis. Biol. Bull., *60:*187–211.

——— 1932 Changes in volume and surface of Urechis eggs upon fertilization. J. Exp. Zool., *63:*155–173.

——— 1937 On the energetics of differentiation. V. Comparison of the rates of development and of oxygen consumption of tight membrane and normal echinoderm eggs. J. Exp. Zool., *76:*395–406.

——— 1939a Extraction of an egg membrane-lysin from sperm of the giant keyhole limpet (*Megathura crenulata*). Proc. Nat. Acad. Sci., *25:*317–323.

——— 1939b Crystalline echinochrome and spinochrome: their failure to stimulate the respiration of eggs and of sperm of Strongylocentrotus. Proc. Nat. Acad. Sci., *25:*523–528.

——— 1940a Sperm agglutination in the keyhole limpet, *Megathura crenulata.* Biol. Bull., *78:*159–178.

——— 1940b Agglutination of sea urchin eggs by means of a substance extracted from the eggs. Proc. Nat. Acad. Sci., *26:*249–256.

——— 1941 The role of fertilizin in the fertilization of eggs of the sea urchin and other animals. Biol. Bull., *81:*190–204.

——— 1942 Specific interacting substances of eggs and sperm. Western J. Surg., Obstet. & Gynecol., *50:*126–138.

——— 1945a Conversion of agglutinins and precipitins into "univalent" (non-agglutinating or non-precipitating) antibodies by photo-dynamic irradiation of rabbit-antisera vs. pneumococci, sheep-red-cells and sea urchin sperm. J. Immunol., *51:*157–172.

——— 1945b Anaphylactic properties of photooxidized rabbit-antisera (vs. sheep-erythrocytes and pneumococci) and horse-antiserum (vs. diphtherial toxin) containing "univalent" antibodies. J. Immunol., *51*:329–338.

Tyler, A. 1946a Loss of fertilizing power of sea urchin and Urechis sperm treated with "univalent" antibodies vs. antifertilizin. Proc. Soc. Exp. Biol. & Med., *62*:197–199.

—— 1946b On natural auto-antibodies as evidenced by anti-venin in serum and liver extract of the Gila monster. Proc. Nat. Acad. Sci., *32*: 195–201.

—— 1947 An auto-antibody concept of cell structure, growth and differentiation. Growth, *10*(suppl.):7–19.

—— 1948a Fertilization and immunity. Physiol. Rev., *28*:180–219.

—— 1948b The chemistry of the fertilizin of the sea urchin *Strongylocentrotus purpuratus*. Anat. Rec., *101*:8–9.

—— 1949 Properties of fertilizin and related substances of eggs and sperm of marine animals. Amer. Nat., *83*:195–219.

—— 1950 Extension of the functional life span of spermatozoa by amino acids and peptides. Biol. Bull., *99*:224.

—— 1953 Prolongation of life span of sea-urchin spermatozoa, and improvement of the fertilization-reaction, by treatment of spermatozoa and eggs with metal-chelating agents (amino acids, versene, DEDTC, oxine, cupron). Biol. Bull., *104*:224–239.

——, and Atkinson, E. 1950 Prolongation of the fertilizing capacity of sea-urchin spermatozoa by amino acids. Science, *112*:783–785.

——, and Dessel, F. W. 1939 Increasing the life span of unfertilized Urechis eggs by acid. J. Exp. Zool., *81*:459–472.

——, and Fox, S. W. 1939 Sperm agglutination in the keyhole limpet and the sea urchin. Science, *90*:516–517.

——, and Fox, S. W. 1940 Evidence for the protein nature of the sperm agglutinins of the keyhole limpet and the sea urchin. Biol. Bull., *79*:153–165.

——, and Humason, W. D. 1937 On the energetics of differentiation, VI. Comparison of the temperature coefficients of the respiratory rates of unfertilized and of fertilized eggs. Biol. Bull., *78*:261–279.

——, and O'Melveny, K. 1941 The role of antifertilizin in the fertilization of sea urchin eggs. Biol. Bull., *81*:364–374.

——, Ricci, N., and Horowitz, N. H. 1938 The respiration and fertilizable life of Arbacia eggs under sterile and non-sterile conditions. J. Exp. Zool., *79*:129–143.

——, and Rothschild, Lord 1951 Metabolism of sea-urchin spermatozoa and induced anaerobic motility in solutions of amino acids. Proc. Soc. Exp. Biol. & Med., *76*:52–58.

——, and Scheer, B. T. 1937 Inhibition of fertilization in eggs of marine animals by means of acid. J. Exp. Zool., *75*:179–197.

——, and Schultz, J. 1932 Inhibition and reversal of fertilization in the eggs of the echiuroid

worm, *Urechis caupo*. J. Exp. Zool., *63*:509–532.

——, and Swingle, S. W. 1945 Protective value of "univalent" antibodies produced by photo-oxidation of antipneumococcal rabbit-serum and antidiphtheric horse-serum. J. Immunol., *51*:339–347.

——, and Tanabe, T. Y. 1952 Motile life of bovine spermatozoa in glycine and yolk-citrate diluents at high and low temperatures. Proc. Soc. Exp. Biol. & Med., *81*:367–371.

Ubisch, L., von 1943 Über die Bedeutung der Diminution von *Ascaris megalocephala*. Acta Biotheoretica, *7*:163–182.

Vandel, A. 1941 Recherches sur la génétique et la sexualité des isopodes terrestres. VII. Sur la longévité des spermatozoïdes à l'intérieur de l'ovaire d' "Armadillidium vulgare." Bull. Biol. France et Belgique, *75*:364–368.

Vasseur, E. 1947 The sulphuric acid content of the egg coat of the sea urchin, *Strongylocentrotus droebachiensis* Müll. Ark. Kemi, Mineral., Geol., *25B*, No. 6.

—— 1948a Chemical studies on the jelly coat of the sea urchin egg. Acta chem. Scandinav., *2*: 900–913.

—— 1948b A spectrophotometric study on the orcinol reaction with carbohydrates. Acta chem., Scandinav., *2*:693–701.

—— 1949 Effect of calcium ions on the agglutination in *Strongylocentrotus droebachiensis* Mull. Ark. Kemi, *1*:No. 14, 105–116.

——, and Hagström, B. 1946 On the gamones of some sea urchins from the Swedish west coast. Ark. Zool., *37A*:No. 17, 1–17.

——, and Immers, J. 1949 Genus specificity of the carbohydrate component in the sea urchin egg jelly coat as revealed by paper chromatography. Ark. Kemi, *1*, No. 6.

Warburg, O. 1908 Beobachtungen über die Oxydationsprozesse im Seeigelei. Z. physiol. Chem., *57*:1–16.

Weismann, A. 1883 Die Entstehung der Sexualzellen bei den Hydromedusen. Gustav Fischer, Jena.

—— 1893 The Germ Plasm. English translation by W. N. Parker and H. Rönnfeldt. C. Scribner's Sons, New York.

Whitaker, D. M. 1931a On the rate of oxygen consumption by fertilized and unfertilized eggs. I. *Fucus vesiculosus*. J. Gen. Physiol., *15*:167–182.

—— 1931b On the rate of oxygen consumption by fertilized and unfertilized eggs. II. *Cumingia tellinoides*. J. Gen. Physiol., *15*:183–190.

—— 1931c On the rate of oxygen consumption by fertilized and unfertilized eggs. III. *Nereis limbata*. J. Gen. Physiol., *15*:191–200.

—— 1933a On the rate of oxygen consumption by fertilized and unfertilized eggs. IV. Chaetopterus and *Arbacia punctulata*. J. Gen. Physiol., *16*:475–495.

—— 1933b On the rate of oxygen consumption by fertilized and unfertilized eggs. V. Comparison and interpretation. J. Gen. Physiol., *16*: 497–528.

—— 1937 Extension of the fertilizable life of

unfertilized Urechis eggs by alcohol and by dextrose. J. Exp. Zool., 75:155–167.

White, M. J. D.   1936   Chromosome cycle of *Ascaris megalocephala.* Nature, 137:783.

———   1946   The cytology of the Cecidomyidae (Diptera). II. The chromosome cycle and anomalous spermatogenesis of Miastor. J. Morphol., 79:323–370.

———   1947a   Chromosome studies on gall midges. Carnegie Inst. Washington Year Book No. 46, pp. 165–169.

———   1947b   The cytology of the Cecidomyidae (Diptera). III. The spermatogenesis of *Taxomyia taxi.* J. Morphol., 80:1–24.

———   1948   The cytology of the Cecidomyidae (Diptera). IV. The salivary-gland chromosomes of several species. J. Morphol., 82:53–80.

Whiteley, A.   1949   Phosphorus compounds of sea urchin eggs and the uptake of radio-phosphate upon fertilization. Amer. Nat., 83:249–267.

Wiener, A. S.   1944   A new test (blocking test) for Rh sensitization. Proc. Soc. Exp. Biol. & Med., 56:173–176.

———   1945a   Rh blood types and some of their applications. Am. J. Clin. Path., 15:106–121.

———   1945b   Conglutination test for Rh sensitization. J. Lab. Clin. Med., 30:662–667.

———, and Gordon, E. B.   1948   Studies on the conglutination test in erythroblastosis fetalis. J. Lab. Clin. Med., 33:183–188.

Wilbur, K. M.   1939   The relation of the magnesium ion to ultra-violet stimulation in the Nereis egg. Physiol. Zool., 12:102–109.

Willier, B. H.   1933   Potencies of the gonad-forming area in the chick as tested in chorio-allantoic grafts. Roux' Arch. Entw.-mech., 130:616–648.

———   1937   Experimentally produced sterile gonads and the problem of the origin of the germ cells in the chick embryo. Anat. Rec., 70:89–112.

———   1939   Embryonic development of sex; in Sex and Internal Secretions (E. Allen, ed.). Williams & Wilkins Co., Baltimore, pp. 64–144.

Wilson, E. B.   1925   The Cell in Development and Heredity. 3d ed. The Macmillan Co., New York.

Wintrebert, P.   1929   La digestion de l'enveloppe tubaire interne de l'oeuf par des ferments issus des spermatozoides, et de l'ovule, chez *Discoglossus pictus* Otth. Compt. rend. Acad. Sci. Paris, 188:97–100.

———   1933   La fonction enzymatique de l'acrosome spermien du Discoglosse. Compt. rend. Soc. Biol., 112:1636–1640.

Witschi, E.   1948   Migration of the germ cells of human embryos from the yolk sac to the primitive gonadal folds. Carnegie Inst. Washington Pub. No. 575, Contributions to Embryology, 32:67–80.

Worley, L. G.   1944   Studies of the vitally stained Golgi apparatus. II. Yolk formation and pigment concentration in the mussel *Mytilus californianus* Conrad. J. Morphol., 75:77–101.

———   1946   The Golgi apparatus: an interpretation of its structure and significance. Ann. New York Acad. Sci., 47:1–56.

Yamane, J.   1930   The proteolytic action of mammalian spermatozoa and its bearing upon the second maturation division of ova. Cytologia, 1:394–403.

———   1935   Kausal-analytische Studien über die Befruchtung des Kanincheneies. I. Die Dispersion der Follikelzellen und die Ablösung der Zellen der Corona radiata des Eies durch Spermatozoen. Cytologia, 6:233–255.

Ycas, M. F.   1950   Studies on the respiratory enzymes of sea-urchin eggs. Ph.D. Thesis, California Institute of Technology.

Zondek, B., and Marx, L.   1939   Lipaemia and calcaemia in the cock induced by diethylstilboestrol. Nature, 143:378–379.

CHAPTER 2

Cleavage, Blastulation and Gastrulation

DONALD P. COSTELLO

THE SPLITTING of the egg into a multitude of cells which build up the body of the metazoon embryo and, eventually, of the adult, is known as the cleavage or segmentation of the egg. Cleavage is the initial series of mitotic cell divisions in the life history of each individual following the egg stage, and an infinitesimally small part of the immense series of cell divisions that has no finite limits in the past or in the future. If the activation of the egg to development is looked upon as the removal of a block to cell-division, then each succeeding generation adds to a continuum that extends back from the present to the dawn of life. There is thus little wonder that the early students of the subject, including Kölliker, Remak, Virchow, Wilson and others, saw in the division process the fundamental basis of cell heredity. During the cleavage period there is little or no increase in total cytoplasmic mass, whereas, typically, the rate of synthesis of nuclear material is relatively high.

Aside from this hereditary significance, one of the major embryological problems is whether cleavage is merely cell multiplication, by which the egg splits up into a number of equivalent or indifferent cells, or whether the cleavage blastomeres have a definite and predetermined pattern in relation to each other and to the embryonic parts for which they will contribute their cell progeny. According to the former view, the process of differentiation must follow cleavage, as a separate phenomenon; according to the latter, cleavage and differentiation proceed concurrently and interrelatedly. Historically, the first attempts to settle this problem led to the type of study known as cell lineage.

Cell lineage is the tracing of the developmental history of each individual blastomere through to its ultimate fate in forming definitive parts of the larva or adult. A synonym is cytogeny. One may study the cell lineage

of any animal, regardless of its pattern of cleavage and type of differentiation. However, such studies have more than casual significance in the case of those forms cleaving with precise and predictable patterns, and especially in those showing so-called "determinate cleavage" (see below).

There are three main categories of cleavage: radial, bilateral, and spiral. In assigning species to these categories, it is necessary to bear in mind that one is not dealing with fixed or rigid characteristics, which persist throughout the cleavage period. In spirally cleaving forms, there is usually a transition to bilateral cleavage following the earlier segmentation of the embryo.

Radial cleavage, well exemplified by the cleavage of the sea urchin egg, occurs when the successive cleavage planes cut straight through the egg, at right angles to one another and symmetrically disposed around the polar axis. Thus, when the egg is viewed from either pole, the blastomeres are arranged in a radially symmetrical form. Radial cleavage is found in the Porifera and Cnidaria as well as among the echinoderms.

In bilateral cleavage, the spindles and cleavage planes are bilaterally arranged with reference to a plane of symmetry which coincides with the median plane of the embryo. Styela and other tunicates, Amphioxus, the Amphibia and higher mammals clearly show this type of segmentation. Richards ('31) classifies the nematodes and rotifers among the bilaterally cleaving forms but it has been pointed out (Costello, '48a) that in their early cleavages, these may actually be variants of a spirally cleaving type. The ctenophores show a type of bilateral cleavage which Richards has called disymmetrical.

Spiral cleavage is found in those forms in which there is a rotational movement of cell parts around the egg axis, leading to a displacement or inclination of the spindles with respect to the symmetrically disposed radii. It could have been called, and more properly, oblique cleavage. Postcleavage rotations of cell parts and blastomeres may also occur. The rotational movements are characterized by a regular alternation of direction, clockwise (right-handed, or dexiotropic) and counterclockwise (left-handed, or laeotropic), in successive cleavages. The inclination of

in four quadrants. In all forms, spiral cleavage becomes modified into bilateral cleavage at some stage in development. The animal types that may be added to the list of spirally cleaving forms include the acoel Turbellaria (which produce duets rather than quartets of micromeres), the Cirripedia, as exemplified by Lepas and Balanus (with cleavage by "monets"), the Nematoda and probably the Rotifera.

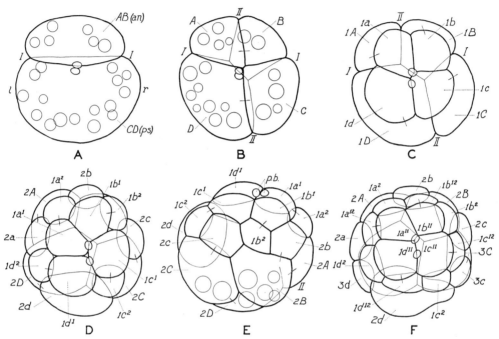

Fig. 69. The normal cleavage of the egg of Nereis (modified after Wilson, 1892). The circles in *A, B* and *E* are oil droplets. The fertilization membrane has been omitted. *A,* Two-cell stage, polar view. *B,* Four-cell stage, polar view. *C,* Eight-cell stage, polar view. *D,* Sixteen-cell stage, polar view. *E,* Sixteen-cell stage, viewed from the right side. *F,* Twenty-two-cell stage, polar view. (From Costello, '45.)

the spindles in spiral cleavage is usually exquisitely clear at the third cleavage, at which time the first quartet of micromeres is formed. During the first and second divisions, the obliquity of the spindles is less clear, and these cleavages are sometimes spoken of as prospectively spiral. In Crepidula (Conklin, 1897), it is a postcleavage rotation of daughter nuclei and of the protoplasmic areas in which these lie that marks the first cleavage as prospectively spiral.

Spiral cleavage (see Fig. 69) is generally assumed to be limited to the polyclad Turbellaria, the Nemertea, the Annelida, and all Mollusca except the Cephalopoda. Actually, spiral cleavage is considerably more widespread, if one considers certain modifications of the typical oblique cleavage taking place

The details of cleavage pattern for various species may be found in MacBride ('14), Dawydoff ('28), and other general texts, as well as in countless original papers describing early development. It has been demonstrated that there are resemblances nothing short of marvelous between the cell lineage of spirally cleaving eggs of even widely separated taxonomic groups. In gastropods, lamellibranchs, annelids and polyclad turbellarians, the ectoderm of the embryo is made up of three quartets of cells, formed from the first four blastomeres; the fourth product of the left posterior macromere contains the mesoblast, except in the turbellarians. The turbellarian ectomesoblast (derived from the second quartet) is represented in the other groups as larval mesoblast; the four basal cells, after producing ectoblast and mesoblast, form entoderm, etc. Superimposed upon these general aspects of the ancestral reminiscences of cleavage are numerous special features of the cleavage of each species. These special features adapt the cleavage of each form to the needs of the future larva, as definitely as the larva is adapted to the actual conditions of its environment. This principle of adaptation in cleavage was enunciated by F. R. Lillie (1893 and later papers).

Almost every detail of the cleavage of the ovum of Unio can be shown to possess some differential significance. The first division is unequal. Why? Because the anlage of the immense shell-gland is found in one of the cells. The apical-pole cells divide very slowly and irregularly, lagging behind the other cells. Why? Because the formation of apical organs is delayed to a late stage of development. The second generation of ectomeres is composed of very large cells. Why? Because they form early and voluminous organs (larval mantle). The left member of this generation is larger than the right. Why? Because it contains the larval mesoblast. The entomeres are very minute. Why, again? Because the intestine remains rudimentary until a late stage; thus a parallel instance to the apical-pole cells. One can thus go over every detail of the cleavage, and knowing the fate of the cells, can explain all the irregularities and peculiarities exhibited.

These peculiarities of cleavage are all due to the precocious segregation of organs or tissues in separate blastomeres. The order and character of the segregation again are ruled by the needs of the embryo. Thus, one of its greatest needs is the large and powerful shell with which it is provided. The necessity of such provision being made has caused the production of a large shell-gland, which has impressed itself on the segmentation stages as the largest of their blastomeres. I could illustrate the principle in each of the cases just enumerated, but will be satisfied with repeating the introductory sentence of this paragraph in a more special form: The peculiarities of the cleavage in Unio are but a reflection of the structure of the glochidium, the organization of which controls and moulds the nascent material. (Lillie, 1895, p. 38.)

The egg is not a cell dividing under the stress of purely mechanical rules. It is "a builder which lays one stone here, another there, each of which is placed with reference to future development" (Lillie, 1895).

In the theoretically simplest forms, the divisions would be expected to be equal and synchronous throughout the embryo. However, departures from this simplicity are actually the rule, in accordance with Lillie's principle. In the egg of the annelid Nereis, the typical succession of cleavages includes the 2-, 4-, 8-, 16-, 20-, 23-, 29-, 32-, 37-, 38-, 41-, and 42-cell stages (see Fig. 69).

Such deviations in synchrony are not dependent upon the amount or distribution of yolk or other substances in the eggs of marine invertebrates. Only in a very rough way may the rule of Balfour (that the rate of division in any region of the embryo is inversely proportional to the amount of deutoplasm it contains) be applied. In the telolecithal ova of the salamander and certain teleosts, the slower rate of division in the lower hemisphere appears to be correlated with the greater quantity of yolk contained therein. However, remarkable differences of tempo of cleavage are often shown by blastomeres that display no appreciable difference in yolk content.

The inequality in size of the two daughter blastomeres is likewise a phenomenon that is inexplicable in terms of yolk content. Among annelids, the first cleavage is unequal in Nereis, and the fifth is uneven in Polygordius. The first four blastomeres of Crepidula and Patella (gastropods), Leptoplana (polyclad turbellarian), and Podarke (annelid) are equal or near-equal in size. Cumingia and Unio (lamellibranchs), Ilyanassa (gastropod), Dentalium (scaphopod), and Amphitrite (annelid) show unequal early cleavages. The extent of the inequality likewise varies among these animals. Treadwell (1899) attributes cleavage inequality to the arrangement of segregated materials within the cell in relation to the direction of the cleavage plane, and points out that this may be a quantitative segregation rather than a qualitative one. Later considerations of the mechanical causes of inequality of cleavage take into account the relation of polar lobe formation to the inequality of cleavage in Ilyanassa and Dentalium, the inequality of the two poles of the first cleavage spindle in Nereis, and the combination of these two factors contributing to unequal first cleavage of the egg of Chaetopterus (Tyler, '30). In Nereis, the difference between the centriolar poles and asters of the first cleavage spindle is foreshadowed by an inequality of the poles of the sperm diaster. Lillie ('09) attributes inequality of spindle poles to the molecular structure of the ground substance, and a more satisfactory explanation of the phenomenon has not yet been suggested. How an asymmetrical liquid crystal structure of the ground substance could effect the production of an asymmetrical pair of asters is not clear.

Since the cleavage furrow passes through the middle of a cleavage spindle, the sizes of the cells formed at a given cleavage are determined by the position of the spindle at the time. This has been admirably demonstrated by the production of giant polar bodies formed by divisions occurring while a maturation spindle is being stretched and displaced by centrifugal force (Conklin, '16; Clement, '35).

There are special inequalities which occur characteristically during the cleavage period in certain eggs, and independently of the equal or unequal nature of the first

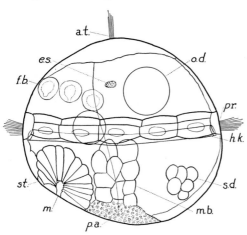

Fig. 70. Normal Nereis trochophore about 20 hours after fertilization of the egg, viewed from the left side. *a.t.*, Apical tuft; *e.s.*, eye-spot; *f.b.*, frontal body; *h.k.*, head-kidney; *m.*, mouth; *m.b.*, mesoblast band; *o.d.*, oil droplet in entodermal cell; *p.a.*, anal pigment area; *pr.*, prototroch; *s.d.*, derivatives of the first somatoblast; *st.*, stomodaeum. (From Costello, '45.)

division. One almost universal case of cleavage inequality is the production of the first quartet of micromeres at the third cleavage of spirally cleaving eggs. These micromeres are usually smaller than the basal macromeres, which fact accounts for the original name designations. In Cerebratulus, however, the first quartet micromeres are actually larger than the basal quartet macromeres. Another well known case of characteristic unequal cleavage is that of turret cell (trochoblast) production at the fourth cleavage. These small cells in Nereis and many other annelids produce the ciliated prototroch (see Fig. 70). In Crepidula they contribute to the ciliated velum. The *2d* and *4d* cells are also smaller than their cell mates. Another example is the separation of the four micromeres at the vegetal pole as the 16-cell stage is attained in the egg of Arbacia and other echinoderms. Here,

differences in the quality of the cytoplasmic contents of the daughter cells are readily apparent, since the micromeres are practically yolk- and pigment-free. This result is brought about by a segregation of granules preceding cleavage. No causal relation is implied between the lack of granules in the micromeres and the inequality of the cleavage by which these cells are produced.

DETERMINATE AND INDETERMINATE CLEAVAGE

Eggs which cleave with a definite and regular pattern are often called "determinate" cleavage types; those in which the cleavage pattern is subject to irregularities and variations, and in which the position of each furrow is not predictable, are called "indeterminate." Obviously, these are not absolute terms, but relative designations.

The original meanings of these terms differed basically from this usage. Conklin ('97) suggested that the determinate cleavage type is that in which cleavage is typically constant with respect to differentiation, as opposed to the indeterminate type, in which cleavage may be changed without interfering with normal development. Synonyms for these terms are, respectively, "mosaic" eggs and "regulative" eggs. Assignment of eggs to one or the other of these arbitrary categories is now recognized as unjustified. There are few, if any, animals in which the normal cleavage pattern does not bear some definite relation to axes, etc., of differentiation, yet there are many animals in which the cleavage pattern may be experimentally altered (as by pressure) without interfering with normal development. (See section on redistribution of egg substances and their relation to cleavage pattern.)

CLEAVAGE WITHOUT NUCLEI

Fragmentation of an enucleated portion of an egg under the influence of an artificial stimulus was apparently first recorded by Delage ('99). This fragmentation, which was described in connection with observations on the non-nucleated cut portions of the eggs of Lanice, Dentalium, and the sea urchin, he considered to be a pseudosegmentation of no special significance, since it did not lead to the formation of a larva capable of movement.

Boveri ('18), McClendon ('08), and Fry ('25) attempted to obtain development of enucleated fragments by activating them parthenogenetically, but with somewhat dubious success. McClendon reported that cells could segment irregularly without nuclei but it is not certain that his Asterias egg-fragments were completely devoid of chromatin. Fry appears to have refuted the earlier evidence of Wilson ('01a,b) that asters can divide in the absence of chromatin. Fry obtained an irregular single cleavage in some of these fragments.

Fankhauser ('29, '34) describes amphiasters and spindles devoid of chromosomes in merogonic Triton embryos; these appeared to cause division of non-nucleated cells. In these same embryos, however, nucleated cells were also present, and were considered to be essential for the continued life of the chromatin-free cells.

Gross ('36), after cold-treating embryos of *Artemia salina*, obtained cleavage of certain blastomeres devoid of nuclei. These divisions apparently occurred under the influence of the cytasters which were observed in the non-nucleated cells.

The general problem was again brought into focus by the observations of E. B. Harvey on the eggs of Arbacia ('36), of other species of sea urchins ('38, '40), and of Chaetopterus ('39). Non-nucleated fragments of Arbacia eggs obtained by centrifuging were treated with parthenogenetic agents. Cytasters appeared but no spindles, and four to six hours after treatment, a "cleavage plane" sometimes appeared between two cytasters. Cleavage is reported to have continued in certain of these eggs, resulting in the formation of blastulae, which could emerge from the fertilization membrane. There is no good evidence that these "embryos" ever differentiated cilia. Chaetopterus "embryos" did not develop this far. Two questions, at least, that might be raised are (1) whether this is really cleavage, as defined above, or merely a type of cellular fragmentation, and (2) whether the furrowing is brought about by the cytasters. Adequate evidence concerning these points is not available from the work on the sea urchin egg.

If one should be willing to concede that "parthenogenetic merogony" is a form of cleavage, the significance of the observations is still open to question. Cleavage of non-nucleated fragments of the sea urchin egg is not cleavage without nuclear material. The sea urchin egg, as obtained from the mature female, is a fully mature egg, with female pronucleus present, both maturation divisions having been completed. When, in

the ovary, the oocyte nucleus (germinal vesicle) ruptured during the formation of the first maturation spindle, all the residual substance of the large germinal vesicle was set free in the cytoplasm. This nuclear material has long been considered to condition the egg cytoplasm for activation and cleavage (O. and R. Hertwig, '87; Delage, '99;

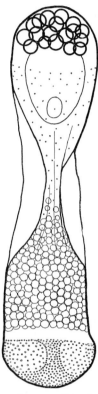

Fig. 71. Strongly centrifuged (61 minutes at 66,000 times gravity) Nereis egg showing zones of stratification, in order from centripetal pole, as follows: large oil drops, hyaline protoplasmic layer, an indistinct layer of fine neutral red–staining granules, zone of yolk spheres, a second hyaline zone, and a centrifugal zone of small jelly-precursor granules, containing a vortex of heavy neutral red-staining granules. (From Costello, '40.)

Wilson, '03; Yatsu, '05; Lillie, '19; and others). A real test of cleavage without nuclear material could therefore be obtained only on fragments of eggs taken before germinal vesicle breakdown. Such an investigation, requiring an egg fertilizable in the germinal vesicle stage, was reported by Costello ('40). Eggs of *Nereis limbata*, which had been stretched by prolonged centrifuging at about 66,000 g., were cut into two halves within the vitelline membrane. The fragments lacking the germinal vesicle could be penetrated by sperm and showed the surface activation phenomena characteristic of fertilization. Not one of these fragments ever cleaved. Cytological examination of sections of these fragments gave evidence that sperm aster formation did not take place. Attempts to activate non-nucleated fragments by means of parthenogenetic agents likewise produced surface activation responses, but no cleavage. The conclusion was reached that substances essential for aster formation are released from the germinal vesicle at the time of its rupture; in the absence of this material, cleavage is not possible.

The report by A. R. Moore (quoted as a personal communication by P. Weiss, '39) that "cleavage substances" may be displaced by centrifugal force in the egg of Dendraster, and hence only one end of the egg can respond to parthenogenetic agents, is of considerable interest. Since Dendraster eggs are fertilizable when fully mature, the theoretical implications are subject to the same criticism as in the case of "parthenogenetic merogony" of the Arbacia egg. This "cleavage substance" in Dendraster cannot be completely analogous to the "cleavage substance" described by Beams and King ('37) on the basis of ultracentrifugation experiments on fertilized Ascaris eggs.

REDISTRIBUTION OF EGG SUBSTANCES AND THEIR RELATION TO CLEAVAGE PATTERNS

Streaming movements of the cytoplasm, and especially those taking place during certain phases of mitosis, are well known from the observations of Spek ('18, '26), Conklin ('38), and many others. Whether these movements can be due to localized changes in surface tension at the egg surface as once suggested is now highly problematical. The measurements of surface behavior of the eggs of several different marine animals by the kaolin particle method of Dan and his co-workers ('37) now give exact data which appear to preclude such an interpretation. The low values for total tension (0.2 dyne per centimeter for the Arbacia egg) obtained by E. N. Harvey ('31), Cole ('32), and Cole and Michaelis ('32) likewise suggest that surface tension cannot be of significance in such cellular activities. With such a low initial tension, any changes due to surface tension–lowering substances would involve negligible amounts of surface force. The flowing movements may therefore

be due to the activity of asters (or centrioles?) or to some other (and unknown) cause.

Over and above such streaming movements taking place during the process of cell division are the extensive redistributions of ooplasmic substances which occur in various eggs at different times during maturation, before or after fertilization, or during early cleavage. In the egg of the sea urchin, Arbacia, which is practically homolecithal when fully mature, an outwardly directed, radial migration of the echinochrome pigment granules follows fertilization, so that these granules come to lie in the gelated cortical region (Wilson, '26). The cortical gelation itself is another consequence of the chain of reactions inaugurated by fertilization. This visible radial segregation is typical of many echinoderm eggs, and perhaps correlated with the differentiation equipotentiality of the first four blastomeres when separated or isolated. An exception, among echinoderms, to this simple corticalward segregation may perhaps be found in the case of Paracentrotus eggs. The eggs of some individuals of *Paracentrotus lividus* are characterized by a certain amount of polar differentiation in the form of a subequatorial pigment band (Boveri, '01). This band has been used (Hörstadius, '28, '39) as a means of orienting the egg for cutting animal or vegetal fragments. It is not a general characteristic of sea urchin eggs, but the accumulation of pigment in this zone may be considered another form of ooplasmic segregation.

The more classic examples of animal-vegetal ooplasmic segregation are to be found in eggs showing the so-called "determinate" type of cleavage. Since there is an original polarity of the egg that can usually be traced back to the earliest stages of the oogonium, it is recognized that the simplest type of ooplasmic segregation along the animal-vegetal axis is essentially a repolarization of certain of the egg constituents. Only this repolarization can be considered to come within the scope of Spek's ('30, '33, '34) term "bipolar differentiation," as applied to the phenomenon in several different egg species.

As a typical example of ooplasmic segregation, the process in the egg of the annelid, Nereis, may be described. The egg of Nereis before fertilization is flattened somewhat in the polar axis and contains a large central germinal vesicle (oocyte nucleus), around which is arranged a double row of relatively large oil droplets. The other cytoplasmic components of the egg (including yolk spheres, mitochondria, neutral red–staining granules, microsomes, etc.) are approximately uniform in their distribution in the remaining space, except in the cortical layer where the small jelly-precursor granules are arranged to simulate alveoli. At fertilization or activation, the jelly-precursor material is extruded through the vitelline membrane to the exterior, where it swells to form the thick enveloping layer of jelly characteristic of the fertilized Nereis egg. The germinal vesicle ruptures a few minutes after fertilization, releasing a quantity of nuclear material into the cytoplasm. As the maturation spindle is formed and undergoes its divisions, there begins a slow movement of hyaline cytoplasm and of cytoplasmic components. The small spherical mitochondria form a subcortical ring below the animal pole. Most of these become incorporated into the CD cell at the unequal first cleavage. These bipolar movements of cytoplasmic materials continue slowly throughout the maturation period and during the first two cleavages. By the time the four-cell stage is reached, ooplasmic segregation is very pronounced. Most of the clear protoplasm and smaller protoplasmic granules are to be found in the animal hemisphere; the neutral red–staining granules form a thin cortical band just above the equator. The oil droplets and yolk spheres occupy the vegetal hemisphere, the oil droplets being nearer the vegetal pole. During cleavage, these are brought into contact and fuse with each other in the four entomeres, until, in later development, only four remain, one in each entodermal cell. Since these several cytoplasmic inclusions take up vital dyes differentially, the segregation is strikingly apparent in vital-stained eggs (Spek, '34). On the basis of this staining with indicator dyes, Spek has concluded that the animal hemisphere of the Nereis egg contains granules which are alkaline in reaction, in an "alkaline" animal plasm. The vegetal hemisphere correspondingly consists of an acid yolk plasm, of which the yolk spheres are the chief constituent. In the equatorial region are some acid granules in a medium of alkaline protoplasm. The so-called "alkaline" region gives rise to the ectodermal structures of the larva, the "acid" yolk-plasm region produces the entoderm, and the border region around the equator, containing acid granules in "alkaline" protoplasm, gives rise to the prototroch of ciliated ectoderm.

However, it appears clear that the substances which take up the vital dyes in the egg of Nereis dumerilii (Raven, '38), in the egg of Aplysia (Ries, '39), and in the egg of Nereis limbata (Costello, '36, '45) are displaceable by centrifuging, if force of a sufficient magnitude is applied (see Fig. 71). It has been pointed out (Costello, '45) that if the vital dyes are used at truly vital concentration, the hyaline protoplasm itself does not stain, all coloration being associated with granules or vacuoles. Many of these inclusions approach the limit of microscopical visibility, but are movable by centrifugal force if centrifuged for a sufficient period of time with an appropriate force. The "acid" and "alkaline" regions, therefore, are not regions of acid or alkaline ground substance (hyaline protoplasm), but are regions of segregated granules or vacuoles which stain differentially. So far as can be ascertained by observation of stained and unstained eggs, with visible or ultraviolet light, there are no differences in the *hyaline protoplasm* of the different regions. Any histogenetic significance that could be attributable, even theoretically, to the formed inclusions should follow the induced pattern of these inclusions in the strongly centrifuged egg. It is well known from a multitude of centrifuging experiments (Morgan, '08, '10; Lillie, '06, '09; Conklin, '16; and others) that no such histogenetic effect can be attributed to the visible granules. Therefore, only localized invisible differences within the hyaline protoplasm itself could be of significance for histogenesis.

This conclusion that the visible cytoplasmic components of invertebrate eggs have no morphogenetic value has been questioned recently by Raven ('38) and Raven and Bretschneider ('42). However, their objections to the conclusions of Conklin ('10) and Clement ('38) appear to be without adequate foundation, since they ignore the fact that Clement obtained normal development of *hyaline* fragments of centrifuged Physa eggs. Harvey ('46) has obtained plutei from the "clear quarter" of the Arbacia egg.

A more complex type of segregation is that found in the egg of the ascidian and described by Conklin ('05). Upon fertilization of the Styela egg, there is a primary segregation of materials resulting from a downflow of the yellow and clear substances from the animal toward the vegetal pole. This active migration is completed within a few minutes after sperm entrance. Then the sperm nucleus moves to one side in the lower hemisphere, inaugurating a secondary segregation to form the posterior yellow crescent. Opposite this region, the light gray crescent arises at the future anterior region of the egg. As a result, the animal hemisphere is occupied by clear protoplasm, the remainder of the vegetal hemisphere (except for the two above-mentioned crescents) by dark gray yolk.

The formation of the gray crescent in the frog egg, which follows fertilization and is correlated in at least a high percentage of cases with the position of the median plane of the embryo, may be considered a segregation phenomenon analogous to crescent formation in the egg of Styela.

It appears possible, by studying a series of different egg species, to establish a correlation between the time of ooplasmic segregation and the degree of embryonic determination. Invertebrate eggs of the various animal groups can be divided into different categories as regards the time of onset, and the pattern, of ooplasmic segregation. It is obvious that there are different relationships between the pattern of segregation and the cleavage pattern in these different forms. An isolated blastomere of an egg cleaving differentially at the first cleavage (such as Chaetopterus, Dentalium, Nereis or Sabellaria) would be expected to develop as a partial embryo because the segregated material is different in the two daughter blastomeres.

The apparent paradox between the correlation of ooplasmic segregation with embryonic differentiation in isolated blastomeres and egg fragments, as compared with the lack of correlation between the sedimentation of visible particles and embryonic differentiation, in the case of centrifuged eggs, can be resolved theoretically as follows: We need only assume that the mechanism of normal ooplasmic segregation segregates both *visible* formed inclusions and invisible histogenetic substances. The invisible histogenetic substances could be presumed to become associated with the hyaline protoplasmic materials which occupy the interstices (as ground substance) between the granules or vacuoles. Centrifuging might easily displace the larger visible particles and vacuoles without displacing the invisible substances (of molecular dimensions or somewhat larger) associated with the hyaline protoplasm (protein framework?) of the cell. This conclusion is basically that reached by Conklin ('31), from his experiments centrifuging the Styela egg. It is not the visible granules that have histogenetic value, but the special lo-

calized hyaline protoplasm of the areas with which these granules are normally associated.

If this view be accepted, it becomes of paramount importance to work out the mechanism by which ooplasmic segregation is brought about. This mechanism must be able to accomplish both a visible stratification of the suspended ooplasmic substances and a parallel, but invisible, segregation of the so-called "formative stuffs."

Eggs of animal species whose cleavage characteristics are known can be aligned in a series with the most determinate (ctenophores, rotifers, and nematodes) at one extreme, the least determinate at the other, and with all degrees of gradation between the two. When this is done, it appears that the most rigidly "determinate" cleavage types are found in the forms which represent the most markedly "mosaic" pattern of differentiation. Nevertheless, the chief differences between the so-called "mosaic" and "regulative" eggs are merely (1) a different morphological relation of the cleavage pattern to certain prelocalized or segregated embryonic areas (i.e., unequal as contrasted with equal distribution of these segregated histogenetic areas between the blastomeres at a given cleavage), (2) different time relationships between the determination of embryonic areas and such developmental events as fertilization, cleavage, and gastrulation, and (3) the regulative (and regenerative) capacity of the developing embryo, including the degree of interaction of the parts involving determination by diffusible substances. It appears that even the most "mosaic" egg has some integrative or regulative powers, which act during normal development as well as under special experimental conditions.

FUNCTION OF PARTITION MEMBRANES IN CELLULAR DIFFERENTIATION

Differentiation without cleavage was first adequately demonstrated by the studies of Lillie ('02, '06) on the eggs of Chaetopterus. Treatment of unfertilized eggs or of uncleaved fertilized eggs with sea water containing a small additional amount (0.25 per cent) of potassium chloride resulted in the development of these into ciliated structures with segregated internal contents. These ciliated "embryos" resembled annelid trochophores in a number of respects. Brachet ('37), among others, has repeated Lillie's observations, and demonstrated that

'27) was that if the late blastula were "water-tight," an absorption of blastocoele fluid by certain cells might cause an invagination because of hydrostatic pressure.

If gastrulation provides a basis for neurulation, the reverse is also true. Glaser ('14), studying the transformation of the neural plate into a neural tube, found that there was no increase in number of cells during the process. Therefore, there is no asymmetrical proliferation of cells to account for neurulation. During the process of folding, however, the volume of the neural plate was found to increase about three-fold by the intake of water. This was assumed to account for the fact that about 80 per cent of the nervous system of an amphibian is made up of water, whereas water constitutes only about 60 per cent of the whole body weight. In a later note (Glaser, '16), the lack of evidence for differential water absorption within the neural plate itself is stressed. Brown, Hamburger, and Schmitt ('41) did not confirm Glaser's values for water intake during gastrulation and neurulation. They obtained very slight changes in density which were interpreted as showing that there are but slight changes in volume or water content of the prospective neural tissue during development.

Holtfreter ('43b, '44) attempted to correlate the movements of the several regions of the amphibian embryo during gastrulation with the inherent properties of certain cell groups, and to the responses of these cell groups to stimuli emanating from their environment. The primary cause of gastrulation in the Amphibia, according to his theory, is a higher relative alkalinity of the blastocoele fluid, which brings about local surface tension changes in the membranes of certain flask-shaped cells. These cells are attached at their outer boundaries to the "surface coat" and exert contractile tension when they elongate in the direction of the blastocoele in response to the surface tension changes at their blastocoelic boundaries. Modern cellular physiologists, however, have all but abandoned surface tension changes at cell surfaces as being of any great significance, since all actual measurements (E. N. Harvey, '31; Cole, '32; Cole and Michaelis, '32) of the magnitude of the tension at the surface of cells have indicated an almost infinitesimally small value. As indicated above, if the surface tension is low, agents producing slight changes in it cannot produce much of a physiological effect.

Lewis ('47) attempts to explain invagination and neurulation in terms of one essential factor. This is an increase or a decrease in the contractile tension of the superficial gel layers on one side of a group of adherent epithelial cells which offer some resistance to distortion. This is a purely mechanical "explanation," since it would be necessary to elucidate the causes of the increase or decrease of contractile tension in relation to the biological variables of time, place, and cell type.

Spek ('20) used as a model of gastrulation a composite strip of two layers of gelatin with different densities. When immersed in water, this composite strip absorbed water differentially and curved to simulate the behavior of a portion of the entodermal plate of the invaginating gastrula. Spek also suggested that the lithium in Herbst's experiments might make the outer portion of the blastula wall lyophilic, as compared with the inner wall, and thus bring about evagination. Moore ('30) has pointed out that in Herbst's original work, it was demonstrated that the characteristic effect of lithium is less if applied after the 16-cell stage. The fact that lithium is not effective in causing evagination if applied to the early blastulae indicates that the cells have been determined in their invaginative pattern at an earlier stage. The Spek hypothesis of the mechanism of lithium action in terms of a direct action to produce lyophilic colloids at a time immediately preceding gastrulation is therefore inadequate.

Moore ('30) tested Assheton's hypothesis by experimentally producing various geometrical relations of nuclei to cells in late blastulae of the sand dollar and sea urchin. The position of the nuclei with respect to the tendency of regions to evaginate or invaginate showed little or no correlation in this experimental material.

In more recent contributions, Moore and Burt ('39) and Moore ('41) attempted to analyze by operative means the question whether the entire blastula takes part in the gastrulation process, or whether the forces of gastrulation are localized in a special region. When the upper half or two-thirds of the early gastrula is cut away, leaving an intact vegetal or entodermal plate, gastrulation is not impaired. This experiment disposes of the idea that differences between the blastocoele fluid and the external medium play a part during invagination. In the cases where the entodermal plate was isolated by cutting away the remainder of the embryo, the plate continued to roll up its rim, eventually closing to form a small spherical invaginated gastrula (see Fig. 74). These experiments lead Moore and Burt to the conclusion that the forces of gastrulation do not act in a median plane through the poles of the embryo, but in the plane of the entodermal plate at right angles to the animal-vegetal axis. This gastrula plate consists of two concentric zones (see Fig. 73, left). The central spot (a) is the first region to show activity, while the remainder of the plate (p), which forms a ring about a, is only secondarily involved in the initial stages of the process. As soon as

pieces of the entodermal plate of echinoderm early gastrulae were unsuccessful because the cut edges showed a tendency to spring apart, leaving an open sector. Moore suggests that the whole entodermal plate is normally under tension, and acts as one concentric unit.

Moore's own proposal that asymmetrically (or excentrically) placed cytoplasmic bridges between the cells could account for gastrulation likewise appears to be inadequate, since such cell bridges by contracting would tend only to draw cell boundaries closer together and would not

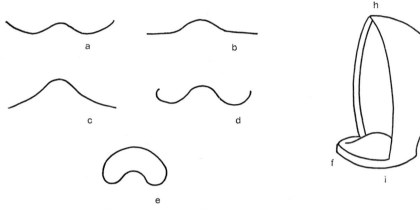

Fig. 74. Left: Diagrams illustrating the positions assumed successively by the gastral plate of *Patiria miniata* during the hour following excision. Horizontal view.

Right: Diagram illustrating the relations of the two planes considered in theories of gastrulation. *fg*, The plane of the gastral plate, at right angles to the plane passing through the animal and vegetal poles, *hi*. (Figures from Moore and Burt, '39.)

a has moved in to form a cone, p (the plastic zone ring) begins to participate actively and moves toward the interior. A wave of activity is then transmitted to a ring of cells immediately below p (the ring r), and these cells take up the work of pushing the archenteric tube inward until gastrulation is complete. It is the region p which determines the subsequent fate of the gastrula, i.e., whether it is to be normal or an exogastrula. The cells of region r must change from moment to moment as the archenteric tube lengthens and the entodermal cells become incorporated into it as integral elements. In gastrulation, the cells of a have the general form (in section) of truncated cones.

Glaser ('14) mentions an experiment in which W. Roux cut out pieces of the early neurula of the frog embryo. These detached fragments, obtained by transverse section, continued to infold. Moore's attempts to repeat such results on isolated radially cut

change the shape of cells unless new connections were made as suggested in the "zipper" hypothesis of Schmitt ('41).

In Herbst's original lithium cultures, certain incomplete exogastrulae were described. In these, the outer part of the gastrula plate had evaginated, while the center had invaginated. Moore takes these incomplete exogastrulae as evidence that the central spot of the entodermal plate is either more stable or determined considerably earlier than the adjacent plastic ring.

Experimentally, it has been possible to suppress invagination osmotically with a non-penetrating sucrose solution, and on the basis of such experiments an attempt has been made to calculate the magnitude of the pressure exerted normally by the invaginating cone of the gastrula plate. The figure Moore ('41, '45) gives is a pressure of 2.6 to 5.5 mg., acting on a cross sectional area of 707 square microns, or about 3.88 to 7.75 gm. per square millimeter. This figure is considerably greater than that calculated by Waddington ('39) for the force of invagination in the Triton embryo (i.e., 0.34 mg. per square millimeter). Until more forms are studied, the significance of such calculations cannot be judged. It appears inconceivable, in view of the general knowledge relating to osmotic pressure in cells, that half the cell (the part bordering the blastocoele) could swell while the half toward the future archenteric cavity shrinks. The changes in cell shape that accompany gastrulation can scarcely be osmotic in origin.

REFERENCES

Assheton, R. 1916 The Geometrical Relation of the Nuclei in an Invaginating Gastrula. Cambridge University Press, Cambridge, England.

Beams, H. W., and King, R. L. 1937 The suppression of cleavage in Ascaris eggs by ultracentrifuging. Biol. Bull., 73:99–111.

Boveri, T. 1901 Die Polarität von Ovocyte, Ei und Larve des Strongylocentrotus lividus. Zool. Jahrbücher, 14:630–653.

——— 1918 Zwei Fehlerquellen bei Merogonieversuchen und die Entwicklungsfähigkeit merogonischer und partiell-merogonischer Seeigelbastarde. Roux' Arch. Entw.-mech., 44:417–471.

Brachet, J. 1937 La différenciation sans clivage dans l'oeuf de Chétoptère envisagée aux points de vue cytologique et métabolique. Arch. Biol., 48:561–589.

Brown, M. G., Hamburger, V., and Schmitt, F. O. 1941 Density studies on amphibian embryos with special reference to the mechanism of organizer action. J. Exp. Zool., 88:353–372.

Bütschli, O. 1915 Bemerkungen zur mechanischen Erklärung der Gastrula-Invagination. Sitz.-Ber. Akad. Wissensch., Heidelberg, 6B (No. 2): 1–13.

Clement, A. C. 1935 The formation of giant polar bodies in centrifuged eggs of Ilyanassa. Biol. Bull., 69:403–414.

——— 1938 The structure and development of centrifuged eggs and egg fragments of Physa heterostropha. J. Exp. Zool., 79:435–460.

Cole, K. S. 1932 Surface forces of the Arbacia egg. J. Cell. & Comp. Physiol., 1:1–9.

———, and Michaelis, E. 1932 Surface forces of fertilized Arbacia eggs. J. Cell. & Comp. Physiol., 2:121–126.

Conklin, E. G. 1897 The embryology of Crepidula. J. Morph., 13:1–226.

——— 1905 The organization and cell-lineage of the Ascidian egg. J. Acad. Nat. Sci. Phila., 2d series, 13:5–119.

——— 1910 The effects of centrifugal force upon the organization and development of the eggs of fresh water pulmonates. J. Exp. Zool., 9:417–455.

——— 1915 Why polar bodies do not develop. Proc. Nat. Acad. Sci., 1:491–496.

——— 1916 Effects of centrifugal force on the polarity of the eggs of Crepidula. Proc. Nat. Acad. Sci., 2:87–90.

——— 1931 The development of centrifuged eggs of ascidians. J. Exp. Zool., 60:1–119.

——— 1938 Disorientations of development in Crepidula plana produced by low temperatures. Proc. Amer. Phil. Soc., 79:179–211.

Costello, D. P. 1936 Some effects of centrifugal force on marine eggs. (Abstract). J. E. Mitch. Sci. Soc., 52:172.

——— 1939 Some effects of centrifuging the eggs of nudibranchs. J. Exp. Zool., 80:473–499.

——— 1940 The fertilizability of nucleated and non-nucleated fragments of centrifuged Nereis eggs. J. Morph., 66:99–114.

——— 1945 Experimental studies of germinal localization in Nereis. I. The development of isolated blastomeres. J. Exp. Zool., 100:19–66.

——— 1948a Spiral cleavage. Biol. Bull., 95:265.

——— 1948b Oöplasmic segregation in relation to differentiation. Ann. New York Acad. Sci., 49:663–683.

Dan, Katsuma 1952 Cyto-embryological studies of sea urchins. II. Blastula stage. Biol. Bull., 102:74–89.

———, and Ono, Tomonao 1952 Cyto-embryological studies of sea urchins. I. The means of fixation of the mutual positions among the blastomeres of sea urchin larvae. Biol. Bull., 102:58–73.

———, Yanagita, T., and Sugiyama, M. 1937 Behavior of the cell surface during cleavage. I. Protoplasma, 28:66–81.

Dawydoff, C. 1928 Traité d'Embryologie Comparée des Invertébrés. Masson et Cie., Paris.

Delage, Y. 1899 Études sur la mérogonie. Arch. de Zool. Exp. et Gén., Sér. 3, 7:383–417.

Fankhauser, G. 1929 Ueber die Beteiligung kernloser Strahlungen (Cytaster) an der Furchung geschnürter Triton-Eier. Revue Suisse Zool., 36:179–187.

——— 1934 Cytological studies on egg fragments of the salamander Triton. IV. The cleavage of egg fragments without the egg nucleus. J. Exp. Zool., 67:349–393.

Fry, H. J. 1925 Asters in artificial parthenogenesis. II. Asters in nucleated and enucleated eggs of Echinarachnius parma and the role of the chromatin. J. Exp. Zool., 43:49–81.

Glaser, O. C. 1914 On the mechanism of morphological differentiation in the nervous system. I. The transformation of a neural plate into a neural tube. Anat. Rec., 8:525–551.

——— 1916 The theory of autonomous folding in embryogenesis. Science, 44:505–509.

Gray, J. 1924 The mechanism of cell-division. I. The forces which control the form and cleavage of the eggs of Echinus esculentus. Proc. Cambr. Philos. Soc. (Biol. Sci.), 1:164–188.

Gross, F. 1936 Cleavage of blastomeres in the absence of nuclei. Quart. J. Micr. Sci., 79:57–71.

Harvey, E. B. 1936 Parthenogenetic merogony or cleavage without nuclei in Arbacia punctulata. Biol. Bull., 71:101–121.

——— 1938 Parthenogenetic merogony or development without nuclei of the eggs of sea urchins from Naples. Biol. Bull., 75:170–188.

Harvey, E. B. 1939 Development of half-eggs of *Chaetopterus pergamentaceus* with special reference to parthenogenetic merogony. Biol. Bull., 76:383–404.

——— 1940 A comparison of the development of nucleate and non-nucleate eggs of *Arbacia punctulata*. Biol. Bull., 79:166–187.

——— 1946 Structure and development of the clear quarter of the *Arbacia punctulata* egg. J. Exp. Zool., 102:253–276.

Harvey, E. N. 1931 The tension at the surface of marine eggs, especially those of the sea urchin, Arbacia. Biol. Bull., 61:273–279.

Herbst, C. 1892 Experimentelle Untersuchungen über den Einfluss der veränderten chemischen Zusammensetzung des umgebenden Mediums auf die Entwicklung der Thiere. I. Versuche an Seeigeleiern. Zeit. wiss. Zool., 55:446–518.

——— 1893 Experimentelle Untersuchungen über den Einfluss der veränderten chemischen Zusammensetzung des umgebenden Mediums auf die Entwicklung der Thiere. II. Weiteres über die morphologische Wirkung der Lithiumsalze und ihre theoretische Bedeutung. Mitt. Zool. Stat. Neapel, 11:136–220.

——— 1900 Über das Auseinandergehen von Furchungs- und Gewebezellen in kalkfreiem Medium. Roux' Arch. Entw.-mech., 9:424–463.

Hertwig, O., and Hertwig, R. 1887 Über den Befruchtungs- und Teilungsvorgang des tierischen Eies unter dem Einfluss äusserer Agentien. Jena. Z. Naturw., 20:120–241, 477–510.

Holtfreter, J. 1943a Properties and functions of the surface coat in amphibian embryos. J. Exp. Zool., 93:251–323.

——— 1943b A study of the mechanics of gastrulation. I. J. Exp. Zool., 94:261–318.

——— 1944 A study of the mechanics of gastrulation. II. J. Exp. Zool., 95:171–212.

Hörstadius, S. 1928 Über die Determination des Keimes bei Echinodermen. Acta Zool., Stockh., 9:1–191.

——— 1939 The mechanics of sea urchin development, studied by operative methods. Biol. Rev. Camb. Phil. Soc., 14:132–179.

Lewis, Warren H. 1947 Mechanics of invagination. Anat. Rec., 97:139–156.

——— 1949 Gel layers of cells and eggs and their role in early development. Lecture Series, Roscoe B. Jackson Memorial Laboratories, Bar Harbor, Maine, pp. 59–77.

Lillie, F. R. 1893 Preliminary account of the embryology of *Unio complanata*. J. Morph., 8: 569–578.

——— 1895 Embryology of the Unionidae. J. Morph. 10:1–100.

——— 1899 Adaptation in cleavage. Biol. Lectures, M. B. L., 1897 and 1898, Boston.

——— 1902 Differentiation without cleavage in the egg of the annelid *Chaetopterus pergamentaceus*. Roux' Arch. Entw.-mech., 14:477–499.

——— 1906 Observations and experiments concerning the elementary phenomena of embryonic development in Chaetopterus. J. Exp. Zool., 3: 153–268.

——— 1909 Polarity and bilaterality of the annelid egg: experiments with centrifugal force. Biol. Bull., 16:54–79.

——— 1919 Problems of Fertilization. University of Chicago Press, Chicago.

MacBride, E. W. 1914 Textbook of Embryology. Vol. I. Invertebrata. The Macmillan Co., London.

McClendon, J. F. 1908 The segmentation of eggs of *Asterias forbesii* deprived of chromatin. Roux' Arch. Entw.-mech., 26:662–668.

Moore, A. R. 1930 On the invagination of the gastrula. Protoplasma, 9:25–33.

——— 1941 On the mechanics of gastrulation in *Dendraster excentricus*. J. Exp. Zool., 87:101–111.

——— 1945 The Individual in Simpler Forms. University of Oregon Press, Eugene, Oregon.

———, and Burt, A. S. 1939 On the locus and nature of the forces causing gastrulation in the embryos of *Dendraster excentricus*. J. Exp. Zool., 82:159–171.

Morgan, T. H. 1908 The location of embryo-forming regions in the egg. Science, N.S., 28:287–288.

——— 1910 Cytological studies of centrifuged eggs. J. Exp. Zool., 9:593–656.

——— 1927 Experimental Embryology. Columbia University Press, New York.

———, and Spooner, G. B. 1909 The polarity of the centrifuged egg. Roux' Arch. Entw.-mech., 28:104–117.

Motomura, I. 1941 Materials of the fertilization membrane in the eggs of echinoderms. Sci. Rep. Tokyo Imp. Univ., Ser. 4:Biol., 16:345–363.

Plough, H. H. 1927 Defective pluteus larvae from isolated blastomeres of Arbacia and Echinarachnius. Biol. Bull., 52:373–393.

Raven, Chr. P. 1938 Experimentelle Untersuchungen über die "Bipolare Differenzierung" des Polychaeten- und Molluskeneies. Acta Neerland. Morph., 1:337–357.

———, and Bretschneider, L. H. 1942 The effect of centrifugal force upon the eggs of *Limnaea stagnalis* L. Arch. Neerland. Zool., 6:255–278.

Rhumbler, L. 1902 Zur Mechanik des Gastrulationsvorganges. Roux' Arch. Entw.-mech., 14: 401–476.

Richards, Aute. 1931 Outline of Comparative Embryology. John Wiley & Sons, New York.

Ries, E. 1938–9 Histochemische Sonderungsprozesse während der frühen Embryonalentwicklung verschiedener wirbelloser Tiere. Arch. Exp. Zellforsch., 22:569–586.

Schmitt, F. O. 1941 Some protein patterns in cells. Growth Suppl., 5:1–20.

Spek, Josef 1918 Differenzen im Quellungszustand der Plasmakolloide als eine Ursache der Gastrulainvagination, sowie der Einstülpungen und Faltungen von Zellplatten überhaupt. Kolloidchem. Beihefte, 9:259–399.

——— 1920 Beiträge zur Kolloidechemie der Zellteilung. Kolloidchem. Beihefte, 12:1–91.

——— 1926 Über gesetzmässige Substanzverteilungen bei der Furchung des Ctenophoreies und ihre Beziehungen zu den Determinationsproblemen. Roux' Arch. Entw.-mech., 107:54–73.

Spek, Josef. 1930 Zustandsänderungen der Plasmakolloide bei Befruchtung und Entwicklung des Nereis-Eies. Protoplasma, 9:370–427.

——— 1933 Die bipolare Differenzierung des Protoplasmas des Teleosteer-Eies und ihre Enstehung. Weitere experimentelle Beiträge zum Studium der kataphoreseartigen Erscheinungen in lebenden Zellen und der Bestimmung des pH der lebenden Zelle. Protoplasma, 18:497–545.

——— 1934 Über die bipolare Differenzierung der Eizellen von *Nereis limbata* und *Chaetopterus pergamentaceus*. Protoplasma, 21:394–405.

Treadwell, A. L. 1899 Equal and unequal cleavage in annelids. Biol. Lect. Woods Hole, 1897–98, pp. 93–111.

Tyler, A. 1930 Experimental production of double embryos in annelids and molluscs. J. Exp. Zool., 57:347–407.

Waddington, C. H. 1939 On the magnitude of morphogenetic forces. Nature, 144:637.

——— 1940 Organizers and Genes. Cambridge University Press, Cambridge, England.

Weiss, P. 1939 Principles of Development. Henry Holt & Co., New York.

Wilson, E. B. 1892 The cell-lineage of Nereis. J. Morph., 6:361–480.

——— 1898 Considerations on cell-lineage and ancestral reminiscence. Ann. N. Y. Acad. Sci., 11:1–27.

——— 1901a The morphological phenomena involved in the chemical production of parthenogenesis in sea urchins. Biol. Bull., 2:347–350.

——— 1901b Experimental studies in cytology. I. A cytological study of artificial parthenogenesis in sea urchin eggs. Roux' Arch. Entw.-mech., 12:529–596.

——— 1903 Experiments on cleavage and localization in the Nemertine-egg. Roux' Arch. Entw.-mech., 16:411–460.

——— 1926 Newer aspects of the alveolar structure of protoplasm. Amer. Nat., 60:105–120.

Yatsu, N. 1905 The formation of centrosomes in enucleated egg-fragments. J. Exp. Zool., 2:287–312.

EMBRYOGENESIS: PROGRESSIVE DIFFERENTIATION

CHAPTER 1

Amphibians

J. HOLTFRETER AND V. HAMBURGER

EGG ORGANIZATION AND DETERMINATION OF AXES

EGG STRUCTURE

ALTHOUGH the uncleaved amphibian egg has been used extensively for experimentation since the beginnings of experimental embryology, our information concerning its organization is very limited (see Fankhauser, '48). External signs of structure are few: the pigment concentration in the cortical layer of the animal hemisphere, the yolk concentration in the vegetal hemisphere, and a clear area near the animal pole, indicating the location of the egg nucleus and of the polar bodies. In some species, a dorsoventral polarization and the plane of symmetry can be detected before fertilization (Pasteels, '37a; Banki, '27b). The descriptions of the internal egg organization indicate regional differences in the size and concentration of yolk platelets and of pigment granules, and a cytoplasmic organization into a more fluid inner plasmasol and a more gelated outer cortex; the latter is covered by a cell membrane and a protective surface coat (Holtfreter, '43a). These components are arranged in a complicated pattern and not in the fashion of simple gradients, as is often postulated for the sake of theoretical simplifications (Fig. 75a) (Ancel and Vintemberger, '48; Pasteels, '51). Banki ('27a) and Lehmann ('42a) have described in the eggs of several urodeles an equatorial ring of specialized, subcortical "marginal plasma" which may be the precursor of the marginal zone of the gastrula.

Shortly after fertilization, the whole egg undergoes a rotation within its jelly coats, whereby its animal-vegetal axis assumes a vertical position ("rotation of orientation," Ancel and Vintemberger, '48). In some anurans and urodeles, dorsoventral polarity and bilateral symmetry become visible shortly before the first cleavage with the appearance of the *gray crescent*, which is a sickle-shaped grayish area at the margin of dark and white material. Observations and vital-staining experiments have confirmed the contention of Roux ('03) and others that the gray crescent demarcates the area above the future blastopore, and thus the dorsal side of the future embryo whose head will be located in the region of the animal pole. As a rule, the plane bisecting the gray crescent becomes the median plane of the embryo (Vogt, '26a; Banki, '27a; Pasteels, '37a; see, however, p. 233).

The formation of the gray crescent is a visible sign of more fundamental changes in the egg organization which begin long before the gray crescent appears. In eggs with a clearly demarcated ventral pigment border (for instance, *Rana fusca*), one observes a rotation of the pigment cap. Its border shifts from its original horizontal position (*m-n*, Fig. 75a) to an oblique position m_1-n_1, Fig. 75b), and the animal pole moves downward (from *an*, Fig. 75a, to an_1, Fig. 75 b), its final inclination amounting to 15 to 30 degrees. The gray crescent appears on the side at which the margin of the pigment cap rises above the equator, and its median plane coincides with the meridian along which the animal pole has moved. Obviously, we are dealing with a second rotation-phenomenon ("rotation of symmetrization," Ancel and Vintemberger, '48). It has been generally assumed that this rotation involves the entire egg, leading to a redistribution of heavy and light materials and to a shift of the center of gravity. However, Ancel and Vintemberger (since '32, see '48) have demonstrated for *R. fusca*, by means of electrocautery marks, that only the egg surface is involved. The cortex glides over the heavy materials of the center, which later remain

Interest in these problems has been revived more recently.

Some authors contend that a bilateral symmetry pre-exists in all unfertilized amphibian eggs and not only in those in which it is actually visible. The appearance of normal symmetry relations in eggs which have been activated by chemical agents or by electrical shock may be cited in support of this contention. Such an inner organization would originate in the ovary.

Numerous investigations have shown that whatever intrinsic organization pre-exists,

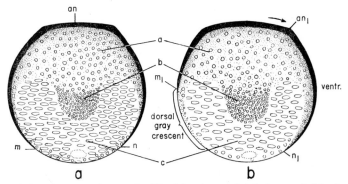

Fig. 75. Diagram of the structure of an unfertilized frog's egg (*a*) before and (*b*) after rotation of symmetrization (after Ancel and Vintemberger, '48, Fig. 35). *a*, Animal pigmented cytoplasm with small yolk granules; *an*, *an₁*, position of animal pole before and after rotation; *b*, central pigmented yolk area; *c*, vegetal unpigmented area with large yolk granules; *m-n*, *m₁-n₁*, ventral margin of pigment before and after rotation.

static except for a slight shift in the marginal plasma (Fig. 75).

The origin of the gray crescent is not clearly understood. According to the above authors, it originates in anurans in the following way: on the future dorsal side, only the cortical plasma carrying pigment moves upward, but the more deeply located pigment is left behind. The latter is thus overlaid by a thin layer of unpigmented plasma, resulting in the gray hue of the crescent. According to Roux ('03), pigment is dispersed into the interior. Vital-staining experiments of Banki ('27a) indicate that in urodeles cortical or subcortical materials spread also towards the vegetal pole during the formation of the gray crescent. The matter requires further elucidation.

AXIAL DETERMINATION

The analysis of the factors involved in axial determination has been a favorite object of experimentation in the first period of experimental embryology (Roux, Pflüger, Born, Schultze, and others; see Morgan, '27).

it is highly labile and modifiable; in fact, it is possible to impose on the uncleaved egg a median plane in any desired meridian. The two classical methods by which this can be accomplished are (*a*) the use of gravitational force (rotation, centrifugation, fixation in abnormal positions) and (*b*) localized insemination.

Effects of Gravitational Force. The following experiment of Ancel and Vintemberger ('48) gives an impressive demonstration of the lability of the internal organization. Unfertilized eggs (*R. fusca*) are mounted on a glass plate, with the animal-vegetal axis inclined 135 degrees (Fig. 76). Following parthenogenetic activation by electric shock, water is added, whereupon the egg undergoes its "rotation of orientation." Marking experiments have shown that the plane in which the animal-vegetal axis moves during this rotation coincides invariably with the median plane of the future embryo. In other words, the meridian in which the animal pole moves during the "rotation of orientation" coincides with the one in which it moves during the subsequent "rotation of symmetrization," and therefore also with the median plane of the gray crescent. The latter originates around that point of the border between dark and white material which was highest on the inclined egg. Since one can mount the egg in any desired position, any meridian can be chosen as the median plane and any point on the circumference of the white vegetal field as the dorsal side of the future embryo.

In an extensive re-investigation of the classic inversion experiment of Schultze (1894), Penners and Schleip ('28a,b) have shown that the plane of symmetry can be altered even after the appearance of the gray crescent. Eggs of *R. fusca* in the 2-cell stage were compressed between glass plates,

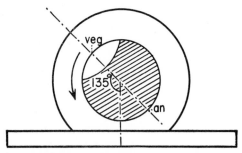

Fig. 76. Diagram of rotation experiment to determine the median plane. An unfertilized frog's egg in its jelly membranes is mounted on a glass plate; the egg axis forms an angle of 135 degrees with the vertical (after Ancel-Vintemberger, '48, Fig. 1).

the positions of their gray crescents were marked on the glass plate, and the fixed eggs were then kept in an upside-down position for several hours. As a result, the yolk and the cytoplasm underwent a complete rearrangement. Several significant points were established: (1) The blastopore, or blastopores (in the case of duplications) were formed invariably at the border of dark and white material. (2) The site of the blastopores was preferentially at, or near, the center of the original gray crescent. (3) The invaginations and their direction were influenced by the abnormal yolk distribution. As a result, the median plane or planes of the embryos could be at any angle to the original plane of symmetry. Similar experiments of Pasteels ('38, '39a) confirmed these results for *Rana esculenta* and Discoglossus. Of particular significance is the second point. It implies that the inversion did not dislocate the original gray crescent. This led the authors to suggest that a factor which determines the site of invagination and thus the dorsal side may reside in the *cortex*. It is

relatively stable at a stage when the symmetry plane is still labile. In other words, the experiment has succeeded in disengaging the factors for *dorsalization* from the factors for *symmetrizations:* The former are stabilized first; they determine a preferential site for invagination but not necessarily its direction. The direction of invagination, and thus the cephalocaudal polarity and bilateral symmetry of the embryo seem to depend on the distribution of yolk. It is possible that the yolk plays a passive role in this respect, serving merely as a support to direct cytoplasmic shifting, similar to the condition in an unfertilized, aged egg kept in hypertonic salt solution. There the pigmented cortex can "invaginate" by moving inside, around a plug of vegetal yolk (Holtfreter, '43b).

Experiments with Localized Insemination. The localized insemination of the frog's egg by Newport (1854), which was probably the first analytical experiment in embryology, and a similar experiment by Roux (1885, 1887), which was conceived independently, demonstrated a close correlation between the sperm entrance point and the plane of first cleavage which latter passed through animal pole, vegetal pole and sperm entrance point. Although the contention that the first cleavage plane coincides invariably with the median plane of the embryo was not borne out by later investigations (Vogt, '26a; Banki, '27b; and others), the correlation between sperm entrance point and median plane was confirmed by Ancel and Vintemberger ('48) and others. It is likely that the sperm actually determines bilateral symmetry under natural conditions, at least in some species (see Pasteels, '37a). However, its role is not universal or indispensable. For instance, normal symmetry relations establish themselves in polyspermic species of urodeles (see Fankhauser, '25) and after experimentally induced parthenogenesis (A. Brachet, '11, and others).

All observers, then, agree that the dorsoventrality and bilateral symmetry of the uncleaved egg are highly labile and readily modifiable by gravity and localized insemination. The former is stabilized first; the latter remains labile at least up to the 2-cell stage.

INITIAL STEPS OF ORGAN DETERMINATION

The axial determination is only one aspect of egg organization. The early determination of organ patterns is of equal significance. This problem has a long tradition; it is the modern version of the "preformation-versus-epigenesis" controversy.

The classic constriction experiments on 2-cell stages of urodeles (Endres, 1895; Herlitzka, 1897; Spemann, '01, '03; and others) and on blastulae of anurans (Schmidt, '33), and the isolation experiments of early blastomeres (Ruud, '25), which resulted in the formation of twin embryos or duplications, demonstrate convincingly that in amphibians no rigid pattern of organ precursors exists in the 2-cell stage. This notion is supported by the fusion experiments of Mangold ('20) and Mangold and Seidel ('27), in which two 2-cell stages were united crosswise, resulting in giant normal embryos or two to four axial systems.

The constriction experiments gave at the same time a clear indication of an incipient difference between the future dorsal and ventral sides. Spemann found that, in numerous cases, only one blastomere formed a normal embryo, whereas the other one formed a viable spherical structure without axial organs, in which only pronephric tubules, mesenchyme and blood cells were differentiated (*Bauchstück*, belly piece). Two complete individuals were formed whenever both separated blastomeres contained part of the upper blastoporal lip. One embryo and a belly-piece resulted when the entire dorsal lip was contained in one blastomere. Apparently, factors or materials which are necessary for invagination and for the formation of axial organs are localized early on one side. Spemann ('14, '28) found by constriction of uncleaved eggs that this prelocalization exists before cleavage begins, and Fankhauser ('30) and Streett ('40) traced it back to stages shortly after fertilization. Centrifugation experiments of Pasteel's ('41) indicate that this precursor of axial organs becomes stabilized at the time of the formation of the gray crescent.

The constriction and fusion experiments do not rule out the possibility that a more detailed pattern of regional differences exists in very early stages; but if so, it is very labile, and reversible. The results are in full agreement with those obtained in the experiments on axial determination; both demonstrate that the prelocalization of a dorsalizing factor is the first step in organ determination. Whereas there is general agreement that the area corresponding to the chorda-mesoderm field of the early gastrula is blocked out first, the theoretical interpretation of its origin has followed different lines.

INTERPRETATION OF DORSALIZATION IN TERMS OF LOCALIZED PRECURSORS

Spemann, Mangold, and others have considered the dorsalizing agent to be the actual precursor material of the chorda-mesoderm, and Lehmann ('42a, '45) has suggested that the pigmented marginal plasma which Banki ('27a) and he himself have found in the equatorial zone of some urodeles corresponds to the marginal zone of the gastrula. This would not necessarily imply that this precursor is already endowed with inductive capacity from earliest stages on. Holtfreter ('34b), Mayer ('35) and Waddington ('38b) have shown that the uncleaved egg contains agents which are capable of inducing neural tissue, but there is no evidence for their prelocalization at the dorsal region.

Certain experimental findings do not seem to be in agreement with the concept of localized precursors. Penners and Schleip ('28a, b) and Penners ('36) found in their inversion experiments that, in exceptional cases, the hemisphere not containing the gray crescent formed a blastopore and subsequently an embryo. Pasteels ('38, '40, '41) observed in rotation and centrifugation experiments that occasionally a blastopore originated at a distance from the site of the gray crescent. Spemann ('38) and Lehmann ('45) have interpreted the results of Penners and Schleip in terms of a translocation or splitting of mesoderm-precursor material due to the rotation, and the results of Pasteels could be explained in the same way.

Dollander and Darby ('49) and Dollander ('50) found in constriction experiments on *Triturus palmatus*, in which the gray crescent had been marked, that the blastomere opposite to the gray crescent gave rise to normal or microcephalic embryos in a considerable number of cases. The indistinctness of the gray crescent in this species introduces a serious source of error. Furthermore, one should realize that the gray crescent is not in all species a reliable indicator of the dorsal side. For instance, Schechtman ('36) found in *Triturus torosus*, in not less than 27 per cent of the eggs, a divergence between the plane of symmetry of the gray crescent and that of the gastrula, ranging between 25 and 90 degrees.

Altogether, the assumption of an early prelocalization of a precursor material for chorda-mesoderm has not been invalidated by experimental data.

INTERPRETATION OF DORSALIZATION IN TERMS OF GRADIENTS

The occurrence of blastopores outside of the gray crescent area has led some authors to propose a more dynamic interpretation of the origin of dorsalization. Penners and Schleip ('28a,b) have contended that the essential condition for blastopore formation is a gradient between dark cortical material and white yolk, and that invagination would occur at that point of the egg surface at which this gradient is steepest. Dalcq and Pasteels ('37, '38; Dalcq, '41a,b) have formulated an elaborate double-gradient theory which encompasses not only the patterning of morphogenetic movements and tissue segregation, but also the subsequent differentiations and inductions. Only a few points of this theory are relevant to the present discussion.

The authors postulate (1) a "yolk-gradient field" with its center at the vegetal pole; it is not necessarily represented by yolk, but more likely by the cytoplasm combined with the yolk; (2) a "cortical gradient field" which resides in the cortex; it has its center in the center of the gray crescent and extends around the entire surface of the egg. Both fields show continuous decrements and both elaborate specific products, V (vitelline) and C (cortical), respectively, which interact with each other to produce a new compound, "organisine." Every region on the egg surface is defined by two variables: the product $C \times V$, and the ratio C/V. The basic point of the theory is the following: The initial egg organization is represented by merely quantitative regional differences between the two variables, and these differences can be modified experimentally. The region of the peak value of $C \times V$ becomes the site of blastopore formation and mesodermization. In the normal egg, this peak would be attained in the area halfway between the centers of the two gradient fields; but the experimental dislocation of the more mobile yolk-gradient field by centrifugation or inversion may raise the $C \times V$ value of any other point on the egg surface to a sufficiently high level to endow it with the capacities of invagination and mesodermal differentiation. The experimental support of this theory cannot be presented here (see reviews in Dalcq, '41a; Pasteels, '51). It is largely based on the inversion experiments of Pasteels ('38, '40) in which the positions of the two fields with respect to each other and their interactions could be controlled experimentally.

A number of criticisms have been levelled against this hypothesis (see Rotmann, '43; Lehmann, '45). The question of whether the yolk-cytoplasm system exerts its influence by producing a chemical substance or merely by providing a favorable mechanical matrix for mesodermal invagination is still open. Furthermore, the significance of the subcortical "marginal plasma" for the processes under discussion remains to be settled. Lehmann ('42a, '45) ascribes to it an important role, whereas Pasteels ('46) denies its existence. According to Pasteels ('51), the subcortical marginal zone is characterized by a special ratio of yolk platelets and basophilic granules. None of the cytological pictures presented so far permit definite conclusions, and detailed studies of serial sections of eggs immediately after rotation and centrifugation are altogether missing. Therefore, much of the discussion is of a highly speculative nature. A more detailed study of the egg structure with modern tools will be necessary before a decision between the two hypotheses becomes possible.

GASTRULATION, FATE MAPS

Gastrulation is a very significant event in vertebrate development. In this phase, the body plan is created and the main organ primordia are blocked out and brought into their definite spatial relations to each other.

The classic vital staining experiments of Vogt ('29) have shown that gastrulation in amphibians is accomplished by complex *morphogenetic movements* which are integrated in space and time. His investigations on urodeles and anurans have clarified numerous controversial issues and have laid the foundation for an understanding of gastrulation in meroblastic vertebrates (see Pasteels, '37b). Space does not permit us to give an adequate presentation of these phenomena; we refer to textbooks on comparative and experimental embryology. A detailed account of Vogt's work may be found in Hamburger ('42).

The transformation of the blastula into the three-layered gastrula is accomplished by an invagination of the lower hemisphere which includes the marginal zone (prospective mesoderm) and the vegetal material (prospective entoderm), and an expansion (epiboly) of the upper hemisphere (prospective ectoderm). Invagination begins at the dorsal lip of the blastopore, where at first pharyngeal entoderm, then prechordal mesoderm and chorda material move inward; somewhat later, invagination of lateral and ventral mesoderm proceeds around the entire rim of the blastopore. Before and during invagination, the mesoderm material undergoes a conspicuous convergence towards the median plane, and at the same time an axial stretching to form the substratum for the medullary plate. At the end of gastrulation, the medullary plate arises as the result of a condensation of the dorsal ectoderm into a columnar epithelium which then converges mediad and folds inward to form the neural tube. Concurrently, the ventral ectoderm continues to expand and flatten (Gillette, '44). The mechanisms underlying the morphogenetic movements cannot be discussed here

Hörstadius and Sellman ('45) and Niu ('47) worked out localizations in the neural crest. The mesoderm mantle was mapped by Yamada ('37) and the entoderm by Balinsky ('47). Concerning the tail, see p. 247.

It is important to realize that these maps indicate merely topographic relations. They represent the "prospective significance" (actual fate) of a given area, in normal development, but do not indicate its state of determination nor its inherent potentialities. These can be evaluated only by transplantation, explantation, and other devices. On the basis of such experiments, Holtfreter ('36; see Fig. 80) has constructed maps represent·

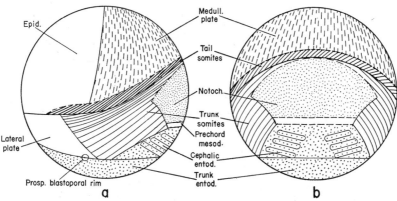

Fig. 77. Maps of the prospective regions of the early gastrula of the axolotl (after Pasteels, '42). *a*, Lateral view; *b*, dorsal view.

(see Holtfreter, '43b, '44a; Lewis, '47, '49).

Once the gastrulation movements were known in detail, it became possible to trace the origin of the different organs back to earlier stages. As a result of his systematic staining experiments on urodeles and anurans, Vogt was in a position to construct the so-called fate maps which represent the projection of the main organ primordia onto the surface of the late blastula or early gastrula. These maps have been an invaluable aid to all subsequent experimental work on pre-neurula stages. Nakamura ('38) and Pasteels ('42) have made significant additions and corrections, and the map of Pasteels for *Amblystoma mexicanum* (Fig. 77) may now be considered as representative of urodeles in general.

No complete maps exist for neurula stages. However, information is available for special areas: Goerttler ('25) and Schechtman ('32) mapped the ectoderm in general, Roehlich ('31) and Carpenter ('37) the ectodermal derivatives of the head, Manchot ('29) and Woerdeman ('29) the prospective eye areas;

ing regulative and differentiation potencies and compared them with the fate maps.

SIGNIFICANCE OF GASTRULATION MOVEMENTS AND INDUCTION AS ORGANIZING FACTORS

TOTAL EXOGASTRULATION

The importance of the morphogenetic movements as an organizing principle is well demonstrated in embryos whose gastrulation movements have become inhibited or disoriented (Holtfreter, '33a,d). When a blastula of the axolotl or of other urodeles, after the removal of the supporting membranes, is placed into a slightly hypertonic physiological salt solution, the entomesoderm, instead of moving inward beneath the ectoderm, moves in an opposite direction, away from the ectoderm (Fig. 78*b*). Even in its "exogastrulated" position the marginal zone proceeds to execute the characteristic gastrulation movements of dorsal convergence and anteroposterior elongation, becoming at the same time embedded in the mass of entoderm which eventually envelops it entirely. The equatorial zone corresponding to the blastoporal rim is successively constricted until it is narrowed down to a thread which connects the attenuated tail-end of the entomesoderm with the empty bag of the stripped-off ectoderm (Fig. 78c). The latter, thus deprived of its normal underlying tissues, proves to be incapable of differentiating into any of its normal derivatives, such as a neural sys-

PARTIAL ORGANIZATION AS A RESULT OF PARTIAL INVAGINATION

The supposition that lack of an ectodermal organization is caused by the absence of subjacent entomesoderm is confirmed by observations on partially exogastrulated embryos. Varying with the concentration of the ambient salt solution and with the time of exposure, one may obtain a continuous

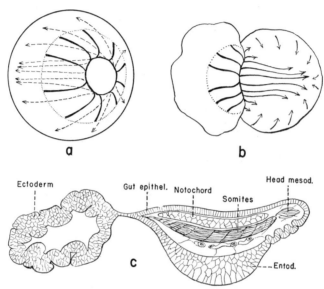

Fig. 78. Diagrammatic illustration of the morphogenetic movements (a) of normal gastrulation and (b) of exogastrulation. c, Main differentiations in an exogastrulated embryo. (After Holtfreter, '33a.)

tem, sense organs or specific epidermal structures. It merely develops into a mass of unspecialized epidermis cells. It follows that the entomesoderm contains determinative factors necessary for any typical ectodermal differentiation.

The exogastrulated material, on the other hand, may adopt the shape of an embryo and differentiate quite normally in the total absence of ectodermal tissues (Fig. 78c). Thus the displaced marginal zone develops into an axial notochord associated with somites and pronephroi, and furthermore into coelomic cavities, head muscles, connective tissue, blood, some cartilage, heart and smooth intestinal muscles. The latter two, though not innervated, may perform rhythmic contractions. These mesodermal tissues are wrapped into entoderm which differentiates into the various kinds of glands and epithelia characteristic of the normal intestinal system. However, the polarity of these epithelia is inverted, their secreting surface being turned toward the external medium.

series of gradations between complete exogastrulae and normally invaginated embryos. Figure 79 gives typical examples of such malformations in R. pipiens, which in this case, however, were obtained by a shock treatment with alkali. This series differs from corresponding ones in urodeles (Holtfreter, '33d) mainly by the fact that the latter rarely exhibit the various degrees of tail duplication and spina bifida which result in anurans from a failure of the lateral primordia to join in the dorsal midline (in contrast to the urodeles, the prospective tail somites in the anuran gastrula are located more laterally). In all cases, however, the extent and type of ectodermal organization can be related to the amount and histological nature of the entomesoderm that has invaginated. Thus the appearance of spinal cord and fin depends upon the presence of underlying notochord and somites while the various ectoderm structures of the head develop only when cephalic entomesoderm has invaginated.

The following chapters will deal in detail with these relationships between the germ layers. We merely draw the general conclusion that the organizing capacity resides primarily in the entomesoderm and not in the ectoderm. The former consists of regionally different tissue components which determine

may cause various degrees of cyclopia and microcephaly: hybridization (Moore, '46); parthenogenesis, androgenesis or over-ripeness of the egg (Rugh, '48); low or high temperatures (Atlas, '35; Hoadley, '38); centrifugation (Jenkinson, '14; Motomura, '31; Pasteels, '40; Pasquini, '42); irradiation

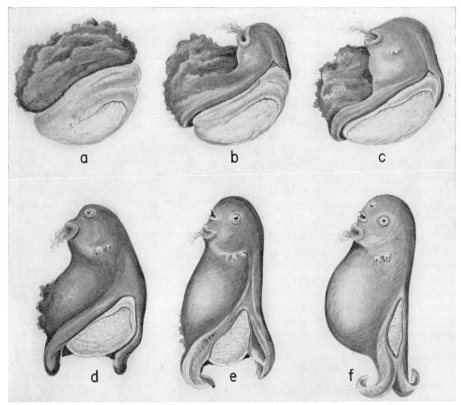

Fig. 79. Varying degrees of hypomorphism in *Rana pipiens*, produced by brief alkali treatment at the early gastrula stage. All six malformations are of the same age. Note the correlation between the extent of invagination and the degree of ectodermal organization. In *a*, the three germ layers have remained side by side; *d* possesses suckers and a single eye; *f* shows spina bifida and a double tail. (Original.)

or "induce" the ectoderm to enter into its various kinds of differentiations. To insure a response, intimate contact between ectoderm and the subjacent "inductor" is necessary.

VARIOUS AGENTS CAUSING SUBNORMAL ORGAN PATTERNS

Hypomorphic forms corresponding to partial exogastrulae occur "spontaneously" in all vertebrates (Schwalbe, '07; Wolff, '48) and they have been produced experimentally by a great diversity of procedures (see Section XIV, on teratogenesis). Confining ourselves to the amphibians and omitting further details, we list some of the procedures which

of the spermatozoa (Rugh, '39); crowded conditions, alkali (Holtfreter, '44c, '48b); fat solvents, acids, and a variety of salts, especially lithium chloride (Jenkinson, '06; Lehmann, '33, '38; Adelmann, '34, '36; Copenhaver and Detwiler, '41; Pasteels, '45).

Thus a great number of unrelated physical and chemical interferences from the outside as well as intrinsic genetic changes can affect development in such a way that the resulting malformations are strikingly similar. Not all of these experimental data have been sufficiently analyzed to decide when, where and by what mechanism the different agents have deranged the developmental processes. However, it can be safely assumed that in all these instances the pattern of the malformations was laid down principally by way of a disturbance of the gastrulation movements. It is furthermore probable that the absence or reduction of brain and sense organs is due to deficiencies of the inductive entomesoderm rather than to primary defects of the ectoderm. There is no experimental evidence in support of the assumption of earlier teratologists that such gross anomalies as microcephaly or cyclopia may arise from a secondary degeneration of originally full-size organ primordia. More generally stated, these malformations are not a problem of abnormal growth but of cell movements and cytological determination. The embryo may possess the cell material necessary for the formation of all ectodermal organs, yet these organs will never begin to differentiate unless their primordia have been mapped out and fixed in their fate by the appropriate inductors.

STATE OF ORGANIZATION OF THE EARLY GASTRULA

The data presented so far have dealt with the problem of embryonic organization in rather generalized outlines. Further analysis of these phenomena requires a more detailed study of the determinative relations between the parts of the early embryo. With this aim in mind, three methods which supplement each other have been employed: isolation, transplantation and defect experiments. Such experiments have been made possible through the introduction of fine glass needles as microsurgical instruments (Spemann, '18, '21b) and through the use of a balanced physiological salt solution (henceforth referred to as "standard solution") for culturing the embryonic fragments (Holtfreter, '31, '43a).

ISOLATION EXPERIMENTS SHOWING THE DIFFERENTIATION CAPACITIES OF PARTS OF THE GASTRULA

Isolation experiments have been carried out on a large scale on the early gastrula of both urodele and anuran species (Holtfreter, '38b, c). We shall confine ourselves to the conditions in urodeles. As the preceding chapter has shown, the gastrula is of particular interest since it is mainly during this stage that the basic pattern of organization is laid down.

The gastrulae were divided up into small fragments which were then cultured in standard solution. The main types of differentiation obtained from hundreds of such explants as projected back upon the gastrula are represented in Figure 80b. This distribution pattern is markedly different from the map of the prospective organ areas (Fig. 80a), indicating that only few of these areas develop true to their prospective significance when they are explanted. Three kinds of behavior can be distinguished which correspond more or less to the regions of the ectoderm, the marginal zone and the vegetal hemisphere, respectively.

The Ectodermal Region. In accordance with the observations on total exogastrulae, the different isolated regions of the ectodermal layer are incapable of forming typical tissues but form merely unspecialized epidermis cells. This holds for both the prospective epidermal and the prospective medullary areas and applies to the axolotl and to various European, American and Japanese Triturus species (Holtfreter, '33a, '38b, '44b; Waddington, Needham and Brachet, '36; Shen, '39; Gallera, '48; Yamada, '50a). When supported by a solid surface such as glass, a piece of ectoderm may spread to form an epithelium which will, however, disintegrate shortly into single cells. In order to maintain an epithelial continuity, ectodermal cells require the presence of connective tissue and a basal membrane (Holtfreter, '34c, '39b).

The failure of the explants to form typical ectodermal derivatives cannot be ascribed to inadequacies of the culture medium but is a true expression of their state of determination at the time of isolation. This is evidenced by the fact that when corresponding ectoderm pieces are isolated from a neurula, they do develop into different tissues whose type conforms more or less to the prospective significance of the areas tested (Holtfreter, '31; Mangold, '33b; Monroy, '37; von Aufsess, '41). Thus an explant taken from the medullary plate of a neurula will no longer form epidermis but neural tissue, epidermal differentiations being now confined to explants derived from the presumptive epidermis. Obviously, the invaginated tissues have changed the determinative state of the neurula ectoderm.

The Dorsal Marginal Zone. Explants taken from the different sectors of the marginal zone of urodele gastrulae are capable of developing into a great variety of tissues, but their histological fate does not conform exactly to the prospective significance of the areas tested. Most illuminating is the behavior of explants from the upper blastoporal region. They undergo vigorous movements and reshufflings of their cell material before they settle down for final differentiation. These rearrangements can be compared with the movements of gastrulation, although, under the present conditions, they

80*b*). Fragments containing the material of the caudal somites and notochord frequently produce merely epidermis which is sometimes associated with ill-defined connective tissue. It appears that the latter represent

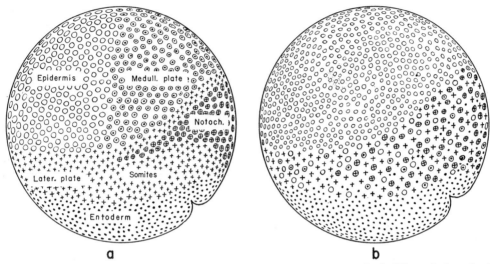

a b

Fig. 80. *a*, Differentiations in normal development (prospective significance); *b*, differentiations obtained when small pieces of the prospective areas are cultured as explants. The results are projected back upon the side-view of an early gastrula. (After Holtfreter, '36.)

are bound to take an abnormal course (Holtfreter, '38b, '39b; Schechtman, '42).

If the differentiations are related to the fate map, it becomes evident that the dorsal blastoporal region has the properties of an "embryonic field." Here are some relevant data:

1. A small piece from the presumptive notochord not only gives rise to a notochord but will also form somites and, frequently, even various neural and epidermal structures. The same array of tissues can be obtained from pieces isolated from the area of the presumptive somites (Fig. 81). This shows that at the time of isolation the explanted areas do not differ noticeably in their tendencies of self-differentiation, all of them producing a greater variety of tissues than they would do when left undisturbed within the embryo.

The gradient nature of this "*chorda-mesoderm field*" (Weiss, '39) is expressed in the distinct decrease of chorda-mesoderm differentiations at its periphery. The frequency of regulative differentiations is highest in explants comprising the prechordal material and the central portion of the prospective chorda-mesoderm; it decreases toward the animal pole and the lateroventral region of the marginal zone (compare Figs. 80*a* and

prospective skeletal muscle which could not differentiate typically because it was not associated with notochord tissue.

2. When attached to glass, a blastoporal fragment tends to form an axial system ex-

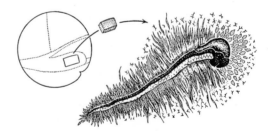

Fig. 81. An explanted piece of the prospective somite region of an early gastrula differentiates into an axial system consisting of median notochord and spinal cord and bilaterally arranged myoblasts. Notice anterior brainlike enlargement of the neural tube, capped by epidermis and surrounded by migrating mesenchyme and "giant cells" which seem to represent cephalic mesectoderm. (After Holtfreter, '38b.)

hibiting cephalocaudal polarity and bilaterally symmetrical arrangement of its myoblasts (Fig. 81). This applies even to pieces from the lateral blastoporal region. Hence, one may ascribe to the chorda-mesoderm field the capacity of a segregative *"self-organization."*

The following experiment shows that a patterning of this field into separate tissues may occur even in explants in which the original cell arrangement has been changed completely. When the entire dorsal regions of several gastrulae are isolated, then dissociated into free cells by means of alkali, and this cell suspension is made to re-aggregate in a neutral medium, the composite body will undergo a sorting out of the intermingled cells (Holtfreter, '44c). The entodermal and ectodermal cells will preferably move into surface positions, while all mesodermal cells accumulate in the interior. The latter, instead of differentiating into a chaotic mosaic of different cell types, tend to form well segregated tissues, such as somites, pronephros, body cavities, and a single, though dendritic, notochord. This self-organization of the disarranged material into a complex and highly integrated structure recalls the reorganization observed in dissociated sponges. It demonstrates that the process of blocking out and determination of the dorsal blastoporal material into distinct tissue primordia is controlled by several morphogenetic principles: directed cell movements, selective cellular adhesions, and mutual determinative processes occurring between the cellular constituents of the aggregate.

The Ventral Marginal Zone. A determinative interdependence did not become apparent in explants containing the prospective areas of pronephros, erythrocytes, smooth intestinal muscle and coelomic walls. These tissues developed from the lateral and ventral sectors of the marginal zone, usually combined with some epidermis and gut epithelium (see also Fernald, '43; Yamada, '50a). Except for the pronephric duct which could appear in any of the lateroventral fragments, the last-mentioned differentiations corresponded largely to the prospective significance of the isolated material as shown on the fate map. However, the conclusion which is suggested by these results, namely that the ventrolateral sectors of the marginal zone are more strictly determined than is the dorsal sector, has become questionable on the basis of subsequent experiments.

The Entoderm. In contrast to the ectoderm and chorda-mesoderm, the entodermal organ areas appear to be locally determined at the early gastrula stage, although some overlapping between them may exist. Explants from the different entodermal areas (vegetal hemisphere) furnished the differentiations of the various epithelia of the intestinal tract, and of liver and pancreas. These structures could develop independently of each other and in the absence of ectoderm and organizer material. Histological regulations could not be detected, an observation which was made on neurula material as well (Kemp, '46), although Balinsky ('47) reports an interchangeability of the anlagen of liver and stomach at the neurula stage. In order to obtain the epithelial arrangement of an intestinal wall, the entoderm cells require a support of connective tissue; in its absence they behave like isolated ectoderm forming an irregular mass of cells which, however, becomes cytologically differentiated into intestinal cells (Holtfreter, '38b,c, '39a,b). Such cell-orienting influences of the environment should not be considered as induction phenomena.

General Conclusions. The differences in developmental capacities of the regions dealt with above indicate that the early amphibian embryo exhibits simultaneously the properties of a determinative and a regulative type of development. The entodermal differentiations show the highest degree of independence, the ectoderm the lowest, and the chorda-mesoderm occupies an intermediate position. It is, therefore, no longer correct to consider the chorda-mesoderm field as a region whose histological determination precedes that of all other regions, and to relate this alleged supremacy to its faculty of determining the fate of other, less specifically determined, parts of the embryo. Actually, the entodermal districts, being earlier determined than the dorsal mesoderm, are not subject to the determinative influence of the latter.

Considering, however, the organological rather than the cytological features of the explants, it is evident that none of the primordia can attain the shape and structure of a typical tissue or organ without the formative assistance of surrounding tissues. In the absence of an epidermal or mesodermal covering, all intestinal primordia develop in an inverted orientation forming an external epithelium instead of inner tubes. Without a supporting matrix, especially of mesenchyme, no ento- or mesodermal epithelia or tubes can be established, the eye vesicle cannot become an eye cup, and no caudal elongation of the axial mesoderm can take place (Holtfreter, '39a,b,c). These environmental factors are mainly of a general mechanical nature and should therefore not be confused with the primary determining factors of differentiation. All evidence points to the conclusion that a cell which in response to inherent or external stimuli has become determined to differentiate in a certain direction, acquires simultaneously the tendencies of motility and adhesion characteristic of this cell type. Varying with the type, the cell may exhibit the tendencies of elongating or spreading, of invaginating, aggregating, dispersing, etc. Proper execution of these tendencies is a prerequisite for the final arrangement of the cells into typical tissues and organs. To manifest the tendencies, environmental conditions of the kind mentioned above are required. But cytological differentiation may proceed to some length even if the external conditions inhibit the execution of collective cell movements. It is incorrect to think that preventing the marginal zone from invagination causes it to become ectoderm, but material which is determined to become mesodermal tends to move into the interior of an embryo. In conclusion, it may be stated that the marshaling of the cells into tissue patterns is controlled by a variety of environmental factors which differ fundamentally from those which initially determine the material and dynamic trend of cellular differentiation.

TRANSPLANTATION AND DEFECT EXPERIMENTS ON THE EARLY GASTRULA

The method of grafting certain parts of the embryo into different regions of another embryo involves two consequences: their separation from the determinative factors of the original tissue environment and, possibly, their exposure to new determinative factors at the site of implantation. Varying with the new site and with the state of determination of the graft, the tissue may develop according to its prospective significance or according to the determinative stimuli emerging from the new tissue environment. If the various grafts are subjected to a sufficiently wide range of different stimuli, one may expect to gain an idea of the range of developmental potencies of the grafts at the time of operation.

Potentialities of the Ectoderm. Whereas the isolated ectoderm of the early gastrula lacks the capacity of differentiation into typical structures, it possesses a very wide range of reaction potencies ("competence") when exposed to inductive stimuli. The interchangeability of prospective epidermis and prospective neural tissue was demonstrated in the classic transplantation and rotation experiments of Spemann ('18). Corresponding xenoplastic experiments gave similar results (Holtfreter, '35a,b, '36). Transplantation to the ventral region which lacks inductive capacity resulted in the formation of unspecialized epidermis (Mangold, '29a; Bytinski-Salz, '29).

Numerous experiments have shown that any part of the early gastrula ectoderm can be induced to form any kind of neural or epidermal structure. Furthermore, given the proper inductive stimuli, gastrula ectoderm can be transformed into any kind of mesodermal tissue. When grafted into the lateroventral marginal zone of another gastrula, it may form pronephric tubules or lateral plate (Mangold, '23), and when grafted into the dorsal blastoporal lip it can differentiate into notochord, somites and neural tissue (Spemann and Geinitz, '27; Raven, '38). In contact with the caudal portion of the archenteron roof it can be induced to form notochord, somites, neural tube, pronephros, meninges, mesonephros, mesenchyme and limb tissues (Holtfreter, '33c, '36; Raven, '35; Spofford, '48). It has been shown that this wide range of differentiation potencies is equally shared by the presumptive epidermal and medullary areas (Holtfreter, '33b, '33c, '44b). There is no evidence for the contention of Goerttler ('27) and Barth ('41) that the ectodermal layer, before being affected by inductive stimuli, possesses an inherent "polarity," or that its different areas are in any way predetermined according to their prospective fate. Whether or not the gastrula ectoderm is fully omnipotent is still an open question. Claims to the effect that it can be transformed into blood cells, liver, and gut tissues (Mangold, '23; Holtfreter, '33c; Raven, '35, '38) require further elucidation.

The mesodermal marginal zone is endowed with about the same range of differentiation capacities as the ectoderm. Unlike the latter, however, it has a certain tendency to form mesodermal rather than ectodermal tissues, and its various potencies can become manifest independently of external inductive stimuli by way of self-organization. Yet, the following observations indicate that determinative factors of the environment cannot be disregarded, if one attempts to analyze the field properties of the chorda-mesoderm. Large defects in the median part of the blastoporal lip involving removal of most of the prospective head mesoderm can be regulated almost perfectly. Obviously the surrounding marginal zone, by filling the gap, becomes converted into head tissues (Töndury, '37; Shen, '37; Holtfreter, '38b; Dalcq, '40). A similar convertibility has been observed when the dorsal blastoporal region comprising the presumptive head and trunk mesoderm is rotated 180 degrees (Waddington and Yao, '50). Musculature forms readily from prospective notochord, as is shown in experiments of Spemann and Bautzmann ('27), Weber ('28), Wang ('33) and Mayer ('35). The rotation and exchange experiments within the marginal zone performed by Bautzmann ('33) demonstrate, in agreement with numerous other observations, that prospective lateroventral mesoderm can be transformed into somites and notochord.

As was found in explantations, the chorda-mesoderm material is furthermore capable of forming not only mesodermal but also various epidermal and neural structures. This occurred, for instance, when a piece of the blastoporal lip was grafted into another embryo, or into a jacket of ectoderm (Lewis, '07; Spemann, '18; Spemann and Mangold, '24; Holtfreter, '36; Dalcq and Lallier, '48a, b). Following excision of a large portion of the ectodermal roof, the defect was closed by the expanding marginal zone and a normal animal could be formed; part of the prospective chorda-mesoderm produced, according to its new position, various ectodermal structures (Bruns, '31; Holtfreter, '38b). When a large dorsal piece including the borderline areas of prospective medullary plate and mesoderm was rotated 180 degrees the dislocated areas developed according to their new position, demonstrating once more their convertibility into each other (Töndury, '36). However, when the prospective head mesoderm of an early gastrula was replaced by prospective trunk-tail mesoderm of an advanced gastrula, no regulation occurred: the embryo developed merely a spinal cord but no head structures (Hall, '37). Obviously, apart from a chorda-mesodermal trunk field, the early gastrula possesses a mesodermal head field, and these two cannot be readily converted into each other.

It is unfortunate that the factors which determine the formation of tissue patterns within the marginal zone have so far eluded further analysis. We shall face the same issue in the discussion of the neurula stage, during which the major segregations take place. The general result of all these studies is epitomized in the statement that the chorda-mesoderm area of the gastrula represents an equipotential field with diffuse outlines and a center of activity near the dorsal lip; this is little more than a formulation of the problem. However, another important idea emerges from these experiments: Whereas the chorda-mesoderm field shows a high degree of self-organizing capacity when explanted, its actual fate in the embryo depends not only on determinative interactions within this area but also upon its topographic relations to the ectodermal (and entodermal) parts of the embryo. Apparently, the surrounding ectoderm is involved in fixing the boundaries of the material which is destined to invaginate and to become mesodermal. This relationship is quite remarkable since later on it is the invaginated material which determines the blocking out and differentiation of the ectodermal structures.

EXPERIMENTS WITH CHEMICAL AND PHYSICAL AGENTS

Further evidence of the labile nature of determination of the entire marginal zone comes from experiments with externally applied chemical or physical agents. Exposure of early Triturus gastrulae to certain concentrations of lithium chloride resulted in larvae lacking all or parts of the notochord (F. E. Lehmann, '33, '37, '38; Pasteels, '45). Vital staining experiments of Lehmann have shown that the prospective notochord was used in the formation of somites. When explants of prospective lateroventral mesoderm were briefly subjected to the disaggregating action of ammonia, they differentiated partly into notochord and somites (Yamada, '50a), and when whole frog gastrulae were exposed to urea solutions, scattered fragments of notochord appeared within such different tissues as the somites, the neural plate, and the entoderm (Jenkinson, '06; Fautrez, '49). Treatment of frog blastulae with thiocyanate resulted in an increase of the notochord diameter in the trunk region (Ranzi and Tamini, '39; Ranzi, Tamini and Offer, '45–'46). But since the outgrowth of the tail of these larvae was delayed or subnormal and since thiocyanate failed to convert explanted lateroventral mesoderm into notochord (Ranzi and Tamini, '40), it is likely that the increase in diameter resulted simply from a failure of the notochord to elongate, an effect which need not involve any tissue conversion since it can be likewise achieved by mechanical inhibition of the tail formation (Holtfreter, '45a).

Suppression of notochord formation has been observed, furthermore, in amphibian larvae which at early stages had been subjected to supranormal temperatures (Hoadley, '38) or to centrifugation (Jenkinson, '14; Pasteels, '40). When early amphibian embryos were raised in a temperature gradient, the warmed side developed faster than the cooled one, but no other deviations from the normal differentiation pattern were observed (Huxley, ' 27; Vogt, '28b; Margen and Schechtman, '39). Therefore, the notion of Child ('29, '46) that simply a raising of the physiological activity of a given embryonic region can shift it into new trends of differentiation does not apply to the amphibian embryo. The few cases of accessory axial systems which Gilchrist ('28) observed after the local application of higher temperatures were probably due to a bifurcation of the invaginating mesoderm rather than to a direct determinative effect of heat upon the differentiation of the ventral mesoderm or ectoderm.

Irradiation of the blastoporal lip with ultraviolet light tended to suppress its differentiation and induction power (Dürken, '36; Reith, '38). When this treatment was applied to the lateral half of the prospective chorda-mesoderm the results varied with the stage of the embryo (Brandes, '38, '40, '42). When early cleavage stages of Rana were irradiated unilaterally, the volumetric ratio between notochord and somites became supranormal, but when later stages, up to the early gastrula, were irradiated, it tended to become subnormal. As compared with the somites of the non-irradiated side of the blastoporal lip, those of the irradiated side would attain, in approximately equal percentages, a larger, smaller, or equal volume, and no clear relationship could be established between the dosage of irradiation and the tendency of the marginal zone to form either somites or notochord.

Attempts to "explain" the experimentally produced chorda-mesodermal conversions by the hypothesis that a "morphogenetic potential" (Dalcq and Pasteels, '37, '38; Pasteels, '40; Brandes, '42; Fautrez, '49) of the affected primordia has been either raised or lowered amount to little more than tautology. There is no information available concerning the chemical mechanisms involved in these conversions. Nor do we know at what critical point of this reaction chain the various chemical and physical agents have interfered, and why some of them had a chordalizing, others a mesodermizing effect. The data suggest that this conversion proceeds with equal facility in either direction. There is therefore no factual basis for the assumption that the segregation of the chorda-mesoderm field results from the differential distribution of a single hypothetic substance, called "organisine" (Dalcq and Pasteels, '38; Dalcq, '41a; Pasteels, '40; Brandes, '42), and it is furthermore arbitrary to assume that the prospective notochord possesses a higher concentration of this substance, hence a higher "morphogenetic potential" than the prospective somites. Some less hypothetical suggestions have been made as to the possible mechanism by which lithium and other agents may bring about their effects (reviewed by Gustafson, '50), but it is clear that much more biochemical work is needed before the conversions, and the field characteristics of the marginal zone in general, can be expressed in other than morphogenetic terms.

ANALYSIS OF THE "ORGANIZER"

INDUCTIVE AND ORGANIZING ACTIVITY OF THE MATERIAL FROM THE UPPER BLASTOPORAL LIP

In our discussion of the factors of organization we have referred frequently to determinative interactions between the germ layers. The present section is devoted largely to the inductive capacities of the chorda-mesoderm field whose self-differentiating capacities have been dealt with in the preceding section.

In their pioneering work on the "organizer," Spemann and H. Mangold ('24) transplanted part of the upper blastoporal lip into the ventral ectoderm of another gastrula of a different species. Another method of bringing this material in contact with the ventral ectoderm consists in inserting it into the blastocoele. If the graft contained a substantial portion of the chorda-mesoderm field, it invaginated, stretched itself between ectoderm and entoderm of the host, tended to establish the cavity of an archenteron (Lehmann, '32) and then organized itself into various tissues, such as notochord, somites, pronephros, prechordal mesoderm and entoderm (sometimes also neural tissue) which we have already encountered in the corresponding explants. Like the latter, the graft tended to form a harmoniously proportioned axial system with a craniocaudal polarity and a bilateral symmetry. This applied even to pieces containing only a lateral half of the dorsal lip (Spemann, '31; Holtfreter, '33d; Mayer, '35; Ekman, '36).

Spemann ('21a) introduced the term "organizer" for the upper blastoporal lip. The choice of this term, which we, like Spemann ('38) himself, shall use only in a provisional sense, was based upon the discovery that the tendency of self-organization of the graft was combined with the induction of host tissue to form an integrated whole. By assimilating adjacent host cells into its mesodermal system and by inducing additional

self-organized blastoporal material (Fig. 82c). (2) The action of the graft may go further by causing "complementary inductions" (Mangold, '32). In this case, the host cells supplement the axial system of the graft by adding to it entire rows of somites, large segments of the notochord, and a pronephric and neural system not containing

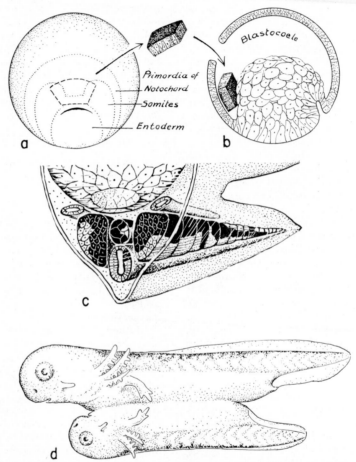

Fig. 82. Diagram of the transplantation of a piece of the upper blastoporal lip into another gastrula (a, b) and the self-differentiations plus inductions of the graft (c, d). In c, the tissues derived from the graft are shown in black, and the induced tissues in white. (Original.)

structures from the overlying ectoderm the graft could give rise to a more or less complete secondary embryo (Figs. 82, 92). There are two somewhat different ways whereby the host can participate in the construction of the secondary formation: (1) A true "assimilative induction" (Spemann and Geinitz, '27) may occur when the host cells become harmoniously incorporated into the grafted tissues thus forming sectors of the notochord, somites, pronephros and neural tissue of the

any grafted cells. Both modes occur usually combined (Spemann and Mangold, '24; Lehmann, '32; Bautzmann, '29, '33). The cephalocaudal axes of the secondary embryo and of the host may be oriented at any angle to each other, but several workers observed a striking preference of the graft for developing its main axis parallel to that of the host, even if its original orientation was at a wide angle to it (Geinitz, '25a; Spemann, '31; Lehmann, '32). Probably the invaginating host tissues tend to deviate the gastrulation movements of the graft, carrying the latter along with their own cell streams.

As a rule, the induced mesodermal tissues seem to result from a conversion of the host's ventrolateral mesoderm, although their derivation from the pluripotential ectoderm is within the range of possibilities. The prospective entoderm apparently cannot be induced to form mesodermal or ectodermal tissues. However, the blastoporal graft may affect the subjacent host entoderm insofar as the latter frequently forms a cavity, resembling that of an archenteron, which follows the length of the grafted notochord. The cavity later becomes confluent with the host's gut lumen. There is no evidence to show that the affected entoderm differentiates contrary to its prospective fate. If induction is defined as a process which determines primarily the cytological fate of the reacting cells, then this entodermal reaction would not fall under the term since it involves merely the cell arrangement and not the trend of differentiation of the entoderm.

The accessory medullary plate folds inward synchronously with that of the host. If the graft is sufficiently large, a correspondingly large plate will be induced which may develop into a complete neural system comprising the various brain portions, sense organs, spinal cord, and neural crest derivatives. The organization of the secondary embryo may be completed by the appearance of typically located gills, limbs, dorsal fin, balancer, teeth and other ectodermal derivatives (Holtfreter, '33d; Ekman, '37; Nieuwkoop, '47). However, in most of the reported cases only parts of the neural system were induced (Figs. 92a, b), such as a brain of reduced size which usually showed defects of various degrees. The incomplete brains were bilaterally symmetrical and they differentiated into the tracts and nuclei which are characteristic of the homologous normal brain divisions (Nieuwkoop, '47).

Together with these morphological characteristics, the secondary embryo appears to acquire the biochemical mechanisms necessary for its normal physiological functions. The muscles of the accessory head and trunk become innervated and exhibit rhythmical contractions, either spontaneously or in response to external stimulation. This occurs likewise if the inductions have been produced in an isolated piece of ectoderm, showing that the muscle innervation is actually supplied by the induced neural system (Holt-

freter, '36). In both the normal and the accessory embryo, the transformation of the medullary plate into a tube is a matter of cellular shiftings and changes of cell shape rather than of differential growth. Subsequently not only the normal neural tube (Burt, '43) but also neural tissue induced by chemical substances (Waddington, '40) show an intense mitotic activity. The cholinesterase activity of the experimentally induced neural structures is of the same order and magnitude as that of the primary nervous system of the host (Boell and Shen, '44).

In conclusion, the grafted blastoporal material has demonstrated the capacity to induce all the ectodermal structures of a normal embryo and, in addition, to supply the mesodermal tissues of an axial system, partly out of its own substance and partly by recruiting them inductively from the host. Taken together with the experimental evidence from our preceding chapters these observations leave no doubt that the organizing mechanisms here disclosed are likewise instrumental in the normal morphogenesis of the amphibian embryo. Comparative studies on the organizer activity in different amphibian species did not reveal any marked differences; in fact, the essential features here described on the basis of experiments on urodeles are also found in various anuran species (Geinitz, '25a; Bytinski-Salz, '29; Schotté, '30; Dalcq, '33, '40, '43; Holtfreter, '35a; Pasteels, '40, '45; Schechtman, '38a,b; Raunich, '40).

DISTRIBUTION OF REGIONALLY SPECIFIC INDUCTORS IN THE EARLY GASTRULA

The formation of a secondary embryo involves an axial self-organization of the blastoporal graft as well as an axial patterning of the induced structures. Brain tissues appear normally in connection with the anterior portion of the invaginated archenteron roof and tail tissues with the posterior portion. That this patterning of the inductions is not due to a regionally different responsiveness of the ectoderm to a general stimulus became clear when it was found that either head or tail structures can be readily induced from any portion of the early ectoderm. Evidently, what has been provisionally called "the organizer" must be subdivided into regional components with specific capabilities of differentiation and induction. It would seem desirable to establish a one-to-one relationship between a particular induced structure and a histologically defined component of the inducing system. This, however, has not been possible, partly because of the tendency of grafted fragments of the organizer to regulate into a variety of tissues, and partly because of the fact that what is induced is not a rigid mosaic of tis-

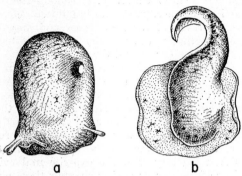

a   **b**

Fig. 83. *a,* Induction of ectodermal head structures by "head organizer" which was grafted into isolated ectoderm. *b,* Induction of trunk and tail structures by "trunk-tail organizer." (After Holtfreter, '36.)

sue primordia but a pattern of overlapping new embryonic fields which then undergo self-organization into definite organs and tissues. But although the regional differences in inductivity have eluded the attempts to localize them precisely, their existence cannot be denied.

The first attempt at demarcating the area capable of causing inductions was made by Bautzmann ('26). He found that in early Triturus gastrulae the material capable of inducing a neural tube is confined to the quadrant above the dorsal blastoporal lip, a region which in isolation undergoes pronounced self-organization. In anurans, the neuralizing material appears to be restricted to a narrower dorsal sector, since in at least four genera studied for this purpose (Rana, Hyla, Discoglossus, Bufo) the neuralizing material extended to about 45 degrees on either side of the dorsal mid-line, as against 90 degrees in Triturus (Schmidt, '36; Schechtman, '38b; Raunich, '40). Grafts from more lateroventral sectors of the marginal zone of the anuran gastrula could induce a tail which frequently lacked a spinal cord but contained the induced derivatives of a neural crest, such as mesenchyme and chromatophores.

This method of testing the induction power of parts of the marginal zone by implanting them into another gastrula gave somewhat ambiguous results because of an occasional interference of determining influences of the host (p. 259). Other methods circumvent this source of complication. A clear specificity of the organizer regions was found when either the anterior or posterior parts of the prospective archenteron roof were grafted xenoplastically into a bag of gastrula ectoderm isolated from the animal pole region (Holtfreter, '36). The anterior part regularly induced head structures: brain, sense organs, visceral cartilage and mouth structures; the posterior part always induced trunk structures: spinal cord and, less frequently, somites, notochord and pronephros, which tended to grow out into a tail (Fig. 83). Mesenchyme and chromatophores could be induced by either of the grafts. Further evidence of inductive differences along the cephalocaudal extent of the archenteron roof could be derived from the partial exogastrulae (p. 236). When gastrula ectoderm was placed upon the exogastrulated endomesoderm, the cephalic portion of the latter induced brain structures, and the trunk portion a tail (Holtfreter, '33d).

More detailed information on the distribution of inductive cell material in the early gastrula has been furnished by the aforementioned isolation experiments (p. 238). The explants which comprised small sectors of the marginal zone frequently developed some ectoderm which either came from the

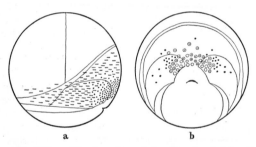

a   **b**

Fig. 84. *a,* The location of the "head-organizer" (dots) and of the "trunk-tail organizer" (dashes) is indicated on the side view of an early urodele gastrula. *b,* Dorsal view of a gastrula; distribution of ears (dots), noses (circles) and eyes (circles with dots), as obtained in small explants from this area. (After Holtfreter, '38b.)

prospective ectoderm that was included in the explant, or had been formed by regulation from prospective chorda-mesoderm. As is indicated in Fig. 84a, cephalic inductions occurred associated with head mesoderm and the anterior portion of notochord and somites, while spinal cord and tail fin differentiated in association with the more posterior portion of notochord and somites which themselves tended to become elongate structures. Adopting the terms of Spemann ('31) one may thus distinguish between head and trunk-tail organizers. (Their regionally specific effects in a host are illustrated in Figs. 92a, b.) The latter extends far into the lateral marginal zone, but fades out toward the ventral sector. The ventral entoderm and the ectoderm of the gastrula showed no inductive capacity. This deserves special mentioning because in later stages certain derivatives of these two germ layers do possess inductive faculty.

It is interesting to note that small explants from the upper blastoporal lip induced out of their own material ectodermal structures which showed again regional specificity. In these instances head structures, such as single eyes, olfactory pits, otocysts or balancers, could appear independently of each other, and from different, though somewhat overlapping, districts of the marginal zone (Fig. 84b). This seems to indicate that even at the gastrula stage the head organizer is not actually an equipotential entity but is subdivided into specialized inductors although distinct boundaries between them do not seem to exist.

THE ORGANIZATION OF THE MESODERM MANTLE AND THE TAIL BUD IN THE NEURULA

MESODERM MANTLE

The following chapters are devoted to the organization of the neurula and, in particular, to the mesoderm mantle and the medullary plate. These primordia represent significant intermediate stages in a gradually increasing stabilization of differentiations. Of particular interest are the interactions between these two structures and the complex relationships between the different components of the mesoderm. For orientation see Figure 85.

Notochord. During neurulation, the dorsal median strip of the mesoderm mantle becomes separated from the lateral parts. Its differentiation tendency for notochord is established from early neurula stages on (Bautzmann, '28; Yamada, '37; Chuang, '47; and others).

Somite Area. Prospective somite material of the early neurula of *Triturus alpestris* and *T. pyrrhogaster*, when reared within epidermal jackets or when transplanted to the midventral body region, does not form skeletal muscle but, unexpectedly, well differentiated pronephric tubules in a high percentage of cases (Yamada, '37, '39b; see Fig. 86). Apparently, the somite material requires for its normal differentiation the intervention of extrinsic factors. The notochord contains these factors, since if it is explanted in combination with somite material, the latter forms typical musculature (Yamada, '39b; Muchmore, '51; see Fig. 86). The notochord, however, holds no monopoly in this respect. For instance, either the transplantation of prospective somites to older hosts (Yamada, '39a), or the explantation of large pieces, containing prospective somite and adjacent

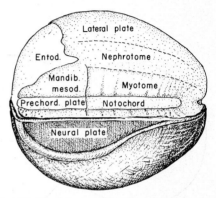

Fig. 85. Urodele neurula; the mesoderm mantle is exposed on the right side of the embryo. (Original.)

pronephros areas (Muchmore, '51), has the same effect. Moreover, typical somites are differentiated after the complete extirpation of the notochord in the early neurula (Kitchin, '49; Hörstadius, '44; Nieuwkoop, '46; Muchmore, '51). In normal development, muscle differentiation is probably brought about by the synergistic action of various neighboring tissues.

In addition to pronephric tubules and musculature, notochord and even neural tissue can be differentiated from prospective somites (Muchmore, '51; Lopashov, '35b).

Pronephros Area. Explants of this region when taken from Triturus neurulae can differentiate into typical pronephric tubules (Yamada, '40), but when isolated from *Amblystoma punctatum* they give rise to few and poorly developed tubules (Muchmore, '51). This area is capable also of forming musculature when isolated in combination with notochord or when grafted to the somite level (Yamada, '37, '40) but it forms ventral mesoderm and blood islands when grafted to ventral regions (Yamada, '37; see Fig. 86).

Lateral plate and blood islands differentiate in explants largely according to their prospective significance, but when grafted to the somite and pronephros level, they differentiate "neighborwise," probably as a result of assimilative induction (Yamada, '37, '40). However, when ventral mesoderm was isolated in combination with notochord, it frequently gave rise to pronephric tubules and the blood cell formation was suppressed (Yamada, '40; Fernald, '43; Muchmore, '51; see Fig. 86).

This situation has been interpreted in different ways: Modifying the ideas of Dalcq and Pasteels ('37, '38), Yamada ('40) assumes that the qualitative differences in the differentiation of the mesoderm originate from quantitative differentials of the morphogenetic activity within the mesoderm mantle. Each specific differentiation would be the manifestation of a certain "morphogenetic potential," and (arbitrarily assigned) thres-

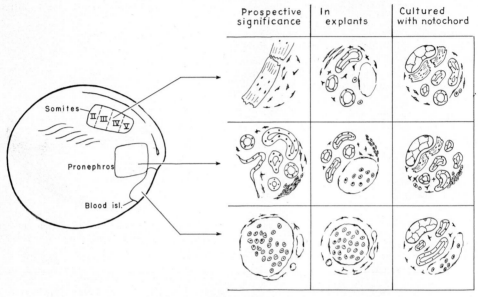

Fig. 86. Schematic representation of the differentiations of prospective somite, pronephros, and blood island regions, respectively, of the early neurula. First vertical row: normal fate; second vertical row: differentiation when isolated in ectodermal vesicle; third vertical row: differentiation when combined with notochord, in ectodermal vesicle. (After Yamada, '40.)

All these data show that some parts of the mesoderm of the early neurula are endowed with stronger differentiation tendencies towards their prospective fate than they were in the early gastrula stage. This applies especially to the prospective notochord. The pronephric and ventrolateral areas, while capable of differentiating selfwise and independently of each other, can still be shifted into other routes of differentiation when exposed to the influence of prospective notochord or somites. The prospective somite region is particularly dependent on environmental factors. Although its tendency to form notochord or neural tissue is clearly reduced as compared to the behavior of explants or transplants from the blastoporal lip of the early gastrula, its transformation into muscle tissue is definitely enhanced by neighboring tissues, among which the notochord plays a predominant role.

hold values would determine the lines of segregation of the primordia. The "potential" of the mid-dorsal area is presumably high enough for notochord differentiation, but that of the prospective somite area is too low for muscle differentiation and just high enough for the differentiation of pronephric tubules. Combination with notochord results in a raise of each level by one step: prospective somite and pronephros are raised to muscle, lateral and ventral mesoderm to pronephros differentiation.

Muchmore ('51) envisages the organization of the mesoderm mantle in terms of several overlapping morphogenetic fields which are characterized by qualitative rather than quantitative differences. Tissues other than the notochord can also direct mesodermal primordia into new channels of differentiation, and there is no evidence that these effects are due to quantitative gradations of a single agent. The overlap of the pronephros over the somite field would account for the formation of tubules in isolates of the somite area, and a mediad extension of the pronephros field would explain the tubule formation from ventrolateral mesoderm. The somite field seems to require extrinsic agents for its materialization to a higher degree than the other mesodermal primordia.

POSTERIOR TRUNK AND TAIL MESODERM

Vogt ('26b, '29) has shown that in urodeles, at the stage of the closed blastopore, only the

tion and elongation of the tail bud begins (for details see particularly Chuang, '47).

According to the studies of Pasteels ('39b, '43), the different structures of the posterior trunk and tail originate from localized tissue primordia which undergo morphogenetic movements considered to be a continuation of the gastrulation movements. They are not the result of differential growth processes, since there was no indication of a high or differential mitotic activity. Therefore, amphibian development does not conform to the concept of Holmdahl (since '25; see '39), who ascribes the organogenesis of the caudal end to an outgrowth from an indifferent growth center, and not to the segregation of

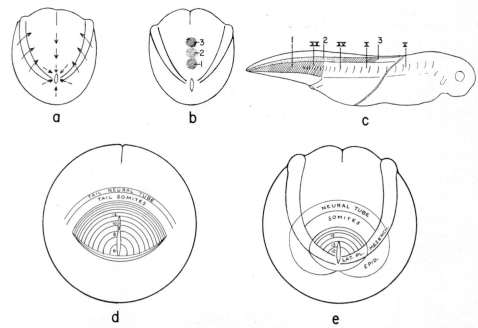

Fig. 87. Maps and morphogenetic movements of posterior trunk and tail in urodeles. *a*, Morphogenetic movements during neurulation; *b*, vital staining of three areas in the posterior medullary plate; *c*, the fate of the three marks. *d*, Topography of prospective tail structures in the neural groove stage; *e*, same in neurula with rising folds. The numbers in *d* and *e* indicate somite numbers. (After Chuang, '47.)

first six to eight somites, the adjacent lateral mesoderm, and the greater part of the notochord are invaginated. The posterior trunk and tail somites are still on the surface occupying the posterior fifth of the medullary plate. Detailed maps of these regions were constructed on the basis of vital staining and transplantation experiments (Vogt, '26b, '29; Bijtel, '31; Nakamura, '38; Pasteels, '39b, '42; Spofford, '45; Chuang, '47; see Fig. 87). During neurulation, the tail material moves inward by way of complicated invagination and folding processes, whereupon the forma-

germ layers characteristic of the more anterior regions. A distinction between "primary" and "secondary" body formation is not warranted in amphibians.

Holmdahl's notion finds still less support in the results from defect, transplantation and isolation experiments. They have shown that, from early neurula stages on, the different primordia of the tail region are even more rigidly determined and less capable of regulation than the more anterior parts of the mesoderm mantle (Bytinski-Salz, '31, '36; Mangold, '32, '33b; Bijtel, '36; Von Aufsess,

'41; Chuang, '47). This restriction of potentialities of the caudal primordia is the more remarkable as in larval stages it is the tail and not the trunk which is outstanding for its capacity of regeneration. Hence, one can no longer subscribe to the notion that the determination of the axial organs proceeds along a cephalocaudal gradient.

The different tissue primordia of the tail, namely notochord, spinal cord, somites and fin, are each independently capable of axial stretching. But it seems that the cooperation of several, or all, of them is necessary for the formation of a complete and straight tail (Vogt, '26b; Holtfreter, '33c; Bytinski-Salz, '36; Chuang, '47; Kitchin, '49).*

REGIONAL INDUCTION CAPACITIES OF THE MESODERM OF THE NEURULA

We saw that even in the young gastrula a distinction can be made between head and trunk-tail organizers, although their borders are ill-defined. At the end of gastrulation, a more distinct localization of the various mesodermal inductors along the cephalocaudal axis is manifested. The axial mesoderm has meanwhile separated into a posterior portion (notochord and somites) and an anterior one (prechordal mesoderm). The latter begins at the level of the midbrain, between the first and second visceral arch. It is subdivided into a narrow median strip, the "prechordal plate," and the lateral "mandibular mesoderm" whose paraxial position corresponds to that of the trunk somites (Vogt, '29; Adelmann, '32; and others; see Fig. 85). Lehmann ('42b, '45, '48) has pointed out that this mesodermal structuration is reflected in differences of inductive capacity. He considers the prechordal mesoderm as a specific inductor for tel- and diencephalon which are designated as "archencephalic" structures, whereas the chordal-parachordal head mesoderm would induce posterior or "deuterencephalic" brain structures. Dalcq ('46) prefers the terms "acrencephalic" and "chordencephalic" inductors. No structural difference can be detected between the latter and the spinal cord–inducing trunk portion of the archenteron roof.

In order to examine possible regional dif-

* This balance between independence and cooperation of the components of the tail is nicely demonstrated in L. S. Stone's time-lapse film of the development of *A. punctatum.* The speeded-up pictures show an up-and-down wiggling of the elongating tail bud, which seems to reflect alternate spurts of stretching in the ventral and dorsal tail portions, respectively.

ferences in the inductive capacity of the archenteron roof, Mangold ('33b) divided the latter into four transverse strips and implanted each under the ectoderm of a gastrula. Grafts of the rostral strip were relatively inactive, possibly because they consisted largely of cephalic entoderm. The second strip induced predominantly anterior head structures (forebrain, eyes, nose, balancers), the third strip mainly posterior head structures (rhombencephalon, otocysts), while the caudal strip induced regularly spinal cord and, frequently, pronephros and tail, but no brain. However, some structures, such as eye or otocysts, could be induced not only by that part of the mesoderm which underlies these structures normally, but by adjacent regions as well. Similar results were obtained by Ter Horst ('48) in explants, and by Okada and Takaya ('42), Okada and Hama ('43, '45) and Hama ('49), who tested the specificity of the cephalocaudal sections of the archenteron roof, before and after their invagination, by implanting them into whole embryos or ectoderm vesicles. These authors confirmed the rather puzzling observation of Mangold ('33b) that the anteriormost part of the archenteron was practically inactive.

Unfortunately, neither Mangold nor the Japanese authors worked heteroplastically, and they disregarded possible effects of the host levels on the regional specificity of the inductions. However, in view of the consistency of their results, the conclusion seems justified that the different levels of the archenteron roof have to a certain degree regionally specific induction capacities. Obviously, we are dealing with overlapping and not sharply delimited "induction fields" (*Organisationsfeld,* Spemann, '21a; *Determinationsfeld,* Weiss, '26).

Indirect evidence for a regional inductive specificity of the archenteron roof may be derived from the experiments of F. E. Lehmann ('38) in which successive gastrula stages of *Triturus taeniatus* were exposed to solutions of lithium chloride for short periods. The treatment resulted in localized defects in the anterior or posterior head or trunk mesoderm, respectively, depending on the stage subjected to lithium chloride. Corresponding deficiencies appeared in the overlying neural system. The results were interpreted in terms of stage-specific ("phase-specific") and localized susceptibilities of the mesodermal regions to lithium, and a rather strict regional correspondence between mesodermal inductors and induced neural structures was assumed. However, Pasteels ('45), who repeated these experiments on urodeles and anurans, obtain a series of continuous rather than discontinuous deficiencies both in the mesoderm and in its inductions, which he interpreted in terms of a cephalocaudal gradient of susceptibility.

The experiments of Dalcq ('46, '47) give an indication of qualitative differences between the inductivity of the prechordal and the chordal-parachordal mesoderm. He bisected the young gastrula of the anuran, Discoglossus, by a horizontal cut, rotated the upper half 180 degrees and healed the halves together. Two axial systems developed, one at the original dorsal side and one on the ventral side. Variations in the distance of the plane of cutting from the blastopore resulted in a series of incomplete axial systems. Isolated forebrains occurred in the ventral systems, and they were invariably correlated with prechordal mesoderm. Whereas the autonomy of an archencephalic inductor region was thus established, no evidence was found for an independent deuterencephalic inductor. Hindbrain and spinal cord were always induced together. The author considers the hindbrain induction merely as the result of a particularly strong inductive capacity of the cranial end of the chordal-parachordal mesoderm. Nieuwkoop ('47, '50) transplanted upper blastoporal lips from different gastrula stages of Triturus into the ventral side of another gastrula and likewise obtained secondary embryos showing successive steps of brain deficiencies. The boundary between the induced archencephalon and deuterencephalon coincided invariably with that of prechordal and chordal-parachordal mesoderm. The detailed study of the deficient brains suggested to the author that the other subdivisions of the brain are not induced by a mosaic of qualitatively different regions of the anterior archenteron roof but that they reflect threshold values of inductive potency within a cephalocaudal gradient of neural inductivity in the archenteron roof.

In the extensive experiments with adult inductive tissues or their fractions it has been found frequently that some of them induce predominantly head structures, others trunk-tail structures, or both (Chuang, '39, '40; Toivonen, '40; and others, see p. 269). Isolated ectoderm, when exposed to neuralizing aqueous solutions formed exclusively anterior head structures (Barth, '41; Shen, '42; Holtfreter, '44b; Yamada, '50a). It may be doubted whether these inductors have any similarity with the normal ones, but the findings indicate again that the factors which bring about an archencephalon differ from those which induce the more caudal parts of the nervous system. However, in all these experiments, no specific inductor for the deuterencephalon was found; the latter occurred always combined with archencephalic or with spinocaudal structures.

It was pointed out above that the posterior fifth of the medullary plate does not form neural but mesodermal structures of the posterior trunk and tail (see Fig. 87e). Hence one might expect that the caudal part of the archenteron roof would have mesoderm-inducing capacities. Spofford ('48) has shown that this is, indeed, the case. He substituted vitally stained pieces of early gastrula ectoderm for caudal medullary plate and found that the implants formed trunk and tail somites and other mesodermal tissues.

Altogether, there is good evidence for a distinction between a large anterior section of the archenteron roof which induces the various parts of the neural system and the mesectoderm, and a short caudal section which induces mesodermal tissues. The prechordal mesoderm operates (in cooperation with the tips of notochord and somites?) as an archencephalic inductor, but no sharp borderline seems to exist between the inductors for hindbrain and for spinal cord. The question of whether the inductive conditions which specify the different brain sections represent a discontinuous series of qualitative differences or a continuous series of merely quantitative differences of a single agent is undecided. This problem has given rise to extensive discussions (see for instance, F. E. Lehmann, '38, '45, '48; Dalcq, '46; Nieuwkoop, '47, '50; Waddington and Yao, '50). We shall return to it later on. Such variables as intensity of inductive effect and period of contact between archenteron roof and overlying ectoderm have to be taken into account (Dalcq, '46).

Whereas in normal development only the median part of the mesoderm mantle subjacent to the medullary plate actually exerts an inductive influence, the more lateral mesoderm also contains latent inductive capacities (Holtfreter, '33c, '38a; Raven, '35; Waddington, '36a). When pieces of gastrula ectoderm were placed over the dorsolateral mesoderm of a neurula, at different levels along the cephalocaudal axis, they were induced to form a great diversity of accessory ecto- and mesodermal structures, such as fragmentary brains, sense organs, somites, pronephros, and others. The different structures occurred at approximately the same sites as the corresponding host structures, their frequencies diminishing with the distance from these sites. This indicates that the dorsolateral mesoderm, like the more median archenteron roof, consists of a cephalocaudal series of specific, yet overlapping, induction fields. Some of the differentiations, such as balancers, gills, or ear vesicles, revealed the presence of induction fields outside the medullary plate which operate in normal development (see p. 255). However, the occurrence of supernumerary brains or tails in a lateral position seems to show that the neural plate inductors actually extend farther into the lateral mesoderm, beyond the boundary of the neural plate. It is probable that these peripheral induction capacities are normally not expressed because the ectoderm of the neurula—in contrast to the grafted gastrula ectoderm—is no longer competent to respond to them (p. 257).

Corresponding experiments on still older hosts have shown that these induction fields remain potentially active far beyond the stage at which they are normally engaged in organ determination. But a significant difference exists between these normally inactive inductors and the early organizer: Whereas the latter tends to assimilate the induced mesodermal tissues into its own field, the various tissues induced by the aged inductors are not incorporated but tend to establish axial systems of their own. For discussion of this problem see p. 279.

ORGANIZATION AND EARLY DIFFERENTIATION OF THE MEDULLARY PLATE

After it had become evident that the different regions of the archenteron roof are instrumental in blocking out the major subdivisions of the medullary plate, the question arose: To what extent is the subjacent mesoderm responsible for the more detailed patterning of the central nervous system? Does it operate merely as a short-term "activator" or does it exert an influence over a longer period participating also in the determination of the tissue organization of the induced areas?

An examination of this question revealed that the capacity for neural differentiation and organization does not arise abruptly but develops progressively during the protracted period of gastrulation. This was demonstrated by transplantations and explantations of circumscribed regions of the prospective or visible medullary plate of *Triturus alpestris* (Mangold, '29a; Mangold and von Woellwarth, '50). A merely epidermal differentiation occurred when the material was removed before it had contact with invaginated mesoderm. When taken from middle or late gastrulae which already possess an archenteron roof, the pieces developed partly into neural structures, but the percentage of identifiable brain parts and eyes was low. From early neurula stages on, the majority of the cases formed typical brain parts and single or synophthalmic eyes. Gallera ('47, '48) and Damas ('47) obtained similar results with Pleurodeles. However, they stressed the point that the grafts from the younger stages differentiate into pigment cells rather than into neural tissue and they assumed that this stage-linked differentiation reflects quantitative dosage effects of the inductive substratum.

After the medullary plate has become visible, its different levels are capable of differentiating into typical fore- or hindbrain, eyes, or spinal cord, respectively, when isolated from the underlying mesoderm (Mangold, '33b; Nakamura, '38; Ter Horst, '48; and others). However, these regions represent but indistinctly outlined morphogenetic fields whose parts are not yet rigidly determined. A variety of experiments has shown that this applies to urodeles as well as to anurans (for references see Mangold, '31a; Adelmann, '36). Extirpations of large parts of the anterior medullary plate, or a rotation through 90 or 180 degrees of the median portion of this region, without the underlying mesoderm (Alderman, '35) failed to produce marked abnormalities in brain and eye development. Small pieces of the prospective spinal cord region implanted in the brain region were assimilated by the latter (Umanski, '35). Hence, the anterior part of the medullary plate does not represent a mosaic pattern of cephalic primordia but a general and labile *eye-forebrain field*. This field seems to possess a mediolateral gradient because heterotopic transplants of its median strip formed an eye six times as frequently as did grafts of lateral strips (Adelmann, '30). Its anteroposterior polarity is fixed as early as the neural groove stage, as was shown by rotation experiments of the entire anterior prospective medullary plate or of its lateral half (Roach, '45). (In the above-mentioned rotation experiments of Alderman, the transplants were much smaller and their inherent polarity was apparently changed by the surrounding tissue.) However, the mediolateral axis was found to be still reversible in the medullary plate stage (Roach, '45). The same holds for the hindbrain field; the extirpation of its lateral half is followed by restitution from the intact half (Harrison, '47).

Systematic studies of Mangold ('31a, '36) and Adelmann ('37) lead to the conclusion that the normal segregation of the field into brain and bilaterally arranged eyes is controlled

Instead of using surgical methods, one can prevent the development of the prechordal plate by exposing early gastrulae to certain concentrations of lithium chloride. In this case, a continuous layer of mandibular head mesoderm forms across the midline, and the induced structures exhibit again the syndrome of a cyclopean head (Lehmann, '33; Adelmann, '34). These results indicate that the bilateral disposition of the material for forebrain and eyes is decisively influenced by the corresponding mass distribution of the

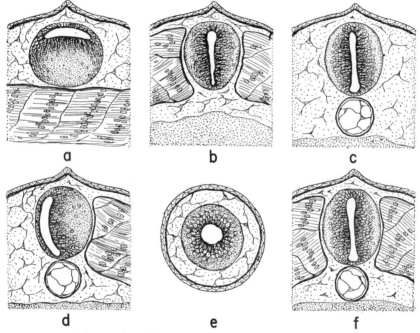

Fig. 88. Semidiagrammatic illustration of the formative effects of somites, notochord and mesenchyme upon the shaping of the neural tube; see text. (Original.)

trolled by formative effects of the underlying parts of the mesoderm. Following extirpation of the whole prechordal mesoderm from a neurula, 75 to 100 per cent of the embryos developed all degrees of synophthalmic to cyclopean abnormalities. The percentage of defects was approximately the same when only the median "prechordal plate" (Fig. 85) was extirpated, but it dropped to 44 per cent when only the paraxial "mandibular" portions of the mesoderm had been removed. Conversely, grafts containing the median strip of the anterior neural plate without the subjacent prechordal plate produced only a single eye, but when grafted together with this substratum, they formed two complete eyes connected by brain tissue, in 70 per cent of the cases.

subjacent mesoderm, especially the prechordal plate, and that this influence is exerted even after the brain-eye field has been induced.

It is doubtful whether this continued formative effect of the mesodermal substratum should be classified as an "induction." Adult tissues having no axial organization can likewise induce brains with bilaterally arranged sense organs (Holtfreter, '34b; Chuang, '39; Toivonen, '40). This makes it likely that the prechordal mesoderm merely provides the unspecific mechanical conditions for the bilateral segregation of the induced field. As such this influence would belong in the same category as that of the (non-inductive) mesenchyme which is necessary as a supporting matrix for the transformation of the optic vesicle into a double-layered optic cup (Holtfreter, '39c).

The mesoderm adjacent to the spinal cord plays apparently the same role in the bilateralization of this structure as does the head mesoderm in the bilateral distribution of the eyes. If the prospective notochord is extirpated (Lehmann, '26, '28; Hörstadius, '44) or its differentiation is suppressed by exposure of early gastrulae to lithium chloride (Lehmann, '37; Pasteels, '45) or to centrifugal force (Pasteels, '40), the somites may fuse across the midline. Under these conditions, the wall of the adjacent neural tube, instead of forming the characteristic thin floor plate, forms a thick mass (Fig. 88a). This occurs likewise when an additional neural tube is induced on the outer surface of older somites (Holtfreter, '33c). On the other hand, when neural tissue differentiates combined with notochord alone, its contacting side flattens out into a thin layer (Fig. 88c), while the presence of notochord together with unilaterally located somites produces the asymmetrical configuration of Figure 88d. But when the spinal cord develops surrounded merely by mesenchyme, its walls are uniformly thick (Holtfreter, '34c, '39c; Fig. 88e). Thus notochord and somites not only represent the inductor system for the spinal cord but they continue to influence the cell distribution within the tube. Although their formative effects are antagonistic, notochord and somites are normally arranged in such a way that their effects supplement each other, producing the typical thinning of the floor plate and the thickening of the lateral walls of the spinal cord (Fig. 88f).

It should be mentioned that the presence of an epidermal covering is equally important for the shaping of the neural tube, since without it the medullary plate fails to close and spina bifida (rachischisis) results. A multitude of externally applied chemical or physical agents can prevent the closure of the plate into a tube. Many of them are identical with the agents which inhibit the movements of gastrulation (p. 237), e.g., hypertonicity, extreme temperatures, detergents, iodo-acetamide.

Undoubtedly, the archenteron roof has an important share in the initial regional specification of the central nervous system. Yet the experimental data give convincing evidence that it is only partly responsible for the subsequent morphological and histological patterning of the morphogenetic fields which it has projected onto the dorsal ectoderm. At best, the inductive substratum facilitates the subsequent processes in a non-specific way. The elaboration of histological details is left to the *self-organizing capacity* of the neural tissue which was referred to above. If adult tissue can induce the ectoderm to form a typical bilaterally symmetrical brain flanked by any of the sense organs (Fig. 99b), then it is plausible to assume that similar autonomous processes occur within the different gradient fields of the normal medullary plate. These self-organizing processes supplement the activities of the archenteron roof and carry on when inductions have ceased to operate.

THE INDUCTION OF NEURAL CREST DERIVATIVES AND OF OTHER ECTODERMAL STRUCTURES

We have followed the progressive differentiation up to the neurula. In subsequent stages, a great variety of new structures appears. Their morphogenesis is analyzed in other chapters of this book. The present chapter is limited to some general aspects of the determination of ectodermal derivatives not belonging to the central nervous system. Prominent among them are the derivatives of the *neural crest* which, in turn, originate from the neural folds. We mention briefly the following crest derivatives: the majority of the chromatophores, large amounts of mesenchyme of the head and trunk region, the principal components of the visceral cartilaginous skeleton and of the cranial ganglia, dental papillae, Schwann's sheath cells, at least part of the corium and of the membranous coverings of the brain, the chromaffin bodies and the medulla of the adrenal glands (see the reviews by Harrison, '38; Du Shane, '43; Rawles, '48; Hörstadius, '50). Ectodermal *placodes* outside of the medullary plate produce the olfactory epithelium and its nerve processes, the lens, the otocyst and its acoustic ganglion, the lateral line sense organs and some components of the cranial ganglia.

NEURAL CREST DERIVATIVES

Since the neural crest originates in the neural folds, one might expect that it is induced in conjunction with the adjacent medullary plate, by the more lateral parts of the archenteron roof. Although some of its derivatives, such as mesenchyme cells, chromatophores and Rohon-Beard neurons, can be induced independently of medullary plate tissues (Holtfreter, '33c; Raven, '35), these elements have occurred in most instances in combination with parts of the central nervous system. In fact, there is hardly any case known in which induced neural tissue has not been accompanied by neural crest derivatives.

Dalcq ('41a, '46) and Raven and Kloos ('45) have interpreted these results in terms of a concentration gradient of a hypothetical inductive substance, "organisine," present in the archenteron roof (see p. 278). The median strip of the archenteron roof, supposedly rich in organisine, would induce neural structures while the more lateral parts which elaborate it in smaller quantities would induce neural crest.

There is little evidence to support this gradient concept. Whereas the experiments of Bautzmann ('28, '29) seemed to indicate that the prospective notochord has a stronger neuralizing effect than the prospective somites, the experiments mentioned above and those of Bytinski-Salz ('31) did not confirm this contention. They have shown that the frequency and amount of neural tissue induced by prospective somites is not inferior to that obtained by prospective notochord. The embryos, in which the formation of large sections of the notochord was suppressed by chemical treatment without any sign of reduction of the neural tube (F. E. Lehmann, '35, '37, '38; Lehmann and Ris, '38), gave further evidence that the prospective somites and the notochord have equal potencies as inductors. The studies of Raven and Kloos ('45) indicate that neural crest derivatives are induced equally well by median and lateral pieces of the archenteron roof, whereas neural tissue was induced more frequently by the former than the latter. However, the small number of the experiments does not permit a statistical evaluation. Furthermore, the absence of neural inductions by lateral mesoderm can be correlated with a very poor differentiation of the transplants themselves. The available evidence thus indicates merely that some neural crest derivatives can be induced in the absence of a neural plate and that, if this happens, paraxial mesoderm was responsible for it. As a matter of principle, the question of whether the emergence of different structures is due to qualitative or quantitative differences in inductive substances can only be answered by experiments in which such substances are isolated and applied in graded dosages. Experiments with normal inductive tissues can never answer this question satisfactorily.

At the stage of rising neural folds, a *regional pattern* of limited differentiation capacities is already laid down in the neural crest: The precursors of melanophores originate mainly from the trunk part of the crest (Niu, '47, for Triturus) and those of visceral cartilage exclusively from the head crest (Harrison, '25; Raven, '31, '33; Hörstadius and Sellman, '45). Little is known concerning the determination of these patterns. However, final differentiation of both types of precursor cells depends on additional factors residing outside the archenteron roof and the neural crest itself. The chromatophore pattern will be discussed elsewhere. The formation of visceral cartilages requires an activation of their precursor cells by pharyngeal entoderm or, under experimental conditions, by notochord or intestinal wall of the trunk (Hörstadius and Sellman, '45; and others). In a similar way, final differentiation and functioning of the other derivatives of the neural crest seem to depend on additional stimuli which are ordinarily furnished at the sites where the migratory crest cells settle down. Thus, the formation of myelin depends on the establishment of contact between Schwann's sheath cells and nerve fibers, and the crest cells migrating into the mouth region produce dentine only when in contact with oral ecto- or entoderm. One may hesitate to give these additional environmental factors the same rank as the initial ones, since it is possible that at least some of them are merely necessary to realize the potencies evoked already by the initial inductive factors.

STRUCTURES OUTSIDE THE MEDULLARY PLATE

The situation is similar with respect to the placode derivatives: nose, lens and otocyst, and some other structures. In these instances, several inductive tissues are involved which operate either simultaneously or in succession, supplementing and reinforcing each other. These inductions thus serve as new illustrations of an important general principle; namely, of the existence of synergistically active *"inductor systems"* (Holtfreter, '35a,b). We have already encountered this principle in the case of the induction of spinal cord by the chorda-somite system and in the case of the brain-eye induction by a multiplicity of primordia of the anterior archenteron roof. In otocyst induction, a conditioning of the ectoderm by lateral head mesoderm is followed by an inductive action on the part of the lateral wall of the rhombencephalon. In the case of the lens, the optic vesicle provides the essential inductive stimulation in most amphibian species, but in at least some species it is preceded by a conditioning influence of the head mesoderm. The latter may be sufficient to call forth a lens in those species which can form it in the absence of an optic vesicle. Probably both the rostral part of the archenteron roof and the prospective forebrain are involved in the induction of the nasal placode, and both head mesectoderm and archenteron roof derivatives are concerned with balancer induction. In the case of the pituitary gland, the invagination of the ectoderm seems to be induced by oral ento-mesoderm, while its final differentiation depends upon a subsequent contact of this ectoderm with the infundibulum.

It has been shown in several of these instances that in the absence of one of the two components, the induced structure fails to attain normal shape and differentiation. When an inductive substratum is deranged, or when its contact area with the ectoderm is abnormally large, double or multiple formations may result, such as supernumerary nasal epithelia (Holtfreter, '36) or medullary plates (Waddington, '40). In order to call forth normal structures, the constituents of the "inductor systems" must be arranged typically with respect to the ectoderm, and they must act at the proper time.

To complete this brief survey of ectodermal inductions we merely enumerate others: epidermal glands, enamel organs, gills, and fin. In addition, the characteristic *perforations* which produce mouth opening, gill slits, and anus have sometimes been listed under the term "induction." It is true that they result from a contact action between specific parts of the intestinal tract and the overlying ectoderm. Yet, the physiological processes making for the thinning out and regression of these ento-ectodermal membranes appear to be quite different from those which cause the cytological determination of the other structures dealt with above.

HOMOIOGENETIC INDUCTION

As pointed out above, certain parts of the nervous system are engaged in the induction of ectodermal organs (nose, lens, otocyst, pituitary). On the other hand, in the early gastrula only the chorda-mesoderm has inductive capacity, whereas the ectoderm lacks

it. Obviously, the medullary portion of the ectoderm becomes inductive in postgastrula stages. Mangold and Spemann ('27) discovered that pieces of the medullary plate of urodeles when transplanted into the blastocoele of young gastrulae would induce a secondary medullary plate in the host, and Mangold ('29a) showed that all parts of the plate acquire the capacities for self-differentiation and induction simultaneously. The authors used the term *"homoiogenetic induction"* for this phenomenon. In accordance with the regional differences in the inductive specificity of the archenteron roof, anterior parts of the plate induce mainly brain and sense organs; middle portions, a spinal cord; and posterior parts, various tail structures (Mangold, '29a, '32, '33b; Bytinski-Salz, '29; Ter Horst, '48).

The experimental conditions leading to the manifestation of homoiogenetic induction are entirely artificial since, normally, the neural plate has no chance to act upon gastrula ectoderm. From this viewpoint, the phenomenon belongs in the category of "abnormal inductions" (see p. 267). However, it is likely that the agents which neuralize gastrula ectoderm are identical with those which are instrumental in the normally occurring induction of the above-mentioned placodal structures, all of which differentiate from neurula and tail-bud epidermis, and that the differences in response are due to changes in the reaction potency (competence) of the ectoderm. In fact, it has been shown that the ectoderm loses its neural competence towards the end of gastrulation, while acquiring local competences for nasal epithelium, otocyst, and so forth. If the above interpretation is correct, then the seemingly atypical phenomenon of "homoiogenetic" neural induction would be merely an expression of the age differences between inductor and reacting tissue.

CHAINS OF INDUCTION

Tissues such as the neural plate which must first be induced in order to become capable of inducing other structures have been termed *"secondary inductors."* Subsequently, the secondarily induced structures may act as *"tertiary inductors":* the otocyst induces the surrounding mesenchyme to form a cartilaginous capsule, and it appears that the lens stimulates the overlying ectoderm to adopt the characteristics of a cornea. Thus differentiation, particularly of the ectodermal structures, proceeds through the mediation of several generations of properly distributed inductors which succeed each other and may combine in various ways to act as coordinated determinative systems. This chain of inductive processes continues to operate beyond embryonic stages, involving the determination of the gonads, the mesonephros and various morphogenetic processes which occur during the metamorphosis of the amphibian larvae. Thus the principle of induction is of great importance for the organization of the amphibian body and, probably, of all other vertebrates.

COMPETENCE

Some districts of the early amphibian embryo, particularly the entodermal ones, do not seem to require specific external stimuli for their normal differentiation, while the mesodermal ones do require them to some extent. This dependence is most pronounced in the prospective ectodermal districts whose typical differentiations do not arise in the absence of exogenous inductive factors. On the other hand, it has been found that the differential fate of the ectoderm depends not only upon regional differences of the inductors but just as much upon a proper state of ectodermal responsiveness which varies with the developmental stage. The physiological state of a tissue which permits it to react in a morphogenetically specific way to determinative stimuli has been termed *"Reaktionsfähigkeit"* (Mangold, '29a), *"Reaktionsbereitschaft"* (Machemer, '32) or *"competence"* (Waddington, '32, '40). Like the capacity of certain cell groups to differentiate normally without specific external stimuli, competence is of course primarily determined by genetic factors. The term "competence" is useful if one wishes to distinguish between cell-inherent and exogenous factors of cell determination.

In using this term, it is necessary to specify embryonic area, stage of development, and the differentiation process to which competence refers. We can define competence only in terms of the products of differentiation because the inner conditions which permit an embryonic area to pursue a certain differentiation when properly stimulated can be grasped today only in a very hypothetical way. It would be advisable to confine the term to a limited phase and not to the terminal steps of differentiation. As an illustration of some fundamental aspects of competence, data collected on the ectoderm have been selected for discussion.

TIME PATTERN OF COMPETENCE

It is well known that the ectoderm from early gastrulae can respond to different inductive stimuli by forming any one of a number of different ecto- or mesodermal derivatives (p. 241). These and other data refute the notion of a dichotomy of progressive differentiation (Lillie, '27), according to which only one of two directions of differentiation is open to an embryonic area at a given stage.

With progressive development, the competence to form a diversity of structures becomes as a rule gradually restricted. Neural induction of the ectoderm occurs normally in advanced gastrula stages. Spemann ('18), Mangold ('29a), Lehmann ('28, '29), and others have shown that the competence of the prospective epidermis for neuralization is lost shortly after this event has taken place. In special studies of this problem, Machemer ('32), using urodeles, and Schechtman ('38a), using Hyla, transplanted the upper blastoporal lip of early gastrulae under ventral and flank epidermis of various stages. They found that the capacity for neuralization decreases markedly in the late gastrula stage, and is completely absent in the early neurula ectoderm. Raunich ('42b), using adult liver as an inductor, obtained similar results.

In a different set-up, Holtfreter ('38a) removed pieces of prospective ectoderm from early Triturus gastrulae, reared them in standard solution for varying lengths of time, and then implanted them homo- or xenoplastically into the dorsolateral regions of neurulae where a variety of inductors were known to be present. It was found that competence changes with time in both a quantitative and a qualitative sense. With increasing age, the grafted ectoderm forms increasingly smaller and at the same time less complex neural structures. Furthermore, new directly induced structures arise. Older ectoderm corresponding to the neurula stage forms only tissues which normally arise from the placodes and neural crest, until finally it becomes entirely refractory to inductive stimuli. The experiments indicate that the gradual change and final loss of competence is due to an autonomous process of ageing within the ectoderm (see also Waddington, '36b).

It is not yet possible to state at which stage the ectoderm acquires its responsiveness to inductive stimuli. Mangold ('26, '29a) and many subsequent workers observed that when living or dead inductors are grafted into an early gastrula, the induced medullary plate appears synchronously with that of the host. Assuming that these grafts begin to release the neuralizing agent immediately after implantation, a precocious medullary plate might have been expected. Since this did not happen, it has been inferred that the ectoderm acquires neural competence not before the middle or late gastrula stages. In view of the following data, the interpreta-

nized with these two inductive events are successive states of competence: the ectoderm of the gastrula and early neurula will respond only to the mesodermal inductor, but is refractory to the neural inductor. During neurulation, the ectoderm acquires the capacity to form otocyst in response to the neural inductor while gradually losing responsiveness to the mesodermal inductor (Fig. 89).

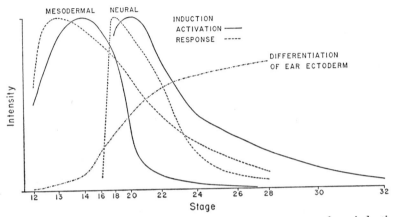

Fig. 89. Graphic representation of relative intensities of various components of ear inductions in Amblystoma. The maxima are placed at the same level arbitrarily. Abscissa: Harrison stages (12 = small yolk plug; 32 = advanced tail bud). Ordinate: Degree of ear differentiation in arbitrary units. (From Yntema, '50.)

tion may be somewhat different. Neuralization could be produced in the ectoderm of early gastrulae by exposing it for only a few minutes to cytolyzing solutions (p. 272). Nevertheless, the induced neural plate appeared synchronously with that of the donors of the ectoderm. Evidently, the early gastrula ectoderm is already competent for neuralization, but there was a latent period between the time of stimulation and visible differentiation.

The analysis of otocyst induction by Yntema ('50) provides a good example of the synchronization of competence and inductions in the normal embryo. Unspecified gastrula ectoderm, or prospective gill ectoderm of older stages, was transplanted to the ear region, including a wide variety of donor and host stages in altogether more than 100 combinations. It has been known that both mesoderm and prospective hindbrain are instrumental in otocyst induction (see Harrison, '45). Yntema showed that the mesodermal action which occurs first is maximally effective in early neurula stages, whereas the hindbrain operates somewhat later with a maximum of activity in the early tail-bud stages. Remarkably synchro-

REGIONAL PATTERNS OF COMPETENCE

The prospective ectoderm of the early gastrula shows no regional differences in neural or other competences (see p. 273), but such differences do develop gradually in the embryo. For instance, in the late neurula and early tail-bud stages, the lens-competence of the ectoderm is in some species narrowly restricted to the normal lens-forming area and its adjacent ectoderm; in *Bombinator pachypus* it is limited to the head epidermis, and in a number of species of Rana and Triturus it extends over the entire head and trunk (reviews of this much-discussed problem in Mangold, '31a; Spemann, '38; Needham, '42). In the same stages, the competence for balancer formation in *A. punctatum* is confined to the balancer-forming epidermis and its immediate neighborhood (Harrison, '25). Similar studies have been made with regard to the competence for mouth and gill formation, but the exact pattern of these competences has not been investigated, and the suggestion of Spemann ('12) that the reaction potencies for different structures may represent overlapping gradient fields ("*Reaktionsfeld*," Mangold,

'31a) has never been subjected to a rigorous test. The observations of Yntema ('33) concerning the distribution of otocyst competence in the late neurula do not substantiate this concept.

We have little information concerning the specific factors responsible for regional differences in competence. In the case of the ear (Yntema, '50) and of the lens (Liedke, '51) it seems that the head mesoderm provides the primary specific stimuli for ear and lens differentiation which are locally different. In all probability, this initial step of determination ("*Bahnung*," Vogt, '28a) involves a loss of reactive potencies for other stimuli. It is conceivable that in this way differentials are set up, at first between head and trunk epidermis in general, and then between different head regions. This problem, which has been touched upon already in connection with the two-step "inductor-systems" (p. 255), awaits clarification by further systematic analysis.

The data presented in this chapter indicate that the competence of the ectoderm changes with time and, in a rather involved way, with the region of the embryo. Since the entoderm and, to a lesser extent, the mesoderm, develop rather independently of external determinative stimuli, we refrain from discussing their particular age-conditioned states of competence. As far as the ectoderm is concerned, it is clear that for the achievement of its typical differentiations, two sets of temporally and spatially matching, yet relatively independent, mechanisms are required: (1) a proper distribution of inductors which are in some measure specific; (2) a proper stage-specific state of responsiveness of the ectoderm.

As was stated above, the genetic constitution determines decisively the response of a given tissue to external stimuli. This point has been mentioned above in connection with the regional distribution of the competence for lens formation.

REGIONAL HOST INFLUENCE

When living or dead inductors were grafted into early gastrulae, results were obtained which could not always be accounted for by inductive specificity of the graft but which indicated the interference of regional host influences. Such effects were first shown in the experiments of Spemann ('31). Whereas "head organizer" would induce brain structures in any body level of the host, "trunk organizer" did not express its specificity when transplanted into the head level, since there it induced eyes and parts of brain which were fused with those of the host.

Various explanations have been offered for this host influence, but before discussing them, it should be pointed out that certain phenomena sometimes listed under this heading may be due to purely mechanical interactions between transplant and host. (1) The fact that the structures induced by grafted blastoporal material tend to appear at the same body level as the corresponding host structures may be due to a deflection of the invagination movements of the graft by those of the host whereby both become concordant. (2) Double or multiple brains and sense organs can arise if the graft acts as a mechanical obstacle, by splitting or deranging the inductors of the host. Grafts which are otherwise rather inactive can produce this effect (Raven, '33; Holtfreter, '34a), and it is not unlikely that some of Spemann's results can be explained in this way.

The elusiveness of this problem is indicated by the fact that normal trunk-tail organizer (Mangold, '33b; Holtfreter, '36) as well as adult organs (Chuang, '39) *can* induce a tail in the host's head region. Obviously, a clarification of this problem can only come from experiments which deal with it on a statistically satisfactory basis and avoid the situations outlined above. Besides, an analysis of the host influences would require a comparison of the inductions obtained by the same grafts in the whole embryo and in isolated ectoderm.

Normal head and trunk inductors express their regional specificity in every case when they are grafted into isolated ectoderm vesicles (Holtfreter, '36; Okada and Hama, '43, '45; Fig. 83). Comparable results were obtained when fresh or boiled adult tissues were implanted into such explants. For instance, Chuang ('38, '39) found that mouse kidney, when acting upon explanted ectoderm, would induce exclusively brain and sense organs, whereas Triturus liver would induce trunk and tail in addition to head structures (Figs. 93–96; Table 14, p. 269). Since the inductions obtained in such explants could be just as complex and well organized as those produced by the same inductor in whole embryos, these findings invalidate the idea of some authors that atypical inductors merely "evoke" a generalized structure such as neural tissue and that an "individuation field" of the host is re-

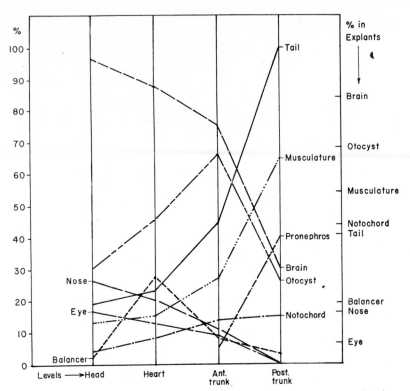

Fig. 90. Influence of host levels on the inductions of different organs by fresh liver of Triturus in Triturus embryos. Abscissa: host levels; left ordinate: frequency of inductions of different organs; right ordinate: frequency of the same organs when induced by fresh Triturus liver in explants (ectodermal vesicles). (After Chuang, '39.)

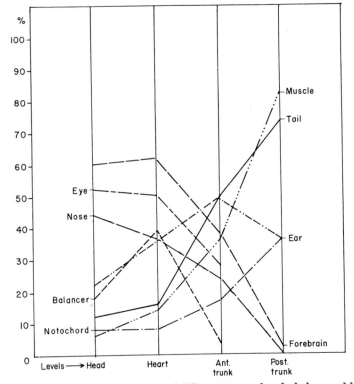

Fig. 91. Influence of host levels on the inductions of different organs by alcohol-treated livers and kidneys of different vertebrates in Triturus embryos (see text). Abscissa: host levels; ordinate: frequency of inductions. This graph is based on the figures given in Table 10, Toivonen ('40).

Fig. 92.

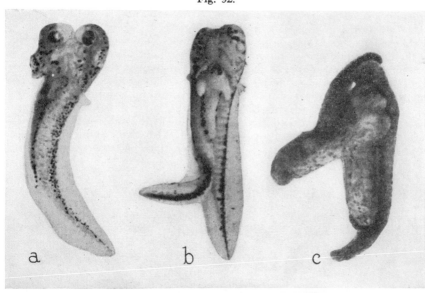

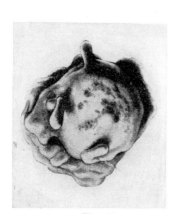

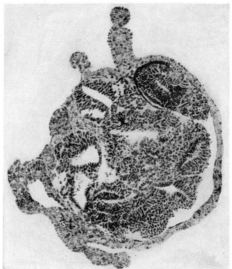

Fig. 93.   Fig. 94.

Fig. 92. *a*, Inductive effects of the "head organizer"; *b*, inductive effects of the "trunk-tail organizer"; *c*, heteroplastic induction of a complete secondary embryo, oriented opposite to the main axis of the host (from Holtfreter, '33d).

Fig. 93. Induction of headlike structure with three balancers, by fresh mouse kidney implanted in ectodermal vesicle of *Triturus alpestris* (from Chuang, '39).

Fig. 94. Induction of neural structures and eye with lens, by fresh mouse kidney implanted in ectodermal vesicle of *Triturus alpestris* (see Fig. 93) (from Chuang, '38).

quired to organize this tissue into regionally specific tissue patterns, such as brain with sense organs (Needham, Waddington and Needham, '34; Woerdeman, '36). Evidently, typical head and trunk patterns can arise within the stimulated ectoderm itself, by way of self-organization, and whatever the

host influence may be, it can only modify the effects of the graft.

Using the same adult tissues as in the preceding experiments, Chuang ('39, '40) grafted them into the ventral region of various levels of whole embryos. To simplify matters we shall discuss only his results obtained with Triturus liver which are based upon a statistically sufficient number of cases (185). As far as the host influence is concerned, the extensive data on mouse kidney gave much the same results. In Figure 90 the distribution of the various induced structures over the host is plotted according to four cephalocaudal levels. No distinction was made between direct and indirect inductions; for instance, the listed ear vesicles could have been induced directly by the graft or indirectly by hindbrain which was induced first.

ways. Unfortunately, the inductive specificity of these tissues had not been tested in ectoderm explants. Nevertheless the diagram of Figure 91 shows again that cephalic inductions tend to increase toward the head region, and trunk-tail inductions toward the tail region of the host. Once more, otocyst and balancer fall out of line, having their maximum of occurrence not in the head but in the anterior trunk region.

The available evidence indicates that there does exist a specifying influence of the host level upon accessory inductions, although

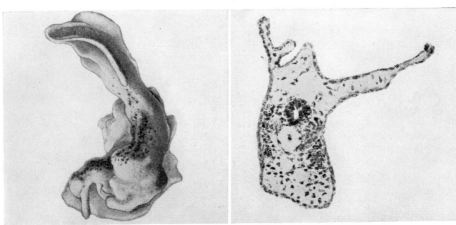

Fig. 95.   Fig. 96.

Fig. 95. Induction by fresh liver of Triturus implanted in ectodermal vesicle of *Triturus alpestris*. Notice tail and balancer. (From Chuang, '38.)
Fig. 96. Induction by fresh liver of Triturus, implanted in ectodermal vesicle of *Triturus alpestris* (see Fig. 95). Notice spinal cord, notochord, somites, tail fins. (From Chuang, '38.)

If one uses the rate of incidence of certain inductions in explants as a control (right ordinate), it is apparent that host influences reinforce the appearance of a given structure in certain levels and reduce the chance of its occurrence in other levels. Brain, nose and eye inductions clearly decrease in a cephalocaudal direction while those of pronephros, muscle and tail decrease in the opposite direction. However, as was the case in explants, head and tail structures *can* be induced simultaneously at any host level. Apparently, specific effects of the graft and regional host influences interact and compete with each other in a complicated way. The former may account for the rather unexpected frequency of otocysts and balancers in trunk levels.

Strikingly similar distribution patterns of specific inductions within a host were observed by Holtfreter ('34b) and Toivonen ('40), who used a great variety of adult tissues which had been pretreated in different

this influence asserts itself only in a certain percentage of cases. This phenomenon does not seem to be covered by our explanations given above and one has to look for other possible interpretations. The following suggestions have been made:

(1) The head mesoderm differs from trunk mesoderm quantitatively and possibly also in its reaction potency (Chuang, '39); hence the difficulty of the grafts to induce mesodermal trunk structures in the head region. (2) The competence of the ectoderm appears to vary along the cephalocaudal axis (Spemann, '31). This point has been discussed before (p. 258). Further indications for such a gradient are found in experiments which show that the ectodermal response to a graft is usually more pronounced in the anterior than in the posterior ventral regions of the embryo (Lehmann, '32; Machemer, '32; Holtfreter, '34b; Schechtman, '38a; Chuang, '39). (3) The primary host inductors may tend to assimilate the accessorily induced

structures into their regional fields. We recall the observation that the inductors in the archenteron roof represent overlapping fields which reach far into the lateral parts of the embryo. The normally unexpressed activity of the periphery of these fields may intervene and superimpose its regional characteristics upon the inductions of the graft. Such an auxiliary effect seems to account for the fact that the closer a graft lies to the dorsal host mesoderm, the more pronounced is its neural induction (Raven, '33).

There is also the "bridge phenomenon": An induced neural plate lying close to that of the host usually links up with the latter, suggesting that sub-threshold inductive factors of the lateral mesoderm can add up with those of the graft to induce the neural bridge. The most impressive indication of such an auxiliary host effect was found by Pasteels ('47a,b, '49a) who produced secondary axial systems by centrifuging blastula and gastrula stages. The secondary formations did not attain perfect differentiation unless they appeared linked up with the primary axial system ("*contagion*," Pasteels).

The interpretation of host effects in terms of regional fields meets with the difficulty that the peaks of frequency of the induced organs are not always at the levels of the respective host organs, where one would expect them.

Obviously, the term "host influence" comprises a group of heterogeneous factors, and their analysis offers serious obstacles. In a given instance, it is difficult to decide whether the graft suppresses the activities of the host inductors, or whether it displaces the host inductors or cooperates with them. Furthermore, the regional specificity of the grafts themselves is somewhat variable and can be expressed only in statistical terms.

HETEROPLASTIC AND XENOPLASTIC TRANSPLANTATIONS*

Born (1897) was the first to accomplish the fusion of parts of amphibian embryos belonging to different species and genera. This new method proved to be of great value in the analysis of some basic problems such as the interactions of genetic and environmental factors in growth (reviewed by Harrison, '35; Twitty, '40), the formation of pigment patterns (see Twitty, '42, '45), and

* "Heteroplastic" usually refers to tissue combinations between different species of the same genus, and "xenoplastic" (Geinitz, '25b) to those between more distantly related forms.

embryonic induction. The following discussion is concerned only with the last-mentioned problem.

The combination of inductors and reacting tissues differing in hereditary characteristics, such as pigmentation, or size of cells and nuclei, allows for an exact distinction between transplanted and host tissues. Therefore, this method has become an irreplaceable tool for the finer analysis of induction. Experiments of this type have established several fundamental principles:

1. Induction operates across the borders of species and even orders. This has been shown in a variety of experiments. For instance, the optic vesicle of a urodele embryo can induce a lens in competent epidermis of other urodele species or of anurans, and the chorda-mesoderm can induce a secondary embryo in the gastrula of a foreign species or order. It follows that the inductive agents are not species-specific.

2. The responses to inductive stimuli are in accordance with the genetic potentialities of the reacting material; they are species-specific with respect to form, growth rate, and other tissue characters. For instance, a balancer induced by head structures of *Triturus cristatus* in transplanted prospective belly ectoderm of *T. taeniatus* is a typical taeniatus-balancer (Rotmann, '35a; see Fig. 106). The genetic constitution is thus recognized as one of the most important limiting factors for the competence of the reacting tissue.

3. The larvae of urodeles and anurans differ in various *order-specific structures*: The urodeles are equipped with a pair of balancers on the ventrolateral side of the head, whereas the anurans have a pair of adhesive glands ("suckers") in a more ventral position. The larvae of urodeles possess dentine teeth, whereas the anuran tadpoles do not develop them until metamorphosis; instead, tadpoles are equipped with horny denticles which are not homologous with the former. There are conspicuous differences in the shape, number and topographic relations of the cartilages of the visceral skeleton, in body pigmentation and other characters. The induction of these structures which are divergent in the two orders has been analyzed by means of xenoplastic transplantations. It was found that the inductors are responsible for the regional specificity of the induced organs, but the pattern and structural characters of the latter are determined by the inherent properties of the reacting material. The following experiments illustrate this point.

When belly ectoderm of an anuran gastrula is transplanted to the prospective head region of a urodele gastrula, it is induced to form suckers on the ventral side of the head (Spemann and Schotté, '32) and horny denticles in the mouth region (Holtfreter, '35b; Schmidt, '37; Spemann, '38; see Fig. 97). In the reciprocal experiment, head structures of the frog or toad induced balancers (Fig. 98) and dentine teeth in the prospective neural ectoderm of a salamander

evolution. This aspect has been stressed particularly by Baltzer and his associates, in their extensive transplantation experiments (Baltzer, '41, '50a,b; Andres, '49; Wagner, '49; Roth, '50).

It seems that when structural divergencies originated in the course of evolution, the underlying inductive mechanisms were retained, in part, and they have remained a common property of both urodeles and anurans. The term "homodynamic" was pro-

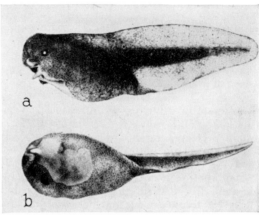

Fig. 97.   Fig. 98.

Fig. 97. Xenoplastic substitution of prospective ventral head ectoderm of Triturus by belly ectoderm of *Rana esculenta*, in early gastrula stage. The urodele head structures have induced mouth implements of anuran type: horny "teeth" and suckers. (From Spemann, '38, after Schotté.)

Fig. 98. Xenoplastic substitution of prospective ventral head ectoderm of the toad (Bombinator) by belly ectoderm of *Triturus taeniatus*, in early gastrula stage. The anuran head structures have induced a urodele balancer. (From Spemann, '38, after Rotmann.)

(Holtfreter, '35a; Rotmann, '35b). The respective inductors are regionally specific since they induce head implements, but they are at the same time sufficiently general to call forth the formation of structures which do not occur in the genetic repertory of the inducing host. Spemann and Schotté ('32; see also Spemann, '38) used the term "general situation stimulus" in describing this condition. The explantation experiments of Holtfreter ('36) have demonstrated that regionally specific structures can be induced xenoplastically, outside of a whole embryo. All these results brought sharply into focus the "release" character of the inductive mechanism, and the important role which the self-organizing capacity as well as the genetic constitution of the reacting tissue play in the inductive process.

The induction of organs which urodeles and anurans do not share has interesting implications for problems of homology and

posed for factors which are equivalent in different taxonomic groups, and the term "specific" for factors in which they differ (Baltzer, '50b). For instance, the cephalic inductors of balancers and suckers would be homodynamic, while the competence of the ectoderm would represent the specific factors. The same situation was revealed in exchange transplantation between *T. taeniatus*, which is equipped with balancers, and the axolotl, which lacks them. It was found that both possess the balancer inductors but that the axolotl ectoderm has lost the capacity to respond to them (Mangold, '31b). The following example may illustrate the point that inductive agents as well as competences can be homodynamic.

When anterior neural crest was exchanged between neurulae of *T. alpestris* and the toad, *Bombinator pachypus*, its derivatives participated in the formation and induction of numerous structures in the foreign head

(Wagner, '49). Dermal bones of the visceral skeleton, which are characteristic of early larvae of urodeles but absent in anuran tadpoles, were formed by the mesectoderm of Triturus in the anuran head in typical location and at the normal time. Conversely, the mesectoderm of Bombinator formed typical rostral cartilages in the urodele head which normally lacks these structures. These results imply that in both orders the entomesodermal head tissues are homodynamic in their capacity to provide a favorable substratum for the migration and final topographic localization of the skeletogenous neural crest derivatives. In addition, the visceral entoderm supplies an agent necessary for chondrogenesis (Hörstadius and Sellman, '45) which is equally effective (that is, homodynamic) in both orders. Anuran mesectoderm formed tooth papillae in the larval Triturus head, although normally the anuran tadpoles do not form teeth until metamorphosis. Bombinator and Triturus mesectoderm are thus shown to be homodynamic in their competence to stimuli which induce papillae.

Baltzer ('50a, b) has pointed out that the homodynamic components of the developmental mechanisms which are a common stock of large taxonomic units represent an as yet unexhausted reservoir for future evolutionary divergencies. The specific components, on the other hand, indicate where genetic changes have occurred in the past. The ectoderm appears to be predominantly a carrier of specific factors, while the inducing mesoderm and entoderm carry the homodynamic factors, although this is by no means a general rule. In several instances, the evolutionary change seems to have involved shifts in the time patterns of differentiation, as is illustrated in the delay of dermal bone and tooth formation in anurans (for a discussion of these and related problems, see DeBeer, '51).

ANALYSIS OF THE PHYSIOLOGICAL MECHANISM OF INDUCTION

From the preceding account rather complete information has been gained concerning the morphological phenomena of induction in the amphibian embryo. Departing from this level, further research proceeded to examine the induction mechanism from a more physiological and biochemical angle. Since it is impossible in this context to review adequately the vast literature in this field, we shall consider only those data which are relevant to our topic.

INDUCTIVE CAPACITY OF DEAD EMBRYONIC TISSUES

In 1932, a short collective report by Bautzmann, Holtfreter, Spemann, and Mangold announced that organizer and medullary plate retained inductive power after they had been killed by heat, cold, or alcohol (Fig. 99). Holtfreter showed in addition that non-inductors, such as ectoderm and entoderm of the gastrula, acquired induction capacity through these treatments. More intensive studies were then devoted to the effects of extreme temperatures and various chemical agents on the inductive capacity of embryonic tissues (Holtfreter, '33e, '34a). The test method consisted largely in grafting the killed tissues into the blastocoele of early Triturus gastrulae.

One of the first surprises in these experiments was the observation that the neuralizing capacity of the inductors was hardly affected by drying, or boiling at 100° C., whereas the mesodermizing capacity disappeared rapidly through these treatments. At temperatures between 100° and 150° C. the neuralizing effect was likewise progressively reduced to zero.

After it had been either dried, heated, frozen, or treated with acid, alcohol, or boiling ether, the posterior part of the medullary plate plus subjacent archenteron roof which, in the living state, can induce trunk and tail tissues, had not only lost its mesodermizing activity but also changed its regional specificity: it now induced brain portions which could be associated with various sense organs (see also Barth and Graff, '38; Okada and Takaya, '42; Holtfreter, '48a). Likewise, ectoderm and ventral entoderm from a gastrula and early neurula which were rendered active by extreme temperatures or fat solvents had a strong tendency to induce brain portions and sometimes free lenses, but they never induced mesoderm. Thus, through the different killing methods, the original regional specificity of the normal inductors was abolished, and all parts of the gastrula or neurula became inductors of cephalic structures. Also inductive were all cytoplasmic regions and the nucleus of the coagulated ovum (Holtfreter, '34a; Waddington, '38b).

In order to disarm the possible criticism that the high degree of organization found in the induced structures might have been due to an activation of the host's determination fields (Weiss, '35; Woerdeman, '36), the host influence was excluded in the following

Fig. 99.

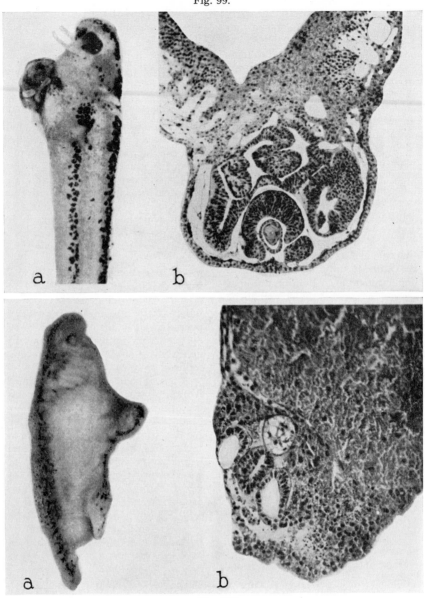

Fig. 100.

Fig. 99. Induction of neural structures and eye with lens, obtained by implantation of heat-killed anterior medullary plate into the blastocoele of an early gastrula of Triturus (from Holtfreter, '33e).

Fig. 100. Induction of a secondary embryo obtained by implantation of a piece of boiled human thyroid gland into the blastocoele of an early gastrula of Triturus. Notice neural tube, notochord and otocysts in *b*. (From Holtfreter, '34b.)

two experimental modifications (Holtfreter, '33e): (1) the heat-killed tissues were sandwiched between two sheets of isolated prospective epidermis from an early gastrula; (2) pieces of prospective epidermis were loosely placed upon the dead tissues. In both cases, voluminous inductions were obtained in the explants representing brainlike forma-

tions (Fig. 101) which were sometimes accompanied by mesenchyme, melanophores, or an olfactory placode.

Graded inactivation of neural inductors by heat was as a rule expressed in three interrelated phenomena: relative frequency, volume, and organological complexity of the induced structures. If large enough, the induced cell mass could organize itself into brain and sense organs. Very small masses formed nondescript neural cell aggregates or vesicles. Finally, there were intermediary cell types between epidermis and neural tissue known as "neuroid" or "palisade" structures which were produced by the weakest inductors (Holtfreter, '33c, '34a;

DISTRIBUTION OF INDUCING AGENTS IN THE ANIMAL KINGDOM

It has been shown that inductions are possible in combinations of tissues from different species or orders (p. 263). It was known, furthermore, that the inducing capacity of at least some tissues is retained in

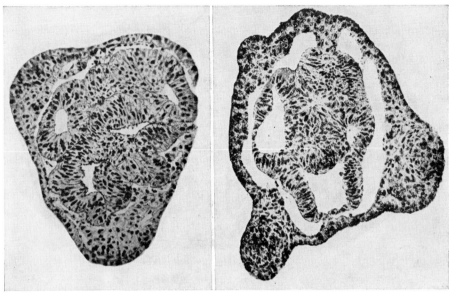

Fig. 101.   Fig. 102.

Fig. 101. Induction of neural structures, obtained by placing a piece of prospective epidermis of the early medullary plate into the blastocoele of an early gastrula of Triturus (from Holtfreter, '33e).

Fig. 102. Neural differentiations in fused pieces of prospective ectoderm of middle gastrulae of *Amblystoma punctatum*, reared (without inductor) in salt solution (from Barth, '41).

Needham, Waddington and Needham, '34). It seems that the size of the induced area plays a more important role in determining the degree of complexity of the induced structure than does any special property of the inductor (see p. 278).

The following conclusions may be drawn: a chemical stimulus which is relatively stable in extreme temperatures and in fat solvents, rather than mere physical stimulation, is instrumental in neural induction. Heating, freezing and drying abolish the mesodermizing but not the neuralizing inductivity. Furthermore, neuralizing agents are present in all germ layers but are normally inactive in the ectoderm and entoderm, either because they cannot diffuse out while these tissues are alive (Holtfreter, '33e; Toivonen, '40) or, more likely, because they occur there in a physically masked, or chemically bound form (Needham, Waddington and Needham, '34) and are liberated only after the cells are killed.

stages in which the ectoderm is no longer competent to react to them. For instance, brain from a swimming larva (Mangold, '29b) and somites and notochord from tailbud stages (Holtfreter, '33c, '36) proved to be inductors. Woerdeman ('33b) reported that even skeletal muscle and sarcoma from adult rat, chick and man can neuralize gastrula ectoderm. Holtfreter ('34b) made an extensive study of the inducing capacity of a variety of tissues from larval and adult organisms. Fragments from practically every organ or tissue from various amphibians, reptiles, birds and mammals, including man, were inductive (Figs. 100, 103, 104). The results were about the same whether the grafts were fresh, or had been dried, or briefly exposed to higher temperatures. Likewise active were cell-free coagulated homogenates from amphibian and chick embryos and from Daphnia and beef liver. Most tissues tended to induce neural structures with cephalic characteristics, while others (e.g., liver, kid-

Fig. 103.   Fig. 104.

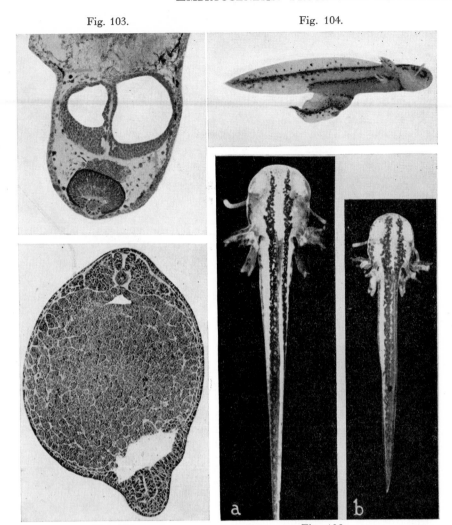

Fig. 105.   Fig. 106.

Fig. 103. Induction of symmetrical brain parts and eye by mouse kidney, boiled for 15 minutes and implanted in the blastocoele of an early gastrula of Triturus (from Chuang, '39).

Fig. 104. Induction of tail in posterior trunk region of Triturus, obtained by implantation of mouse kidney which had been killed by dipping briefly in boiled water (from Chuang, '39).

Fig. 105. Induction of a neural tube by 3,4-benzpyrene, using coagulated egg albumen as a carrier. Axial organs of host above, and induced neural tube adjacent to transplant below. (From Needham, '42, after Waddington.)

Fig. 106. Heteroplastic induction of balancer. a, Larva of *Triturus cristatus*. The prospective head epidermis on the right side had been replaced in the early gastrula by prospective belly epidermis of *Triturus taeniatus*. The right balancer induced in the transplant by underlying *T. cristatus* structures is of *T. taeniatus* type. Notice its size, shape, direction of outgrowth, absence of terminal club. b, Normal larva of *Triturus taeniatus*, for comparison. (From Rotmann, '35a.)

ney, thyroid of some mammals) induced preferentially spinocaudal structures. Less conspicuous and complex inductions were obtained with grafted tissues from various invertebrates. Inactive were agar, starch, glycogen, wax, charcoal.

Similar results were obtained by Needham, Waddington and Needham ('34) and Wehmeier ('34) on urodeles, and by Raunich ('42b) on anurans. The implantation of plant tissues (cambium, root tip) produced merely ectodermal thickenings (Ragosina, '37; Toivonen, '38); but Brachet ('43, '50) obtained neuralizations by applying nucleoprotein fractions from yeast and wheat embryos.

DIFFERENCES IN INDUCTIVITY OF ADULT TISSUES

The phenomenon that some adult tissues imitate the action of normal head inductors and others that of trunk-tail inductors was investigated further by Chuang ('38, '39), who used mouse kidney and Triturus liver as inductors, testing their effects both on whole Triturus gastrulae and on isolated gastrula ectoderm which served as a jacket for the grafts (Figs. 93–96, 103, 104).

Table 14 shows that, whereas Triturus liver induced head as well as trunk-tail structures in both experimental series, mouse

into two groups: liver, thymus and kidney of certain animals induced almost exclusively "archencephalic" structures* (tel- and diencephalon with eyes, nose, balancers), whereas the kidneys of other animals acted as "deuterencephalic" (rhombencephalon, otocysts) and spinocaudal inductors. Undoubtedly, regional influences of the host complicate the situation. However, even if due allowance is made for this factor, differences of different organs with respect to their archencephalic and spinocaudal inductivities are uncontestable. Yet no relationship of a general kind can be established between the histological type of certain adult organs

TABLE 14. *Inductive Specificity of Fresh Mouse Kidney and Triturus Liver (from Chuang, '39)*

GRAFT	NO. OF CASES	RESULTS IN PERCENTAGE								
		BRAIN	NOSE	EYE	BAL- ANCER	EAR VESICLE	TAIL	MUSCLE	NOTO- CHORD	PRO- NEPHROS
In Explants										
Kidney	97	100	44.3	23.7	11.3	23.7	—	—	—	—
Liver	63	82.5	17.4	6.3	19.0	68.4	41.2	52.6	44.4	—
In Whole Gastrulae										
Kidney	186	97.8	9.1	9.6	8.6	63.9	39.7	27.9	1.07	13.9
Liver	198	73.2	13.6	9.6	9.0	46.4	47.0	31.3	13.6	13.6

kidney would do so only when grafted into a whole gastrula but confined itself to purely ectodermal cephalic structures when enclosed in isolated ectoderm. This difference can be explained by assuming that mouse kidney is unable to induce mesodermal structures out of ectoderm, but can induce them from the mesoderm which is available in whole embryos. Triturus liver, on the other hand, can induce mesodermal trunk structures from either ectoderm or mesoderm. These results show that differences do exist in the effect-specificity of adult organs. In agreement with the data on heat-treated embryonic tissues, Chuang ('39, '40) found that in both kidney and liver the mesodermizing capacity is much more readily abolished by boiling water (within two seconds) than is the neuralizing capacity (still present after one hour of boiling, Fig. 103). This indicates the presence of different inducing factors which are possibly similar to those present in embryonic inductors.

Inductor-specific differences were brought out even more strikingly in the experiments of Toivonen ('40), who tested various adult vertebrate tissues which were first treated with 70 per cent alcohol and then implanted in whole Triturus gastrulae. The tissues fall

(such as liver or kidney) and the type of their inductions. For instance, the alcohol-treated kidney of the viper induced archencephalic structures, that of the guinea pig spinocaudal structures and that of the beef induced both (Toivonen, '40; Toivonen and Kuusi, '48). If one compares these results with those of Holtfreter ('34b), Chuang ('39) and Hama ('44) on the inductivity of liver and kidney from various species, it becomes even more difficult to draw general conclusions as to the inductive specificity of adult tissues. In addition to species differences, such factors as age (Rotmann, '42) and starvation (Toivonen, '51) of the donor animal, as well as pretreatment of the inducing material and the competence condition of the reacting tissue, influence the results. This applies not only to such complex inductions as head and trunk structures but also to single tissues such as a free lens, which can be induced by a variety of fresh or killed embryonic and adult tissues.

* A terminological inconsistency should be pointed out: Lehmann ('42b) introduced the terms "archencephalic" and "deuterencephalic" as designations of parts of the brain, whereas Toivonen and others use them to designate different regions of the head, including non-neural structures.

ATTEMPTS TO ISOLATE AND IDENTIFY THE INDUCTIVE AGENTS

Several groups of workers set out to subject embryonic amphibian tissues and inductive adult organs to various extraction methods in the hope that the active agents could be isolated and chemically identified. In addition, a large number of well characterized chemical compounds were tested. The extracts and substances were usually included in supporting material, such as agar or albumen, which was then grafted into the blastocoele cavity of early urodele gastrulae. Needham ('42) and Brachet ('45) have discussed these experiments extensively. We shall confine ourselves to some pertinent points.

At the beginning, we wish to emphasize the methodological difficulties involved in this kind of investigation. They arise mainly from the fact that the ectoderm and entoderm of the gastrula contain neuralizing agents in a masked form which can be liberated or activated by practically any treatment that kills the tissue. The implanted tissue or substance may be toxic and kill surrounding host cells which, in turn, would release their liberated agents into the adjacent, non-injured ectoderm (Barth and Graff, '38; Okada, '38; "relay mechanism," Holtfreter, '45b). Furthermore, as Brachet points out, implanted dead or adult tissue is subject to degradations by the enzyme systems of the host. For these reasons, it is impossible, in principle, to obtain conclusive direct evidence that any of the tissues or substances which were implanted contains, or is identical with, the neuralizing agent of the living archenteron roof.

The following "inductors" operate probably indirectly ("relay"), by cytolyzing host tissue: inorganic substances, such as silica and kaolin (Okada, '38), cephalin and digitonin (Barth and Graff, '38; Barth, '39). Likewise methylene blue, claimed by Waddington, Needham and Brachet ('36) and by Beatty, deJong and Zielinski ('39) to have neuralizing effects, was found to be effective only in toxic concentrations (Holtfreter, '45b).* This was true also of sulfhydryl compounds for which Brachet and Rapkine ('39) claimed a neuralizing activity. As to the inductivity of thiocyanate (Ranzi and Tamini, '39), the evidence suggests that the observed neuralizations were either due to a toxicity of the chemical or to contamination of the ectoderm with mesoderm. The much-

discussed question whether or not glycogen can induce is still open; very likely, the positive cases reported can be attributed to impurities of some glycogen preparations.

The Cambridge workers contended that the naturally occurring neural inductor ("evocator") is a *steroid compound*. This claim was based on the effectiveness of the unsaponifiable fraction of ether extracts from embryos and adult tissues, and furthermore, on the effectiveness of a variety of chemically identified steroids (see Fig. 105; for references, see Waddington, '40; Needham, '42). Concerning the first point, the evidence is not very striking with respect to the frequency and the histological type of inductions observed. Unfortunately, control experiments showed that coagulated egg albumen, which usually served as carrier, could by itself induce similar palisade structures and neuroid cell aggregations, which further weakens the case. Fischer ('35) and H. Lehmann ('38) found the unsaponifiable fraction to be inactive when freed from acids and salts, but the saponifiable fraction, containing fatty acids, to be strongly active. This was confirmed by Barth and Graff ('38) and Toivonen ('49, '50), who found, furthermore, that the extracted residues were far more active than their ether extracts. The second point, the effectiveness of chemically identified polycyclic hydrocarbons, most of which had been prepared synthetically (Waddington, '38a), deserves more serious consideration. Some of these compounds are known as estrogenic, others as carcinogenic agents; however, some otherwise biologically inactive substances did induce as well, and there was no parallelism between the neurogenic and the estrogenic or carcinogenic activity of these compounds.

Experiments of Shen ('39) with a water-soluble polycyclic hydrocarbon (a carcinogen) have been used as the main argument in support of the steroid nature of the normal neural evocator. The substance, in very low doses, was mixed with crystalline albumen which was then implanted into the blastocoele. The alleged correlation between dosage and percentage of inductions is not clear: a peak for neural inductions seems to be at a concentration of 0.0125γ,† while the percentage of neuroid structures simply increases with decreasing dosage.

The effectiveness of very low concentrations of this hydrocarbon was taken by Waddington ('40) and Needham ('42) as an

---

* Pasteels ('51) reports that data of his own do not support the latter conclusion.

† This peak has statistically little significance (chi square test).

indication that it has a direct effect, similar to that of the normal neural inductor, rather than a "relay" effect. However, Shen did observe necrotic cells in all of his experimental series. Furthermore, as has been pointed out by Needham himself ('39, '42) and by Brachet ('45), some substances, at extremely low concentrations, may be comparatively more toxic, diffusible, or biologically active than others. It appears, therefore, that the questions of whether polycyclic hydrocarbons act directly or indirectly and whether such substances are at all involved in normal neural induction cannot yet be answered.

The same uncertainty seems to apply to *fatty acids* and *nucleic acids*. Their neuralizing action was on the whole more pronounced than that of steroids. Since such entirely different substances as purified fatty acids from plants (e.g., oleic acid) or animals (e.g., muscle adenylic acid), and completely lipid-free nucleoproteins and nucleotides were equally effective, the investigators (Fischer and collaborators, '33, '35; H. Lehmann, '38) refrained from identifying any of them with the hypothetical neuralizing agent of normal development and ascribed their common effect to an unspecified "acid stimulus." Possible cytolytic effects of the substances used have not been considered by these workers, although they have been demonstrated (Holtfreter, '45b; Brachet, '49). A relay-effect of the "acid stimulus" is therefore within the range of possibility.

FRACTIONATION OF TISSUE EXTRACTS

One might hope to break the deadlock by comparing the activities of various tissue extracts, obtained by different fractionation methods, with the inductive capacity of the residues. The pioneering experiments were done by Toivonen and Kuusi ('48) and Toivonen ('49, '50), who analyzed the specific inductive capacities of guinea pig liver ("archencephalic inductor") and kidney ("spinocaudal inductor") by testing a great variety of fractions of these tissues obtained by extraction with alcohol and petroleum ether, dialysis, treatment with salt solutions, and heat treatment. All implants were made in whole Triturus embryos. The authors suggest that there exist two qualitatively different inducing substances, an archencephalic agent which is dialyzable, thermostable and ether-soluble, and a spinocaudal agent which is thermolabile and not ex-

tractable in ether. Kuusi ('51) continued the analysis of the same tissues, testing tissue homogenates, isolated nuclei, protein fractions, cytoplasmic granules, ribonuclease-treated homogenate, formol-treated tissue and others. The capacity for spinocaudal inductions was not associated with cytoplasmic granules or with extracted nucleoproteins but seemed to be linked with protein and was easily lost by fractionation procedures. The capacity for archencephalic inductions seemed to be rather stable. However, no clear-cut chemical separation of the two hypothetical agents has been obtained.

In order to avoid the interference of regional host effects, Yamada (personal communication) used isolated gastrula ectoderm as the reacting material. He found that a 0.14 M sodium chloride extract (supernatant) of guinea pig kidney induces somites and spinal cord. The extract after heat treatment, and an RNA-protein fraction isolated from the original extract, induced archencephalic structures. DNA-protein of the same tissue gave also archencephalic inductions. The results are interpreted in terms of a "dorsalizing" and a "caudalizing" factor.

Although the techniques employed by these workers were not yet adequate for a chemical characterization of the different agents, this type of experiment seems to be a particularly promising approach to the problem of induction.

RELATION BETWEEN INDUCTION AND NUCLEIC ACIDS

Brachet ('45) has marshalled a variety of data in support of his contention that nucleic acids, and particularly RNA found in small granules of the cytoplasm, are responsible for inductions by both normal and abnormal inductors.

In sectioned amphibian embryos stained with pyronin or toluidine blue, Brachet ('40, '43) found an abundance of basophilic cytoplasmic elements whose stainability was lost after treatment with ribonuclease, suggesting that the basophilia was due mainly* to the presence of RNA. Microscopic study of the distribution of basophilic elements in amphibian embryos showed a high concentration in the upper blastoporal lip which decreased during invagination of this mate-

* Toluidine blue, unless applied within a strongly acid range, stains proteins in addition to nucleic acid (Herrmann, Nicholas, and Boricious, '50). Brachet does not mention having controlled the *p*H.

rial.* A simultaneous increase in stainable elements in the medullary plate suggested a transfer of RNA from the inductor to the neural plate. Later, basophilia was again strong in the notochord, decreasing in the mesoderm in a ventral direction, but the epidermis contained these granules as well.† Exact quantitative determinations of this distribution pattern have not been made.

Using the ultracentrifuge, Brachet and co-workers ('40, '42, '44) isolated from homogenized embryonic and adult tissues small cytoplasmic granules which contained all or most of the RNA, besides phosphatides, proteins with —SH groups, and certain enzymes which varied with the type of tissue. These granules which were assumed to be identical with the basophilic elements in sections proved to be inductive when applied as coagulated grafts, as was also tobacco mosaic virus. Treatment of organizer tissue, adult organs, or tobacco mosaic virus with ribonuclease resulted in a conspicuous decrease or loss of their inductive capacity. All these data suggested that either RNA or its nucleotides are instrumental in normal and experimental neuralization.

Persuasive as these data may appear, they are subject to several objections which reduce their conclusiveness. (1) The basophilic elements of the amphibian embryo occur over much wider ranges of tissues and developmental stages than are normally involved in induction. Their distribution seems to reflect rates of general metabolic activity rather than inductive activity. (2) The scanty histological evidence offered by Brachet ('45) indicates that the implanted granules are much less effective inductors than are whole tissues. Kuusi ('51) found that the isolated granules from guinea pig liver and kidney are not more potent than are the cell residues, or the supernatant of the homogenates. Contrary to Brachet, Kuusi did not find any relationship between the RNA content of the various preparations

and their inductive capacity. The results obtained with tissues that had been hydrolyzed with crystalline ribonuclease led Kuusi to the conclusion that this treatment fails to reduce their inductivity both in a quantitative and in a qualitative sense. (3) Doubts about a correlation between RNA content and inductivity of a graft are strengthened by the observation of Toivonen and Kuusi ('48) that *proteolytic* enzymes practically inactivate inductive tissues. (4) Different preparations of crystalline ribonuclease contain proteolytic enzymes (Cohen, '44; McDonald, '48), and it appears that the preparations used by Brachet have not been assayed for such impurities; on the other hand, its efficiency in removing the RNA present in isolated granules or in tobacco mosaic virus has been questioned (Loring, '42; Claude, '44). (5) Observations of Brachet himself ('49) make it likely that the neuralizing activity of pure nucleic acids and nucleotides is due to a relay mechanism because these substances in low concentrations cytolyze ectoderm explants of the axolotl.

The above studies have the merit of drawing attention to the possible significance of cytoplasmic granules in morphogenetic processes, but they do not settle the problem of the chemical nature of the neuralizing agent in favor of nucleic acids or any of the other components of the basophilic elements.

NEURALIZATION IN RESPONSE TO A TRANSIENT CELL INJURY

A new approach to the analysis of induction was opened by the discovery of Barth ('41) that the isolated ectoderm of *A. punctatum*, in contrast to the ectoderm of other species, can form neural structures in the absence of a tangible inductor, namely when reared in standard solution (Fig. 102). Holtfreter ('44b) confirmed this result. He showed that it is correlated with cellular disaggregation of the explant, the degree of disaggregation being proportional to that of subsequent neuralization. Obviously, *A. punctatum* is more susceptible than other urodeles to ordinary standard solution which hitherto had been considered as "neutral" with regard to factors that direct cell determination. One could anticipate that if ectoderm of *A. punctatum* were cultured in a less injurious medium it would become epidermal, and that the ectoderm of other species, for which standard solution is not injurious, could be neuralized if it would undergo a transient disaggregation. Subse-

---

* Pasteels ('49b) found a steady increase of basophilic granules in the prechordal mesoderm.

† In late gastrulae and neurulae of *T. alpestris*, Cagianut ('49) found pyronin-stainable cell structures distributed in both the neural plate and the archenteron roof along a cephalocaudal gradient and diminishing in density toward the ventral regions of the ectoderm and mesoderm. These structures consisted mainly of perinuclear and cortical caps, and of long filaments such as Brachet ('40, '43) has already described. It appears rather hazardous to identify these gross structures with the granules of various sizes that have been isolated from centrifuged homogenates.

quent experiments on *A. punctatum* and *T. torosus* verified this assumption (Holtfreter, '45b, '47b).

Cellular adhesion and integrity of the cell membrane in isolated amphibian tissues depend largely on the *p*H and the presence of an adequate amount of calcium ions in the isotonic salt solution. A lowering of *p*H to 4.5 or the addition of glucose, sucrose or histone to the culture medium usually resulted in an epidermal differentiation of *A. punctatum* explants, probably owing to a fortification of the cell membrane. On the contrary, neural differentiation was obtained in gastrula ectoderm of *T. torosus* which had been briefly treated with inorganic acids, or alkali, alcohol, distilled water, or calcium-free standard solution. These agents are known to increase cell permeability; they cause swelling and ameboid dispersal of the cells, and finally cytolysis when applied for longer periods. Reintegration of the dispersed cells was produced by their transfer to a neutral balanced medium. The closer the cells were brought to the brink of death, the more pronounced was their tendency to become neural. Yamada ('50a) obtained similar neuralizations in isolated ectoderm of *T. pyrrhogaster* by exposing it briefly to ammonia.

In the above experiments the prospective epidermal and medullary areas of the gastrula reacted alike. Any portion of the ectoderm could form brain-like structures associated with olfactory placodes, rudimentary eyes, mesenchyme and pigment cells. Since this pattern of cephalic structures developed in the absence of a structured inductor and of any determination field of the host, it must have arisen by self-organization of the stimulated explants. The absence of a locally applied inductor expressed itself in the fact that the brain diverticula were not bilaterally symmetrical but multiple formations; they could be associated with as many as twelve olfactory placodes in one explant.

It was thought at first that we were dealing once more with a "relay" mechanism, killed cells acting as inductors for the intact cells. If this were the case, then all further progress would have been stalled. However, neuralization was also observed in the absence of any permanently damaged or dying cells (Holtfreter, '47b). Obviously, the external stimulus liberated the inductive agent within the reacting cells themselves by causing initial and reversible steps of cytolysis. The similarity between this process in living

cells and the "unmasking" of the neuralizing agent in killed cells is underlined by the fact that in either case many different injurious treatments can cause this liberation. The essential and common mechanism by which the cytolytic agents initiate neuralization of the explants seems to be: (1) increase of permeability of the cell membrane; (2) flooding of the cytoplasm with water and the electrolytes of standard solution; (3) dissociations and, after recovery from the shock, new combinations of certain cytoplasmic compounds whose specific synthetic activity would shift differentiation from epidermal to neural. It is unlikely that the initial steps of this mechanism occur in normal development also.

Some of the inductive effects discussed above can conceivably be reinterpreted in the light of these experiments. For instance, neuralization by methylene blue, organic acids, water-soluble carcinogens or sulfhydryl compounds could be due to a reversible cell injury rather than to a relay mechanism. The mechanism by which certain carcinogens exert their neuralizing effect may be similar to the unmasking effect of subcytolytic agents. Waddington and Goodhart ('49) found that such a hydrocarbon becomes selectively fixed to the large granular cell inclusions (lipochondria) which may entail the liberation of the neurogenic factor.

The fact that an abnormally high water imbibition of the cell, caused by unspecific injurious agents, is apparently sufficient to elicit neuralization demonstrates once more the futility of the attempts to identify any of the experimentally applied chemicals with the normal neuralizing factor. On the other hand, our conviction is strengthened that the key to an understanding of the induction phenomena is to be sought in the reacting cells rather than in the inductors. This supposition led to a comparative study of some cytological phenomena in differentiating epidermal and neural cells.

CELLULAR POLARITY, MOTILITY AND ADHESIVENESS AS RELATED TO INDUCTION

The recognition of the polar structure of early embryonic cells is of fundamental importance for an understanding of neural induction. The entire surface of the embryo is coated with a protective film having a low permeability. Cellular motility is mainly confined to the inner uncoated surface, which becomes the ameboid anterior pole when a cell migrates or exhibits "outgrowth." Inductive agents, whether represented by formed inductors or by injurious aqueous media, act only when applied to the uncoated cell surfaces or after the coat has been dissolved (Holtfreter, '43a, '48b).

As a consequence of neural induction, ectodermal cells acquire the tendencies (1) to elongate reversibly into cylindrical bodies

uptake, suggested by Glaser ('14, '16), do not control the neurulation process (Brown, Hamburger and Schmitt, '41).

Determination of a cell to become a neuron is immediately reflected in new tendencies for adhesiveness and ameboid motility (Holtfreter, '47a). An isolated Rohon-Beard neuroblast adopts a pear shape, its anterior pole projecting mobile filopodia into the liquid medium and its tapering posterior pole

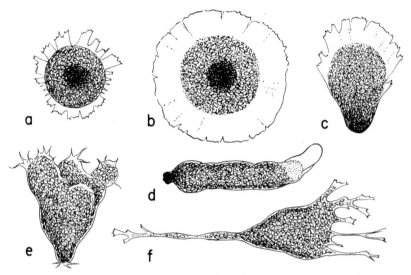

Fig. 107. Kinetic tendencies of isolated embryonic cells. *a, b, c*, Ectodermal cells, determined to become epidermis, exhibit flattening (epiboly) over the substrate; *d*, an isolated cell of the medullary plate elongates into a cylindrical body; *e, f*, isolated neuroblasts form dendritic processes. (After Holtfreter, '48b.)

(Fig. 107*d*), (2) to move from the periphery into the depth, (3) to detach themselves from non-neural cells. The same three tendencies appear in other induced ectodermal structures (lens, otocyst, pituitary, placodes). By contrast, ectoderm cells which have not received inductive stimuli and are destined to form epidermis become spherical when floating in a culture medium; they flatten out when provided with a proper surface of contact, and they do not invaginate (Holtfreter, '47a, '48b; see Fig. 107*a,b*). These different kinetic tendencies are due to forces inherent in each isolated cell and they are the first cytological indication that induction has occurred. According to the measurements of Gillette ('44) these kinetic properties are instrumental in normal development: the medullary plate arises as the result of a proximodistal elongation and corresponding contraction of the outer surface of the dorsal ectoderm cells, while the prospective epidermis cells undergo a compensatory flattening. Volume changes by differential water

having a pronounced adhesiveness (Fig. 107*e,f*). Given an appropriate contact surface, a neuroblast may migrate ameba-fashion, but if the cell body remains attached, the advancing ameboid projections are spun out to form branching processes, and the configuration of a dendritic neuron is obtained (Harrison, '10).

In a similar way, the morphogenesis of other cell types, their properties of aggregation or dispersal, and the direction of their movements, are largely determined by their inherent axial organization. Stage-specific and tissue-specific differences of motility and adhesiveness are instrumental not only in cyto-differentiation but also in organ formation. Holtfreter ('46a, '48b) has suggested that shape and kinetic properties of embryonic cells result primarily from local and temporal variations of the expansibility of the cell membrane, reflecting changes in the composition and molecular arrangement of this structure which may be considered as being essentially an organized lipo-protein film subject to various states of hydration. He assumed furthermore that induction and cytological determination in general involve the elaboration of new tissue-specific compounds, some of which become integrated localized elements of the cell membrane and are thus responsible for the different new types of cellular shape, motility, selective adhesiveness, and metabolism. The problem of how, and in which parts of the cell, these specific morphogenetic changes originate is a matter of conjecture (see discussion below).

GENERAL CONSIDERATIONS

Before entering into a discussion of some general notions on amphibian embryogenesis, we should point out that our preceding presentation is somewhat unbalanced: much emphasis has been placed upon the phenomenon of induction, but other, equally important principles of organogenesis have not received their due share of consideration. We did stress the importance of morphogenetic movements and of self-organization, but we have neglected such aspects as selective cell adhesion; structural, mechanical, hydrostatic factors of development; space-time patterns of physiological processes and identified substances; problems of energy metabolism; phenomena of differential growth; genetic and comparative-embryological considerations. For information on these latter aspects, which are in many ways interconnected with the problems dealt with above, the reader is referred to other chapters of this book.

In the following discussion our attention shall be mainly focussed upon the concepts of embryonic fields and gradients which have played a predominant role in the analysis of induction, and of organogenesis in general.

GENERAL CHARACTERISTICS OF INDUCTION PHENOMENA

Since the term "induction" has sometimes been used in a loose way, let us try to circumscribe it for our present purposes. Unlike hormones, inductive stimuli operate only at certain stages, as a rule, during early development, and they are normally ineffective unless there is an intimate contact between inducing and reacting tissues. The effects of the inductive tissues are undeniable, since in their absence none of the ectodermal and probably few of the mesodermal differentiations would ever arise. Once stimulated, the cells proceed along their new course of differentiation independently of a continued application of the inducing stimulus. The newly acquired characteristics are self-maintaining and handed on to subsequent cell generations. In this respect, too, the inductive stimuli differ from hormones which must be applied continuously in order to sustain the differentiations initiated by them (for further discussion of these and related problems, see Medawar, '47).

Thus, normally, "inductors" are living and as a rule embryonic tissues which determine the *cytological* fate of the reacting, adjacent cells. This inauguration of a new trend of differentiation is almost invariably associated with new trends of *kinetic* activities of the induced cells, such as invaginations, delaminations, new rates of cell division, etc. But kinetic activities may arise independently of inductive stimuli, as for instance when the blastoporal rim invaginates into the blastocoele, or when certain cells establish an epithelium in response to a favorable non-specific substratum. In the same sense, the transformation of cuboidal into temporarily elongated cells, which is practically always associated with ectodermal inductions (medullary plate, lens and other placodes: Ruffini, '25; Lehmann, '29; McKeehan, '51), merely indicates that these cells proceed to invaginate. The invaginating cells of the blastoporal lip likewise stretch into long bodies; their change of shape is not due to an inducing substratum but to an inherent migration tendency of these cells (Holtfreter, '44a). Columnar cell elongations also appear frequently in intestinal epithelia and their glandular evaginations. Therefore, we cannot subscribe to the idea that there is necessarily a causal relationship between cell elongation and induction mediated by attracting and orienting molecular forces acting across the inductive contact surface (Weiss, '47, '50).

Hence, when speaking of induction, emphasis should be placed upon the "material" and irreversible rather than upon the "dynamic" and temporary cellular changes (Vogt, '23–'24) following this kind of stimulation. In the terms of Weiss ('39), the latter are merely "modulations," that is, reversible manifestations of one among a variety of possible cellular adaptations, the range of which is determined genetically and often with the cooperation of inductors. Therefore, we are reluctant to call the epithelial perforations produced by contact action in the mouth, pharynx and anus regions "inductions," just as one would hesitate to apply this term to the secondary formative effects of the archenteron roof upon the bilaterality of the neural system, or to the accumulation of limb blastema cells following amputation or the insertion of a graft. The kinetic response of cells to certain stimuli in itself does not indicate the presence of inductive stimuli (see inflammatory reactions). Likewise, to extend the term "induction" to the effects of external factors upon the rate of tissue growth (as opposed to cell determination) would result in a confusion in terminology.

There is no doubt that in the course of development new kinds of specific inductors come into play. They may involve the derivatives of all three germ layers, and these primordia may cooperate so as to form synergistic "inductor systems." The different tissue components of such a system may act simultaneously or in succession but they must be arranged in a typical pattern in order to induce a single structure, such as a typical neural tube or an acoustic organ. At this point, we should remind the reader that the outcome of an induction is not only determined by the specific properties of the different inductors but just as much by those of the stimulated cells. The reaction potencies of the latter were found to be limited by the following inherent factors: genetic potentialities, stage-specificity, and tissue-specificity. The two independent sets of properties, namely those of the inductors and those of the reacting cells, must be interlocked in space and time in order to insure normal development. This is principally achieved by directed cellular mass-movements.

COMMENTS ON THE TRANSMISSION OF INDUCTIVE STIMULI

Although we can no longer doubt that induction involves some sort of an activating chemical mechanism, we really do not know the chemical nature and the mode of transmission of these stimuli.

Schmitt ('41) drew attention to the possibility that the columnar shape of the neural plate cells might result from a molecular zipper effect operating by means of dehydrating agents between the adjoining surfaces of these cells. This interpretation has become improbable in view of the fact mentioned above that isolated medullary cells can elongate reversibly without any surface of contact. But Schmitt applied considerations of molecular surface interactions also to the problem of the inductive mechanism, and other workers have speculated along similar lines.

On the basis of physicochemical models, Needham ('42, p. 289) suggested that induction may not actually involve the transmission of a chemical agent but may be primarily a matter of polar orientation and attraction of long-chain molecules at the inductor-facing side of the reacting cell; this effect might reach into the deeper zones of the cell, creating an increasing complexity of structuration which would lead to neural differentiation. Holtfreter ('44b) also believed that interfacial attraction forces and surface adsorptions might be instrumental in the induction process. Weiss ('47, '49a, b, '50) has elaborated and expanded the concept of intercellular surface actions, making it part of a general hypothesis on the role of "molecular ecology" in morphogenesis. We cannot discuss here the full background and the ramifications of this highly interesting hypothesis but shall deal only with its application to induction.

The concept of "molecular ecology" is stated by the author as follows: "Each cell and organized cell part (nucleus, chromosome, etc.) consists of an array of molecular species whose densities, distribution, arrangement and groupings are determined by their mutual dependencies and interactions as well as by the physical conditions of the space they occupy. These species range from the elementary inorganic compounds to the most complex 'key' species characteristic of a given cell. Chemical segregation and localization within the cell result from free molecular interplay, as only groups of elements compatible with one another and with their environment can form durable unions. . . . Among the principal segregative factors of molecular mixtures are interfaces. Interfacial forces between partly immiscible molecular populations concentrate certain selected molecular species of the interior along the border. By their surface positions, these border species acquire power over the further behavior of the enclosed system. . . . Various considerations suggest that in biological systems fixation of a given molecular species in a surface is not due solely to unspecific factors, such as surface tensions, adsorption, etc., but that in addition, highly selective chemical affinities are involved. These may be based on the steric interlocking of characteristically shaped end groups of the surface molecules of adjacent systems" (Weiss, '49b, p. 476).

The highly specific molecular configurations at the cell surface are thought to play a particularly important role in differentiation, tissue affinities and embryonic induction. Assuming that the cell surfaces of inductive tissue are characterized by specific, oriented end groups, "the molecular surface film of the inducing layer (e.g., retina) would selectively attract key molecules of complementary or otherwise conforming configuration from the interior of the cells of the adjacent layer (e.g., epidermis) and thus decide the further differentiation of these cells" (Weiss, '49b, p. 478). The incorporation of certain key molecules in the surface would result in the competitive removal of others from the surface, and this redistribution would initiate a specific trend of differentiation within the reacting cell. The inductor itself would operate only on the interface of inducing and reacting tissue by creating on the surface of the latter a "steric conformance, i.e., complementary spatial configurations between molecules or certain exposed atomic groups of them enabling them to conjugate in key-lock fashion" (Weiss, '47, p. 256).

A diffusion of molecules from the inducing cells to the interior of the reacting cells is not considered as an alternative mechanism. Since attempts to test the diffusibility of inductive agents of normal inductors by the use of separating membranes of known porosity have failed so far (Brachet, '50; McKeehan, '51), the old assumption that under normal conditions close contact between inducing and reacting cells is necessary, remains unchallenged.*

The above concept of Weiss meets with serious difficulties when we consider that freely floating ectodermal explants can be neuralized by different liquid media which have no fixed molecular configuration. This can occur in the absence of any disintegrating cells (Holtfreter, '47b). Consequently, there is no likelihood that, as Weiss ('49a) suggests, an "inductive protein film" might become adsorbed at the surface of the floating explant. Furthermore, it is difficult to apply this hypothesis to the following observations: transformation of noninductors, such as ectoderm or entoderm, into neural inductors by different killing procedures;

* Very recently, Niu and Twitty ('53) demonstrated that the inductive factors of living tissues are indeed diffusible. Ectoderm explants differentiated into neural and mesodermal tissues through the application of the salt solution in which pieces of embryonic inductors had previously been cultured.

the neuralizing capacity of such diverse substrata as the normal archenteron roof, adult organs of all sorts and their cell-free extracts. It can hardly be assumed that all of them possess the same specific molecular surface pattern to account for their common neuralizing effects.

It appears, therefore, that the kinetic and differentiation tendencies of induced cells can arise independently of a molecule-orienting inductor and that the new cell properties are evoked by the introduction of non-oriented chemical agents rather than by the orienting or attracting forces of a specifically structured substratum. A cytotypical molecular configuration of the cell surface which seems to be very important for cell-specific motility, adhesion and differentiation, may very well arise secondarily and independently of a contact with other cells. Hence the burden of organizing the cellular constituents for cytodifferentiation would be carried by the reacting rather than by the inducing cells, a relationship similar to that between sperm and egg development or between a hormone and the differentiations initiated by it. We do not question the fact that polarity, shape, arrangement and movements of all embryonic and adult cells including cellular "modulations" (Weiss, '39) are subject to controlling factors of the environment. However, the latter are merely subsidiary and not determinative factors. Their presence enables the cells to manifest their inherent potentialities which have been previously determined by cell-inherent or extraneous factors.

THE QUESTION OF QUANTITATIVE VERSUS QUALITATIVE CHEMICAL DIFFERENCES BETWEEN THE DIFFERENT INDUCTORS

Once the chemical nature of inductive processes was established, there arose the question: how does the diversity of induced structures come about? This question is very complex, as may be deduced from the fact that histologically different primordia can induce the same kind of tissue, and that a single primordium can induce one structure in one germ layer and another one in another germ layer. In a simplifying fashion this problem has been reduced to the question of whether the stimuli of the different inductors vary in a quantitative or in a qualitative sense.

It should be realized that this question cannot be answered satisfactorily by any experiments with normal living inductors. The elucidation of this problem must wait until more is known about the chemical nature of the inducing agents, of their distribution in the embryo, and of their effects at different concentrations. At present, only more or less plausible assumptions can be made.

Quantitative Aspects. In connection with what will become evident from our later discussion, one may accept the view that differences in the size of the inductive substratum, or in the concentration of the inductive agent, can bring about different induction patterns. Thus the formation of a brain, in contrast to that of a spinal cord, is perhaps due in part, though certainly not entirely, to differences in the size of the stimulated area. It is conceivable, furthermore, that the different components of a synergistic "inductor system" release the same kind of inductive agent and that differential effects arise from differences in concentration, or in the spatial or temporal application of this agent. The fact that a lens normally arises in contact with the optic vesicle, but that, in the absence of an eye, a lens *can* be induced by various other tissues of the head (Ikeda, '38) may be ascribed to the existence of a widely extending gradient of the lens-inducing agent. Within this gradient, the optic vesicle would constitute the dominating center which normally prevents the appearance of accessory lenses. This consideration may be applicable to other structures, such as balancer or sucker.

There is no convincing evidence that quantitative variations of one and the same inductive agent can change its effect-specificity. It is true that progressively heat-inactivated neural inductors induce increasingly smaller and less organized formations. Nevertheless, the grafts remain neural inductors. This applies also to living inductors, such as the medullary plate: when increasingly smaller grafts of this tissue are used, the resulting inductions become smaller and less complex, but no shift to other types of inductions, as for instance mesodermal ones, occurs. When a neuralizing hydrocarbon was applied at different concentrations, the histological type of the inductions remained unchanged (Shen, '39).

Many attempts have been made to determine in what respect neuralizing grafts differ from lens-inducing grafts, but no definite conclusions could be drawn from these experiments. Pasteels ('40, '45) has interpreted the successive cephalocaudal disappearance of entomesodermal tissues in centrifuged or chemically treated embryos by assuming that the treatments produce a progressive lowering of a "morphogenetic potential" or, in other words, a depression of the concentration gradient of "organisine." This interpretation, however, still lacks a biochemical foundation. Similarly, attempts at ascribing the induction of neural tissue, as against neural crest derivatives, to different concentrations of "organisine" have remained questionable.

Altogether, it appears unlikely that merely quantitative differences of one type of agent can account for the diversity of the induction phenomena observed. The fact that of the wide range of reaction capabilities only one becomes manifest in a given case seems to indicate that at least some of the inductive stimuli differ from each other qualitatively and that they act selectively upon the array of multiple capabilities (competence).

Qualitative Aspects. When normal trunk inductor or certain adult tissues are devitalized by heat, cold, or drying, they lose abruptly their capacity of inducing mesodermal structures, but their neuralizing capacity is fully retained, if not increased, and only after prolonged boiling in water, or exposure to temperatures above 100°, does the latter decrease slowly and finally disappear.

On the other hand, treatment with various fat solvents does not appreciably reduce the mesodermizing but may strongly diminish the neuralizing capacities of adult tissues. Extraction with salt solutions or proteolytic enzymes nearly abolished both capacities. It appears, therefore, that some tissues contain simultaneously several kinds of inducing agents which can be eliminated selectively. On the basis of these and other findings, Holtfreter ('34a), Chuang ('39) and Toivonen ('40) have distinguished between a "neuralizing" and a "mesodermizing" agent.

In most instances when mesodermal tissues arose under the influence of either normal or atypical inductors, they did not appear singly but as an array of different tissues which could exhibit the characteristic pattern of a trunk or tail (Fig. 104). These experiments therefore could not determine whether or not the emergence of the different components of the chorda-mesoderm material is due to the action of different stimuli. However, the data obtained from the treatment of prospective mesoderm with lithium, urea, or ammonia have shown that some of these chemicals have a specific chordalizing and others a somite-producing effect. This seems to suggest that qualitative rather than quantitative differences in the inductive agents cause these divergent differentiations.

It should be pointed out that, so far, no purified tissue extracts or chemicals have been found which transform ectoderm into mesodermal tissues, and the claim that the mesodermizing agent may be represented by proteins and the neuralizing agent by nucleic acids (Brachet, '45, '50; Kuusi, '51) is based on inconclusive data.

Since it has not been possible to convert neuralizing tissues or chemicals into inductors for non-neural structures, e.g., for those of lens, ear or teeth, it is likely that the latter owe their emergence to the action of still other agents. No doubt, temporal and regional changes of competence are involved in the distribution of these secondary inductions, but it is questionable whether the principle of competence is sufficient to account for this regional diversity. Especially in cases of a two-step inductive mechanism, as is exemplified in the determination of teeth, branchial cartilage and pituitary, where the histogenetic effect of the first stimulus differs strikingly from that of the subsequent stimulus, it seems plausible to assume that successively different inductive agents are engaged.

THE "ORGANIZER" AND THE INDUCTIONS CONSIDERED AS MORPHOGENETIC FIELDS

The main difficulty in the analysis of induction arises from the fact that in most cases both the inductors and the induced material originally constitute "morphogenetic fields" which defy further breakdown into localizable subunits. We are dealing with complex dynamic systems and not with an assembly of independent fixed primordia. Let us briefly retrace these difficulties and then try to untangle them as far as it seems possible at this moment.

Field Characteristics of the "Organizer." The concept of "morphogenetic fields" (Spemann, '21a; Gurwitsch, '22; Weiss, '26, '39) emerged from the older concept of "harmonious-equipotential systems" (see Driesch, '29), which stressed the regulative capacities inherent in the majority of embryonic systems. However, the doctrinal formulations of Driesch barely did justice to the actual conditions in the embryo (see the critical discussion of Needham, '42, p.

119). A typical example of a morphogenetic field is the chorda-mesodermal area of the early gastrula: any isolated part of it tends to regulate into a well-proportioned axial system comprising considerably more kinds of tissues than would arise from this material in a normal embryo; parts of this field can be removed or interchanged without causing abnormal development; two chorda-mesoderm fields can be fused to form a single axial system. This means that the histological fate of any part of the field depends upon its topographic relationship to the other parts of the field. There are many other examples of such regulative fields both in vertebrate and invertebrate development (see Huxley and De Beer, '34; Weiss, '39).

We do not know how the chorda-mesoderm field comes into existence, but we do know that there are complicated determinative inter-relationships between the constituents of this field leading to its segregative differentiation. This poses the question of whether the determinative effects within the field involve principally the same physiological mechanisms as are operative in induction. The latter is characterized by a unidirectional action of inducing upon reacting tissues. In a morphogenetic field, however, there seem to exist reciprocal determinative actions which are not strictly confined to close contact-relationships. Furthermore, there was evidence that the ectoderm of the gastrula, itself not an inductor, contributes to the fixation of the boundaries of the chorda-mesoderm field. Contrary to the conditions in ordinary induction, this ectodermal effect would have to operate in a tangential direction and not between two superimposed cell layers.

These considerations are a challenge to find common principles which govern both the inductions and the self-organization which occur within a morphogenetic field.

It is a peculiar property of the chorda-mesoderm field ("trunk-tail organizer") and of the dorsal blastoporal lip proper ("head organizer") to induce adjacent tissues, particularly the overlying prospective ectoderm, to start new trends of differentiation. This capability of induction should not be included in a general definition of morphogenetic fields (see Waddington, '34; Weiss, '35). However, in vertebrate development, these two properties—self-organization of the primary inductors, and their regionally specific inductive capacities—are intricately associated.

It would be entirely misleading to conceive of the "organizer" material as of a kind of general manager which determines the destiny of the entire remainder of the embryo. Large portions of the embryo are not subject to its influence and, as has been pointed out already, the demarcation and invagination of the "organizer" itself are largely controlled by factors outside this area.

The "organizer" has suffered further devaluation. It is true that when part of this area is grafted into another gastrula it not only reorganizes itself into an incomplete axial system but it supplements its own differentiations by way of "assimilative induction," i.e., adjacent host cells (mainly mesoderm) become harmoniously incorporated into the system. Rather than considering this integrating action as a unique property of the "organizer," one may interpret it as just another demonstration of the characteristics of a morphogenetic field. The graft extends its field properties into the adjacent non-determined host cells, probably because it is merely a fragment of the "organizer" and as such in an "unsaturated" condition. In the unfragmented normal embryo there is no necessity for assimilative induction. There, the organizing effect of the "organizer" is confined to its own material, namely the chorda-mesoderm mantle.*

While the "organizer" becomes segregated into distinct tissue primordia it loses the regulation tendencies of a field and, at the same time, the capacity of assimilating experimentally supplied additional material into its system. Yet these primordia, let us say of an advanced neurula, retain strong and complex inductive powers. When experimentally confronted with gastrula ectoderm, they may induce a complete tail, or brain and sense organs. However, the structural pattern of these inductions has no relationship to that of the inductors; it is autonomously organized. Thus the derivatives of the "organizer" behave essentially like dead or adult tissues which can likewise induce highly complex organ systems but do not contribute to the patterning of their inductions.

Field Characteristics of the Inductions. It has been argued that there are two kinds of inductive agents: (1) "evocators" (Needham,

* Some difficulty of interpretation arises in the case of the induction of tail somites by the posterior part of the archenteron roof. This process might be considered as a rather belated assimilative field effect of the "organizer."

Waddington and Needham, '34), which are supposedly present in normal inductors as well as in dead tissues and certain chemicals, and which evoke merely amorphous cell masses; (2) "modulators" (Waddington, '40) or "eidogens" (Needham, '42), which are present in normal inductors only and are thought to specify the induction so as to acquire organotypical patterns ("individuation"). This concept has been discussed recently by Holtfreter ('51). We shall confine ourselves to brief statements which are largely based upon the data presented in the preceding chapters.

It has been shown that fresh or dead adult tissues can call forth perfectly individuated inductions outside of a whole host, namely in an isolated piece of ectoderm (Figs. 93–96). This excludes the necessity of an intervention of "eidogens" for the emergence of highly complex and normal anatomical patterns. Since the atypical inductors possess no structure which they have in common among themselves or with the inductions, it seems reasonable to conclude that they simply activate the ectoderm to establish a new head or tail field which then organizes itself into typical tissue patterns. If there are such substances as individuating "eidogens," they did not come from the inductors but arose de novo within the induced ectoderm. This would make it futile to attempt a distinction between "inducing" and "evocating" agents.

There is good reason to assume that in normal development the archenteron roof acts not much differently from a dead inductor. The neural plate is induced in the form of *new* complex field systems which have no point-to-point relationship to the inductors and are capable of organizing themselves into anatomical patterns. This independence applies also to secondary inductions (lens, ear vesicle), since their complex structures have evidently no counterpart in the structural properties of their inductors. Striking evidence for this notion that independent fields and not specific organs or structures are induced has been provided by the xenoplastic experiments. They showed that although the parts of the archenteron roof have regionally specific effects, the elaboration of anatomical and histological patterns is due to inherent properties of the reacting material. In this respect, therefore, the inductive action of the "organizer" may be compared with the action of hormones which can stimulate certain tissues to undergo specific differentiations but which have no control over the organized pattern of these differentiations.

To conclude, then, the "organizer" has the characteristics of a morphogenetic field which is, however, not really harmonious-equipotential in the strict definition of Driesch, and it induces another, or several other, fields, which are likewise capable of regulation and of self-organization.

Self-organization of Fields. We have had several occasions to emphasize the important role which the self-organization of morphogenetic fields plays in progressive differentiation: an area which is capable of self-differentiation and of regulation breaks up into smaller units which may represent fields on a smaller scale and with more restricted differentiation potencies. They, in turn, may subsequently be subjected to further segregation, until the final organization of an organ is achieved. One of the outstanding characteristics of the process of "self-organization" is its autonomous character; it is illustrated by the morphogenetic behavior of the chorda-mesoderm field (Fig. 81) and the limb field, and by the highly organized differentiations induced by adult organs (Figs. 100, 103, 104) and in xenoplastic combinations (Fig. 97).

This issue, and its significance for vertebrate development, has been recognized early by different investigators. Weiss has stressed its importance under the heading of "autonomization" ('26) and "emancipation" ('35, '39); Lillie ('27) has used the term "embryonic segregation" and Lehmann ('42b) the term "autonomous self-organization." The earlier cell-lineage studies and isolation experiments on invertebrate eggs had already focussed the attention to this principle.

In contrast to the extensive analysis to which embryonic induction has been subjected in the last 50 years, our information on the mechanisms involved in the process of self-organization is negligible. Tentative approaches to this problem have been made. In connection with his investigations on the development of the limb and otocyst in Amblystoma, Harrison ('45) has suggested that the emergence of axial structuration in a field might be based on the presence of a supracellular paracrystalline lattice of dipolar molecules. Spiegelman and Steinbach ('45) have interpreted the differentiation of morphogenetic fields in terms of physiological competition between transforming cells, in the framework of a more general and more elaborate theory which we cannot discuss in detail. Weiss ('50) points out that neither electrodynamic theories nor simple concentration gradients nor differences in position and exposure of cell groups can account for the complex behavior of segregating fields. He suggests ('50, p. 194) that "It may become necessary to assume that at any given point of a particular field, conditions of such specific constellation arise that certain molecular groupings will be selectively favored or energized by a sort of resonance relation between field and molecular pattern."

The lack of precision and the diversity of these notions testify to our present-day ignorance of the physicochemical factors operating in the process of field segregation. But the progress which is being made in the elucidation of some instances of embryonic fields (see below) is encouraging enough to support the belief that the crucial and universal problem of self-organization is not entirely refractory to further analysis.

Morphogenetic Movements as an Organizing Principle. The patterning of an embryonic field involves more mechanisms than determinative (inductive?) interactions of its parts. In some instances, implication of the latter is even doubtful. For example, the re-individuation of a disaggregated adult sponge is mainly, if not entirely, mediated by the principles of directed movements and selective adhesion of the different types of cells. Corresponding morphogenetic cell movements are of equal importance for the tissue patterning of the chorda-mesoderm field. That these movements of invagination, spreading or stretching which make for the regroupings and final segregation of the tissue components are inherent properties of the cells concerned is clearly demonstrated in explants from the blastoporal region, especially if such explants have been previously disaggregated.

Embryonic Fields as Related to Their Initial Mass. Graded inactivation by heat of either normal or atypical inductors reduces their effectiveness in a quantitative as well as a qualitative sense. The inductions not only become progressively smaller but they exhibit less organized patterns until they have the aspects of non-specific neural or neuroid cell groups. This reduction and final loss of patterning seems to show that the organological complexity of a neurogenic field depends primarily on the number of cells which have experienced stimulation. In other words, the size of the field appears to be a determining factor in its future organ pattern.

Other observations tie up with this notion. Lopashov ('35a) states that the differentiations produced by explants from the dorsal blastoporal region increase in complexity with the number of fused identical explants. It is well known, furthermore, not only that if the cephalic entomesoderm is progressively reduced in mass it induces increasingly smaller head organs, but also that there are lower limits beyond which well proportioned and complete head structures can no longer be formed. Instead of decreasing proportionally in all its parts, the tissue pattern of the reduced heads changes qualitatively. Thus, in the graded series of micro- to anencephalic animals, the lateral structures, such as gills, balancers, eyes, or ear vesicles, become shifted mediad, then appear as single organs, and finally drop out entirely. But even in the complete absence of eyes, the diencephalon may still exhibit a rather normal structure (Nieuwkoop, '47). These recessions in a lateromedian direction are invariably associated with a stepwise reduction and final absence of all head structures in a cephalocaudal direction.

Lehmann ('45, '48) circumscribes these changes of pattern in terms of *"Realisationsstufen"* and he points out that corresponding situations exist in other blastemas, such as those of the ear vesicle (Andres, '48) or the limb (Bretscher, '49). As a matter of fact, this relationship between initial size of the field and the diversity of its final differentiations has been found previously in many other instances, especially in invertebrates, where this phenomenon was described under headings such as vegetative budding, regeneration, or reconstitution of disarranged organismic fields (for references see Child, '41; Huxley and De Beer, '34; Berrill, '41; Holtfreter, '51). In all these instances, the initial size of the field seemed to determine its future organological complexity, each field having its own series of critical size thresholds which determine type and configuration of the tissues that will emerge from the originally pluripotential mass of cells.

AMPHIBIAN DEVELOPMENT AS RELATED TO CHEMICAL GRADIENTS

Child's Gradient Theory, according to which structural patterns are preceded and determined by axial gradients of metabolic activity, is well known and need not be elaborated here. This theory, which has its main and legitimate field of application in reconstitution processes of invertebrates, has also been applied to amphibian development (general references: Huxley and De Beer, '34; Child, '41, '46). From what follows it appears, however, that the factual basis for this latter application is rather slim.

Let us first acknowledge that not all embryonic fields originate through induction. In an aggregation of a sufficiently large number of amebocytes of Dictyostelium (Raper, '41), a field arises "autonomously," that is, under "unspecific" external conditions. A corresponding self-establishment of a field appears to occur in an isolated piece from any region of the gastrula ectoderm of anurans which tends to segregate into epidermal and sucker cells (Holtfreter, '33a, '36, '38c; Yamada, '38; Raunich, '42a). As in the classical experiments on hydrozoans and worms, the mere act of "physiological isolation" from controlling factors of the whole organism (Child, '15, '41) seems to create the new field.

No other examples of this sort are known in amphibian development, and it has been mentioned already that no new fields could be produced simply by raising the rate of metabolism of an embryonic district. The production of a brain-field in ectoderm explants by means of injurious treatments certainly resembles the individuations obtained by Child ('41) in injured hydrozoa, but it is doubtful that Child's rather vague concepts of differential susceptibility, recovery and dominance are of much help for a concrete physiological interpretation of the above results.

Principally on the basis of the data of Bellamy ('19) on the regionally different susceptibility of amphibian gastrulae to the cell-dispersing action of potassium cyanide, Child postulated a region of "physiological dominance" in the ectoderm around the animal pole, and a dorsoventral gradient with its center above the dorsal blastoporal lip. The differential susceptibility to potassium cyanide was interpreted as indicating differences of oxygen consumption. However, later workers refuted this interpretation (Buchanan, '29; Holtfreter, '43a). Subsequent quantitative determinations did reveal regional differences, although not exactly gradients, in the distribution of certain compounds, or physiological processes, within the early amphibian embryo. This was shown in the case of sulfhydryl compounds, RNA, alkaline phosphatase, degree of reducing power, glycolytic activity, and rate of oxygen consumption, all of which follow more or less the same pattern of distribution (for references see Brachet, '45; Boell, '48). These patterns, however, do not coincide at all with those of the inducing fields or their inductions. All they appear to show are regional differences in the rate of metabolic activity of the various germ layers or primordia. These differences seem to be largely a reflection of tissue-specific differences in the ratio between inert yolk and physiologically active cytoplasmic components. Some parts of the embryo—notably the ectoderm, which is poor in yolk reserves—differentiate comparatively faster than others, but the biochemical data have so far failed to throw any light upon the phenomena of induction, regulation or tissue determination. Even if there were a close parallelism between metabolically especially active and morphogenetically "dominant" regions in the sense of Child, one may still advance the argument of Spemann ('38) and others that it is difficult to decide whether such metabolic patterns are the cause or the effect of tissue determination.

The Double Gradient Theory of Dalcq and Pasteels ('37, '38; Dalcq, '41a) follows similar lines. These authors have postulated that all embryonic tissue differentiations, including the intramesodermal segregations, are caused by one and the same hypothetical agent ("organisine") and that qualitative differences between the inductions are due to different concentrations of this agent. The premises of this gradient concept and some of its applications to embryological problems have already been discussed in previous chapters. No doubt this concept aims to be all-embracing. It attempts to attribute such diverse phenomena as egg organization, morphogenetic movements, field segregation, and regional induction to the interplay of just two hypothetical factors, a cortical and a vitelline factor, whose interactions would result in the establishment of the aforementioned gradient of "organisine" that pervades the whole embryo. It is impossible in this review to evaluate critically the factual and theoretical aspects of this hypothesis. It is based upon assumptions which seem to be controversial or arbitrary, and some of the interpretations offered are merely circumscriptions of the problems to be solved. Similar criticisms were raised by Rotmann ('43). We assert again that in most instances when this concept has been applied to certain observations, other hypotheses would serve as well, if not better. It seems that too

many unrelated, though partly overlapping, processes are engaged in embryogenesis to allow for their unitary interpretation in terms of an oversimplified gradient concept.

Yamada ('50a, b) has proposed a different version of a double gradient theory. He postulates two qualitatively different activities distributed in a gradient fashion and changing their values with time. One of these "morphogenetic potentials" would be related to the dorsoventral pattern of organization in ectoderm and mesoderm and have its highest concentration at the dorsal side. The other would be related to stretching and convergence activities; it would be represented by a cephalocaudal gradient with its peak at the caudal end. The specific differentiation of a germ area would be determined by the combined effects of both.

The spatiotemporal patterns of both potentials are thought to be controlled by extrinsic as well as intrinsic factors and therefore modifiable experimentally. For instance, the dorsoventral and cephalocaudal potentials of ventral ectoderm remain low when the ectoderm is isolated, resulting in atypical epidermis. A change of pH results in brain-like differentiations which are interpreted as a raise of the d-v potential ("dorsalization") without a change of the cephalocaudal potential. The same ventral ectoderm, when combined with guinea pig kidney, differentiates into tail-like structures including spinal cord and somites, which is considered to be the result of the raising of both potentials ("dorsalization" and "caudalization"). Other experiments are interpreted along the same lines. However, the experimental data on normal and atypical inductions can be interpreted equally well in terms of "neuralizing" and "mesodermizing" inductors, and more factual evidence would be required for a critical evaluation of this hypothesis.

Inside-Outside Gradients as Determining Factors in the Organization of Embryonic Fields. Concentration gradients involving not just one, but many kinds of chemical substances as well as more complex organic entities are bound to develop in any embryological system in response to its environment (Gibbs phenomenon). The concentric organization of an amphibian egg into ovoplasm, pigmented cortex and coat can be partly attributed to this principle of sorting out of surface-active substances and their subsequent reactions with each other and with external factors. Such inside-outside gradients are significant even in the multicellular embryonic stages where the inward movement of certain primordia and the outward movement and epibolic spreading of others can hardly be explained without invoking chemical gradients of some sort which control the direction of the cellular migrations (Holtfreter, '44a).

In a stimulating article dealing with the individuation of slime molds from the aggregation of equipotential myxamebae, Cohen ('42) points out that in response to the external inorganic medium, an initially homogeneous cell aggregate most likely elaborates concentric patterns of distribution and concentration of different substances. Critical levels of pH, oxygen tension, salts and other diffusible compounds will be established in certain regions; in this way, the necessary conditions are provided for chemical processes that cannot occur in other regions. From these reactions new patterns of complexity will arise which in turn initiate further local structurations. Provided the differentially distributed new compounds are of cell-determinative significance, it is quite conceivable that the initially merely quantitative gradations play a fundamental role in the segregation of an originally equi- and pluripotential cell-aggregate into definite tissue patterns.

We believe that such considerations will be very helpful in the analysis of the factors responsible for the self-organization of the various fields in the embryos of higher organisms. Clearly, the location of a prospective field within the organism and the size of its cell population would have a decisive bearing on the establishment and effectiveness of such inside-outside gradients. Furthermore, regional differences in the accessibility and composition of the environmental factors would determine the outcome.

It is important to realize that the structuration of a field can be inaugurated both by "unspecific" and "specific," that is, inductive, factors. Globular cell-aggregates of a potential field which float freely in an "unspecific" medium may be expected to elaborate a concentric and radially symmetrical organization; this is exemplified in the multiple brain formations of shock-activated ectoderm explants. Local attachment to a substratum, even if it is inert, would introduce polarity into the system. This is demonstrated not only in the basal-apical polarization of attached cell aggregates of sponges, slime molds and hydrozoa (Child, '41), but also in the axial organization of embryonic fields of vertebrates which are exposed to a differential of external conditions. The neuralized ectoderm explants develop an apical-basal polarity when attached to glass. Similarly, the elaboration of a bilateral symmetry in glass-attached explants of blastoporal material (Fig. 81) is undoubtedly enhanced by external differentials, since freely floating explants of this kind fail to manifest their tendency for axial organization. When inductors of any kind are grafted into a whole embryo their action is more or less unidirectional upon the overlying tissues, which simulates the conditions in normal development. In either case, the induction tends to establish a bilateral symmetry and dorsoventral polarity. But such patterns are very rare when the same inductors are placed into a mantle of isolated ectoderm, thus affecting the latter throughout its circumference; under these topographic conditions an irregular multiplicity of structures tends to appear. Obviously, and this is in accord with Child's ideas, the emergence of axial patterns in a prospective field requires the application of external factors in certain directions. This seems to be true not only of "unspecific" environmental conditions but still more so of inductive stimuli.

CYTOPLASMIC FACTORS OF DIFFERENTIATION

It would be desirable to connect the data and concepts derived from the study of amphibians with those obtained in other fields of biology so as to arrive at a generalizing hypothesis of the factors that determine cellular differentiation. This enterprise is, however, too involved to be tackled satisfactorily within the limited space available. We propose, nevertheless, to venture a few steps into this little explored yet very stimulating field of speculation.

There seems to be agreement among embryologists that the regionally different fate of the parts of an egg, and of its subsequent embryonic fields, is determined by cytoplasmic rather than nuclear differences of the cells concerned. One cannot doubt that the nuclear genes control the emergence and maintenance of the cytoplasmic differentiations, yet there is an impressive body of evidence indicating that once local cytoplasmic differences are established, they may for long periods become relatively independent of continued gene control. (See, for instance, Hadorn, '36; Sonneborn, '47; Rhoades, '49.) This has led to the supposition that, apart from self-reproducing genes, there are cytoplasmic entities, designated by the various authors as plasmones, cyto-genes, plasmagenes or gene products, which become likewise capable of reduplication and mutation, and which are directly responsible for the physiological and morphological properties of the various types of differentiating cells (Wright, '41, '45; Darlington, '44; Haddow, '44; and others).

It has been suggested by several authors that the hypothetical plasmagenes are comparable to, or located within, the basophilic granules (mitochondria, microsomes) referred to above, which in turn share some properties with the virus (for further references see Brachet, '45, '50). Needham ('42) compares homoiogenetic induction with the mechanism of virus infection. Many workers are inclined to think that some tumors originate from the transformation of normal microsome-like entities into virus particles. This idea seems to be supported by the findings of Claude ('40, '41), who isolated from normal chick tissues small nucleoprotein particles which could not be distinguished chemically from the infective virus which renders these tissues malignant. Thanks to the investigations of Claude ('46), Brachet and collaborators ('40, '42, '44) and many others, it has been established that cytoplasmic granules of a comparable composition, though of various sizes, are present in at least the majority of embryonic and adult tissues. Many of the essential enzymes have been found to be localized in the larger granules (mitochondria), and it has been suggested that the alleged capability of reduplication of these granules is due to their richness in ribonucleic acid.

It will be recalled that Brachet attaches great importance to the function of the nucleoprotein granules in morphogenesis. Although we were reluctant to accept the data now available as evidence to show that any of the described constituents of these granules are specifically engaged in neural induction, one can hardly doubt that in view of their being the carriers of so many important compounds, the granules play an essential role not only in the metabolic specification of adult tissues but also in the developmental elaboration of the different tissues.

On the basis of his studies on enzymatic adaptation of yeasts, Spiegelman ('48) has arrived at similar ideas and has proposed a concrete scheme which he considers to be applicable to embryonic differentiation. The chief merit of this scheme consists in its attempt to translate the notions of potential-ity, competence and induction into the more tangible terms of enzymology. As is pointed out, it is the uniqueness of the enzyme patterns more than anything else that distinguishes the tissues from each other. According to Spiegelman, genes determine merely the potentiality of enzyme formation, but whether or not a particular enzyme is actually formed in the cytoplasm depends upon other factors, of which the substrate is obviously one. It is assumed that enzyme formation is governed by autosynthetic reduplication and that in this process the various enzyme-forming precursors or "plasmagenes" compete with each other for nitrogenous compounds. An externally applied specific substrate is presumed to combine with one of the inactive and rather unstable precursors to form a specific plasmagene-enzyme system which thereafter can reproduce itself faithfully. Thus the substrate enhances the continued production and accumulation of one type of enzyme at the expense of other potential enzyme-precursors which through competition are more or less crowded out. However, owing to cytoplasmic patterns of distribution and to certain "symbiotic" relations and ecological interactions within the population of the competing entities, there remains room for the co-existence of different enzymes within a cell. Just the same, "the fate of any given cell during morphogenesis will be determined by the outcome of the competitive interactions amongst the initial plasmagene population." (Spiegelman, '48; see also Steinbach and Moog, Section III, Chap. 2 of this book.)

If plasmagene population means "competence," and activating substrate "inductor," then the above considerations may serve as a model for interpreting the relations between these phenomena. Competence may then be ascribed to the stage-specific preponderance of certain enzymatic or morphogenetic precursors which can combine selectively with certain inductive agents. By doing so, the newly formed self-reproducing compounds would gain an advantage over the other competing precursors, and the cell would progressively narrow down its competence to become eventually unipotent. But since competence changes with time independently of external stimulation, either progressive transformation of the plasmagenes themselves, or their selective elimination through cell-bound competition must be assumed. The prevailing irreversibility and "canalization" of differentiation (Waddington, '48) would result from the "survival of the fittest," namely the accumulative and self-reinforcing propagation of tissue-specific compounds extending over successive cell generations. Yet some cells, especially those capable of sexual or asexual reproduction, remain omnipotent throughout the life cycle. How did they avoid specialization? Other cells, having become incapable of shifting into a new trend of normal differentiation, may still react to proper stimuli by "mutating" cytoplasmically into cancerous tissues (Graffi, '40; Haddow, '44; Potter, '45; Holtfreter, '48a).

This comparison of enzymatic adaptation of yeasts with tissue determination has some weaknesses: whereas the former requires continued external application of a specific substrate (as in the case of hormones), embryonic tissues proceed to differentiate independently of the initial inductive stimulus. Moreover, it remains to be explained how ectoderm explants can be switched into neural differentiation simply by an unspecific injury. Finally, some primordia, especially those of the entoderm, do not seem to require exogenous inductive stimuli for their normal differentiation.

To fit these data into the above concept it seems necessary to assume that the substrates required for the autocatalytic synthesis of specific tissue proteins pre-exist in the reacting cells, and that the inducing stimulus acts neither like a virus nor as an enzymatic substrate but as an agent which activates or liberates certain intracellular substrates. The "unmasking" of the neuralizing agent in killed or slightly injured ectoderm may be due to autolytic dissociations comparable to those which occur in dying amphibian cells (Holtfreter, '48a; Brachet, '49, '50) and in the isolated nucleoprotein granules (Claude, '46). It has also been suggested that some enzymes are inactive in the living cell because they are separated from their proper substrates. This may give a clue to the observations of Pasteels ('47a,b; '49a) that centrifuged blastulae give rise to accessory neural and mesodermal structures in the affected ectoderm. The cell content of the latter becomes clearly stratified, suggesting that these "auto-inductions" (Holtfreter, '47b, '48a) may originate from a mechanically produced union and reaction of morphogenetic precursors with certain substrates present in the same cell.

In a thoughtful article, Waddington ('48) has discussed these problems from a somewhat different angle, emphasizing likewise

that one must assume the existence of different intracellular substrates and gene products, subject to competitive interactions, in order to account for the autocatalytic synthesis of tissue-specifying protein compounds.

At present, such attempts to arrive at general concepts by coordinating genetic, physiological and embryological data are liable to be of a highly speculative nature. However, they suggest outlines for future research.

REFERENCES

Adelmann, H. B. 1930 Experimental studies on the development of the eye. III. The effect of the substrate ("Unterlagerung") on the heterotopic development of median and lateral strips of the anterior end of the neural plate of Amblystoma. J. Exp. Zool., 57:223–281.

——— 1932 The development of the prechordal plate and mesoderm of *Amblystoma punctatum*. J. Morph., 54:1–67.

——— 1934 A study of cyclopia in *Amblystoma punctatum* with special reference to the mesoderm. J. Exp. Zool., 67:219–281.

——— 1936 The problem of cyclopia. Quart. Rev. Biol., 11:161–182.

——— 1937 Experimental studies on the development of the eye. IV. The effect of the partial and complete excision of the prechordal substrate on the development of the eyes of *Amblystoma punctatum*. J. Exp. Zool., 75:199–227.

Alderman, A. L. 1935 The determination of the eye in the anuran, *Hyla regilla*. J. Exp. Zool., 70: 205–232.

——— 1938 A factor influencing the bilaterality of the eye rudiment in *Hyla regilla*. Anat. Rec., 72:297–302.

Ancel, P., and Vintemberger, P. 1948 Recherches sur le déterminisme de la symétrie bilaterale dans l'oeuf des amphibiens. Bull. Biol. France et Belg., Suppl. 31:1–182.

Andres, G. 1948 Realisationsgrade bei der Entwicklung des Amphibienlabyrinths. Arch. J. Klaus-Stiftung., 23:562–568.

——— 1949 Untersuchungen an Chimären von Triton und Bombinator. I. Entwicklung xenoplastischer Labyrinthe und Kopfganglien. Genetica, 24:1–148.

Atlas, M. 1935 The effect of temperature on the development of *Rana pipiens*. Physiol. Zool., 8: 290–310.

Aufsess, A. von 1941 Defekt- und Isolationsversuche an der Medullarplatte und ihrer Unterlagerung an *Triton alpestris*- und Amblystoma-Keimen, mit besonderer Berücksichtigung der Rumpf- und Schwanzregion. Roux' Arch. Entw.-mech., 141:248–339.

Balinsky, B. I. 1947 Kinematik des entodermalen Materials bei der Gestaltung der wichtigsten Teile des Darmkanals bei den Amphibien. Roux' Arch. Entw.-mech., 143:127–166.

Baltzer, F. 1941 Untersuchungen an Chimären

von Urodelen und Hyla. Rev. suisse Zool., *48:* 413–482.

Baltzer, F. 1950a Chimären und Merogone bei Amphibien. Rev. suisse Zool., *57:*93–114.

———— 1950b Entwicklungsphysiologische Betrachtungen über Probleme der Homologie und Evolution. Rev. suisse Zool., *57:*451–477.

Banki, O. 1927a Die Lagebeziehungen der Spermium-Eintrittsstelle zur Medianebene und zur ersten Furche, nach Versuchen mit örtlicher Vitalfärbung am Axolotlei. Anat. Anz., *63:* Erg. H., 198–209.

———— 1927b Die Entstehung der äusseren Zeichen der bilateralen Symmetrie am Axolotlei; nach Versuchen mit örtlicher Vitalfärbung. Verh. X. Internat. Zool. Kongress Budapest, pp. 375–384.

Barth, L. G. 1939 The chemical nature of the amphibian organizer: III. Stimulation of the presumptive epidermis of Ambystoma by means of cell extracts and chemical substances. Physiol. Zool., *12:*22–29.

———— 1941 Neural differentiation without organizer. J. Exp. Zool., *87:*371–384.

————, and Graff, S. 1938 The chemical nature of the amphibian organizer. Cold Spring Harbor Symp. Quant. Biol., *6:*385–391.

Bautzmann, H. 1926 Experimentelle Untersuchungen zur Abgrenzung des Organisationszentrums bei *Triton taeniatus*. Roux' Arch. Entw.-mech., *108:*283–321.

———— 1928 Experimentelle Untersuchungen über die Induktionsfähigkeit von Chorda und Mesoderm bei Triton. Roux' Arch. Entw.-mech., *114:*177–225.

———— 1929 Über Induktion durch vordere und hintere Chorda der Neurula. Roux' Arch. Entw.-mech., *119:*1–46.

———— 1933 Über Determinationsgrad und Wirkungsbeziehungen der Randzonenteilanlagen (Chorda, Ursegmente, Seitenplatten und Kopfdarmanlage) bei Urodelen und Anuren. Roux' Arch. Entw.-mech., *128:*666–765.

————, Holtfreter, J., Spemann, H., and Mangold, O. 1932 Versuche zur Analyse der Induktionsmittel in der Embryonalentwicklung. Naturwiss., *20:*972–974.

Beatty, R. A., DeJong, S., and Zielinski, M. A. 1939 Experiments on the effect of dyes on induction and respiration in the amphibian gastrula. J. Exp. Biol., *16:*150–154.

Bellamy, A. W. 1919 Differential susceptibility as a basis for modification and control of early development in the frog. Biol. Bull., *37:*312–361.

Berrill, N. J. 1941 Spatial and temporal growth patterns in colonial organisms. Growth (Suppl.), *5:*89–111.

Bijtel, H. 1931 Über die Entwicklung des Schwanzes bei Amphibien. Roux' Arch. Entw.-mech., *125:*448–486.

———— 1936 Die Mesodermbildungspotenzen der hinteren Medullarplattenbezirke bei *Amblystoma mexicanum* in Bezug auf die Schwanzbildung. Roux' Arch. Entw.-mech., *134:*262–282.

Boell, E. J. 1948 Biochemical differentiation during amphibian development. Ann. New York Acad. Sci., *49:*773–800.

————, and Shen, S. C. 1944 Functional differentiation in embryonic development: I. Cholinesterase activity of induced neural structures in *Amblystoma punctatum.* J. Exp. Zool., *97:*21–41.

Born, G. 1897 Über Verwachsungsversuche mit Amphibienlarven. Roux' Arch. Entw.-mech., *4:* 349–465.

Brachet, A. 1911 Études sur les localisations germinales et leur potentialité réelle dans l'oeuf parthenogénétique de *Rana fusca.* Arch. de Biol., *26:*337–363.

Brachet, J. 1940 Étude histochimique des proteines au cours du développement embryonnaire des poissons, des amphibiens et des oiseaux. Arch. de Biol., *51:*167–202.

———— 1941 La localisation des acides pentosenucléiques dans les tissus animaux et les oeufs d'Amphibiens en voie de développement. Arch. de Biol., *53:*207–257.

———— 1943 Pentosenucleoproteides et induction neurale. Bull. de l'Acad. Roy. de Belgique, 5th Serie, *29:*707–718.

———— 1945 Embryologie Chimique. Masson, Paris. (English edition, 1950.)

———— 1949 Le rôle et la localization des acides nucléiques au cours du développement embryonnaire; in Acidi Nucleici, Proteine e Differenziamento Normale e Patologico, pp. 1–25. Rosenberg and Sellier, Torino.

———— 1950 Characteristiques biochimiques de la compétence et de l'induction. Rev. suisse Zool., *57:*57–75.

————, and Chantrenne, H. 1942 Nucleoproteides libres et combinés sous forme de granules chez l'oeuf d'Amphibiens. Acta biol. Belg., *4:* 451–454.

————, and Jeener, T. 1944 Recherches sur les particules cytoplasmiques de dimensions macromoléculaires riches en acide pentosenucléique. Enzymologia, *11:*196–211.

————, and Rapkine, L. 1939 Oxydation et réduction d'explantats dorsaux et ventraux de gastrulas (Amphibiens). Compt. rend. Soc. de biol., *131:*789–791.

Brandes, J. 1938 Modification de la morphogénèse primordale chez les Amphibiens, par l'action précoce des rayons ultraviolets. Acad. roy. de Belgique Sci., *24:*92–108.

———— 1940 Action des rayons ultraviolets sur la morphogénèse des Amphibiens. II. Arch. de Biol., *51:*219–292.

———— 1942 Action des rayons ultraviolets sur la morphogénèse des Amphibiens. II. Arch. de Biol., *53:*150–206.

Bretscher, A. 1949 Die Hinterbeinentwicklung von *Xenopus laevis* und ihre Beeinflussung durch Colchicin. Rev. suisse Zool., *56:*33–96.

Brown, M. G., Hamburger, V., and Schmitt, F. O. 1941 Density studies on amphibian embryos with special reference to the mechanism of organizer action. J. Exp. Zool., *88:*353–372.

Bruns, E. 1931 Experimente über das Regulationsvermögen der Blastula von *Triton taeniatus* und *Bombinator pachypus.* Roux' Arch. Entw.-mech., *123:*682–718.

Buchanan, J. W. 1929 The relation between embryo volume and the susceptibility of *Amblystoma punctatum* embryos to potassium cyanide. Physiol. Zool., *2:*125–147.

Burt, A. 1943 Neurulation in mechanically and chemically inhibited Amblystoma. Biol. Bull., *85:*103–115.

Bytinski-Salz, H. 1929 Untersuchungen über die Determination und die Induktionsfähigkeit einiger Keimbezirke der Anuren. Roux' Arch. Entw.-mech., *118:*121–163.

―――― 1931 Untersuchungen über die Induktionsfähigkeit der hinteren Medullarplattenbezirke. Roux' Arch. Entw.-mech., *123:*518–564.

―――― 1936 Kombinative Einheitsleistungen in der Entwicklungsgeschichte. Compt. rend. XII. Congrès Intern. de Zool. Lisbonne, 1935, pp. 595–618.

Cagianut, B. 1949 Zur Wirkung von Sexualhormonen auf die Primitiventwicklung von *Triton alpestris.* Zeitschr. Zellf., *34:*471–501.

Carpenter, E. 1937 The head pattern in Amblystoma studied by vital staining and transplantation methods. J. Exp. Zool., *75:*103–129.

Child, C. M. 1915 Individuality in Organisms. University of Chicago Press, Chicago.

―――― 1929 Physiological dominance and physiological isolation in development and reconstitution. Roux' Arch. Entw.-mech., *117:*21–66.

―――― 1941 Patterns and Problems of Development. University of Chicago Press, Chicago.

―――― 1946 Organizers in development and the organizer concept. Physiol. Zool., *19:*89–148.

Chuang, H. H. 1938 Spezifische Induktionsleistungen von Leber und Niere im Explantationsversuch. Biol. Zentrbl., *58:*472–480.

―――― 1939 Induktionsleistungen von frischen und gekochten Organteilen (Niere, Leber) nach ihrer Verpflanzung in Explantate und verschiedene Wirtsregionen von Tritonkeimen. Roux' Arch. Entw.-mech., *139:*556–638.

―――― 1940 Weitere Versuche über die Veränderung der Induktionsleistungen von gekochten Organteilen. Roux' Arch. Entw.-mech., *140:*25–38.

―――― 1947 Defekt- und Vitalfärbungsversuche zur Analyse der Entwicklung der kaudalen Rumpfabschnitte und des Schwanzes bei Urodelen. Roux' Arch. Entw.-mech., *143:*19–125.

Claude, A. 1940 Particulate components of normal and tumor cells. Science, *91:*77–78.

―――― 1941 Particulate components of the cytoplasm. Cold Spring Harbor Symp. Quant. Biol., *9:*263–271.

―――― 1943 Distribution of nucleic acids in the cell and the morphological constitution of cytoplasm. Biol. Symp., *10:*111–125.

―――― 1944 Distribution of enzymatic activities in fractions of mammalian liver; in A. A. A. S. Research Conference on Cancer. Washington, D. C., pp. 223–226.

―――― 1946 Fractionation of mammalian liver cells by differential centrifugation. J. Exp. Med., *84:*51–89.

Cohen, A. L. 1942 The organization of protoplasm: a possible experimental approach. Growth, *6:*259–272.

Cohen, S. S. 1944 The enzymatic degradation of thymus nucleohistone. J. Biol. Chem., *158:*255–264.

Copenhaver, W. M., and Detwiler, S. R. 1941 Developmental behavior of Amblystoma eggs subjected to solutions of indolebutyric acid. Anat. Rec., *79:*247–261.

Dalcq, A. 1933 La détermination de la vésicule auditive chez le discoglosse. Arch. d'Anat. Micr., *29:*389–420.

―――― 1940 Contribution à l'étude du potentiel morphogénétique chez les Anoures. I. Arch. de Biol., *51:*387–586.

―――― 1941a L'Oeuf et son Dynamisme Organisateur. A. Michel, Paris.

―――― 1941b Contributions a l'étude du potentiel morphogénétique chez les Anoures. III. Arch. de Biol., *53:*2–124.

―――― 1943 Le phénomène d'induction en embryologie. Bull. Acad. Roy. Méd. de Belgique, Ser. VI., *8:*300–312.

―――― 1946 Recent experimental contributions to brain morphogenesis in Amphibians. 6th Growth Symposium, pp. 85–119.

―――― 1947 Sur l'induction de l'épiphyse et sa signification pour la morphogénèse du cerveau antérieur. Arch. Portug. Sci. Biol., *9:*18–41.

――――, and Lallier, R. 1948a Transplantations de territoires variés de la zone marginale médio-dorsale de la jeune gastrula chez le Triton. Arch. de Biol., *59:*268–378.

――――, and Lallier, R. 1948b Neuralisation directe de greffons chordo-mésoblastiques chez le Triton. Compt. rend. de l'Assoc. des Anatomistes Strasbourg, pp. 160–163.

――――, and Pasteels, J. 1937 Une conception nouvelle des bases physiologiques de la morphogénèse. Arch. de Biol., *48:*669–710.

――――, and Pasteels, J. 1938 Potentiel morphogénétique, régulation et "axial gradients" de Child. Bull. Acad. Roy. Méd. de Belgique, Ser. VI, *3:*261–308.

Damas, H. 1947 Effet de la suspension précoce du flux inducteur sur la détermination du neurectoblast medullaire. Arch. de Biol., *58:*15–57.

Daniel, F. J., and Yarwood, E. A. 1939 The early embryology of *Triturus torosus.* Univ. Calif. Publ. Zool., *43:*321–356.

Darlington, C. D. 1944 Heredity, development and infection. Nature, *154:*164–169.

DeBeer, G. R. 1947 The differentiation of neural crest cells into visceral cartilage and odontoblasts in Amblystoma, and a reexamination of the germ-layer theory. Proc. Roy. Soc. B., *134:*377–398.

―――― 1951 Embryos and Ancestors. Clarendon Press, Oxford, England.

Dollander, A. 1950 Étude des phénomènes de régulation consécutifs à la separation des deux premiers blastomères de l'oeuf de Triton. Arch. de Biol., *61:*1–110.

――――, and Derby, G. 1949 Données complémentaires sur la régulation consécutive à la ligature frontale de l'oeuf aux stades jeunes chez le Triton (*T. helveticus*). Ann. Soc. Roy. Zool. Belg., *80:*9–19.

Driesch, H. 1929 The Science and Philosophy of

the Organism. 2d ed. Black and Co., London.

Dürken, B. 1936 Über Bestrahlung des Organisatorbezirkes im Tritonkeim mit Ultraviolett. Zeitschr. wiss. Zool., *147:*295–356.

Du Shane, G. 1943 The embryology of vertebrate pigment cells. Part I. Amphibia. Quart. Rev. Biol., *18:*108–127.

Ekman, G. 1936 Beobachtungen über den Bau durch halbseitige obere Urmundlippe induzierter Embryonen bei Triton. Ann. Acad. Sci. Fenn., Ser. A., *45:*1–100.

———— 1937 Zwei bemerkenswerte induzierte Embryonen bei Triton. Acta Soc. pro. Fauna et Flora Fenn., *60:*113–128.

Endres, H. 1895 Über Anstich- und Schnürversuche an Eiern von *Triton taeniatus.* Schles. Ges. Vaterländ. Kultur. 73.

Fankhauser, G. 1925 Analyse der physiologischen Polyspermie des Triton-Eies auf Grund von Schnürungsexperimenten. Roux' Arch. Entw.-mech., *105:*501–580.

———— 1930 Zytologische Untersuchungen an geschnürten Triton-Eiern. I. Die verzögerte Kernversorgung nach hantelförmiger Einschnürung des Eies. Roux' Arch. Entw.-mech., *122:*117–139.

———— 1948 The organization of the amphibian egg during fertilization and cleavage. Ann. New York Acad. Sci., *49:*684–708.

Fautrez, J. 1949 De "chordaliserende" invloed van urea up het ei van *Rana temporaria.* Medel. Koninkl. Vlaamse Acad. Wetensch., *11:*1–30.

Fernald, R. L. 1943 The origin and development of the blood island of *Hyla regilla.* Univ. Calif. Publ. Zool., *51:*129–148.

Fischer, F. G. 1935 Zur chemischen Kenntnis der Induktionsreize in der Embryonal-Entwicklung. Verhandl. dtsch. Zool. Ges. (Zool. Anz. Suppl.), pp. 171–176.

————, Wehmeyer, E., and Jühling, L. 1933 Zur Kenntnis der Induktionsmittel in der Embryonalentwicklung. Nachr. Ges. Wiss. Göttingen, VI. Biologie, *9:*394–400.

————, Wehmeyer, E., Lehmann, L., Jühling, L., and Hultzsch, K. 1935 Zur Kenntnis der Induktionsmittel in der Embryonal-Entwicklung. Ber. dtsch. Chem. Ges., *68:*1196–1199.

Gallera, J. 1947 Effets de la suspension précoce de l'induction normale sur la partie préchordale de la plaque neurale chez les Amphibiens. Arch. de Biol., *58:*221–264.

———— 1948 Recherches comparées sur le développement du neurectoblaste préchordal transplanté sur l'embryon ou enrobé dans l'ectoblaste in vitro (*Triton alpestris*). Rev. suisse Zool., *55:*295–303.

Geinitz, B. 1925a Embryonale Transplantation zwischen Urodelen und Anuren. Roux' Arch. Entw.-mech., *106:*357–408.

———— 1925b Zur weiteren Analyse des Organisationszentrums. Zeitschr. f. ind. Abstamm.-L., *37:*117–119.

Gilchrist, F. G. 1928 The effect of a horizontal temperature gradient on the development of the egg of the urodele, *Triturus torosus.* Physiol. Zool., *1:*231–268.

Gillette, R. 1944 Cell number and cell size in the ectoderm during neurulation (*Amblystoma maculatum*). J. Exp. Zool., *96:*201–221.

Glaser, O. C. 1914 On the mechanism of morphological differentiation in the nervous system. Anat. Rec., *8:*527–551.

———— 1916 The theory of autonomous folding in embryogenesis. Science, *44:*505–509.

Goerttler, K. 1925 Die Formbildung der Medullaranlage bei Urodelen im Rahmen der Verschiebungsvorgänge von Keimbezirken während der Gastrulation und als entwicklungsphysiologisches Problem. Roux' Arch. Entw.-mech., *106:*503–541.

———— 1927 Die Bedeutung gestaltender Bewegungsvorgänge beim Differenzierungsgeschehen. Roux' Arch. Entw. Mech., *112:*517–576.

Graffi, A. 1940 Einige Betrachtungen zur Aetiologie der Geschwülste, speziell zur Natur des wirksamen Agens der zellfrei übertragbaren Hühnertumoren. Zeitschr. f. Krebsforsch., *50:*501–551.

Gurwitsch, A. 1922 Über den Begriff des embryonalen Feldes. Roux' Arch. Entw.-mech., *51:*383–415.

Gustafson, T. 1950 Survey of the morphogenetic action of the lithium ion and the chemical basis of its action. Rev. suisse Zool. (Suppl.), *57:*77–91.

Haddow, A. 1944 Transformation of cells and viruses. Nature, *154:*194–199.

Hadorn, E. 1936 Übertragung von Artmerkmalen durch das entkernte Eiplasma beim merogonischen Triton-Bastard, palmatus-Plasma × cristatus-Kern. Verh. Dtsch. Zool. Ges., pp. 97–104.

Hall, E. K. 1937 Regional differences in the action of the organization centre. Roux' Arch. Entw.-mech., *135:*671–688.

Hama, T. 1944 On the inductive specificity of fresh and boiled tissues of vertebrate liver and kidney. Annot. Zool. Japon., *22:*165–172.

———— 1949 Explantation of the urodelan organizer and the process of morphological differentiation attendant upon invagination. Proc. Jap. Acad., *25:*No. 9.

Hamburger, V. 1942 A Manual of Experimental Embryology. University of Chicago Press, Chicago.

Harrison, R. G. 1910 The outgrowth of the nerve fiber as a mode of protoplasmic movement. J. Exp. Zool., *9:*787–848.

———— 1925 The development of the balancer in Amblystoma, studied by the method of transplantation and in relation to the connective tissue problem. J. Exp. Zool., *41:*349–427.

———— 1935 Factors concerned in the development of the ear in *Amblystoma punctatum.* Anat. Rec., *63:*(Suppl. 1) 38–39.

———— 1938 Die Neuralleiste. Anat. Anz., *85:*Erg. Heft:3–30.

———— 1945 Relations of symmetry in the developing embryo. Trans. Connecticut Acad. Arts Sci., *36:*277–330.

———— 1947 Wound healing and reconstitution of the central nervous system of the amphibian embryo after removal of parts of the neural plate. J. Exp. Zool., *106:*27–84.

Herlitzka, A. 1897 Sullo sviluppo di embrioni completi da blastomeri isolati di uova di Tritone (*Molge cristata*). Roux' Arch. Entw.-mech., *4:* 624–658.

Hermann, H., Nicholas, J. S., and Boricious, J. K. 1950 Toluidine blue binding by developing muscle tissue. J. Biol. Chem., *184:*321–322.

Hoadley, L. 1938 The effect of supramaximum temperatures on the development of *Rana pipiens*. Growth, *2:*25–48.

Hörstadius, S. 1944 Über die Folgen von Chorda-Exstirpation an späten Gastrulae und Neurulae von *Amblystoma punctatum*. Acta Zool., *25:*1–13.

——— 1950 The Neural Crest. Oxford University Press, Oxford, England.

———, and Sellman, S. 1945 Experimentelle Untersuchungen über die Determination des knorpeligen Kopfskelettes bei Urodelen. Nov. Acta Soc. Scient. Uppsala., Ser. IV, *13:*1–170.

Holmdahl, D. E. 1939 Die Morphogenese des Vertebratorganismus vom formalen und experimentellen Gesichtspunkt. Roux' Arch. Entw.-mech., *139:*191–226.

Holtfreter, J. 1931 Über die Aufzucht isolierter Teile des Amphibienkeimes. II. Roux' Arch. Entw.-mech., *124:*404–465.

——— 1933a Die totale Exogastrulation, eine Selbstablösung des Ektoderms vom Entomesoderm. Roux' Arch. Entw.-mech., *129:*669–793.

——— 1933b Nicht typische Gestaltungsbewegungen, sondern Induktionsvorgänge bedingen die medullare Entwicklung von Gastrulaektoderm. Roux' Arch. Entw.-mech., *127:*591–618.

——— 1933c Der Einfluss von Wirtsalter und verschiedenen Organbezirken auf die Differenzierung von angelagertem Gastrulaektoderm. Roux' Arch. Entw.-mech., *127:*620–775.

——— 1933d Organisierungsstufen nach regionaler Kombination von Entomesoderm mit Ektoderm. Biol. Zentrbl., *53:*404–431.

——— 1933e Nachweis der Induktionsfähigkeit abgetöteter Keimteile. Roux' Arch. Entw.-mech., *127:*584–633.

——— 1934a Der Einfluss thermischer, mechanischer und chemischer Eingriffe auf die Induzierfähigkeit von Tritonkeimteilen. Roux' Arch. Entw.-mech., *132:*225–306.

——— 1934b Über die Verbreitung induzierender Substanzen und ihre Leistungen im Triton-Keim. Roux' Arch. Entw.-mech., *132:*307–383.

——— 1934c Formative Reize in der Embryonalentwicklung der Amphibien, dargestellt an Explantationsversuchen. Arch. exp. Zellf., *15:* 281–301.

——— 1935a Morphologische Beeinflussung von Urodelenektoderm bei xenoplastischer Transplantation. Roux' Arch. Entw.-mech., *133:*367–426.

——— 1935b Über das Verhalten von Anurenektoderm in Urodelenkeimen. Roux' Arch. Entw.-mech., *133:*427–494.

——— 1936 Regionale Induktionen in xenoplastisch zusammengesetzten Explantaten. Roux' Arch. Entw.-mech., *134:*466–550.

——— 1938a Veränderungen der Reaktionsweise im alternden isolierten Gastrulaektoderm. Roux' Arch. Entw.-mech., *138:*163–196.

——— 1938b Differenzierungspotenzen isolierter Teile der Urodelengastrula. Roux' Arch. Entw.-mech., *138:*522–656.

——— 1938c Differenzierungspotenzen isolierter Teile der Anurengastrula. Roux' Arch. Entw.-mech., *138:*657–738.

——— 1939a Studien zur Ermittlung der Gestaltungsfaktoren in der Organentwicklung der Amphibien. I. Roux' Arch. Entw.-mech., *139:* 110–190.

——— 1939b Studien zur Ermittlung der Gestaltungsfaktoren in der Organentwicklung der Amphibien. II. Roux' Arch. Entw.-mech., *139:* 227–273.

——— 1939c Gewebeaffinität, ein Mittel der embryonalen Formbildung. Arch. f. exp. Zellf., *23:*169–209.

——— 1943a Properties and functions of the surface coat in amphibian embryos. J. Exp. Zool., *93:*251–323.

——— 1943b A study of the mechanics of gastrulation. I. J. Exp. Zool., *94:*261–318.

——— 1944a A study of the mechanics of gastrulation. II. J. Exp. Zool., *95:*171–212.

——— 1944b Neural differentiation of ectoderm through exposure to saline solution. J. Exp. Zool., *95:*307–340.

——— 1944c Experimental studies on the development of the pronephros. Rev. Canad. de Biol., *3:*220–249.

——— 1945a Differential inhibition of growth and differentiation by mechanical and chemical means. Anat. Rec., *93:*59–74.

——— 1945b Neuralization and epidermization of gastrula ectoderm. J. Exp. Zool., *98:*161–207.

——— 1946a Structure, motility and locomotion in isolated embryonic amphibian cells. J. Morph., *79:*27–62.

——— 1946b Experiments on the formed inclusions of the amphibian egg. I. J. Exp. Zool., *101:* 355–406.

——— 1947a Changes of structure and the kinetics of differentiating embryonic cells. J. Morph., *80:*57–92.

——— 1947b Neural induction in explants which have passed through a sublethal cytolysis. J. Exp. Zool., *106:*197–222.

——— 1948a Concepts on the mechanism of embryonic induction and its relation to parthenogenesis and malignancy. Symposia Soc. Exp. Biol., *2:*17–48.

——— 1948b Significance of the cell membrane in embryonic processes. Ann. New York Acad. Sci., *49:*709–760.

——— 1951 Some aspects of embryonic induction. Growth (Suppl.), *10:*117–152.

Huxley, J. S. 1927 The modification of development by means of temperature gradients. Roux' Arch. Entw.-mech., *112:*480–516.

———, and DeBeer, G. R. 1934 The Elements of Experimental Embryology. Cambridge University Press, Cambridge, England.

Ikeda, Y. 1938 Über die wechselseitigen Beziehungen der Sinnesorgane untereinander in ihrer normalen und experimentell bedingten Entwicklung. Anat. Inst. Imp. Jap. Univ. Sendai., *31*:1–44.

Jenkinson, J. W. 1906 On the effect of certain solutions upon the development of the frog's egg. Roux' Arch. Entw.-mech., *21*:367–460.

—— 1914 On the relation between the structure and the development of the centrifuged egg of the frog. Anat. J. Micr. Sci. (NS) *60*:61–158.

Kemp, N. E. 1946 Regulation in the entoderm of the tree frog, *Hyla regilla*. Univ. Calif. Publ. in Zool., *51*:159–184.

Kidd, J. G. 1946 Distinctive constituents of tumor cells and their possible relation to the phenomena of autonomy, anaplasia and cancer causation. Cold Spring Harbor Symp. Quant. Biol., *11*:94–112.

Kitchin, I. C. 1949 The effects of notochordectomy in *Amblystoma mexicanum*. J. Exp. Zool., *112*:393–416.

Kuusi, T. 1951 Über die chemische Natur der Induktionstoffe. Ann. Zool. Soc. Zool. Bot. Fenn. "Vanamo," *14*:1–98.

Lehmann, F. E. 1926 Entwicklungsstörungen in der Medullaranlage von Triton, erzeugt durch Unterlagerungsdefekte. Roux' Arch. Entw.-mech., *108*:243–282.

—— 1928 Die Bedeutung der Unterlagerung für die Entwicklung der Medullarplatte von Triton. Roux' Arch. Entw.-mech., *113*:123–171.

—— 1929 Die Entwicklung des Anlagenmusters im Ektoderm der Tritongastrula. Roux' Arch. Entw.-mech., *117*:312–383.

—— 1932 Die Beteiligung von Implantats- und Wirtsgewebe bei der Gastrulation und Neurulation induzierter Embryonalanlagen. Roux' Arch. Entw.-mech., *125*:566–639.

—— 1933 Die Augen- und Linsenbildung von Amphibienembryonen unter dem Einfluss chemischer Mittel. Rev. suisse Zool., *40*:251–264.

—— 1935 Die Entwicklung von Rückenmark, Spinalganglien und Wirbelanlagen in chordalosen Körperregionen von Tritonlarven. Rev. suisse Zool., *42*:405–415.

—— 1937 Mesodermisierung des präsumptiven Chordamaterials durch Einwirkung von Lithiumchlorid auf die Gastrula von *Triton alpestris*. Roux' Arch. Entw.-mech., *136*:111–146.

—— 1938 Regionale Verschiedenheiten des Organisators von Triton. Roux' Arch. Entw.-mech., *138*:106–158.

—— 1942a Über die Struktur des Amphibieneies. Rev. suisse Zool., *49*:223–228.

—— 1942b Spezifische Stoffwirkungen bei der Induktion des Nervensystems der Amphibien. Naturwiss., *30*:515–526.

—— 1945 Einführung in die Physiologische Embryologie. Birkhäuser, Basel.

—— 1948 Realisationsstufen in der Ontogenese als entwicklungsphysiologisches und genetisches Problem. Arch. J. Klaus Stiftg., *23*:568–573.

——, and Ris, H. 1938 Weitere Untersuchungen über die Entwicklung der Achsenorgane bei partiell chordalosen Triton-Larven. Rev. suisse Zool., *45*:419–423.

Lehmann, H. 1938 Dissert. inaug., Freiburg im Breisgau.

Lewis, W. H. 1907 Transplantation of the lips of the blastopore in *Rana palustris*. Amer. J. Anat., *7*:137–143.

—— 1947 Mechanics of gastrulation. Anat. Rec., *97*:139–156.

—— 1949 Gel layers of cells and eggs and their role in early development. Lecture Ser., Jackson Mem. Lab., pp. 59–77.

Liedke, K. B. 1951 Lens competence in *Amblystoma punctatum*. J. Exp. Zool., *117*:573–592.

Lillie, F. R. 1927 The gene and the ontogenetic process. Science, *66*:361–368.

Lopashov, G. 1935a Die Entwicklungsleistungen des Gastrulaektoderms in Abhängigkeit von Veränderungen der Masse. Biol. Zentrbl., *55*:606–615.

—— 1935b Die Umgestaltung des präsumptiven Mesoderms in Hirnteile bei Tritonkeimen. Zool. Jahrb., *54*:299–312.

Loring, H. S. 1942 Action of ribonuclease on tobacco mosaic disease virus. J. Gen. Physiol., *25*:497–505.

Machemer, H. 1932 Experimentelle Untersuchungen über die Induktionsleistungen der oberen Urmundlippe in älteren Urodelenkeimen. Roux' Arch. Entw.-mech., *126*:391–456.

Manchot, E. 1929 Abgrenzung des Augenmaterials und anderer Teilbezirke in der Medullarplatte; die Teilbewegungen während der Auffaltung. Roux' Arch. Entw.-mech., *116*:689–709.

Mangold, O. 1920 Fragen der Regulation und Determination an umgeordneten Furchungsstadien und verschmolzenen Keimen von Triton. Roux' Arch. Entw.-mech., *47*:249–301.

—— 1923 Transplantationsversuche zur Frage der Spezifität und der Bildung der Keimblätter. Roux' Arch. Entw.-mech., *100*:198–301.

—— 1926 Über formative Reize in der Entwicklung der Amphibien. Naturwiss., *14*:1169–1175.

—— 1929a Experimente zur Analyse der Determination und Induktion der Medullarplatte. Roux' Arch. Entw.-mech., *47*:249–301.

—— 1929b Das Determinationsproblem, I. Ergebn. d. Biol., *3*:152–227.

—— 1931a Das Determinationsproblem, III. Ergebn. d. Biol., *7*:193–404.

—— 1931b Versuche zur Analyse der Entwicklung des Haftfadens bei Urodelen. Naturwiss., *19*:905–911.

—— 1932 Autonome und komplementäre Induktionen bei Amphibien. Naturwiss., *20*:371–374.

—— 1933a Isolationsversuche zur Analyse der Entwicklung bestimmter Kopforgane. Naturwiss., *21*:394–397.

—— 1933b Über die Induktionsfähigkeit der verschiedenen Bezirke der Neurula von Urodelen. Naturwiss., *21*:761–766.

—— 1936 Experimente zur Analyse der Zusammenarbeit der Keimblätter. Naturwiss., *29*:753–760.

——, and Seidel, F. 1927 Homoplastische und heteroplastische Verschmelzung ganzer Triton-

Keime. Roux' Arch. Entw.-mech., *111:*594–665.

Mangold, O., and Spemann, H. 1927 Über Induktion von Medullarplatte durch Medullarplatte im jüngeren Keim, ein Beispiel homöogenetischer oder assimilatorischer Induktion. Roux' Arch. Entw.-mech., *111:*341–422.

——, and Woellwarth, C. von 1950 Das Gehirn von Triton. Naturwiss., *37:*365–372.

Margen, S., and Schechtman, A. M. 1939 Effect of localized increased temperatures on a frog egg (*Hyla regilla*). Proc. Soc. Exp. Biol. & Med., *41:*47–48.

Mayer, B. 1935 Über das Regulations- und Induktionsvermögen der halbseitigen oberen Urmundlippe von Triton. Roux' Arch. Entw.-mech., *133:*518–581.

—— 1939 Versuche zum Nachweis der Induktionsfähigkeit jüngster Entwicklungstadien von Triton. Naturwiss., *27:*277.

McDonald, M. 1948 A method for the preparation of "protease-free" crystalline ribonuclease. J. Gen. Physiol., *32:*33–42.

McKeehan, M. S. 1951 Cytological aspects of embryonic lens induction in the chick. J. Exp. Zool., *117:*31–64.

Medawar, P. B. 1947 Cellular inheritance and transformation. Biol. Rev., *22:*360–389.

Monroy, A. 1937 Sulle capacità di sviluppo della placca midollare in condizioni di espianto. Roux' Arch. Entw.-mech., *136:*580–592.

Moore, J. A. 1946 Incipient intraspecific isolating mechanisms in *Rana pipiens*. Genetics, *31:*304–326.

Morgan, T. H. 1927 Experimental Embryology. Columbia University Press, New York.

Motomura, J. 1931 Notes on the effect of centrifugal force on the frog's egg. Sci. Rep. Tohoku Imp. Univ. (Biol.), *6:*251–256.

—— 1935 Determination of the embryonic axis in the eggs of Amphibia and echinoderms. Sci. Rep. Tohoku Imp. Univ. (Biol.), *10:*213–245.

Muchmore, W. B. 1951 Differentiation of the trunk mesoderm in *Amblystoma maculatum*. J. Exp. Zool., *118:*137–186.

Nakamura, O. 1938 Tail formation in the urodele. Zool. Mag., *50:*442–446.

Needham, J. 1939 Biochemical aspects of organizer phenomena. Growth (Suppl.), *3:*45–52.

—— 1942 Biochemistry and Morphogenesis. Cambridge University Press, Cambridge, England.

——, Waddington, C. H., and Needham, D. M. 1934 Physico-chemical experiments on the amphibian organizer. Proc. Roy. Soc. London Ser. B., *114:*393–422.

Newport, T. 1854 Researches on the impregnation of the ovum in the Amphibia, and on the early stages of development of the embryo. Philos. Trans. Roy. Soc. London, *144:*229–244.

Nieuwkoop, P. D. 1946 Experimental investigations on the origin and determination of the germ cells. Arch. Neerl. Zool., *8:*1–205.

—— 1947 Investigations on the regional determination of the central nervous system. J. Exp. Biol., *24:*145–183.

—— 1950 Neural competence and neural

fields. Rev. suisse Zool., *57:*23–40.

Niu, M. C. 1947 The axial organization of the neural crest, studied with particular reference to its pigmentary component. J. Exp. Zool., *105:*79–114.

——, and Twitty, V. C. 1953 The differentiation of gastrula ectoderm in medium conditioned by axial mesoderm. Proc. Nat. Acad. Sci., *39:*985–989.

Okada, Y. K. 1938 Neural induction by means of inorganic implantation. Growth, *2:*49–53.

——, and Hama, T. 1943 Examination of regional differences in the inductive activity of the organizer by means of transplantation into ectodermal vesicles. Proc. Imp. Acad. Tokyo, *19:*48–53.

——, and Hama, T. 1944 On the different effects of the amphibian organizer following culture, transplantation, and heat treatment. Proc. Imp. Acad. Tokyo, *20:*36–40.

——, and Hama, T. 1945 Regional differences in the inductive capacity of the dorsal roof of the archenteron of the urodele, *Triturus pyrrhogaster*. Proc. Jap. Acad., *21:*240–247.

——, and Takaya, H. 1942 Experimental investigation of regional differences in the inductive capacity of the organizer. Proc. Imp. Acad. Tokyo, *18:*505–519.

Pasquini, P. 1942 Sulla fine struttura dell'encefalo nei diversi casi di anomalie oculari. Arch. Ital. Anat. e Embriol., *47:*310–341.

Pasteels, J. 1937a Sur l'origine de la symétrie bilatérale des Amphibiens anoures. Arch. d'Anat. microsc., *33:*279–300.

—— 1937b Études sur la gastrulation des vertébrés méroblastiques. III. Oiseaux. Arch. de Biol., *48:*381–488.

—— 1938 Recherches sur les facteurs initiaux de la morphogénèse chez les Amphibiens anoures. I. Arch. de Biol., *49:*627–667.

—— 1939a Recherches sur les facteurs initiaux de la morphogénèse chez les Amphibiens anoures. II. Arch. de Biol., *50:*291–320.

—— 1939b La formation de la queue chez les vertébrés. Ann. Soc. Roy. Zool. de Belg., *70:*33–51.

—— 1940 Recherches sur les facteurs initiaux de la morphogénèse chez les Amphibiens anoures. IV. Arch. de Biol., *51:*335–386.

—— 1941 Recherches sur les facteurs initiaux de la morphogénèse chez les Amphibiens anoures. V. Arch. de Biol., *52:*321–329.

—— 1942 New observations concerning the maps of presumptive areas of the young amphibian gastrula (Amblystoma and Discoglossus). J. Exp. Zool., *89:*255–282.

—— 1943 Proliférations et croissance dans la gastrulation et la formation de la queue des vertébrés. Arch. de Biol., *54:*1–41.

—— 1945 Recherches sur l'action du LiCl sur les oeufs des Amphibiens. Arch. de Biol., *56:*105–183.

—— 1946 Sur la structure de l'oeuf insegmenté d'axolotl et l'origine des prodromes morphogénétiques. Acta Anat., *2:*1–16.

—— 1947a Sur l'apparition d'organes variés dans l'ectoblaste, à la suite de la centrifugation de la blastula et de la gastrula chez les Amphibiens. Experientia, *3*:30–32.

Pasteels, J. 1947b Sur les interactions entre l'axe embryonnaire normal et les formations secondaires produites par la centrifugation de la blastula et de la gastrula chez les Amphibiens. Experientia, *3*:73–74.

———— 1949a Résultats complémentaires sur les effets de la centrifugation de la blastula-gastrula des Amphibiens. J. Cyto-embryol. belgo-néerland., pp. 88–91.

———— 1949b Observations sur la localisation de la plaque préchordale et de l'entoblaste présomptifs au cours de la gastrulation chez *Xenopus laevis*. Arch. de Biol., *60*:235–250.

———— 1951 Centre organisateur et potentiel morphogénétique chez les batraciens. Bull. Soc. Zool. de France, *76*:231–270.

Penners, A. 1936 Experimente zur Frage nach der Potenz der ventralen Keimhälfte von *Rana fusca*. Zeitschr. wiss. Zool., *148*:189–220.

————, and Schleip, W. 1928a Die Entwicklung der Schultzeschen Doppelbildungen aus dem Ei von *Rana fusca*. I–IV. Zeitschr. wiss. Zool., *130*:305–454.

————, and Schleip, W. 1928b Die Entwicklung der Schultzeschen Doppelbildungen aus dem Ei von *Rana fusca*. V–VI. Zeitschr. wiss. Zool., *131*:1–156.

Potter, V. R. 1945 The genetic aspects of the enzyme-virus theory of cancer. Science, *101*:609–610.

Ragosina, M. N. 1937 Die Induktionswirkung pflanzlicher Gewebe auf das Ektoderm der Gastrula. Roux' Arch. Entw.-mech., *137*:317–326.

Ranzi, S., and Tamini, E. 1939 Die Wirkung von NaSCN auf die Entwicklung von Froschembryonen. Naturwiss., *27*:566–567.

————, and Tamini, E. 1940 Einfluss von NaSCN auf Fragmente von Axolotlkeimen. Naturwiss., *28*:458–459.

————, Tamini, E., and Offer, E. S. 1945–46 Alterazioni dello sviluppo embrionale di anfibi prodotte da solfocianato e da altre sostanze. Recond. Istit. Lomb. di Sci. e Lett., *79*:161–197.

Raper, K. B. 1941 Developmental patterns in simple slime molds. Growth (Suppl.), *5*:41–76.

Raunich, L. 1939 Sulla determinazione della piastra midollare negli urodeli. Arch. Zool. Ital., *26*:69–91.

———— 1940 Sulle proprietà induttrici del cordomesoderma negli embrioni di Anuri. Rivista di Biol., *30*:1–30.

———— 1942a Contributo alla conoscenza della determinazione dell'organo adhesivo degli Anfibi Anuri (*Bufo viridis*). Monitore Zool. Ital., *53*:17–26.

———— 1942b Induzioni da organizzatori anormali in embrioni di diversa età di *Triton taeniatus* e *Bufo viridis*. Monitore Zool. Ital., *53*:227–235.

Raven, C. P. 1931 Zur Entwicklung der Ganglienleiste. I. Die Kinematik der Ganglienleistenentwicklung bei den Urodelen. Roux' Arch. Entw.-mech., *125*:210–292.

———— 1933 Zur Entwicklung der Ganglienleiste. III. Die Induktionsfähigkeit des Kopfganglienleistenmaterials von *Rana fusca*. Roux' Arch. Entw. Mech., *130*:517–561.

———— 1935 Zur Entwicklung der Ganglienleiste. IV. Roux' Arch. Entw.-mech., *132*:509–575.

———— 1938 Über die Potenz von Gastrulaektoderm nach 24-stündigem Verweilen im äusseren Blatt der dorsalen Urmundlippe. Roux' Arch. Entw.-mech., *137*:611–713.

————, and Kloos, J. 1945 Induction by medial and lateral pieces of the archenteron roof. Acta Neerl. Morph., *5*:348–362.

Rawles, M. E. 1948 Origin of melanophores and their role in the development of color patterns in vertebrates. Physiol. Rev., *28*:383–408.

Reith, F. 1938 Über die Induktionsfähigkeit mit Ultraviolett bestrahlter Organisatorbezirke nach Implantation in eine Gastrula bei Triton. Z. wiss. Zool., *150*:179–205.

Rhoades, C. P. 1949 Neoplastic abnormal growth; in The Chemistry and Physiology of Growth, edited by A. K. Parpart, pp. 217–265. Princeton University Press, Princeton, New Jersey.

Roach, F. C. 1945 Differentiation of the central nervous system after axial reversals of the medullary plate of Amblystoma. J. Exp. Zool., *99*:53–71.

Roehlich, K. 1931 Gestaltungsbewegungen der präsumptiven Epidermis während der Neurulation und Kopfbildung bei *Triton taeniatus*. Roux' Arch. Entw.-mech., *124*:66–81.

Roth, H. 1950 Die Entwicklung xenoplastischer Neuralchimaeren. Rev. suisse Zool., *57*:621–686.

Rotmann, E. 1935a Der Anteil von Induktor und reagierendem Gewebe an der Entwicklung des Haftfadens. Roux' Arch. Entw.-mech., *133*:193–224.

———— 1935b Reiz und Reizbeantwortung in der Amphibienentwicklung. Verhandl. dtsch. Zool. Ges., pp. 76–83.

———— 1942 Zur Frage der Leistungspezifität abnormer Induktoren. Naturwiss., *30*:60–62.

———— 1943 Entwicklungsphysiologie. Fortschr. d. Zool., *7*:167–255.

———— 1950 (See discussion of Toivonen, 1950.)

Roux, W. 1885 Über die Bestimmung der Hauptrichtungen des Froschembryo im Ei und über die erste Theilung des Froscheies. Breslauer ärztl. Zeitschr., pp. 1–54 (Ges. Abh. No. 20).

———— 1887 Die Bestimmung der Medianebene des Froschembryo durch die Copulationsrichtung des Eikernes und des Spermakernes. Arch. mikr. Anat., *29*:157–211 (Ges. Abh. No. 21).

———— 1903 Über die Ursachen der Bestimmung der Hauptrichtungen des Embryo im Froschei. Anat. Anz., *23*:65–91.

Ruffini, A. 1925 Fisiogenia. F. Vallardi, Milano.

Rugh, R. 1939 Developmental effects resulting from exposure to x-rays. I. Effect on the embryo of irradiation of frog sperm. Proc. Amer. Philos. Soc., *81*:447–471.

———— 1948 Experimental Embryology. Burgess Publishing Co., Minneapolis, Minnesota.

Ruud, G. 1925 Die Entwicklung isolierter Keim-fragmente frühester Stadien von *Triton taeniatus*. Roux' Arch. Entw.-mech., *105:*209–293.

Schechtman, A. M. 1932 Movement and localization of the presumptive epidermis in *Triturus torosus*. Univ. Calif. Publ. Zool., *36:*325–346.

——— 1934 The organizer in *Triturus torosus* and its role in the development of the medullary plate. Univ. Calif. Publ. Zool., *39:*277–290.

——— 1936 Relation between the gray crescent and the organizer center of a urodele egg (*Triturus torosus*). Roux' Arch. Entw.-mech., *134:* 207–208.

——— 1938a Competence for neural plate formation in *Hyla regilla* and the so-called nervous layer of the ectoderm. Proc. Soc. Exp. Biol. & Med., *38:*430–433.

——— 1938b Localization of the neural inductor and tail mesoderm in a frog egg (*Hyla regilla*). Proc. Soc. Exp. Biol. & Med., *39:*236–239.

——— 1942 The mechanism of amphibian gastrulation. I. Univ. Calif. Publ. Zool., *51:*1–40.

Schmidt, G. A. 1933 Schnürungs- und Durchschneidungsversuche am Anurenkeim. Roux' Arch. Entw.-mech., *129:*1–44.

——— 1936 Über die Unterschiede in den Induktionsfähigkeiten des Organisationszentrums der Urodelen und Anuren. Zool. Anz., *15:*323–330.

——— 1937 Bildung des Haftnapfes und der Mundbewaffnung von Anuren im Tritonkeim. Zool. Anz., *117:*26–30.

Schmitt, F. O. 1941 Some protein patterns in cells. Growth (Suppl.), *5:*1–20.

Schotté, O. 1930 Der Determinationszustand der Anurengastrula im Transplantations-Experiment. Roux' Arch. Entw.-mech., *122:*663–664.

Schultze, O. 1894 Die künstliche Erzeugung von Doppelbildungen bei Froschlarven mit Hilfe abnormer Gravitationswirkung. Roux' Arch. Entw.-mech., *1:*269–305.

Schwalbe, E. 1907 Die Morphologie der Missbildungen des Menschen und der Tiere. II. Doppelbildungen. G. Fischer, Jena.

Shen, G. 1937 Experimente zur Analyse der Regulationsfähigkeit der frühen Gastrula von Triton. Roux' Arch. Entw.-mech., *137:*271–316.

Shen, S. C. 1939 A quantitative study of amphibian neural tube induction with a water-soluble hydrocarbon. J. Exp. Biol., *16:*143–149.

——— 1942 Neural induction in epidermal explants in liquid medium. J. Exp. Biol., *19:*5–10.

Sonneborn, T. H. 1947 Recent advances in the genetics of Paramecium and Euplotes. Advances Genetics, *1:*263–358.

Spemann, H. 1901 Entwicklungsphysiologische Studien am Tritonei. I. Roux' Arch. Entw.-mech., *12:*224–264.

——— 1903 Entwicklungsphysiologische Studien am Tritonei. III. Roux' Arch. Entw.-mech., *16:*551–631.

——— 1912 Zur Entwicklung des Wirbeltierauges. Zool. Jahrb. Abt. allg. Zool. u. Phys., *32:* 1–98.

——— 1914 Über verzögerte Kernversorgung von Keimteilen. Verhandl. dtsch. Zool. Ges., pp. 216–224.

——— 1918 Über die Determination der ersten Organanlagen des Amphibienembryo. I–VI. Roux' Arch. Entw.-mech., *43:*448–555.

——— 1921a Die Erzeugung tierischer Chimaeren durch heteroplastische embryonale Transplantation zwischen *Triton cristatus* und *taeniatus*. Roux' Arch. Entw.-mech., *48:*533–570.

——— 1921b Mikrochirurgische Operationstechnik; in Handbuch der biologischen Arbeitsmethoden, edited by Emil Abderhalden, Abt. V., *3:*1–30. Urban und Schwarzenberg, Berlin.

——— 1928 Die Entwicklung seitlicher und dorso-ventraler Keimhälften bei verzögerter Kernversorgung. Zeitschr. wiss. Zool., *132:*105–134.

——— 1931 Über den Anteil von Implantat und Wirtskeim an der Orientierung und Beschaffenheit der induzierten Embryonalanlage. Roux' Arch. Entw.-mech., *123:*390–516.

——— 1938 Embryonic Development and Induction. Yale University Press, New Haven, Connecticut.

———, and Bautzmann, E. 1927 Über Regulation von Tritonkeimen mit überschüssigem und fehlendem medianen Material. Roux' Arch. Entw.-mech., *110:*557–577.

———, and Geinitz, B. 1927 Über Weckung organisatorischer Fähigkeiten durch Verpflanzung in organisatorische Umgebung. Roux' Arch. Entw.-mech., *109:*129–175.

———, and Mangold, H. 1924 Über Induktion von Embryonalanlagen durch Implantation artfremder Organisatoren. Arch. f. mikr. Anat. u. Entw. Mech., *100:*599–638.

———, and Schotté, O. 1932 Über xenoplastische Transplantation als Mittel zur Analyse der embryonalen Induktion. Naturwiss., *20:*463–467.

Spiegelman, S. 1948 Differentiation as the controlled production of unique enzyme patterns. Symp. Soc. Exp. Biol., *2:*286–325.

———, and Steinbach, H. B. 1945 Substrate-enzyme orientation during embryonic development. Biol. Bull., *88:*254–268.

Spofford, W. R. 1945 Observations on the posterior parts of the neural plate in Amblystoma. I. J. Exp. Zool., *99:*35–52.

——— 1948 Observations on the posterior parts of the neural plate in Amblystoma. II. J. Exp. Zool., *107:*123–164.

Streett, J. C. 1940 Experiments on the organization of the unsegmented eggs of *Triturus pyrrhogaster*. J. Exp. Zool., *85:*383–408.

Suzuki, S. 1929 Defektversuche an ventralen und lateralen Bezirken der Randzone von Pleurodeleskeimen. Roux' Arch. Entw.-mech., *114:*371–457.

Ter Horst, J. 1948 Differenzierungs- und Induktionsleistungen verschiedener Abschnitte der Medullarplatte und des Urdarmdaches von Triton im Kombinat. Roux' Arch. Entw.-mech., *143:* 275–303.

Toivonen, S. 1938 Über das Verhalten des Gastrulaektoderms von *Triton taeniatus* bei Anwendung von pflanzlichen Implantaten. Ann. Zool. Soc. Zool. Bot. Fenn. "Vanamo," *5:*1–12.

——— 1940 Über die Leistungsspezifität der abnormen Induktoren im Implantatversuch bei Triton. Ann. Acad. Sci. Fenn., Ser. A., *55*:1–145.

Toivonen, S. 1949 Zur Frage der Leistungsspezifität abnormer Induktoren. Experientia, *5*:323–326.

———— 1950 Stoffliche Induktoren. Rev. suisse Zool., *57*:41–56.

———— 1951 Verschiedenheit der Induktionsleistungen des Lebergewebes von hungernden und gut ernährten Meerschweinchen im Implantatversuch bei Triturus. Arch. Soc. Zool. Bot. Fenn. "Vanamo," *6*:63–71.

————, and Kuusi, T. 1948 Implantationsversuche mit in verschiedener Weise vorbehandelten abnormen Induktoren bei Triton. Ann. Zool. Soc. Zool. Bot. Fenn. "Vanamo," *13*:1–19.

Töndury, G. 1936 Beiträge zum Problem der Regulation und Induktion. Roux' Arch. Entw.-mech., *134*:1–111.

———— 1937 Über experimentell erzeugte Mikrokephalie bei Urodelen. Roux' Arch. Entw.-mech., *136*:529–562.

Twitty, V. C. 1940 Size-controlling factors. Growth (Suppl.), *4*:109–120.

———— 1942 The role of genetic differentials in the embryonic development of Amphibia. Biol. Symp., *6*:291–310.

———— 1945 The developmental analysis of specific pigment patterns. J. Exp. Zool., *100*:141–178.

Umanski, E. 1935 Über gegenseitige Vertretbarkeit der präsumptiven Anlagen der Rückenmark- und Gehirnteile bei den Amphibien. Zool. Anz., *110*:25–30.

Vogt, W. 1923–24 Morphologische und physiologische Fragen der Primitiventwicklung. Sitz. Ber. Gesellsch. Morph. Physiol. München, *35*:22–32.

———— 1926a Die Beziehungen zwischen Furchung, Hauptachsen des Embryo und Ausgangsstruktur im Amphibienei, nach Versuchen mit örtlicher Vitalfärbung. Sitz. Ber. Gesellsch. Morph. Physiol. München, *37*:60–70.

———— 1926b Über Wachstum und Gestaltungsbewegungen am hinteren Körperende der Amphibien. Anat. Anz., *61*(Erg. H.):62–75.

———— 1928a Mosaikcharakter und Regulation in der Frühentwicklung des Amphibieneies. Verhandl. dtsch. Zool. Ges., pp. 26–70.

———— 1928b Ablenkung der Symmetrie durch halbseitige Beschleunigung der Frühentwicklung. Anat. Anz., *66*(Erg. H.):139–155.

———— 1929 Gestaltungsanalyse am Amphibienkeim mit örtlicher Vitalfärbung. Roux' Arch. Entw.-mech., *120*:384–706.

Waddington, C. H. 1932 Experiments on the development of chick and duck embryos, cultivated in vitro. Philos. Trans. Roy. Soc. London, Ser. B., *221*:179–230.

———— 1934 Morphogenetic fields. Science Progress, No. 114, pp. 336–345.

———— 1936a A failure of induction in normal development. J. Exp. Biol., *13*:75–85.

———— 1936b The origin of competence for lens formation in the amphibia. J. Exp. Biol., *13*:86–91.

———— 1938a Evocation by some further chem-

ical compounds. Proc. Roy. Soc. London, Ser. B., *125*:365–372.

———— 1938b The distribution of the evocator in the unfertilized egg. J. Exp. Biol., *15*:371–384.

———— 1940 Organizers and Genes. Cambridge University Press, Cambridge, England.

———— 1941 Translocation of the organizer in the gastrula of Discoglossus. Proc. Zool. Soc. London, Ser. A., *111*:189–198.

———— 1948 The genetic control of development. Symp. Soc. Exp. Biol., *2*:145–154.

————, and Goodhart, C. B. 1949 Location of absorbed carcinogens within the amphibian cell. Quart. J. Micro. Sci., *90*:209–219.

————, Needham, J., and Brachet, J. 1936 The activation of the evocator. Proc. Roy. Soc. London, Ser. B., *120*:173–207.

————, and Wolsky, A. 1936 The occurrence of the evocator in organisms which possess no nerve cord. J. Exp. Biol., *13*:92–94.

————, and Yao, T. 1950 Studies on regional specificity within the organization centre of urodeles. J. Exp. Biol., *27*:126–144.

Wagner, G. 1949 Die Bedeutung der Neuralleiste für die Kopfgestaltung der Amphibienlarve. Untersuchungen an Chimären von Triton und Bombinator. Rev. suisse Zool., *56*:520–620.

Wang, S. C. 1933 Die regulative Entwicklung dorsal-lateraler Verbandskeime von *Triton taeniatus*. Roux' Arch. Entw.-mech., *130*:243–256.

Weber, H. 1928 Über Induktion von Medullarplatte durch seitlich angeheilte Keimhälften bei *Triton taeniatus*. Roux' Arch. Entw.-mech., *113*:669–703.

Wehmeier, E. 1934 Versuche zur Analyse der Induktionsmittel bei der Medullarplatteninduktion von Urodelen. Roux' Arch. Entw.-mech., *132*:384–423.

Weiss, P. 1926 Morphodynamik. Abh. z. theoret. Biol., *23*:1–43.

———— 1935 The so-called organizer and the problem of organization in amphibian development. Physiol. Rev., *15*:641–674.

———— 1939 Principles of Development. H. Holt and Co., New York.

———— 1947 The problem of specificity in growth and development. Yale J. Biol. & Med., *19*:235–278.

———— 1949a Differential growth; in The Chemistry and Physiology of Growth, edited by A. K. Parpart, pp. 137–186. Princeton University Press, Princeton, New Jersey.

———— 1949b Growth and differentiation on the cellular and molecular levels. Proc. 6th Internat. Congress Exp. Cytology, pp. 475–482.

———— 1950 Perspectives in the field of morphogenesis. Quart. Rev. Biol., *25*:177–198.

Woerdeman, M. W. 1929 Experimentelle Untersuchungen über Lage und Bau der augenbildenden Bezirke in der Medullarplatte beim Axolotl. Roux' Arch. Entw.-mech., *116*:220–241.

———— 1933a Über den Glykogenstoffwechsel des Organisationszentrums in der Amphibiengastrula. Proc. Kon. Akad. Wetensch. (Amsterdam), *36*:189–193.

———— 1933b Embryonale Induktion durch Geschwulstgewebe. Proc. Kon. Akad. Wetensch. (Amsterdam), *36:*477–481.

Woerdeman, M. W. 1933c Über die chemischen Prozesse bei der embryonalen Induktion. Proc. Kon. Akad. Wetensch. (Amsterdam), *36:*842–849.

―――― 1936 Embryonic induction by chemical substances. Proc. Kon. Akad. Wetensch. (Amsterdam), *39:*306–314.

Wolff, E. 1948 La Science des Monstres. Gallimard, Paris.

Wright, S. 1941 The physiology of the gene. Physiol. Rev., *21:*487–527.

―――― 1945 Genes as physiological agents. Amer. Nat., *79:*289–303.

Yamada, T. 1937 Der Determinationszustand des Rumpfmesoderms im Molchkeim nach der Gastrulation. Roux' Arch. Entw.-mech., *137:*151–270.

―――― 1938 Weitere Analyse der Determination der Haftdrüse bei *Rana nigromaculata* mit einigen Bemerkungen über die Induktion anderer Kopforgane. J. Fac. Sci. Tokyo Imp. Univ., *5:*133–163.

―――― 1939a Über den Einfluss von Wirtsalter auf die Differenzierung von verpflanztem Ursegmentmaterial des Molchembryo. Jap. J. Zool., *8:*265–283.

―――― 1939b Über bedeutungsfremde Selbstdifferenzierung der präsumptiven Rückenmuskulatur des Molchkeimes bei Isolation. Okajimas Fol. Anat. Jap., *18:*565–568.

―――― 1939c Wechselseitige Induktion zwischen Medullaranlage und Ursegmentmaterial des Molchkeimes, dargestellt an zusammengesetzten Isolaten. Okajimas Fol. Anat. Jap., *18:*569–572.

―――― 1940 Beeinflussung der Differenzierungsleistung des isolierten Mesoderms von Molchkeimen durch zugefügtes Chorda- und Neuralmaterial. Okajimas Fol. Anat. Jap., *19:*131–197.

―――― 1947 An extension of the potential theory of the morphogenesis. Zool. Mag. (Tokyo), *57:*124–126.

―――― 1950a Dorsalization of the ventral marginal zone of the Triturus gastrula. I. Ammonia-treatment of the medio-ventral marginal zone. Biol. Bull., *98:*98–121.

―――― 1950b Regional differentiation of the isolated ectoderm of the Triturus gastrula induced through a protein extract. Embryologia, *1:*1–20.

Yntema, C. L. 1933 Experiments on the determination of the ear ectoderm in the embryo of *Amblystoma punctatum*. J. Exp. Zool., *65:*317–357.

―――― 1950 An analysis of induction of the ear from foreign ectoderm in the salamander embryo. J. Exp. Zool., *113:*211–244.

CHAPTER 2

Teleosts and Birds

DOROTHEA RUDNICK

IN THE course of divergence from primitive vertebrate stock, two modern groups—the fish and the sauropsidans—have separately become characterized by a large-yolked egg as a framework for ontogeny. Necessarily the eggs of both groups share certain mechanical adaptations: the discoid meroblastic cleavage pattern, the ultimate envelopment of the yolk by the spreading protoplasmic disc. These likenesses are of such superficial nature as scarcely to be likenesses at all, morphogenetically speaking. Movements of material—that is to say, the relative situation of prospective areas of the disc—differ radically in the two classes of egg. The characteristic vertebrate axis that eventuates is in each case achieved by a quite different morphogenetic sequence. The adnexa, by the same token, differ strikingly in their origin and relations.

In contrast, the experimental analysis of independent behavior of various parts of these blastoderms has tended to emphasize the basic likeness of development in all vertebrate groups. Where comparable experiments have been performed on eggs of fish and bird, the results seem likewise to be comparable. There is so far no suggestion of divergence in the fundamental pattern of differentiation processes.

THE PRE-CLEAVAGE PERIOD

The massive telolecithal eggs, like other eggs, are started in the main course of their genesis in the peculiarly specialized environment of the ovary, in relation to other cells and to maternal body fluids. Significant experimental interventions in this complex situation are extremely difficult to realize. From cytological and cytochemical studies it seems clear that not only a surface-interior differential, but morphological polarity appears fairly early in the growth period; it may be assumed that, like other animal eggs, these leave the ovary with at least

provisional axes of polarity and symmetry established. The effect of the sperm at fertilization on this pattern is not known.

In the teleost egg, the early radial pattern of the primary oocyte is reinforced by a gradual migration of material from the periphery of the nucleus to the cell membrane where a cortical layer is differentiated. This migration has been observed by Spek ('33) and inferred by Brachet ('44, p. 72) from figures in the literature; whether more than one material or process is involved in these diverse observations is not clear. Yolk formation follows this radiating phase, accompanied by marked increase in the diameter of the cell. Sometime during this period —evidently not at first—eccentricity of the nucleus is observed; this body eventually comes to rest against one pole of the egg cortex, the micropyle region, and maturation is initiated (Spek). The interpretation suggested by these accounts is that the basic cortex-interior pattern, reinforced during the early radial period when the nucleus is visibly active with reference to the cytoplasm, is given a slight axial differential at this time, and that the oocyte grows on this framework as a polarized system. Subsequently, as in many eggs, after release into water, active streaming of cytoplasmic material establishes a sharp layering along the polar axis: protoplasmic cap, basal vacuolar area, yolk, and usually "oil" droplets. Many teleost eggs display great surface activity at this time and during cleavage (cf. Yamamoto, '38, etc.; Roosen-Runge, '38; Lewis and Roosen-Runge, '42); several workers have interpreted results of injury and transplantation experiments (see p. 299) as showing that not only does material continue to stream into the blastodisc during cleavage, as is apparent in the Lewis–Roosen-Runge film, but that this material is of critical morphogenetic significance. However, nobody as yet has observed the actual incorporation of marked material from the yolk by the blastodisc.

In the early days of morphogenetic experimentation (Morgan, 1893; also Lewis, '12, Hoadley, '28) it was established that considerable cytoplasm of the uncleaved blastoderm in Fundulus may be removed by puncture without disturbing subsequent development. More recently (Tung and Tung, '44), there has been a report of puncturing the goldfish egg in the equatorial region, just before fertilization while the protoplasm

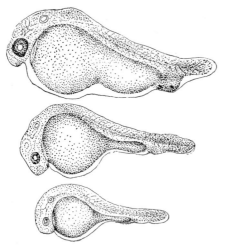

Fig. 108. From top to bottom: a giant embryo of *Carassius* produced by fusion of two four-celled eggs; a normal embryo of corresponding stage; and an embryo formed from half an egg (cf. Fig. 110). (Redrawn from Tung and Tung, '44, Fig. 16.)

is still flowing upward to form the blastodisc. A normal embryo may form from as little as one-half the material of the egg under these circumstances. All fragments, however, do not form normal or nearly normal embryos: over half form monstrosities where head, trunk or tail predominates; in a few, gastrulation is suppressed. Clearly, some sort of spatially arranged system is being displaced in these cases.

Polar arrangement in the vast fluid ovarian egg of the bird is even more impressive than it is in the case of the fish. The eccentricity of the nucleus has an obvious intimate relation to the pattern of yolk deposition. It must be recalled, when discussing axiation in the meroblastic eggs, that as yolk content becomes more extreme in proportion to protoplasm, the animal-vegetal axis tends more and more to represent the future dorsoventral axis of the embryo, while the anteroposterior axis of the embryo proper is repre-

sented by a smaller and smaller meridional arc of the egg. In the pigeon, Bartelmez ('12) has traced not only anteroposterior but left-right axes back to slight eccentricities of the nucleus in early oocyte stages. In the chick, too, the statistically regular orientation of the egg rotating in the oviduct, during or immediately following fertilization, would indicate previous establishment of the major axes.

THE CLEAVAGE PERIOD

It has long been known (Clapp, 1891; Morgan, 1893) that cleavage in the teleost egg, although following a predictable pattern, bears only an imprecise relation to the future embryonic axis. The vital stain studies of Oppenheimer ('36b) have demonstrated explicitly the variability of this relation in Fundulus. These considerations have undoubtedly promoted the tendency among embryologists to regard the cleavage period as a purely mitotic interlude, not involving profound changes in quantity or location of critical protoplasmic materials. The figures of Oppenheimer in the publication cited do not indicate spatial rearrangements of any magnitude within the blastodisc, until the blastula stage is reached. However, addition of some material to the blastodisc from the surrounding yolk or periblast has been repeatedly reported (cf. Roosen-Runge, '38). There is experimental evidence to indicate that some progressive change takes place in blastodisc, yolk, or both while the segmentation process continues at top speed.

Data on regulation of defects in Fundulus eggs have been most recently summarized by Nicholas and Oppenheimer ('42). Two- and 4-celled stages may regulate 50 per cent loss completely: i.e., the removal of one or two blastomeres. Tung and Tung, as Figure 108 demonstrates, have shown for the goldfish that at this early stage not only can a half egg form a complete embryo (see Fig. 110) but two eggs may be, under proper conditions, fused into one.

In Fundulus it appears that in the 8-celled stage (Hoadley, '28) or 16-celled stage, certain defects, at least, can entirely prevent gastrulation. The basis of this relative lack of regulability in later cleavage stages is not at all clear. It may be that surface relations of cells do not permit adequate covering of the wound, and that this apparent progressive differentiation is not due to any profound change in organization. On the other hand, the 16-celled stage marks the initiation of nuclear contribution to periblast formation, and the appearance of special osmiophile and other staining properties has been reported in the peripheral cells destined to form the germ ring (Rauber, 1883;

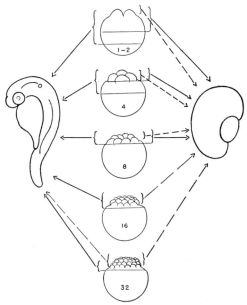

Fig. 109. Results of removal of blastodiscs with varying amounts of yolk, followed by culture in Holtfreter's solution. Interrupted arrows: work of Oppenheimer ('36c) on Fundulus; solid arrows, that of Tung, Chang and Tung ('45) on Carassius. In the first series, the blastodiscs were invariably removed clean of yolk; in the second, a small amount of yolk was always left adherent, and in early stages differing amounts of yolk, as indicated, were purposely included. The diagram shows only the most radical results; fragments capable of forming complete embryos may also develop incompletely in many cases.

Agassiz and Whitman, 1884) in Gobius and Ctenolabrus; there is a possibility that an important step in differentiation is involved here.

Morgan was the first to report that the entire yolk mass is not necessary to the differentiation of the embryonic axis in teleosts. Figure 109 summarizes and compares the relations worked out more recently in Fundulus and Carassius, independently. Blastodiscs were removed, with or without some yolk, as indicated, and cultured in saline medium. Results ranged from non-gastrulating "hyperblastulae" through varying degrees of abnormal or defective embryo formation, to quite perfect embryos. In general, the results suggest comparable progressive

changes in the two forms. Fundulus blastodiscs may form hyperblastulae after isolation at any stage. The 32-celled stage is the youngest isolate able to form an embryo. In Carassius, the eight-celled blastodisc, isolated except for a minimal quantity of yolk, is the oldest stage capable of forming a hyperblastula. Occasionally this type of isolate may form an embryo. In younger stages, three-fifths of the yolk must be included

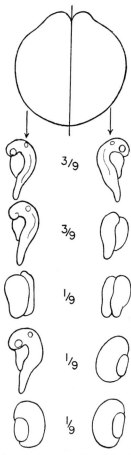

Fig. 110. Summary of results of Tung and Tung ('44) on raising both halves of bisected eggs. The frequency and types of result are schematized below. A half-egg may form a complete or nearly complete embryo, a defective embryo, or a hyperblastula. Out of nine successfully raised pairs, three consisted of two nearly complete embryos, one of two hyperblastulae, and the rest, as indicated, showed intermediate combinations.

(1- and 2-celled stages) or half the yolk (4-celled stage) if an embryo is to result. Explants with less yolk fail to gastrulate or to form axes. These results may possibly indicate, as the authors suggest, a flow of material necessary for gastrulation upward from the equator, reaching the blastodisc at about the time of the third cleavage in Carassius but later in Fundulus.

The types of abnormality appearing in cultured blastodiscs seem not to be the same in Carassius as in Fundulus, and may imply some morphodynamic divergence. In the former, trunk axis seems to differentiate in preference to head or tail; in the latter, head differentiates preferentially whereas trunk and tail are most easily suppressed. Devillers ('49) suggests that these differences may be referred to distinctive patterns of axial elongation in the two species. This is probably only part of the story; interpretation should perhaps be deferred until the course of morphogenetic movements in Carassius is understood.

In addition to the latitudinal separation of the cleaving egg, Tung and Tung ('44) have succeeded in a remarkable feat, the meridional bisection of the whole egg at the 2-celled stage or later, followed by the rearing of both halves. Nine such pairs are described in their report: Figure 110 attempts to summarize these descriptions. It is seen that the successful pairs range from two perfect embryos down to two non-gastrulating fragments. Some particularly interesting pairs occurred: one case of two complete embryos showed slight complementary asymmetry reminiscent of amphibian embryo pairs obtained by constriction methods (Spemann and Falkenberg, '19). In another remarkable pair, the notochord is confined to one member, and is disproportionately large; the nerve cord appears quite normal in the deficient twin, where the position of the chorda is occupied by median somites. The interpretations that unilateral localization (in the yolk mass) of material necessary for gastrulation is responsible for this series of results, or that some spatial localization of chorda material in the blastodisc is indicated, are possible but not necessary conclusions from such a series as this. Clearly, defective gastrulation is indicated in many cases; localized materials may or may not play a role.

In summary, then, while some experiments on Fundulus indicate great plasticity of organization during cleavage, this form is possibly not completely equipotent, nor, probably, is Carassius. We are not yet in a position to analyze these differences. In both forms, some progressive stabilization of material within the blastodisc seems to occur, making it able to carry on development independently of the yolk over the subsequent period. Devillers ('47, '49) has shown that at the end of the cleavage period, the blastodisc of the small-yolked egg of Esox is similarly independent, whereas that of Salmo must have a carbohydrate source in the culture medium.

At present the cleavage stage in the bird's egg is terra incognita experimentally; it is possible only to make conjectures based on the situation found after laying; this will be discussed in the following section.

EVENTS DURING GASTRULATION

In the meroblastic eggs under consideration, the blastula stage is the period during which a cell size characteristic of the species is being established in the blastodisc, which thus acquires stable epithelial properties. A constant subgerminal cavity indicates equilibration of fluid relations between yolk and blastoderm. At this time are initiated the major changes of form which continue through gastrulation to the molding of the embryonic axis.

In the teleost, rapid spreading of the blastodisc is combined with thickening and invagination of material at the peripheral blastopore or germ ring. The hypothesis expressed by Lewis ('49) that this epiboly is due to contraction of the yolk gel layer, pulling the blastoderm down over the yolk, has inspired considerable experimental work. In the trout egg, Devillers ('51b) points out that independent movements of the blastodisc in relation to its specific substratum (the periblast) are of at least as much importance as any gel-layer contraction. Trinkaus ('51) gives strong evidence against the effectiveness of any gel-layer traction in Fundulus, and substitutes the interpretation that the gel-layer controls and coordinates growth of the blastodisc, but that the growth itself is due to factors intrinsic in the disc, or in its relation to the periblast. The latter structure he has shown to have remarkable independent powers: in the absence of a blastodisc it can spread over the yolk and even close a "blastopore." The gel layer, he submits, solates as the periblast margin advances, and hence cannot exert traction on either periblast or blastodisc.

In the avian egg, the blastoderm also spreads rapidly over the yolk, and Schlesinger ('52) has recently shown this to be due to active growth of the cellular margin. Movements of invagination, however, are confined to the central posterior area, where there is established the elongated blastopore more commonly known as the primitive streak. Figure 111 is intended to illustrate the broad lines of these morphogenetic differences during the gastrulation period. The striking features here are the peripheral

longitudinal line and its closure hence entirely dissociated from the overgrowth of the yolk by the periphery of the blastoderm.

The diagrams of Figure 111A, taken from the sequence in Fundulus, can serve as a model for teleost development only in a very

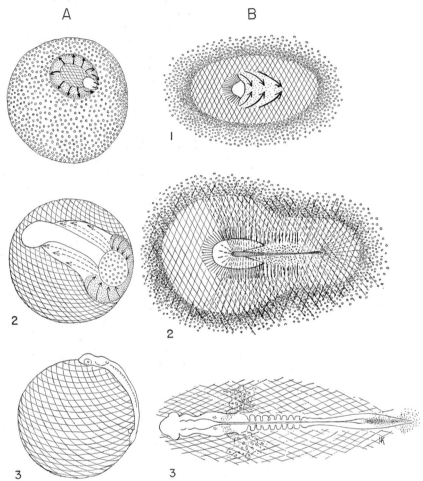

A   B

1

2   2

3   3

Fig. 111. Diagrams comparing major prospective divisions of the germ in (A) teleost (Fundulus: Oppenheimer, '37) and (B) chick (Rudnick, '48; Spratt, '52) during gastrulation and later. For obvious reasons most of the yolk mass is omitted in the chick figures. White: ectoderm. Radiating lines in B1 and B2: non-medullary ectoderm. Stippled: superficial material which will later be invaginated. Broken lines: invaginated material. Mesh: extraembryonic ectoderm. Circles: yolk. 1, Blastula stage; 2, late gastrula, blastopore nearly closed; 3, embryo formed.

position of the material to be invaginated, in the teleost blastoderm, as contrasted with its central-posterior position in the bird; conversely, the central position of the extraembryonic material in the fish, and the peripheral location of all extraembryonic material in the bird. The blastopore in the first case is the periphery of the disc; in the second case, it is reduced to a central

general way. Fish eggs vary widely in their proportion of protoplasm to yolk, in the relative time necessary for closure of the blastopore, and hence in the relation of axis formation to invagination. The two best-known forms experimentally, Salmo and Fundulus, are widely separated in the series. Figure 112 diagrams comparable stages as regards blastopore closure in these eggs;

the marked precocity of axis formation in the large-yolked Salmo is thus made clear. On the enlarged diagrams of the early gastrula at the top, prospective areas have been projected in lateral view. As in the case of all vertebrates so far studied, invagina-

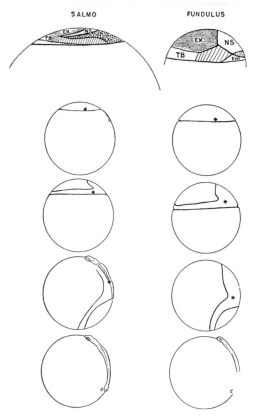

Fig. 112. Comparative lateral diagrams of prospective areas in the early gastrula and diagrams of gastrulation stages. White: prospective nervous system. Stippled: prospective chorda. Oblique lines: future somites. Shaded: extraembryonic area (yolk sac). *TB*, tailbud material; *Ent*, entoderm. The boundary between chorda and entoderm in the Fundulus diagram is purely conventional; experimentally it has not been specified. The asterisk in the gastrulation series represents the migration of a group of cells on the germ ring into the somite mesoderm. (From Pasteels, '36a; Oppenheimer, '36b, '37.)

tion of material to lower layers is accompanied by marked convergence of both invaginating and superficial material to the dorsal midline of the future embryo. Hence, prospective areas for nervous system, chorda and other mesoderm extend at first some distance laterally to the position they will later occupy. The convergence movements

in the mesoderm are summarily indicated by migration of the asterisk in the lower figures. Contrary to what might be expected a priori, the trout blastodisc, which has so much centrifugal growth and stretching to accomplish, likewise undergoes much more marked convergence movements. Mesodermal trunk material in Fundulus lies originally closer to the embryonic shield than it does in Salmo. In both, ultimately, the ventral lip enters the tailbud.

For the avian embryo, we have almost no comparative material for this period; our information derives almost exclusively from the egg of the domestic fowl. Surface diagrams are presented in Figure 113 for the stages corresponding to those just indicated for teleosts. What emerges from the sometimes conflicting studies is that the following order of gastrulation takes place: (1) The hypoblast is formed by a process of sporadic delamination from the posterior region of the pellucid area; this process is not shown in the diagrams of Figure 113. (2) In the same general region, the primitive streak appears soon afterward as an irregular thickening, followed by invagination and emigration of mesoderm beneath the superficial layer. The first invaginated mesoderm moves laterally and posteriorly, becoming extraembryonic. The posterior part of the streak through which it invaginates thus corresponds roughly to the ventrolateral blastopore lips. (3) Gradually, more anterior material is incorporated in the streak and anterolateral emigration of mesoderm ensues; the front end of the streak thus corresponds to the dorsal half of the blastopore. The anteriormost axial mesoderm remains in the lower layers of the anterior streak for considerable time: this concentration of material constitutes Hensen's node. Lateral and extraembryonic mesoderm continues to invaginate through the posterior three-fourths of the streak even after the axial mesoderm, as notochord and somites, is elongating and differentiating anterior to the node.

This order of events in the chick is clearly associated with convergence of superficial areas toward the invaginating zone, the most extensive migration being performed by the more peripheral *area pellucida* regions which enter the early (posterior) primitive streak. The arrows in Figure 111*B–1* are intended to show the approximate extent of convergence. The movements thus differ in order, tempo and magnitude from those outlined for the teleost.

In both types, it should be noted, convergence and concentration of material that is to enter the embryonic axis is in sharp contrast to thinning and rapid epibolic spreading of material destined to be extraembryonic. Luther ('37) was able to show an antagonism between embryo formation

tion from the rest of the blastoderm. Future ventral or extraembryonic areas react to explantation in vitro by spreading and vesiculating (Rudnick, '38b).

In embryonic and extraembryonic areas, in teleost and chick, before and during gastrulation, the innate migration tendencies of

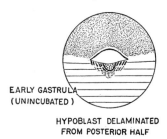

EARLY GASTRULA
(UNINCUBATED)

HYPOBLAST DELAMINATED
FROM POSTERIOR HALF

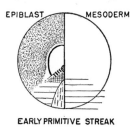

EPIBLAST — MESODERM

EARLY PRIMITIVE STREAK

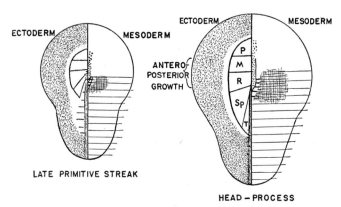

ECTODERM — MESODERM

ANTERO-POSTERIOR GROWTH

ECTODERM — MESODERM

LATE PRIMITIVE STREAK

HEAD — PROCESS

Fig. 113. Gastrulation stages in the chick: prospective areas, from marking experiments by Wetzel ('29), Pasteels ('36b), Spratt ('46, '47, '52), Spratt and Condon ('47). In all but the unincubated stage, the left half shows superficial areas, the right half, invaginated mesoderm. The following prospective areas are indicated: extraembryonic ectoderm, shaded. Embryonic ectoderm, white: the medullary plate is enclosed by a heavy line and its anteroposterior levels demarked in the head-process diagram as *P*, prosencephalon; *M*, mesencephalon; *R*, rhombencephalon; *Sp*, spinal cord; *T*, tail nerve cord. Chorda and prechordal plate, stippled. Mesodermal somites, heavy parallel lines. Heart, cross-hatched. Lateral plate and extraembryonic mesoderm, light horizontal lines. The blastopore or primitive streak is indicated by vertical shading. The boundaries of the posterior and lateral mesodermal areas are conjectural; those of the anterior axis (notochord and somites) as well as of the ectodermal areas have been carefully mapped by Spratt and his co-workers, on explanted blastoderms. In the head-process stage, the region of greatest anteroposterior growth, most pronounced in the median line, is bracketed. (Spratt, '47; Gaertner, '49.)

and epiboly by defect experiments in Salmo. In this same form, Devillers ('48a) has shown that the onset of gastrulation introduces a marked localization of the spreading tendency, which becomes restricted to the future extraembryonic region at that time (cf. Fig. 114). This may indicate the first appearance of a relatively persistent physiological differentiation between these two major areas.

In the chick, explanation experiments show a similar characteristic tendency of axial materials to condense, even in isola-

the epithelia do not interfere with wound healing, or with regulation of excised parts, provided the latter are not disproportionately large. The role of the surface coat in this process has been studied for the trout egg by Devillers ('48a, '51b), in Fundulus by Trinkaus ('49, '51). No surface coat as such has been demonstrated in the chick blastoderm or yolk, but the behavior of the former after lesions would indicate that a continuous intercellular material must be present and must function similarly after wound healing.

It has been emphasized for the chick that invagination in the primitive streak must involve a de-epithelization process (Waddington and Taylor, '37) where individual cells lose connection with other cells (detach from the surface coat?) and become rounded and heaped up in the streak. Evidence from a wide variety of histological and histochemical studies is continually accumulating to indicate that this invagination process is accompanied by a whole series of cellular

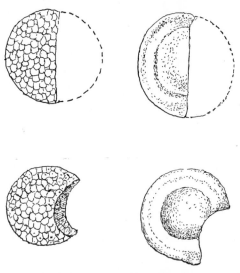

Fig. 114. Healing of trout blastodisc after removal of one-half its substance. Left side, morula stage. The lower figure shows that wound healing and closure take place evenly from all sides. Right, gastrula stage. Only the ventral (top) half stretches to heal the wound (see lower figure). (After Devillers, '48a, Fig. 55.)

changes: increased affinity for dyes in the upper layers of the streak at least; increased reducing capacity for oxidation-reduction indicators (Rulon, '35); loss of lipids upon invagination (Jacobson, '38); increased ribonucleic acid content followed by its loss in laterally migrating mesoderm—not, evidently, in the axial mesoderm which migrates anteriorly (Gallera and Oprecht, '48); increased sulfhydryl (reported by Brachet; cf. also Buño, '51); concentration of indophenol oxidase and phosphatase (Moog, '43, '44). The anteroposterior gradient of activity observed so frequently in these studies on the streak is of course morphologically a dorsoventral gradient of the blastopore and may be at least in part a function of differential massing and tempo of invagination of cells in the different parts of the streak.

In the teleost, invagination is primarily an ingression of a continuous sheet of cells; Devillers ('51b) has figured in Salmo the process of loss of connection with the surface coat, as in the amphibian gastrula, and has also described loss of basophilia during the process. According to Oppenheimer ('36b), some individual detachment of cells from anterior portions of the embryonic shield epiblast, to join the mesoderm, occurs in addition to ingression at the dorsal lip. It is difficult to avoid comparing these de-epithelizations to the more radical experimental situation demonstrated by Holtfreter ('47) in explants of amphibian ectoderm, where neural differentiation appears to be associated with the margin of the epithelial mass, under conditions promoting slight cytolysis and eventual sloughing of cells.

The experimental analysis of the amphibian egg has led to the identification of the region actively concerned in induction of central nervous system, with the invaginating chordamesoderm. It would be expected from the distribution of the latter areas that Salmo and Fundulus (cf. Fig. 112) might also differ in spatial extent of material capable of performing the primary induction. This property has not been compared directly in the two forms. It is known, for both, that a bit of dorsal lip or already invaginated material will induce a supernumerary axis from material that would not normally form dorsal axis. A phenomenon that would seem to bear some relation to such direct tests of induction is the differentiation of axial tissues in isolated pieces or grafts taken from regions which normally do not contribute to the dorsal axis. In Salmo in the blastula stage, according to Luther ('36a), all quadrants of the blastoderm are equipotent for the formation of axial structures when grafted to the yolk sac of hatched fry. It is hard to imagine that the neural tubes in these grafts arose by independent differentiation of ventral ectoderm: we are forced to interpret such formations as "self-organizations" involving release, among other things, of some latent neural-plate–inducing potency somewhere in the isolate.

The ability of the ventral side of the trout blastoderm to form an axis when released from the influence of the dorsal side was confirmed (Luther, '37) by combining two ventral half-blastulae: an axis regularly formed, usually from the half that was slightly younger. Devillers ('51a) in extending this work has made the striking discovery that if the preparation is made using as a host

culiarities of the ectoderm at the tips of the limb buds in the chick, point to how much there remains to learn about the properties of non-neural ectoderm.

THE LOWER LAYERS

As gastrulation progresses, not only do induction capacity, neural competence, and the specific competences for different levels in the ectoderm become gradually restricted to the appropriate embryonic area: the invaginating layers themselves ultimately must become a mosaic of areas of definite differentiation tendencies. It is believed that all these areas have at first the properties of *fields*, of indefinite boundaries, possibly overlapping one another. Toward the time of beginning morphogenesis, the boundaries of the fields evidently become more restricted and more precise, as if brought into focus by some microscope capable of reading the future; each field then coincides with the corresponding organ-forming area.

In the forms under discussion, our experimental knowledge of this course of events in the lower layers is based only on the results of transplantation experiments in which at least two layers were involved, and which resulted in differentiation of complexes of several tissues. The desirable isolation experiment has not yet been technically possible. The succession of figures which form the matter of the present section is an abstraction, presented in order to help the reader to visualize, for each major embryonic structure, the spatial distribution of its origin in grafts, delimited as well as the experimental material allows. Many of the studies on which these abstractions are based have not been carried through to the stage where the potency field corresponds with the actual organ-forming area; but the tendency in that direction is clearly observable.

Figure 117 deals with the axial mesoderm, in so far as notochord and somites (or skeletal muscle) are found to occur differentially in grafts of parts of blastoderms. The reported data are unsatisfactory for the blastula stage; in particular the distributions indicated for the chick (Fig. 117D, J) in the unincubated stage are based on a few positive cases and may not be valid. The trout, however, shows an understandable sequence, with a notochord field converging toward the dorsal lip (Fig. 117B, C), followed by later invaginated somite material (Fig. 117H, I). The strict delimitation of

the chorda field in the chick gastrula (Fig. 117E, F) is in striking contrast, and would indicate that this structure, at least, is localized relatively early in the latter form—a

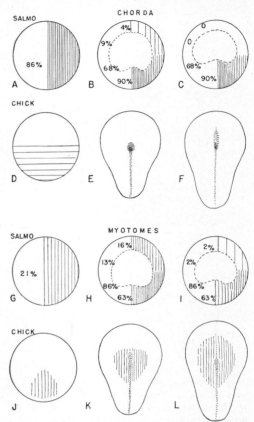

Fig. 117. Progressive changes in fields for production of chorda and somites in grafts from Salmo (Luther, '36a) and the chick (Butler, '35; Hunt, '31, '32; Rudnick, '32; Rawles, '36). In the diagrams for Salmo, the left half of the figure shows the actual percentages of differentiation in various sectors, on which the scheme of the right half is based. No such quantitative estimate has been attempted in the case of the chick. Localization in blastula stages is based on very incomplete information, which may be of no significance. The marked restriction of chorda-forming material in the chick (E,F) is based on reliable data. The extent of the somite field in the chick (J,K,L) is based merely on differentiation of skeletal muscle, and so is not critical, nor are the lateral boundaries established.

condition not reached even in the late gastrula in Salmo.

The interpretation of this localization in the chick is not easy, as examination of Figure 118 will lead us to reflect. Here we have similar figures showing progressive localization of two more lateral mesodermal

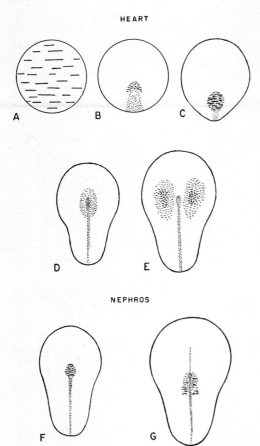

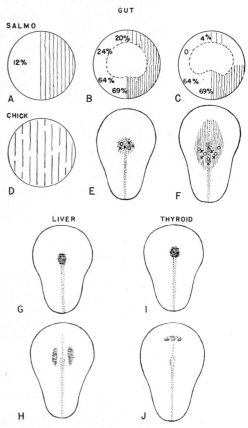

region gives the highest proportion of differentiation of each tissue. It is possible that the thick mesodermal streak in this area contains definitely localized autonomous primordia of notochord and somites, as well as still migrating heart and nephros fields; the results could equally well be interpreted on the basis of high concentration of growth factors plus a few key inducing substances, quite irrespective of morphological localizations.

Entodermal derivatives must largely be considered in association with mesodermal ones. Grafts from trout blastodiscs show a distribution not very different from that of somites, for example, for gut tubules (Fig. 119A–C). In the chick, the progressive pat-

Fig. 118. Progressive localization in the chick of heart muscle and nephros (Butler, '35; Rudnick, '32, '38b,c; Rawles, '43). The situation in the unincubated blastoderm is somewhat uncertain; it is possible that some localization exists even then. It is established that as soon as the primitive streak appears (B,C), a limited area only can form cardiac muscle in vitro or in grafts (D,E), and that until the head-process stage the median part of this area is most active. In E and G the boundaries of the areas have been carefully determined; in the other stages, they are somewhat conjectural, the shaded areas representing positive cases.

structures: heart and nephros. Heart-forming areas (i.e., those which will form cardiac muscle) follow fairly well the course that would be expected of invaginating lateral mesoderm, as probably does the more posterior nephric field. A comparison of the various diagrams for the definitive primitive streak stage (Figs. 117E, 118D,F) shows a remarkable concentration of potencies in the immediate vicinity of Hensen's node: an expression of the experimental fact that grafts from this center develop into larger, more varied masses than do more lateral or anterior or posterior regions; the medianmost

Fig. 119. Localization of entodermal potencies: A–C from Luther ('36a); D–F from Butler ('35), Rudnick and Rawles ('37); G–J from Rudnick ('32) and Rawles ('36); data all from grafts. In the chick material, lateral and posterior limits of areas have not been determined in stages earlier than the head process. In D–F, the shading indicates gut not formed into recognizable organ units; crosses, organized small intestine; circles, identifiable segments of colon.

terns, if we compare definitive streak stages for entoderm and heart (Fig. 119E, G, I; Fig. 118D) with the corresponding head-process diagrams (Fig. 119F, H, J; Fig. 118E), are understandable on the basis of migration toward definitive positions: thyroid anteriorly, liver laterally, intestine posteriorly. The lateral movement of median material and a sharp anterior stretching of material just in front of the node correspond with known germinal movements. In these cases, at least, the hypothesis of migration of definitely localized cell groups in mesoderm and entoderm, together, is tenable and preferable.

Of recent years there has been a tendency to focus attention on the heart area not only as an early autonomous region, present at least as early as localized dorsal axial material, but also as possibly playing an organizing role in the anteroventral region of the body analogous to that of the dorsal lip for the dorsal axis. Direct evidence for this view is lacking; the considerations are early autonomy of the heart, and its tendency to be associated with foregut structures (pharynx, thyroid, liver) in experimental situations.

In the case of the intestine (Fig. 119E, F), no cell migrations have been described that will account for the posterior displacement of the area during the head-process stage. It is only fair to say that they have not been looked for, and that the mesodermal portion of the streak would be the place to look. There is evidence that in gut formation, mesoderm plays a large role (Hunt, '37) and that hypoblast is, to say the least, dispensable in the process. It would be very convenient if such slight but definite posterior displacement of mesoderm in the streak could be found, since it would then explain very well the posterior expansion of the mesonephric area between the definitive primitive streak and head-process stages, indicated in Figure 118F, G; this material might be considered to undergo a spurt of posterolateral migration at this time, and to push the lateral plate ahead of it, posterior and lateral to the node field.

CONCLUDING REMARKS

The meroblastic vertebrate eggs, by their pattern of differentiation within the ovary, have realized an almost complete separation of the factors and materials involved in primary differentiation, from those necessary for later growth. Thus most teleost blastodiscs can very early be separated from the yolk and complete most of the histogenetic and embryogenetic sequence in a saline medium. The trout and chick blastodiscs differ in requiring at least some carbohydrate from outside (Spratt, '49; Devillers, '49) in order to carry through a comparable sequence of events. It is doubtful if these isolates grow to any appreciable degree, if a rigorous definition of growth as increase in mass be insisted on; by contrast, differentiation is remarkably complete. Whether this primary semi-independent phase is also represented in some form in holoblastic eggs, and whether a key to developmental kinetics may be seen in this feature and its variants, is not certain.

Within the protoplasmic blastodisc of both fish and bird, it seems safe to say that any differentials present during cleavage are fairly easily reversed or negated. That differentials exist in the fish egg would be indicated by some varieties of experiment where injury or separation results in a defective embryo; to balance these, there are clearcut cases of totipotence of halves or even quarters of the blastodisc, continuing up to the blastula stage. Parts of the whole can, when suitably isolated, become wholes themselves. Whether every part of the germ shares this property is still debatable.

At some time, during or after the onset of gastrulation, some fairly stable differentials appear. Thus in Fundulus the dorsal lip region, as soon as identifiable, has potencies sharply different from those of the rest of the circumference of the blastodisc; this situation appears to be achieved only gradually in Salmo. Similarly, the duck egg at laying is evidently largely equipotent, whereas all our information on the unincubated chick egg points to the posterior or blastoporal sector as having properties not shared by other regions. Thus within each group are found variations of timing.

Between the two groups, bird and fish, is the major and striking difference of spatial pattern: the position of the blastopore, the relative rate of its formation, the continuity of invagination, and complexities of movement in the blastoporal area itself. We can contrast the elaborate history of the primitive streak, with its posteroanterior order of appearance, its delayed invagination and emigration, and its complex incompletely understood pattern of cellular movement, with what seems to be a much more simple and direct invagination pattern in the teleost. It must be said, however, that great technical difficulties have impeded study of details of invagination in the fish, and that the notion that the process is simple may merely indicate our ignorance.

Gastrulation, then, shifts germinal regions having a tentative or reversible pattern into definitive positions related to the blastopore. The axial ectoderm, whatever its primary pattern, is undoubtedly given its final stamp of independent differentiation tendency by the mesoderm that comes to underlie it. As for the invaginated material, there is no evidence in the fish, and but one case in the chick (heart), to show that any specific differentiation tendency is present before the material undergoes invagination. At this stage of our knowledge, then, most of the embryonic fields appear to originate at gastrulation. Whatever future investigations will show, it is clear that gastrulation is a critical process, separating and reinforcing if not originating the embryonic pattern of potential areas.

We know too little of the details of any two of the experimental forms under discussion to compare accurately the course of events whereby any one field moves into definitive position and becomes restricted to the territory of its embryonic anlage. In the teleost neurula we seem to have a fairly well localized system; defects made in the axis may not even be regulated. In the chick, regulation of some parts remains possible for considerable time. Are these differences real, or an accident of the difference in absolute size and scale of organization between the two embryos, whereby it is difficult to make a really minute defect in the teleost, without much subsidiary damage? Again, in gastrulation stages, it is clear that Fundulus behaves much as the amphibian embryo does, in that transplants to the embryonic shield are induced to form a variety of structures, somewhat but not exactly corresponding to the level of the host axis: a result presumably of the wide imprecise nature of the host induction fields. In the chick, no convincing experiments show such histological effect of host on transplant, though polarity may be decidedly affected (Waddington and Schmidt, '33). This peculiarity may be only because the usual transplant tested is a piece of primitive streak, the normal fate of which is not known precisely, or because the chick blastoderm reacts in a special way to transplanted tissue: either by joining with it inextricably in a complex induction, or by walling it off, physiologically speaking, so that it develops as a separate intrusive graft.

It is obvious that in every way the picture we construct of the progressive invisible changes in any embryo, leading to visible differentiation, depends on the experiments possible with that embryo. Slight differences in texture or in chemical surface, perhaps, may determine whether it is possible to make transplants or explants of any given portion; whether defects will heal or an epithelium respond to induction. These factors are only a small part of the equipment of embryonic cells, but they loom very large experimentally. If we are to be able to make valid comparisons, our task must be to disentangle these properties from the intrinsic genetic mechanisms, and to discover the role of both in cellular differentiation. This is for the future.

REFERENCES

The following list contains only titles actually cited in the text. Recent comprehensive reviews of the material covered are to be found in Oppenheimer ('47), Rudnick ('44, '48), and Waddington ('52).

Agassiz, L., and Whitman, C. O. 1884 On the development of some pelagic fish eggs. Proc. Am. Acad. Arts & Sci., 20:23–75.

Alexander, L. E. 1937 An experimental study of the role of optic cup and overlying ectoderm in lens formation in the chick embryo. J. Exp. Zool., 75:41–68.

Bartelmez, G. W. 1912 The bilaterality of the pigeon's eggs. J. Morph., 23:269–329.

Brachet, Jean 1944 Embryologie Chimique. Masson, Paris.

Buño, W. 1951 Localization of sulfhydryl groups in the chick embryo. Anat. Rec., 111:123–128.

Butler, Elizabeth 1935 The developmental capacity of regions of the unincubated chick blastoderm as tested in chorio-allantoic grafts. J. Exp. Zool., 70:357–389.

Clapp, Cornelia 1891 Some points in the development of the toad-fish (Batrachus tau). J. Morph., 5:494–501.

Clarke, L. F. 1936 Regional differences in eye-forming capacity of the early chick blastoderm as studied in chorio-allantoic grafts. Physiol. Zool., 9:102–128.

Devillers, Ch. 1947 Explantations in vitro de blastodermes de Poissons (Salmo, Esox). Experientia, 3:71–74.

——— 1948a Le cortex de l'oeuf de Truite. Ann. Stat. Cent. d'Hydrobiologie appl., 2:29–49.

——— 1948b Suppression du matériel chordal dans la gastrula de Truite. Compt. rend. Acad. sci., 227:1411–1413.

——— 1949 Explantations en milieu synthétique de blastodermes de Truite (Salmo irideus). J. Cyto-embryol. Belgo-Neérland., pp. 67–73.

——— 1951a Symétrisation et régulation du germe chez la Truite. Compt. rend. Ass. Anat. Nancy, XXXVIII Réun., pp. 1–7.

——— 1951b Les mouvements superficiels dans

la gastrulation des poissons. Arch. d'Anat. Microscop., *40*:298–309.

Eakin, R. M. 1939 Regional determination in the development of the trout. Roux' Arch. Entw.-mech., *139*:274–281.

Gaertner, R. A. 1949 Development of the posterior trunk and tail of the chick embryo. J. Exp. Zool., *111*:157–174.

Gallera, J., and Oprecht, E. 1948 Sur la distribution des substances basophiles cytoplasmiques dans le blastoderme de la Poule. Rev. suisse Zool., *55*:243–250.

Hoadley, L. 1928 On the localization of developmental potencies in the embryo of *Fundulus heteroclitus.* J. Exp. Zool., *52*:7–44.

Holtfreter, J. 1947 Neural induction in explants which have passed through a sublethal cytolysis. J. Exp. Zool., *106*:197–222.

Hunt, T. E. 1931 An experimental study of the independent differentiation of the isolated Hensen's node and its relation to the formation of axial and non-axial parts in the chick embryo. J. Exp. Zool., *59*:395–427.

———— 1932 Potencies of transverse levels of the chick blastoderm in the definitive-streak stage. Anat. Rec., *55*:41–70.

———— 1937 The development of gut and its derivatives from the mesectoderm and mesentoderm of early chick blastoderms. Anat. Rec., *68*:349–370.

Jacobson, W. 1938 The early development of the avian embryo. II. J. Morph., *62*:445–488.

Levi-Montalcini, R. 1946 Ricerche sperimentali sulla determinazione del placode otico nell'embrione di pollo. Accad. Naz. Lincei Rendic. Cl. Sci. fis-mat. e nat., ser. VIII, *1*:445–448.

Lewis, W. H. 1912 Experiments on localization in the eggs of a teleost fish (*Fundulus heteroclitus*). Anat. Rec., *6*:1–6.

———— 1949 Gel layers of cells and eggs and their role in early development. Roscoe B. Jackson Mem. Lab. Lect., pp. 59–77.

————, and Roosen-Runge, E. C. 1942 The formation of the blastodisc in the egg of the zebra fish, *Brachydanio rerio*, illustrated with motion pictures. Anat. Rec., *84*:463.

Luther, W. 1935 Entwicklungsphysiologische Untersuchungen am Forellenkeim: die Rolle des Organisationszentrums bei der Entstehung der Embryonalanlage. Biol. Zbl., *55*:114–137.

———— 1936a Potenzprüfungen an isolierten Teilstücken der Forellenkeimscheibe. Roux' Arch. Entw.-mech., *135*:359–383.

———— 1936b Austausch von präsumptiver Epidermis und Medullarplatte beim Forellenkeim. Roux' Arch. Entw.-mech., *135*:384–388.

———— 1937 Transplantations- und Defektversuche am Organisationszentrum der Forellenkeimscheibe. Roux' Arch. Entw.-mech., *137*:404–424.

Lutz, H. 1948 Sur l'obtention expérimentale de la polyembryonie chez le Canard. Compt. rend. Soc. Biol., *142*:384–385.

McKeehan, M. S. 1951 Cytological aspects of embryonic lens induction in the chick. J. Exp. Zool., *117*:31–64.

Moog, Florence 1943 Cytochrome oxidase in early chick embryos. J. Cell. Comp. Physiol., *22*:223–231.

———— 1944 Localizations of alkaline and acid phosphatases in the early embryogenesis of the chick. Biol. Bull., *86*:51–80.

Morgan, T. H. 1893 Experimental studies on teleost eggs. Anat. Anz., *8*:803–814.

Nicholas, J. S., and Oppenheimer, J. M. 1942 Regulation and reconstitution in Fundulus. J. Exp. Zool., *90*:127–157.

Oppenheimer, J. M. 1934 Experiments on early developing stages of Fundulus. Proc. Nat. Acad. Sci., *20*:536–538.

———— 1935 Processes of localization in developing Fundulus. Proc. Nat. Acad. Sci., *21*:551–553.

———— 1936a Transplantation experiments on developing teleosts (Fundulus and Perca). J. Exp. Zool., *72*:409–437.

———— 1936b Processes of localization in developing Fundulus. J. Exp. Zool., *73*:405–444.

———— 1936c The development of isolated blastoderms of *Fundulus heteroclitus.* J. Exp. Zool., *72*:247–269.

———— 1937 The normal stages of *Fundulus heteroclitus.* Anat. Rec., *68*:1–8.

———— 1938 Potencies for differentiation in the teleostean germ ring. J. Exp. Zool. *79*:185–212.

———— 1947 Organization of the teleost blastoderm. Quart. Rev. Biol., *22*:105–118.

Pasteels, J. 1936a Études sur la gastrulation des vertébrés méroblastiques. I. Téléostéens. Arch. Biol., *47*:205–308.

———— 1936b Analyse des mouvements morphogénétiques de gastrulation chez les oiseaux. Bull. Acad. Roy. Belg., series V, *22*:737–752.

Rauber, A. 1883 Neue Grundlegungen zur Kenntnis der Zelle. Morph. Jb., *8*:233–338.

Rawles, M. E. 1936 A study in the localization of organ-forming areas in the chick blastoderm of the head-process stage. J. Exp. Zool., *72*:271–315.

———— 1943 The heart-forming areas of the chick blastoderm. Physiol. Zool., *16*:22–41.

Roosen-Runge, E. C. 1938 On the early development—bipolar differentiation and cleavage—of the zebra fish, *Brachydanio rerio.* Biol. Bull., *75*:119–133.

Rudnick, D. 1932 Thyroid-forming potencies of the early chick blastoderm. J. Exp. Zool., *62*:287–317.

———— 1938a Contribution to the problem of neurogenic potency in post-nodal isolates from chick blastoderms. J. Exp. Zool., *78*:369–383.

———— 1938b Differentiation in culture of pieces of the early chick blastoderm. I. Anat. Rec., *70*:351–368.

———— 1938c Differentiation in culture of pieces of the early chick blastoderm. II. J. Exp. Zool., *79*:399–427.

———— 1944 Early history and mechanics of the chick blastoderm. Quart. Rev. Biol., *19*:187–212.

———— 1945 Limb-forming potencies of the chick blastoderm: including notes on associated trunk structures. Trans. Conn. Acad. Arts & Sci., *36*:353–377.

Rudnick, D.   1948   Prospective areas and differentiation potencies in the chick blastoderm. Ann. N. Y. Acad. Sci., 49:761–772.

——, and Rawles, M. E.   1937   Differentiation of the gut in chorio-allantoic grafts from chick blastoderms. Physiol. Zool., 10:381–395.

Rulon, O.   1935   Differential reduction of Janus green during development of the chick. Protoplasma, 24:346–364.

Saunders, J. W., Jr.   1948   The proximo-distal sequence of origin of the parts of the chick wing and the role of the ectoderm. J. Exp. Zool., 108: 363–403.

Schlesinger, A. B.   1952   Analysis of growth of the chick marginal blastoderm. Science, 116:64–65.

Seevers, C. H.   1932   Potencies of the end bud and other caudal levels of the early chick embryo with special reference to the origin of the metanephros. Anat. Rec., 54:217–246.

Spek, J.   1933   Die bipolare Differenzierung des Protoplasmas des Teleosteer-Eies und ihre Entstehung. Protoplasma, 18:497–545.

Spemann, H., and Falkenberg, H.   1919   Über asymmetrische Entwicklung und Situs inversus viscerum bei Zwillingen und Doppelbildungen. Roux' Arch. Entw.-mech. 45:371–422.

Spratt, N. T., Jr.   1942   Location of organ-specific regions and their relationship to the development of the primitive streak in the early chick blastoderm. J. Exp. Zool., 89:69–101.

——   1946   Formation of the primitive streak in the explanted chick blastoderm marked with carbon particles. J. Exp. Zool., 103:259–304.

——   1947   Regression and shortening of the primitive streak in the explanted chick blastoderm. J. Exp. Zool., 104:69–100.

——   1949   Nutritional requirements of the early chick embryo. I. J. Exp. Zool., 110:273–298.

——   1952   Localization of the prospective neural plate in the early chick blastoderm. J. Exp. Zool., 120:109–130.

——, and Condon, Leon   1947   Localization of prospective chorda and somite mesoderm during regression of the primitive streak. Anat. Rec., 99: 653.

Stockard, C. R.   1907   The artificial production of a single median cyclopian eye in the fish embryo by means of sea water solutions of magnesium chlorid. Roux' Arch. Entw.-mech., 23: 249–258.

Street, S. F.   1937   The differentiation of the nasal area of the chick embryo in grafts. J. Exp. Zool., 77:49–80.

Trinkaus, J. P.   1949   The significance of the periblast in epiboly of the Fundulus egg. Biol. Bull., 97:249.

——   1951   A study of the mechanics of epiboly in the egg of Fundulus heteroclitus. J. Exp. Zool., 118:269–320.

Tung, T. C., Chang, C. Y., and Tung, Y. F. Y.   1945   Experiments on the developmental potencies of blastoderms and fragments of teleostean eggs separated latitudinally. Proc. Zool. Soc. London, 115:175–188.

——, and Tung, T. F. Y.   1944   The development of egg-fragments, isolated blastomeres and fused eggs in the goldfish. Proc. Zool. Soc. London, 114:46–64.

Twiesselmann, F.   1938   Expériences de scisson précoce de l'aire embryogène chez le Poulet. Arch. Biol., 49:285–367.

Waddington, C. H.   1932   Experiments on the development of chick and duck embryos cultivated in vitro. Phil. Trans. Roy. Soc. London, B221: 179–230.

——   1933   Induction by the endoderm in birds. Roux' Arch. Entw.-mech., 128:502–521.

——   1935   The development of isolated parts of the chick blastoderm. J. Exp. Zool., 71:273–288.

——   1937   The determination of the auditory placode in the chick. J. Exp. Biol., 14:232–239.

——   1952   The Epigenetics of Birds. University Press, Cambridge, England.

——, and Schmidt, G. A.   1933   Induction by heteroplastic grafts of the primitive streak in birds. Roux' Arch. Entw.-mech., 128:522–563.

——, and Taylor, J.   1937   Conversion of presumptive ectoderm to mesoderm in the chick. J. Exp. Biol., 14:335–339.

Wetzel, R.   1929   Untersuchungen am Hühnchen. Die Entwicklung des Keims während der ersten beiden Bruttage. Roux' Arch. Entw.-mech., 119: 118–321.

Willier, B. H., and Rawles, M. E.   1935   Organ-forming areas in the early chick blastoderm. Proc. Soc. Exp. Biol. & Med., 32:1293–1296.

Woodside, G. L.   1937   The influence of host age on induction in the chick blastoderm. J. Exp. Zool., 75:259–282.

Yamamoto, T.   1938   Contractile movement of the egg of a bony fish, Salanx microdon. Proc. Imp. Acad. Tokyo, 14:149–151.

Zwilling, E.   1942   Restitution of the tail in the early chick embryo. J. Exp. Zool., 91:453–463.

CHAPTER 3

Selected Invertebrates

RAY L. WATTERSON

PROGRESSIVE differentiation involves changes in the constitution of regions of the egg or of cells or groups of cells which amount to either permanent gains or permanent losses. These changes are accompanied by temporal and spatial restrictions of potencies of the several parts of the egg and embryo as development proceeds.

VISIBLE DIFFERENCES ALONG THE ANIMAL-VEGETAL AXIS OF POLARITY

The earliest visible differences in the eggs of many aquatic invertebrates are those which occur along one heteropolar axis, the animal-vegetal axis of polarity. Similarly, the earliest invisible differentiation in these eggs, as revealed by experimental analysis, usually occurs along this same axis. This axis stands revealed in a variety of ways. Some eggs are more or less elongated along the animal-vegetal axis. The specific weight of the animal half is frequently less than that of the rest of the egg. The germinal vesicle is usually displaced towards the animal pole. Maturation spindles form normally at the animal pole and the polar bodies mark the animal pole insofar as they remain at their point of origin. In many forms a micropyle exists in the chorion at the animal pole, in others at the vegetal pole. More or less striking accumulations of plasm (pole plasms) may occur at the animal pole or at the vegetal pole, or at both. Distinct transverse pigment bands may appear perpendicular to this axis. In some eggs, whether or not a micropyle exists, the sperm enters preferentially in the animal half, in others at the vegetal half; this is a further indication of structural and/or physiological differences at different levels of this axis. Visible differences along the animal-vegetal axis arise at different developmental stages in eggs of different animals. In some eggs, for example those of Dentalium, a

mollusk, such differences are evident before maturation occurs (Wilson, '04a); in these living eggs there is recognizable a white animal pole region, a broad middle transverse pigment girdle, and a white vegetal pole region. In other eggs, changes occur during maturation which reveal the axis of polarity more clearly. For example, in Paracentrotus, a sea urchin, the immature egg contains a uniform distribution of red pigment in the ectoplasm, but after maturation this pigment is concentrated and restricted to a distinct subequatorial transverse band (Boveri, '01) which has proved to be so useful as an indicator of polarity in the hands of Hörstadius. Similarly, in the leech, Clepsine, the visibly distinct animal and vegetal pole plasms are first in evidence after maturation; prior to this time the distribution of yolk and plasm provides no visible evidence of polarity (Schleip, '14). In still other eggs, for example those of the tunicates, the polar axis is only weakly indicated in early stages, but fertilization results in redistributions of visibly different constituents within the egg until their stratification clearly reveals the polar organization. Thus in Styela (Conklin, '05a) the yolk then lies at the animal pole, the yellow material at the vegetal pole, and in between these two layers there is a zone of clear cytoplasm.

Cleavage planes can usually be described readily in relation to the axis of polarity which is revealed as described above: cleavage planes cut through this axis, run parallel or perpendicular to it, micromeres are cut off at the animal pole (annelids, mollusks, ctenophores) or at the vegetal pole (echinoderms, ctenophores), etc. (see Costello, Section V, Chap. 2).

Even more important than this, the animal-vegetal axis of polarity is the chief axis of differentiation. As a rule the material situated near the animal pole may be traced to ectodermal structures, whereas material around the vegetal pole becomes incorporated in entodermal structures. A question immediately arises as to whether the developmental capacities of animal and vegetal halves differ from the earliest stages or whether these differences arise progressively. To date operations have not been possible on ovarian eggs, but certain experiments on uncleaved eggs provide some information bearing on this question.

EXTENT OF SPECIFICATION OF CYTOPLASM ENCOUNTERED IN UNCLEAVED EGGS

Unfertilized eggs of the nemertine, Cerebratulus, can be separated into animal and vegetal halves or into meridional halves. Hörstadius ('37a, p. 335) summarizes his studies on the developmental capacities of such halves as follows: "Our isolation of animal and vegetative halves prior to fertilization confirms the results of Wilson ('03) and Yatsu ('10),—that any fragment of the unfertilized egg may develop into a pilidium."* However, evidence from defect experiments on the egg of Cerebratulus indicates that cytoplasmic specification increases progressively in the uncleaved egg from fertilization up to the first cleavage (Yatsu, '04). Non-nucleated regions of the cytoplasm were removed at each of the following stages: before dissolution of the germinal vesicle, at the metaphase of the first meiotic division, at the period of conjugation of the egg- and sperm-nuclei, and after constriction of the first cleavage had appeared. For the first three developmental stages listed above the percentages of normal pilidia decreased progressively as follows: 85.7 per cent, 52.3 per cent and 24 per cent; too few operations were carried out at the fourth stage to provide significant percentage values. Yatsu interpreted these results as demonstrating that there must take place some progressive changes in the general make-up of the egg during the period extending from the time of dissolution of the germinal vesicle to the union of the germ nuclei, in other words, that cytoplasmic localization has been progressively established.†

* Similarly animal and vegetal halves, as well as meridional halves of unfertilized eggs of the ascidian *Ascidiella scabra*, can gastrulate and develop into remarkably normal tadpole larvae, although there are many exceptions to this statement (Dalcq, '38).

† Centrifugation experiments on uncleaved eggs of the mollusks *Physa ancillaria* and *Lymnaea cata-*

By contrast, isolated animal halves and vegetal halves of unfertilized eggs of other invertebrates develop into larvae which differ from each other and from normal larvae in certain characteristic ways. For example, Hörstadius ('28, '37b) has demonstrated that isolated animal halves of unfertilized sea urchin eggs (Paracentrotus, Arbacia) develop into blastulae with enlarged apical tufts and that these blastulae fail to gastrulate or form a skeleton, whereas isolated vegetal halves of the same eggs gastrulate and form a skeleton and develop in some cases into quite normal plutei, although usually they develop into larvae with an ovoid body shape, no mouth, and a malformed skeleton. By contrast, meridional halves of unfertilized sea urchin eggs developed into more or less typical plutei.‡ Similarly Wilson ('04a) has demonstrated characteristic differences in development of isolated animal and vegetal halves of unfertilized eggs of the mollusk, Dentalium, whereas such differences appear to be lacking in isolated meridional halves. He states (p. 69), "Fertilized fragments of the unsegmented unfertilized egg, obtained by hori-

scopium (Conklin, '10) and *Physa heterostropha* (Clement, '38) seemed to indicate that the effects of centrifugation are least injurious just after the completion of maturation and most injurious just before the first cleavage. Again it was suggested that this might indicate increasing differentiation of the egg with time prior to the first cleavage. However, Raven and Bretschneider ('42) obtained no definite increase in injurious effects with time in their centrifugation experiments on *Limnaea stagnalis*; thus their experiments lend no support to the hypothesis of a progressively increasing differentiation of ooplasm between maturation and first cleavage; they feel that their results are more critical since their material was examined histologically whereas that of Conklin and Clement was not.

‡ Contrary to the above results, Taylor and Tennent ('24, p. 205), using eggs of the sea urchin *Lytechinus (Toxopneustes) variegatus*, find that "From many pairs of both horizontal and vertical sections we obtained blastulae with mesenchyme, normal gastrulae with triradiate skeletal spicules, and plutei, which, except for size, could not be distinguished from those developing from normally developing entire eggs." Tennent, Taylor and Whitaker ('29, p. 4) stated, ". . . the results showed that both halves of the egg, no matter what the plane of section, might form normal identical larvae. The animal halves, like the vegetal halves, produced larvae with mesenchyme and an archenteron." Hörstadius ('37b) feels strongly that such results must have been due to some error in orientation of the cut or to a rotation of the egg during cutting, and his arguments are convincing.

zontal or oblique section, differ in development according as they do or do not contain the lower white area. The upper fragment . . . produces a larva similar to the lobeless ones. The lower one . . . may produce a normally formed dwarf trochophore. Fragments obtained by vertical section through the lower white area may . . . produce nearly normally formed dwarf trochophores."

Taken together these experiments on uncleaved eggs suggest that in the developmental history of the egg there is probably no structural organization along an animal-vegetal axis at first, that such a pattern probably arises progressively, and that it may be realized earlier in some uncleaved eggs (sea urchin, mollusk) than in others (nemertine, tunicate). This is the same conclusion that was reached concerning the establishment of visible differences along the axis of polarity.

ARE EXTRINSIC OR INTRINSIC FACTORS RESPONSIBLE FOR ESTABLISHMENT OF AN AXIS OF POLARITY?

As a general rule the attached end of the egg in the ovary becomes the vegetal pole, the free end the animal pole. There are those who believe that this relationship is a causal one, such that the different environments at the two ends of the egg *cause* those ends to develop differently. If this were true, the basic organization of the egg along the animal-vegetal axis would be imposed upon it from the outside. Child ('41) has emphasized the importance of extrinsic factors in the establishment of polarity in animal eggs. Although such a causal relationship may actually exist, it has not been proved experimentally for eggs of invertebrate animals, and such proof would be difficult to obtain. It is equally difficult to prove that such a causal relationship does not exist.

Be this as it may, one important feature of egg organization, at least in snails, appears to be controlled by intrinsic factors, i.e., by the genotype of the unreduced egg. The resulting egg organization in some way controls (1) the position of the cleavage spindles for the second cleavage, whether dexiotropic or laeotropic; (2) the position of the primary mesoderm cell, *4d*, whether to the left or the right of the first cleavage plane; (3) the direction of coiling of the visceral mass and shell, whether clockwise or counterclockwise. Sturtevant ('23) has suggested that one pair of genes is involved, a dominant dextral factor and a recessive sinistral factor. In terms of the usual Mendelian inheritance a cross between two heterozygous parents should give 3 dextral: 1 sinistral offspring; actually all are dextral. A cross between a homozygous recessive female from the above cross and a homozygous dominant male should give all dextral offspring; actually all are sinistral. Thus the genotypic make-up of the egg seems to have exerted a permanent effect upon the egg organization prior to onset of the maturation divisions. Even though Sturtevant's interpretation may not account for the results of all crosses (consult Morgan, '27), this does not detract from the generalization that intrinsic, as well as extrinsic, factors play important roles in the establishment of egg organization.

STRATIFICATION OF EGG CONSTITUENTS ALONG THE AXIS OF POLARITY IS THE RESULT, NOT THE CAUSE, OF POLAR ORGANIZATION

It can be demonstrated experimentally by centrifugation that the specific distribution assumed by the various visible constituents of the egg does not create the basic polar organization which underlies regional differentiation, but is a consequence of that polar organization. The latter basic organization remains unchanged if a new axis of stratification of visible constituents is imposed by centrifugation (although the position of maturation spindles and cleavage planes may be modified to conform to the axis of centrifugation). Thus in sea urchin eggs the axis of stratification imposed by centrifugation was found to bear every possible relationship to the axis of differentiation (Morgan, '27), and a similar situation characterized the eggs of the annelids Chaetopterus and Nereis (Lillie, '09), of such mollusks as Cumingia (Morgan, '27), Physa and Lymnaea (Conklin, '10), and of the tunicate Styela (Conklin, '31), etc.* It therefore appeared that polar organization of the egg was a property of the ground substance, by which Lillie ('06, p. 156) meant the "fluid that contains and suspends all the granules and droplets." According to Lillie ('09), polarity must depend on some definite architecture of the ground substance, and movements of visible constituents produced by the centrifuge cannot be mass movements of entire protoplasmic areas, but only granule movements through the ground sub-

* Raven and Bretschneider ('42) disagree with this conclusion.

stance, whose structure is therefore not essentially disturbed by centrifuging. The possibility that this architecture of the ground substance might involve liquid crystals has been discussed (Needham, '42; Harrison, '45). Conklin ('24) stated that the organization of the egg resides in the internal framework of entoplasm and the cortical layer of ectoplasm.

EVIDENCE THAT THE STRUCTURAL BASIS OF EGG ORGANIZATION RESIDES IN THE EGG CORTEX

If some permanent internal framework exists in the entoplasm of the ground substance, it should be possible to obtain evidence of its existence from viscosity measurements (Howard, '32). The presence of cohering molecular aggregates ramifying through a liquid phase would be expected to cause plastic flow of the system as a whole, as a result of a certain amount of mechanical rigidity to shear which is characteristic of such structures. Centrifugation experiments on two sea urchins (*Arbacia punctulata* and *Strongylocentrotus purpuratus*) revealed no unequivocal plasticity and led Howard to conclude (p. 368) that ". . . no continuous structure is present which can significantly affect diffusion within the resting egg." If so, there is no constant protoplasmic structure in the entoplasm which could account for the relatively stable organization of the egg. It has been noted that usually the ectoplasm (cortex) of the egg is relatively unaffected by centrifugation experiments, and it was natural to suggest that the ultrastructural basis for egg organization must be localized in the egg cortex (Motomura, '35; Raven and Bretschneider, '42; and others). The importance of the ectoplasm in this respect would also seem to be indicated by the work of Hörstadius, Lorch and Danielli ('50), who withdrew large quantities of entoplasm from the sea urchin egg (reducing the volume of the egg by more than 50 per cent) and still obtained normally proportioned plutei; nevertheless, these authors seem reluctant to suggest that their experiments provide any conclusive evidence on the problem.

If the basic polar organization of the egg does reside in the cortex, it would be essential that at least some components of the cortex maintain their relative positions throughout cleavage; otherwise cleavage would disrupt such an organization. Runnström ('28a, '28b) has described a dark-field ring in the cortex of the vegetal half of the sea urchin egg

which maintains its position unchanged throughout cleavage; during gastrulation the cells in which this dark-field ring is localized largely become invaginated to form the walls of the archenteron. Accordingly, part of the cortex, at least, seems not to be dislocated during formation of cleavage furrows and could serve as the locus of the basic organization of the egg along the animal-vegetal axis (see Lehmann, '45).

In general it may be said that the axis of differentiation rarely becomes dissociated from the original axis of polarity; consequently it is of basic importance for an understanding of differentiation that we arrive at some concept of the ultrastructure of the egg responsible for the basic polarity made visible by morphological and physiological differences. Recent speculations by Weiss ('49a, '49b, '50) in terms of molecular ecology provide a model of the way in which an initial organization of the egg crust could impose organization upon the more fluid egg core.

SPECIFICATION OF BLASTOMERES ACCORDING TO THE PORTION OF THE CYTOPLASM SEGREGATED WITHIN THEM

The most striking feature about the descriptive embryology of certain annelids, mollusks, ctenophores and tunicates is the precocious localization of visibly different cytoplasmic areas and the segregation of these areas into specific blastomeres or groups of blastomeres. In many instances isolation and transplantation experiments prove that such blastomeres or groups of blastomeres differ markedly from other blastomeres in their developmental capacities.

ANNELIDS AND MOLLUSKS

Experiments on Eggs Lacking Polar Lobes and Pole Plasms. Especially clear-cut evidence for specification of blastomeres according to the portion of the cytoplasm segregated within them comes from experiments on the eggs of the mollusk Patella (Wilson, '04b) and the annelid Nereis (Costello, '45). The trochophore larva of Patella is illustrated in Figure 120*A*. If a single cell of the first quartette of micromeres is isolated (Fig. 120*B*), it develops into a partial larva consisting of four primary trochoblasts, two smaller secondary trochoblasts, two apical tuft cells, and a group of non-ciliated ectoblast cells (Fig. 120*C*). The first quartette of micromeres divides into four upper cells

($1a^1$-$1d^1$) and four lower cells ($1a^2$-$1d^2$); see Figure 120D. If $1a^1$ is isolated (Fig. 120E), it develops into two secondary trochoblasts, several non-ciliated cells and a small number of apical tuft cells, whereas an isolated $1a^2$ are isolated or remain as part of the whole egg. Each cell or group of cells differentiates in a specific way because specific portions of a heterogeneous cytoplasm are segregated into them.

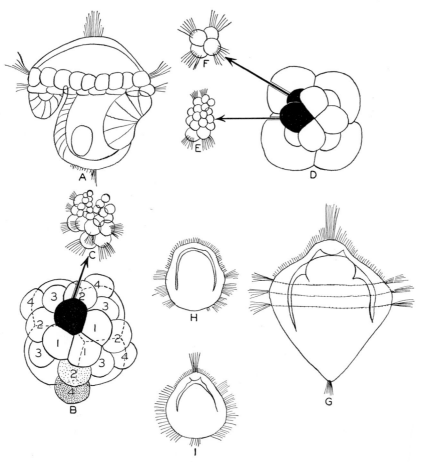

Fig. 120. Specification of blastomeres in molluscan eggs. (A, C, E and F from Wilson, '04b; G, H and I from Wilson, '04a.) A, Normal trochophore larva of the mollusk Patella. B, Generalized scheme of cleavage in annelids and mollusks (from Wilson, 1899). The first somatoblast (2d) is indicated by sparse stippling; the second somatoblast (4d) is indicated by heavy, dense stippling. C, Differentiation of isolated cell of first quartette of micromeres of Patella. D, Generalized scheme of cleavage of first quartette of micromeres. E, Differentiation of isolated $1a^1$ cell of Patella. F, Differentiation of isolated $1a^2$ cell of Patella. G, Normal trochophore larva of the mollusk Dentalium. H, Type of larva which differentiates from the Dentalium egg lacking first polar lobe, or from the following cells when isolated: AB, A, B, C, 1a, 1b or 1c. Note absence of apical tuft and post-trochal region. I, Type of larva which differentiates from the Dentalium egg lacking only the second polar lobe, or from an isolated 1d cell. Note that only the post-trochal region is lacking.

blastomere (Fig. 120F) divides only twice to produce four primary trochoblasts; etc. Essentially the same results were obtained with the Nereis egg except for minor differences which correspond to slight differences in cell lineage in these two animals. Thus with each successive cleavage, cells become more sharply specified for one fate only, and that fate is realized whether the cells involved

Experiments on Eggs Possessing Polar Lobes. In the eggs of some annelids (Sabellaria, Chaetopterus) and mollusks (Dentalium, Ilyanassa) a peculiar phenomenon known as polar lobe formation occurs, the first polar lobe appearing just before the first cleavage furrow, the second polar lobe appearing just as the second cleavage is initiated. The cytoplasmic contents of the polar lobes enter the

CD cell when the first cleavage is completed and the D cell when the second cleavage has terminated. The trochophore larva of Dentalium is illustrated in Figure 120G. If, in Dentalium (Wilson, '04a), the AB blastomere or the A, B, or C blastomeres, all of which lack the substance of the polar lobes, are isolated, they develop into larvae lacking an apical tuft and a post-trochal region (Fig. 120H). The same type of defective larva develops if the first polar lobe is extirpated while the first cleavage furrow is forming. Thus it appears that the formation of apical tuft and post-trochal region is dependent upon that part of the cytoplasm contained in the first polar lobe. If the first polar lobe is not removed, but instead the second one is extirpated, the resulting larva develops an apical tuft, but still lacks the post-trochal region (Fig. 120I). Thus it appears that the portion of the cytoplasm essential for apical tuft formation is not present in the second polar lobe, although the portion of the cytoplasm essential for formation of the post-trochal region is contained therein. At the third cleavage the first quartette of micromeres forms, and when the cells of this quartette ($1a$-$1d$) are isolated, only cell $1d$ forms an apical tuft (none of the micromeres forms a post-trochal region). Thus it appears that the portion of the cytoplasm essential for apical tuft formation is progressively translocated from the first polar lobe into the CD cell and finally into the $1d$ blastomere. The latter cell alone is then able to develop into a larva with an apical tuft because a special portion of the heterogeneous cytoplasm has been segregated into it. Similarly the $1D$ cell receives the portion of the cytoplasm contained in the second polar lobe, and it alone of the macromeres of the 8-cell stage has the capacity to form the post-trochal region. Strikingly similar results have been obtained with eggs of the annelid Sabellaria by Hatt ('32) and Novikoff ('38), although there are differences in detail.

Experiments on Eggs Possessing Pole Plasms. The eggs of Oliogochaeta and Hirudinea are characterized by the accumulation of an area of distinctive protoplasm at the animal pole and another one at the vegetal pole just after the second maturation division; such localized protoplasmic areas are termed pole plasms. In Tubifex (Penners, '22) these two pole plasms are progressively restricted during cleavage to the CD cell, then to the D cell where they fuse, then to the $1D$ cell. About half this pole plasm then enters the $2d$ cell (first somatoblast—see Fig. 120B) of the second quartette and finally enters one of its derivatives ($2d^{111}$), which then consists almost exclusively of pole plasm. This cell divides into Tl (to the left of the dorsal midline) and Tr (to the right), and from these two cells all *ectodermal* structures are derived (ventral nerve cord, cerebral ganglion, circumesophageal commissures, circular muscle, epidermis, and probably the setal sacs). The rest of the pole plasm (Penners, '24a), after passing through cells $2D$ and $3D$, finally enters cell $4d$ (second somatoblast—see Fig. 120B) which divides into Myl (to the left of the dorsal midline) and Myr (to the right). From these two cells all *mesodermal* structures are derived (the somatic mesoderm and the longitudinal musculature derived from it, the splanchnic mesoderm, the septa and the nephridia). The possibility exists that the portion of the pole plasm entering cell $2d^{111}$ specifies the derivatives of that cell to become ectodermal structures, whereas the portion of the pole plasm entering cell $4d$ specifies the derivatives of that cell to become mesodermal structures.

Blastomeres of Tubifex eggs are very sensitive to radiation by ultraviolet light; individual radiated blastomeres are cast out from the developing system by non-radiated cells (Penners, '26). As stated above, half of the pole plasm appears to be segregated progressively into cells $2D$, $3D$, $4d$ and finally Myl and Myr; mesodermal structures fail to form if any of these blastomeres are destroyed. The other blastomeres develop quite normally but parts are frequently displaced from their normal positions relative to one another and metamerism is lacking. Penners ('38) concluded that the pole plasm passing through the blastomeres listed above specified Myl and Myr for mesodermal differentiation and further that the mesoderm must exert some organizing influence upon the ectoderm and entoderm. Similarly, half of the pole plasm appears to be segregated progressively into blastomeres, $2d$, $2d^1$, $2d^{11}$ and $2d^{111}$; in early experiments (Penners, '26) ectodermal structures failed to form if any of these blastomeres were destroyed. The rest of the blastomeres developed quite normally and Penners concluded that the pole plasm passing through these blastomeres specified $2d^{111}$ for ectodermal differentiation. However, Penners ('37) discovered that if he kept these embryos alive as long as possible, considerable regulation occurred in the absence of derivatives of $2d^{111}$, with all parts normally forming from this cell now arising from derivatives of Myl and Myr. Thus the mesodermal part of the embryo can regulate to such an extent that it produces derivatives normally of ectodermal origin.

Therefore the Tubifex egg is not as striking an example of specification of blastomeres by segregation of specific portions of the cytoplasm into them as it was once thought to be. Essentially similar results have been obtained with the egg of Clepsine (Leopoldseder, '31; Mori, '32), although certain differences in detail are encountered.

CTENOPHORES

Isolation, deformation and defect experiments on the ctenophore egg (Driesch and Morgan, 1895a, b; Fischel, 1897, 1898; Ziegler, 1898; Yatsu, '12) give the following results, which indicate a progressive restriction of the capacity to form swimming plates to the first octet of animal micromeres and which indicate that each micromere of the first octet receives the developmental factors necessary for formation of one row of swimming plates. Each of the first two blastomeres, when isolated, develops into a larva with four rows of swimming plates; each of the first four blastomeres into a larva with two rows of swimming plates; each of the first eight blastomeres into a larva with one row of swimming plates. If two macromeres are removed in the 16-cell stage, such that six macromeres and eight micromeres remained, the resulting larva possessed all eight rows of swimming plates. From this it was concluded that the morphogenetic factors essential for formation of one row of swimming plates had been segregated into each of the first octet of micromeres (Fischel, 1897). But in the case described by Fischel two of the rows of swimming plates were much shorter than the others, and the possibility was not eliminated that this deficiency was due to the lack of the second set of micromeres in two octets, due in turn to the absence of the macromeres (see Schleip, '29). Yatsu ('12), however, seems to have furnished evidence that only the first octet of micromeres is concerned with formation of swimming combs. If he separated two cells of the 8-cell stage from the remaining six, a larva with two rows of swimming plates developed from the former. If, however, he separated two macromeres together with their two micromeres from the rest of the blastomeres in the 16-cell stage, and then removed the two micromeres, the two macromeres formed a larva lacking swimming plates.

Spek ('26) has demonstrated that a progressive segregation of corticoplasm into the first octet of micromeres parallels this progressive restriction of potency during cleavage. This corticoplasm appears green in eggs of Beroë under dark-field illumination. In the fertilized but uncleaved egg it forms a distinct and uniform layer over the egg. As the first cleavage furrow develops the green corticoplasm accumulates at the animal pole, but as this furrow advances towards the vegetal pole, much of the corticoplasm is swept downwards towards the vegetal pole and accumulates there temporarily. It then becomes uniformly distributed again. These shiftings of corticoplasm are repeated in the second division and in the third cleavage, except that in the latter the green corticoplasm remains as a cap at the animal pole of each cell. At the following cleavage each of these green caps is cut off almost completely into one of the first octets of animal micromeres. Again a segregation of specific portions of the cytoplasm into certain blastomeres is accompanied by a restriction of certain developmental capacities to those blastomeres.*

TUNICATES

The greatest variety of visibly distinct and sharply localized cytoplasmic areas ever discovered occurs in the egg of the tunicate Styela. The progressive segregation of these areas into the blastomeres is spectacular to watch in living eggs (Conklin, '05a, b). Unfertilized eggs contain three protoplasmic regions which are differently colored and are distributed around the animal-vegetal axis (Fig. 121A). Following fertilization, striking rearrangements of these regions occur, involving a rapid flowing of the yellow protoplasm first to the vegetal pole (Fig. 121B), then to the future posterior end of the egg where it accumulates as a distinct yellow crescent (Fig. 121C). The animal half then contains clear protoplasm and the vegetal

* But some of the green corticoplasm enters the second octet of micromeres and some of it later enters micromeres which arise at the vegetal pole, and these cells are not involved in formation of swimming plates. Moreover, not all derivatives of the first octet of micromeres form swimming plates; some form non-ciliated ectoderm between the eight rows of swimming plates and between swimming plates within each row. Thus only a part of the green corticoplasm appears to be utilized in the formation of swimming combs. Spek emphasized that the green color of the comb-forming cells differed in no way from that in other ectodermal derivatives.

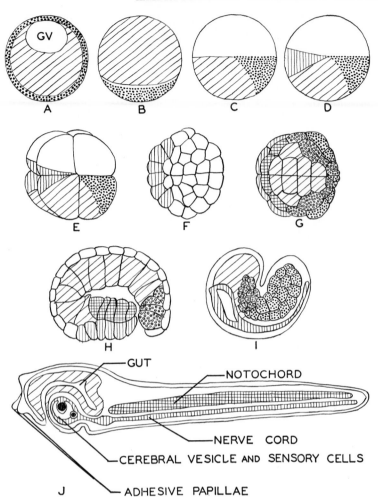

Fig. 121. Cleavage stages and prospective fates of specific regions of the egg of the tunicate *Styela* (*Cynthia*) *partita*. In all illustrations the anterior end is to the left, the posterior end to the right. (*A, B, C, F, G* and *I* from Conklin, '05a; *D* and *E* from Conklin, '05b.) *A*, Unfertilized egg showing germinal vesicle (*GV*), central gray yolk (oblique hatching), and peripheral yellow protoplasm (dotted). *B*, Fertilized egg showing accumulation of yellow protoplasm and clear protoplasm at the vegetal pole. *C*, Uncleaved, fertilized egg with yellow protoplasm accumulated as a crescent across the posterior end of the egg. *D*, 2-cell stage showing light gray crescent (vertical hatching) across the anterior end of the egg. *E*, 8-cell stage. *F*, Animal half of 64-cell stage viewed from the animal pole; vertically-hatched cells represent prospective cerebral vesicle. *G*, Vegetal half of 64-cell stage viewed from vegetal pole; vertically-hatched cells represent prospective nerve cord; cells hatched vertically and horizontally represent prospective chorda; solid dots represent prospective muscle cells; circles represent prospective mesenchyme. *H*, Gastrulation stage; diagrammatic. *I*, Young tadpole larva. *J*, Definitive tadpole larva; diagrammatic.

half anterior to the yellow crescent contains dark gray protoplasm. The first cleavage furrow passes through the mid-sagittal plane (the plane of the paper in Figs. 121*C, D*), bisecting the yellow crescent, and also bisecting a light gray crescent which has now become visible around the anterior end of the egg (Fig. 121*D*), extending slightly above the equator. Thus there is in this egg shortly after fertilization an early, sharp, and visible localization of several indices of underlying

differences in cytoplasmic composition. Cleavage progressively segregates these regions from one another until by the 64-cell stage each cell is "pure" for cytoplasm of one type only (Figs. 121*E, F, G*). The structures of the tadpole larva derived from each group of distinctively colored cells can be determined at a glance (Figs. 121*H, I, J*). These ooplasmic regions are sufficiently distinct that every important step of their localization and segregation can be followed in black and white photographs of living eggs (Conklin, '05b).*

Do differences in developmental capacities of blastomeres parallel the visible differences? Conklin ('05c, '06) sought an answer to this question by defect experiments. Eggs in the 2-, 4-, 8-cell stages, etc., contained within the chorion, were strongly spurted with a pipette or were shaken in a vial, whereby some of the blastomeres were injured and others remained uninjured and continued to develop. Injured blastomeres were rarely killed, but their nuclei were frequently broken and their chromosomes scattered, such that these cells could not undergo cleavage. By such crude treatment, eggs were obtained with injured and uninjured blastomeres in various combinations. These could be sorted into groups as follows: eggs with the right half uninjured, the left half injured, and vice versa; those with the anterior half uninjured and the posterior half injured, and vice versa. In this way Conklin obtained sufficient material to study in detail the development of right and left half embryos, three-quarter embryos, anterior and posterior half embryos, quarter embryos and eighth or sixteenth embryos. Regulation of the fragments was limited entirely to closure of the larva (or organ) on the injured side and there was no restitution of missing parts. For example, the anterior half-egg gave rise to an embryo consisting of ectoderm, neural plate, sense spots, notochord and entoderm, but lacking muscles and mesenchyme; the posterior half-egg gave rise to an embryo consisting of ectoderm, muscles (at least myoblasts), mesenchyme and entoderm, but lacking neural plate, sense spots and notochord. Each fragment of the egg under these circumstances gave rise to those structures which it would have formed as part of the whole developing egg (see Fig. 121). From results of this sort Conklin concluded that development of the ascidian

* No such elaborate color scheme exists in other tunicate eggs, although Berrill ('29) reports an orange substance in the eggs of *Boltenia hirsuta* which segregates into the muscle and mesenchyme cells exactly as does the yellow substance in Styela. In *Ciona intestinalis, Phallusia mamillata* and *Molgula manhattensis* the eggs are not colored; nevertheless the same ooplasmic regions can be recognized in stained sections, and have the same prospective fates. Various ooplasmic regions in yet another ascidian egg (*Ascidiella aspersa*) have the same prospective fates, although the fates of these regions can be demonstrated only with the aid of vital stains (Tung, '32). In *Ascidiella scabra* slight differences in the position of organ-forming regions have been demonstrated (Dalcq, '38).

egg is a mosaic work since the individual blastomeres or groups of blastomeres are composed of different kinds of ooplasmic materials, and moreover since the developmental fate of any ascidian blastomere or group of blastomeres is primarily a function of its material content. He saw no indication of dependent differentiations or inductions. He reached similar conclusions following defect experiments on the eggs of the European tunicate, *Phallusia mamillata* (Conklin, '11). His conclusions received strong support from the studies of von Ubisch ('39a) who removed blastomeres at later stages (32- and 64-cell stages) when each kind of ooplasm was restricted to separate blastomeres. Systematically removing each group of blastomeres, he found only one instance where the potency of the remaining cells was greater than their prospective fate, viz., ectoblast could give rise to entoderm.†

DIFFERENTIATION WITHOUT CLEAVAGE

In annelids, mollusks, ctenophores and tunicates progressive differentiation (i.e., temporal and spatial restriction of potencies) seems to involve primarily a precocious localization of visibly different cytoplasmic areas and the segregation of these areas into specific blastomeres or groups of blastomeres whose developmental capacities then prove to differ markedly from other blastomeres. To what extent can differentiation occur if cleavage fails to segregate these localized areas? Lillie ('02) was able to suppress cleavage by treating unfertilized or fertilized Chaetopterus eggs with sea water containing potassium chloride. His most striking illustration of the degree to which differentiation can progress without cleavage is illustrated in Figure 122A (which should be compared with the normal trochophore larva of Chaetopterus illustrated in Fig. 122B). His description reads as follows (p. 481): "This structure possesses a certain undeniable resemblance to a trochophore: if the smaller hemisphere be com-

† Isolation experiments (Berrill, '32; Tung, '34; Cohen and Berrill, '36; Rose, '39; von Ubisch, '40; Reverberi and Minganti, '46a,b; Pisanò, '49) gave essentially similar results. There was some disagreement as to whether cerebral vesicles could form in isolated animal halves, although there was agreement that sensory spots could not form in such halves; similarly there was disagreement as to whether entoblast could give rise to ectoderm in isolated vegetal halves.

pared to the pre-trochal, and the larger to the post-trochal region, the large vacuoles occupy approximately the position of the prototroch. It is interesting to note that a similar girdle of large vacuoles is found in this position in the trochophore. Continuing the comparison, we may note that the aggregation of yolk is in a similar position to the gut of the trochophore." Unusually strong and active cilia were formed and were arranged with great regularity. Thus considerable differentiation can occur when cleavage fails to segregate sharply localized cytoplasmic regions.

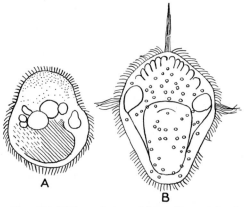

Fig. 122. Differentiation without cleavage in the annelid Chaetopterus (from Lillie, '02). A, Experimental larva; optimal differentiation without cleavage. B, Control larva.

Although similar results have been obtained by other investigators, this still remains the classic example of this phenomenon. This experiment would seem to indicate the primary importance in differentiation of the precocious localization of different cytoplasmic areas and the secondary importance of the segregation of these areas by the cleavage process.*

CHEMICAL CHARACTERIZATION OF LOCALIZED CYTOPLASMIC AREAS IN MOSAIC EGGS

If precocious localization of cytoplasmic areas is of primary importance for the differentiation of eggs of annelids, mollusks,

* Brachet ('37) has demonstrated that such differentiation without cleavage is impossible when oxidations are inhibited by cyanide, and also when metabolism is interfered with by monoiodoacetic acid, although some localization of cytoplasmic materials can take place in the presence of the latter agent.

ctenophores and tunicates, it is essential that the chemical and physical nature of these areas be analyzed by cytochemical methods or by any other methods which can be applied to minute objects. Examples of this approach to the study of differentiation have been illustrated, summarized and evaluated by Needham ('42, pp. 131–140) and by Brachet ('50, pp. 271–291). Needham states (p. 139), ". . . in many eggs showing mosaic development a profound chemical heterogeneity of the parts of the egg sets in very early, parallel with the early determination. Histochemical and experimental methods confirm each other. The former alone will not carry us much further, but with the micro-chemical technique which should before long be available, it ought to be possible to establish by unimpeachable chemical methods the differences between the determined areas." A step in this direction has been taken by Berg and Kutsky ('51), who studied differences in oxygen uptake of isolated blastomeres and polar lobes in the egg of the mollusk *Mytilus edulis*. They report a lower respiratory rate of the cytoplasm of the *CD* blastomere when compared with the *AB* blastomere and demonstrate that the lower rate of the former is due to the lower respiratory rate of the polar lobe cytoplasm which is incorporated into the *CD* cell. The importance of the polar lobe cytoplasm in development has been stressed above.

INTERACTION BETWEEN BLASTOMERES IN DEVELOPMENT

IN MOSAIC EGGS

In the preceding section emphasis was placed on the independent differentiation of blastomeres in certain phyla, i.e., on the apparent lack of interaction between blastomeres. Thus far interpretations have been based largely upon results of defect experiments or isolation experiments. Attention may now be turned briefly to experiments involving transplantation, fusion of eggs, etc., to see whether they provide any evidence for interaction between blastomeres in nemertines, annelids, mollusks or tunicates. Hörstadius ('37a) found that from the 8-cell stage onward, separation of the egg of the nemertine Cerebratulus into animal and vegetal halves, into an_1, an_2, veg_1 and veg_2 layers, various combinations of these layers of blastomeres, as well as fusion of animal halves with meridional halves, provided no evidence for interaction of blastomeres. This is in distinct contrast to identical combinations of sea urchin blastomeres, as noted below. Each set of blastomeres simply self-differentiated regardless of the other blastomeres present simultaneously. Novikoff ('38) combined halves and quarters of the egg of the annelid Sabellaria with another whole egg. The addition of these extra egg fragments gave no inductions in the host; any added fragment simply self-differentiated into those structures characteristic of its prospective fate

lation is possible in the eggs of annelids and mollusks under special conditions. It was noted earlier that in the absence of the normal source of ectodermal structures in the Tubifex egg, such structures could arise from cells originally believed to be specified for mesodermal differentiation only (Penners, '38). Also it was noted that in the absence of mesodermal structures metamerism was lacking and ectodermal and entodermal structures were displaced, suggesting an organizing influence of the mesoderm upon the

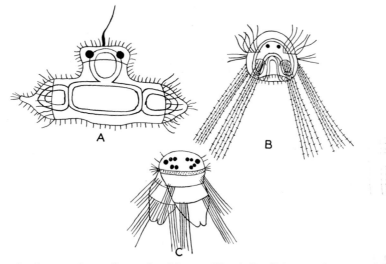

Fig. 123. Types of twins experimentally produced in annelids. *A*, Duplicitas cruciata twin of Chaetopterus (from Titlebaum, '28). *B*. Duplicitas cruciata twin of Sabellaria (from Novikoff, '40). *C*, Duplicitas cruciata twin of Nereis (from Tyler, '30).

(i.e., an extra *A* or *B* cell added extra apical cilia, an extra *C* cell added an extra apical tuft, and an extra *D* cell added an extra post-trochal region, etc.). The localization of cytoplasmic factors for development of apical tuft and post-trochal region in the polar lobes of annelids and mollusks has already been discussed; attempts by Novikoff to transplant polar lobes to entire eggs of Sabellaria were unsuccessful in that nothing additional formed in the hosts to which such polar lobes were attached (although the union of polar lobes to eggs was sufficiently close that vital stain passed from the former into the latter). Fusion of two or more eggs (Hatt, '31; Novikoff, '38) did not result in a single giant larva of unit structure but yielded double embryos or more complex monsters, each egg in the fused mass differentiating independently of the others.

In spite of these negative results insofar as demonstrating interaction of blastomeres is concerned, a considerable amount of regu-

distribution of ectodermal and entodermal derivatives. Moreover, in Tubifex an isolated *CD* or *D* cell containing the pole plasm regulates itself into a normally proportioned, though small, worm. But even more striking is the observation that if the vegetative pole plasm be equally distributed to the first two blastomeres (Tubifex, by heat or deprivation of oxygen, Penners, '24b; Chaetopterus, Nereis and Cumingia by compression, high or low temperatures, centrifugation or anaerobiosis, Titlebaum, '28, Tyler, '30; Sabellaria by treatment with potassium chloride, Novikoff, '40), double monsters of the duplicitas cruciata type are formed (Fig. 123), or the blastomeres may, if isolated, give rise to more or less complete larvae. Costello ('45) has emphasized that the treatment must do more than distribute pole plasm equally to the first two blastomeres; it must set up an effective barrier between the two cells such that each of the first two blastomeres and their derivatives do not react with one another, but give rise to a separate individual. This would seem to imply that they *do* interact with one another under normal circumstances.

Tung ('34) has accomplished the fusion of two tunicate eggs in the 2-cell stage, obtaining results which favor rigid mosaic development in that two complete sets of organs formed. However, von Ubisch ('38, especially '39a) was able to produce giant tadpole larvae from fusion of two tunicate eggs oriented in such a way that their animal-vegetal axes were parallel. It appeared that a point-to-point fusion of identical cytoplasmic areas occurred, with each such area then forming an organ larger than normal. Thus no evidence for interaction of blastomeres was furnished by either investigator. Nevertheless there is evidence from other experiments for the induction of at least two structures in the tadpole larva of tunicates, viz., adhesive papillae and sensory cells. Tung ('34) separated the animal half from the vegetal half in the 8-cell stage and rotated the former through 90 to 180 degrees before replacing it. Adhesive papillae were frequently absent following such rotation; when present they always occurred at the original anterior extremity of the vegetal half, although they originate from cells of the animal half. This means that they have formed from ectoderm which does not normally produce them and that the stimulus for their formation originated in the anterior vegetal cells. This appears to be an example of true induction. Similarly in centrifugation experiments in which various structures underwent relatively normal histogenesis, but occurred in abnormal relationships to one another, Tung, Ku, and Tung ('41) observed that adhesive papillae differentiated only from ectoderm which was in contact with entoderm (no exception in 49 cases). Reverberi and Minganti ('51) agree that the stimulus necessary for development of adhesive papillae emanates from anterior vegetal cells, but they find, in contrast to Tung ('34), that such adhesive papillae can be stimulated to form only from anterior animal cells, i.e., from cells which normally form adhesive papillae. They prefer, therefore, to speak of the stimulus as an "evocation" rather than as an "induction."

Similar evidence is available that interaction of blastomeres is involved in the differentiation of sensory cells. Isolated lateral halves of the 8-cell stage form sensory cells, as do isolated anterior halves; by contrast, isolated posterior halves or isolated animal and vegetal halves do not form sensory cells (Berrill, '32; Tung, '34; von Ubisch, '40). Such cells originate from the animal half, but it appears that some stimulus from the anterovegetal half is necessary for their differentiation. This conclusion is supported by Rose ('39), who found that cerebral vesicles and sensory cells formed in 15 of 46 cases when the two posteroanimal cells were combined with the two anterovegetal cells, whereas in reciprocal combinations (two anteroanimal plus two posterovegetal cells) neither cerebral vesicles nor sensory cells formed in 20 attempts.[*] Rose had some evidence that the inductor of the sensory cells was restricted to the prospective entodermal portion of the two anterovegetal cells; however, von Ubisch ('40) obtained sensory cells in defect experiments involving complete removal of prospective entoderm. Reverberi and Minganti ('51) agree that some stimulus necessary for development of brain and sensory cells emanates from the anterior vegetal cells; but, as in the case of adhesive papillae, they believe that the development of such structures can be stimulated only from cells which usually give rise to them, i.e., only from anterior animal cells. Again, then, they prefer to speak of an "evocation" of brain and sensory cells, rather than of their "induction." They are convinced that this evocation is mediated by a chemical substance.

In the words of Reverberi and Minganti ('51), "all other presumptive territories (of muscle cells, notochord, epidermis, mesenchyme, endoderm) present a complete capacity of self-differentiation, even in the absence of this 'center,' that is of the anterior vegetal blastomeres."[†]

[*] But there must be species differences in this respect, since Tung ('34) obtained differentiation of sensory cells when he rotated the animal half of the 8-cell stage through 180 degrees which would place the anterior animal cells above the two posterior vegetal cells.

[†] Both Rose ('39) and von Ubisch ('40) noted that myoblasts complete their differentiation into muscle cells only when the anterior vegetal cells are present together with the posterior vegetal cells from which myoblasts originate. However, it seems likely that this stimulus necessary for complete differentiation of myoblasts may be simply a mechanical one imposed normally by the elongating chorda which originates from cells of the anterovegetal region, and of quite a different nature from the inductive stimulus necessary for formation of adhesive papillae and possibly of sensory cells. For more recent experiments see Reverberi and Minganti ('47).

From this brief survey it appears that interaction between blastomeres is of minor importance in the development of nemertines, most annelids and mollusks; it appears to be essential to the development of a few structures of tunicate larvae, viz., cerebral vesicle, sensory organs, and adhesive papillae. By contrast, interaction between blastomeres appears to be involved in the development of almost every larval structure of echinoderms. Such interactions have been analyzed most extensively in developing eggs of sea urchins and sand dollars.

IN ECHINODERM EGGS

That fragments of sea urchin eggs are capable of considerable regulation (as also

ingly, the two meridional halves of the sea urchin blastula can regulate into a normal, though small, pluteus larva. Obviously the fate of individual blastomeres or even of groups of blastomeres must become rigidly fixed much later than in the eggs thus far examined; otherwise those in each half blastula could not respond to the altered relationships produced by such experimental interference by collectively producing a normal individual.

Existence of Animalizing and Vegetalizing Influences. The sea urchin egg is by no means devoid of organization. Not every part of it can form a whole (as Driesch originally believed); for if the egg is divided into two halves *equatorially* either before fertilization or at the 8-cell stage by separating the four

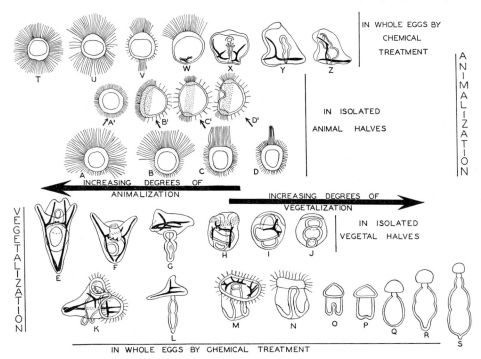

Fig. 124. Modifications of sea urchin development by operative and chemical procedures (*A* through *J* from Hörstadius, '35). *A–D*, Series of animalizations characteristic of isolated animal halves; increasing degrees of animalization from right to left. *A'–D'*, Series of definitive animalizations arising from transitory types *A–D*. *E–J*, Series of vegetalizations characteristic of isolated vegetal halves; increasing degrees of vegetalization from left to right. *K–S*, Series of vegetalizations of whole eggs produced by LiCl treatment; increasing degrees of vegetalization from left to right (*K*, *M* and *N* from Herbst, 1896; others from Child, '40). *T–Z*, Series of animalizations of whole eggs produced by treatment with NaSCN; increasing degrees of animalization from right to left (from Lindahl, '36).

are fused eggs) has long been known. Each of the first two blastomeres, or each of the first four blastomeres *can* produce, when isolated, a relatively normal, though small, pluteus larva (Driesch, 1891, 1892; Hörstadius and Wolsky, '36); even more strik-

animal cells from the four vegetal cells, the resulting larvae usually differ considerably, not only from each other but also from the normal pluteus (Fig. 124). The most extreme larva derived from the animal half is characterized by (1) an apical tuft which is too large (Fig. 124*A*), often covering as much as three-fourths of the surface, although it later disappears and the surface becomes uniformly ciliated (Fig. 124*A'*); (2) the absence of both stomodaeum and ciliated band, normally derived from cells of the animal half; (3) the absence of skeleton; (4) failure to gastrulate. Such larvae are said to be "animalized" or "ectodermized." But in less extreme cases the apical tuft is more restricted (Figs. 124*C, D*) and in such cases a ciliated band (Fig. 124*C'*) and even a stomodaeum (Fig. 124*D'*) may develop (Hörstadius, '39). The vegetal halves of eggs, the isolated animal halves of which produce overdevelopment of the apical tuft, may form quite normal plutei (Figs. 124*E, F*), or they may form exogastrulae (Fig. 124*G*) with poorly developed skeleton and arms. At the other extreme the vegetal halves of eggs, the isolated animal halves of which produce a restricted apical tuft (Figs. 124*C, D*), may produce very abnormal larvae (Figs. 124*H, I, J*). The latter consist mostly of gut contained within an ectodermal vesicle which may develop a ciliated field at its most animal border (Fig. 124*H*) and a skeleton which has not advanced beyond the spicule stage (Figs. 124*H, I*) or which may be entirely absent (Fig. 124*J*). Such larvae are said to be "vegetalized" or "entodermized."

It is not necessary to separate the animal half completely from the vegetal half in order to produce such developmental modifications. If the egg is simply stretched along its animal-vegetal axis (Lindahl, '36), or if a constriction is formed by a single silk fiber around the equator of the egg (Hörstadius, '38), the partially separated animal and vegetal halves develop much as if they were completely isolated. Thus it appears that some influence from the vegetal half (vegetalizing influence) normally passes into the animal half and exerts the following effects upon development of the latter: (1) restriction of the apical tuft; (2) stimulation of stomodaeum invagination; (3) stimulation of formation of a ciliated band on the ventral side parallel to the animal-vegetal axis. Similarly, it appears that some influence from the animal half (animalizing influence) normally passes into the vegetal half and exerts the following effects upon the latter: (1) restriction of the size of the gut; (2) control of skeletal development. Recent experiments (Hörstadius, Lorch and Danielli, '53) seem to demonstrate that enucleated vegetal halves cannot exert vegetalizing influences, but that enucleated animal halves can still exert animalizing influences.

Time Required for Animalizing and Vegetalizing Influences to Exert Their Effects. Experiments designed to answer this question can best be summarized by paraphrasing the words of Hörstadius ('39, pp. 160–161). Animal halves are isolated every second hour from the 16-cell stage (4 hours post-fertilization) up to the beginning of gastrulation (16 hours post-fertilization); if isolated 4 to 6 hours after fertilization they produce a large apical tuft and develop into ciliated blastulae or blastulae with a ciliated field (Figs. 124 *A, A', B, B'*), whereas if isolated later (10 to 16 hours post-fertilization) they produce a restricted apical tuft and develop a ciliated band and stomodaeum (Figs. 124*D, D'*), the structures which they should produce as parts of the intact egg. The change in differentiation of the animal halves occurring about 8 or 10 hours post-fertilization (blastula before formation of primary mesenchyme) indicates that by that stage the vegetalizing influences have so interacted with the animal half that the latter can then self-differentiate according to its prospective fate. Isolation of the most animal quarter of the egg, corresponding to an_1, indicates that vegetalizing influences have modified its fate somewhat later, from 14 to 16 hours after fertilization. This indicates that determination, as regards the influence of vegetative material upon the animal, proceeds from the vegetative towards the animal pole. The isolated vegetal halves produce ovoid plutei until 14 to 16 hours post-fertilization when suddenly they develop into a new type of larva, a pluteus with long anal arms, but entirely without oral lobe, i.e., they develop as if still part of the entire egg. This change in differentiation indicates that by that stage the animalizing influences have so interacted with the vegetal half that the latter can self-differentiate according to its prospective fate.

Do Isolated Animal Halves Lose Their Competence to Respond to the Vegetalizing Influences at the Same Time that Capacity for Self-differentiation Is Attained? To answer this question animal halves are isolated from vegetal halves at progressively later stages and micromeres are then added to such isolated halves to determine how late a normal pluteus with gut can be induced from animal halves. If four micromeres are added to isolated animal halves even as late as the stage when onset of gastrulation normally occurs (16 hours post-fertilization), a gut can still be induced from cells of the animal half, and the necessary shiftings of the position of stomodaeum and ciliated band can still take place such that an almost normal pluteus results. Thus the animal half is competent to respond to vegetalizing influences of the micromeres at a stage later than it is capable of self-differentiation. This must mean that determination is progressive, that when it has advanced far enough to enable an isolated region to self-differentiate, it is still only a labile determination and can be changed if brought under appropriate influences.*

Do Animal Halves and Vegetal Halves Lose Their Capacity to Exert Animalizing and Vegetalizing Influences in Advanced Stages? Hörstadius ('50) demonstrated that an animal half from an advanced stage (blastula before formation of primary mesenchyme) can still exert animalizing influences on much younger vegetal halves, and similarly that a vegetal half of a beginning gastrula can still exert vegetalizing influences on a younger animal half sufficient to inhibit extension of the apical tuft and evoke formation of a ciliated band and stomodaeum.

Graded Intensity of Animalizing and Vegetalizing Influences. Transplantation experiments (Hörstadius, '39) suggested that animalizing and vegetalizing influences were not distributed uniformly throughout the animal and vegetal halves respectively, but existed as overlapping gradients with polar concentrations. Animalizing influences seemed strongest in an_1, less strong in an_2, less still in veg_1 and least in veg_2; vegetalizing influences seemed to be strongest in the micromeres, less strong in veg_2, weaker still in veg_1 and weakest in the animal hemisphere. Normal development appeared to depend upon a proper balance between animalizing and vegetalizing influences, rather than upon their absolute intensities. The evidence for this has been reviewed by Hörstadius ('39, '49).

Chemical Modifications of Development. *Vegetalization (Entodermization) of Entire Eggs.* If entire sea urchin eggs are fertilized in normal sea water and are then transferred

* It should be noted that animal halves retain their competence only if they remain in contact with the vegetal halves until just before micromeres are added; if animal halves are isolated 4 hours after fertilization and the isolated animal halves remain in isolation until 16 hours post-fertilization, at which time micromeres are added, the animal halves are no longer competent to respond to the vegetalizing influences. They form no stomodaeum, no ciliated band, no restricted apical tuft and no gut.

to sea water containing lithium chloride, many of the resulting larvae resemble in a striking way those derived from isolated vegetal halves (Herbst, 1892, 1893, 1896; Runnström, '28a; Child, '40). This is very evident upon comparison of Figure 124K with 124F, 124L with 124G, 124M with 124H, 124N with 124I, J, etc. Treatment with lithium apparently shifted the boundary between ectodermal and entodermal development above the equator (i.e., prospective ectoderm was converted to entoderm) such that an excessively large gut developed.† That this is the correct interpretation is indicated by two types of information. It is known that primary mesenchyme cells aggregate into two masses at a level along the animal-vegetal axis determined by the ectoderm (von Ubisch, '39b); a skeletal spicule forms within each such aggregation. Following lithium treatment these micromere derivatives aggregate much closer to the animal pole, suggesting that the lithium treatment has restricted ectodermal differentiation to a level closer to the animal pole. Moreover, the dark-field ring mentioned earlier as associated with the cortex of prospective entodermal cells likewise extends further towards the animal pole in lithium-treated eggs (Runnström, '28a, b). Lithium can also modify development of isolated animal halves in the same direction as micromeres do (von Ubisch, '29); lithium-treated animal halves can develop into pluteus-like larvae just as they can when micromeres are added.

Animalization (Ectodermization) of Entire Eggs. If entire sea urchin eggs are treated before fertilization with calcium-free sea water to which isotonic sodium thiocyanate has been added (Lindahl, '36), and are then returned to sea water, are fertilized and allowed to develop, many of the resulting larvae resemble in a striking way those derived from isolated animal halves. With increasing degrees of animalization modifications occur in the following sequence: the gut fails to connect with the stomodaeum

† Only such development is true vegetalization. According to Lindahl ('42), only a few treatments result in true vegetalization, and of these lithium is definitely most effective. Vegetalization and exogastrulation are not synonymous; there are many chemical and physical agents which produce simple exogastrulation of the type illustrated in Figure 124L without increasing the ratio of entoderm/ectoderm (see Child, '41, footnote, p. 222). Extreme reduction of ectoderm and enlargement of entoderm occurs when lithium-treated embryos are returned to sea water (Figs. 124O–S).

(Fig. 124Y); the skeleton becomes abnormal (Figs. 124X, W); gut fails to form (Figs. 124W, V, etc.) and no coelom forms. With increasing animalization an apical tuft also appears at the most vegetal pole (Fig. 124V), and with continued animalization spreads in proportion as the animal apical tuft spreads (Fig. 124U) until finally the most extreme animalized form (Fig. 124T) is completely covered with apical tuft cilia. Such modifications constitute animalization, since ectodermal differentiations occupy a greater part of the body than normally.

Hypotheses to Account for Vegetalization and Animalization by Chemical Agents. RUNNSTRÖM-LINDAHL HYPOTHESIS. Runnström ('33) suggested that the gradient of animalizing influences decreasing from the animal pole might be the expression of a graded distribution of animalizing substance, and similarly that the gradient of vegetalizing influences decreasing from the vegetal pole might be the expression of a graded distribution of vegetalizing substance. Lindahl ('36) attempted to account for the origin of these hypothetical substances by suggesting that there are two specific kinds of metabolism in the egg, carbohydrate metabolism in the animal half, protein metabolism in the vegetal half, producing animalizing and vegetalizing substances, respectively. Lindahl assumes that lithium treatment blocks carbohydrate metabolism and reduces the amount of animalizing substance formed, thus reducing the intensity of the animalizing influence and thereby enabling the unmodified vegetalizing influence to turn the development of a larger proportion of the egg than usual in an entodermal direction. And conversely Lindahl suggests that ectodermization is the result of a block to protein metabolism, reducing the amount of vegetalizing substance formed, thereby reducing the intensity of the vegetalizing influence and enabling the unmodified animalizing influence to turn the development of a larger proportion of the egg than usual in an ectodermal direction. This hypothesis has stimulated an enormous amount of research, far too extensive to be reviewed and evaluated here; fortunately this has been done in recent years by Lindahl ('42), Needham ('42), Lehmann ('45), Hörstadius and Gustafson ('48), Hörstadius ('49) and Brachet ('50). Needham evaluates this hypothesis as follows (pp. 494–495): "That there are two centres of morphogenetic influence and a gradient system which reforms after certain experimental interferences

must be regarded as established. It is undeniable also that the actions of these centres may be imitated by a variety of chemical agencies, and it is at least exceedingly probable that the two centres are characterised by two different kinds of metabolism. That they produce each a definite morphogenetic substance or substances is likely. But with the statement that the animal pole is associated with carbohydrate catabolism and the vegetal pole with that of protein, we reach a point where caution is necessary." For more recent attempts to demonstrate differences in metabolism in animal and vegetal halves, and to relate these differences to differentiation, see Hörstadius ('49), Gustafson and Hjelte ('51) and Gustafson and Lenicque ('52).

CHILD-RULON HYPOTHESIS. Instead of a double gradient system, Child ('40) proposes a single gradient system diminishing from the animal towards the vegetal pole. Child interprets the mechanics of vegetalization as follows (p. 29): "If prospective entoderm originates from the lower levels of a primary apico-basal gradient, as dye reduction and differential lethal susceptibility indicate, entodermization may result from depression or inhibition of prospective ectoderm below a certain 'physiological level'; that is, the specific difference between ectoderm and entoderm may be a secondary result of a nonspecific, primarily quantitative difference. According to this suggestion, entodermization occurs first in the most basal levels of prospective ectoderm and progresses acropetally with increasing inhibition because lower levels of ectoderm require only relatively slight inhibition, higher levels, more extreme inhibition, to bring them down to the entodermal level." Rulon ('41), accepting Child's concept of a single physiological gradient, accounts for ectodermization by sodium thiocyanate as follows (pp. 312–313): "Exposure of unfertilized eggs to NaSCN in Ca-free sea water apparently results in a general depression or slowing down of physiological processes, the apical or more active region being retarded to a greater extent than the less active region. Such differential inhibition may be sufficient to decrease the apical dominance to such a degree that the axiate pattern is partly obliterated. With the stimulation to increased activity, resulting from return to normal sea water and fertilization, the lower levels of the gradient, being wholly or partly physiologically isolated, may recover and develop in the same, or almost the same, way as higher levels. In other words, the whole egg may now develop in a manner similar to the original apical portion. Since the apical region normally gives rise to ectoderm and ectodermal derivatives, the whole egg may now give rise to ectoderm alone, with neither mesenchyme nor gut developing."

The chief difference in the approach of these two hypotheses has been an emphasis on the specific effects of chemical treatment on certain aspects of metabolism on the one hand (Runnström-Lindahl) versus an emphasis on non-specific inhibition of vaguely defined physiological activities on the other (Child-Rulon), i.e., an emphasis upon *kinds* of metabolism versus *rates* of activities. More recently Rulon (literature summarized '52) has attempted to characterize the animal-vegetal activity gradient in terms of enzymes involved by exposing sand dollar eggs to specific enzyme inhibitors.

In commenting upon attempts to correlate metabolism and enzyme activities with differentiation, Holter ('49, p. 73) stated, "The indications are that in the stream of chemical and metabolic events that constitute the life of the embryo from fertilization to hatching, the true morphogenetic processes are only like ripples on the surface and their quantitative share in the chemistry of the whole is very small. It seems rather doubtful whether we can hope to reveal the mechanisms which cause those ripples by studying overall metabolism and general enzyme distribution. We are obtaining very interesting results as to the general biochemistry of the egg and embryo, but the crucial problems of morphogenesis may be beyond reach of the enzyme chemist." In spite of this discouraging outlook some advance seems to have been made towards analysis of determination of dorsoventrality in terms of enzyme activities.

ESTABLISHMENT OF DORSOVENTRALITY AND BILATERALITY

Most animal eggs reveal earlier or later a bilaterally symmetrical organization. There is then recognizable a median plane separating the egg into right and left halves. In some echinoderms, for example the holothurians *Psolus phantopus* and *Cucumaria frondosa* (J. and S. Runnström, '21), bilaterality of the egg is revealed visibly even in oocyte stages. Much more commonly the median plane stands revealed visibly and becomes rigidly determined relatively late in development compared with the axis of polarity. Nevertheless there is some evidence both in tunicates and in sea urchins that some steps in the determination of the plane of bilateral symmetry have occurred at very early stages. In the egg of the tunicate Styela (Conklin, '05a) the sperm can enter at any point within 30 degrees of the vegetal pole; the sperm nucleus then moves towards one side of the egg and much of the yellow protoplasm located at that time at the vegetal pole (Fig. 121B) is drawn over with it, forming the yellow crescent just below the equator (Fig. 121C). The center of the yellow crescent indicates the future median plane. The sperm nucleus often travels through a considerable distance to reach this side of the egg and Conklin believes it is traveling towards a preformed area, in other words, that the meridian which becomes the median plane is already fixed in the uncleaved egg. Certain experiments on development of fragments of unfertilized tunicate eggs (Dalcq, '38) likewise suggested the possibility that bilateral symmetry is already determined in the tunicate egg before fertilization. Foerster and Örström ('33) have presented physiological evidence for the early existence of a dorsoventral organization in fertilized (uncleaved) sea urchin eggs. If such eggs are exposed to potassium cyanide a smaller and a larger hollow arise opposite each other; these hollows later disappear, but if the position of the larger one is marked by vital stain, the resulting larva is stained ventrally. Such an experiment suggests a dorsoventral distribution of some condition of the cytoplasm which gives the same reaction to potassium cyanide, but a more vigorous one ventrally. Crowding of eggs, reducing availability of oxygen, has the same effect. If such hollows are suppressed by treatment with anionic detergents (Gustafson and Sävhagen, '50), the resulting larvae are radially symmetrical. Moreover, complementary deficiencies which arise in meridional halves of unfertilized sea urchin eggs also indicate that a bilateral organization is already established in this egg before the entrance of the sperm (Hörstadius and Wolsky, '36).

There is also evidence that external factors can control the position of the median plane. Just ('12) has demonstrated that the first cleavage plane consistently passes through the sperm entrance point in the egg of Nereis (an annelid); the first cleavage plane is perpendicular to the longitudinal axis of the body. Just concludes (pp. 250–251), "Since . . . the sperm may enter at any point and since the first cleavage plane passes through this point, the structure of the ovocyte of Nereis at the time of insemination must be the same in all meridians." Morgan and Tyler ('30) have investigated this relationship in more detail in annelids and mollusks. Differences of opinion exist as to the relation between the sperm entrance point and the median plane in the sea urchin egg. Hörstadius ('39) stained the side opposite the point of sperm entry and found this point in all positions in relation to the first cleavage furrow. Since the first cleavage furrow in sea urchin eggs has no rigid relation to the future median plane, it remains uncertain how the sperm entrance point is related to the median plane. Lillie ('09) examined development of fragments of unfertilized Chaetopterus (annelid) eggs separated by centrifugation. He believed that his study of cleavage pattern in these fragments indicated that bilaterality developed subsequent to their fertilization. He concluded (p. 65), ". . . if bilaterality can develop in the parts there is no reason for assuming its prior existence in the whole; and its origin must be regarded as a purely epigenetic process." Similarly Pease ('38), upon discovery that he could control the position of the ventral surface in eggs of the annelid Urechis by centrifugation, concluded (p. 422), "It seems best to regard this bilateral determination as induced in the egg and not as a rotation or shift of a bilateral axis or predisposition already present in the egg, although such may be present in a weakly defined form."

The most detailed studies of determination of dorsoventrality are those on sea urchin and sand dollar eggs. If sea urchin eggs are stretched perpendicular to the animal-vegetal axis by forcing eggs through a fine capillary tube (Lindahl, '32a) or by constricting them meridionally by a single silk fiber (Hörstadius, '38), the axis of stretching becomes the dorsoventral axis. In the experiments with the capillary tubes Lindahl found that the end of the stretched egg which usually develops into the ventral surface becomes the dorsal surface instead if it is overstained with vital stain. Similarly in centrifugation experiments the dorsoventral axis coincides roughly with the axis of centrifugation (Runnström, '26; Lindahl, '32b; Pease, '39). Pease concluded from his experiments on sand dollar eggs that two factors are involved in ventral determination: (1) a ventral determinant present in gradient form with its greatest intensity

on the prospective ventral side; this he considered to be located in the egg cortex and not shifted by centrifugation; (2) a substrate located in the entoplasm, uniformly distributed in a normal egg, but concentrated at the centripetal pole in centrifuged eggs. He suggested that the ventral determinant may be an enzyme adsorbed in the cortical layers. He proceeded to test this hypothesis ('41, '42a, b) by exposing eggs in the 8-cell stage to gradients of known enzyme inhibitors. With certain specific enzyme inhibitors the ventral surface formed only on the side away from the source of the inhibitors, suggesting that the enzyme systems concerned specifically with dorsoventral determination will cause a ventral side to form wherever their activity is greatest. It has been known for a long time that many chemical treatments of echinoderm eggs completely suppress bilaterality and produce radially symmetrical forms; more recent experiments by Rulon ('49, '51, listed in Rulon, '52) with specific enzyme inhibitors, followed by return of the treated eggs to sea water, seemed to cause a spread of ventral determination over a greater portion of the egg than usual, i.e., they caused a "ventralization" of the egg.

If sea urchin eggs are separated meridionally in advanced blastula stages, and the separation surfaces are vitally stained, some pairs of larvae are obtained in which one twin is stained dorsally, the other ventrally (Hörstadius and Wolsky, '36). This would be the expected result if dorsoventrality were already determined at the time of the operation and if the cut happened by chance to pass through the frontal plane. By contrast, if the first two blastomeres are separated, followed by staining of the surface of separation, pairs of larvae are found in which both are stained dorsally. One larva in such a pair tends to develop more slowly and to form less perfect ventral structures than the other. Presumably the latter represents the prospective ventral half of the egg, the former the prospective dorsal half, and the first cleavage plane happened to pass through the prospective frontal plane. If so, the original dorsoventral axis has been retained in the prospective ventral half, reversed in the prospective dorsal half. Since such a reversal of dorsoventrality is possible in early stages, and not in later ones, establishment of a rigid dorsoventral organization must be a progressive process. Similar results have been obtained by Gustafson and Sävhagen ('50) using anionic detergents (see above). Up to 6 hours after fertilization such detergents prevent development of the oral (ventral) side and radial symmetry results; but between 6 and 9 hours after fertilization the detergents gradually lose their effects and after 9 hours they can no longer inhibit development of bilaterality.

REFERENCES

Berg, W. E., and Kutsky, P. B. 1951 Physiological studies of differentiation in *Mytilus edulis*. I. The oxygen uptake of isolated blastomeres and polar lobes. Biol. Bull., *101:*47–61.

Berrill, N. J. 1929 Studies in tunicate development. I. General physiology of development of simple ascidians. Phil. Trans. Roy. Soc. London, *B, 218:*37–78.

——— 1932 The mosaic development of the ascidian egg. Biol. Bull., *63:*381–386.

Boveri, T. 1901 Die Polarität von Ovocyte, Ei und Larve des *Strongylocentrotus lividus*. Zool. Jahrb. Abt. Anat. u. Ontogenie, *14:*630–653.

Brachet, J. 1937 La différenciation sans clivage dans l'oeuf de Chétoptère envisagée aux points de vue cytologique et métabolique. Arch. Biol., *48:*561–589.

——— 1950 Chemical Embryology. Interscience Publishers, Inc., New York.

Child, C. M. 1940 Lithium and echinoderm exogastrulation: with a review of the physiological-gradient concept. Physiol. Zool., *13:*4–42.

——— 1941 Patterns and Problems of Development. University of Chicago Press, Chicago.

Clement, A. C. 1938 The structure and development of centrifuged eggs and egg fragments of *Physa heterostropha*. J. Exp. Zool., *79:*435–460.

Cohen, A., and Berrill, N. J. 1936 The development of isolated blastomeres of the ascidian egg. J. Exp. Zool., *74:*91–117.

Conklin, E. G. 1905a The organization and cell-lineage of the ascidian egg. J. Acad. Nat. Sci. Philadelphia, *13:*1–119.

——— 1905b Organ-forming substances in the eggs of ascidians. Biol. Bull., *8:*205–230.

——— 1905c Mosaic development in ascidian eggs. J. Exp. Zool., *2:*145–223.

——— 1906 Does half of an ascidian egg give rise to a whole larva? Roux' Arch. Entw.-mech., *21:*727–753.

——— 1910 The effects of centrifugal force upon the organization and development of the eggs of fresh water pulmonates. J. Exp. Zool., *9:*417–454.

——— 1911 The organization of the egg and the development of single blastomeres of *Phallusia mamillata*. J. Exp. Zool., *10:*393–407.

——— 1924 Cellular differentiation; Section IX in General Cytology, edited by E. V. Cowdry. University of Chicago Press, Chicago.

——— 1931 The development of centrifuged eggs of ascidians. J. Exp. Zool., *60:*1–119.

Costello, D. P. 1945 Experimental studies of germinal localization in Nereis. I. The develop-

ment of isolated blastomeres. J. Exp. Zool., *100:*19–66.

Dalcq, A. M. 1938 Form and Causality in Early Development. Cambridge University Press, Cambridge, England.

Driesch, H. 1891 Entwicklungsmechanische Studien. I. Der Werth der beiden ersten Furchungszellen in der Echinodermenentwicklung. Experimentelle Erzeugung von Theil- und Doppelbildungen. II. Über die Beziehungen des Lichtes zur ersten Etappe der thierischen Formbildung. Zeit. f. wiss. Zool., *53:*160–184.

——— 1892 Entwicklungsmechanische Studien. III. Die Verminderung des Furchungsmaterials und ihre Folgen (Weiteres über Theilbildungen). IV. Experimentelle Veränderungen des Types der Furchung und ihre Folgen (Wirkungen von Wärmezufuhr und von Druck). V. Von der Furchung doppelt befruchteter Eier. VI. Über einige allgemeine Fragen der theoretischen Morphologie. Zeit. f. wiss. Zool., *55:*1–62.

Driesch, H., and Morgan, T. H. 1895a Zur Analysis der ersten Entwickelungsstadien des Ctenophoreneies. I. Von der Entwickelung einzelner Ctenophorenblastomeren. Roux' Arch. Entw.-mech., *2:*204–215.

———, and Morgan, T. H. 1895b Zur Analysis der ersten Entwickelungsstadien des Ctenophoreneies. II. Von der Entwickelung ungefurchter Eier mit Protoplasmadefekten. Roux' Arch. Entw.-mech., *2:*216–224.

Fischel, A. 1897 Experimentelle Untersuchungen am Ctenophorenei. I. Von der Entwickelung isolirter Eitheile. Roux' Arch. Entw.-mech., *6:*109–130.

——— 1898 Experimentelle Untersuchungen am Ctenophorenei. II. Von der künstlichen Erzeugung (halber) Doppel- und Missbildungen. III. Über Regulationen der Entwickelung. IV. Über den Entwickelungsgang und die Organisationsstufe des Ctenophoreneies. Roux' Arch. Entw.-mech., *7:*557–630.

Foerster, M., and Örström, A. 1933 Observations sur la prédétermination de la partie ventrale dans l'oeuf d'oursin. Trav. de la Stat. Biol., Roscoff, *11:*63–83.

Gustafson, T., and Hjelte, M.-B. 1951 The amino acid metabolism of the developing sea urchin egg. Exptl. Cell Res., *2:*474–490.

———, and Lenicque, P. 1952 Studies on mitochondria in the developing sea urchin egg. Exptl. Cell Res., *3:*251–274.

———, and Sävhagen, R. 1950 Studies on the determination of the oral side of the sea-urchin egg. I. Ark. för Zool., *42A*(10):1–6.

Harrison, R. G. 1945 Relations of symmetry in the developing embryo. Trans. Acad. Arts Sci. Connecticut, *36:*277–330.

Hatt, P. 1931 La fusion expérimentale d'oeufs de "*Sabellaria alveolata* L." et leur développement. Arch. Biol., *42:*303–323.

——— 1932 Essais expérimentaux sur les localisations germinales dans l'oeuf d'un annélide (*Sabellaria alveolata* L.). Arch. d'Anat. micros., *28:*81–98.

Herbst, C. 1892 Experimentelle Untersuchungen über den Einfluss der veränderten chemischen Zusammensetzung des umgebenden Mediums auf die Entwicklung der Thiere. I. Versuche an Seeigeleiern. Zeit. f. wiss. Zool., *55:*446–518.

Herbst, C. 1893 Experimentelle Untersuchungen über den Einfluss der veränderten chemischen Zusammensetzung des umgebenden Mediums auf die Entwicklung der Thiere. II. Weiteres über die morphologische Wirkung der Lithiumsalze und ihre theoretische Bedeutung. Mittheil. aus der Zool. Stat. zu Neapel, *11:*136–220.

———— 1896 Experimentelle Untersuchungen über den Einfluss der veränderten chemischen Zusammensetzung des umgebenden Mediums auf die Entwicklung der Thiere. III. Über das Ineinandergreifen von normaler Gastrulation und Lithiumentwicklung (Züchtung von Lithiumlarven mit Entoderm und Mund). IV. Die formative Wirkung des Lithiums auf befruchtete Eier von *Asterias glacialis*. V. Über die Unterdrückung von Entwicklungsprozessen (Wirkung von Kalium rhodanatum und Natrium butyricum). VI. Über den Einfluss einiger anderer organischer Salze. Roux' Arch. Entw.-mech., *2:*455–516.

Hörstadius, S. 1928 Über die Determination des Keimes bei Echinodermen. Acta Zoologica, *9:*1–191.

———— 1935 Über die Determination im Verlaufe der Eiachse bei Seeigeln. Pubbl. Staz. Zool. Napoli, *14:*251–429.

———— 1937a Experiments on determination in the early development of *Cerebratulus lacteus.* Biol. Bull., *73:*317–342.

———— 1937b Investigations as to the localization of the micromere-, the skeleton-, and the entoderm-forming material in the unfertilized egg of *Arbacia punctulata.* Biol. Bull., *73:*295–316.

———— 1938 Schnürungsversuche an Seeigelkeimen. Roux' Arch. Entw-mech., *138:*197–248.

———— 1939 The mechanics of sea-urchin development, studied by operative methods. Biol. Rev., *14:*134–179.

———— 1949 Experimental researches on the developmental physiology of the sea-urchin. Pubbl. Staz. Zool. Napoli, *21* (Suppl.):131–172.

———— 1950 Transplantation experiments to elucidate interactions and regulations within the gradient system of the developing sea urchin egg. J. Exp. Zool., *113:*245–276.

————, and Gustafson, T. 1948 On the developmental physiology of the sea urchin. Symposium Soc. Exp. Biol., *2:*50–56.

————, Lorch, I. J., and Danielli, J. F. 1950 Differentiation of the sea urchin egg following reduction of the interior cytoplasm in relation to the cortex. Exptl. Cell Res., *1:*188–193.

————, Lorch, I. J., and Danielli, J. F. 1953 The effect of enucleation on the development of sea urchin eggs. II. Enucleation of animal or vegetal halves. Exptl. Cell Res., *4:*263–274.

————, and Wolsky, A. 1936 Studien über die Determination der Bilateralsymmetrie des jungen Seeigelkeimes. Roux' Arch. Entw.-mech., *135:*69–113.

Holter, H. 1949 Problems of enzyme localization in development. Pubbl. Staz. Zool. Napoli, *21* (Suppl.):60–76.

Howard, E. 1932 The structure of protoplasm as indicated by a study of sea-urchin eggs at various shearing forces. J. Cell. Comp. Physiol., *1:*355–369.

Just, E. E. 1912 The relation of the first cleavage plane to the entrance point of the sperm. Biol. Bull., *22:*239–252.

Lehmann, F. E. 1945 Einführung in die physiologische Embryologie. Verlag Birkhäuser, Basel.

Leopoldseder, F. 1931 Entwicklung des Eies von Clepsine nach Entfernung des vegetativen Polplasmas. Zeit. f. wiss. Zool., *139:*201–248.

Lillie, F. R. 1902 Differentiation without cleavage in the egg of the annelid *Chaetopterus pergamentaceus.* Roux' Arch. Entw.-mech., *14:*477–499.

———— 1906 Observations and experiments concerning the elementary phenomena of embryonic development in Chaetopterus. J. Exp. Zool., *3:*153–268.

———— 1909 Polarity and bilaterality of the annelid egg. Experiments with centrifugal force. Biol. Bull., *16:*54–79.

Lindahl, P. E. 1932a Zur experimentellen Analyse der Determination der Dorsoventralachse beim Seeigelkeim. I. Versuche mit gestreckten Eiern. Roux' Arch. Entw.-mech., *127:*300–322.

———— 1932b Zur experimentellen Analyse der Determination der Dorsoventralachse beim Seeigelkeim. II. Versuche mit zentrifugierten Eiern. Roux' Arch. Entw.-mech., *127:*323–338.

———— 1936 Zur Kenntnis der physiologischen Grundlagen der Determination im Seeigelkeim. Acta Zool., *17:*179–365.

———— 1942 Contributions to the physiology of form generation in the development of the sea urchin. Quart. Rev. Biol., *17:*213–227.

Morgan, T. H. 1927 Experimental Embryology. Columbia University Press, New York.

————, and Tyler, A. 1930 The point of entrance of the spermatozoön in relation to the orientation of the embryo in eggs with spiral cleavage. Biol. Bull., *58:*59–73.

Mori, Y. 1932 Entwicklung isolierter Blastomeren und teilweise abgetöteter älterer Keime von *Clepsine sexoculata.* Zeit. f. wiss. Zool., *141:*399–431.

Motomura, I. 1935 Determination of the embryonic axis in the eggs of amphibia and echinoderms. Sci. Rep. Tohoku Univ., *10:*211–245.

Needham, J. 1942 Biochemistry and Morphogenesis. Cambridge University Press, Cambridge, England.

Novikoff, A. B. 1938 Embryonic determination in the annelid, *Sabellaria vulgaris.* II. Transplantation of polar lobes and blastomeres as a test of their inducing capacities. Biol. Bull., *74:*211–234.

———— 1940 Morphogenetic substances or organizers in annelid development. J. Exp. Zool., *85:*127–155.

Pease, D. C. 1938 The influence of centrifugal force on the bilateral determination of the spirally-cleaving eggs of Urechis. Biol. Bull., *75:*409–424.

Pease, D. C. 1939 An analysis of the factors of bilateral determination in centrifuged echinoderm embryos. J. Exp. Zool., *80*:225–247.

———— 1941 Echinoderm bilateral determination in chemical concentration gradients. I. The effects of cyanide, ferricyanide, picrate, dinitrophenol, urethane, iodine, malonate, etc. J. Exp. Zool., *86:* 381–404.

———— 1942a Echinoderm bilateral determination in chemical concentration gradients. II. The effects of azide, pilocarpine, pyocyanine, diamine, cysteine, glutathione, and lithium. J. Exp. Zool., *89:*329–345.

———— 1942b Echinoderm bilateral determination in chemical concentration gradients. III. The effects of carbon monoxide and other gases. J. Exp. Zool., *89:*347–356.

Penners, A. 1922 Die Furchung von *Tubifex rivulorum* Lam. Zool. Jahrb. Abt. f. Anat. u. Ontog., *43:*323–368.

———— 1924a Doppelbildungen bei *Tubifex rivulorum* Lam. Zool. Jahrb. allg. Zool., *41:*91–120.

———— 1924b Experimentelle Untersuchungen zum Determinationsproblem am Keim von *Tubifex rivulorum* Lam. I. Die Duplicitas cruciata und organbildende Keimbezirke. Arch. f. mikr. Anatomie, *102:*51–100.

———— 1926 Experimentelle Untersuchungen zum Determinationsproblem am Keim von *Tubifex rivulorum* Lam. II. Die Entwicklung teilweise abgetöteter Keime. Zeit. f. wiss. Zool., *127:*1–140.

———— 1937 Regulation am Keim von *Tubifex rivulorum* Lam. nach Ausschaltung des ektodermalen Keimstreifs. Zeit. f. wiss. Zool., *149:*86–130.

———— 1938 Abhängigkeit der Formbildung vom Mesoderm im Tubifex-Embryo. Zeit. f. wiss. Zool., *150:*305–357.

Pisanò, A. 1949 Lo sviluppo dei primi due blastomeri separati dell'uovo di Ascidie. Pubbl. Staz. Zool. Napoli, *22:*16–25.

Raven, C. P., and Bretschneider, L. H. 1942 The effect of centrifugal force upon the eggs of *Limnaea stagnalis* L. Arch. Néerlandaises de Zool., *6:*255–278.

Reverberi, G., and Minganti, A. 1946a Le potenze dei quartetti animale e vegetativo isolati di *Ascidiella aspersa*. Pubbl. Staz. Zool. Napoli, *20:*135–151.

————, and Minganti, A. 1946b Fenomeni di evocazione nello sviluppo dell'uovo di Ascidie. Risultati dell'indagine sperimentale sull'uovo di *Ascidiella aspersa* e di *Ascidia malaca* allo stadio di otto blastomeri. Pubbl. Staz. Zool. Napoli, *20:* 199–252.

————, and Minganti, A. 1947 La distribuzione delle potenze nel germe di Ascidie allo stadio di otto blastomeri, analizzata mediante le combinazioni e i trapianti di blastomeri. Pubbl. Staz. Zool. Napoli, *21:*1–35.

————, and Minganti, A. 1951 Concerning the interpretation of the experimental analysis of the ascidian development. Acta Biotheoretica, *9:*197–204.

Rose, S. M. 1939 Embryonic induction in the ascidia. Biol. Bull., *77:*216–232.

Rulon, O. 1941 Modifications of development in the sand dollar by NaSCN and Ca-free sea water. Physiol. Zool., *14:*305–315.

———— 1952 The modification of developmental patterns in the sand dollar by glucose. Physiol. Zool., *25:*346–357.

Runnström, J. 1926 Experimentelle Bestimmung der Dorso-Ventralachse bei dem Seeigelkeim. Ark. för Zool., *18 A*(4):1–6.

———— 1928a Zur experimentellen Analyse der Wirkung des Lithiums auf den Seeigelkeim. Acta Zool., *9:*365–424.

———— 1928b Plasmabau und Determination bei dem Ei von *Paracentrotus lividus* Lk. Roux' Arch. Entw.-mech., *113:*556–581.

———— 1933 Kurze Mitteilung zur Physiologie der Determination des Seeigelkeims. Roux' Arch. Entw.-mech., *129:*442–444.

————, and Runnström, S. 1921 Über die Entwicklung von *Cucumaria frondosa* Gunnerus and *Psolus phantopus* Strussenfelt. Bergens Mus. Aarbok, 1918–1919, *2*(No. 5):1–100.

Schleip, W. 1914 Die Entwicklung zentrifugierter Eier von *Clepsine sexoculata*. Verh. deutsch. Zool. Ges., pp. 236–253.

———— 1929 Die Determination der Primitiventwicklung. Akademische Verlags-Austalt, Leipzig.

Spek, J. 1926 Über gesetzmässige Substanzverteilungen bei der Furchung des Ctenophoreneies und ihre Beziehungen zu den Determinationsproblemen. Roux' Arch. Entw.-mech., *107:*54–73.

Sturtevant, A. H. 1923 Inheritance of direction of coiling in Limnea. Science, *58:*269–270.

Taylor, C. V., and Tennent, D. H. 1924 Preliminary report on the development of egg fragments. Yearbook Carnegie Institution, *23:*201–206.

Tennent, D. H., Taylor, C. V., and Whitaker, D. M. 1929 An investigation on organization in a seaurchin egg. Pap. Tortugas Lab., *26:*1–104.

Titlebaum, A. 1928 Artificial production of Janus embryos of Chaetopterus. Proc. Nat. Acad. Sci., *14:*245–247.

Tung, T. 1932 Experiences de coloration vitale sur l'oeuf d'*Ascidiella aspersa*. Arch. de Biol., *43:* 451–469.

———— 1934 Récherches sur les potentialités des blastomères chez *Ascidiella scabra*. Experiences de translocation, de combinaison et d'isolement de blastomères. Arch. d'Anat. micros., *30:*381–410.

————, Ku, S., and Tung, Y. 1941 The development of the ascidian egg centrifuged before fertilization. Biol. Bull., *80:*153–168.

Tyler, A. 1930 Experimental production of double embryos in annelids and molluscs. J. Exp. Zool., *57:*347–407.

Ubisch, L. von 1929 Über die Determination der larvalen Organe und der Imaginalanlage bei Seeigeln. Roux' Arch. Entw.-mech., *117:*80–120.

———— 1938 Über Keimverschmelzungen an *Ascidiella aspersa*. Roux' Arch. Entw.-mech., *138:* 18–36.

———— 1939a Über die Entwicklung von Ascidienlarven nach frühzeitiger Entfernung der einzelnen organbildenden Keimbezirke. Roux' Arch. Entw.-mech., *139:*438–492.

Ubisch, L. von 1939b Keimblattchimärenforschung an Seeigellarven. Biol. Rev., *14:*88–103.

———— 1940 Weitere Untersuchungen über Regulation und Determination im Ascidienkeim. Roux' Arch. Entw.-mech., *140:*1–24.

Weiss, Paul 1949a Differential growth; in Chemistry and Physiology of Growth, edited by A. K. Parpart, pp. 35–186. Princeton University Press, Princeton, New Jersey.

———— 1949b Growth and differentiation on the cellular and molecular levels. Exptl. Cell Res., *1*(Suppl.):475–482.

———— 1950 Perspectives in the field of morphogenesis. Quart. Rev. Biol., *25:*172–198.

Wilson, E. B. 1899 Cell-lineage and ancestral reminiscence. Biol. Lect. Marine Biol. Lab., Woods Hole, *6:*21–42.

———— 1903 Experiments on cleavage and localization in the nemertine egg. Roux' Arch. Entw.-mech., *16:*411–460.

———— 1904a Experimental studies on germinal localization. I. The germ-regions in the egg of Dentalium. J. Exp. Zool., *1:*1–72.

———— 1904b Experimental studies in germinal localization. II. Experiments on the cleavage mosaic in Patella and Dentalium. J. Exp. Zool., *1:*197–268.

Yatsu, N. 1904 Experiments on the development of egg fragments in Cerebratulus. Biol. Bull., *6:*123–136.

———— 1910 Experiments on germinal localization in the egg of Cerebratulus. J. Coll. Sci. Tokyo, *27*(17):1–37.

———— 1912 Observations and experiments on the ctenophore egg. III. Experiments on germinal localization of the egg of *Beroë ovata.* Annot. Zool. Jap., *8:*5–13.

Ziegler, H. E. 1898 Experimentelle Studien über die Zelltheilung. III. Die Furchungszellen von *Beroë ovata.* Roux' Arch. Entw.-mech., *7:*34–64.

CHAPTER 4

Insects

DIETRICH BODENSTEIN

PROGRESSIVE differentiation is the process by which the fertilized insect egg is transformed into the complete embryo through developmental events closely coordinated in time and space. The initiation and progress of organization in the egg depend upon the realization of certain dynamic phenomena which mold the embryonic material for particular functions. It is the special physico-chemical nature of the insect egg that provides the substrate and conditions for the action and interaction of these dynamic forces.

THE INITIATION OF EARLY EMBRYONIC ORGANIZATION

The insect egg is usually rich in yolk. Its nucleus lies in a central position and is embedded in a small cytoplasmic island. Fine cytoplasmic strands of this island ramify through the yolk and often condense at the periphery of the egg, forming here a cortical layer. After the nucleus has divided and its daughter nuclei have populated the yolk, the majority of them move toward the egg surface. Here they arrange themselves with the formation of cell boundaries into a single cell layer, the blastoderm. The first visible differentiation of the embryo is the germ band. It appears in the blastoderm in the region of the presumptive prothorax and from here continues its differentiation anteriorly and posteriorly. These beginnings of organization in the egg are governed by two different centers, the activation center and the differentiation center (Seidel, '29). Through an alternation of dynamic processes and material reactions, these two centers interact, thus setting into motion the whole process of embryonic organization.

The activation center is located at the posterior pole of the egg. Its function depends on the interaction of the cleavage nuclei with some factor in the region of the center. The product of this reaction, presumably

a specific material substance, spreads forward in the egg, evoking in its course another reaction which changes the structure of the yolk system. This in turn causes a contraction of the yolk system. The latter reaction provides the necessary situation for the aggregation of the blastoderm cells to form the germ band.

The contraction begins at the site of the presumptive prothorax and spreads from here anteriorly and posteriorly in a wavelike fashion. This region is known as the differentiation center; in this same region the first visible differentiation of the germ band may be witnessed. The morphologically defined differentiation center hence can be visualized as a center of morphodynamic movement which provides the stimulus for the aggregation of the cells that form the germ band. The chain of reactions evoked by the activation center is thus essential for the function of the differentiation center, which represents the focal point for all subsequent processes of differentiation of the embryo.

While the described phenomena do not directly concern the formation of the blastoderm, it must be realized that the entire specialized organization of the insect egg as a dynamic system, including the yolk system, the cleavage nuclei with their cytoplasmic connections, and the blastoderm, is the prerequisite for the normal sequence of the described reactions.

DETERMINATION AND REGULATION

The problem of regulation and determination is closely related to, and can only be understood in the light of, the above discussed general principles of insect development. It has been shown that the regulative capacity of the egg varies greatly within the different groups of insects (Seidel, Bock, and Krause, '40). As a matter of fact, all transitions from eggs with great regulative powers to eggs exhibiting strictly mosaic development may be found. For instance, in the dragonfly Platycnemis, twin embryos of harmonious proportions can be experimentally produced by injuring of the presumptive germ band in early cleavage stages. In this form, the embryonic material maintains its regulative capacity until some time after the blastoderm is formed. In Diptera, on the other hand, the determination of the presumptive embryonic parts is already accomplished at the time of fertilization, for when egg parts at this early stage are removed, the remaining parts are unable to develop beyond their prospective significance (Reith, '25; Pauli, '27). An intermediate position between these two extremes is taken by the honeybee (Schnetter, '34) or the pea weevil Sitonia (Reith, '35); in these the determination of the embryo is completed at the early blastoderm stage. The regulative capacity of the embryonic material is gradually restricted and finally lost as development proceeds. In Platycnemis, where in early development the various regions of the presumptive embryo can still replace each other, these regions become more and more committed to special tasks with continued development. Finally the entire embryonic zone reaches the mosaic stage, in which each part is irrevocably determined and destined to a specific end. This state of affairs prevails not only in the determination of the early embryonic material but also in the determination of parts within organ fields of larval or imaginal character, and extends even to the processes of regeneration: it is a general principle and well founded indeed.

Thus the principle of progressive determination applies to insects as well as to other forms. Is the difference between regulative and mosaic insect development to be explained by this principle? If, as we usually assume, it is the early or late determination of embryonic parts for their final destiny that distinguishes the regulative from the mosaic type, then this principle does not apply. For eggs exhibiting mosaic characteristics in early stages of development can in the course of their development acquire the capacity to regulate (Ewest, '37). The differences between the determinate and indeterminate egg type are not based on alterations of events in time, but are found in the specialized architecture of the different insect eggs. Specializations in the configuration of the internal egg structure which restrict or enhance the freedom of movement of the embryonic material in the dynamic egg

system are the factors that decide and distinguish the determinate from the indeterminate type (Seidel, Bock, and Krause, '40).

EMBRYONIC INDUCTION BETWEEN GERM LAYERS

Among the causal factors of embryonic determination, we must include the processes of embryonic induction. The experiments supplying this important information for insects were carried out on the eggs of the neuropteron *Chrysopa perla* (Bock, '39). The decisive facts are briefly as follows: When at an early stage of germ layer formation ectoderm is removed at one side of the segment, the mesoderm spreads normally below the ectoderm-free regions, but fails to form an epithelium and soon degenerates. Thus the epithelization of this layer is dependent on the presence of ectoderm. The question whether the ectoderm also decides the further differentiation of the underlying mesoderm was determined by other experiments. Within one half of a segment large parts of ectoderm located near the median line or more lateral to it were removed. The mesoderm below the median as well as the lateral remains of ectoderm formed coelom-epithelium of diminished proportions, corresponding in size to the reduced ectoderm portions above. The epithelium differentiated in due course into intestinal muscles and cardioblasts below the lateral ectoderm, while these differentiations were absent below the median ectodermal region. In other words, the mesoderm always differentiated according to position, regardless of its prospective significance. From these results and from other experiments showing that the mesoderm was isopotent for the structures in question, it was concluded that the various ectodermal regions determine the type of differentiation of the mesoderm below them. The lateral ectoderm regions hence contain factors necessary for the formation of intestinal muscles and cardioblasts, which factors were absent in the median ectodermal portions. Thus the capacity of the ectoderm to imprint its specific demands on the underlying mesodermal substratum must be considered as a phenomenon of real embryonic induction. In the light of these facts, it is interesting to venture a comparison of the types of organizing events between amphibians and insects. The decisive factors for the organization of the embryo are located in a definite germ layer in amphibians as well as in Chrysopa. In amphibians they are found in the mesoderm, in Chrysopa in the ectoderm. The inducing material of amphibians enjoys a great freedom of movement. The extent of these movements determines to a large degree the size and proportions of the induced structures. In Chrysopa, on the other hand, the inductor, the ectoderm, is a relatively rigid system, endowed with a mosaic of inductive potency. The mesoderm underlies this system and responds with specific differentiations to the stimuli emanating from it. The movements of the embryonic material, different as they are in both classes of animals compared, undoubtedly have the same basic significance, namely the bringing together of developmental systems for the purpose of interactions that provide the basis for the organization of the embryo (Seidel, Bock, and Krause, '40).

CYTOPLASMIC DETERMINERS

In the determinate egg type, the cortical cytoplasm is usually heavy and already in the fertilized egg seems to consist of a mosaic of differentials that determine the various parts of the future embryo. When in the beetles Leptinotarsa (Hegner, '11) or Bruchus (Brauer and Taylor, '34) small areas of the cortical cytoplasm are destroyed before the cleavage nuclei have arrived and without apparent injury to them, those parts of the embryo are missing which would have developed from the destroyed regions. Since no degeneration of the cleavage nuclei occurred, it follows that they must have taken part in the development of some other parts of the egg. The cortical cytoplasm they happen to invade as the result of the experimentally altered conditions must have determined their fate. The fact that these nuclei were able to respond to the cytoplasmic influences of regions normally foreign to them indicates their totipotency. The totipotency of cleavage nuclei in early stages of development, it might here be added, was definitely proved in experiments on other forms, notably Platycnemis, where it persists at least until the seventh cleavage division (Seidel, '32). These experiments show quite conclusively that the cortical cytoplasm is a differentiated continuum in which localized differentials exert specific influences on the cleavage nuclei, leading them towards special assignments. One has to assume that the cytoplasmic regions possess their specific qualities only when in

normal topographic relationship to the cortical cytoplasmic layer as a whole. Their influences must be regarded as of a general directive nature in that they set up differentials in the cleavage nuclei, thereby creating a definite pattern within the framework of the blastoderm, which forms the basis for the ensuing developmental events. If one could excise the cytoplasm of the presumptive eye region and supply it with any number of the totipotent nuclei, the isolated bit of tissue would in all probability never give rise to an eye or to any specialized structure.

Within the realm of cytoplasmic determiners one has to include the pole-plasm. The cortical cytoplasm at the posterior pole of the egg is in certain insects distinguished from the rest of this layer by the presence of deeply staining granules. This region is called the pole-plasm. The cleavage nuclei which penetrate this region become known as pole cells; they represent the germ-cell primordia. When in the egg of the beetle Leptinotarsa (Hegner, '11), the polar cytoplasm is removed before the cleavage nuclei have entered the pole, germ cells are lacking in the embryo. This shows that the polar cytoplasm contains some factor essential for the formation of the germ cells. The polar region of the cortical cytoplasm is thus endowed with a specific organ-forming principle which takes effect at an early stage in development and which determines the cleavage nuclei towards their future destiny. It has been assumed that the formative role of the polar influences was such as to predetermine rigidly the polar cells for their fate. That this is not the case has recently been demonstrated in Drosophila (Poulson, '47). For some time it has been known that not all the pole cells take part in the formation of the gonad, but that some of them go astray on their way to their final location in the interior of the embryo. These "lost" cells were formerly supposed to degenerate, apparently because of their failure to become germ cells. Now Poulson has made the striking discovery that these "lost" cells do not degenerate at all, but that they can become incorporated into the epithelium of the gut, of which they actually become a part. This fact deserves emphasis, for it demonstrates that the cytoplasmic pole factors do not decide finally the ultimate fate of the pole cells. They obviously endow the pole cells with the potentialities necessary for the formation of germ cells. But whether or not these or other potentialities become realized is decided much later in the course of development, apparently at or near the site these cells finally occupy.

PROGRESSIVE FIXATION OF CHARACTERS

The entire process of embryonic determination, it will be noted, is a step by step affair. First, a general body zone is mapped out (differentiation center). This zone subdivides into smaller more specialized zones, with less power of change (germ layers). Progressive specialization continues, bringing about a more detailed subdivision of the various embryonic zones into organ fields. Segregation of material, and with it restriction of potencies, is now so advanced that the different organ fields can no longer replace each other. Yet the capacity for limited regulation might still prevail in certain organ fields even at relatively late stages of development (Lüscher, '44). Soon the power of regulation subsides even in these fields; finally, at the time of visible organ segregation all power of regulation is apparently lost.

The organism developing in the egg is the larval form of the species. It is the determination of its parts that has been discussed so far. When the fully developed larva leaves the egg, it carries in its body (holometabolous insects) reservoirs of cell groups from which many structures of the adult animal take their origin. These groups of cells are called imaginal discs; they represent the primitive anlagen of the future imaginal organs, such as legs, wings, eyes, etc. Not all these discs are morphologically distinct at the time the larva hatches from the egg. The time of their appearance varies greatly within different insect groups and even within the various organs of the same individual. In Lepidoptera, for instance, the imaginal wing discs are already visible in the youngest caterpillar stage, while the leg discs make their appearance only in the last larval instar (Bodenstein, '36). In Diptera, both leg and wing discs are visible as small cell aggregations at the time the larva hatches (Auerbach, '36). The regions in the larval body from which these various imaginal discs arise are mapped out long before the discs become actually visible (Bodenstein, '36). Now the evidence suggests that the determination of these imaginal regions already occurs in embryonic development, and that it takes place a short time after the larval structures in the egg

are determined (Lüscher, '44; Geigy, '31). The insect egg, as it has been said, thus becomes the carrier of a double embryo— a larval and an imaginal embryo (Geigy, '31). The imaginal anlagen or their presumptive regions may remain in an undifferentiated embryonic state till very late in postembryonic development and maintain throughout this period a remarkable degree of regulative capacities. The different elements of the imaginal organs become determined at different times. The character of the scales in adult Lepidoptera legs or the type of cuticle sheath formed by the legs at pupation is already determined in the third instar larva while at this time the presumptive materials for femur, tibia, or tarsus can still replace each other. The determination of these latter parts apparently takes place shortly before the leg discs become visible at the last larval instar (Bodenstein, '37). The appearance of the imaginal discs per se does not mark the final state of determination, for in Drosophila, where the leg discs are present in the first instar larva, isolation experiments showed that the discs of young last instar larvae are still capable of regulation (Vogt, '46), reaching their final mosaic state in a later period of this instar (Bodenstein, '41). The genital discs of last instar Drosophila larvae also still possess considerable powers of regulation (Hadorn, Bertani, and Gallera, '49). At this advanced stage these discs are composed of a mosaic of separate fields, each of which gives rise to a special element of the imaginal genital apparatus. These fields cannot replace each other, but the various parts within a single field can regulate; they differentiate into normally shaped adult structures of characteristic size. Duplications of various other Drosophila organs, such as wing, antenna, palpus, or scutellum, following x-ray treatment (Waddington, '42) or temperature treatment (Vogt, '47a) of young last instar larvae gave further proof of the indeterminate state of these organs in late stages of development.

The determination of all imaginal systems is not necessarily completed at the end of the larval period. The venation in wings of some Lepidoptera is not finally determined before the pupa is several days old (Henke, '33). It is also during the pupal stage that the color pattern of the wing becomes determined. This wing pattern is a complicated developmental system, composed of different zones which are determined at different times. In the determination of the wing pattern a succession of determination streams passes over the wing surface determining the various component parts of this system. The nature of the determining influences is not known. The experimental analysis of wing pattern formation has furnished a wealth of information concerning the state of determination of the various zones at different times in development and has brought to light the interdependency of these zones in the formation of the entire pattern (Caspari, '41).

DEVELOPMENTAL INTERACTIONS IN LATER STAGES

Although the different elements comprising the component parts of an organ can still replace each other in organ anlagen of postembryonic stages, the imaginal discs or the prospective regions from which they arise are at these late stages usually committed to the type of organ or body part they eventually form. There are, however, experiments indicating that the plasticity of the formative disc material goes beyond the limit of regulations of its own parts. It has been shown that the developmental path of one type of disc can be changed into another. In late postembryonic stages of development, therefore, the prospective significance of these discs is not yet organ specific. For example, the presumptive antenna material of last instar Drosophila larvae can be changed into leg material by appropriate temperature treatment (Vogt, '46b) or x-ray treatment (Waddington, '42). Also in Drosophila the change of presumptive head chitin into eye facets (Steinberg, '41; Chevais, '44) and wing tissue into body skin (Waddington, '42) by similar methods are other instances of the same sort. Developmental modifications produced by treating Drosophila larvae or pupae with ether (Gloor, '46, '47) reveal effects with like implications, and so do many other investigations dealing with phenocopies. It is of interest to note further that transformations of presumptive antenna material into leg material were obtained in Drosophila by the use of two chemicals, colchicin (Vogt, '47b) and a nitrogen mustard compound (Bodenstein, '47)—chemicals that are known to have a marked effect on cell division. The long-suspected importance of growth relations (Goldschmidt, '38) between the various organ-fields as decisive factors in determining the type of organ differentiation has thus gained support. The phenomenon

known as homoeosis, i.e., the replacement by regeneration of one organ by one belonging to another region of the body, needs to be mentioned in this connection. In studying this type of regeneration, it was found that regional specific regeneration occurs if relatively little of the original organ is removed, while amputation of larger parts is usually followed by heteromorphic regeneration (Brecher, '24). It thus seems that in the first instance the organ-field of the original organ takes the lead in determining the new structure, while in the second instance this lead is taken by a neighboring field. In ontogenesis as in regeneration, therefore, it is the interaction between zones within one organ-field, or that between neighboring fields, which determines the type of organ finally to be formed.

An interesting and special case showing a change from one type of development into another has been reported in the moth Orgyia (Lep.). Here, the secondary sexual characters of the female wing discs are still not irrevocably determined in fourth instar caterpillars, for fourth instar wing discs when transplanted into male hosts and made to regenerate in their new surroundings will form male wings. In the reverse experiments, however, transplanted male wings will regenerate male wings in the female environment (Paul, '37). It might well be pointed out that this case is a singular instance of this kind, although the problem has been studied extensively in other insects. The experiments usually quoted as proof for the complete determination of secondary sexual characters are castration experiments and transplantations of gonads between individuals of the opposite sex. It may be added that the above cited case is not only singular in its results but also in its method. In Orgyia, in contrast to all other investigations, the organ exhibiting the secondary sexual character was brought into contact with the entire developing system of the opposite sex and hence subjected to influences additional to those of the gonads. It is perhaps the lack of appropriate experimentation rather than the special condition of the Orgyia wing that made the obtained results exceptional.

Finally, mention should be made of developmental interactions between systems which already possess a considerable degree of differentiation. There are species of Drosophila that have spiral, and others that have nonspiral, ellipsoid adult testes. Now it has been found (Stern, '41a, '41b) that when vasa efferentia from species with spiral testes are brought experimentally into contact with normally non-spiral testes, the latter coil, i.e., become spiral shaped. And vice versa, the vasa of non-spiral species when connected to normally spiral testes prevent the coiling of these organs. The vasa thus determine the final shape of the adult testis. This effect is only produced when testes and vasa, which originate independently of each other, become attached, i.e., come into cellular contact. The attachment of both organs takes place during pupal life, at which time both components involved are already quite well differentiated.

Another type of interaction between tissues far advanced in development is illustrated in the following example. If female genital discs of Drosophila are transplanted into male hosts, the host testes suffer extensive degeneration when the oviducts developed from the transplanted disc become attached to the host testes. As in the previous case, the phenomenon is only brought about if cellular contact is established between these two organs; the principle causing it is not species specific (Bodenstein, '46). In both cases cited, the stimuli eliciting the characteristic response are located in the genital ducts. There seems to exist an inductor-reactor relationship between these two organs; the inductor in the vasa calls forth a growth reaction in the testis, and the inductor in the oviduct a degenerative process. The inductors act only when in contact with the reacting material.

A similar mechanism of transmitting determining influences through the substance of adjacent cells has been suggested in explaining the determination of certain structural units in the cuticle pattern of the bug Rhodnius (Wigglesworth, '40a). In this insect, the nymphal cuticle bears bristles arising from small plaques which are distributed regularly over the surface of the abdomen. The closeness of these plaques to each other seems to affect the determination of new plaques. Each plaque apparently exerts through the substance of the epidermis cells that surround it an inhibiting influence which prevents the development of a new plaque within a certain radius. The distance over which this influence acts is dependent upon the number of epidermal cells between the existing plaques. It is noteworthy that the number of cells intervening between the plaques decides the limitation of the inhibiting influence. Since the cell number is the result of previous cell division, the role of

growth processes in the determination events again becomes evident. In the mechanism of determination, influences of this kind are perhaps of major importance, although they are not easily detected experimentally. They might function fundamentally in the developmental interactions between cell populations, prospective organ regions, discs or body parts discussed in this chapter.

HORMONES IN GROWTH AND DIFFERENTIATION

While the processes of determination establish, by progressive restriction of developmental potencies, the determination of organs and body parts to attain fixed fates, it is hormones that in many instances are known to be responsible for the realization of these fates. Hormone activity thus is an integral mechanism in the development of insects. For instance, the imaginal differentiation of Drosophila leg or eye discs can only take place after a specific hormone released by the ring gland has exerted its influence (Bodenstein, '43). Similarly, the nymphal cuticle of the blood-sucking bug Rhodnius (Wigglesworth, '34 and '36) or of the cockroach (Scharrer, '46) or the skin of caterpillars (Piepho, '38a) can only develop imaginal character when stimulated by the appropriate hormones. Moulting in insects is also under humoral control. Since moulting is an essential feature in insect growth, it is growth that is controlled by hormones. This fact is also well illustrated by the behavior of Drosophila discs which grow only in an organic environment especially conditioned by hormones (Bodenstein, '43). The ability of the different tissues to react to hormonal stimuli varies greatly. Some tissues become competent for response early in development, others later. Thus the epidermis of first stage Rhodnius nymphs (Wigglesworth, '34) or of caterpillars just hatched from the egg (Piepho, '38b) already responds at this early stage to metamorphosis hormones and can hence be changed experimentally into imaginal epidermis. On the other hand, imaginal discs of first instar Drosophila larvae do not respond to these hormones but acquire the ability to do so at the next larval stage (Bodenstein, '44). Moreover, not all tissues respond with like ease to the same hormone level (Bodenstein, '43; Kühn and Piepho, '36). The factors that make the discs or body parts competent to respond, or what this competence means in physicochemical terms, is obscure, as is the nature of the mechanism of determination in discs in general.

Now it should be understood that hormones are not merely general stimulators, creating a situation through which the invisibly fixed organization of the organic pattern becomes realized. They do more, for they often decide specifically which of the developmental possibilities existing in the reacting material shall become manifest. In fact, it is often only through the specific action of these hormones that we can detect the existence of latent developmental potentialities. Take the case of the young caterpillar epidermis. Under normal conditions, the young epidermis at the ensuing moult would have laid down caterpillar cuticle under the influence of the juvenile hormone. Yet, under experimental conditions, prematurely supplied with metamorphosis hormone, the same epidermis lays down pupal cuticle. In the reacting material, therefore, several competences must have existed side by side and the hormone decided when and which of these became manifest. As far as the determination of definite fates is concerned, the young larval epidermis is but labilely determined, for by the appropriate hormone it can be switched from larval to imaginal development. Not only epidermis but also organ anlagen show this dual type of determination (Bodenstein, '42). Apparently a similar state of affairs prevails in the reversal of secondary sex characters in the Lepidoptera wing cited above. Here influences presumably hormonal in nature emanating from the organic environment were able to shift the development from a female into a male direction. Even at the end of development, when the adult organism emerges, it seems that absolute stability, i.e., a definite determination of the parts to pursue fixed fates, is never reached. This is most strikingly demonstrated by the fact that adult insects can be made to moult in the presence of juvenile hormone and that part of the organism now possesses nymphal or larval character (Wigglesworth, '40; Piepho, '38a). The developmental systems necessary for this reversion of development were hence latent in the cells, but needed special conditions for their realization. There are other instances with like implication. One of special interest is the case of the walking-stick Dixippus in which, by extirpation of the corpora allata, the normal hormonal balance was upset; this resulted in the formation of an eye-like structure in the ectoderm of the head. This eye, though never normally observed in this species, is characteristic for related species (Pflugfelder, '39a). Now the purpose of presenting this information is to emphasize the fact that apparently rigidly determined systems may still contain latent developmental powers of amazing plasticity which, however, become manifest only under certain conditions.

The role of hormones in growth has been mentioned. It is not astonishing that we find them playing an important part in the activation of growth as a component process in regeneration. The walking-stick Dixippus loses its ability to regenerate new appendages in the adult stage, while it freely regenerates these organs in nymphal stages. If the imago is induced to moult again by the transplantation of young corpora allata and thus supplied with juvenile hormone, the animal once again regains its powers to regenerate. Conversely, extirpation of the corpora allata in young nymphs results in the loss of the regeneration power, while reimplantation of these glands restores this capacity (Pflugfelder, '39a, '39b). Removal of the corpora allata in young nymphal stages also causes severe changes in all tissues (Pflugfelder, '38; Scharrer, '46). Many tissues degenerate, others show abnormal uncontrolled growth often resembling certain tumors familiar to vertebrate pathologists. Mesodermal organs seem to be affected first, and more drastically than skin. Normal conditions may be restored by providing the abnormal animals again with corpora allata. Internal secretion and tissue proliferation as well as cell pathology are closely related. In general, we can visualize the part played by hormones in insect development as follows: In addition to their more specific actions in controlling the manifestation of certain morphogenetic and histogenetic features in development, the hormones play the more general role of metabolic regulators. By virtue of their reintegrating function, they bring the various parts of the organism under a common control. Thus any disturbance of this prominent integrating system results in severe developmental modifications and functional alterations.

REFERENCES

Auerbach, C. 1936 The development of the legs and the wings and halteres in wild type and some mutant strains of *Drosophila melanogaster*. Trans. Royal Soc. Edinburgh, *53*:787–815.

Bock, E. 1939 Bildung und Differenzierung der Keimblätter bei *Chrysopa perla* (L). Z. Morph. u. Ökol. Tiere, *35*:615–700.

Bodenstein, D. 1936 Das Determinationsgeschehen bei Insekten mit Ausschluss der frühembryonalen Determination. Ergeb. d. Biol., 13:174–234.

——— 1937 Beintransplantationen an Lepidopterenraupen, IV. Roux' Arch. Entw.-mech., 136:745–785.

——— 1941 Investigations on the problem of metamorphosis. VIII. Studies on leg determination in insects. J. Exp. Zool., 87:31–53.

——— 1942 Hormone controlled processes in insect development. Cold Spring Harbor Symp. on Quant. Biol., 10:17–26.

——— 1943 Hormones and tissue competence in the development of Drosophila. Biol. Bull., 84: 34–58.

——— 1944 The induction of larval molts in Drosophila. Biol. Bull., 86:113–124.

——— 1946 Developmental relations between genital ducts and gonads in Drosophila. Biol. Bull., 91:288–294.

——— 1947 Chemical alteration of development in Drosophila. Anat. Rec., 99:No. 4, p. 34.

Brauer, A., and Taylor, A. C. 1934 Experiments to determine the presence, location and effects of an organization center in Bruchid (Coleoptera) eggs. Anat. Rec., 60 (Suppl.):61.

Brecher, L. 1924 Die Bedingungen für Fühlerfüsse bei Dixippus morosus. Roux' Arch. Entw.-mech., 102:549–572.

Caspari, E. 1941 The morphology and development of the wing pattern of Lepidoptera. Quart. Rev. Biol., 16:249–273.

Chevais. S. 1944 Determinisme de la taille de l'oeil chez la mutant Bar de la Drosophile. Intervention d'une substance diffusible specifique. Bull. Biol. Fr. Belg., 78:1–39.

Ewest, A. 1937 Struktur und erste Differenzierung im Ei des Mehlkäfers Tenebrio molitor. Roux' Arch. Entw.-mech., 135:689–752.

Geigy, R. 1931 Erzeugung rein imaginaler Defekte durch ultraviolette Eibestrahlung bei Drosophila melanogaster. Roux' Arch. Entw.-mech., 125:406–447.

Gloor, H. 1946 Die experimentelle Erzeugung von homoeotischen Modifikationen im Metathorax der Drosophila melanogaster. Arch. Jul. Klaus-stift., 21:308–311.

——— 1947 Phänokopie-Versuche mit Äther an Drosophila. Rev. suisse Zool., 54:637–712.

Goldschmidt, R. 1938 Physiological Genetics. McGraw-Hill Book Co., New York.

Hadorn, E., Bertani, G., and Gallera, J. 1949 Regulationsfähigkeit und Feldorganisation der männlichen Genital-imaginalscheibe von Drosophila melanogaster. Roux' Arch. Entw.-mech., 144:31–70.

Hegner, R. W. 1911 Experiments with Chrysomelid beetles. III. The effects of killing parts of the eggs of Leptinotarsa decemlineata. Biol. Bull., 20:237–251.

Henke, K. 1933 Untersuchungen an Philosamia cynthia Drury zur Entwicklungsphysiologie des Zeichnungsmusters auf dem Schmetterlingsflügel. Roux' Arch. Entw.-mech., 128:15–107.

Kühn, A., and Piepho, H. 1936 Über hormonale Wirkungen bei der Verpuppung der Schmetterlinge. Abh. Ges. Wiss. Gottingen, Math. physik. Kl., N.F., 2:No. 9, pp. 141–154.

Lüscher, M. 1944 Experimentelle Untersuchungen über die larvale und die imaginale Determination im Ei der Kleidermotte (Tineola biselliella Hum.). Rev. suisse Zool., 51:531–627.

Paul, H. 1937 Transplantation und Regeneration der Flügel zur Untersuchung ihrer Formbildung bei einem Schmetterling mit Geschlechtsdimorphismus, Orgyia antiqua L. Roux' Arch. Entw.-mech., 136:64–111.

Pauli, M. E. 1927 Die Entwicklung geschnürter und centrifugierter Eier von Calliphora erythrocephala und Musca domestica. Z. wiss. Zool., 129:483–540.

Pflugfelder, O. 1938 Weitere experimentelle Untersuchungen über die Funktion der Corpora allata von Dixippus morosus. Z. wiss. Zool., 151: 149–291.

——— 1939a Beeinflussung von Regenerationsvorgängen bei Dixippus morosus Br. durch Exstirpation und Transplantation der Corpora allata. Z. wiss. Zool., 152:159–184.

——— 1939b Wechselwirkungen von Drüsen innerer Sekretion bei Dixippus morosus Br. Z. wiss. Zool., 152:384–408.

Piepho, H. 1938a Über die Auslösung der Raupenhäutung, Verpuppung und Imaginalentwicklung an Hautimplantaten von Schmetterlingen. Biol. Zbl., 58:481–495.

——— 1938b Über die experimentelle Auslösbarkeit überzähliger Häutungen und vorzeitiger Verpuppung an Hautstücken bei Kleinschmetterlingen. Naturwissenschaften, 26:841–842.

Poulson, D. F. 1947 The pole cells of Diptera, their fate and significance. Proc. Nat. Acad. Sci., 33:182–184.

Reith, F. 1925 Die Entwicklung des Musca-Eies nach Ausschaltung verschiedener Eibereiche. Z. wiss. Zool., 126:181–238.

——— 1935 Über die Determination der Keimesanlage bei Insekten (Ausschaltungsversuche am Ei des Rüsselkäfers Sitona lineata). Z. wiss. Zool., 147:77–100.

Scharrer, B. 1945 Experimental tumors after nerve section in an insect. Proc. Soc. Exp. Biol. & Med., 60:181–186.

——— 1946 The role of corpora allata in the development of Leucophaea maderae (Orthoptera). Endocrinology, 138:35–45.

Schnetter, M. 1934 Physiologische Untersuchungen über das Differenzierungszentrum in der Embryonalentwicklung der Honigbiene. Roux' Arch. Entw.-mech., 131:285–323.

Seidel, F. 1929 Untersuchung über das Bildungsprinzip der Keimanlage im Ei der Libelle Platycnemis pennipes, I–IV. Roux' Arch. Entw.-mech., 119:322–440.

——— 1932 Die Potenzen der Furchungskerne im Libellenei und ihre Rolle bei der Aktivierung des Bildungszentrums. Roux' Arch. Entw.-mech., 126:213–276.

Seidel, F., Bock, E., and Krause, G. 1940 Die Organisation des Insekteneies. Naturwissenschaften, 28:433–446.

Steinberg, A. G. 1941 A reconsideration of the mode of development of the bar eye of *Drosophila melanogaster*. Genetics, *26:*325–346.

Stern, C. 1941a The growth of testes in Drosophila. I. The relation between vas deferens and testis within various species. J. Exp. Zool., *87:* 113–158.

——— 1941b The growth of testes in Drosophila. II. The nature of interspecific differences. J. Exp. Zool., *87:*159–180.

Vogt, M. 1946a Zur labilen Determination der Imaginalscheiben von Drosophila, I. Biol. Ztrbl., *65:*223–238.

——— 1946b Zur labilen Determination der Imaginalscheiben von Drosophila, II. Biol. Ztrbl., *65:*238–254.

——— 1947a Zur labilen Determination der Imaginalscheiben von Drosophila, III. Biol. Ztrbl., *66:*81–105.

——— 1947b Beeinflussung der Antennendifferenzierung durch Colchicin bei der Drosophilamutante Aristopedia. Experientia, *3:*156.

Waddington, C. H. 1942 Growth and determination in the development of Drosophila. Nature, *149:*264.

Wigglesworth, V. B. 1934 The physiology of ecdysis in *Rhodnius prolixus* (Hemiptera). II. Factors controlling moulting and metamorphosis. Q. Jour. Micro. Sci., *77:*191–222.

——— 1936 The function of the corpus allatum in the growth and reproduction of *Rhodnius prolixus* (Hemiptera). Q. Jour. Micr. Sci., *79:*91–121.

——— 1940a Local and general factors in the development of "pattern" in *Rhodnius prolixus* (Hemiptera). J. Exp. Biol., *17:*180–200.

——— 1940b The determination of character at metamorphosis in *Rhodnius prolixus* (Hemiptera). J. Exp. Biol., *17:*201–222.

SPECIAL VERTEBRATE ORGANOGENESIS

CHAPTER 1

Nervous System

(Neurogenesis)

PAUL WEISS

THE OBJECT AND THE PROBLEMS

WE ARE to deal here with the causal analysis of "the development of the nervous system." In that generality, the task is simply unmanageable. Of the innumerable aspects the mature nervous system offers to the observer, each one has had its characteristic ontogenetic history, hence raises separate questions as to time and manner of its origin and as to mode and means of its ontogenetic transformations. This points us to the only practical approach, which lies in resolving the confusing complexity of the system into simpler components and addressing our questions to the more elementary events thus singled out. Most of the following account will be essentially a sample exercise in phrasing and sorting such questions of sufficient concreteness as to offer hope for precise answers. The answers themselves are mostly still in a very fragmentary state and will be presented without glossing over their often provisional character. I have chosen topics and examples chiefly in the spirit of the guiding theme of this book, which is to illuminate, rather than cover, the processes of development. This also explains the argumentative, rather than reportorial, manner of presentation. It reflects the effort to give a coherent and consistent picture, in which facts and data are rated not as isolated items, but as tools for the clarification and solution of problems—not as sheer statements, but as answers to questions; which makes the text useful as a guide more to the understanding, than to the literature, of the field.

Some familiarity with the main morphological, physiological, and embryological features of the nervous system will be taken for granted. Yet a brief listing of the most prominent ones may help to keep our analytical questions properly focussed from the start. Somewhat arbitrarily we shall separate the discussion of the central nervous system, which serves intercommunication among its constituent units, from that of the peripheral nerves, which serve communication between the former and the non-nervous tissues of the body.

THE PERIPHERAL NERVE

Nerves are composite structures, containing bundles of nerve fibers of different classes, associated in variable numbers, proportions, and groupings, and held together and sheathed by connective tissue, in which course blood and lymph vessels and endoneurial fluid. In the so-called plexuses, nerves regroup or exchange some of their fibers. Farther peripherally, they branch by successive dichotomies and distribute their branches over the periphery according to patterns characteristic of the given peripheral sector or organ, with considerable latitude for individual variation.

The component nerve fibers themselves are composite (Fig. 125), with the axis cylinder (axon or neurite, *a*)—a protoplasmic extension of the centrally located cell body (perikaryon)—at the core; covered by a membrane or medullated sheath (*m*) consisting of alternating layers of myelin and protein; surrounded by the thin protoplasm of the sheath cells of Schwann (*s*), arrayed in tandem and (in medullated fibers) corresponding each to an internodal segment (between two nodes of Ranvier); the whole enclosed in a collagenous tube (*t*). Axons vary in diameter (caliber) according to the classes to which they belong (sympathetic, somatic motor, tactile sensory, etc.) and, within each class, according to length and peripheral distribution; the thickness of the myelin sheath and usu-

different types of neurons differ substantially in their constitution (molecular content), as evidenced by selective reactions to poisons, drugs, histological stains, hormones, and the production of specific secretions (neurosecretions). This specificity of neurons may be assumed to extend into the axis cylinders, which are true protoplasmic extensions of the cell. Many more items could be added to this list. In their totality, they make up what may be described as the "functional architecture" of the CNS.

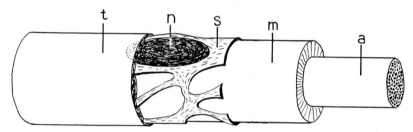

Fig. 125. Diagram of composition of single nerve fiber (explanation in text).

ally also the length of internodes vary proportionately. These parameters are importantly related to functional properties (conduction velocity, threshold, susceptibility, etc.). Fibers remain single or branch out, either by terminal flaring or by side shoots (collaterals), in accordance with functional needs. Each branch ends either blindly or on a specific end-organ with which it forms transmissive and trophic connections ("innervation"). Nerve fibers of a given class generally are found connected with the appropriately matching type of end-organ. The density of innervation varies regionally and with the type of innervated organ.

THE CENTRAL NERVOUS SYSTEM (CNS)

The CNS and its outpost ganglia contain the cell bodies (perikarya) of the peripheral neurites, and the former also a host of intracentral fibers, either in orderly bundles (fiber tracts, funiculi, commissures) or irregularly dispersed as "neuropil." In addition, these neural masses are interlaced with various types of glia cells, blood vessels, and, according to some, ground substance of ill-defined nature. Morphologically, the cell bodies vary characteristically in size, location, grouping, number, distribution of processes, and mode of interconnections, all of which may be called "geometrical" criteria. In addition to these distinctions, however,

NEUROGENESIS

Every feature thus singled out raises a separate question as to its origin. We have noted the finished products; but how have they come about? This circumscribes the task of neurogenesis. Our goal is to reconstruct the whole causal chain of events that leads from the properties of the egg cell to each particular item on our list. These events include complex molecular interactions with the emergence of new molecular species and the loss of others; displacements and rearrangements of substance on a molecular, micellar, cellular, and supracellular scale; metabolic energy production and consumption; electric, thermal, hydrodynamic, and mechanostatic (pressure-tension) phenomena, etc.; at any rate, processes that are in principle observable, measurable, and describable in terms of the substances, forces, interactions, and conditions actually present at each step. This is the object of ontogenetic analysis. Phylogenetic (evolutionary) considerations, introducing past history, do not enter into this causal (or operational) analysis at all; they only explain why of the infinite conceivable number of possible causal chains of events, only a very limited selection has found materialization.

Causal analysis must be preceded by a complete description of the events that are to be explained; description, of course, in objective and, wherever possible, quantitative terms. Much of the current research in neurogenesis is still in this descriptive phase, even though, in order to get the necessary data, it makes extensive use of experiments. The mode of the formation of a nerve fiber is a case in point. At the turn of the century, there were two opposing schools of thought given to different interpretations of inconclusive static observations. The one maintained that the axis cylinder is produced in fractions by tandem chains of peripheral cells, which are then secondarily joined together into a single strand, drainpipe fashion; while the other contended the axon to be a protoplasmic sprout of a single central neuroblast cell. The ingenious experimental feat of Harrison ('07a, '10) in isolating the supposed neuroblasts in extraneous media devoid of peripheral cells to test whether or not they could still form axons, settled the issue: they could. A descriptive datum had been ascertained by an experimental method. Then, passing on to explore the reaction of cells in vitro to solid fiber substrata, Harrison ('14) carried his research into the strictly analytical sphere, where one examines why things happen as they do—in the given case, why the nerve fiber follows one course rather than another. The Hows and Whys of our questions are thus intimately related and often enough blend into one. With this in mind we may now attempt to carve out some specific neurogenetic questions from the body of neurological data presented above. Evidently, this can only be a crude and fragmentary sample.

Why and where does the axon arise from the neuroblast? What causes its elongation? What gives it its course? Do the trunks and branches of the mature nerves reflect the orientation of early outgrowth? Is that outgrowth strictly oriented or is it haphazard, followed by selective abolition of unsuccessful connections? What determines deflections or other changes of course? What causes branches to arise, and where? Are tissues flooded with nerve fibers, or is admission selective? If the latter, how is invasion held in check? And is penetration tantamount to functionally effective innervation? What causes the association of sheath cells and nerve fibers, and what is the mechanism of myelin formation? How do fibers group into bundles—by active aggregation or by the enveloping action of connective tissue? And what determines the places and proportions in which the various tissue elements combine to form nerves? How does it happen that fibers of similar function are often grouped together, and how do they each reach their appropriate destinations? Or do they? And, if not, how can central functions fail to be confused? How does a nerve fiber gain in width, and what decides its final caliber? And does it change with body growth? What controls the number of fibers available for a given area—size of the source, frequency of branching, overproduction followed by terminal screening, or all of these? And if the size of the source is a factor, what determines it? This points us to the centers.

How does the neural plate transform into primordia of brain, spinal cord, and ganglia? How does it grow? How do its cell groups specialize for their respective formative tasks, how early, in what places and what sequence? What makes them divide or cease to divide? What causes them to migrate and in what directions, and what to assemble in defined locations? What sets the numbers and quotas of the different neuron types, and adjusts them to the functional needs of the individual? How do they achieve selective interconnections on which their later functioning will depend? And which ones of these are really relevant to the specific patterns, rather than just the general execution, of central functions? What provides the neuron population with the proper contingent of supportive, protective, and nutrient cells and structures of other origins, in varying combinations according to the local needs? And how much interdependence and interaction in growth and differentiation is there between different central regions before and after they have become segregated? If there are interactions, what is their nature and how are they transmitted? Does exercise and practice have a constructive, or at least modifying, effect on central pathways or central size? Are fluctuating peripheral demands taken into account in the development of centers, and, if so, by what means? Can growing centers adjust to lesions or deformation, and how—by regeneration, compensatory growth, or substitutive functional corrections? And can the development of overt behavior be correlated with, or even explained by, the stepwise emergence of neural apparatuses?

Specific questions like these, rather than noncommittal generalities about "the development of the nervous system being a matter of metabolic processes, gradient fields and enzymatic reactions," are effective guides to useful research.

NERVE REGENERATION

Since our insight into nerve development and growth has been greatly aided by studies on nerve regeneration, the essentials of this phenomenon may be briefly recapitulated here for later reference; for fuller reviews, see Cajal ('28), Nageotte ('22), and Boeke ('35).

freezing, chemical damage, etc.), the segment lying distally to the lesion (the "distal" or "peripheral" stump), within a few days loses conductivity, and the individual nerve fibers in it become converted into non-conducting plasmatic strands ("Schwann cords" or "Buengner's cords"); myelin and axis cylinder remnants break down (o, Fig. 126B). and as they are being resorbed, their place

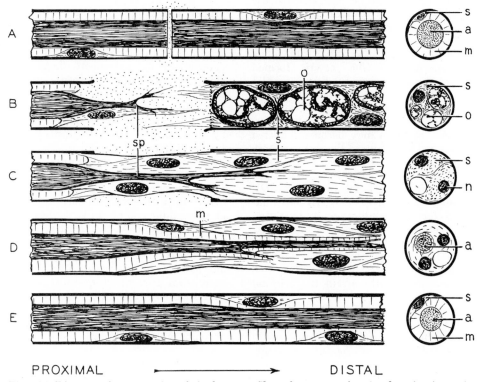

PROXIMAL ⟶ DISTAL

Fig. 126. Diagram of regeneration of single nerve fiber after transection (explanation in text).

Nerve regeneration is the restoration of morphological and physiological continuity in a transected nerve. The older supposition that this may take place *per primam fusionem* of the severed ends has proved untenable; the observation that cut ends of axons in tissue culture that lie within a distance of a few micra may merge during the first hours after severance (Levi, '34), does not apply to nerves in the body, where this condition is practically never realized. In the body, the nerve is restituted by renewed outgrowth of fibers from the proximal stump, repeating with some modifications the process of embryonic outgrowth. Briefly, the events are as follows (Fig. 126).

After a nerve has been severed or otherwise locally disrupted (e.g., by pressure,

is taken by the hypertrophying and multiplying sheath cells of Schwann (s, Fig. 126C). This combination of regressive and proliferative processes is generally referred to as "Wallerian degeneration." In the "proximal" or "central" stump, it remains confined to the immediate vicinity of the lesion, and although the whole injured neuron, including the central perikaryon, shows some traumatic reaction, the part that has retained its continuity with the central cell body soon becomes the source of the regenerative process.

The free tip of each proximal axon stump assumes amoeboid activity and extends into the surroundings much the same as in the first development (sp, Fig. 126B). Branching is frequent, but many of the branches are arrested in their course and remain abortive. While the outgrowing axon branches roam about the wound area, Schwann cells spill from the cut nerve ends, notably from the "degenerating" peripheral stump. When an advancing axon tip meets such a Schwann cord, it follows it and is thus guided into the peripheral stump (Fig. 126C), and through it to the peripheral tissues, where new transmissive connections can be established if the arriving nerve branch is of the proper type.

The highly irregular connective tissue that seals the cut nerve ends, commonly referred to as "scar," causes the dissipation of a large proportion of the newly formed branches, which may form dense tangles called "neuromas." Nerve regeneration thus involves a great deal of overproduction and wastage of sprouts. Eventually, a near-normal number of fibers may become collected in the deserted channels of the distal stump. The new branches, small at first (1μ or less), gradually gain in width and develop on their surface a new myelin sheath (m, Fig. 126D), which thickens proportionately. In this manner, lines for the conduction of excitation between centers and periphery are reestablished. However, owing to the misdirection of many fibers into wrong channels, the physiological control restored by regenerated nerves does not usually attain the original perfection.

In contrast to the practically unlimited power of regeneration observed in peripheral nerves, regenerative growth of intracentral nerve fibers declines with age and phylogenetic rank so as to be little more than abortive in brain and spinal cord of adult mammals under ordinary circumstances. Whether this is due to an intrinsically lower growth potential of the neurons or to less favorable growth support, perhaps even greater active obstruction, by the central, as compared to the peripheral, environment, is still a matter of debate.

ANALYSIS OF THE DEVELOPMENT OF A NEURON

OUTGROWTH OF AXIS CYLINDER

Mechanism of Elongation. As was indicated above, it is now indisputably established that the neurite (axon) develops as a direct protoplasmic extension of the nerve cell. At a given point along the circumference of the neuroblast, cytoplasm is protruded to form a short thread with a highly mobile tip. Presumably any breach in the cell surface may serve as outlet. The fact that in the

embryo the sprouts tend to emerge from the same sides in all neuroblasts of a given group must be ascribed to certain polarizing factors in the cellular environment, analogous to the determination of rootlet formation in Fucus eggs by the polar action of electric fields, ultraviolet light, pH gradients, etc. (Whitaker, '40).

The young sprout of axoplasm has no rigid axis skeleton, no firm sheath, nothing to propel it in a predetermined direction. The sprout continues to elongate by virtue of forces residing chiefly within the cell of origin, but the course of the elongation is determined by extraneous factors. In his classic observations on axon outgrowth in tissue culture, Harrison ('10) correctly identified the mode of advance as of the amoeboid type, which view has been fully borne out by later observations in explants (Lewis and Lewis, '12; Levi, '34) and in the living tadpole (Speidel, '33). Adopting and partly amplifying Lewis' ('50) interpretation, we may conceive of the sprout as a cylinder of firmly gelated ectoplasm surrounding a core of more fluid entoplasm streaming from the cell body distad. At the free tip, this central stream would erupt in numerous pseudopodial processes, which then compete among one another hydrodynamically for the common axial current (Fig. 127). The branch that succeeds in draining the inflow into its own channel thus automatically obliterates the weaker pseudopods, and as its surface becomes gelated, it adds its length to the already consolidated older parts of the fiber lying behind it. Meanwhile, the tip bursts forth anew, and thus the fiber advances in a continuous series of steps of protrusion of pseudopods, competition, and consolidation. Evidently, the protoplasm for the fiber is produced in the cell body, but it is added at the tip to which it is conveyed by the central stream. The motive mechanism of this convection is still obscure, but it may consist of peristaltic contraction-relaxation waves of the fiber surface. It provides some sort of "pumping" action, which after the fiber has ceased to elongate, continues to supply protoplasm for its further growth in width (see p. 363). In contrast to true amoeboid locomotion, however, the rear end of the nerve cell remains anchored to its surroundings so that instead of dragging the bulk of the cell after it, the advancing tip merely spins out a thread of increasing length between itself and the cell body.

The described active advance ends as soon as the free tip of a fiber attaches itself permanently to a peripheral receptor or effector cell. Further elongation becomes essentially a matter of passive extension, the fiber being in tow by the terminal tissues, which are subject to considerable migrations (e.g., muscle buds) and displacements during the subsequent phases of growth (Fig. 128). Because of this "towing" process, the primary growth pattern of nerves becomes greatly

problem, and a variety of "tropisms" and "attractions" of chemical, electrical, mechanical or undefined physiological nature have been suggested as the orienting agents (see Harrison, '35a,b). At present, we are approaching a rather unified concept of the mechanism of nerve fiber orientation, which is summarized in the following account (condensed from Weiss, '41c, '44, '50c).

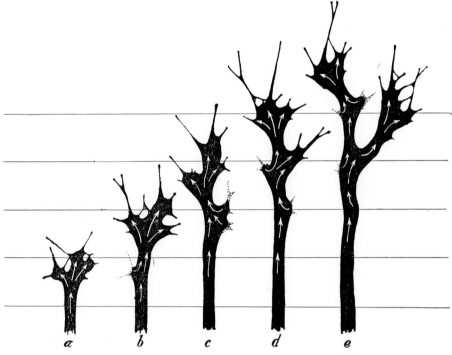

Fig. 127. Five consecutive phases in the advance of an axon tip (semidiagrammatic). Arrows indicate directions of flow, thrust and drain of neuroplasm. In *e*, dichotomous branching of fiber has been initiated. Dotted portions represent the location of earlier protrusions that have been sucked back by the draining force of the axial stream.

distorted. This explains why ontogenetic shifts, hence phylogenetic relations, of individual muscles can often be traced through their nerve supply, as in the pelvic fins of fishes that have migrated far forward until they have come to lie ahead of the pectoral fins.

During its period of free advance, the orientation of the nerve fiber is of course determined by the course which its roving tip takes. The early "pioneer" or pathfinder fibers thus lay down the primary nerve connections to the nerveless tissues which they invade. Since later fibers simply follow the course of the earlier ones, the problem of nerve orientation concerns primarily the pioneers. Much experimental work, and even more speculation, has been devoted to this

Mechanism of Orientation. Without recounting the trials and errors of the past, it is yet instructive to point to one basic fallacy of earlier concepts, namely, the tacit assumption that nerve fibers can penetrate structureless space in the manner in which plants can grow into air or water—an impression strengthened by the selective nerve stains, which impregnate nerve fibers to the exclusion of their surroundings. The suggestiveness of plant growth as a model of nerve growth is clearly reflected in the widespread use of botanical similes in neurological terminology; e.g., "dendrites," "rami," "roots," "arborization," "sprouts." Actually, however, according to the best available experimental evidence, nerve processes, like most animal tissue cells, are unable to push freely into

a liquid, but can only proceed along interfaces, either between a solid and a liquid, or
between two immiscible liquids, or between
a liquid and a gas. The nearest analogon
among plants would be the clinging vine.
A nerve tip can traverse not even a small
liquid gap without an interfacial bridge.

Interfaces capable of serving as the requisite substrata are furnished in the body by

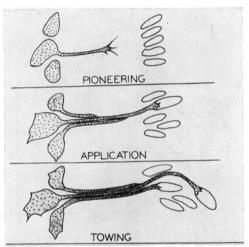

Fig. 128. Three phases in development of nerves
(diagrammatic). *Top:* Pioneering phase (free fiber
tip advances into surroundings). *Middle:* Application phase (pioneering tip has become attached to
peripheral cell, younger tips apply themselves to
course of older ones). *Bottom:* Towing phase (shift
of peripheral cell produces corresponding displacement of attached nerve fiber).

all the fibrous units (fibrils, fibers, filaments)
that pervade the liquid spaces in and between
cells and tissues and constitute the solid
framework of the "ground substances" (see
Section III, Chapter 1, by Schmitt). They
consist mostly of chains of filamentous protein molecules combined into bundles and
networks of submicroscopic and microscopic
dimensions. Along such filaments the terminal filopodia of the nerve fiber are drawn
out by interfacial forces of still unresolved
nature which cause protoplasm to spread
out along the interface, grossly comparable
to a "wetting" process. The linearity of the
fibrous units along which they extend is a
major factor in guiding the extending nerve
fibers. In a planar interface, they would
fuse to a sort of "terminal web." However,
the linear guide structures are the ones of
greatest practical importance, since even
planar surfaces commonly contain inhomo-
geneities that describe linear tracts within
the common plane (e.g., the fibrous constitu-

ents of coats or membranes). The principle
according to which nerve fiber tips are
guided in their course by contact with surrounding structures has been designated as
"contact guidance" (Weiss, '41c).

In an irregular network, fibrils intersect
at countless places and angles. Nerve tips
advancing on such a trellis will be split at
each intersection, but, as was explained
above, competition will usually obliterate all
but one of these terminal branches, and only
this one will proceed. The decision of which
one of the multiple projections will endure
in any given instance may be essentially a
matter of the accidents of the local situation.
If so, the resulting nerve course will be
irregular and tortuous (Fig. 129b, e), as is
the case in the neuropil of the nerve centers,
in scar tissue (e.g., between severed nerve
stumps), and in the plasma clots of ordinary
tissue cultures. On the other hand, the more
the meshes of the fibrillar network are oriented in a given prevailing direction, the
more the resulting nerve fiber course, tracing
the common directional component, will likewise become definitely oriented (Fig. 129a).
The extreme of this condition is attained when
the fibrous matrix consists of parallel guide
rails which leave the single-tracked nerve
fibers no alternative course (Fig. 129c,d).
In this case, nerve orientation resolves itself
completely into a matter of the orientation
of the underlying substratum and can therefore be controlled by way of the latter, as
has been proved by a variety of observations
and experiments both in the living animal
and in vitro. The following examples may
serve as illustrations.

When tension is applied in tissue culture
to a blood plasma clot, either during or after
coagulation, the meshes of the random network of fibrin threads are drawn out in the
general direction of the lines of stress. Nerve
fibers allowed to grow out in such a medium
then move in the same prevailing direction
(Weiss, '34a). Thus, by orienting the colloidal matrix, tension can indirectly orient
nerve growth. The immediate factor is the
orientation of the matrix, irrespective of how
it has been obtained. Fibrous tissue exudates
spreading along surfaces and being drawn out
in the direction of flow, for instance, act in
like manner (Weiss, '45). That this principle
of contact guidance is equally valid within
the living body has been substantiated in
numerous instances, most strikingly by the
directional control of nerve regeneration.
Without intervention, regenerating nerve
fibers commonly take random courses. But

it has been possible to direct them into a straight oriented course by forcing the underlying matrix into parallel alignment. This has been achieved both in the gelatinous fin tissue of larval amphibians (Weiss, '50a) and in the blood clots binding severed nerve stumps of adult mammals (Weiss, '44; Weiss and Taylor, '43). In the latter case

tion. If the nerve course depends on preneural guide structures in the colloidal matrices, our attention must therefore turn to the factors producing structural orientation. Tension being presumably the commonest orienting agent, let us examine first the potential sources of tensional stresses in the body. Oriented tensions arise from external stretch-

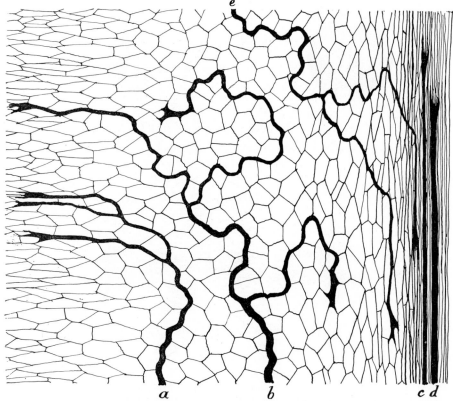

Fig. 129. Advance of nerve fibers in fibrous media of different degrees of ultrastructural organization (randomness in center turning into prevailing horizontal orientation in left part, and strict vertical orientation in right part of diagram). Along random meshes of center strip, the course of fibers *a*, *b* and *e* is tortuous, with frequent branching; in the more orderly parts of the medium, fiber courses become correspondingly aligned; in a rigorously oriented medium, fibers (*c*, *d*) run straight and remain undivided.

there is a primary phase, during which longitudinal tensions orient the fibrin of the blood clot in a prevailing direction from stump to stump, followed by a secondary phase, during which fibrinolytic agents discharged in the wound dissolve all remaining disoriented crosslinks between the longitudinal fibrin strands. This gives a good illustration of the multiplicity of factors involved in orientation.

In view of the ubiquitous presence of fibrous elements in the tissue spaces, these examples may be considered to be fair models of the normal mechanism of nerve orienta-

ing or internal shrinkage of a cohesive system. Differential growth, resulting in extensive displacement of body parts relative to one another, is an ample source of stretch effects. Nerve growth may thus be expected to trail actively advancing organs even prior to being taken in tow by them. Localized shrinkage is perhaps even more important as a source of stress. Such shrinkage occurs, for instance, around any intensely proliferating area as a result of a peculiar dehydrating effect which proliferating cells exert on surrounding colloids (Weiss, '29, '34a; Grossfeld, '34). The resulting local contraction of the fibrillar network automatically distorts the meshes into a radial pattern converging upon the proliferating center (Fig. 130, top). Subsequent nerve growth, being guided over these radial pathways toward the center, naturally will give the illusion of having been "attracted" by it. We may call this the

structures, cogently explicable in terms of demonstrable chains of physico-chemical events. This may appropriately be called the "two-center effect."

Although tension has been revealed as the most common effector mechanism in the production of guide structures, it is conceiv-

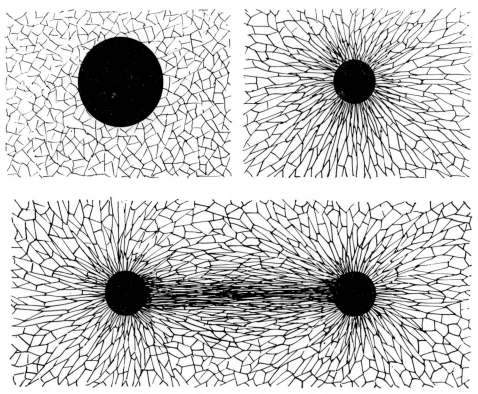

Fig. 130. Effect of local contraction on ultrastructure of a fibrous medium. *Top:* "One-center effect." Shrinkage of area indicated by black circle from the dimensions of the left panel to those of the right panel produces radial distortion of contiguous network. *Bottom:* "Two-center effect." Two "one-center effects" in a common network yield resultant preferential orientation along connecting line between the two centers.

"one-center effect." It is a concrete example of one way in which localized chemical activity can translate itself into structural patterns.

In the presence of two separate centers of proliferation (hence, two contracting foci), the intermediate fibrous matrix is being stretched, hence becomes aligned, along the connecting line. There is thus established a fibrillar bridge which any nerve fibers in that area are bound to follow (Fig. 130, bottom). Figure 131, top, shows, for example, the straight tract of nerve fibers grown reciprocally between two proliferating spinal ganglia in a thin plasma lamella, guided not by spurious "attractions" from the distance, but by contact with tangible guide

able that other vectorial agents besides tension, such as hydrodynamic currents, high electrostatic potentials, electrophoresis, or perhaps still wholly unsuspected processes, could effect fibrillar orientation of the requisite kind.

On a strictly oriented substratum, nerve fiber growth is thus fully determined by contact guidance. On a substratum of random configuration, that is, one not previously subjected to orienting factors, nerve growth would remain correspondingly random unless additional factors became operative. Since each one of the countless intersections of an irregular pathway system presents the nerve tip with alternative directions, any factor that systematically favors one general

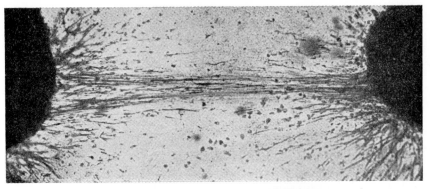

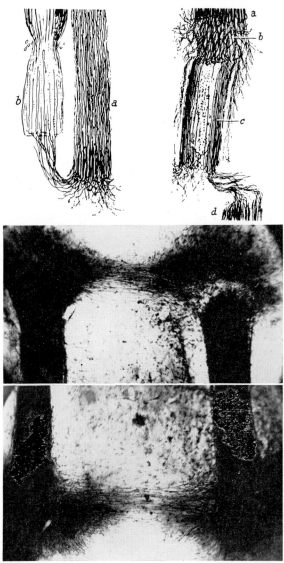

Fig. 131. Two-center effect. *Top:* "Bridge" of cells and nerve fibers that has formed between two embryonic spinal ganglia of chick (dark areas) cultured in vitro in thin blood plasma membrane. × 48. (From Weiss, '34.) *Middle:* Regenerated nerve fibers forming "bridges" between "proximal" stumps (*a, c*) and dislocated "peripheral" stumps (recurrent, *b;* laterally displaced, *d*) (from Cajal, '28). *Bottom:* "Bridges" of Schwann cells that have grown out between the open ends of two fragments of adult rat nerve explanted in a thin blood plasma clot (from Weiss, '52b).

355

direction over another would entail a statistical deviation of the fibers in the favored direction—an over-all trend rather than a common course. Many dendritic fields, for instance, show such a trend. The gradual deflection, rather than definite orientation, toward the cathodal site of neurons in tissue cultures exposed to electric fields of proper density (Marsh and Beams, '46) presents all the aspects of this picture, indicating simply relative inhibition of filopodial protrusion on the anodal side with no cathodal "stimulation" or "attraction," a view confirmed by direct observations on slime moulds (Anderson, '51). These electric effects evidently operate not by laying down pathways, but by prohibiting some of the existing ones (see Fig. 48 in Weiss, '50a).

It must be further postulated that the chemical characteristics of the pathway systems endow contact guidance with an element of selectivity. It would seem impossible otherwise to explain the fact reported below that different kinds of nerve fibers tend to choose different pathway systems when faced with a choice. Only a faint trace of such selectivity has thus far been observed in tissue culture in the preference of nerve tips for interfaces of tissue exudate rather than of fibrin (Weiss, '45). At any rate, such discriminatory ability is based on affinity for the chemical constitution of the contact surface rather than on the perception of concentration gradients of diffusing substances as surmised in the theory of chemotropism. A singularly strong affinity of this kind seems to exist between axoplasm and the protoplasm of the sheath cells of Schwann (see p. 367).

The described mode of advance of the nerve tip makes it clear that the "rate of free outgrowth" is a function of both the neuron itself and the configuration of the pathway system. The rates are of similar magnitude whether determined in the embryo, in nerve regeneration or in tissue culture (Harrison, '35b). It must be borne in mind, however, that these are over-all values of length over time without implying uniform speed. Actually, the advance consists of alternating spurts and delays, the frequency of the latter mounting with increasing irregularity ("intersectedness") of the substratum (see Weiss and Garber, '52). Consequently, the total rate is fastest along straight oriented pathways (e.g., during nerve regeneration inside old Schwann tubes; Gutmann, Guttmann, Medawar and Young, '42) and slowest in the dense and confused fiber tangle of a scar. The maximum rate of advance under optimal conditions is of the order of a few millimeters per day (at 37° C.), which is close to the autonomous rate of proximodistal movement of axoplasm observed in the perpetual growth of neurons, as described below (p. 364). Any faster elongation of nerve fibers (e.g., Wislocki and Singer, '46) suggests passive elongation by towing.

Neurotropism. "Contact guidance," as here described, is but a modified and more detailed version of such concepts of nerve orientation as have been proposed by His (1887), Harrison ('14), and Dustin ('10). They all imply that the nerve fiber is conducted on its way by markings of its immediate contact surroundings, rather than directed from a distance by the tissue of destination issuing "attractive" forces or merely acting in the manner of a beacon. Such "distance action," commonly referred to as "neurotropism" and assumed to be a form of either galvanotropism or chemotropism, has been invoked to explain oriented nerve growth in the embryo (e.g., Kappers, '17), as well as during later nerve regeneration (foremost: Cajal, '28; Forssman, 1900). This concept dates from a period in which the mechanism of nerve growth was still poorly understood; before it was realized, for instance, that nerve fibers cannot penetrate into the interior of a structureless fluid in the manner of plants. It was assumed that remote tissues, by virtue of their electric charges or of specific chemical emanations, could "attract" nerve growth from a distance. This assumption implies (1) that the supposed gradients be steady and durable, and undisturbed by any activities within the intervening distance, and (2) that the nerve tip has means not only for perceiving the required minute differentials of potential or concentration, but also for translating them into corresponding steering actions. Neither these premises nor the basic thesis of distance attraction has ever been critically demonstrated. On the contrary, overwhelming evidence has accumulated over the years to disprove them.

Repeated attempts to obtain directed nerve growth along the stream lines of an electric field have remained unsuccessful. Indeed the very possibility of an electric guidance is ruled out by the fact that nerve growth often proceeds simultaneously in diametrically opposite directions (e.g., the ascending and descending branches of dorsal root fibers; recurrent fibers in nerve regeneration; re-

Fig. 132. Nerve growth in "alternate-choice" experiment (from Weiss and Taylor, '44). *Top:* Diagram of operation. Proximal nerve stump (left) is introduced into stem of Y-shaped artery; one branch of artery is sealed off distally, the other branch contains degenerating nerve as supposed "lure." *Middle:* Experimental case, 20 weeks after operation, showing both the blind and the connected branches filled with regenerated nerve fibers. *Bottom:* Detail from same case at bifurcation at higher magnification.

ciprocal fiber tracts in the brain, etc.). Thus, the only known electric effects are the inhibitory ones mentioned above (p. 356).

Chemical "attractions" have been postulated largely on the strength of Cajal's ('28) varied experiments demonstrating a tendency of regenerating nerve fibers to converge upon the open end of any degenerated nerve stump (Fig. 131, middle), as if the latter were a source of "neurotropically" active substances. While the observations were correct, the interpretation was not. The nerve fibers are guided toward the peripheral stump, not by a chemical concentration gradient, but by a structural bridge of Schwann cells which has previously spanned the gap as a result of the orienting "two-center effect" (see p. 354) which the two proliferating cut surfaces exert upon the intervening blood clot. It is easy to demonstrate this effect directly in tissue culture (Fig. 131, bottom) by placing two fragments of degenerated (axon-free) peripheral nerve into a thin plasma clot (Weiss, '52b). Evidently, if axons were to

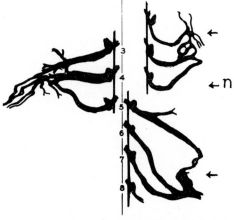

Fig. 133. Deflection of peripheral limb nerve plexus toward transplanted limb buds (combined from Detwiler, '36b). The left half shows the plexus of a normal forelimb (contribution from segments 3, 4, 5), the right half nerve supply in two experimental cases in which limb buds had been transplanted from their normal site (*n*) to anterior or posterior levels, respectively, as indicated by arrows.

grow from one of the stumps, the connecting strand of Schwann cells would automatically lead them over into the other stump. The chemical activity of the degenerated stump thus plays no part other than that of an accessory aid to structural orientation. In confirmation of this fact, degenerated nerve in a liquid medium leaves nerve growth wholly unaffected despite enhanced diffusion (Weiss and Taylor, '44), and conversely, oriented structural pathways are followed by nerve fibers regardless of whether or not they lead to supposedly "attractive" destinations. For instance, when a proximal nerve stump as fiber source is introduced into the stem of a bifurcated blood-filled tube, one branch of which contains degenerated nerve while the other ends blindly (Fig. 132), regenerating nerve fibers fill both branches equally well and abundantly (Weiss and Taylor, '44).

In conclusion, the idea that remote tissues of destination can attract nerve fibers directly may be safely discounted; such tissues do, however, contribute to the formation of nerve patterns indirectly by the creation of pathways, as here outlined, as well as by various secondary effects on later neuron development to be detailed below.

Ontogeny of Nerve Patterns. Our task is now to explore whether what we have outlined in the foregoing pages for nerve orientation in general is sufficient to account adequately for the specific nerve patterns observed in the organism.

Nerve Deflection Toward Growing Organs. Evidence that embryonic nerve growth is often actively routed toward rapidly growing peripheral organs rests largely on the experimental work of Detwiler (summarized in Detwiler, '36b). Transplanting urodele limb buds, prior to the outgrowth of segmental nerves, to farther anterior or posterior sites entailed a certain shift of their nerve supply, as is illustrated in Figure 133, which is a composite of two typical cases. It can be seen that there is a tendency for the limb plexus to originate in more anterior or more posterior segments than normally. Yet, since this shift of the nerve source is less extensive than the displacement of the limb, the nerve trunks appear to slant forward or backward, as if "attracted" by the actual limb site (see also Lovell, '31). Such deflection toward the actively growing limb can readily be understood as an instance of the "two-center effect" outlined above. That the effect is quite unspecific is demonstrated by the fact that the limb nerves are similarly deflected toward transplanted eyes and nasal placodes (Detwiler and Van Dyke, '34), although in the latter case it has not been made clear how much of the observed cord-nasal connection originated in the cord and how much in the olfactory epithelium. Brain grafts on the other hand exert no such effect (Detwiler, '36a), perhaps because the proliferating cell layer is shut in and not exposed to the surrounding matrix.

Frog limb buds deprived of their ipsilateral nerve source often secure vicarious supply from the opposite side (Hamburger, '29). It must be considered, however, that this is initiated during an early stage, when both hind limbs are still close together, and that subsequent dislocations of the plexus and fasciculation of the successful branches (see below, p. 366) tend to create an exaggerated idea of the power of nerves to reach their destination by detours.

Despite this qualification, it seems fairly obvious that pioneer fibers often do take directive courses toward growing organs, which by their very growth activity have become hubs of pathway systems. It is in line with this view that nerves can be made to converge upon a transplanted limb bud only if the operation is performed prior to their first outgrowth; once established, their course can no longer be redirected (Detwiler, '24b).

Intracentral Connections. There are hardly any systematic investigations on the manner in which the different intracentral nerve tracts are laid down, the routing of which is of such paramount importance to orderly function. In attempting a causal analysis, it is well to keep in mind two basic factors. First, there is no microprecision, in the sense of rigidly determined connection patterns, on the level of the individual neuron. Only the gross group characters of the various tracts are determined, while the details are merely statistically defined, the individual elements conforming to some "norm" but being otherwise indeterminate. This considerably reduces the number of relevant patterns to be accounted for. Second, the incredibly complex structure of the adult brain owes its intricacy to the fact that it is the compound result of innumerable elementary patterns laid down one after another in a long succession of separate ontogenetic steps, each one in itself rather simple. If we assume that intracentral fibers, like peripheral fibers, trace oriented pathways in their colloidal surroundings, then each pathway system that temporarily dominates a given embryonic period will leave a permanent record behind in those neuron systems which happen to grow out during that period. As conditions change, the colloidal matrix will adapt to the change, assume new orientation and thus establish new nerve courses, often unrelated geometrically to the earlier ones. However, actually to resolve central nerve patterns into such simple constituent steps is still largely a task for the future.

That it promises success is indicated, for instance, by the observation that fiber tracts tend to develop between central neuron groups that develop contemporaneously (Coghill, '29). This looks like the "two-center effect" at work again. Reasonable guesses are also possible regarding the pathway structures underlying the longitudinal fiber tracts, the commissural fiber systems and the early internuncial connections of the cord. The longitudinal tracts appear to be determined by the longitudinal stretch to which the

neural tube is subjected by the growth in length of the surrounding body (see below). This assumption finds support in the early appearance of axial birefringence in the neural tube (Hobson, '41), indicating polar orientation of the substratum. The arched transverse pattern of the ventral commissures might be attributable to transverse stresses which the median strip of the medullary plate suffers during the bending of the plate into the tube. The early internuncial fibers travel along an interface clearly demarcated

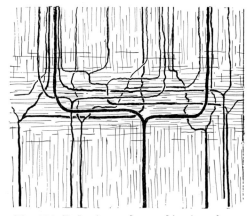

Fig. 134. Deflection and recombination of nerve fibers (plexus formation) along intersecting systems of ultrastructural pathways.

between the dense neural epithelium surrounding the central canal and the more loosely packed mantle zone.

All these preneural guide structures, however, can only account for the initial orientation of nerve patterns. Other sets of factors determine their further elaboration with regard to numbers, size, and connections (see below).

Deflection and Plexus Formation. Many nerve courses show a sudden angular deflection from one direction into another. This may be the result of a passive distortion—for instance, by sudden change of course of a towing organ or by wedging in of another organ—or it may be a sign of actual angular outgrowth. The latter condition is realized whenever pioneering fiber tips proceeding along one pathway system come upon another one running crosswise (Fig. 134). Depending on how completely the intersecting system obliterates the original system, fewer or more of the tips will be diverted into the new direction; a tight barrier (e.g., membrane) will produce total deflection. Intersecting structures of this kind arise, for instance, in the border zone between fibrous colloids of different concentrations, and model experiments in tissue culture have verified the tangential deflection of radial nerve fiber growth along such borders (Weiss, '34a). Similar cross patterns may arise in the body at the boundary between masses or layers of cells of different kinds which exert different effects on the surrounding colloids. Many other processes that would lead to the same end are imaginable, all of them thus far untested.

Striking examples of angular deflection in the embryo are the dorsal roots of the cord, the various central and peripheral plexuses, and the partially decussating systems in the brain. Dorsal root fibers, after entering the cord laterally, turn abruptly into a longitudinal course (with or without branching), forming thus the dorsal funiculi. Evidently the switch is produced by the encounter with longitudinal pathways in the marginal veil oriented lengthwise by the passive elongation of the tube mentioned before (p. 359). Plexus formation is to be expected wherever layers with predominantly radial structure alternate with tangentially oriented ones, as in the retina or in the various strata of the cortex (see Fig. 134). Thus the horizontal interconnections among the vertical projection systems, which are such an important functional feature, are presumably anticipated by lamination in the texture of the ground substance, which in turn might be due either to the differential growth expansion of the various cell strata or to differential impregnation of the ground substance from different concentric cell layers (see Weiss, '39, p. 509). Peripheral nerve plexuses are probably likewise caused by "crossroads"; the brachial and pelvic plexuses, for instance, by the tangentially disposed girdle mesenchyme which lies across the nerve paths radiating toward the limb base. A cross structure in the optic chiasma, whose angle of intersection changes with the relative shifts between eyes and brain, could account for the ipsilateral deflection of optic fibers in forms with partial decussation, with the probability of diversion, hence the proportion of uncrossed fibers (important in binocular vision) being perhaps a function of the chiasmatic angle during the growth phase.

Hypothetical though many of these detailed applications of the principle of contact guidance to concrete embryological problems may be, they at least formulate the problems involved for practical experimental attack. For final judgment, the results of the latter must be awaited. At any rate, it appears clear that plexus formation as such, with fibers turning off their former course at a sharp angle and intermingling in a common plane, often to emerge again later as independent bundles, defeats any but a structural concept of guidance.

Branching. Individual neurons may remain essentially unbranched, as in many sensory types, or they may branch more or less profusely, as do the motor neurons. Since, according to the all-or-none principle, the neuron can only act as a unit, the extent of branching has great functional significance and must be either preadapted to, or actively regulated by, functional needs. Extensive branching, economical in the motor field where it enables a single neuron to engage several hundred muscle fibers at a time, would be undesirable in the sensory field, where it would blur discrimination. Despite its biological importance, however, the problem of branching has not yet been systematically studied (Sunderland and Lavarack, '53).

Branching occurs either at the tip of a growing fiber by dichotomy (terminal branching) or along the stem some distance behind the tip which is either still free or already connected (collateral branching). Terminal branching results whenever two simultaneous terminal pseudopods (see Fig. 127e) are of equal strength so that they can divide the inflow of protoplasm between themselves and continue to advance with independent tips (see Speidel, '33). The frequency of this occurrence depends on the structure of the pathway system; the more intersected the latter, the higher the incidence of branching (Fig. 129). Accordingly, terminal branching is profuse in the maze of central neuropil, as well as in peripheral scar tissue (e.g., after nerve severance), but is infrequent along well-oriented pathways.

Collateral branches arise as side sprouts from already consolidated fiber stems, presumably in response to local irritations, mechanical, chemical or electrical (Peterfi and Kapel, '28; Speidel, '33; Edds, '53). The repeated branching of motor fibers, for instance, could be ascribed to a seriation of such irritations as would attend consecutive divisions of young muscle fibers. The size of a "motor unit" (number of muscle fibers attached to a single neuron) would then simply reflect the degree of ulterior growth of that muscle after receiving its primary quota of fibers. The systematic occurrence of similar irritations near certain layers or nuclei of the brain and spinal cord could account for the regular emergence of collaterals at those sites. Possibly different fiber types might even react in different degrees to the same irritant so that one type would give off a branch while another type would not. These are merely some pointers to future work. Concrete information is scanty.

In view of the labile state of the neuron (see later), we must expect it to spring minor leaks in its surface all the time, especially in its unsheathed terminal branches and at the nodes of Ranvier. Whether such weak spots will be repaired or become the source of a collateral branch will presumably depend on the vigor and rate of growth of the neuron and the competitive strength of the main stem of the fiber, which counteracts accessory outgrowths. Agents capable of either loosening the axonal surface or invigorating neuronal growth or merely reducing the drain into the main axis of the fiber (as after amputation) should, therefore, automatically increase the frequency of collateral branching. The compensatory sprouting of peripheral collaterals after partial denervation of muscles or after injection of substances from degenerated muscles (Hoffman, '50; Edds, '53), as well as the "parasitic" branches forming from severed or otherwise truncated neurons (Nageotte, '22), seem to bear out this expectation.

Nerve Patterns Within Peripheral Organs. Usually, the factors that guide nerves to a given organ are not the same that will determine the distribution pattern within the organ (Hamburger, '29). For instance, when limb buds are transplanted to the head region and innervated by foreign cranial nerves, the latter assume a distribution pattern which is essentially a typical limb pattern. It is from this very observation that Harrison ('07b) first deduced the structural guidance of nerve fibers, a conclusion which was soon also adopted by Braus ('11), who had previously interpreted his own similar observations as evidence of a peripheral (autonomous) origin of nerves. Evidently, the growing limb can impose a limb-specific arrangement upon nerve fibers coming from whatever source (see also Hamburger, '29; Piatt, '41; Weiss, '37a). This plainly contradicts the gratuitous contention (Ruud, '29) that nerves from a given source contain the geometry of their future distribution in themselves. Rather, the "limb pattern" of distribution is determined by a complex, multifactorial chain of events, roughly divisible into two phases—a primary one governed by the structural and chemical properties of the preneural pathways in the limb blastema, and a secondary one of elaboration of the primary pattern by towing, fasciculation (see below, p. 366), and the differential survival, growth, and resorption of fibers, depending on the physiological adequacy of their terminal connections. The decisive patterning effect of the primary phase is revealed by the observation that virtually all nerve branches of the mature limb (in the frog) are already recognizable as such in the early limb bud at a very primitive stage of morphogenesis (Taylor, '43). The principal nerve paths are thus laid down by factors in the early limb blastema.

If, on the other hand, a limb is kept nerveless ("aneurogenic") during its differentiation and is then grafted to a normal host body from which it can derive belated innervation, the invading nerves follow quite irregular and aberrant courses (Piatt, '52). A certain predilection for some major invasion routes at times creates some gross resemblance to a limb pattern (Piatt, '42), but this could be due simply to trivial anatomical features, offering only limited spaces between skin, muscles and skeleton for the massive advance of nerve fibers. In this instance, major blood vessels may also play a leading role (Hamburger, '29), although in normal development the noted parallelism between vascular and nerve trunks is more likely to be a sign of common guidance of both systems by the same ultrastructural pattern in the common matrix. Whether the nerve distribution pattern within the limb follows normal or aberrant lines is of no consequence, however, as far as the later functional activity is concerned. As will be described below (p. 384), functional coordination between the central nervous system and receptor and effector organs remains orderly even if the anatomical nerve connections are utterly confused. The relative stereotypism of peripheral nerves is presumably significant only as a means of insuring ubiquitous innervation of adequate quantity.

PERIPHERAL CONNECTIONS

Specificity of Preneural Pathways. Nerve fibers of a given kind can penetrate foreign organs with ease. After heterotopic transplantations or other deviations, cranial nerves have been followed into limbs (see above; Harrison, '07b; Braus, '11; Nicholas, '33; Piatt, '41), midbrain fibers into trunk muscles (Hoadley, '25) in the chick (not observed in comparable experiments in urodeles: Det-wiler, '36a), spinal fiber tracts into limbs (Nicholas, '29; Weiss, '50a), limb nerves into tumors (Bueker, '48; Levi-Montalcini and Hamburger, '51), optic nerves into the nose (Weiss, '41c) or the pharynx (Ferreira-Berutti, '51).

Yet, the peripheral nervous system of normal individuals is relatively stereotyped, not only in the mode of its arborization but also in its terminal connections. By and large, ventral root fibers end in skeletal muscles, spinal ganglion fibers in sensory end organs, sympathetic fibers in glands or smooth muscles. Since the attempts to refer this specificity of connections to selective neurotropic attractions have proved unten-able, other explanations must be sought.

Mindful of the fact that the first outgrowth of motor fibers antedates that of sensory fibers (Coghill, '29), it has been suggested (Harrison, '35b; Weiss, '39) that a systematic change in the peripheral pathway structure, with the earlier pathways leading to muscles, the later ones to skin, would automatically account for the correct routing. However, this time-lag explanation is ruled out by the observation that motor and sensory fibers take each their typical courses even when both grow out simultaneously, as for in-stance, in the innervation of the hind limb of the anuran tadpole. When the bud makes its late appearance, both motor and sensory nerve masses are already waiting at its base ready to invade it (Taylor, '43). As they penetrate the limb bud, they assort them-selves according to kinds into specifically muscular and cutaneous branches, respec-tively, coursing sometimes jointly, but often also independently. This has been revealed by withholding either the sensory or the motor nerve quota from the limb (Ham-burger, '29), and most conclusively by ex-tirpating the appropriate spinal ganglia or spinal cord segments (Taylor, '44); the developed limbs then lacked the correspond-ing kind of nerve branches.

It seems difficult to account for these facts otherwise than by the assumption of selec-tive contact affinities of given nerve fiber types for matching types of preneural path-ways. This view is strengthened by the pre-dilection which nerves with aberrant origins or courses show for their typical sites or channels, as has been described for the lateral line nerve (Harrison, '03), the dorsal roots (Detwiler and Maclean, '40; Holtzer, '52b), and Mauthner's fibers (Oppenheimer, '41; Piatt, '44; Stefanelli, '50; Holtzer, '52b). Such selective application of one tissue to

another is not uncommon in development (see, for instance, the guided growth of the pronephric duct; Holtfreter, '44); but, save for a hypothetical reference to its possible stereochemical basis (Weiss, '47), the under-lying mechanism is still obscure.

Specificity in Regeneration. The ability of given kinds of nerve fibers to select con-forming pathways seems to last beyond the pioneering phase. After transection of the mixed nerves to a young differentiating limb, the regenerating motor fibers retrace essen-tially the original muscular branches, and the regenerating sensory fibers the cutaneous branches (Taylor, '44). Similarly, regenerat-ing lateral line nerves have been reported to give preference to an old lateral line branch over a nearby cutaneous branch (Speidel, '48), which even suggests finer subspecificities within the sensory class. Yet, with the prog-ress of maturation, this selectivity of out-growth is lost. Adult nerves of different qualities, when cross-connected, regenerate into each other's channels indiscriminately and without difficulty. For example, sensory fibers regenerate into motor stumps (Boeke, '17; Gutmann, '45; Weiss and Edds, '45) and vice versa (Weiss and Cummings, '43), somatic nerves into sympathetic stumps and vice versa (Simpson and Young, '45; Ham-mond and Hinsey, '45), etc. Apparently, the residual Schwann cords of degenerated stumps, which serve as pathways to the re-generating fibers, are of the same quality in motor, sensory, somatic and autonomic nerves, hence are indistinguishable to the regenerating fibers, which, as will be shown below, have not lost their constitutional dif-ferentials.

Terminal Connections. Nerve fibers may reach the peripheral tissues either preassorted over proper pathways or intermingled over aberrant routes (see above), but neither mode of approach is decisive for whether or not they will make transmissive connections, that is, connections which will permit im-pulses to pass between nerve fiber and end organ. A clear distinction must be made be-tween (a) penetration of a tissue by nerve fibers ("neurotization"), (b) microscopic contiguity between nerve ending and effector or receptor cell, and (c) physiologically effec-tive junction. No absolute specificity prevails in (a) and (b), but (c) occurs only if end-organ and nerve fiber are generally related.

For example, when sensory nerve fibers are led into muscles, they terminate on the muscle fibers in what histologically appear to be intimate motor connections (Boeke, '17); yet electric stimulation of such nerves never yields muscular contraction (Gutmann, '45; Weiss and Edds, '45). Cross unions between somatic, sympathetic and parasympathetic nerves that have been tried in various combinations likewise are physiologically sterile. Cholinergic and adrenergic nerves fail to achieve physiological innervation of each other's peripheries (Langley and Anderson, '04; Dale, '35), not because of lack of regenerative penetration, but because of transmissive failure of the terminal junction.

The fact of neuro-terminal selectivity is proof of the existence of specific protoplasmic differences both among the major classes of neurons (sensory, motor, etc.) and among the corresponding terminal tissues. Within each class, however, transmissive junctions can be made indiscriminately. Any motor nerve shows functional affinity to any skeletal muscle (Weiss, '37a; Weiss and Hoag, '46); cross connections of different kinds of sensory nerves have likewise been effected successfully (Anokhin, '35), and the paradoxical sensations noted after irregular sensory nerve regeneration in man (Stopford, '30) also indicate interchangeability within the sensory field. There are additional finer functional selectivities, beyond those controlling junction, but these are imposed upon the connected neurons from their endings and will be discussed later (see p. 384).

Synaptic Connections. Naturally, the question arises whether specificities similar to those observed in peripheral connections govern the establishment of central synaptic junctions. In the few instances thus far examined, intracentral neurons have shown a remarkable lack of discrimination in making terminal connections. Limb buds inserted into gaps of the embryonic neural tube receive effective motor innervation from central fiber tracts (Nicholas, '33), and the central gray matter of isolated fragments of larval spinal cord or medulla oblongata establishes fully functional connections with both muscles and skin in the complete absence of primary motor and sensory neurons (Weiss, '50a). The promiscuity of junctional relations manifested in these cases contrasts sharply with the acute selectivity of functional response relations (see below, p. 384), which throws doubt upon any theory explaining the latter purely in terms of specific anatomical connections. The fact that a junction capable of transmitting an impulse has been established does not explain when and how it will be actuated in the coordinated group activities of the centers, nor indeed whether or not it will be used at all. Whether disuse entails eventual rupture of junctions has not yet been clearly decided.

AXON GROWTH

Growth of Axon Caliber. While the elongation of the nerve fiber is essentially a phenomenon of protoplasmic convection, it proceeds pari passu with real growth, that is, increase of the total protoplasmic mass of the neuron, and is actually sustained by the latter. This growth process continues after the fiber has reached its final length and can, in fact, best be studied during that later period, when all further protoplasmic gain accrues solely to the width of the fiber. Since the eventual caliber of the axon, usually referred to as "fiber size," is of considerable functional significance, as it determines velocity of impulse conduction, thresholds of excitability and susceptibility to noxious agents, etc. (Erlanger and Gasser, '37), a study of axonal growth offers both physiological and developmental interest. Nerve fiber caliber increases as animals grow to mature size (Hursh, '39).

Analytical information on axon growth is mostly derived from recent experiments dealing with the restoration of fiber diameter in regenerated nerve fibers (Weiss and Hiscoe, '48). These experiments are schematically summarized in Figure 135, which shows a series of mature neurons in various stages of normal (*A-E*) and modified (*F-I*) regeneration. The nucleated cell body is at the left, the peripheral end-organ at the right, both connected by the neurilemmal tube that envelops the fiber. From the proximal stump of the severed fiber (*B*), a thin axonal sprout advances toward the periphery (*C*), effects peripheral connection (*D*) and gradually grows in width until it approximates its old caliber and the width of the tube (*E*). This recovery, however, can be significantly impeded if one constricts the distal stump and thereby reduces the diameter of all tubes at a given spot. At first, regeneration proceeds normally (compare *D* and *F*), but as soon as the axon has reached the girth at which it fills the narrow (constricted) part of the tube, the portion lying distally to the constriction ceases to gain in width, while at the proximal side of the constriction excess axoplasm begins to pile up in configurations such as are ordinarily assumed by a steadily propelled column of plastic material suddenly faced with an obstruction (*G, H*). If, later, the constriction is released allowing the tube to re-expand, the dammed-up material moves on peripherad, thus widening the formerly stunted distal portion (*I*). The rate of this movement was estimated to be of the order of a few millimeters per day, which corresponds closely to the optimal rate of free advance in regenerating fibers (see p. 356).

These results have led to the conclusions that (1) axoplasm is synthesized solely in the

terminal swellings of blocked regenerating nerve fibers (see Cajal, '28; Nageotte, '22). Although we know nothing about the nature of the axonal pumping mechanism,* it is reasonable to assume that it is the same for first outgrowth (see p. 350) and regeneration. While the fiber tip advances, the material is used for elongation; after the fiber has ceased to elongate, the continuing sup-

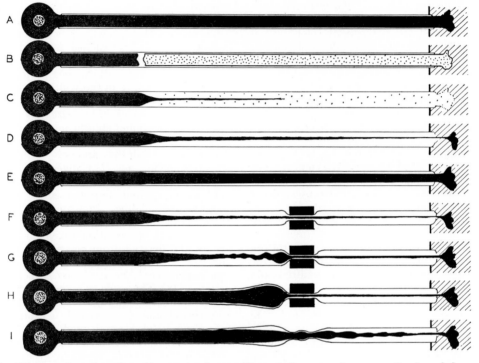

Fig. 135. Damming of axoplasm in constricted nerve fibers. *A–E*, consecutive stages of unimpeded regeneration; *F–H*, consecutive stages of regeneration with "bottleneck"; *I*, following *H* after release of constriction. (From Weiss and Hiscoe, '48.)

central cell body near the nucleus; (2) axoplasm is conveyed peripherad in a steady movement accommodated to the width of the tube which serves as channel; (3) axoplasm is subject to continuous catabolic degradation all along the fiber. Accordingly, any local reduction of the width of the channel throttles downward flow, hence reduces the rate of replacement of the "downstream" portion, while excess material accumulates on the "upstream" side. Thus is visualized directly what used to be postulated by earlier students of nerve growth as "vis a tergo" (Held, '09) or "formative turgor" (Cajal, '28).

Damming of axoplasm can now be taken as a direct sign of obstructed axonal transport. As such it is seen, for instance, in the

ply adds to its width until a steady state is reached between rate of supply and rate of catabolic consumption. Since there is evidence (Weiss and Hiscoe, '48) that this centrifugal supply stream continues throughout the life of the mature neuron, nerve regeneration turns out to be but a special manifestation of a perpetual growth process. This explains why nerves can regenerate repeatedly in succession with undiminished vigor (Duncan and Jarvis, '43).

* If the rhythmic pulsations demonstrated for central glia cells (Pomerat, '51) were also a property of peripheral Schwann cells and if these were coordinated in the manner of heart muscle contractions or ciliary beats, this might offer a mechanism for the massaging of axoplasm downward within its sheath.

The caliber of a nerve fiber is thus determined essentially by three factors: (1) the amount of synthesis of new axoplasm in the cell body; (2) the rate of its centrifugal movement; and (3) the rate of its peripheral breakdown. Since the rate of movement is limited by the width of the channel in which it occurs, large nerve fibers regenerating into narrower tubes fail to gain full normal width (Holmes and Young, '42; Sanders and Young, '44; Simpson and Young, '45; Hammond and Hinsey, '45). However, no such limitation is to be expected during embryonic growth, before firm neurilemmal tubes have formed. Assuming, furthermore, rather uniform rates of catabolism, we are left with the rate of central synthesis as the main variable in the determination of fiber caliber, which, in turn, is rather closely correlated with the size of the nerve cell body.

Factors Controlling Neuron Growth. Early in development different neuron groups seem to acquire constitutional growth differentials which place them in different size classes. Within each class itself, however, growth rate and size are subject to further modifications which are due to extraneous conditions, as illustrated in the following.

When a nerve fiber is severed, hence disconnected from its terminal organ, the whole neuron begins to atrophy (Weiss, Edds and Cavanaugh, '45; Sanders and Young, '46; Aitken, Sharman and Young, '47). If we disregard certain acute traumatic changes ("ascending degeneration," "axon reaction") referable to the injury as such, the main long-range effect of the loss consists of a progressive reduction of the dimensions of the neuron, beginning with the nucleolus and spreading to the nucleus, the cell body, and finally the diameter of the axon (Cavanaugh, '51). Conversely, upon reconnection with a peripheral organ, the dimensions enlarge again. Moreover, when a neuron is "overloaded," that is, made to innervate a larger volume of peripheral tissue than originally (e.g., by collateral branching into a denervated field), nucleus and cell body enlarge above their normal dimensions (Terni, '20; Edds, '49; Cavanaugh, '51). The production center of neuronal synthesis thus adapts itself sensitively to the demands of the peripheral innervation volume.

Variations of functional activity have similar effects. Not only do neurons tend to atrophy, when they are chronically deprived of excitation (e.g., Edds, '51), but they hypertrophy, again starting from the nucleus, in response to intensified physio-logical demands (Hamberger and Hydén, '49). Enlargement of the nuclei and nucleoli of the cells in certain brain centers following induced hyperfunction of these centers (e.g., antidiuretic center in the hypothalamus) has also been recorded (Ortmann, '51). The interpretation of all these facts requires caution, because nuclear enlargement may signify either true protoplasmic growth generally associated with increase in desoxyribonucleic acids (Hydén, '50), or merely water uptake, accumulation of functional products and other transitory changes subserving functional activity rather than true growth (see Leuchtenberger and Schrader, '52).

At any rate, the realization that the size of a neuron is subject to continual upward or downward regulations in accordance with extraneous influences received from both its afferent and (ascendingly) efferent ends, certainly controverts the classic view which has endowed the central nervous system, at least in morphological regards, with a nimbus of static and rigid fixity.

The significance of this demonstrated plasticity for our concepts of central activity is evident. The backward projection of peripheral conditions into the centers, which we encounter here for the first time in our discussion and which will be amplified below, is particularly noteworthy. This makes it all the more important to stress the fact that the reported influences do not "determine" activity, growth, or size, of a neuron in any absolute sense, but simply enhance or depress its inherent activities, and within relatively narrow limits at that (for instance, even the chronically disconnected ganglion cell still retains about 60 per cent of its normal mass).

Biochemistry of Neuron Growth. The morphological evidence for the localized growth of the neuron from the nuclear territory (Weiss and Hiscoe, '48) is supported by the cytochemical demonstration of abundance of desoxyribonucleic acids and a high rate of protein synthesis in the nuclear territory (Caspersson, '50; Hydén, '50), with fluctuations that closely parallel the growth activity of the neuron. Thus, the intensity of these syntheses increases during the regenerative phase following nerve section (Bodian, '47), during the growth reaction resulting from hyperactivity (Hamberger and Hydén, '45) and, embryonically, during the phase of the functional alerting of brain cells (Flexner, '50).

In agreement with this monopoly of the nuclear territory as the growth center of the neuron, the well-known impairment of nerve growth in thiamine deficiency (beriberi) is observed only if the cell bodies are bathed by the deficient medium (in vitro), even though the rest of the nerve, including the growing tips, lies in normal medium (Burt, '43a).

The correlation of cytological, biochemical and physiological data for normal and deficiency states of the nervous system is making encouraging progress (see p. 376). One of the major tasks in these studies which remains is to distinguish clearly between the relative contributions of the metabolic machinery of the neuron to its growth (i.e., protoplasmic reproduction) on the one hand, and to its functional activity on the other; a task rendered more difficult by the fact just outlined, that having reached a stationary size, a neuron keeps "growing" without change of total mass.

DEVELOPMENT OF GROUP RELATIONS

Fasciculation. Outside the gray matter and the terminal arborizations, nerve fibers

of pioneering fibers, the routing is achieved not by "attraction" but by a form of contact guidance. When a nerve source and a peripheral organ, e.g., a limb, are implanted at some distance from each other in a loose connective tissue bed (e.g., the dorsal fin of an amphibian larva), a strong nerve cable soon develops between them (Fig. 136) in the following manner (Weiss, '50a). Pioneering fibers from the nerve center invade the surroundings. Those that happen upon the limb and succeed in connecting with its tissues thereby become somehow adhesive for other nerve fibers growing out subsequently; older fibers thus become guides to the limb for younger ones, endowing them, in turn, with adhesiveness, and so forth, in a sort of chain reaction. It is not known what eventually terminates the agglomeration; perhaps fasciculation ceases automatically as soon as peripheral saturation (see p. 368) has been reached, that is, when further newcomer fibers no longer find functional attachments, hence, do not become adhesive.

The lessons of nerve anatomy which show that nerve fibers of identical functional

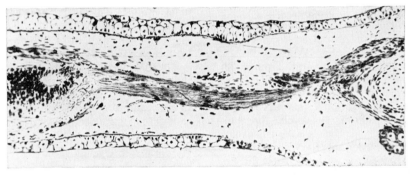

Fig. 136. Fasciculation. Nerve cable that has formed between a fragment of spinal cord (left) and a limb (right), both deplanted to the dorsal fin of a urodele larva (frontal section, showing the loose connective tissue of the fin between the two borders of epidermis). (From Weiss, '50a.)

rarely appear solitary. They commonly associate with other nerve fibers to form bundles, as well as with the Schwann cells and connective tissue cells. The grouping of fibers into bundles seems to come about in two ways: (*a*) by a primary tendency of younger fibers to follow the course of older fibers in close application of one to the other ("fasciculation"); and (*b*) by the secondary gathering of small groups into larger assemblies through the formation of common connective tissue sheaths.

Primary fasciculation is not a chance event but a systematic device to route a sufficient number of nerve connections toward a destination in need of them. As in the outgrowth

properties (e.g., fibers subserving pain or special sensations) often course together, both in peripheral nerve trunks and central funiculi, indicate an element of selectivity in the process of fasciculation. Young fibers of a given kind would apply themselves preferentially to older fibers belonging to the same, rather than to another, category. Some experimental proof for "selective fasciculation" by contact affinities may be seen in the observation that supernumerary Mauthner's fibers of the amphibian brain run alongside the normal Mauthner's fibers of that side much more frequently than could be expected on mere chance; and in the further observation that transected longitudinal fiber tracts of the spinal cord, when regenerating through a connective tissue gap, even over great distances, tend to retain their fascicular identity (Hooker, '30; Holtzer, '52b). Evidently, such selectivity of association implies two things: first, that nerve fibers of different functional designations are constitutionally (i.e., substantially) different, and second, that they can recognize and distinguish one another according to kind.

Fasciculation occurs by non-detachment among fibers that have made contact, rather than by active association. It therefore is promoted by conditions furthering the chances of contact. These chances are low in compact tissues containing innumerable separate fibrous guide lines, but high in tissues with large liquid spaces, where the nerve pathways are crowded into the relatively few land bridges. Judging from tissue cultures, established nerve fibers may themselves bring about the latter condition by liquefying surrounding colloids (Weiss, '34a) and thus facilitate bundling. Moreover, liquefaction around attached nerve fibers will cause their floating stems to cling together, according to the same principle that makes wet threads stick together in air, thus assembling them secondarily into trunks. These considerations furnish a ready explanation of the fact that fibers tend to remain separate in the gray matter, in the peripheral tissues and in nerve scars, whereas they are aggregated into bundles in the more liquid-filled interstices, particularly along the blood vessels. However, much remains still to be found out about the mechanisms of fasciculation; particularly the factors effecting the sorting and collecting of fascicles into still larger assemblies by wrappings of connective tissue are still wholly unexplored.

Association with Sheath Cells; Myelinization. The specific affinity between Schwann cells and axons appears to be mutual. Sheath cells attach themselves to nerve sprouts (Speidel '32). The tips of nerve fibers, conversely, show a definite predilection for strands of Schwann cells (Nageotte, '22; Dustin, '17), and it is doubtful whether naked sprouts, not enveloped by sheath cells, can persist over appreciable distances. The two cell types, when in contact, thus seem to form firm unions, which actively resist separation (Abercrombie, Johnson and Thomas, '49). Sheath cells have been seen to shuttle freely between nerve fibers of different kinds (Speidel, '33), with a certain preference for transfer from unmyelinated to myelinated ones (Speidel, '50). Sheath cells,

however, do not share the specificity of the nerve fibers which they coat; this can be inferred from the fact that regenerating sensory or motor nerve sprouts penetrate Schwann cords of either nerve type with equal ease (see p. 362).

Myelin is presumably formed in the surface of the axon, with the sheath cells (or, in the central nervous system, the glia cells) furnishing some essential stimulus or complement (Speidel, '33, '35), but the details of the process are not known. Since the same sheath cell has been observed either to induce, or fail to induce, myelin formation, depending on whether it joined the branch of a potentially myelinated or a potentially unmedullated fiber (Speidel, '33), the differential faculty for myelinization must be a property of the nerve fiber itself. The laminated structure of the myelin sheath (see p. 347) and the proportionality between its thickness and the caliber of the axon suggest that successive layers are shed by the surface as the axon grows in width (see Geren and Raskind, '53).

As Schwann cells line up in tandem along the axons, myelin formation progresses in a general proximodistal sequence, starting in each cell from the region of the nucleus. The length of the cell defines a myelin segment, and the junction of two cells, the node of Ranvier. The standard length of individual segments (internodes) amounts to about 300 micra, which agrees with the average length of an extended Schwann cell in tissue culture. The same average length is found in regenerated nerve fibers regardless of diameter (Hiscoe, '47; Vizoso and Young, '48). The greater internodal length in primary (non-regenerated) fibers, which varies directly with fiber diameter attaining up to about 1500 micra, is presumably to be ascribed to passive elongation by the stretching of the nerves in tow of growing organs (Hiscoe, '47; Young, '50). The longest fibers having undergone the greatest extension would also end up with the longest segments, and since the longest fibers (within the same class) have the largest caliber (Kölliker, 1896), a general proportionality between fiber diameter and internodal length would result (Thomas and Young, '49), which fact has recently assumed added significance in connection with the saltatory theory of nerve conduction.

Saturation Factors. Volume and density of peripheral innervation vary relevantly from organ to organ and from region to region within the same systems (skin, intestine, connective tissue). This characteristic distribution is grossly anticipated in the relative allocations of neurons to different peripheral sectors (see below, p. 374), in the frequency of preterminal branching and in the peripheral control of fasciculation. Since this rough preallocation would still leave a wide margin of variability in the number of fibers actually arriving in a tissue in a given individual, there are additional screening factors in operation in the terminal tissues themselves which adjust the final quota of terminals to a stable norm. Each tissue would thus maintain a characteristic "saturation" density of innervation. While not much is known about the means by which this control is exerted, it is already becoming obvious that they are different for different tissues, and that the mechanisms for upward regulation from a deficient source are of a different kind than those involved in the downward regulation from an excessive source. They will therefore be considered separately.

When supernumerary (Detwiler, '36b) or excessively large (Harrison, '35a) limbs are transplanted to the limb region of urodele embryos, the enlarged periphery, while causing no adaptive increase in the central nerve source (see below, p. 382), yet derives from that undersized source the full contingent of nerve fiber branches appropriate to its larger mass. Similarly, limbs transplanted in later larval stages, and provided with only a small branch for regenerative innervation, contain eventually the full contingent of fibers normal for a limb (Weiss, '37a). In nerve regeneration in the adult, likewise, the number of regenerated fibers in the distal stumps approximates the normal quota, even if the proximal source of fiber stems has been drastically reduced (Dogliotti, '35; Litwiller, '38a; Weiss and Campbell, '44; Billig, van Harreveld and Wiersma, '46).

This compensatory increase of the volume of innervation is due to more extensive peripheral branching of the individual neurons. Being the rule in the regeneration of transected nerves (see above, p. 350), such branching is satisfactorily accounted for in the cases just mentioned in which nerves have been severed. However, compensatory branches may also arise, as if in response to peripheral needs, from nerves that have not been deliberately traumatized. When musculature is partially denervated by the experimental elimination of part of its tributary ventral roots, the residual healthy intra-

muscular fibers develop "spontaneously" collateral branches that take over the innervation of the neighboring denervated muscle elements (see Edds, '53). The fact that such collateral branching can be artificially induced by intramuscular injection of extracts from degenerating muscle (Hoffman, '52) suggests an active participation of the denervated muscle fibers in tapping the locally available nerve sources for extra branches. As indicated in our discussion of branching mechanisms (p. 361), this need imply nothing more than the weakening of the axonal surface, particularly at the nodes, to permit ever-present abortive axonal leaks to yield durable offshoots. Perhaps substances reported to enhance nerve regeneration (von Muralt, '46) should be viewed in the same light, as facilitating the protrusion of branches or diminishing the resistance of tissues to penetration by them.

Compensatory collateral innervation, comparable to that observed in muscle, has also been described to occur in denervated sectors of skin, whose infiltration by side branches from nerves of the surrounding intact area has been either observed directly in experimental cases (Weddell, Guttmann and Gutmann, '41) or deduced from clinical results (Livingston, '43). Again, the explanation may lie either in a true activation of branching by emanations from the denervated tissue or, conversely, in the removal of an active suppressing principle that could be assumed to emanate from nerve-saturated tissue as a bar to its invasion by nerve branches continually forming as a result of intra-axonal growth pressure and surface instability. The latter alternative seems plausible since the assumed abortive branching has actually been observed in living preparations (Speidel, '42). Negative microscopic evidence, on the other hand, would be meaningless in view of the electronmicroscopic demonstration of fiber collaterals far below the range of microscopic visibility (Fernández-Morán, '52).

In conclusion, if overproduction of branches is a regular occurrence, it would account for a reservoir of fibers sufficiently large to supply the needs of even a considerably enlarged periphery; on the other hand, it may be necessary in addition to assume peripheral factors that facilitate, if not the production, at least the further outgrowth and consolidation, of branches in accordance with the size of the periphery to be innervated. Either mechanism insures to the peripheral tissue a full quota of innervation even from an undersized nerve fiber source.

Equally important, however, is the upper limitation set to nerve density, referred to above as "saturation." Even in the face of a superabundant supply of nerve fibers, the tissue restricts the admission of terminals to its normal quota. The best-studied examples are muscle, peripheral nerve, and regenerating limbs. Individual muscle fibers rarely contain more than one ending of nerve fibers of the same kind. That this embodies an active self-protection of the muscle fiber against multiple innervation ("hyper-

Of different causation, but of comparable effect, is the peripheral control of nerve fiber numbers in nerve regeneration. Irrespective of the size of the nerve fiber source and even in the presence of an excessive amount of branches produced, the number contained in the regenerated distal stumps approximates the normal number closely enough to intimate active regulation (e.g., Davenport, Chor and Dolkart, '37; Weiss, '37a; Weiss and Campbell, '44; Litwiller, '38a; Weiss and Cummings, '43). Since new fibers course both inside and between old nerve tubes (Holmes and Young, '42), the

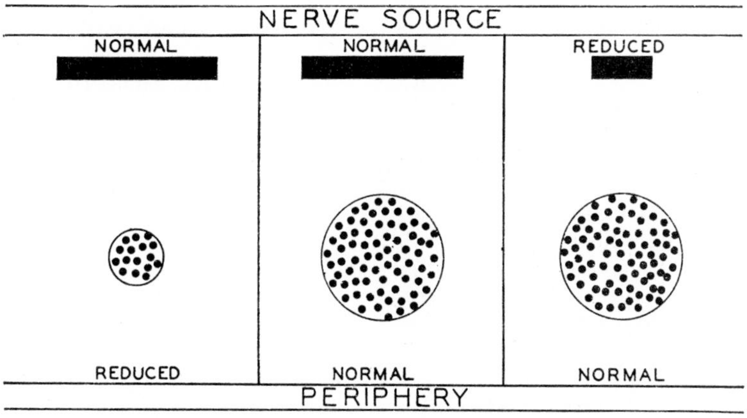

Fig. 137. Diagram summarizing the regulation of density of peripheral innervation in instances of abnormal ratios of nerve source to peripheral field.

neurotization"), comparable to the self-protection of fertilized eggs against multiple insemination (Harrison, '10), is evidenced by the fact that it is impossible to force appreciable surplus innervation upon a muscle even by inserting an excessive supply of nerve fibers right into it (Elsberg, '17; Fort, '40; Weiss and Hoag, '46). Only uninnervated muscle fibers seem to be ready to accept nerve endings, but once a connection has been effected, the muscle fiber shields itself somehow from further impregnation. Since this physiological insulation requires some time to develop, there exists, of course, an open interim during which additional endings can take. This explains why there is always a certain percentage of muscle fibers found with multiple endings, and why the incidence of "hyperneurotization" is higher when superabundant nerve masses are allowed to pervade the muscle simultaneously (Hoffmann, '51). The nature of the protective reaction is unknown, but may be looked for in a change of surface properties.

capacity of the latter cannot be the limiting factor. Indeed, the numerical restriction is observed even if the peripheral nerve stumps have been evulsed (Litwiller, '38a). Even more instructive is the similarly restrictive influence exerted by regenerating limbs on the quota of nerve branches they admit to their territory. When a urodele limb is amputated, the cut nerves promptly sprout branches in numbers superabundant for the supply of a full-sized limb. Nevertheless, only a small fraction enters the young regeneration blastema, and this fraction increases only gradually, in direct proportion to the growth of the blastema (Weiss and Walker, '34; Litwiller, 38b), with a saturation constant of ca. 40 nerve terminals per cubic millimeter of tissue. It is difficult to escape the conclusion that each innervated tissue fragment establishes an inhibitory field around it which prevents the penetration of competing fiber branches (analogous to territorial dominance observed in other tissue complexes; see Wigglesworth, '48; Willier, '52; Weiss, '53). Similar factors may be responsible for the great local differences in the density of the central neuropil (see Herrick, '48, pp. 29-39).

It is interesting to note, in this connection, that topical application of carcinogens entails a marked rise in the density of the local cutaneous nerve net (Julius, '30), and that the presence of mouse sarcomata in chick embryos similarly opens certain visceral organs, e.g., the mesonephros, which normally would have remained uninnervated, to profuse invasion by sympathetic fibers (Levi-Montalcini and Hamburger, '53). These observations seem to indicate that the mechanisms controlling saturation density can be suspended by certain agents, among which tumor agents seem to be prominent.

The peripheral density control (Fig. 137), whatever its nature may be, serves to insure, in combination with the other numerical controls outlined earlier, the attainment and maintenance of an adequate functional state despite wide fluctuations of the individual developmental histories. It should have become clear from our discussion that such purportedly goal-directed performances, when properly analyzed, are resolvable into chains of causal mechanisms.

DEVELOPMENT OF THE CENTRAL NERVOUS SYSTEM (CNS)

DETERMINATION OF THE CNS

The foregoing chapters, devoted to nerve fibers, have taken the existence of nerve cells for granted. To consider the origin of the nerve cells themselves, we must now turn back to an earlier phase of the embryonic history. As for the manner in which neural differentiation is initiated and the primordia of the neural system are mapped out in the early embryo, we may simply refer to the article in this book by Holtfreter and Hamburger. We shall take up the story from the time when the anterodorsal sector of the ectoderm has become irrevocably earmarked for the formation of the neural organs and endowed with the capacity to produce parts with the morphological, histological and chemical characteristics of central nervous system even when isolated from the rest of the germ. At that stage, by virtue of anteceding interactions of induction and segregation, the neural plate has become constituted as a system of fields, the median ones directing the transformation to central nervous structures—anteriorly, brain and its derivatives;

posteriorly, spinal cord—while the marginal ones give rise to neural crest. That this area already has biochemical properties that are distinctly neural is indicated by its selective immune response to antibodies prepared against adult neural antigens (Ebert, '50). At least in anteroposterior direction, it constitutes a definite mosaic of fields (Dalcq, '47; Nieuwkoop, '52), the individual regions of which already contain differential conditions guiding the subsequent steps of morphogenesis toward the formation of specific localized parts of the CNS. It is these steps, involving mainly folding, cell movements, proliferation, cell growth, cytodifferentiation, secretion, and cell degeneration, that we shall now consider in greater detail.

EARLY MORPHOGENESIS

Neurulation. Transformation of the neural plate into the neural tube occurs by means of forces residing within the plate itself, for as was shown by Roux (1895), the folding takes place even in excised and isolated plates. The expansive pressure of the surrounding epidermis in the germ plays merely an adjuvant role (Giersberg, '24). The dynamics of the folding process, as those of similar invaginations (e.g., gastrulation; see article by Costello in this book) are still not fully understood. They are based on the development of differences in surface expanse between the outer and inner sides of the plate. An earlier suggestion, attributing this difference to differential water uptake (Glaser, '14), has now been discounted (Glaser, '16; Brown, Hamburger and Schmitt, '41). Differential cell growth or cell multiplication has likewise been ruled out (Burt, '43b; Gillette, '44; Hutchinson, '44). The most likely assumption is that of an active contraction of the outer surface of the plate, the contractile elements, presumably fiber proteins, being either in the cells (Lewis, '47) or in their outer coating (Holtfreter, '43), or perhaps in the intercellular fiber cement around the outer cell poles seen under the microscope as "terminal web" (Sauer, '35). Active elongation of the medullary cells may normally assist this process (Brown, Hamburger and Schmitt, '41; Holtfreter, '46); ultraviolet irradiation of the germ with wave lengths near the absorption maximum of sterols inhibits it (Davis, '44).

When the raised folds meet from the two sides, epidermis fuses with epidermis, and neural layer with neural layer. Since this occurs even in asymmetrically mutilated embryos under mechanically wholly aberrant conditions (Holtzer, '51), it cannot be simply a mechanical accident, but must be viewed as a case of selective fusion of tissues according to their respective affinities (see Holtfreter, '39; Chiakulas, '52). Similarly, the extrusion at this stage of the neural crest cells from the confines of the neural plate might be an expression of a

cylindrical lumen. This actually occurs in isolated pieces of plate in homogeneous surroundings (Holtfreter, '34). The slit-shape of the normal tube has been shown to depend on the presence of notochord (Lehmann, '35) (Fig. 138C, E). The effect may be credited to a vertical system of fibers, spanning the thickness of the plate along a median strip coextensive with the notochord and apparently attached to it, which

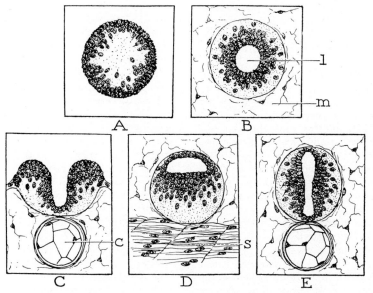

Fig. 138. Shape of neural tube under different conditions (from Holtfreter, '34). A, Solid neural mass developed in explantation: nuclei of gray matter crowded near the surface; white matter in the interior. B, Neural tube surrounded by mesenchyme: shape cylindrical with central lumen; nuclei massed at the inner (free) surface. C, Asyntaxia dorsalis (failure of the tube to close); thinning of the floor of the tube in contact with the notochord; gray matter along the free surface. D, Neural tube underlain by musculature; lumen eccentric at far side; white matter at near side. E, Neural tube underlain by notochord; normal appearance; slit-shaped lumen, oriented towards notochord. l, Lumen; m, mesenchyme; c, notochord; s, segmented musculature.

transient incompatibility (or disaffinity) between the two groups. Thus, visible movements and shaping processes appear as the observable results of more intimate physicochemical distinctions within the prospective neural system.

Early Morphogenesis of Brain and Cord. The gross shapes of the early brain and cord, respectively, are anticipated in the proportions of the neural plate, whose wide anterior part, upon folding upward, forms the large vault of a brain ventricle, while the narrower posterior part encloses the narrow lumen of the central canal of the spinal cord.

The shape of the canal varies with the details of the folding process (Fig. 138). Uniform curling of the plate would leave a

holds the midline firmly anchored as a hinge about which the flanks of the plate fold up (Weiss, '50c). A similar fibrous plane seems to define the border between the alar and basal plate cell masses; as the latter grow and bulge, it gives rise to the lateral sulcus. Because of their importance for the later regular distribution and grouping of cell columns, such tangible traces of early subdivisions would merit more intensive study; at present, we have no more than vague hints as to their presumable role.

After the closure of the groove, the turgor of the fluid in the lumen assumes the morphogenetic role of firm support for the limp walls, which otherwise would collapse. The source of this turgor has been found in the secretion of fluid from the cells of the inner lining of the early ventricles (Weiss, '34b; Holtzer, '51). Furthermore, the ciliary beat of the lining may propel the fluid anteriorly, which in the normal embryo would help to maintain the distention of the brain cavity. In cyclostomes and teleosts, in which the CNS is laid down initially as a solid cell cord, this same secretion process seems to be the method by which the central lumen is secondarily established in the interior. The shrinkage of the central canal by partial fusion of its walls (see Hamburger, '48), paralleled by the decline of mitotic activity, may reflect a reduction of turgor in the spinal portion.

With hydrostatic pressure on the inside and the confining skull capsule on the outside, continued enlargement of the brain wall by growth, cell migrations and the deposition of white matter must be expected to lead to deformations, which, depending on the local conditions, manifest themselves as cave-ins, outpocketings, fissures or folds. Practically nothing is known about the mechanics of these elementary shaping processes, although there are at least some indications that the fissures between major divisions of the cortex actually arise as cave-ins along lines of least resistance in the wall which tends to expand in confined space (Clark, '45; Källén, '51). It must be emphasized, however, that the systematic pattern, according to which such mechanical events take place, is intrinsically prepared by the inequalities established previously by the locally differing processes of proliferation, migration, aggregation and differentiation (see Bergquist and Källén, '53a); the gross mechanical factors do not create these differentials, but merely translate them into more conspicuous spatial configurations.

Accordingly, the attainment of normal brain configuration depends not only on the typical development of the brain wall, but also on the proper harmony between the latter and the growth of the skull capsule (or in the case of the cord, the spine) on the outside, and the turgor of the cerebrospinal liquor on the inside. If this harmony is disturbed, either by a genetically determined imbalance between the component tissues or by later trauma or nutritional deficiencies, serious aberrations of the CNS will ensue. Genetically conditioned hypersecretion of central fluid, for instance, leads to hydrocephalus and brain herniation (Little and Bagg, '24; Bonnevie, '34; see Section

XIV, Teratogenesis, by Zwilling); delayed closure of the folds past the onset of secretion, to various grades of spina bifida with draining fistulae (for an example of mechanical production of spina bifida, see Fowler, '53); and retardation of skull growth in vitamin A deficiency, with unimpeded growth of the CNS, to brain compression and herniation (Wolbach and Bessey, '42). The early cartilaginous capsule, at least in the spinal region, can accommodate its size to the actual dimensions of the enclosed CNS (Holtzer, '52a), but this adaptability is certainly greatly reduced in later stages.

Morphogenesis of the Neural Crest. The neural crest, which contains precursor cells for spinal ganglia, sympathetic ganglia, Schwann cells, pigment cells, and, in lower vertebrates, also branchial skeleton and ordinary mesenchyme, is regionally specialized even before its cells start on their migrations away from the dorsal midline (Hörstadius, '50; Niu, '47). The bilateral cell masses first move down in rather coherent sheets (Detwiler, '37b); the parts of prime interest here, those giving rise to the ganglia, then settle down in two major columns, one between spinal cord and myotomes, the other alongside the aorta, with further outposts moving into the viscera. The localization of the ganglionic columns is hardly a simple matter of filling open grooves between the tissues, but rather an expression of specific contact affinities between the crest cells and the surrounding cell systems. We find a model of this process in the formation of pigment bands by neural crest–derived melanophores (Twitty, '49), where the migrating cells likewise aggregate along certain tracts preformed in the surrounding tissues.

Later the continuous columns break up into segmental clusters. The tendency to separate into smaller groups seems to be intrinsic to the cells, but the segmental localization of these groups is determined by the segmental arrangement of the myotomes, for the experimental removal (or disarrangement) of the latter abolishes (or correspondingly disarranges) the segmental array of the ganglia (Lehmann, '27; Detwiler, '34, '35). The segmental arrangement of the nerve roots and neural arches is likewise dependent on the presence of axial mesoderm (Detwiler, '37b), but just how these processes are causally interrelated is not yet clear.

GROWTH PATTERNS

Proliferative Sources. In the ganglia, cell division is rather ubiquitous. In the CNS, on the other hand, mitoses are, in post-neurulation stages, confined to the inner surface, lining central canal and brain ventricles (Fig. 139). More peripheral layers are essentially devoid of mitotic figures; the cells there continue to grow in size, but without ensuing divisions. Whether the inner "germinal" layer is subject to some active mitogenic stimulation by its exposure to the lumen, or rather division in the outer layers is actively inhibited by local conditions in the mantle, is uncertain. However, upon injury to the early CNS (Hooker, '25), as well as after unilateral ablation (cord: Detwiler, '44; Holtzer, '51; not observed in midbrain: Detwiler, '46b), mitotic cells may appear throughout the mantle, which seems to disprove an early loss of divisory faculty. There is a remote possibility that the confinement of mitotic figures to the inner surface might not truly express the position of the germinal cells in the resting stage, but that the latter might merely rise to the surface during mitosis (Sauer, '35). The observation that x-irradiation of embryos destroys a cell layer somewhat deeper than the inner lining (Hicks, '52) could be interpreted in two ways: either these deeper cells are the true germinal ones, but are impaired in their normal premitotic centripetal movement, or else they are postmitotic cells defying the general supposition that germinal cells are the most sensitive to radiation (Hicks, '53). At any rate, once neuronal differentiation has become marked, none of the resulting nerve cells would ever divide again under ordinary circumstances. We therefore can confine our consideration of proliferative patterns to the inner, "germinal," layer, whatever its precise delineation may be. In this layer, mitotic density and rate vary characteristically both along the longitudinal and in the dorsoventral direction, as will be described more fully below.

Growth and Shape. Daughter cells of a germinal mitosis may either remain in the germinal layer or move off into the deeper layers. In the former event, they can continue to proliferate, while in the latter event, they merely add to the bulk of the mantle without further reproduction. Since the relative frequency of the two events will depend on the spatial arrangement, the configuration of

early brain and cord assumes significance for their over-all growth rate. According to Hertwig's rule, the plane of division of a radially elongate medullary cell should lie parallel to the surface; hence, of the two daughter cells only one would remain a germinal cell. We know neither what rearrangements take place after division, nor what actuates and guides the movement of the proliferated cells. However, it seems that, at least in the earlier stages, they glide along other medullary cells stretching across the

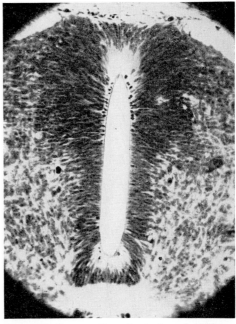

Fig. 139. Cross section of spinal cord (15th segment) of 6½-day chick embryo showing mitotic activity of germinal layer, predominantly in dorsal half (from Hamburger, '48).

neural tube and brain wall, or along radial fibers deposited by the medullary cells. If all new cells kept on being thus displaced in the radial direction, the neural tube would gain only in width, but not in length.

The factor counteracting this trend seems to be the longitudinal stretch to which the tube is passively subjected by the lengthwise extension of the surrounding tissues, especially the notochord (Hörstadius, '44; Kitchin, '49). This would divert a certain fraction of the new cells in the longitudinal, rather than radial, direction, and by extending the germinal surface area, also lead to a progressive expansion of the proliferative source. While still hypothetical, this view is supported by the observation that isolated sections of the spinal cord, transplanted to the flank, where they are deprived of axial stretch, do become much thicker and shorter than if they had developed in continuity with the rest of the cord (Zacharias, '38). The ease with which lateral halves of the cord are regenerated with the participation of transverse cell shifts from the intact half (Detwiler, '47b; Harrison, '47; Holtzer, '51), contrasted with the failure to repair major gaps in the longitudinal direction, likewise indicates the

tivity declines at some levels and flares up at others. Moreover, the centers of proliferation often form a quiltlike pattern with foci at the intersections of four longitudinal columns with transverse bands (neuromeres) (Bergquist and Källén, '54). Some of the segmental peaks coincide with the appearance of prominent peripheral organs in the corresponding sector, for instance, in the limb segments. As will be shown later (p. 381), part of this correspondence is due to an active control exerted upon the centers by their respective

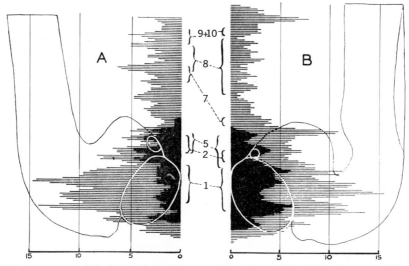

Fig. 140. Mitotic pattern of the brain of Amblystoma (after Burr, '32). *A*, Earlier stage (31, after Harrison). *B*, Later stage. (35, after Harrison).

To facilitate comparison, the two stages are represented side by side in symmetrical arrangement. The outline of the brain is indicated. Horizontal lines express the number of mitotic figures contained in serial brain slices of 30μ each. Abscissa: Number of mitoses. Full black: Mitoses in forebrain and hypothalamus. Individual bars: Mitoses in the rest of the brain. Brackets indicate position and extent of sensory placodes. Note the change in the distribution of peaks from *A* to *B*.

need of extraneous stretch for elongation. In the brain, the hydrostatic turgor deserves similar attention as a potential regulator of the expanse of the proliferative surface, hence of the over-all growth rate. These considerations would not apply, of course, to those parts of the CNS which arise, not as transformations of the original neural plate, but by secondary budding processes (e.g., the posterior parts of midbrain and spinal cord in amphibians).

Regional Patterns of Proliferation. Regional variations of mitotic activity within the germinal layer have been mapped out for several species and stages (urodele spinal cord: Coghill, '24, '36; urodele brain: Burr, '32; chick cord: Hamburger, '48; comparative studies: Bergquist and Källén, 53b). Each stage has its own characteristic pattern (Fig. 140); that is, as development proceeds, ac-

peripheries. But there are also some basic intrinsic growth differentials among different regions of the CNS (Coghill, '36; Detwiler, '24a, '36b; Hamburger, '48), the origin of which remains in need of explanation.

It has been proposed that local proliferation is regulated by the number of intracentral tract fibers ending in a given locality (Detwiler, '36b). This has been inferred from experiments in which posterior cord pieces of potentially smaller end size (of urodele tail-bud stages) and anterior ones of potentially larger size had been mutually exchanged and found to develop in accordance with their new sites, the former growing beyond, the latter remaining below, the sizes they would have attained in their original positions (Detwiler, '23, '24a). Since more descending brain fibers terminate at more anterior than at more posterior levels, these fibers were thought to have determined the site-specific growth rates. Confirmatory evidence was seen in the fact that when the anterior cord segments were replaced by a supernumerary medulla as extra fiber source, the spinal host segments lying immediately posterior to the graft became abnormally large (Detwiler, '25c).

In the light of later work, however, this view has become untenable. For instance, when the normal medulla as the supplier of supposedly stimulating fiber tracts was replaced by a spinal fragment of much lower fiber productivity, the host spinal cord behind developed quite normally, without the expected diminution (Detwiler, '37c). Similarly, suppression of forebrain development entails no deficienies in the medulla (Detwiler, '45). In the chick, cord segments which have been transected and prevented from receiving down-growing fiber tracts still gain normal dimensions (Levi-Montalcini, '45; Hamburger, '46). Also, the assumption that descending fibers would have an intrinsic preassigned length at which they would stop is gratuitous; free nerve fibers do not stop spontaneously, but are stopped by their surroundings, usually a recipient cell. Hence, fiber tracts cannot be the major determinants of axial growth patterns, although they can exert some modifying effects (see p. 383).

All evidence thus leads to the conclusion that the closed neural tube represents a longitudinal mosaic of specifically different local fields, each guiding the further fate of the area under its control; differential proliferation is but one expression of these different fates, with which we shall deal more fully below in the proper context (p. 376).

Besides the longitudinal pattern, there is also a notable dorsoventral differential of mitotic activity, both in regard to intensity and time course. Proliferation is more abundant and lasts longer in the dorsal than in the ventral half of the cord, with a rather sharp demarcation between the two zones (see Fig. 139). Generally noted in amphibians (Detwiler, '25a; Maclean, '32; Coghill, '33), this fact has been most conclusively demonstrated in the chick (Hamburger, '48). It may be related to the general precocity of the ventral, as compared to the dorsal, portions, including the precession of motor over sensory function (Coghill, '29). Dorsal and ventral halves also differ in other respects, the ventral one being far richer in alkaline phosphatase (Moog, '43), and at the same time being the first to receive vascularization (Feeney and Watterson, '46).

Growth Rate. Conventionally, the term "growth rate" refers to average increment of an organic object per unit of time. It is determined by measuring the object at the beginning and end of given intervals and dividing by the times elapsed. The resulting values are useful for rough orientation, but are often meaningless for analytical and comparative purposes, except for homogeneous systems. If the dimensions of one part of the CNS increase faster than those of another part, this need not mean that the intrinsic growth activity of the former has been greater or that its mitotic rate has been higher. If we consider, for example, a given subdivision of the CNS bounded by certain landmarks by which it can be identified at successive stages, its volume increase is the resultant of the following tributary processes: cell growth, accompanied by division in the germinal layer; cell growth without division in the mantle; immigration of nerve cells and other cell types (glia) from neighboring regions; emigration of cells; outgrowth of axons and deposition of myelin (with that portion of the axons which meanwhile has moved beyond our landmarks being unaccountably lost); passage of axons from other areas; invasion of blood vessels; accumulation of interstitial fluid; and cell disintegration. Large-scale destruction and resorption of cells is a common, if neglected, feature of embryonic development (Glücksmann, '51), and as we shall see presently, is quite prominent in the embryonic nervous system.

From this listing, it should be plain that comparisons of the "growth" of different parts of the CNS on the basis of mere measurements of volume or mass cannot be very revealing and must be interpreted with due caution. There is an even wider margin for error when, instead of volume determinations, only one, supposedly representative, dimension is sampled; e.g., cord diameter. The case is illustrated by the fact that the increase in area observed in cross sections of isolated cord segments (Severinghaus, '30) often was interpreted as hyperplasia until more complete determinations disclosed that there had been a corresponding reduction in length (Zacharias, '38) (see p. 374).

This comment should not detract from the value of the summary quantitative treatment usually accorded to CNS growth, which has been a true advance over earlier, purely verbal, descriptions; rather is it to stress the need for going even further and identifying precisely and quantitatively the various component processes of unequal kind and weight, whose disparate contributions are indistinguishably lumped in any bulk determination.

REGIONAL AND CYTOLOGICAL DIFFERENTIATION

Histochemistry of Differentiation. Superimposed upon the growth processes just discussed appear the cytological specializations usually designated as "differentiations." It is an axiom of development, however, that the morphological (i.e., microscopically discernible) "differentiation" of a cell (other than trivial geometrical changes) is but the visible expression of intimate changes in the composition and distribution of at least part of the molecular population which constitutes that cell (cf. Weiss, '49, '53). Any fundamental distinction between physicochemical (sometimes called "physiological") and morphological differentiation is thus purely artificial, for it refers not to any dichotomy in the properties of a cell but merely to two different techniques of observation, both with definite limitations, hence, supplementing each other. Accordingly, marked differences in morphology point to antecedent physicochemical changes, even though the latter may not yet be detectable by our relatively crude analytical tools, and conversely, demonstrable differences of physicochemical constitution (including differential staining in histological preparations) signify basic differences of protoplasmic properties (cytodifferentiation) even if these have failed to express themselves in corresponding differences of structural detail. It is with these qualifications in mind that the results of correlated studies between morphological and chemical ontogeny of the nervous system should be viewed (see also Section III, Chapter 1, by Schmitt).

A mental separation must be made between those chemical systems that are common to all cells (e.g., the ones engaged in respiration, energy transfer, protein reproduction, etc.) and those that are peculiar to the nervous system. In practice, this is not feasible because of the fragmentary state of our present knowledge and because there are undoubtedly quantitative variations of the former class which are as distinctive of nerve cells as are qualitatively specific compounds. Cytochemical studies of neuron growth have already been referred to above (p. 365). Even less is known about the specific biochemistry of neural differentiation.

Among the most profitable contributions to this field have been studies on the development of the cerebral cortex in which cytological, chemical, metabolic and functional observations were correlated for a series of sample stages. They have led to the recognition of certain critical phases during which differentiation advances in spurts. Within the same brief interval, the nucleus reaches mature dimensions, Nissl bodies appear in quantity, dendrites become more numerous, neurofibrils more prominent, the activities of cytochrome c, adenylpyrophosphatase, and succinic dehydrogenase rise sharply, and electric brain potentials are recordable for the first time (Flexner, '50). In amphibians, motility develops in close parallelism with the production of acetylcholinesterase (Youngstrom, '38; Sawyer, '43; Boell and Shen, '50), which is instrumental in nerve conduction, and experimental modifications of the size of the brain (see p. 383) are reflected in corresponding changes in its content of these products (Boell and Shen, '51).

These examples may suffice to discourage the practice of divorcing morphological from underlying physicochemical considerations. At the same time, much of this work must still be counted in the descriptive class, furnishing important data of information but not yet much causal understanding.

Appearance of Regional Differences. As mentioned above, different levels along the longitudinal axis of the early CNS enter different developmental courses, which subsequently express themselves in the overt mosaic of morphological, histological, and eventually, functional specializations. Although some gross mosaic features may be conceded to the neural plate from its very first appearance (e.g., Nieuwkoop, '52; see above, p. 370), its finer parcellation is a continuing process the progress of which can be tested by appropriate experiments (see Section VI, Chapter 1, by Holtfreter and Hamburger). The standard test consists of displacing the part in question (by explantation, inversion, or heterotopic transplantation) in a graded series of stages and establishing precisely from what stage it can carry on a course of development typical of its original site even under aberrant environmental conditions.

This test presupposes that features attained under the original and under the aberrant conditions are sufficiently distinct to be used as criteria. Individual blood cells, muscle cells and pigment cells, for instance, can be easily distinguished by their inclusions, different gland cells by their secretions; but individual nerve cells, judged by their shapes, whose normally great variability is further exaggerated under experimental conditions,

within each class, which must be postulated on functional evidence (see below, p. 384), for instance, between motor cells innervating different muscles or between neurons subserving different sensory modalities. The

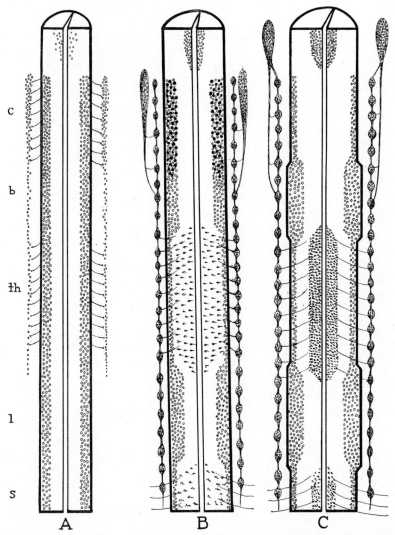

Fig. 141. Diagrammatic frontal sections of the spinal cord of chick embryos of 4 days (*A*), 5 days (*B*) and 8 days (*C*), showing the regionally differing formation of the motor columns from a morphologically rather uniform condition. In *B*, degeneration of cells in the cervical region (*c*, black circles), and centripetal emigration of cells in the thoracic and sacral regions (*th*) have set in, resulting in the distribution shown in *C*. (From Hamburger and Levi-Montalcini, '50.)

cannot always be so readily identified as to the precise type to which they belong. Large motor cells, Rohon-Beard cells, spinal ganglion cells, commissural cells, and a very few others are sufficiently distinctive to be used as cytological indicators for the respective neuron types. But there are no corresponding microscopic signs for the finer distinctions

only individual cell that can be strictly identified as such is Mauthner's neuron, of which there is in many species only a single pair, situated at the otic level of the hindbrain of lower vertebrates, and which can be recognized by its giant size. For the rest, one must rely on general morphological group criteria, such as cross-sectional configuration, characteristic location and distribution of cell columns within the unit, and the like.

Applying these tests, it has been found that the consolidation of regional properties follows a definite time sequence: in general, more anterior parts have a head start over more posterior ones, and fixation along the longitudinal axis seems to precede fixation in the mediolateral direction. Presumptive medulla oblongata of a urodele tail-bud embryo transplanted in the place of the first cord segments of another embryo develops into a supernumerary medulla oblongata (Detwiler, '25c). Even an isolated lateral half of presumptive medulla grafted into a lateral gap of spinal cord develops according to its origin, quite incongruously for the location, into half a medulla (Detwiler, '43a). Yet, while anterior spinal levels at the same stage show similar capacity for self-differentiation (Maclean, '32), more posterior segments are still able in some measure to conform to site-specific determinative influences (p. 387).

All existing evidence leads to the conclusion that, in the later neurula stage, allocation of differential developmental properties within the CNS has already made notable progress. The cord seems to lag slightly behind the brain, but by the time different cord segments have first become externally distinguishable (in birds), each one after transfer to another region develops essentially as if it were still in the original place, mosaic-fashion (B. Wenger, '51). The regionally specific "developmental properties" contain the whole ground plan for all subsequent transformations, that is, they determine pattern and basic rate of proliferation, specific differentiation of cell types, migration, establishment of specific mutual group relations, patterns of cell destruction, and the physiological mechanisms underlying functional activity and coordination. Thus segmental organization in the chick embryo, for instance, which begins to emerge on the fifth day of incubation, shows up (Fig. 141) in abundant cell degeneration in the cervical segments, segregation of a large lateral motor column in the brachial segments, absence of a lateral column and presence of a characteristic column of preganglionic autonomic cells (nucleus of Terni) at the thoracic and sacral levels (Levi-Montalcini, '50; Hamburger and Levi-Montalcini, '50). In the amphibians, where functional tests have been carried further, it includes such properties as the ability of the limb seg-

ments to engender coordinated limb movements, in contrast to the lack of this faculty in the trunk and head regions (see below, p. 387).

Similar early differences of properties at different levels of the main axis have been demonstrated for the spinal ganglia in regard to cell proliferation and regulatory ability (amphibians: Lehman and Youngs, '52) and incidence of cell degeneration (chick: Hamburger and Levi-Montalcini, '49).

It must be stressed that even as the mosaic of diverse parts of the CNS emerges, each area at first seems to operate "field"-fashion, that is, while its general fate is fixed, the detailed course of its component elements would still be variable. This is indicated by such observations as the following. At a time when the development of the medulla oblongata has already become irrevocably identified with the part of the tube lying at the presumptive hindbrain level (see above), one can still turn that piece around, reversing its anteroposterior axis, and yet see it yield a medulla of normal (unreversed) configuration (Detwiler, '43b). Cord regions of the same stage after anteroposterior reversal regulate similarly (Detwiler, '24a).

However, the interpretation of these regulatory effects calls for some caution. While shape and proliferation rates, which served as criteria, may indeed be as adaptable as indicated, this need not apply equally to the segregation of the various qualitatively specialized cell strains, which might follow a totally different time pattern and whose determination might be either precocious or delayed relative to those other features.

Experiments with Mauthner's cell (M-cell) seem to be pertinent to this problem. Unilateral extirpation in a post–tail-bud stage of the hindbrain at the prospective M-cell level leads to permanent absence of an M-cell on the operated side (Detwiler, '33). Since heterotopic grafts of the same area from a neurula yield supernumerary M-cells (Piatt, '44; Stefanelli, '50)—and assuming that the history of the M-cell is representative of that of other, less conspicuous, cell types—we must conclude that even at this early stage a rather detailed fixation of type characteristics has occurred in the various precursor cells of the later cerebral neuron strains. Repetition of the experiments in earlier stages using the M-cell as marker has narrowed the critical period of determination to the late gastrula (in frogs). At that stage, while an explant or transplant from the presumptive M-cell region can already give rise to an M-cell independently, another M-cell may develop at the normal site from amidst the residual neural cells that have closed the gap from adjacent levels (Stefanelli, '50). This proves that the factors localizing M-cell development in the hindbrain had already been in operation but were still enough active to turn out a second set; furthermore, that there were still cells in the surrounding brain regions sufficiently labile in character to respond to redirection. These results suggest that the character of cell strains is fixed much earlier than are the numbers, distribution and arrangement of their descendent cells.

Determination in the transverse direction, that is, along the mediolateral axis of the neural plate, is likewise a gradual process. This can be concluded from the fact that at stages at which transverse strips of neural plate manifest definite "self-differentiation" of regional character after displacement, they still are capable of extensive regulation in the lateral direction (Roach, '45). However, at the stage of the closure of the neural folds, some further mosaic subdivision has also developed in the mesiolateral direction (which after folding appears as ventrodorsal direction); for in birds, localized defects placed in the neural epithelium at that stage result in cords in which the whole radial sector that would normally arise from and cover the destroyed patch is completely missing (E. Wenger, '50).

It is to be noted that these results prove only the loss of capacity for regulative redistribution of tasks within the residual fragment of nervous system itself; no regeneration of the missing sectors had been initiated. If regeneration, i.e., mobilization of new cell material to replace missing parts, can be activated, as has been possible in amphibians, the regulative faculty extends into considerably later stages; again, it is far wider in the lateral than in the longitudinal direction. After the excision of a lateral half of presumptive midbrain, medulla or spinal cord segments from the neural tube, increased proliferation and migration of cell masses across the midline from the residual intact half restore the missing portion with remarkable morphological and, in earlier stages, also histological, perfection (Detwiler, '44, '46b, '47b; Harrison, '47; Holtzer, '51).

A comparative view of all these results

leads us to distinguish rather sharply between determination of individual cell fate, strictly cell-wise, on the one hand, and "determination" of a cell complex, on the other, the latter connoting the imparting of some frame of conditions to the cell group which only in further consequence would gradually fix the characters of the individual component cells. In the case of the CNS, this presents us with the alternative that either (a) the diverse cell types of the later mantle are already preformed as such in a corresponding variety of precursor cells in the neural epithelium, or (b) the cells of the neural epithelium are still equipotential and acquire their differential type characteristics only through local influences of the different mantle portions in which they come to lie.

There is not enough evidence on hand to decide this alternative crucially one way or the other. Except for some indirect morphological and pathological indications (Globus and Kuhlenbeck, '44), it has not even been definitely settled whether the dichotomy between glia (spongioblasts) and nerve cells (neuroblasts) is already effected in the germinal epithelium or whether both are derived from common stem cells. In the case of Mauthner's cell described above one could assume, according to (a), that during neurulation a particular cell of the plate is endowed with the ability either to turn into an M-cell itself or to undergo an orderly sequence of unequal divisions eventuating in the segregation of one of the descendents as an M-cell. A model for such a process is known, for instance, in the production of the mother cells of scales in certain insects (Henke, '53). The occasional occurrence of twin M-cells in haploid embryos (Fankhauser, '52) could be taken as a sign of the disturbance of the regular cell lineage because of the undersized mass of the haploid cells. According to (b), one would assume that a particular cell block in the presumptive hindbrain would be endowed with "inductive" activities that would reach a rather sharp peak at a given focus, and that the cell that happened to be thus pin-pointed would thereby be singled out to grow up into an M-cell.

There is some suggestive, but meager, evidence pointing to early cell type divergence according to (a). In the experiments on the repair of excised halves of spinal cord from cell sources of the opposite half (see above, this page), it was noted that when the operation was performed in successively older embryos, definite cell types would begin to be missing in otherwise morphologically well restituted halves, with the large motor cells dropping out first, commissural neurons next and general internuncials last (Holtzer, '51). This indicates that the regenerated cell types stem each from the homologous cell type of the intact half; that the various types lose their mobility or become otherwise unavailable as sources of replacement, one by one, in the observed time sequence; and that the descendent cells of different strains can no longer substitute for one another.

If this be the case, the term "indifferent," commonly given to cells of no particular morphological distinctiveness, is misleading. Actually, these cells would constitute a heterogeneous population, each with definite differential type characteristics, which may or may never come to the fully mature expression amenable to morphological classification; they would not be a common pool of truly equivalent elements, which could still be switched into the various types of specific neurons by determinative local influences. It is by no means unlikely that eventually both assumptions (a) and (b) will turn out to be partly correct in the sense that some distinctive type specificity is already inherent in the cells leaving the germinal layer for the mantle, but that additional diversity is imposed upon them by conditions along their path and at their final locations.

The appearance of qualitative diversity among sensory neurons has also been demonstrated for the spinal ganglia. Aside from indirect deductions from the fact of selective fasciculation (see above, p. 366), tangible microscopic, topographical and behavioral differences between cell groups subserving different functions have been revealed under the microscope (Levi-Montalcini and Levi, '43); as will be shown below, they likewise represent qualitatively different segments of a heterogeneous neuron population.

In conclusion, there is ample evidence for the early emergence in the CNS of qualitatively diverse cell strains, the number of recognized varieties being severely limited by the inadequacy of our means of discrimination; there is some evidence that the diversity of strains can at least partly be projected right back to a corresponding diversity within their production source, the neural epithelium; and that this mode of development of qualitative regional diversity leaves an adequate margin for quantitative adjustments of numbers within each type—the adjustments which will form the subject of the following pages.

PERIPHERAL EFFECTS ON CENTRAL DEVELOPMENT

Historical Remarks. A quantitative correspondence between nerve centers and their peripheral area of innervation has long been inferred from comparative and pathological studies. Congenital absence of an extremity, for instance, was found to be reflected in unilateral underdevelopment of the corresponding spinal segments (e.g., Edinger, '21). However, whether the missing parts had failed to develop from the start or had been formed but secondarily degenerated from lack of peripheral outlets could not be decided by such static observations. The first attempt to reproduce the results experimentally by removing limb buds in chick embryos (Shorey, '09) led essentially to a confirmation of the fact that centers faced with a reduced periphery became (or remained) undersized; they also proved that the relation was a causal one, without, however, elucidating its nature. In further corroboration, removal of an eye in early amphibian larvae was found to entail reduced size of the optic centers in the corresponding (i.e., contralateral) midbrain hemisphere (Steinitz, '06; Dürken, '13). Yet, not until these defect experiments were supplemented by overloading experiments could the actively stimulating nature of the peripheral influence be regarded as firmly established. The first well attested case was the excessive development of spinal ganglia in trunk segments whose peripheral mass had been increased by the addition of a grafted limb (Detwiler, '20). Continued experimentation in amphibians (chiefly by Detwiler and his school), and later even more penetratingly in birds (by Hamburger and co-workers), has reiterated an old lesson of biological research: a relation that on first acquaintance appears simple and transparent, when subject to more minute analysis more often than not turns out to be much more complex, if not more obscure, than originally suspected. Significant differences were discovered in the response of different species, of spinal ganglia vs. spinal cord, between brain parts, and among different regions of the cord. Meanwhile, other types of peripheral influences upon central development have been discovered, such as the control of neuronal size reported above

(p. 365) and the functional specialization of centers by their end-organs discussed below (p. 384), all of which add to our conviction that the potent role of the periphery is exerted not by a single unitary mechanism, but by a multiplicity of interlocking ones.

In the earlier studies of peripheral rebound on central development, attention was focussed almost solely on the final size (number of cells and total mass) of the affected central part. Depending on whether it was above or below the expected normal size (mostly calculated from the asymmetry between the experimental and opposite control halves of normally symmetrical systems), the difference was described as "hyperplasia" or "hypoplasia," signifying an overproduction or underproduction of cells. However, since final size is determined not only by proliferation rate but also by cell migration, cell growth, cell destruction, etc (see above, p. 375), these terms are apt to be misleading and will not be used in the following discussion (see also Hamburger and Levi-Montalcini, '49). When speaking of "periphery," we shall mean tissues to be innervated, not just any extra-neural environment.

Peripheral Rebound on Primary Neurons. *Ganglia.* No conspicuous excess of brachial over trunk ganglia can be detected after the respective peripheries have been roughly equalized by the suppression of the development of the limb (Detwiler, '24c; Hamburger and Levi-Montalcini, '49). The intrinsic development in the absence of a limb may therefore be taken as the baseline over which effects of peripheral increase build up. Suppression of trunk muscles by myotomectomy results in still smaller ganglia (Detwiler, '27), but in view of the relative uniformity of myotomes in the normal animal, this fact can have no influence on the shape of our "baseline." When a single limb develops (i.e., in the normal case) there results then a rise of this base value to the (normal) magnitude typical of intact limb levels. Adding a limb to a trunk segment raises the base value of the latter so that the spinal ganglia turn out larger than those of normal trunk segments (Detwiler, '20; Hamburger, '39b). In amphibians, the effect can be obtained throughout the larval stages until after metamorphosis (Carpenter, '32, '33). Cranial ganglia likewise enlarge when they are made to innervate a supernumerary organ grafted to the head (Detwiler, '30b). These increases are only partly due to increased proliferation; for the most part they result from the fact that more of the "indifferent" neuroblasts (see above, p. 380) in the ganglion are caused to mature into large typical dorsal root neurons (Hamburger and Levi-Montalcini, '49), which thus add not only to the tally of identifiable sensory cells, but being larger, also to the mass of the ganglion. Besides, there occurs normally in various ganglia a certain amount of cell degeneration, which in the presence of a larger periphery, e.g., a limb, is held in check (Hamburger and Levi-Montalcini, '49). Thus, the final count of cells is regulated through at least three devices: proliferation, maturation and elimination.

Whether the effect is of a generalized kind, involving all neurons of the overloaded region, or a selective response of specifically matching types is still an open question. That there is some selectivity is definitely indicated by the ganglionic response to tumor transplantation. Ganglia at the level of a transplanted mouse sarcoma (in chick embryos) show the typical increase commonly observed under conditions of peripheral overload (Bueker, '48). The effect is selective in that it exempts the motoneurons of the cord, remains confined to the mediodorsal neurons in the spinal ganglia, and reaches its greatest intensity in the purely sympathetic para- and prevertebral ganglia (Levi-Montalcini and Hamburger, '51, '53).

This whole problem has recently been complicated by the discovery that the sympathetic ganglia of the chick embryo develop excessively even when the inducing sarcoma graft has been placed on the allantoic membrane, beyond the reach of actual fiber connections, evidently exerting its effect by some humoral agent (Levi-Montalcini, '52; Levi-Montalcini and Hamburger, '53). One could tentatively assume that the primary effect of the tumor agent consists of a general unstabilization of cell surfaces. The nerve cell bodies would thereby be enabled to issue more sprouts, and the nerve fibers more branches (see above, p. 361); this effect has actually been observed in tissue culture (Levi-Montalcini et al., '54). The visceral organs, on the other hand, would lose their surface protection against fiber invasion and could absorb the outgrowing branches (see p. 370). But the relation, if any, between these events and the ganglionic hyperplasia is by no means clear, and the factual analysis will have to be driven much further before any definitive explanation can be adopted.

Spinal Cord. As in the spinal ganglia, the

peripheral rebound on the development of the spinal cord is superimposed upon an intrinsic pattern of regional differences (see p. 374), which may again serve as "baseline." Even without limbs, this baseline is higher in limb segments than in cervical and thoracic segments (Bueker, '43; Hamburger, '46). As for its potential alteration by changes in peripheral area, the results seemed at first to vary according to species. In urodeles, the presence of a limb caused no increase in the number of cells in the "motor" half of the respective cord region (Detwiler, '24c), although in accordance with the conclusions reported under *Factors Controlling Neuron Growth*, p. 365, the individual neurons, hence the cross sections of the motor roots, were larger (Detwiler and Lewis, '25). In anurans (May, '33) and birds (Hamburger, '34), on the other hand, the presence of a limb entailed a considerable enlargement of the "motor" cell columns of the cord. This apparent discrepancy turned out to be one of terminology. Whereas in the latter group the large cell bodies of motoneurons are compactly assembled in separate cell columns ("motor horns") and therefore can be tallied separately, in urodeles they lie intermingled with other cell types so that for practical reasons the total number of cells in the ventral half of the cord was counted as "motor." Subsequent cell counts in the chick (Hamburger and Keefe, '44) showed that in this form likewise the total cell numbers in the ventral cord were not appreciably different whether or not a limb was there, but that in the presence of one, the ratio of "indifferent" to fully matured motor horn cells was shifted in favor of the latter, and only the latter had been counted in the earlier studies.

It is clear from these facts that one of the effects of the actual presence of a limb in the limb segments is a recruitment process by which neuroblasts that would otherwise have remained less distinctive are induced to mature into large motoneurons. However, this is only part of the story. First, there seems to be also a certain, though minor, stimulation of (mitotic) cell proliferation (Hamburger and Keefe, '44); why this does not lead to an increased cell number in cases with overloaded peripheries has not been resolved. Second, the ways in which the "baseline" values are attained in different regions vary markedly and the ways of the peripheral influences vary accordingly. As outlined before (p. 378), in the chick the various levels of the spinal cord, initially of comparable cell content, gradually assume unequal sizes owing to increased cell degeneration in the cervical region, increased maturation of ventral horn cells in the brachial region, and characteristic migrations of the cell bodies (or just the nuclei?) of preganglionic sympathetic and parasympathetic neurons in the thoracic and sacral regions, respectively (Levi-Montalcini, '50) (see Fig. 141). A limb added to any of these regions will then cause segmental enlargement by either reducing degeneration, or promoting maturation, or checking emigration, respectively.

This diversity of ways in which the final cell tally can be altered complicates the search for the underlying mechanisms and raises doubts in the assumption of a single common mechanism. As in the case of the spinal ganglia, one could maintain that it takes a primary connection between a center and its peripheral district by some pioneering fibers in order to furnish that center with an estimate of its peripheral domain. But how does the pioneering neuron convey its information to others still in immature state? We have already commented on those changes in metabolic activity and other properties of a successfully connected neuron that express themselves in its size (p. 365) and fasciculation (p. 366). One need only assume that certain effects of these changes spread to neighboring cells (Hamburger, '39b; Hamburger and Keefe, '44). Observations in sheep embryos, showing coincidence between the arrival of motoneurons at the periphery and the development of their dendritic fields, have led to the contention that spreading dendrites might be the transmitters of the inducing stimulus (Barron, '43, '46). But this explains little. For one thing, it could not apply to spinal ganglion cells, which lack dendritic interconnections, and moreover, the unknown influence becomes no better known by being transferred from the perikaryon to the dendrites.

The numerical increase of peripherally overloaded centers is limited by the output capacity of the respective centers. Thus, whereas the addition of a limb produces a marked increase over the limbless state, the further addition of one, two or even three extra limbs to the plexus fails to produce an appreciable further augmentation (Verzár and Weiss, '30; Weiss, '37a; Bueker, '45). It is perhaps for this reason that large limbs transplanted orthotopically to a small body fail to evoke a corresponding cellular increase in the spinal limb centers (Schwind, '31; Harrison, '35a). On the other hand, genetically hyperdactylous mice have been reported to have larger limb cord segments (Tsang, '39; Baumann and Landauer, '43). Whether this increase of central cell number as a result of the presence of extra toes is as limited as that observed in urodeles or whether the limb centers of rodents have perhaps retained a higher output capacity from their phylogenetic past, when they possessed more toes, is an open question.

Rebound on Secondary Units. Modifications of the size of spinal ganglia due to alterations of the periphery are also reflected in corresponding variations of the sensory columns of the spinal cord with which the former connect (Hamburger, '34; Barron, '45). This demonstrates the existence of transneuronal effects "in series" similar to the transneuronal effects "in parallel" just discussed. Instead of a non-neural periphery affecting its correlated neurons, one neuronal group now influences the quantitative development of another to which it bears an effector relation. No numerical increase of the internuncial cells discharging into the motor columns has as yet been seen to follow an induced increase of the latter, although the reverse, secondary degeneration of more proximal neurons in consequence of destruction of central fiber tracts, has been observed (see Bodian, '42).

Results comparable to those in the spinal segments have also been obtained with cranial nerves. Elimination of the labyrinth including the acoustic ganglion entails underdevelopment of some associated cell groups of the medulla (Levi-Montalcini, '49). After the early removal of one eye in larval amphibians, the midbrain roof of the opposite side, end station of the crossed optic nerve fibers, develops defectively. Its size remains subnormal (Steinitz, '06; Dürken, '13; Larsell, '31), mitotic activity being reduced and the segregation of typical cell strata being impaired (Kollros, '53). As in the spinal centers, the effect is complex in nature, involving proliferation, migration and cell enlargement, although in the present case it is transmitted not directly but through intermediary neurons.

It is not surprising to find that the morphological underdevelopment of an eyeless midbrain hemisphere is reflected in a deficit of its chemical products. Thus, the activity of acetylcholinesterase, an obligatory constituent of neural tissue, is reduced in proportion to the reduced number of nerve cells (Boell and Shen, '51).

Midbrain centers connected with eyes of subnormal size (transplantation from small to large animals) are intermediate between those of normal and anophthalmic specimens (Twitty, '32). Genetically determined reduction or suppression of eye development (microphthalmia, anophthalmia) has the same effect on the size of the optic brain centers as has the corresponding experimental interference (Chase, '45). It is noteworthy that in insects, too, eye reduction, either experimentally produced (Kopeć, '22) or genetically caused (Power, '43), is correlated with reduction of optic ganglia. Cephalopods react similarly (Ranzi, '28).

An artificial increase in the volume of optic nerve fibers reaching the brain yields the expected central enlargement. This has been obtained in the midbrain after replacement of the normal eye by one of excessive size (Harrison, '29; Twitty, '32), or after adding a supernumerary eye (Pasquini, '27); and in the medulla, in response to the entry of an aberrant optic nerve from an eye grafted in the place of an ear (May and Detwiler, '25).

In conclusion, there is widespread evidence of quantitative regulation of the maturation of nerve centers from both the effector and receptor ends. Although the modes of action may differ, the principle is the same whether the "receptors" and "effectors" concerned are sensory organs and muscles or other neuron groups. Presumably some of the intracentral regulations outlined below (p. 386) are manifestations of this same principle. Its operation provides the nerve centers with the necessary latitude of adjustment to insure adequate central control despite the wide individual variability and unpredictability of the detailed patterns of innervation illustrated throughout this article. It is important, however, to remember that the degree of adaptive latitude is limited by intrinsic properties of the responding centers which date back to their earlier prefunctional and even preneural stages.

Specific Modulation and Resonance. The peripheral encroachment upon central development reaches its climax of refinement in the process of qualitative adaptation ("modulation") of neurons in conformance with the type of effector or receptor organ with which they connect. Let us explain this phenomenon in the case of muscle innervation where it was first discovered (Weiss, '24).

In discussing nerve outgrowth, we have referred to several provisions for the over-all guidance of masses of motoneurons to muscle masses as their appropriate destinations (selective contact guidance, selective fasciculation, etc.), as well as for the preclusion of peripheral connections with inappropriate kinds of tissues. It must be remembered, however, that orderly motor function presupposes that the whole muscle mass of a region be not thrown into contraction indiscriminately or all at once, but that at any one moment, only definite selections of individual muscles be made to contract in combinations yielding a "coordinated" movement. Physiological concepts of coordination are still rather controversial but they all agree on one point, namely, that the coordination of muscle contraction is the result of the selective excitation of the motor ganglion cells connected with the muscle fibers to be actuated. Thus, in order to effect an orderly movement, the motor centers must "know" precisely which ganglion cells are hitched to what muscles.

Theoretically, the way in which this knowledge is acquired could be conceived of about as follows: Either (a) there is a predestined motor cell group for each individual muscle and some detailed mechanism exists by which the axons of that cell group are routed precisely to the matching muscle to the exclusion of all other muscles, so that the pattern of connections would be stereotyped for all individuals; or (b) lacking such stereotyped connections, the centers would "learn" about their specific relations to the periphery by "trial-and-error," actuating muscles at first in random combinations and then fixing somehow those central linkages that had incidentally yielded useful movements. Most past and current thinking about coordination implies either one or the other of these assumptions. Yet, both are contradicted by the facts. As for (a), predestination of motor fibers for particular muscles (rather than just muscles in general) is ruled out not only by the normal variability in plexus formation, but above all by the experimental proof that any motor fiber will innervate equally readily any individual muscle (see above, p. 363) and that, as will be described presently, coordinated function can be obtained even after deliberate randomization of the peripheral pathways. And as regards (b), not only has the "trial-and-error" period supposed to produce basic coordination by gradual learning never been

observed (see later, p. 391), but, as we shall show below, the very crux of this thesis, that the degree of utility to the individual of an achieved movement is at all critical for the development of coordination, has been experimentally invalidated. Neither alternative being tenable, the solution came from a third and unexpected direction.

In condensed version, it is as follows: (1) Each individual muscle has some constitutional specificity by which it is distinguished (presumably in its finer protoplasmic chemistry) from all other muscles (except homologous ones); (2) it imparts its specificity to the motor nerve fiber to which it has become attached, and through the axon, to the ganglion cell; this progressive specification of motoneurons by, and in conformance with, their individual terminations has been termed "nerve modulation." It is through this direct epigenetic backward projection of the mosaic of muscular specificities upon the population of motor ganglion cells that the centers are informed as to just where their communication lines terminate. For fuller information, the reader may be referred to earlier reviews (Weiss, '36, '50b, '52a). Only the basic experiment will be briefly summarized here.

When a limb muscle of a larval amphibian is transplanted near a normal limb and provided with innervation from a nerve branch diverted from the normal limb plexus—any limb nerve branch—the transplanted muscle is always found to contract simultaneously with the muscle of the same name in the normal limb (principle of "myotypic" function). With several supernumerary muscles, the rule applies to each of them separately, so that if a whole limb with a full extra set of muscles is added, their total activity duplicates the overt actions of the normal limb; or if transplant and normal limb are of reverse asymmetry, their movements mirror each other (Fig. 142). Thus, ganglion cells of the limb level of the cord that happen to innervate muscles of the same name (i.e., of identical constitutional specificity) become functionally linked, even though the functional effects of supernumerary muscles or limbs are useless, or outright detrimental, to the animals. Since in these experiments the choice of ganglion cells for the test muscle was entirely a matter of chance or assignment by the experimenter, it is evident that the muscle must have conveyed its name to the central cell, and since this happens even in the complete absence of sensory innervation (Weiss, '41a), it must have occurred by way of the motor axon itself.

While the earlier experiments were carried out in functional larval stages, requiring the remodulation of neurons that had already been modulated once before, the results are the same after embryonic transplantations (Detwiler, '25b, '42). On the other hand, modulation has thus far been proven experimentally only in larval amphibians. After

the locality of origin of the transplanted patch, rather than bearing the "local sign" (Miner, '51). Similar results have been described for vestibular neurons (Sperry, '45). The retina likewise consists of a mosaic of sectors of different constitutional specificities which are projected into the optic nerve fibers, thereby enabling the latter to establish selective discharge relations with a corresponding central mosaic of specific receptor units in the midbrain roof (Sperry, '43,

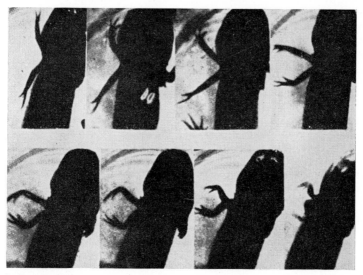

Fig. 142. Myotypic function of supernumerary muscles. A transplanted limb with reversed symmetry (right limb) near a normal left limb mirrors the movements of the latter. (From motion picture, Weiss, '52a.)

metamorphosis, neurons lose their plasticity and retain the specificity acquired previously. Rat nerves transposed to other muscles postnatally likewise failed to undergo remodulation (Sperry, '41). At the same time, there is strong evidence that modulation takes place in prenatal stages in all mammals, including man (Weiss, '35).

Sensory neurons are subject to the same qualitative modulation by their respective end-organs as are motoneurons. Proprioceptive fibers connected with any kind of muscle signal to the cord the correct name of the particular muscle (Verzár and Weiss, '30). Trigeminal neurons of the skin newly made to innervate transplanted cornea thereby acquire corneal character and corresponding reflex relations (Weiss, '42; Kollros, '43b). A transplanted larval skin patch from a foreign sector imparts its foreign specificity to the local cutaneous fibers that innervate it; thereafter when these fibers are stimulated they evoke reflexes characteristic of

'44). In urodele embryos this qualitative mosaic condition is attained about the neurula stage (Stone, '44).

While the rather general validity of the principle of specific neuron modulation by effector and receptor organs seems thus well established, the nature of the processes involved is still undefined. To judge from its slow rate, as well as its qualitative diversity, modulation belongs to quite a different class of processes than nerve conduction. Its specificity sets it apart from more general "trophic" effects. Perhaps it resembles most closely phenomena of induction, infection and immunological sensitization.

Modulation, it must be stressed, clarifies only one aspect of what really is a two-sided phenomenon. By labelling, as it were, the ganglion cells according to their terminations, it produces a qualitative point-for-point replica in the centers of the peripheral receptor and effector units. Possibly the "labelled" neurons can, in turn, transfer their specificities to other, more proximal neurons (Weiss, '41a; Sperry, '51). None of this, however, touches on the problem of coordination and its origin as such; that is, on the mechanisms by which the individual units are actuated in such orderly groupings and sequences that their total effect yields an integrated movement, such as walking, swimming, feeding, etc. As the physiological study of the neural elements has far outdistanced the understanding of their group behavior, we are still without a concept of coordination that could claim cogency or general applicability. This matter would be of no particular concern to us in the present context but for two reasons: first, no consideration of neurogenesis would be complete unless it included some account of the development of the "integrated activity" of behavior; with this we shall deal briefly later. And second, much light can be shed on the nature of coordination from a study of its ontogeny; for this, the experiments just reported offer a relevant example.

The experiments have shown that not only does an extra set of muscles operate in the correct combinations and time sequences required for normal coordination (as expressed by the near-by normal limb), but a single original set of muscles, when scrambled or otherwise abnormally arranged and innervated, also operates in the same stereotyped order; that is, each muscle as an individual contracts at such time and in such strength as would be called for in the particular movement of a normal limb (Weiss, '41a), regardless of the fact that, owing to the anatomical disarrangement, this blind execution of sequences designed for normal arrangement results in a wholly senseless performance. Thus, an amphibian provided with limbs of reverse symmetry (by exchanging right and left limbs) executes all movements in reverse, e.g., walks backwards whenever it is due to advance, and vice versa, all its life (Weiss, '37b). Since this occurs likewise in animals in which the limbs had been reversed as buds and which therefore had never experienced the use of normal limbs, it is plain that the basic coordinating mechanisms, which call the different muscles for a given movement into operation in the proper selection and sequence, are intrinsic and stereotyped products of CNS development and operate blindly regardless of the effectiveness or inefficacy of the resulting movements. These central mechanisms in which the various coordination patterns are preformed might be called,

with a non-committal term, "central action systems." They deal not with the muscles as such, but with the ganglion cells modulated by the latter. Modulation merely sets the muscles into the proper response relations with the central action systems, but it does not govern their construction. Formally, the relation between central action systems and the modulated receptor and effector neurons resembles communication by "resonance."

In conclusion, the response relations within the CNS are now recognized to be ruled by qualitative specificities of great subtlety, far beyond morphological detection, and not simply by geometrical relations of otherwise equivalent units.

DEVELOPMENT OF CENTRAL ACTION SYSTEMS

The realization that in order to call forth, for instance, a coordinated elbow movement, the CNS must have developed the specific means to excite ganglion cells modulated by elbow muscles, presents us with a practical test of the presence or absence of specific action systems in a given central sector: a muscle group transplanted to the sector will not operate unless the center contains the matching set of specific activators. Applying this test, it was found that coordinated limb activities are engendered only within the normal limb segments of the cord (Detwiler and Carpenter, '29). Even a completely isolated brachial cord section can yield coordinated activities in a limb innervated by it, whereas an isolated piece of trunk cord in otherwise identical circumstances cannot (Rogers, '34). The function of limbs innervated by trunk nerves alone remains abortive. Similarly, limbs transplanted to the head and innervated by cranial nerves, while twitching in association with head muscles, never exhibit orderly independent movements (Detwiler, '30b); moreover, such movements as are observed are attributable chiefly to local eye, gill or gular muscles that have attached themselves to the skeleton of the grafted limb, with the limb muscles themselves being essentially uninvolved (Weiss, '36; Piatt, '41). We learn from these results that the regional differences within the cord, some of whose quantitative expressions we have previously encountered (under *Regional and Cytological Differentiation*, p. 376), are really much more profound, pertaining not only to numbers and configurations of cells but to all those other properties on which coordinated function depends. Since the mere attachment of a limb to a foreign spinal or cerebral region does not induce there the differentiation of effective limb control, the experiments also confirm our conclusion that modulation plays no constructive part in the design of central coordination patterns.

The prevalent tendency to base orderly central function on precise patterns of neuronal connections gains little support from the experimental work in embryonic and larval stages. Any sufficiently large fraction of the limb level of the cord contains the full coordinative machinery for a limb; in amphibians one-third of the normal segments is sufficient (Detwiler and Carpenter, '29; Detwiler and McKennon, '30; Weiss, '36). Not only reduction but considerable morphological disarrangement may be inflicted upon the spinal limb centers without abolishing the essentially coordinated development of their typical action systems. For instance, lateral halves of the limb cord restituted after ablation by regeneration from the opposite half (Detwiler, '47b; Holtzer, '51), as well as limb segments grafted in dorso-ventral inversion (Holtzer, '50), still yield the typical limb coordination patterns. Antero-posterior reversal of the early tailbud medulla (Detwiler, '51) or midbrain (Detwiler, '48) likewise fail to impair functional activity appreciably (Detwiler, '52).

The existence of serial functional localization in the spinal cord raises the question of the time sequence and manner of its origin. Is it already inherent in the early neural plate organization, or is it acquired only in the course of subsequent morphogenesis as a result of intracentral segregations and inductive interactions? The appropriate test is the standard one of heterotopic transplantation or isolation. Overt morphological criteria, such as architecture, growth rates, cell numbers, and the like, indicate that some of the regional differences are rather firmly laid down as early as the neural fold stage (see above, p. 376). However, we do not know to what extent these morphological features signify distinctive functional properties. Only a combination of morphological and functional tests can tell. Of the few thus far made, the following are pertinent.

When the prospective limb segments of the cord of a urodele embryo in the neurula stage are replaced by a corresponding length of trunk cord, which would normally have remained smaller and incapable of control-ling a limb, the grafted piece acquires the approximate size, as well as the functional qualifications, of true limb segments (Detwiler, '23). Conversely, prospective limb segments shifted to the trunk region remain undersized and fail to develop the action systems for limb control (Moyer, '43). Since this positional adaptation appears prior to the development of the limb, it must be ascribed to intracentral regulatory interactions, rather than to peripheral influences. If trunk segments are grafted to the brachial region in the later tail-bud stage, however, the adjustment is incomplete and limb function remains defective (Table 6 in Detwiler, '36b). Evidently, the spinal action systems become fixed during that period.

The spinal region anterior to the limb centers, when tested at the comparable stage as before, shows less plasticity and tends to "self-differentiate" in disharmony with its new site (Detwiler, '25a). In its turn, however, it causes certain conforming modifications in the adjacent posterior host segments (judged by their enlargement, as functional tests have not been carried out). This tendency toward self-differentiation followed by some "inductive" influence spreading caudad is even more marked when brain parts are transplanted to more posterior sites, e.g., a supernumerary medulla oblongata in the place of anterior spinal cord (Detwiler, '25c).

It thus appears that functional localization along the spinal axis continues into postneurulation stages, proceeding in anteroposterior sequence. Whether the determination of regional cell number, the "baseline" of our earlier discussion, is effected by a separate agency from that determining functional pattern is uncertain. If it were, some sort of transneuronal stimulation such as that noted above (p. 383) at the junction of optic fibers and midbrain centers might be invoked (Detwiler, '36b; see, however, the objections raised on p. 375 regarding this hypothesis). There are so few facts to go by that speculation has free rein. What is needed is more critical analytical research.

Parenthetically, we may point to the potential usefulness of heteroplastic transplantation in the further exploration of this field. Since exchange of parts between different species is feasible during the younger stages of lower vertebrates, unique test combinations could readily be produced. Exchange of parts of essentially similar function would, of course, be less instructive than exchange of those with regard to which the two species differ crucially. So far, heteroplastic work has dealt largely with the former. The limbs of a given species of salamander are readily controlled by limb spinal cord of another species, no matter whether the strange combination is effected by transplanting the limb to the foreign host (Detwiler, '30a; Twitty and Schwind, '31; Harrison, '35a) or by substituting foreign limb cord segments for those of the host (Wieman, '26; Detwiler, '31); even newt cord can coordinate salamander leg function (Hertwig, '26). But then, activities do not differ markedly between these species. The exchange of limbs between anurans and urodeles should be more rewarding, since the combination is feasible (Guyénot, '27), and one could test whether or not a urodele center can make a frog leg jump. Recent studies on the behavior of animals with hybrid vestibular organs show clearly the great potentialities of such research (Andres, '45).

Taking all these sketchy fragments of information together, the conclusion emerges that spinal cord and brain develop early a gross topographic mosaic of functionally specialized areas, each with specific physico-chemical and structural peculiarities not fully shared by the others, whereas each sector of this mosaic within itself manifests wide powers of regulation and substitution; so much so that any theory of coordination that would rely on a rigidly predetermined order of microconnections among neurons (rather than merely statistical regularities) seems clearly controverted by the facts of experimental embryology. It is highly instructive that these embryological data parallel closely the results of work on functional localization in the cortex, which have likewise revealed macrolocalization of functional districts without microlocalization on the cellular level (Lashley, '42). It is in problems of this kind that embryology, physiology and psychology become confluent so that a conjoint approach promises to lead to much deeper insight than we now possess.* The techniques of experimental morphology, able to manufacture crucial test situations in young animals never attainable in the adult, have hardly yet been called upon to contribute their share to this team-work. Their exploitation seems to hold rich prizes, but space restrictions do not permit us to elaborate the matter in this place.

* See the Survey of Neurobiology; Publication No. 237 by the National Academy of Sciences–National Research Council, Washington, D. C., 1952.

THE HUMORAL MILIEU IN NEURAL DEVELOPMENT

It is beyond the scope of this article to review the specific nutrient requirements of the various components of neurogenesis. As in other organ development, the internal milieu must provide not only all factors requisite for general cell life, growth and differentiation, but must in addition satisfy the more specialized needs of the countless steps of which "the development of the nervous system" is composed. Even in its early formative stage, the CNS is already distinguished from other organ rudiments by its different metabolic requirements (Spratt, '52). Neuropathology, on the other hand, has been able to trace many neural defects of the adult to deficiencies in the availability or utilization of nutrients, thus identifying the role of the latter in neurogenesis. Nerve degeneration in thiamine deficiency (beriberi) is a familiar example. Yet, the still obscure "demyelinization" diseases prove that we do not even yet know the requirements of such a common process as myelin formation. Mental derangements have been related to the lack of certain metabolic enzymes (Hoagland, '47), but the effects of metabolic disturbances on the earlier phases of neural development have not yet been adequately explored. There is need for much more systematic investigation.

The condensed outline of neurogenesis presented in this article ought to have given some idea of the almost endless array of peculiar conditions of chemical and physical nature called for at every turn of this complicated course. To satisfy these ever-changing needs, the milieu presumably undergoes phase-specific changes of composition. In this, non-neural parts or even some other parts of the nervous system may act as providers of the required supplements—in a sense, as sources of specific nutriment. Yet this "symbiotic" interdependence among the tissues is practically unexplored.

It can readily be seen that the role of hormones, the circularized products of endocrine glands, is but a special case in this general category of relations. Just a few cursory remarks can be made here on this topic. For convenience, one may distinguish functional from developmental hormone effects, the former modifying the performance of nervous systems that already possess their full complement of neurons, the latter influencing the growth and differentiation of still incomplete nervous systems; although in view of our concept of the continuous growth of neurons (see p. 364) and the instability of their connections (see p. 363), particularly in the submicroscopic realm, the distinction between the two groups is apt to fade. The former group is best illustrated by the hormonal effects on sexual behavior (see Beach, '47), the latter by the hormone dependence of the transformation of neural structures and functions from the larval to the adult state in metamorphosing species.

thyroxine carrier) near the abducens nucleus, which effects the central linkage (Kollros, '43a). Similarly, the morphological signs of brain metamorphosis, such as increased proliferation, cell increase and histogenetic changes, can be locally evoked (Kollros et al., '50; Weiss and Rossetti, '51). Particularly instructive in the latter sense is the response of Mauthner's neuron, which normally regresses during metamorphosis; if metamorphosis of the hindbrain is enforced by the local application of a thyroxine source, the nerve cell bodies enlarge

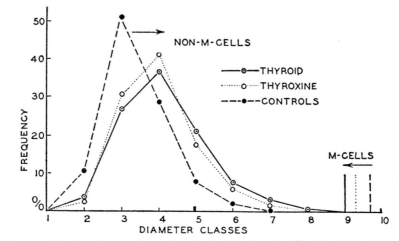

Fig. 143. Metamorphic size changes of opposite sign in Mauthner's cells (M-cells) and their surrounding neuron population (non-M-cells) in urodele larvae with thyroid or thyroxine-agar implants near brain. Histograms of nuclear diameters in 1000 non-M-cells each of control, thyroid and thyroxine cases, as well as mean diameters of M-cells for the corresponding groups of animals. (From Weiss and Rossetti, '51.)

As outlined in Section XII, amphibian metamorphosis is under the direct control of the thyroid hormone; insect metamorphosis similarly depends upon the hormones of certain head glands. The directness of the control is proven by the fact that upon localized topical application of hormone, only the surrounding local region of the tissue undergoes transformation. The same has now been demonstrated for the "adaptive" changes in the nervous control mechanism which must necessarily accompany the other bodily transformations if the metamorphosed animal is to function properly. That these neural changes are likewise under the primary control of the hormone is revealed by the following experiment. The "wink" reflex of the frog, which is normally not executed by the larva although sensory and motor elements are present and individually capable of functioning (Kollros, '42), can be made to mature precociously by the implantation of thyroid gland (or an artificial

markedly (Fig. 143) save for Mauthner's cell, which shrinks (Weiss and Rossetti, '51). This result proves that the various neuron types respond to the hormone each in its own distinctive fashion, determined by preformed metabolic patterns, which further substantiates the qualitative diversity within the neuronal population emphasized throughout our discussion.

Again these experiments are only modest openings into a rich field of future investigation, for in no other event of neurogenesis do we find such a favorable constellation of circumstances as in metamorphosis, where dramatic changes in neural composition, architecture and function, crowded into a relatively brief span of time, supervene in a nervous system that had already attained an advanced state of functional perfection, whose parts are distinct, relatively large and easily accessible to manipulation, and whose transformations can be set off by a controllable agent.

DEVELOPMENT OF BEHAVIOR

No account of neurogenesis can be complete without relating itself to the problems of behavior. After all, behavior is not only another overt sign of the molecular, cytological, morphological and functional organization of the nervous system, but is its dominant manifestation to the accomplishment of which all other features have been made subservient by phylogenetic and ontogenetic adaptation. Unfortunately, space restrictions do not permit me to give the topic its due treatment. However, in order to indicate at least some major aspects, I repeat here, with slight modifications, a summary published on an earlier occasion (Weiss, '50c).

It is a healthy sign that the sharp separation once advocated between a purely phenomenological study of behavior, on the one hand, and the physiological study of its possible neurological foundations, on the other, has not been generally adopted. The pursuit of any one scientific field under an injunction against trespassing into another is neither rational nor productive, especially if both have common objects. It simply is not true that nothing can be learned about the "organism as a whole" by studying its constituent parts and their interrelations. On the other hand, it would, of course, be equally erroneous to assume that mere preoccupation with the elements will tell the full story of their collective behavior. In the light of developments, it would seem unwarranted to subscribe to either a purely holistic or a purely elementarian theory of neural functions and behavior to the exclusion of the other, or to pursue studies on behavior alone or on its neurological foundations alone without the benefits that each field can derive from the advances of the other. Regardless of the pertinence of his detailed propositions, it certainly has been the historical merit of Coghill to have built a strong case for the conjoint attack on the problems of behavior and against the separatist trends of technical disciplines.

The realization that much can be learned about behavior by the study of its development is of relatively recent date. But, as frequently happens in the history of science, the formation of theory outraced the acquisition of factual knowledge, and soon students of the development of behavior were found to be rallied around two opposite doctrines, one stressing the primacy of the holistic, the other the elementarian, viewpoint. Each centered its arguments on cer-

tain objects, observations, and techniques different from those of the other, and evidently each party felt justified in considering its particular niche as a fair sample of the behavioral universe. Thus what in sober evaluation would have become a fruitful stimulus to further clarification of the issues assumed the dogmatic aspect of an irreconcilable antithesis. Again, as often happens in the course of scientific history, the conflict is turning out to be a matter of one-sided viewpoints and undue generalizations rather than of facts. Contrasting views on whether neural functions emerge as mass actions (Coghill, '29; Hooker, '52) or in localized fragments (Windle, '50) can be reconciled if the diversity of sample species and techniques is duly considered and if one refrains from raising observations gathered from a limited field to the dignity of doctrines of universal and unqualified validity.

PHENOMENOLOGY OF THE DEVELOPMENT OF BEHAVIOR

The phenomenology of behavioral development is actually an old discipline. It started with the recognition of the fact that behavior does have a stepwise ontogenetic history, and it went on to describe the steps involved. Only in the second instance did it proceed to test the significance of the steps as instruments or causal links in the development of the whole sequence. However, ever since the demonstration that embryos raised in narcosis would develop behavioral patterns of normal organization (Carmichael, '26; Matthews and Detwiler, '26), even though the overt expression of the whole series of precursor steps had been suppressed, it has been clear that the behavioral steps are merely external manifestations of underlying intrinsic developments rather than practice steps. The complex performances of later stages cannot possibly be founded upon the tested success of their simpler precursors, since they seem none the worse for the omission of the intermediate functional tests due to narcosis. Again, undue generalizations must be avoided, and what is said here for the early and fundamental steps of behavioral development does not apply equally to the terminal phases, in which the inherent developmental patterns are polished and perfected by actual practice and adjustment.

The phenomenological study of the development of behavior has revealed that, like all development, it follows a trend from the general to the specific and from more widespread involvement of elements to more restricted and differential activation. Coghill's principle of "individuation" from a background of mass reaction is based on this realization. It still holds true as designating a trend of events, even if the initial performance under consideration has never been a total activity of the whole body. In some cases and for some functions the primordial activity undoubtedly involves all the neural apparatuses capable of functioning at the same time (Hooker, '52; Barron, '50), while in other cases and for some other functions, it seems equally clear that activity is territorially localized from the beginning (Windle, '50).

To give a clear-cut example of the latter type, we need only refer to the appearance of the lid-closure reflex in amphibians (Kollros, '42, '43b). This reflex appears only at metamorphosis after having been completely absent in the otherwise fully functional larva (p. 389). But from its very onset it constitutes a strictly localized and circumscribed act, which has never been part of a "total pattern" of central functions. Evidently, individuation from mass action does not apply to this type of response, but this, in turn, does not invalidate the principle for other performances. The sobering lesson from all this work has been that we cannot find a key formula for the development of behavior which will save us the trouble of investigating each component of behavioral development in its own right.

THE NEURAL BASIS OF INDIVIDUATION

The development of behavior shows clearly two phases—an early expansive and a later restrictive one (Carmichael, '33). During the expansive phase, wider and wider areas of the body come under neural control. This sequence has been clearly correlated with the gradual expansion of intracentral nerve connections and pathways (Coghill, '29). In a sense this correlation is obvious, as it merely expresses the fact that where there is no neural pathway, there can be no neural function. Reactions during this early phase are remarkably stereotyped, indicating absence of discriminative response mechanisms. However, the more the nervous system approaches structural completion, the more prominent becomes its ability to activate restricted portions and patterns of the exist-

ing network independently in selected and coordinated combinations. It is this restrictive "individuation" for which the proper neural correlate is still to be revealed.

It had been thought that the development of limb innervation in amphibians could serve as an exquisite model of "individuation" in strictly anatomical terms (Coghill, '29; Youngstrom, '40). The limbs move at first only in association with trunk movements, which was explained by the fact that their early innervation consists of collaterals from the motor neurons of trunk muscles. Later "dissociation" from the trunk appeared linked to the development of a secondary separate fiber system from the limb segments of the cord (Youngstrom, '40). Other studies (Taylor, '43), however, suggest that the so-called "primary" associated limb movements are, in reality, passive movements effected through the trunk muscles of the shoulder, while the intrinsic true limb movements do not appear until after the limb muscles have received the independent set of segmental "secondary" neurons. Hence the intrinsic limb function arises as a separate and individualized activity from the very first rather than as an "individuated" offshoot of an earlier mass response. Although some aspects of the situation are still in doubt (Herrick, '48, p. 128), it is quite evident that this singular instance cannot possibly serve as the key model for "individuation" in general, as originally proposed. The neural correlate of individuation thus remains as obscure as ever, nor is it very likely to reveal itself in gross microscopic features. Moreover, the progressive refinement and localization of coordinated function are only in part attributable to improvements in the central action systems, as the progressive muscle-specific modulation of effector neurons (see p. 384), establishing more discriminatory relations with the central action systems, undoubtedly has a share in the process (Weiss, '36; Barron, '50).

CENTRAL ORIGIN OF COORDINATION

Many modern concepts of neurophysiology attempt to derive the properties of the output of the nervous system directly from the pattern of the sensory input. Such a concept is clearly contradicted by the studies on development. The fact that the appearance of motor performance antedates sensory control has often been stressed (see Coghill, '29; Herrick, '48). Even more striking is the evidence of animals in which the development of the sensory nervous system had been experimentally suppressed. The basic patterns of motor coordination in such anesthetic areas develop without major impairment, and limbs lacking sensory innervation from the beginning function coordinately without sensory control having ever had a chance to play a constructive part in the development of the motor patterns (Weiss, '41a; Yntema, '43; Detwiler, '47a). Since neither learning nor patterns of sensory stimuli have any basic part in the development of orderly central functions, we must look to the autonomous processes of central development itself, outlined earlier in this chapter (pp. 376–388), as the main source of coordination patterns. The one fact that has been conclusively established by experimental results is that the central nervous system develops a finite repertory of behavioral performances which are pre-functional in origin and ready to be exhibited as soon as a proper effector apparatus becomes available (Weiss, '41a).

A clear distinction must be made between the mere generation of a central discharge and the pattern of its distribution (coordination). Contrary to a widespread belief, a central discharge does not depend for its generation upon afferent influx but can originate within the centers. Many instances of rhythmic automatisms of nerve centers have been reported (see Bremer, '53) and referred to underlying fluctuations in the metabolic and electric state of the neurons in interaction with the humoral milieu. The observation that any isolated and deranged fragment of medulla or spinal cord will permanently exhibit trains of spontaneous rhythmic discharges (Weiss, '41b) suggests that such activity is a basic property of pools of neurons rather than a specialty of certain centers only. The different rates of "spontaneity" in urodeles with removed or variously exchanged brain parts (Detwiler, '48) may be indicative of differential pacemaker loci in the central generator network.

The sole purpose of these very sketchy comments on behavioral development has been to illustrate the crucial role the methods of experimental embryology and morphology are destined to play in arriving at objective and exact information, and in dispelling misinformation, concerning the principles of behavior.

CONCLUSIONS

The only valid summary of this chapter on neurogenesis is to say that, by the very nature of the developmental process, it does not lend itself to verbal summarization. Any attempt to embrace such intricately complicated events as those dealt with in this chapter in a simple and glibly summarizing formula would end up with either meaningless platitudes or fictitious oversimplica-

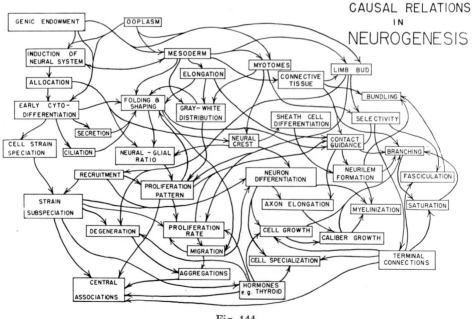

Fig. 144.

tions, undoing all the gains achieved by laborious factual analysis. If it were more generally realized that the subject matter of biology is really more nearly cognate to that of engineering than that of plain physics—that in biology we not only have to establish and reconfirm the validity of general laws and principles, but also have to clarify the complex mechanisms of their operation—then the demand for sweeping generalizations would rapidly subside. The deeper we have penetrated into the analysis of neurogenesis, the more component processes we have been able to identify and single out for methodical analysis. From this analysis, and only after it, have we gained certainty that the component processes are really of many diverse kinds—that the complexity which we encounter is not due to our dearth of knowledge or lack of comprehension but is inherent in our subject, much as it is in a machine. Simplicity, and not complexity, is the illusion.

But faced with this reality, the task of disentangling the complexity and reducing it to an irreducible minimum of elementary events and their interactions becomes all the more challenging. The picture that emerges is a most intricate web of interrelations, each thread definable and either known or amenable to further experimental or conceptual resolution. It seems fitting, therefore, to conclude our discussion with a pictorial representation of this web, constructed according to the analytical results detailed in the text (Fig. 144). The single- and double-headed arrows express causal relations and interrelations, respectively. Most of these can be found documented in our discussion. This diagram, however crude and incomplete, is still the most pertinent summary of neurogenesis that there could be; as such it gives a fair portrayal in miniature of the developmental process in general.

REFERENCES

Abercrombie, M., Johnson, M. L., and Thomas, G. A. 1949 The influence of nerve fibers on Schwann cell migration investigated in tissue culture. Proc. Roy. Soc., B, *136:*448–460.

Aitken, J. T., Sharman, M., and Young, J. Z. 1947 Maturation of regenerating nerve fibers with various peripheral connections. J. Anat., *81:*1–22.

Anderson, J. D. 1951 Galvanotaxis of slime mold. J. Gen. Physiol., *35:*1–16.

Andres, G. 1945 Über die Entwicklung des Anurenlabyrinths in Urodelen (Xenoplastischer Austausch zwischen Bombinator und *Triton alpestris*). Rev. suisse Zool., *52:*400–406.

Anokhin, P. 1935 Reports on the Problem of Center and Periphery in the Physiology of Nervous Activity. State Publishing House, Gorky.

Barron, D. H. 1943 The early development of the motor cells and columns in the spinal cord of the sheep. J. Comp. Neur.. *78:*1–27.

——— 1945 The role of the sensory fibers in the differentiation of the spinal cord in sheep. J. Exp. Zool., *100:*431–443.

——— 1946 Observations on the early differentiation of the motor neuroblasts in the spinal cord of the chick. J. Comp. Neur., *85:*149–169.

——— 1950 Genetic neurology and the behavior problem; in Genetic Neurology, edited by P. Weiss, pp. 223–231. University of Chicago Press, Chicago.

Baumann, L., and Landauer, W. 1943 Polydactyly and anterior horn cells in fowl. J. Comp. Neur., *79:*153–163.

Beach, F. A. 1947 Hormones and mating behavior in vertebrates. Recent Prog. Hormone Res. (Proc. Laurentian Conf.), *1:*27–63.

Bergquist, H., and Källén, B. 1953a On the development of neuromeres to migration areas in the vertebrate cerebral tube. Acta Anat., *18:*65–73.

——— 1953b Studies on the topography of the migration areas in the vertebrate brain. Acta Anat., *17:*353–369.

——— 1954 Notes on the early histogenesis and morphogenesis of the central nervous system in vertebrates. J. Embryol. Exp. Morph., *2:* in press.

Billig, H. E., Harreveld, A. van, and Wiersma, C. A. G. 1946 On re-innervation of paretic muscles by the use of their residual nerve supply. J. Neuropath. & Exp. Neur., *5:*1–23.

Bodian, D. 1942 Cytological aspects of synaptic function. Physiol. Rev., *22:*146–169.

——— 1947 Nucleic acid in nerve-cell regeneration. Symp. Soc. Exp. Biol., *1:*163–178.

Boeke, J. 1917 Studien zur Nervenregeneration II. Die Regeneration nach Vereinigung ungleichartiger Nervenstücke (heterogene Regeneration), und die Funktion der Augenmuskelund Zungennerven. Die allgemeinen Gesetze der Nervenregeneration. Verh. Akad. Wet., Amst., *19:*1–71.

——— 1935 Nervenregeneration; in Bumke-Foerster, Handbuch der Neurologie, vol. 1, pp. 996–1122. Springer, Berlin.

Boell, E. J., and Shen, S. C. 1950 Development of cholinesterase in the central nervous system of *Amblystoma punctatum.* J. Exp. Zool., *113:*583–600.

———, and Shen, S. C. 1951 Appearance and development of cholinesterase in the amphibian midbrain. Science, *114:*477.

Bonnevie, K. 1934 Embryological analysis of gene manifestation in Little and Bagg's abnormal mouse tribe. J. Exp. Zool., *67:*443–520.

Braus, H. 1911 Die Entstehung der Nervenbahnen. Vhdlg. Ges. deutsch. Natf. u. Ärzte, *83:*114–148.

Bremer, F. 1953 Some Problems in Neurophysiology. Athlone Press, London.

Brown, M. G., Hamburger, V., and Schmitt, F. O. 1941 Density studies on amphibian embryos with special reference to the mechanism of organizer action. J. Exp. Zool., 88:353–372.

Bueker, E. D. 1943 Intracentral and peripheral factors in the differentiation of motor neurons in transplanted lumbo-sacral spinal cords of chick embryos. J. Exp. Zool., 93:99–129.

—— 1945 Hyperplastic changes in the nervous system of a frog (Rana) as associated with multiple functional limbs. Anat. Rec., 93:323–331.

—— 1948 Implantation of tumors in the hind limb field of the embryonic chick and the developmental response of the lumbo-sacral nervous system. Anat. Rec., 102:369–390.

Burr, H. S. 1932 An electro-dynamic theory of development suggested by studies of proliferation rates in the brain of Amblystoma. J. Comp. Neur., 56:347–371.

Burt, A. S. 1943a Growth of spinal ganglia in plasma from vitamin B₁ deficient chickens. J. Cell. & Comp. Physiol., 22:205–222.

—— 1943b Neurulation in mechanically and chemically inhibited Amblystoma. Biol. Bull., 85:103–115.

Cajal, S. Ramon y 1928 Degeneration and Regeneration of the Nervous System, translated and edited by Raoul M. May. Oxford University Press, Humphrey Milford, London.

Carmichael, L. 1926 The development of behavior in vertebrates experimentally removed from the influence of external stimulation. Psychol. Rev., 33:51–58.

—— 1933 Original and prenatal growth of behavior; in A Handbook of Child Psychology, 2d ed., edited by C. A. Murchison, pp. 31–159. Clark University Press, Worcester, Massachusetts.

Carpenter, R. L. 1932 Spinal-ganglion responses to the transplantation of differentiated limbs in Amblystoma larvae. J. Exp. Zool., 61:149–173.

—— 1933 Spinal-ganglion responses to the transplantation of limbs after metamorphosis in Amblystoma punctatum. J. Exp. Zool., 64:287–301.

Caspersson, T. O. 1950 Cell Growth and Cell Function. Norton and Company, New York.

Cavanaugh, M. W. 1951 Quantitative effects of the peripheral innervation area on nerves and spinal ganglion cells. J. Comp. Neur., 94:181–220.

Chase, H. B. 1945 Studies on an anophthalmic strain of mice. V. Associated cranial nerves and brain centers. J. Comp. Neur., 83:121–139.

Chiakulas, J. J. 1952 The role of tissue specificity in the healing of epithelial wounds. J. Exp. Zool., 121:383–417.

Clark, W. E. Le G. 1945 Deformation patterns in the cerebral cortex; in Essays on Growth and Form, edited by W. E. Le Gros Clark and P. B. Medawar, pp. 1–22. Clarendon Press, Oxford, England.

Coghill, G. E. 1924 Correlated anatomical and physiological studies of the growth of the nervous system of Amphibia. IV. Rates of proliferation and differentiation in the central nervous system of Amblystoma. J. Comp. Neur., 37:71–120.

—— 1929 Anatomy and the Problem of Behavior. Cambridge University Press, Cambridge, England.

—— 1933 Correlated anatomical and physiological studies of the growth of the nervous system of Amphibia. XI. The proliferation of cells in the spinal cord as a factor in the individuation of reflexes of the hind leg of Amblystoma punctatum, Cope. J. Comp. Neur., 57:327–345.

—— 1936 Correlated anatomical and physiological studies of the growth of the nervous system of Amphibia. XII. Quantitative relations of the spinal cord and ganglia correlated with the development of reflexes of the leg in Amblystoma punctatum, Cope. J. Comp. Neur., 64:135–167.

Dalcq, A. 1947 Recent experimental contributions to brain morphogenesis in amphibians. 6th Growth Symp., pp. 85–119.

Dale, H. 1935 Pharmacology and nerve endings. Proc. Roy. Soc. Med., 28:15–28.

Davenport, H. A., Chor, H., and Dolkart, R. E. 1937 The ratio of myelinated to unmyelinated fibers in regenerated sciatic nerves of Macacus rhesus. J. Comp. Neur., 67:483–491.

Davis, J. O. 1944 Photochemical spectral analysis of neural tube formation. Biol. Bull., 87:73–95.

Detwiler, S. R. 1920 On the hyperplasia of nerve centers resulting from excessive peripheral loading. Proc. Nat. Acad. Sci. (USA), 6:96–101.

—— 1922 Experiments on the transplantation of limbs in Amblystoma. Further observations on peripheral nerve connections. J. Exp. Zool., 35:115–161.

—— 1923 Experiments on the transplantation of the spinal cord in Amblystoma, and their bearing upon the stimuli involved in the differentiation of nerve cells. J. Exp. Zool., 37:339–393.

—— 1924a Further observations on proliferation of nerve cells in grafted units of spinal cord. Anat. Rec. 27:87–94.

—— 1924b Experiments on the transplantation of limbs in Amblystoma. The innervation and function of limbs transplanted after the outgrowth of peripheral nerves. Am. J. Anat., 33:407–419.

—— 1924c The effects of bilateral extirpation of the anterior limb rudiments in Amblystoma embryos. J. Comp. Neur., 37:1–14.

—— 1925a An experimental study of cellular proliferation in the anterior portion of the spinal cord of Amblystoma. J. Exp. Zool., 42:333.

—— 1925b Coordinated movements in supernumerary transplanted limbs. J. Comp. Neur., 38:461–493.

—— 1925c The results of substituting an extraneous medulla for the cephalic end of the embryonic spinal cord in Amblystoma. J. Exp. Zool., 41:293–347.

—— 1927 The effects of extensive muscle loss upon the development of spinal ganglia in Amblystoma. J. Exp. Zool., 48:1–26.

—— 1928 Experiments on the reversal of the anterior end of the spinal cord in Amblystoma embryos. J. Comp. Neur., 45:191–209.

—— 1930a Some observations upon the

growth, innervation and function of heteroplastic limbs. J. Exp. Zool., *57:*183–203.

Detwiler, S. R. 1930b Observations upon the growth, function, and nerve supply of limbs when grafted to the head of salamander embryos. J. Exp. Zool., *55:*319–379.

——— 1931 Heteroplastic transplantations of embryonic spinal-cord segments in Amblystoma. J. Exp. Zool., *60:*141–171.

——— 1933 Further experiments upon the extirpation of Mauthner's neurones in amphibian embryos (*Amblystoma mexicanum*). J. Exp. Zool., *64:*415–431.

——— 1934 An experimental study of spinal nerve segmentation in Amblystoma with reference to the plurisegmental contribution to the brachial plexus. J. Exp. Zool., *67:*395–441.

——— 1935 The development of spinal ganglia following transplantation of the spinal cord with or without somites. Anat. Rec., *61:*441–455.

——— 1936a Growth responses of spinal nerves to grafted brain tissue. J. Exp. Zool., *74:*477–495.

——— 1936b Neuroembryology: An Experimental Study. The Macmillan Co., New York.

——— 1937a Substitution of lateral for axial mesoderm in relation to the development and segmentation of spinal ganglia. J. Exp. Zool., *76:*36–45.

——— 1937b Observations upon the migration of neural crest cells, and upon the development of the spinal ganglia and vertebral arches in Amblystoma. Am. J. Anat., *61:*63–94.

——— 1937c Does the developing medulla influence cellular proliferation within the spinal cord? J. Exp. Zool., *77:*109–122.

——— 1942 Thirteen years of homologous function in normal and supernumerary grafted limbs. Proc. Soc. Exp. Biol. & Med., *51:*176–177.

——— 1943a Unilateral substitution of the brachial region of the spinal cord by the corresponding half of the medulla in Amblystoma. J. Exp. Zool., *92:*247–261.

——— 1943b Reversal of the medulla in Amblystoma embryos. J. Exp. Zool., *94:*169–179.

——— 1944 Restitution of the medulla following unilateral excision in the embryo. J. Exp. Zool,. *96:*129–142.

——— 1945 The results of unilateral and bilateral extirpation of the forebrain of Amblystoma. J. Exp. Zool., *100:*103–117.

——— 1946a Experiments upon the midbrain of Amblystoma embryos. Am. J. Anat., *78:*115–138.

——— 1946b Midbrain regeneration in Amblystoma. Anat. Rec., *94:*229–238.

——— 1947a Further observations on the function and posture of limbs following removal of the trunk neural crest in Amblystoma. J. Exp. Zool., *106:*299–312.

——— 1947b Restitution of the brachial region of the cord following unilateral excision in the embryo. J. Exp. Zool., *104:*53–68.

——— 1948 Further quantitative studies on locomotor capacity of larval Amblystoma following surgical procedures upon the embryonic brain. J. Exp. Zool., *108:*45–74.

——— 1951 Structural and functional adjustments following reversal of the embryonic medulla in Amblystoma. J. Exp. Zool., *116:*431–446.

——— 1952 Further observations on motor responses of Amblystoma larvae following transplantation of primary brain segments. J. Exp. Zool., *119:*189–204.

———, and Carpenter, R. L. 1929 An experimental study of the mechanism of coordinated movements in heterotopic limbs. J. Comp. Neur., *47:*427–447.

———, and Lewis, R. W. 1925 Size changes in primary brachial motor neurons following limb excision in Amblystoma embryos. J. Comp. Neur., *39:*291.

———, and Maclean, B. 1940 Substitution of limbs for brachial somites. J. Exp. Zool., *83:*445–456.

———, and McKennon, G. E. 1930 Further studies upon the nerve supply and function of supernumerary grafted limbs. Biol. Bull., *59:*353–363.

———, and Van Dyke, R. H. 1934 Further observations upon abnormal growth responses of spinal nerves in Amblystoma embryos. J. Exp. Zool., *69:*137–164.

Dogliotti, A. M. 1935 Etudes expérimentales et première application clinique d'une nouvelle opération destinée à augmenter et à équilibrer la fonction neuromusculaire dans la paralysie partielle des nerfs. J. Chir. (Paris), *45:*30–48.

Dürken, B. 1913 Über einseitige Augenexstirpation bei jungen Froschlarven. Zeitschr. wiss. Zool., *105:*192.

Duncan, Donald, and Jarvis, W. H. 1943 Observations on repeated regeneration of the facial nerve in cats. J. Comp. Neur., *79:*315–327.

Dustin, A. P. 1910 Le rôle des tropismes et de l'odogénèse dans la régéneration du système nerveux. Arch. Biol., *25:*269–388.

——— 1917 Les lésions posttraumatiques des nerfs. Contribution à l'histopathologie du système nerveux periphérique chez l'homme. Ambulance de "L'Ocean," Paris, *1:*71–161.

Ebert, J. D. 1950 An analysis of the effects of anti-organ sera on the development, in vitro, of the early chick blastoderm. J. Exp. Zool., *115:*351–378.

Edds, M. V., Jr. 1949 Experiments on partially deneurotized nerves. II. Hypertrophy of residual fibers. J. Exp. Zool., *112:*29–47.

——— 1951 Atrophy of motor root fibers following destruction of sensory roots in the rat. Anat. Rec., *109:*369–370.

——— 1953 Collateral nerve regeneration. Quart. Rev. Biol., *28:*260–276.

Edinger, L. 1921 Einführung in die Lehre vom Bau und den Verrichtungen des Nervensystems, 3d ed., revised by Goldstein and Wallenberg. Vogel, Leipzig.

Elsberg, C. A. 1917 Experiments on motor nerve regeneration and the direct neurotization of paralyzed muscles by their own and by foreign nerves. Science, *45:*318–320.

Erlanger, J., and Gasser, H. S. 1937 Electrical signs of nervous activity. Johnson Foundation

Lectures, University of Pennsylvania Press, Philadelphia.

Fankhauser, G. 1952 Nucleo-cytoplasmic relations in amphibian development. Internat. Rev. Cytology, 1:165–193.

Feeney, J. F., and Watterson, R. L. 1946 The development of the vascular pattern within the walls of the central nervous system of the chick embryo. J. Morph., 78:231–304.

Fernández-Morán, H. 1952 The submicroscopic organization of vertebrate nerve fibers. Exp. Cell Res., 3:282–359.

Ferreira-Berutti, P. 1951 Experimental deflection of the course of the optic nerve in the chick embryo. Proc. Soc. Exp. Biol. & Med., 76:302–303.

Flexner, L. B. 1950 The cytological, biochemical, and physiological differentiation of the neuroblast; in Genetic Neurology, edited by P. Weiss, pp. 194–198. University of Chicago Press, Chicago.

Forssman, J. 1900 Zur Kenntnis des Neurotropismus. Weitere Beiträge. Beitr. path. Anat., 27:407–430.

Fort, W. B. 1940 An experimental study of the factors involved in the establishment of neuromuscular connections. Dissertation, University of Chicago.

Fowler, I. 1953 Responses of the chick neural tube in mechanically produced spina bifida. J. Exp. Zool., 123:115–152.

Geren, B. B., and Raskind, J. 1953 Development of the fine structure of the myelin sheath in sciatic nerves of chick embryos. Proc. Nat. Acad. Sci. (USA), 39:880–884.

Giersberg, H. 1924 Beiträge zur Entwicklungsphysiologie der Amphibien. II. Neurulation bei Rana und Triton. Roux' Arch. Entw.-mech., 103:387–424.

Gillette, R. 1944 Cell number and cell size in the ectoderm during neurulation (Amblystoma maculatum). J. Exp. Zool., 96:201–222.

Glaser, O. C. 1914 On the mechanism of the morphological differentiation in the nervous system. Anat. Rec., 8:525–551.

——— 1916 The theory of autonomous folding in embryogenesis. Science, 44:505–509.

Globus, J. H., and Kuhlenbeck, H. 1944 The subependymal cell plate (matrix) and its relationship to brain tumors of the ependymal type. J. Neuropath. & Exp. Neur., 3:1–35.

Glücksmann, A. 1951 Cell deaths in normal vertebrate ontogeny. Biol. Rev., 26:59–86.

Grossfeld, H. 1934 Zellstreckung und Kohäsionskräfte im gallertigen Wachstumsmedium. Roux' Arch. Entw.-mech., 131:324–332.

Gutmann, E. 1945 The reinnervation of muscle by sensory nerve fibres. J. Anat., 79:1–8.

Gutmann, E., Guttmann, L., Medawar, P. B., and Young, J. Z. 1942 The rate of regeneration of nerve. J. Exp. Biol., 19:14–44.

Guyénot, E. 1927 La perte du pouvoir régénérateur des Anoures, étudiée par la méthode des hétérogreffes. Rev. suisse Zool., 34:1–53.

Hamberger, C.-A., and Hydén, H. 1945 Cytochemical changes in the cochlear ganglion caused by acoustic stimulation and trauma. Acta Oto-laryngol., 61 (suppl.):5–89.

——— 1949 Production of nucleoproteins in the vestibular ganglion. Acta Oto-laryngol., 75:53–81.

Hamburger, V. 1929 Experimentelle Beiträge zur Entwicklungsphysiologie der Nervenbahnen in der Froschextremität. Roux' Arch. Entw.-mech., 119:47–99.

——— 1934 The effects of wing bud extirpation on the development of the central nervous system in chick embryos. J. Exp. Zool., 68:449–494.

——— 1939a The development and innervation of transplanted limb primordia of chick embryos. J. Exp. Zool., 80:347–389.

——— 1939b Motor and sensory hyperplasia following limb-bud transplantations in chick embryos. Physiol. Zool., 12:268–284.

——— 1946 Isolation of the brachial segments of the spinal cord of the chick embryo by means of tantalum foil blocks. J. Exp. Zool., 103:113–142.

——— 1948 The mitotic patterns in the spinal cord of the chick embryo and their relation to histogenetic processes. J. Comp. Neur., 88:221–284.

———, and Keefe, E. L. 1944 The effects of peripheral factors on the proliferation and differentiation in the spinal cord of chick embryos. J. Exp. Zool., 96:223–242.

———, and Levi-Montalcini, R. 1949 Proliferation, differentiation and degeneration in the spinal ganglia of the chick embryo under normal and experimental conditions. J. Exp. Zool., 111:457–502.

———, and Levi-Montalcini, R. 1950 Some aspects of neuroembryology; in Genetic Neurology, edited by P. Weiss, pp. 128–160. University of Chicago Press, Chicago.

Hammond, W. S., and Hinsey, J. C. 1945 The diameters of nerve fibers in normal and regenerating nerves. J. Comp. Neur., 83:79–92.

Harrison, R. G. 1903 Experimentelle Untersuchungen über die Entwicklung der Sinnesorgane der Seitenlinie bei den Amphibien. Arch. f. mikr. Anat. u. Entw.-gesch., 63:35–149.

——— 1907a Observations on the living developing nerve fiber. Anat. Rec., 1:116–118.

——— 1907b Experiments in transplanting limbs and their bearing upon the problems of the development of nerves. J. Exp. Zool., 4:239–281.

——— 1910 The outgrowth of the nerve fiber as a mode of protoplasmic movement. J. Exp. Zool., 9:787–848.

——— 1914 The reaction of embryonic cells to solid structures. J. Exp. Zool., 17:521–544.

——— 1929 Correlation in the development and growth of the eye studied by means of heteroplastic transplantation. Roux' Arch. Entw.-mech., 120:1–55.

——— 1935a Heteroplastic grafting in embryology. Harvey Lectures, 1933–34, p. 116–157.

——— 1935b The Croonian lecture on the origin and development of the nervous system studied by the methods of experimental embryology. Proc. Roy. Soc., London, B, 118:155–196.

Harrison, R. G. 1947 Wound healing and reconstitution of the central nervous system of the amphibian embryo after removal of parts of the neural plate. J. Exp. Zool., *106*:27–84.

Held, Hans 1909 Die Entwicklung des Nervengewebes bei den Wirbeltieren. J. A. Barth, Leipzig.

Henke, K. 1953 Über Zelldifferenzierung im Integument der Insekten und ihre Bedingungen. J. Embryol. exp. Morph., *1*:217–226.

Herrick, C. J. 1948 The Brain of the Tiger Salamander. University of Chicago Press, Chicago.

Hertwig, G. 1926 Die Funktions- und Regenerationsfähigkeit artgleicher und artfremder Extremitätentransplantate. Sitzber. u. Abh. naturf. Ges. Rostock, series III, *1*:62–65.

Hicks, S. P. 1952 Some effects of ionizing radiation and metabolic inhibition on the developing mammalian nervous system. J. Pediat., *40*:489–513.

————— 1953 Developmental malformations produced by radiation. Am. J. Roentgenol., Radium Therapy & Nuclear Med., *69*:272–293.

His, W. 1887 Die Entwicklung der ersten Nervenbahnen beim menschlichen Embryo. Uebersichtliche Darstellung. Arch. Anat. Physiol. (Anat. Abt.), Jg. 1887:368–378.

Hiscoe, H. B. 1947 Distribution of nodes and incisures in normal and regenerated nerve fibers. Anat. Rec., *99*:447–476.

Hoadley, L. 1925 The differentiation of isolated chick primordia in chorio-allantoic grafts. III. On the specificity of nerve processes arising from the mesencephalon in grafts. J. Exp. Zool., *42*:163–182.

Hoagland, H. 1947 Enzyme kinetics and the dynamics of behavior. J. Comp. & Physiol. Psych., *40*:107–127.

Hobson, L. B. 1941 On the ultrastructure of the neural plate and tube of the early chick embryo, with notes on the effects of dehydration. J. Exp. Zool., *88*:107–134.

Hörstadius, S. 1944 Über die Folgen von Chordaexstirpation an späten Gastrulae und Neurulae von *Amblystoma punctatum*. Acta Zool., *25*:75–87.

————— 1950 The Neural Crest. Oxford University Press, Oxford, England.

Hoffman, H. 1950 Local re-innervation in partially denervated muscle: A histophysiological study. Australian J. Exp. Biol. & Med. Sci., *28*:383–397.

————— 1951 Fate of interrupted nerve-fibres regenerating into partially denervated muscles. Australian J. Exp. Biol. & Med. Sci., *29*:211–219.

————— 1952 Acceleration and retardation of the process of axon-sprouting in partially denervated muscles. Australian J. Exp. Biol. & Med. Sci., *30*:541–566.

Holmes, W., and Young, J. Z. 1942 Nerve regeneration after immediate and delayed suture. J. Anat., *77*:63–96.

Holtfreter, J. 1934 Formative Reize in der Embryonalentwicklung der Amphibien dargestellt an Explantationsversuchen. Arch. exp. Zellforsch, *15*:281–301.

————— 1939 Gewebeaffinität, ein Mittel der embryonalen Formbildung. Arch. exp. Zellforsch., *23*:169–209.

————— 1943 Properties and functions of the surface coat in amphibian embryos. J. Exp. Zool., *93*:251–323.

————— 1944 Experimental studies on the development of the pronephros. Rev. Can. de Biol., *3*:220–250.

————— 1946 Structure, motility and locomotion in isolated embryonic amphibian cells. J. Morph., *79*:27–62.

Holtzer, H. 1950 Differentiation of the regional action systems in the urodele spinal cord. Anat. Rec., *108*:127–128.

————— 1951 Reconstitution of the urodele spinal cord following unilateral ablation. I. Chronology of neuron regulation. J. Exp. Zool., *117*:523–558.

————— 1952a An experimental analysis of the development of the spinal column. I. Response of pre-cartilage cells to size variation of the spinal cord. J. Exp. Zool., *121*:121–148.

————— 1952b Reconstitution of the urodele spinal cord following unilateral ablation. II. Regeneration of the longitudinal tracts and ectopic synaptic unions of the Mauthner's fiber. J. Exp. Zool., *119*:263–302.

Hooker, D. 1925 Studies on regeneration in the spinal cord. III. Reestablishment of anatomical and physiological continuity after transection in frog tadpoles. J. Comp. Neur., *38*:315–347.

————— 1930 Studies on regeneration in the spinal cord. IV. Rotation about its longitudinal axis of a portion of the cord in *Amblystoma punctatum* embryos. J. Exp. Zool., *55*:23–38.

————— 1952 The Prenatal Origin of Behavior. University of Kansas Press, Lawrence, Kansas.

Hursh, J. B. 1939 The properties of growing nerve fibers. Am. J. Physiol., *127*:140–153.

Hutchinson, C. 1944 Cell number-volume relationship in the medullary plate of *Amblystoma punctatum*. Anat. Rec., *88*:439.

Hydén, H. 1950 Spectroscopic studies on nerve cells in development, growth, and function; in Genetic Neurology, edited by P. Weiss, pp. 177–193. University of Chicago Press, Chicago.

Julius, H. W. 1930 Nervenreaktionen in der Mäusehaut bei Teerpinselungen und anderen chronischen Schädigungen. Virchows Arch. f. path. Anat., *278*:518–528.

Källén, B. 1951 On the ontogeny of the reptilian forebrain. Nuclear structures and ventricular sulci. J. Comp. Neur., *95*:307–348.

Kappers, C. U. A. 1917 Further contributions on neurobiotaxis. IX. An attempt to compare the phenomena of neurobiotaxis with other phenomena of taxis and tropism. J. Comp. Neur., *27*:261–298.

Kitchin, I. C. 1949 The effects of notochordectomy in *Amblystoma mexicanum*. J. Exp. Zool., *112*:393–416.

Kölliker, A. 1896 Handbuch der Gewebelehre des Menschen. II. Nervensystem. Engelmann, Leipzig.

Kollros, J. J. 1942 Experimental studies on the development of the corneal reflex in Amphibia.

I. The onset of the reflex and its relationship to metamorphosis. J. Exp. Zool., 89:37–67.

Kollros, J. J. 1943a Experimental studies on the development of the corneal reflex in Amphibia. II. Localized maturation of the reflex mechanism effected by thyroxin-agar implants into the hindbrain. Physiol. Zool., 16:269–279.

——— 1943b Experimental studies on the development of the corneal reflex in Amphibia. III. The influence of the periphery upon the reflex center. J. Exp. Zool., 92:121–142.

——— 1953 The development of the optic lobes in the frog. I. The effects of unilateral enucleation in embryonic stages. J. Exp. Zool., 123:153–188.

———, Pepernik, V., Hill, R., and Kaltenbach, J. C. 1950 The growth of mesencephalic V nucleus cells as a metamorphic event in anurans. Anat. Rec., 108:565.

Kopeć, S. 1922 Mutual relationship in the development of the brain and eyes of Lepidoptera. J. Exp. Zool., 36:459–467.

Langley, J. N., and Anderson, H. K. 1904 The union of different kinds of nerve fibers. J. Physiol., 31:365–391.

Larsell, O. 1931 The effect of experimental excision of one eye on the development of the optic lobe and opticus layer in larvae of the tree-toad (*Hyla regilla*). J. Exp. Zool., 58:1–20.

Lashley, K. S. 1942 The problem of cerebral organization in vision. Biol. Symposia, 7:301–322.

Lehman, H. E., and Youngs, L. M. 1952 An analysis of regulation in the amphibian neural crest. J. Exp. Zool., 121:419–447.

Lehmann, F. E. 1927 Further studies on the morphogenetic role of the somites in the development of the nervous system of amphibians. The differentiation and arrangement of the spinal ganglia in *Pleurodeles waltli*. J. Exp. Zool., 49:93–129.

——— 1935 Die Entwicklung von Rückenmark, Spinalganglien und Wirbelanlagen in chordalosen Körperregionen von Tritonlarven. Rev. suisse Zool., 42:405–415.

Leuchtenberger, C., and Schrader, F. 1952 Variation in the amounts of desoxyribose nucleic acid (DNA) in cells of the same tissue and its correlation with secretory function. Proc. Nat. Acad. Sci. (USA), 38:99–105.

Levi, G. 1934 Explantation, besonders die Struktur und die biologischen Eigenschaften der in vitro gezüchteten Zellen und Gewebe. Ergebn. Anat. Entw. Gesch., 31:125–707.

Levi-Montalcini, R. 1945 Corrélations dans le développement des différentes parties du système nerveux. II. Corrélations entre le développement de l'encephale et celui de la moelle épinière dans l'embryon de poulet. Arch. Biol., 56:71–81.

——— 1949 The development of the acoustico-vestibular centers in the chick embryo in the absence of the afferent root fibers and of descending fiber tracts. J. Comp. Neur., 91:209–242.

——— 1950 The origin and development of the visceral system in the spinal cord of the chick embryo. J. Morph., 86:253–284.

——— 1952 Effect of mouse tumor transplanta-

tion on the nervous system. Ann. N. Y. Acad. Sci., 55:330–343.

———, and Hamburger, V. 1951 Selective growth stimulating effects of mouse sarcoma on the sensory and sympathetic nervous system of the chick embryo. J. Exp. Zool., 116:321–362.

———, and Hamburger, V. 1953 A diffusible agent of mouse sarcoma, producing hyperplasia of sympathetic ganglia and hyperneurotization of viscera in the chick embryo. J. Exp. Zool., 123:233–288.

———, and Levi, G. 1943 Recherches quantitatives sur la marche du processus de différenciation des neurones dans les ganglions spinaux de l'embryon de poulet. Arch. Biol., 54:198–206.

———, Meyer, H., and Hamburger, V. 1954 *In vitro* experiments on the effects of mouse sarcomas 180 and 37 on the spinal and sympathetic ganglia of the chick embryo. Cancer Res., 14:49–57.

Lewis, W. H. 1947 Mechanics of invagination. Anat. Rec., 97:139–156.

——— 1950 Motion picture of neurons and neuroglia in tissue culture; in Genetic Neurology, edited by P. Weiss, pp. 53–65. University of Chicago Press, Chicago.

———, and Lewis, M. R. 1912 The cultivation of sympathetic nerves from the intestine of chick embryos in saline solutions. Anat. Rec. 6:7–31.

Little, C. C., and Bagg, H. J. 1924 The occurrence of four inheritable morphological variations in mice and their possible relations to treatment with x-rays. J. Exp. Zool., 41:45–91.

Litwiller, R. 1938a Quantitative studies on nerve regeneration in Amphibia. I. Factors controlling nerve regeneration in adult limbs. J. Comp. Neur., 69:427–447.

——— 1938b Quantitative studies on nerve regeneration in Amphibia. II. Factors controlling nerve regeneration in regenerating limbs. J. Exp. Zool., 79:377–397.

Livingston, W. K. 1943 Pain Mechanisms. The Macmillan Co., New York.

Lovell, H. B. 1931 Innervation and function of grafted hind limbs in *Amblystoma punctatum*. Proc. Soc. Exp. Biol. & Med., 29:180–182.

Maclean, B. L. 1932 Growth responses in caudally grafted brachial segments of the embryonic spinal cord of Amblystoma. J. Exp. Zool., 64:71–108.

Marsh, G., and Beams, H. W. 1946 In vitro control of growing chick nerve fibers by applied electric currents. J. Cell. & Comp. Physiol., 27:139–157.

Matthews, S. A., and Detwiler, S. R. 1926 The reactions of Amblystoma embryos following prolonged treatment with Chloretone. J. Exp. Zool., 45:279–292.

May, R. M. 1933 Réactions neurogéniques de la moelle à la greffe en surnombre, ou à l'ablation d'une ébauche de patte postérieure chez l'embryon de l'anoure, *Discoglossus pictus*, Otth. Biol. Bull., 67:327–349.

———, and Detwiler, S. R. 1925 The relation of transplanted eyes to developing nerve centers. J. Exp. Zool., 43:83–103.

Miner, N. 1951 Cutaneous localization following 180° rotation of skin grafts. Anat. Rec., *109:* 326–327.

Moog, F. 1943 The distribution of phosphatase in the spinal cord of chick embryos of one to eight days incubation. Proc. Nat. Acad. Sci. (USA), *29:* 176–183.

Moyer, E. K. 1943 The innervation of supernumerary limbs by heterotopically grafted brachial cords in *A.punctatum.* J. Exp. Zool., *94:* 97–114.

Muralt, A. v. 1946 Die Signalübermittlung im Nerven. Birkhäuser, Basel.

Nageotte, J. 1922 L'Organisation de la Matière dans ses Rapports avec la Vie. Felix Alcan, Paris.

Nicholas, J. S. 1929 An analysis of the responses of isolated portions of the amphibian nervous system. Roux' Arch. Entw-mech., *118:* 78–120.

———— 1933 The correlation of movement and nerve supply in transplanted limbs of Amblystoma. J. Comp. Neur., *57:*252–283.

Nieuwkoop, P. D. 1952 Activation and organization of the central nervous system in amphibians. J. Exp. Zool., *120:*1–108.

Niu, M. C. 1947 The axial organization of the neural crest, studied with particular reference to its pigmentary component. J. Exp. Zool., *105:*79–114.

Oppenheimer, J. M. 1941 The anatomical relationships of abnormally located Mauthner's cells in Fundulus embryos. J. Comp. Neur., *74:* 131–167.

Ortmann, R. 1951 Über experimentelle Veränderungen der Morphologie des Hypophysenzwischenhirnsystems und die Beziehung der sog. "Gomorisubstanz" zum Adiuretin. Z. Zellforsch., *36:*92–140.

Pasquini, P. 1927 Ricerche di embriologia sperimentale sui trapianti omeoplastici della vesicola ottica primaria in *Pleurodeles waltli.* Boll. dell'-Ist. Zool., Roma, *5:*1–83.

Peterfi, T., and Kapel, O. 1928 Die Wirkung des Anstechens auf das Protoplasma der in vitro gezüchteten Gewebezellen. III. Anstichversuche an den Nervenzellen. Arch. exp. Zellforsch., 5:341–348.

Piatt, J. 1941 Grafting of limbs in place of the eye in Amblystoma. J. Exp. Zool., *86:*77–85.

———— 1942 Transplantation of aneurogenic forelimbs in *Amblystoma punctatum.* J. Exp. Zool., *91:*79–101.

———— 1944 Experiments on the decussation and course of Mauthner's fibers in *Amblystoma punctatum.* J. Comp. Neur., *80:*335–353.

———— 1952 Transplantation of aneurogenic forelimbs in place of the hindlimb in Amblystoma. J. Exp. Zool., *120:*247–285.

Pomerat, C. M. 1951 Pulsatile activity of cells from the human brain in tissue culture. J. Nerv. & Ment. Dis., *114:*430–440.

Power, M. E. 1943 The effect of reduction in numbers of ommatidia upon the brain of *Drosophila melanogaster.* J. Exp. Zool., *94:*33–71.

Ranzi, S. 1928 Correlazioni tra organi di senso e centri nervosi in via di sviluppo. Roux' Arch. Entw.-mech., *114:*364–370.

Roach, F. C. 1945 Differentiation of the central nervous system after axial reversal of the medullary plate of Amblystoma. J. Exp. Zool., *99:*53–75.

Rogers, W. M. 1934 Heterotopic spinal cord grafts in salamander embryos. Proc. Nat. Acad. Sci. (USA), *20:*247–249.

Roux, W. 1895 Beiträge zur Entwicklungsmechanik des Embryo. I; in Roux' gesammelte Abhandlungen über Entwicklungsmechanik der Organismen, vol. 2, pp. 143–255. Engelmann, Leipzig.

Ruud, G. 1929 Heteronom-orthotopische Transplantationen von Extremitätenanlagen bei Axolotlembryonen. Roux' Arch. Entw-mech., *118:* 308–351.

Sanders, F. K., and Young, J. Z. 1944 The role of the peripheral stump in the control of fibre diameter in regenerating nerves. J. Physiol., *103:* 119–136.

———— and Young, J. Z. 1946 The influence of peripheral connexion on the diameter of regenerating nerve fibers. J. Exp. Biol., *22:*203–212.

Sauer, F. C. 1935 The cellular structure of the neural tube. J. Comp. Neur., *63:*13–23.

Sawyer, C. H. 1943 Cholinesterase and the behavior problem in Amblystoma. J. Exp. Zool., *94:* 1–31.

Schwind, J. L. 1931 Heteroplastic experiments on the limb and shoulder girdle of Amblystoma. J. Exp. Zool., *59:*265–295.

Severinghaus, A. E. 1930 Cellular proliferation in heterotopic spinal cord grafts. J. Comp. Neur., *51:*237.

Shorey, M. L. 1909 The effect of the destruction of peripheral areas on the differentiation of the neuroblasts. J. Exp. Zool., *7:*25–63.

Simpson, S. A., and Young, J. Z. 1945 Regeneration of fibre diameter after cross-unions of visceral and somatic nerves. J. Anat., *79:*48–65.

Speidel, C. C. 1932 Studies of living nerves. I. The movements of individual sheath cells and nerve sprouts correlated with the process of myelin-sheath formation in amphibian larvae. J. Exp. Zool., *61:*279–331.

———— 1933 Studies of living nerves. II. Activities of ameboid growth cones, sheath cells, and myelin segments, as revealed by prolonged observation of individual nerve fibers in frog tadpoles. Am. J. Anat., *52:*1–79.

———— 1935 Studies of living nerves. IV. Growth, regeneration, and myelination of peripheral nerves in salamanders. Biol. Bull., *68:* 140–161.

———— 1942 Studies of living nerves. VII. Growth adjustments of cutaneous terminal arborizations. J. Comp. Neur., *76:*57–73.

———— 1948 Correlated studies of sense organs and nerves of the lateral line in living tadpoles. II. Am. J. Anat., *82:*277–320.

———— 1950 Adjustments of peripheral nerve fibers; in Genetic Neurology, edited by P. Weiss, pp. 66–77. University of Chicago Press, Chicago.

Sperry, R. W. 1941 The effect of crossing nerves

to antagonistic muscles in the hind limb of the rat. J. Comp. Neur., 75:1–19.

Sperry, R. W. 1943 Visuomotor coordination in the newt (*Triturus viridescens*) after regeneration of the optic nerve. J. Comp. Neur., 79:33–55.

―――― 1944 Optic nerve regeneration with return of vision in anurans. J. Neurophysiol., 7: 57–70.

―――― 1945 Centripetal regeneration of the 8th cranial nerve root with systematic restoration of vestibular reflexes. Am. J. Physiol., 144:735–741.

―――― 1951 Regulative factors in the orderly growth of neural circuits. Growth Symp., 10:63–87.

Spratt, N. T., Jr. 1952 Metabolism of the early embryo. Ann. N. Y. Acad. Sci., 55:40–49.

Stefanelli, A. 1950 Studies on the development of Mauthner's cell; in Genetic Neurology, edited by P. Weiss, pp. 210–211. University of Chicago Press, Chicago.

Steinitz, E. 1906 Über den Einfluss der Elimination der embryonalen Augenblasen auf die Entwicklung des Gesamtorganismus beim Frosche. Roux' Arch. Entw.-mech., 20:537–578.

Stone, L. S. 1944 Functional polarization in retinal development and its re-establishment in regenerating retinae of rotated grafted eyes. Proc. Soc. Exp. Biol. & Med., 57:13–14.

Stopford, J. S. B. 1930 Sensation and the Sensory Pathway. Longmans, Green & Co., New York.

Sunderland, S., and Lavarack, J. O. 1953 The branching of nerve fibres. Acta Anat., 17:46–61.

Taylor, A. C. 1943 Development of the innervation pattern in the limb bud of the frog. Anat. Rec., 87:379–413.

―――― 1944 Selectivity of nerve fibers from the dorsal and ventral roots in the development of the frog limb. J. Exp. Zool., 96:159–185.

Terni, T. 1920 Sulla correlazione fra ampiezza del territorio di innervazione e grandezza delle cellule ganglionari. II. Arch. ital. di Anat. e di Embryol., 17:235–212.

Thomas, P. K., and Young, J. Z. 1949 Internode lengths in the nerves of fishes. J. Anat., 83:336–350.

Tsang, Y. C. 1939 Ventral horn cells and polydactyly in mice. J. Comp. Neur., 70:1–8.

Twitty, V. C. 1932 Influence of the eye on the growth of its associated structures, studied by means of heteroplastic transplantation. J. Exp. Zool., 61:333–374.

―――― 1949 Developmental analysis of amphibian pigmentation. Growth (suppl.), 9:133–161.

――――, and Schwind, J. L. 1931 The growth of eyes and limbs transplanted heteroplastically between two species of Amblystoma. J. Exp. Zool., 59:61–86.

Verzár, F., and Weiss, P. 1930 Untersuchungen über das Phänomen der identischen Bewegungsfunktion mehrfacher benachbarter Extremitäten. Zugleich: Direkte Vorführung von Eigenreflexen. Pflügers Arch., 223:671–684.

Vizoso, A. D., and Young, J. Z. 1948 Internode length and fibre diameter in developing and regenerating nerves. J. Anat., 82:110–134.

Weddell, G., Guttmann, L., and Gutmann, E. 1941

The local extension of nerve fibers into denervated areas of skin. J. Neurol. Psychiat., 4: 206–225.

Weiss, P. 1924 Die Funktion transplantierter Amphibienextremitäten. Aufstellung einer Resonanztheorie der motorischen Nerventätigkeit auf Grund abgestimmter Endorgane. Roux' Arch. Entw.-mech., 102:635–672.

―――― 1929 Erzwingung elementarer Strukturverschiedenheiten am in vitro wachsenden Gewebe. Die Wirkung mechanischer Spannung auf Richtung und Intensität des Gewebewachstums und ihre Analyse. Roux' Arch. Entw.-mech., 116: 438–554.

―――― 1934a In vitro experiments on the factors determining the course of the outgrowing nerve fiber. J. Exp. Zool., 68:393–448.

―――― 1934b Secretory activity of the inner layer of the embryonic midbrain of the chick, as revealed by tissue culture. Anat. Rec., 58:299–302.

―――― 1935 Homologous (resonance-like) function in supernumerary fingers in a human case. Proc. Soc. Exp. Biol. & Med., 33:426–430.

―――― 1936 Selectivity controlling the central-peripheral relations in the nervous system. Biol. Rev., 11:494–531.

―――― 1937a Further experimental investigations on the phenomenon of homologous response in transplanted amphibian limbs. II. Nerve regeneration and the innervation of transplanted limbs. J. Comp. Neur., 66:481–535.

―――― 1937b Further experimental investigations on the phenomenon of homologous response in transplanted amphibian limbs. IV. Reverse locomotion after the interchange of right and left limbs. J. Comp. Neur., 67:269–315.

―――― 1939 Principles of Development. Henry Holt & Co., New York.

―――― 1941a Self-differentiation of the basic patterns of coordination. Comp. Psychol. Monographs, 17:1–96.

―――― 1941b Further experiments with deplanted and deranged nerve centers in amphibians. Proc. Soc. Exp. Biol. & Med., 46:14–15.

―――― 1941c Nerve patterns: The mechanics of nerve growth. Growth (suppl.), 5:163–203.

―――― 1942 Lid-closure reflex from eyes transplanted to atypical locations in *Triturus torosus*: Evidence of a peripheral origin of sensory specificity. J. Comp. Neur., 77:131–169.

―――― 1944 The technology of nerve regeneration: A review. Sutureless tubulation and related methods of nerve repair. J. Neurosurg., 1:400–450.

―――― 1945 Experiments on cell and axon orientation in vitro: The role of colloidal exudates in tissue organization. J. Exp. Zool., 100:353–386.

―――― 1947 The problem of specificity in growth and development. Yale J. Biol. & Med., 19:235–278.

―――― 1949 Differential growth; in Chemistry and Physiology of Growth, edited by A. K. Parpart, pp. 135–186. Princeton University Press, Princeton, New Jersey.

―――― 1950a The deplantation of fragments of nervous system in amphibians. I. Central reorganization and the formation of nerves. J. Exp. Zool., *113:*397–461.

Weiss, P. 1950b Experimental analysis of co-ordination by the disarrangement of central-peripheral relations. Symposia Soc. Exp. Biol., *4:* 92–111.

———— 1950c Introduction to genetic neurology; in Genetic Neurology, edited by P. Weiss, pp. 1–39. University of Chicago Press, Chicago.

———— 1952a Central versus peripheral factors in the development of coordination. Res. Publ. Ass. Nerv. Ment. Dis., *30:*3–23.

———— 1952b "Attraction fields" between growing tissue cultures. Science, *115:*293–295.

———— 1953 Some introductory remarks on the cellular basis of differentiation. J. Embryol. exp. Morph., *1:*181–211.

————, and Campbell, C. J. 1944 Nerve fiber counts and muscle tension after nerve regeneration in the rat. Am. J. Physiol., *140:*616–626.

————, and Cummings, J. B. 1943 Regeneration of the lateral line nerve of Amblystoma from different nerve fiber sources. Anat. Rec., *87:*119–125.

————, and Edds, Jr. 1945 Sensory-motor nerve crosses in the rat. J. Neurophysiol., *8:*173–193.

————, Edds, M. V., Jr., and Cavanaugh, M. W. 1945 The effect of terminal connections on the caliber of nerve fibers. Anat. Rec., *92:*215–233.

————, and Garber, B. 1952 Shape and movement of mesenchyme cells as functions of the physical structure of the medium. Contributions to a quantitative cell morphology. Proc. Nat. Acad. Sci. (USA) *38:*264–280.

————, and Hiscoe, H. B. 1948 Experiments on the mechanism of nerve growth. J. Exp. Zool., *107:*315–396.

————, and Hoag, A. 1946 Competitive reinnervation of rat muscles by their own and foreign nerves. J. Neurophysiol., *9:*413–418.

————, and Rossetti, F. 1951 Growth responses of opposite sign among different neuron types exposed to thyroid hormone. Proc. Nat. Acad. Sci. (USA) *37:*540–556.

————, and Taylor, A. C. 1943 Histomechanical analysis of nerve reunion in the rat after tubular splicing. Arch. Surg., *47:*419–447.

———— 1944 Further experimental evidence against "neurotropism" in nerve regeneration. J. Exp. Zool., *95:*233–257.

————, and Walker, R. 1934 Nerve pattern in regenerated urodele limbs. Proc. Soc. Exp. Biol. & Med., *31:*810–812.

Wenger, B. S. 1951 Determination of structural patterns in the spinal cord of the chick embryo studied by transplantation between brachial and adjacent levels. J. Exp. Zool., *116:*123–164.

Wenger, E. L. 1950 An experimental analysis of relations between parts of the brachial spinal cord of the embryonic chick. J. Exp. Zool., *114:*51–86.

Whitaker, D. M. 1940 Physical factors of growth. Growth, 2nd Symp. (suppl.), pp. 75–90.

Wieman, H. L. 1926 The effect of heteroplastic grafts of the spinal cord on the development of the limb in Amblystoma. J. Exp. Zool., *45:*335–348.

Wigglesworth, V. B. 1948 The role of the cell in determination; in Growth in Relation to Differentiation and Morphogenesis. Symp. Soc. Exp. Biol., *2:*1–16.

Willier, B. H. 1952 Cells, feathers and colors. Bios, *23:*109–125.

Windle, W. F. 1950 Reflexes of mammalian embryos and fetuses; in Genetic Neurology, edited by P. Weiss, pp. 214–222. University of Chicago Press, Chicago.

Wislocki, G. B., and Singer, M. 1946 The occurrence and function of nerves in the growing antlers of deer. J. Comp. Neur., *85:*1–20.

Wolbach, S. B., and Bessey, O. A. 1942 Tissue changes in vitamin deficiencies. Physiol. Rev., *22:*233–289.

Yntema, C. L. 1943 Deficient efferent innervation of the extremities following removal of neural crest in Amblystoma. J. Exp. Zool., *94:*319–349.

Young, J. Z. 1950 The determination of the specific characteristics of nerve fibers; in Genetic Neurology, edited by P. Weiss, pp. 92–104. University of Chicago Press, Chicago.

Youngstrom, K. A. 1938 On the relationship between choline esterase and the development of behavior in amphibia. J. Neurophysiol., *1:*357–363.

———— 1940 A primary and a secondary somatic motor innervation in Amblystoma. J. Comp. Neur., *73:*139–151.

Zacharias, L. R. 1938 An analysis of cellular proliferation in grafted segments of embryonic spinal cord. J. Exp. Zool., *78:*135–157.

CHAPTER 2

Eye

VICTOR TWITTY

THE EYE has long served as a classic object for the analysis of causal relations in development and regeneration. Composed of structurally discrete parts that are mobilized with precision from diverse sources, the eye immediately challenges the attention of the experimental morphologist and at the same time lends itself almost uniquely to his purposes. By excision, transplantation, and recombination of the eye components, he has exposed many of the influences that integrate the development of these parts and accordingly shape the final form and size of the organ. In the account that follows, sections will be devoted to experiments on (1) the determination of the retinal cup; (2) induction of the lens and cornea; (3) growth of the eye and its associated structures; and (4) regeneration of the eye. Limitations of space preclude extensive coverage of the literature on these subjects, and certain aspects of eye development must be omitted entirely from consideration. For an exhaustive survey of the literature before 1931 the reader is referred to Mangold's monumental review published in that year; other invaluable sources are the books of Spemann ('38) and Needham ('42). In several instances, to shorten the bibliography on the earlier literature, the names of investigators will be cited without specifying publication dates. In all such cases the literature references are available in the reviews of both Mangold and Spemann.

DETERMINATION OF THE RETINA

The first step in the initiation of retinal development, the establishment of paired primordia in the anterior part of the neural plate, has already been treated in the chapter of this book devoted to the organization of the central nervous system. Suffice it to repeat here that this localization proceeds under the influence of the subjacent archenteric roof and, once effected, enables the anlagen

to continue their development into relatively well formed cups when grafted to heterotopic positions. From this it does not follow, however, that the eye begins its development as a mosaic of rigidly prescribed parts. The examples which follow show that the distribution of specific assignments to the constituent cells of the rudiment is referable to morphogenetic influences that continue to operate throughout the period of retina formation.

The ability of retinal and pigmented layers of the optic cup to interchange prospective fates is strongly indicated by the formation of complete eyes by partial rudiments (e.g., following incomplete excision in medullary plate stages), and by the fusion of two optic vesicles to form essentially normal single eyes (Pasquini; Detwiler). Direct and conclusive evidence of this interchangeability has been provided by Dragomirow ('32, '33, '34, '36). Small pieces of prospective pigment epithelium, grafted between lens and cornea, or even to heterotopic positions elsewhere on the head, regulated to form small cups comprised of both sensory and pigmented layers. Even cells already beginning to show pigmentary differentiation were capable of reorganization into sensory tissue. In fact, the ability of pigment epithelium to undergo this transformation persists into adult stages, as will be seen when we come to experiments on the regeneration of the eye. Dragomirow also found that in young optic vesicle stages the prospective sensory layer can give rise to pigment epithelium. The lability of this portion of the vesicle is short lived, however, and by Harrison stage 29 (in *Triturus taeniatus*) it can deliver only retinal tissue.

In the chick, each of the two layers of the optic cup will form both pigmented and nervous tissue when transplanted separately as late as the 36-somite stage (Alexander, '37), and Dorris ('38) has provided confirmation of the regulatory capacity of the two components of the chick optic cup by isolating them in vitro.

Dragomirow, invoking Child's concept of metabolic gradients, believes that the divergent development of the two parts of the vesicle is an expression of simple quantitative differences in physiological activity imposed by environmental influences. He suggests that in normal development it may be contact with the lens or lens ectoderm that initiates the differential in question, a proposal in keeping with the fact that the distal (retinal) wall of the vesicle is the first to become channeled in a fixed course of development. The polarizing action of the lens is not specific in nature, however, since Dragomirow has shown that the epithelium of the ear vesicle may serve in the same capacity. When an eye cup is grafted adjacent to the ear placode, the portion of the pigment layer in contact with the wall of the developing labyrinth is subsequently induced to form a secondary retina. In fact, Ikeda ('37a) reports that the nasal placode, and perhaps other epithelia as well (e.g., peritoneum), are capable of evoking retina formation through contact with the pigment layer of the eye.

Holtfreter ('39) has shown that intimate association with mesenchyme is another condition that must be fulfilled if the eye vesicle is to realize its potentialities for normal organotypic and histotypic differentiation. Eyes evaginating from medullary plates isolated in vitro, under conditions that preclude access to the matrix of mesenchyme that normally surrounds the developing vesicles, attain only the most rudimentary level of organization. His experiments show further that when circumstances permit, the eye vesicle seems actually to "seek" association with mesenchyme, as if in response to a positive physical attraction or affinity between the two. These experiments of Holtfreter serve to expose, perhaps better than any others, the extreme limitations of the eye rudiment as an autonomous developmental unit. These limitations are not fully revealed by ordinary tests, such as heterotopic transplantation, which leave the vesicle in its normal context insofar as association with mesenchyme, epidermis or other epithelia, etc., is concerned. When stripped of these relationships, the anlage appears to be quite incapable of realizing the potentialities assigned to it at the time of its first delineation.

Eakin ('47) has demonstrated that long after the inner layer of the cup becomes channeled as sensory tissue, it remains labile with respect to another fundamental feature of its organization. By reversing surgically the outer and inner faces of the sensory layer, Eakin found that the mediolateral axis of its development does not become fixed until the actual beginning of histological differentiation. Retinae reversed prior to this time develop with sensory and neural layers in proper polar adjustment to the rest of the eye, while those reversed at later stages preserve their original or prospective polar constitution, with rods and cones facing toward the lens. Eakin suggests that physical and perhaps chemical influences exerted by the lens and the pigment epithelium are the possible morphogenetic forces responsible for establishment of polarity within the inner layer of the cup.

Another aspect of retinal determination, the localization of function in the quadrants of the retina, has been studied by Stone ('48) in experiments involving the 180 degree rotation of the optic cup and lens. When this operation is performed prior to the stage when the embryos first become motile, the larvae subsequently show normal motor responses to visual tests. However, rotation at a somewhat later stage, when the beating of the heart first becomes prominent, results in reversed visuo-motor behavior. Efforts to capture moving prey are misdirected, and movements in response to rotating black and white striped drums are the opposite of those shown by normal animals.

The choroid fissure is another feature of retinal topography that is not yet imprinted or localized in beginning stages of eye development. This is shown by the failure of fissures to develop in eyes grafted embryonically to heterotopic positions, and by the "host-wise" formation of the fissure in the normal ventral position after 180 degree rotation of the optic vesicle (Sato, '33a) during early tail-bud stages. The vesicle becomes less adaptive in this respect as development proceeds, but occasionally eyes with normally situated choroid fissures develop following rotation as late as the stage when contractile responses are first exhibited by the embryo. Sato believes that the formation of the fissure at the ventral margin of the cup is determined by the attachment at this point between cup and brain, possibly through exertion of growth-inhibiting influences or even simple mechanical traction by the optic stalk. The results of Sato on the determination of the choroid fissure have been confirmed by Barden ('42,

'43), in connection with his interesting studies on the origin and development of the iris pigment.

INDUCTION OF THE LENS

Although it had been proposed earlier that lens formation is influenced by the developing optic cup, Spemann ('01) was the first to test the issue by direct experiment. First by cautery, and later by surgical excision, he removed the rudiment of the retina in the open medullary plate stage of *Rana fusca*. As a consequence the lens failed to form, and since the results were so unequivocal, it seemed natural at the time to assume that a similar dependency of the lens would be found to obtain universally. However, this conclusion soon proved to be unwarranted. Mencl reported instances of spontaneous lens occurrence in Salmo, and King found that the lens developed in *R. palustris* following experimental removal of the optic cup. Spemann, at first critical of these reports, was nevertheless stimulated to extend his investigations to other forms ('12) and, although he verified completely his original results with *R. fusca*, found that complete removal of the optic rudiment in *R. esculenta* was followed by the development of well formed lenses. In Bombinator, although normal lenses never arose in the absence of the optic cup, there were nevertheless unmistakable indications of incipient lens development.

Along with these early experiments on the ablation of the optic vesicle, the lens-inducing capacity of the vesicle was further tested by replacing the normal lens-forming epidermis with epidermis from other regions and also by introducing the optic vesicle beneath the epidermis in foreign positions on the embryo. The latter procedure was first employed by W. H. Lewis, who found that in numerous cases lenses formed in *R. sylvatica* and *R. palustris* over the transplanted vesicle. He also obtained lenses when epidermis from the trunk was transplanted in substitution of the normal lens-forming epidermis.

Whereas in *R. palustris* and *R. sylvatica* epidermis from any portion of the body was capable of giving rise to a lens, Spemann found that in Bombinator only epidermis from the head region had this capacity, and in *R. esculenta* the lens-forming capacity was restricted to the presumptive lens-forming cells themselves. Spemann called attention to the inverse relationship here revealed between the degree of dependency of the lens upon the optic vesicle and the distribution of lens-forming potency within the epidermis. Thus in *R. palustris*, in which apparently the entire epidermis is capable of forming a lens, the predisposition to do so is at no point strong, whereas in *R. esculenta*, in which the lens-forming potency is limited to the presumptive lens-forming tissue itself, it is—in this circumscribed region—highly developed.* Bombinator occupies an intermediate position, both with respect to the extent of the area (head ectoderm) capable of forming a lens, and in the degree of dependency of the lens ectoderm upon stimulation by the vesicle.

One must of course bear in mind that the distribution of lens-forming competence in the epidermis of these species is largely a function of time, i.e., stage of development. Even in *R. esculenta*, lens competence is presumably widespread in the ectoderm of the young gastrula, while in species like *R. palustris* reactivity eventually narrows to the lens placode itself. In *R. catesbiana*, in which the dependence of the lens is especially pronounced, the competence of trunk ectoderm persists until relatively advanced tail-bud stages (Pasquini, '32). Even after the lens rudiment has been initially determined, or in fact has already begun to show visible thickening, continued association with the optic cup is necessary in order for it to achieve normal structure. If isolated from the cup at these stages by heterotopic transplantation, it gives rise only to abortive lenses. To varying extents, the lens in all other species as well is probably dependent on similar reinforcement for completion of its differentiation and particularly its growth in size (see, for example, LeCron; Woerdeman, '39, '50).

The sharpness of the distinctions between the degree of dependence of the lens upon the vesicle in the species studied by Spemann was questioned by von Ubisch, whose results indicated that external conditions such as temperature influence the percentages of lenses obtained. An even stronger qualification of Spemann's results with *R. esculenta* is provided by the more recent findings of Woerdeman, to be cited shortly. The necessity for caution in drawing conclusions con-

* Although the development of the lens in *R. esculenta* appears to be independent of the optic vesicle, the latter nevertheless possesses the ability to induce a lens. This was shown by Filatow, who found that the optic vesicle of esculenta grafted beneath ventral epidermis of *Bufo vulgaris* was capable of inducing a lens.

cerning the degree of lens dependence in different species is further illustrated by the results of Harrison on *Amblystoma punctatum*. Removal of the retinal rudiment in the medullary plate stage or of the vesicle shortly after closure of the neural folds results in failure of lens development. Surprisingly, however, the presumptive lens ectoderm will differentiate into a lens when grafted to other regions of the head, provided the transplantation is made after closure of the medullary folds. From this difference in results with a single species "it is apparent that . . . secondary circumstances of some unknown character may dominate more fundamental ones and thus lead to mistaken conclusions" (Harrison, '20).

In spite of these seemingly conflicting results, however, the development of the lens continues to provide one of the clearest and most classic examples of dependent differentiation. In most species the optic vesicle appears to be the agent primarily responsible for initiating its development, but even in forms such as *R. esculenta,* where this generalization has not seemed to apply, recent work has shown there is no basis for assuming that the lens is capable of developing independently of inductive influences. Perri ('34) has shown that presumptive lens epidermis of *R. esculenta* will not yield lenses when isolated in vitro. Mangold ('31) called attention to the possibility that the roof of the archenteron, which ordinarily evokes lens formation only indirectly, through prior induction of the retina, may instead act directly upon the lens epidermis in such species as *R. esculenta* (see also Needham, '42, p. 294). New and strongly suggestive clues are provided by the recent work of Liedke ('51) on *A. punctatum*. In this form, in which the optic vesicle is clearly involved in lens induction, Liedke has shown that the head mesoderm must first prepare or activate the lens epidermis during neurula stages before it becomes competent to respond to the retinal stimulus. There is a close parallel in the development of the ear (Harrison, '45; Yntema, '50), where both mesodermal and neural tissues participate in labyrinth induction. The results of Ten Cate as reported by Woerdeman ('50) also help resolve the seeming paradox presented by such forms as *R. esculenta*. Woerdeman had earlier ('39) been unable to confirm Spemann's results on independent lens formation in *R. esculenta*, and proposed that this might be attributable to the difference in temperature

at which he and Spemann commonly maintained their embryonic material prior to experimentation. At Woerdeman's instigation Ten Cate compared the effects of retinal ablation at the neurula stage on embryos previously reared at 10° C. and at 25° C. In the latter series lens formation was very rare, while in the cold-treated group lenses of varying perfection developed in almost all cases. In an independent study, Ten Cate showed that the progress of respiratory and related physiological changes during amphibian development is less retarded by low temperature than is the pace of morphological differentiation; from this it may be presumed to follow that at a given stage of development the tissues (e.g., the epidermis) of a cold-treated embryo will have attained a more advanced level of intrinsic chemical differentiation or maturation than those of an embryo reared at ordinary laboratory temperatures. Ten Cate found that this dissociability of morphological and physiological differentiation at low temperatures is particularly marked in *R. esculenta*. These considerations, together with the striking effects of temperature on lens dependence, and also the finding of Liedke concerning the role of head mesoderm, seem to point to the following picture of lens induction in Amphibia: Probably in all species lens formation is ordinarily elicited by the action of at least two supplementary or mutually reinforcing inductors,* the head mesoderm and the retinal rudiment. Under average environmental circumstances and in most species the component events of development are geared with one another in such manner that the epidermis is insufficiently differentiated at the neurula stage to be fully receptive to the action of the head mesoderm, and requires a subsequent and final impetus from the optic vesicle. At low temperatures, however, and especially in species like *R. esculenta* in which such treatment causes morphological development to lag substantially behind chemical differentiation, the lens epidermis has already become sufficiently mature and responsive at neurulation to require no further incitement beyond that provided by the head mesoderm.

Dependent development of the lens has also been clearly established for the chick. Lens formation fails when contact with the optic vesicle is blocked, and transplanted

* Indications have been encountered that other neighboring elements, notably the nasal placode, may be capable of eliciting lens formation (e.g., Holtfreter, '35; Ikeda, '38).

or explanted vesicles will induce lenses from foreign epidermis (Alexander, '37; van Deth, '40; McKeehan, '51). In other groups of vertebrates the evidence is mostly fragmentary or indirect (see Mangold, '31).

The results of efforts to ascertain the nature of the lens-inducing stimulus are of uncertain implication, and can be properly discussed and evaluated only in conjunction with those of similar studies on the primary organizer. Optic vesicles killed by heat or other treatments, although they may induce neural complexes including eye vesicles, which in turn evoke lens formation from the host ectoderm, seldom if ever induce lenses directly (see Needham, '42). The formation of isolated lenses has been elicited, however, by a variety of foreign tissues, such as fresh salamander liver and boiled salamander heart (Holtfreter, '34). One is also reminded of the isolated lenses and lentoids appearing in Fundulus embryos following treatment with acetone and alcohol, as reported by Werber (who erroneously attributed his results to the inductive action of optic fragments or substances dispersed to other parts of the embryo through the "blastolytic" effects of the toxic agents). Toivonen ('49) finds that alcohol-treated liver, which he has shown to be relatively specific for the induction of head structures, may occasionally stimulate the formation of independent lenses. This archencephalic inductor is thermostable, soluble in organic solvents, and, in fractionations, accompanies the fatty acids and nucleoproteins.

Although these experiments point to the intervention of specific diffusible substances in lens induction, interpretation and extrapolation of the results must be undertaken with caution. One is reminded, for example, of Holtfreter's ('34, '45, '47) finding that many instances of neural induction by artificial agents appear to be the indirect consequence of toxic action by the foreign tissues and chemical substances employed. Even unfavorable pH, by producing sublethal "shock," can seemingly launch chemical sequences in gastrula ectoderm cells that lead to their neuralization; and it is conceivable that the foreign tissues or tissue extracts that elicit lens formation are equally nonspecific in their mode of action.

Even more difficult than identifying the agents responsible for lens induction is the task of analyzing the manner in which their effects upon the lens epidermis are mediated and expressed. Although little concrete information is available on these points, the problem has been approached in a novel and stimulating way by Weiss ('50). Weiss has long stressed the importance of physical factors in development, and has recently presented a concept of induction based on the consequences, at the molecular level, of simple contactual relationships between cells. It has often been demonstrated that embryonic inductors are effective only when they are in direct physical contact with the reacting tissue, and this is well exemplified in the case of the eye; interposition between optic vesicle and epidermis of a narrow gap or an extremely thin layer of mesenchyme cells is sufficient to block lens induction. Weiss's concept, as applied to the eye, is that lens formation results from selective accumulation of particular species of molecules at the surfaces of the epidermal cells, in response to specific physical affinities that exist between these molecules and those arrayed superficially in the cells of the vesicle. His concept "illustrates how interfaces, by selectively adsorbing, orienting, and aligning molecular key species from the cellular content, produce the physical conditions of spatial order which enable stereochemically complementary compounds, such as antibody-antigen or enzyme-substrate systems, to interact most effectively. According to this concept, . . . when a cell comes into contact with another body whose surface is settled with molecules with specifically formed end groups, . . . molecules of conforming configuration will be trapped by their correspondingly shaped counterparts. Thus, a specific fraction of the cell content will gradually become concentrated and segregated along the contact surface [and] . . . a whole train of events determining the future chemical history of the cell has thus been set into motion."

Weiss's student, McKeehan ('51), finds that at the time of contact between optic vesicle and ectoderm in the chick, the cells of the ectoderm become elongated and oriented in the direction of the subjacent retinal cells. This response, together with the firm adhesion developing during this period between retina and lens ectoderm, is precisely the type of behavior to be expected in terms of Weiss's thesis. An important feature of this concept is that it accounts for the induction of a lens or other structure without invoking the actual passage of diffusible substances from inductor to reacting tissue.

Once the lens placode is established, its

invagination into vesicular form is probably the consequence of tensions created by local contraction of the continuous "surface coat" which binds together the free ends of the epidermal cells. The effect of mechanical pull by the invaginating retinal cup, once proposed as a causal or contributory factor, can be discounted in view of the formation of lenses independently of the cup (as in *R. esculenta*), and their induction by fragmentary or abnormally folded optic vesicles and dead tissues.

The development of lens fibers ensues by elongation of the cells forming the proximal (medial) wall of the lens vesicle. This polarization is apparently acquired during early lens stages, since Woerdeman ('34) has shown that vesicles developing from placodes isolated at closure of the neural folds by insertion beneath the flank epidermis preserve their original polarity even when the implants have been introduced with mediolateral faces reversed. Normally the polarity of the lens is probably imparted by the retinal rudiment, but judging from the results of Dragomirow ('29) the influence is not highly specific in nature. When an eye cup is grafted to the auditory region, and the lens induced from host epidermis lies partly interposed between retina and labyrinth, a secondary fiber-forming center develops at the point where the lens touches the ear epithelium. Another feature of lens asymmetry, the presence of vertical and horizontal sutures on its distal and medial surfaces, respectively, also appears to reflect the impact of localizing factors in the lens environment. By rotating the lens epidermis or the retinal rudiment through 90 degrees in Rana, Bombinator and the axolotl, Woerdeman ('34) has shown that the position of the sutures is still a labile feature of lens organization during early neurula stages, but becomes ingrained shortly thereafter; rotation at the time of fold formation does not disturb the normal topographical relationships, but rotation of either component during or after closure of the folds results in the formation of suture lines at atypical angles with reference to the cup.

The development recently of serological methods by Ten Cate and Woerdeman (see Woerdeman, '50) for detecting the first appearance and subsequent development of specific lens proteins in the lens rudiment promises to provide a valuable tool for more penetrating studies of lens induction and differentiation.

INDUCTION OF THE CORNEA

The epidermis covering the eye after separation of the lens undergoes depigmentation and fails to develop the gland cells and chromatophores characteristic of other epidermis. Meanwhile an unvascularized and pigment-free stroma of mesenchymal origin begins to form, and together with the epithelium constitutes the transparent cornea. For the attainment, and also the maintenance, of its histological differentiation the cornea is clearly dependent on association with the rest of the eye. No cornea forms when the eye is lacking, as after extirpation of the retinal rudiment in neurula or tail-bud stages, and the corneal epithelium transforms into ordinary epidermis after removal of the lens and eye cup in young larval stages. Moreover, when the cornea is replaced by skin from other body regions, even in advanced larval stages, the graft will undergo histological modification into typical cornea. Not only the eye as a whole, but component portions of it acting alone (lens, cup, retinal fragments, iris), are capable of eliciting corneal differentiation. Inert objects such as glass pellets introduced beneath foreign skin may cause thinning of the overlying epidermis through mechanical tension, but true histological transformation into cornea, including disappearance of the gland cells, apparently requires a specific inductive stimulus. (For literature on cornea, see Mangold, '31.)

GROWTH OF THE EYE AND ITS ASSOCIATED STRUCTURES

The determination of the initial scale of the retinal and lens rudiments, the maintenance of harmonious size relationships between these and other components of the eye, and the growth of the entire organ relative to the rest of the animal, have been studied primarily by transplantation of the eye or its parts between species of different size or hereditary growth rates. Most of these experiments have already been summarized in an earlier review by me ('40), and in the present section I shall draw from portions of that account.

Rotmann ('39), employing two species of European Triturus, cristatus and taeniatus, has studied the factors that determine the size of the retinal and lens anlagen at the time of their first demarcation in the embryo. Of the two embryos, *T. cristatus* is the larger, and its eye vesicle is correspondingly larger. We know that it is first determined as retinal material while it is still a portion of the open medullary plate, and hence before it actually evaginates to form a vesicle. Thus if a piece of ectoderm from some other region, say ectoderm ordinarily destined to form flank skin, is grafted into this region at a sufficiently early stage it will subsequently form the eye vesicle. One of the possibilities considered by Rotmann is that the area of retinal material thus determined, and hence the initial size of the eye vesicle, is arbitrarily prescribed by the inductor itself. An alternative is that the inductor merely releases retina-forming potentialities, and that the actual scale of the rudiment is an independent expression of genetic qualities in the reacting tissue. This was tested by grafting gastrula ectoderm of *T. cristatus* in place of the future eye region of the smaller *T. taeniatus* embryo. The eye vesicle later forming from the graft was generally of the same size as the normal host eye, suggesting that the inductor not only "determines" the retinal material as such, but also specifies its scale. In a few cases, however, the vesicle was larger than that of its host; and in the reciprocal experiment, *T. taeniatus* ectoderm on the larger *T. cristatus* formed a vesicle appropriate in size for the donor species, that is, much smaller than the normal host vesicle.

Incidentally, initial conformity of the optic vesicle to the size prescribed by the host, as in the first combination, does not mean that its subsequent growth rate and eventual size are similarly altered. Rotmann's experiment was performed independently by the writer (unpublished), and it was found that such vesicles, although starting at the same size, later grew into eyes considerably larger than the normal organs of the host. This is in accordance with the more rapid larval growth rate of the donor species.

Rotmann ('39) obtained a more definite answer to the question of initial size in similar experiments with the lens. Here the scale of the rudiment is apparently an expression of genetic qualities in the lens-forming tissue itself. Thus *T. cristatus* ectoderm grafted over an optic vesicle of *T. taeniatus* forms a lens that already adheres to the *T. cristatus* scale at its earliest recognizable stage of development. This lens was formed at the behest of the small *T. taeniatus* eye vesicle, but apparently the "instructions" do not include specifications concerning the size of the structure elicited. By using haploid embryos as donors of the grafted ectoderm, Rotmann later ('40) showed that the initial size of the rudiment results from the mobilization, not of a specific *number* of epidermal cells, but of an epidermal *area* of specific extent. The induced haploid rudiments, at the stage when they could first be clearly demarcated, contained about 70 per cent more cells, but were of the same total dimensions, as diploid lenses of the same species. This is in keeping with the recent finding of McKeehan ('51) that the area of epidermis incorporated into the lens rudiment in the chick coincides precisely with that enjoying direct physical contact with the optic vesicle. McKeehan's observation does not in turn, however, seem to harmonize well with Rotmann's earlier report that lenses induced from *T. cristatus* ectoderm by the small *T. taeniatus* vesicles are of *T. cristatus* scale from the beginning.

These results on the heteroplastic transplantation of the lens raise a further question that is of even greater pertinence to the problem of eye growth. A chimeric eye is created in which the lens and optic cup are of disharmonious proportions, and one may inquire what the consequences will be during subsequent growth of such an organ. This question has also been studied by Rotmann, but it was first tested by Harrison ('29) in experiments with two species of Amblystoma differing markedly in rate of growth. The eye of the more rapidly growing species, *A. tigrinum*, is much larger than that of *A. punctatum*, so that when the optic vesicle of one and the lens epidermis of the other are combined into a single eye, a potential maladjustment of considerable magnitude is created. This does not materialize, however. Optic cup and lens exert a mutual influence on the growth of one another, with the result that the chimeric eye eventually develops harmonious proportions. For example, an *A. punctatum* cup, when combined with an *A. tigrinum* lens, exceeds its normal size, while in turn the lens fails to attain its usual dimensions. These results have been confirmed and extended by Ballard ('39).

No direct information is available concerning the way in which this growth adjustment is effected, although one is tempted to suggest that differences in metabolic rate between the two components of the chimeric eyes may somehow be involved. Wills ('36) and Hopkins and Handford ('43) have shown that the level of oxygen consumption is decidedly higher in the more rapidly growing species, *A. tigrinum*. Simple physical factors (e.g., the mere mechanical pressure of one part on the other) do not seem to be responsible, since Ballard (personal communication) finds that the growth of the A. *punctatum* cup is not increased by grafting a supernumerary lens of the same species into the pupillary space.

When the entire eye (optic vesicle together with lens epidermis) is grafted between embryos of these two species, it pursues its genetic or predestined growth rate independently of the size of the host (Harrison, '24; Twitty and Schwind, '31). Unlike its component parts, the size increase of the total organ appears to be relatively unaffected by the growth intensity of its immediate environment. Thus an A. *tigrinum* eye becomes disproportionately large for its A. *punctatum* host, and an A. *punctatum* eye grafted to A. *tigrinum* preserves its characteristic small size in spite of the fact that it is nourished by a much larger and more actively growing host.

This greater autonomy of the eye as a whole is not surprising, however, since the organ develops as a relatively self-contained and discontinuous entity. This is not true of its constituent parts, the retina and lens, which are very intimately engaged throughout their development. Numerous examples of local size adjustments between parts intricately related during their development could be offered, including further instances drawn from the eye itself. Not only in amphibians (Twitty, '32), but in birds (Amprino, '49, '50) and mammals (Wessely, '20) as well, the extrinsic ocular muscles and also the skeletal structures associated with the eye partly adjust their size to that of the bulb.* Thus when an A. *tigrinum* vesicle and lens is grafted to an A. *punctatum* embryo, the eye muscles developing from host tissue become considerably enlarged beyond their prospective size, in keeping with the more massive proportions of the organ to which they are now attached. It is of interest to note that their enlargement is effected by increase in the number, not size,

* In the chick there appears to be a relatively fixed amount of scleral mesenchyme, whose disposition over the surface of the eyeball and, accordingly, the thickness of the scleral cartilage, are determined by mechanical stress resulting from growth of the bulb. Following experimental reduction of the size of the eye and thus of its surface area, cartilage comes to invest the eyeball as a markedly thickened layer (Weiss and Amprino, '40). In the amphibian the amount of scleral cartilage which forms seems to be more closely proportional to the size of the eye.

of the constituent muscle fibers (see also Amprino, '49). Since ordinary functional hypertrophy of muscles results from enlargement of the individual fibers, without increase in their number, one is led to suggest that the adjustment in muscle size following heteroplastic transplantation of the eye is attributable to factors more subtle than mere functional demand.

The influence of the eye on the dimensions of the orbit as demonstrated by experimental alteration of bulb size in various animals is discussed by Washburn and Detwiler ('43) in relation to its bearing on problems of comparative physical anthropology.

In addition to grafting embryonic eyes between species of different growth rate, there is another means of producing disharmonious size relationships between the organ and the rest of the animal. This is by exchanging eyes between younger and older larvae, whether of the same or different species. Thus when an eye of an advanced larva is replaced by one from a donor half the size or age of the host, the grafted organ is at first much "too small" for its new host. This experiment was performed by Twitty ('30) and Twitty and Elliott ('34), who found that the small eye, through its more active growth, overtakes the normal host organ and thereby restores the normal size equilibrium. Their results indicated that during its period of regulatory growth the young transplant exceeded its customary rate of increase, and to account for this acceleration it was postulated (Twitty, '40) that with increasing age the larval blood stream affords progressively richer nutrient opportunities. This appeared to be confirmed by chemical determinations that showed an increase with age in the concentration of nonprotein and amino acid blood nitrogen (Twitty and van Wagtendonk, '40). Meanwhile, however, Handford ('45, '48) has reported that young eyes continue to grow at their normal or predestined rate following transplantation to older hosts. Until the issues raised by his results can be subjected to further investigation, conclusions concerning the control of proportionate eye growth must accordingly be held in reserve.

REGENERATION OF THE EYE

Complete regeneration of the urodele eye is possible following removal of all except a relatively small remnant of the organ. Reconstitution is effected mostly through a part by part replacement; that is, cornea, sclera, choroidea and retina are renewed from the corresponding components of the eye fragment (Colucci). Of particular interest is the regeneration of the sensory retina after surgical removal of this layer alone, or following its degeneration as a result of section of the optic nerve. Since it separates readily from the pigment epithelium, the sensory retina may be forced out by slitting the eyeball and exerting pressure, or by flooding the vitreous chamber with a gentle stream of physiological salt solution. Wachs ('20) described the formation of new nervous retina through proliferation jointly from the iris and the pigment layer of the retina; but according to the recent studies of Stone ('50a and b) on the adult Triturus eye, replacement appears to proceed exclusively from the pigmented epithelium of the retina.

Following removal of the sensory retina the cells of the pigment layer become rounded and enlarged, undergo depigmentation, and increase in number through active mitotic division. Some of the daughter cells then differentiate into a normal sensory retina, which establishes functional connection with the brain through ingrowth of new optic nerve fibers, while the others develop pigment again and reform a typical pigment epithelium. The same sequence of events occurs following degeneration of the sensory retina resulting from replantation or transplantation of the eyeball. Even minor defects in the retina, produced by sucking out small areas with a micropipette introduced through a slit in the cornea, are repaired by proliferation from the underlying pigmented retina, instead of from the cells of the sensory layer bordering the wound. Mere detachment of a limited area of the sensory retina from the underlying pigment epithelium is sufficient to provoke formation of secondary retina by the pigment cells. Stone also found that pieces of pigment epithelium grafted into the pupillary space following removal of the lens consistently give rise to sensory retina. Ikeda ('35) describes the regeneration of retinal cups from the pars iridica retinae of iris pieces grafted to the eye cavity, or even to foreign sites such as the fourth brain ventricle. But according to Stone, pure iris tissue never forms retina when implanted in the chambers of the eye. Stone believes that earlier workers, in claiming regeneration of retina from the iris, were misled as a result of incomplete removal of the peripheral portion

(ciliary border) of the retina. Since this region remains proliferative as the source of new retinal cells throughout normal eye growth, its continued activity when left as a remnant following removal of the retina might well account for erroneous conclusions concerning the importance of peripheral regions as a zone of retinal regeneration.

Wolffian Regeneration of the Lens. Regeneration of the lens, normally an epidermal derivative, from the dorsal margin of the iris has intrigued embryologists since it was first described by Colucci and by Wolff. "Wolffian regeneration" usually connotes replacement from this source after removal of the lens from differentiated eyes, but it has frequently been reported that the faculty of lens formation is also possessed by the rim of the optic cup in embryonic stages of development (e.g., Beckwith; Ikeda, '37b; Woerdeman, '39, '50). When the normal channel of lens formation was blocked, as after replacement of the lens placode by foreign, nonreactive epidermis, the dorsal rim of the embryonic retinal cup was sometimes found to enlarge and pinch off as a vesicle which differentiated into a lens of normal structure. Also in the chick, van Deth ('40) has obtained lens regeneration from young optic cups developing in vitro. However, Stone and Dinnean ('40) believe this phenomenon to be of much rarer occurrence in Amphibia than has been reported; and Reyer ('50) finds that in *Triturus viridescens* the margin of the cup is unable to begin regeneration of a lens until young larval stages, after it has already attained a high degree of functional differentiation.

Renewal from the iris epithelium following removal of the lens in larval and adult stages was earlier believed to be of widespread occurrence among Amphibia, but reinvestigation by Stone and his students suggests the possibility that true Wolffian regeneration is characteristic principally of the species of Triturus. The positive results reported for other forms are attributed by Stone to reconstitution from lens fragments remaining after incomplete extirpation. In Triturus, however, the phenomenon is clearly established, and has been described in detail by Wachs ('14), Sato ('30), Dinnean ('42), Zalokar ('44), and Reyer ('48). As summarized from the accounts of Reyer and Dinnean, the principal histological changes following removal of the original lens are as follows: swelling of the dorsal iris, involving an increase in height of the cells, especially those of the inner layer; separation of the inner and outer layers; depigmentation of the inner layer and pupillary border of the iris; cell proliferation at the pupillary border and downgrowth of an unpigmented epithelial vesicle; formation of a lens nucleus through elongation and differentiation into lens fibers of the cells of the inner wall of the vesicle; formation of secondary lens fibers from the equatorial zone; and finally, detachment of the lens from the dorsal iris. Van Deth ('40), who has described lens regeneration from explanted eye cups of the chick, finds that the steps are substantially different in this organism. A plate of tissue grows across the pupillary space and then curls inward to close into a lens vesicle. Equally odd, in comparison with the Amphibia, is the fact that the lens arises from the ventral instead of from the dorsal margin of the cup.

In the normal eye, the regenerative capacity of the iris epithelium is held in check by an inhibitory influence, apparently chemical in nature, exerted by the resident lens. This was first demonstrated by Wachs ('14), who found that an isolated piece of dorsal iris introduced into the vitreous chamber fails to regenerate when situated in an intact eye, but forms a lens readily in a lensless eye. If the regenerate comes in contact with the lens forming simultaneously from the host iris, the two sometimes fuse into a single harmonious lens (Sato, '30, '33b). If implantation is delayed until the host iris has begun to regenerate the lens, the latter will suppress lens formation by the implanted iris. According to Sato ('35) the host lens begins to exert this inhibiting effect during the early stages of its regeneration.

The second condition essential to Wolffian regeneration was revealed by Wachs in transplantations of dorsal iris to an extraocular site, the cavity of the ear capsule (see also Ikeda, '36). Pieces thus isolated were incapable of regenerating lenses unless accompanied by transplanted retinal tissue. On the basis of these results it was postulated that the behavior of the dorsal iris is controlled by a "secretory balance" existing between lens and retina. According to this concept a retinal secretion conducive to lens formation is normally counteracted by another originating from the resident lens; with the removal of the lens the retinal secretion is then free to stimulate regenerative transformation of the iris epithelium.

However, the actual nature of this retinal stimulus, and its relationship to that exerted by embryonic retina in eliciting lens formation from epidermis, are completely unknown.

Lens regeneration from the intact iris always proceeds from the middle of its upper pupillary margin, and it is likewise this part of the iris that manifests the greatest regenerative potency following isolation of iris pieces in the vitreous chamber (Sato, '30). Adjoining portions of the dorsal iris are also capable of delivering lenses under these conditions, but regeneration is often less complete, and pieces of ventral iris give negative results or at best undergo changes suggestive of early stages in lens regeneration. On the basis of the regenerative behavior of eyes that had been rotated 180 degrees in embryonic stages, Sato ('33b) attributes this graded distribution of lensforming capacity in the iris to influences associated with choroid fissure formation at the ventral margin of the developing optic cup. Correlated with the stage at which the rotations were performed, the choroid fissures appeared ventrally (host-wise) in some cases, dorsally (donor-wise) in others; occasionally two fissures, one better developed than the other, arose in a single eye. When these eyes were lentectomized in late larval stages, the new lenses arose from the portion of the iris directly opposite the point where fissure formation had occurred; or, when two fissures were present, opposite the one that was most strongly developed. It thus appears that the lens-forming capacity of the Triturus iris, although eventually restricted to its dorsal border, is originally widespread, and becomes inhibited secondarily at the ventral margin by influences involved in the determination or formation of the choroid fissure. On its face, the finding of van Deth ('40) that in the chick lens regeneration proceeds principally from the ventral instead of from the dorsal margin of the cup would appear to call Sato's interpretation into serious question, but it remains to be seen whether localization of regenerative capacity within the iris is referable to the same factors in the two groups of animals.

In a recent study Sato ('51) has extended his survey of the distribution of lens-regenerative potency in the eye, and finds that it extends into the dorsal portion of the pigment layer of the retina above the iris. Pieces of pigment epithelium taken at increasing distances from the iris along the distoproximal axis of the eye, and implanted in the vitreous chamber of lensless eyes, deliver lenses with decreasing frequency or of decreasing perfection.

It will have become evident from the foregoing abbreviated summary that the mobilization, elaboration, and growth of the many components of the eye, as well as their reconstitution following injury or loss, are dependent at almost every step upon formative influences operating within the system or brought to bear from without. This welding together of diverse parts into an interlocking, harmonious whole of remarkable complexity and functional perfection represents one of the best investigated and at the same time most challenging examples of epigenetic phenomena in vertebrate morphogenesis.

REFERENCES

Alexander, L. E. 1937 An experimental study of the role of optic cup and overlying ectoderm in lens formation in the chick embryo. J. Exp. Zool., 75:41–68.

Amprino, R. 1949 Corrélations entre les organes pendant le développement. Recherches expérimentales sur l'oeil et ses annexes. Compt. Rend. Assoc. Anat., 36:1–9.

——— 1950 Les conditions qui règlent l'organogénèse et la croissance des muscles. Acta Anat., 10:38–80.

Ballard, W. W. 1939 Mutual size regulation between eye-ball and lens in Amblystoma, studied by means of heteroplastic transplantation. J. Exp. Zool., 81:261–285.

Barden, R. B. 1942 The origin and development of the chromatophores of the amphibian eye. J. Exp. Zool., 90:475–519.

——— 1943 Changes in the pigmentation of the iris in metamorphosing amphibian larvae. J. Exp. Zool., 92:171–197.

Deth, J. H. M. G. van 1940 Induction et régénération du cristallin chez l'embryon de la poule. Acta Neerlandica Morph., 3:219–236.

Dinnean, F. L. 1942 Lens regeneration from the iris and its inhibition by lens reimplantation in Triturus torosus larvae. J. Exp. Zool., 90:461–478.

Dorris, Frances 1938 Differentiation of the chick eye in vitro. J. Exp. Zool., 78:385–407.

Dragomirow, N. 1929 Ueber die Faktoren der embryonalen Entwicklung der Linse bei Amphibien. Roux' Arch. Entw.-mech., 116:633–668.

——— 1932 Ueber Entwicklung von Augenbechern aus transplantierten Stückchen des embryonalen Tapetums. Roux' Arch. Entw.-mech., 126:635–662.

——— 1933 Ueber Koordination der Teilprozesse in der embryonalen Morphogenese des Augenbechers. Roux' Arch. Entw.-mech., 129:522–560.

——— 1934 Ueber die Determination der Augenbecherblätter bei Triton taeniatus. Roux' Arch. Entw.-mech., 131:540–542.

——— 1936 Ueber Induktion sekundärer Retina in transplantierten Augenbechern bei Triton und Pelobates. Roux' Arch. Entw.-mech., 134:716–737.

Eakin, R. 1947 Determination and regulation of polarity in the retina of Hyla regilla. Univ. Calif. Publ. Zool., 51:245–287.

Handford, S. W. 1945 The relation of age and temperature to the relative growth of the eyes of Amblystoma. J. Exp. Zool., 98:127–152.

——— 1948 The relative growth of transplanted and normal eyes of Amblystoma larvae under normal conditions. Anat. Rec., 101:10–11.

Harrison, R. G. 1920 Experiments on the lens in Amblystoma. Proc. Soc. Exp. Biol. & Med., 17:199–200.

——— 1924 Some unexpected results of the heteroplastic transplantation of limbs. Proc. Nat. Acad. Sci., 10:69–74.

——— 1929 Correlation in the development and growth of the eye studied by means of heteroplastic transplantation. Roux' Arch. Entw.-mech., 120:1–55.

——— 1945 Relations of symmetry in the developing embryo. Trans. Conn. Acad. Arts & Sci., 36:277–330.

Holtfreter, J. 1934 Der Einfluss thermischer, mechanischer und chemischer Eingriffe auf die Induzierfähigkeit von Triton-Keimteilen. Roux' Arch. Entw.-mech., 132:225–306.

——— 1935 Morphologische Beeinflussung von Urodelenektoderm bei xenoplastischer Transplantation. Roux' Arch. Entw.-mech., 133:367–426.

——— 1939 Gewebeaffinität, ein Mittel der embryonalen Formbildung. Arch. exp. Zellforsch., 23:169–209.

——— 1944 Neural differentiation of ectoderm through exposure to saline solution. J. Exp. Zool., 95:307–340.

——— 1945 Neuralization and epidermalization of gastrula ectoderm. J. Exp. Zool., 98:161–209.

——— 1947 Neural induction in explants which have passed through a sublethal cytolysis. J. Exp. Zool., 106:197–222.

Hopkins, H. S., and Handford, S. W. 1943 Respiratory metabolism during development in two species of Amblystoma. J. Exp. Zool., 93:403–414.

Ikeda, Y. 1935 Ueber die Regeneration von Augenbechern an verschiedenen Körperstellen durch isolierte Irisstücke. Arb. Anat. Inst. Kais.-Jap. Univ. Sendai., 17:11–54.

——— 1936 Neue Versuche zur Analyse der Wolffschen Linsenregeneration. Arb. Anat. Inst. Kais.-Jap. Univ. Sendai., 18:1–16.

——— 1937a Ueber die Bildung akzessorischer Retina aus dem Tapetum bei Hynobius. Roux' Arch. Entw.-mech., 136:676–680.

——— 1937b Ueber die Linsenbildung aus dem embryonalen Augenbecher des Hynobius un-

nangso Tago, untersucht auf Grund der Transplantation der Augenbecheranlage in verschiedenen Entwicklungsstadien. Arb. Anat. Inst. Kais.-Jap. Univ. Sendai., *20:*17–51.

Ikeda, Y. 1938 Ueber die wechselseitigen Beziehungen der Sinnesorgane untereinander in ihrer normalen und experimentell bedingten Entwicklung. Arb. Anat. Inst. Kais.-Jap. Univ. Sendai., *21:*1–44.

Liedke, K. B. 1951 Lens competence in *Amblystoma punctatum.* J. Exp. Zool., *117:*573–589.

Mangold, O. 1931 Das Determinationsproblem. III. Das Wirbeltierauge in der Entwicklung und Regeneration. Ergeb. Biol., *7:*193–403.

McKeehan, M. S. 1951 Cytological aspects of embryonic lens induction in the chick. J. Exp. Zool., *117:*31–64.

Needham, J. 1942 Biochemistry and Morphogenesis. Cambridge University Press, Cambridge, England.

Pasquini, P. 1932 Sulla determinazione e sul differenziamento del cristallino in *Rana catesbiana* (Shaw). J. Exp. Zool., *61:*45–108.

Perri, T. 1934 Ricerche sul comportamento dell'-abbozzo oculare di anfibi in condizioni di espianto. Roux' Arch. Entw.-mech., *131:*113–134.

Reyer, R. W. 1948 An experimental study of lens regeneration in *Triturus viridescens viridescens.* I. Regeneration of a lens after lens extirpation in embryos and larvae of different ages. J. Exp. Zool., *107:*217–267.

———— 1950 An experimental study of lens regeneration in *Triturus viridescens viridescens.* II. Lens development from the dorsal iris in the absence of the embryonic lens. J. Exp. Zool., *113:* 317–346.

Rotmann, E. 1939 Der Anteil von Induktor und reagierendem Gewebe an der Entwicklung der Amphibienlinse. Roux' Arch. Entw.-mech., *139:* 1–49.

———— 1940 Die Bedeutung der Zellgrösse für die Entwicklung der Amphibienlinse. Roux' Arch. Entw.-mech., *140:*124–156.

Sato, T. 1930 Beiträge zur Analyse der Wolffschen Linsenregeneration. I. Roux' Arch. Entw.-mech., *122:*451–493.

———— 1933a Ueber die Determination des fetalen Augenspalts bei *Triton taeniatus.* Arch. Entw.-mech., *128:*342–377.

———— 1933b Beiträge zur Analyse der Wolffschen Linsenregeneration. II. Roux' Arch. Entw.-mech., *130:*19–78.

———— 1935 Beiträge zur Analyse der Wolffschen Linsenregeneration. III. Roux' Arch. Entw.-mech., *133:*323–348.

———— 1951 Ueber die linsenbildende Fähigkeit des Pigmentepithels bei *Diemyctylus pyrrhogaster.* I. Pigmentepithel aus dorsalem Augenbereich. Embryologia (Biol. Inst., Nagoya Univ.), *1:*21–58.

Spemann, H. 1901 Ueber Korrelationen in der Entwicklung des Auges. Verh. anat. Ges., 15 Vers. Bonn:61–79.

———— 1912 Zur Entwicklung des Wirbeltierauges. Zool. Jahrb., *32:*1–98.

———— 1938 Embryonic Development and Induction. Yale University Press, New Haven, Connecticut.

Stone, L. S. 1948 Functional polarization in developing and regenerating retinae of transplanted eyes. Ann. N. Y. Acad. Sci., *49:*856–865.

———— 1950a Neural retina degeneration followed by regeneration from surviving pigment cells in grafted adult salamander eyes. Anat. Rec., *106:*89–110.

———— 1950b The role of retinal pigment cells in regenerating neural retinae of adult salamander eyes. J. Exp. Zool., *113:*9–26.

————, and Dinnean, F. L. 1940 Experimental studies on the relation of the optic vesicle and cup to lens formation in *Amblystoma punctatum.* J. Exp. Zool., *83:*95–125.

Toivonen, S. 1940 Ueber die Leistungsspezifität der abnormen Induktoren im Implantatversuch bei Triton. Ann. Acad. Sci. Fenn., Ser. A, *45:*3–150.

———— 1945 Zur Frage der Induktion selbständiger Linsen durch abnorme Induktoren im Implantatversuch bei Triton. Ann. Zool., Soc. Vanamo, *11:*1–28.

———— 1949 Zur Frage der Leistungsspezifität abnormer Induktoren. Experientia, *8:*323–325.

Twitty, V. C. 1930 Regulation in the growth of transplanted eyes. J. Exp. Zool., *55:*43–52.

———— 1932 Influence of the eye on the growth of its associated structures, studied by means of heteroplastic transplantation. J. Exp. Zool., *61:* 333–374.

———— 1940 Size-controlling factors. Growth Supplement, pp. 109–120.

————, and Elliott, H. A. 1934 The relative growth of the amphibian eye, studied by means of transplantation. J. Exp. Zool. *68:*247–291.

————, and Schwind, J. L. 1931 The growth of eyes and limbs transplanted heteroplastically between two species of Amblystoma. J. Exp. Zool., *59:*61–86.

————, and van Wagtendonk, W. J. 1940 A suggested mechanism for the regulation of proportionate growth, supported by quantitative data on the blood nutrients. Growth, *4:*349–360.

Wachs, H. 1914 Neue Versuche zur Wolffschen Linsenregeneration. Roux' Arch. Entw.-mech., *39:*384–451.

———— 1920 Restitution des Auges nach Exstirpation von Retina und Linse bei Tritonen. Roux' Arch. Entw.-mech., *46:*328–390.

Washburn, S. L., and Detwiler, S. R. 1943 An experiment bearing on the problems of physical anthropology. Am. J. Phys. Anthrop., N. S., *1:* 171–190.

Weiss, Paul 1950 Perspectives in the field of morphogenesis. Quart. Rev. Biol., *25:*177–198.

————, and Amprino, R. 1940 The effect of mechanical stress on the differentiation of scleral cartilage in vitro and in the embryo. Growth, *4:* 245–258.

Wessely, K. 1920 Ueber Korrelationen des Wachstums (nach Versuchen am Auge). Zeit. Augenheilk., *43:*654–681.

Wills, I. A. 1936 The respiratory rate of developing amphibia with special reference to sex differentiation. J. Exp. Zool., *73:*481–510.

Woerdeman, M. W. 1934 Ueber die Determination der Augenlinsenstruktur bei Amphibien. Z. mikr.-anat. Forsch., *36:*600–606.

———— 1939 On lens-induction. Proc. Kon. Ned. Akad. Wetensch., Amst., *42:*290–292.

———— 1950 L'induction du cristallin chez les amphibians. Ann. Biol., *26:*699–709.

Yntema, C. L. 1950 An analysis of induction of the ear from foreign ectoderm in the salamander embryo. J. Exp. Zool., *113:*211–243.

Zalokar, M. 1944 Contribution a l'étude de la régénération du cristallin chez le Triton. Rev. suiss. Zool., *51:*443–521.

CHAPTER 3

Ear and Nose

C. L. YNTEMA

LOCALIZATION OF RUDIMENTS

THE POSITIONS of the presumptive areas of the auditory and nasal placodes as indicated in the diagrams have been determined primarily by vital staining in Amphibia and by explantations in the chick (Figs. 145 and 146). In the former group the placodal areas are underlaid by chordamesoderm during late gastrular stages. The ear ectoderm comes to lie next to the myelencephalic part of the neural tube; the paired areas of nasal ectoderm are closely associated for a time with the neural folds of the prosencephalon.

THE EAR
DIFFERENTIATION OF EAR ECTODERM

A differentiation of the ear rudiment from adjacent cells is present in the late gastrula of Amblystoma (Yntema, '39) and in the early neurula of Rana (Zwilling, '41). Obviously, this demonstrated determination does not imply either presence or lack of an earlier differentiation. Since this differentiation in late gastrular and early neurular stages can be reversed easily, its demonstration depends upon using an environment favorable to expression of the tendency to form an ear vesicle. Transplantation to the region between the eye and ear rudiments of a head process stage serves this purpose in urodeles. Adjacent structures influence the transplanted ectoderm, but only ear ectoderm gives rise to ear vesicles in this position.

During neurulation differentiation of the rudiment advances; increasingly normal ears form from ectoderm transplanted to favorable sites and determination is acquired to develop in less favorable environments. This has been demonstrated or is implied by the results of several investigators on amphibian embryos (Kaan, '26; Röhlich, '29; Yntema, '33; Domacavalli, '37; Sidorov, '37; Ginsberg, '39; Schmalhausen, '40). A saline medium is so unfavorable an environment that a vesicle does not form from neurular ear ectoderm of anurans (Guareschi, '35).

Its differentiation also can be disturbed by ultraviolet radiation (Dürken, '51). A progressive differentiation occurs during comparable stages of the chick (Waddington, '37; Stcherbatov, '38; Waterman and Evans, '40; Levi-Montalcini, '46). Sensory areas become self-differentiating in the chick at an early stage and their development does not depend upon the presence of nerve fibers (Evans, '43).

Shortly before the ear plate has formed, the ear ectoderm has characteristics of an equipotential system in that a whole ear can form from a part and a single normal ear from two fused rudiments (Harrison, '24). After the vesicle has formed, this ability is lost and the vesicle becomes a mosaic (Kaan, '26; Guareschi, '30). From observations on normal and experimental embryos the definitive parts of the labyrinth can be related to parts of the ear plate (Norris, 1892; Kaan, '26). The endolymphatic duct and sac along with the macula of the saccule arise from the dorsal half, mainly the dorsoposterior quadrant. The utricle and its associated canals arise from the ventral half.

Although the ear ectoderm has started to differentiate during gastrulation, the ectoderm about the ear rudiment and the underlying tissues form a field capable of reconstituting a more or less normal labyrinth until the ear rudiment itself is a mosaic. This stands in contrast to the rapid loss of ability of prospective epidermis to form neural plate during the end of gastrulation. Regenerative capacity following extirpation of the ear rudiment is gradually lost and it also varies inversely with the amount of ectoderm removed (Kaan, '26). The relative ability of foreign ectoderm to form an ear in the late neurula decreases with increase in distance from the ear region in a given direction; the most competent ectoderm at this stage lies ventral to the ear region, the least competent anterior to the ear region (Yntema, '33).

Even after the ear rudiment has become

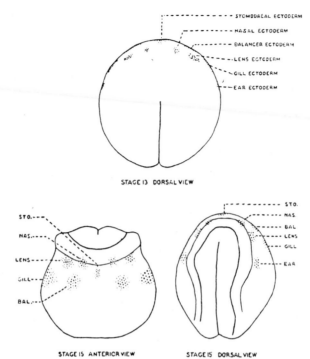

Fig. 145. Relative positions of ectodermal rudiments of the head in neurular stages of *Amblystoma punctatum* (Carpenter, '37; Harrison, '45).

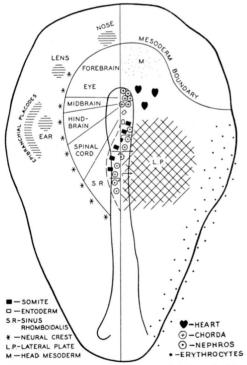

Fig. 146. Map of prospective areas in the primitive streak blastoderm of the chick (Rudnick, '44).

a mosaic its differentiation may be adversely affected by relationship with parts of the central nervous system other than the region with which it is normally related (Detwiler and Van Dyke, '50; Detwiler, '51). It has been concluded that the medulla exerts a late morphogenetic influence on the otic vesicle. However, it can be shown that the medulla is not necessary for late differentiation. If the hindbrain is removed at an ear plate stage a normal labyrinth forms (Yntema, unpublished). Mechanical factors are of importance, especially the formation of a capsule (Kaan, '38) and a functional endolymphatic sac which may regulate hydrostatic pressure of the endolymph (Harrison, '36a). However, presence of capsule and of endolymphatic sac do not in themselves assure normal development (Detwiler and Van Dyke, '50). The size of the ear in the salamander influences the number of cells in the acoustic area of the medulla (Richardson, '32), and absence of the labyrinth in the chick results in less marked differentiation of some associated medullary nuclei (Levi-Montalcini, '49). Neurons of the auditory ganglion are derivatives of the wall of the auditory vesicle (Yntema, '37); hence they serve as an index of differentiation rather than an inductor of the ear along with the facial ganglion as held by Szepsenwol ('33).

Some of the results indicated above involve comparisons between a system at one stage with the same system at another stage. As will be evident in later discussion, the states of one variable in such a continuum are not obvious unless other variables are

the four cardinal positions so that in respect to the two main axes of the ear, both, either one, or none are harmonic with the host axes (Fig. 147). The resulting vesicles may be classed as belonging to four types: (1) harmonic, (2) disharmonic, (3) reduplicated, (4) irregular or vesicular. In transplants with the AP axis disharmonic, the asymmetry is reversed and a harmonic

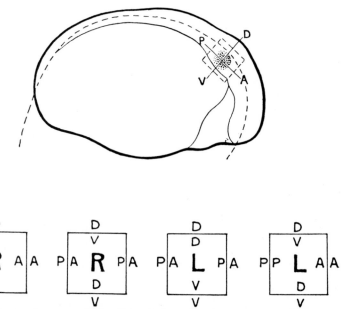

Fig. 147. Scheme of operations to test the effect of changed orientation. The profile of an Amblystoma embryo (stage 21) is shown above. The curved broken line represents the embryonic axis; the stippled area, the rudiment of the ear placode; the square area, the graft. The four squares below show the positions of the axes in four orientations for the right side of the embryo; R, a graft from the right side; L, a graft from the left side. The letters inside the squares give the orientation of the graft; those outside, the direction of the cardinal points of the embryo (Harrison, '45).

held constant. The results do show a progressive loss of ear-forming ability on the part of the system as a whole but do not demonstrate whether such loss is due to changes in one or more parts of the system.

POLARIZATION OF THE EAR ECTODERM

Before and during development of a mosaic pattern the ear rudiment of Amblystoma becomes irreversibly polarized along its main axes, anteroposterior (AP) and dorsoventral (DV), as the experiments of Harrison ('24, '36a, '36b, '45) have shown. The ear rudiment from a donor is grafted into the ear region of a host at the same stage of development as the donor (homostadic transplantation). The graft is placed in one of

ear develops in a majority of experiments done when the neural folds are approximated but not fused (Fig. 148A, stage 19). In later stages the disharmonic AP polarity is usually not reversed. The DV axis becomes fixed during tail-bud stages (stages 25–27); later rotations of the DV axis tend to produce disharmonic labyrinths. Similarly, the AP axis is reversible in Bufo when the neural folds appear but is fixed when the neural folds are fused (Choi, '31).

If the AP axis is reversed during critical stages at the end of neurulation in Amblystoma the polarization of its ectoderm is frequently adjusted only partially to its new environment and an enantiomorphic twin ear results (Fig. 149). "These are always mirrored across the transverse plane and may consist of either two anterior or

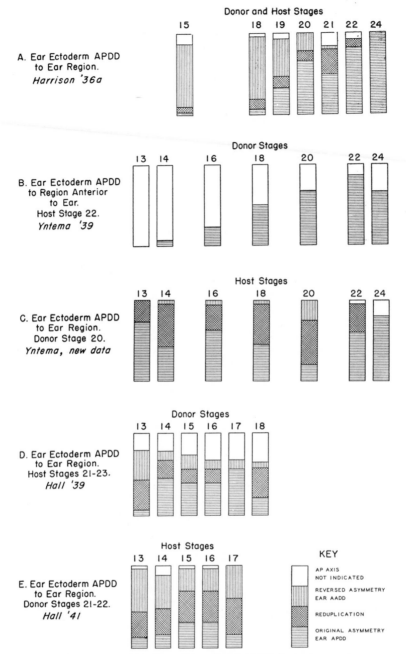

Fig. 148. Differentiation of ear ectoderm placed APDD in various environments.

A, Host and donor are at the same stage of development at the time of operation. Harmonic labyrinths usually develop from grafts in which the AP axis has been rotated before fusion of the neural folds (stage 20); in operations on older stages, the labyrinths are more frequently disharmonic.

B, The AP axis is disharmonic in the heterotopic labyrinths which have recognizable axes; at stage 14 the ear ectoderm may show indication of AP polarization. The site and stage used for receiving the graft show no indication of reversing polarity to produce harmonic ears.

C, The influence of the stage of the host on expression of the graft in homeotopic position is illustrated. Stage 20 is more likely to produce harmonic ears from disharmonic stage 20 ectoderm than earlier or later stages. The high incidence of reduplication when stage 14 is host indicates that this stage influences the expression of polarity more than slightly younger or older embryos. In comparison with *A* it is seen that reduplications occurred in the stage 20 to 20 combination more frequently than in the results of Harrison.

D, A polarity of the ear ectoderm is indicated at the beginning of neurulation which may be expressed in hosts at head process stages at the time of operation.

E, A reversal of polarity is accomplished in some cases by grafting older ear ectoderm to neurulae; as shown in *A*, this ectoderm would more frequently develop disharmonically if grafted to hosts at the same stage of development as the donor.

two posterior halves. Partial twinning, involving either the semicircular canals, which develop from the ventral half of the ear plate, or the saccule, which develops from the dorsal half, also occurs" (Harrison, '45, pp. 295–296).

On the basis of his experiments, Harrison has concluded that the ectoderm of the ear

of harmonic equipotentiality after fixation of the AP axis and before that of the DV axis. These observations led to further investigations on the polarity of the ear ectoderm.

In the experiments indicated above, both host and donor are at the same stage of development for any one experiment. As has

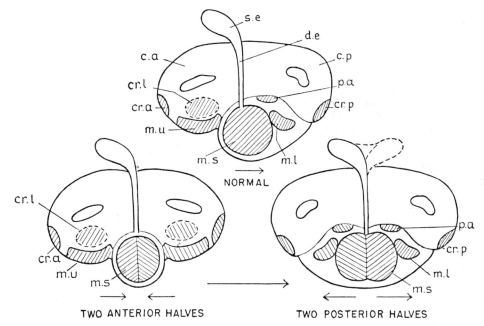

Fig. 149. Normal right labyrinth and two types of enantiomorphic twins, medial surface. The large arrow points to the posterior end of the embryo; the small arrows point posteriorly with respect to the labyrinth or half labyrinth to which they refer. *c.a,* Anterior semicircular canal; *c.p,* posterior canal; *cr.a* and *cr.p,* the corresponding sensory cristae; *cr.l,* lateral crista, projected from the ventrolateral wall but not visible in this view; *d.e,* endolymphatic duct; *m.l,* macula of lagena; *m.s,* macula of sacculus; *m.u,* macula of utriculus; *p.a,* papilla amphibiorum; *s.e,* endolymphatic sac (Harrison, '45).

region and the surrounding area is at first isotropic about the axis perpendicular to its surface. Just as the neural folds are closing a change supervenes. The ear plate becomes polarized with respect to its AP axis. A little later conditions again change, indicating a transition from an indifferent DV axis to one which is definitely polarized. A correlation between the polarization of the ear ectoderm and a regularity in the molecular arrangement of the constituent cells has been postulated and an attempt to demonstrate this by x-ray diffraction, though unsuccessful, indicates a possible means of extending fundamental knowledge of embryology (Harrison, Astbury, and Rudall, '40).

In Amblystoma Hall ('37) studied labyrinths whose ectoderm had been rotated 90 degrees. In these experiments, the ear rudiment may still respond to some of the tests

been indicated, conditions in the hosts as well as the grafts are variables. When the stage of either host or donor is constant in a series, a further analysis of the problem is possible; this has been done in heterostadic transplants to homeotopic and heterotopic positions in Amblystoma (Hall, '39, '41; Yntema, '39). The results of these experiments call for modifications in the conclusions drawn from homostadic operations (Fig. 148B-E). Expression of polarity depends in part on the strength of polarization in the rudiment, in part on the intensity of the polarizing factors in the environment. A labile AP polarity is found in the ear rudiment of the early neural plate stage; this anisotropism is masked in Harrison's experiments by the ability of the hosts used to reverse it. A similar inclination along the DV axis was not demonstrated. Host factors concerned with the arrangement of structures along the two main axes of the laby-rinth may act both before and after the critical stages for the axes indicated by Harrison. The AP polarity of the ear ecto-derm appears to differentiate gradually along with other characteristics of the ear ectoderm.

Some studies on the ciliary beat of the ectoderm within the ear vesicle bear on this subject (Woerdeman, '41). The direction of the beat is already fixed in the presumptive ectoderm of the Triton gastrula, although the stages for polarization of the main axes of the labyrinth are comparable with those of Amblystoma. Hence a polarity is demon-strable in the ectodermal region of the gas-trula. The polarization of the ear rudiment may be a local expression of a general po-larity: this is indicated by some experiments on Amblystoma (Yntema, '48) in which prospective gill ectoderm was placed *apdd* (anteroposterior axis inverted, dorsoventral axis not inverted) into the ear region, using donors and hosts shortly before and after the end of neurulation. As a result the for-eign ectoderm may form disharmonic or reduplicated labyrinths. Under these condi-tions polarization and induction are sep-arable processes. Fixation of polarity of the ciliary beat precedes that of the ear vesicle, as Woerdeman and others have shown. From this Woerdeman concluded that the proc-esses of polarization were not the same for the two systems. It is also possible that polarities of various organs, fixed at different stages, are differential derivatives of a basic but labile pattern in the cells involved. In such a system one derivative of polarity might be fixed, the basic polarity then re-versed, and a second derivative of the same cells would then be disharmonic with the first.

The amphibian ear vesicle has been ro-tated experimentally after it has become a mosaic and its axes fixed (Spemann, '10; Streeter, '07, '14; Ogawa, '21, '26; Tokura, '24, '25; Hall, '37). Under some conditions the vesicle develops in its new position; under others it tends to turn back to its normal position, either partially or com-pletely. The factors which produce such a turning remain undetermined; Streeter ('14, '21) has suggested some possibilities.

INDUCTION OF THE AUDITORY VESICLE

As Harrison ('35, '38) has pointed out, the formation of a normal ear results from the interplay of several factors: the position of the rudiment, as well as ectoderm, meso-derm, and myelencephalon, is involved. Two relations of tissues are to be noted especially: (1) that chordamesoderm comes to lie under the prospective ear ectoderm during gastrulation, and (2) that the raising of the neural folds brings the hindbrain rudiment in relation to the ear ectoderm (Yntema, '46; Ginsberg, '46).

A mesodermal inductor, implied by some earlier results (e.g., Dalcq, '33; Holtfreter, '33), was demonstrated in Amblystoma by Harrison ('35, '38, '45). Belly ectoderm is grafted in place of the neural plate and folds of the hindbrain; subsequently two vesicles form on each side, a lateral one from the presumptive ear ectoderm, a medial one from the graft overlying the chorda-mesoderm which has served as the inductor. Induction by mesoderm of Rana has been reported by other workers (Albaum and Nestler, '37; Zwilling, '41), and the ob-servations of Kogan ('44) on Triton neu-rulae indicate that chorda of the hindbrain level is an active inductor. However, when chorda from the Triton neurula is trans-planted to the gastrula, posterior chorda may induce ear formation in the trunk of the host (Borghese, '42). Ability to induce ear is spread throughout the roof of the archen-teron but it is greatest at the anterior level of the notochord; heat destroys this capacity. These same cells while still part of the dorsal lip of the blastopore can induce ear. Even the uninvaginated mesoderm on the posterior neural plate of the early neurula retains this ability in Triturus (Kawakami, '43, '49). Development of vesicle in absence of adjacent brain in the chick (Szepsenwol, '33), in Discoglossus (Pasteels, '39), or after its early removal in the chick (Levi-Montal-cini, '46), and studies on Rana hybrids by Moore ('46) indicate that paired mesodermal inductor regions are localized in the pri-mary organizer of the early gastrula. The induction of the ear begins as a part of the primary organization occurring during gastrulation and continues through later stages.

The beginning of the second period of induction is characterized by the approxima-tion of the presumptive ear ectoderm to the adjacent neural fold. The inductive capacity of the hindbrain rudiment has been demon-strated by the formation of the ear vesicle from ectoderm next to a heterotopic hind-brain in Amblystoma (Stone, '31), and in Triton, Rana and Bombinator (Gorbunova,

'39). A developmental dependence of the ear vesicle upon the hindbrain is shown by explantation experiments in Rana and Bufo (Guareschi, '35), and in Triton (Mangold, '37); it is also implied when auditory vesicles occur along with induced neural tis-neural tube is associated with induction of the ear.

The normal inductors of the ear are not species specific in Amphibia (Holtfreter, '35; Albaum and Nestler, '37; Schmidt, '38; Kogan, '39). Ears induced xenoplastically

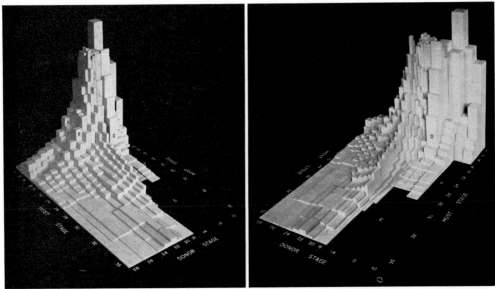

Fig. 150.   Fig. 151.

Fig. 150. Three-dimensional graph indicating the normality of ears induced from gill ectoderm grafted into the ear region. The two horizontal axes are determined by the duration of stages at a given temperature; the vertical axis represents the normality of labyrinths induced from various combinations of donor and host stages.

The view indicates primarily the results obtained when older donors are used with hosts ranging from yolk-plug to motile stages (stages 12 to 35). The peak of the graph represents the normal response of the stage 12 to 12 combination; no other combination of stages consistently produced normal labyrinths. The two ridges labelled A and B represent periods of maximal activation at stages 14 and 20, respectively. The normality of vesicles falls off as hosts and donors become more developed.

Fig. 151. Another aspect of the graph, showing the more complicated results which are produced when younger donor stages are used. The face of the wall labelled C indicates the acquisition of competence to respond to neural activation by stage 18 gill ectoderm. The wall to the right of the label D indicates a marked rise by stage 13 ectoderm in competence to respond to mesodermal activation. The ridges to the left of these walls separated by a shallow recession represent the stages of maximal competence; D indicates the period of maximal competence to respond to mesodermal activation—stage 13; C indicates the same for neural activation—stage 18.

The region E represents negative results obtained by placing ectoderm lacking neural competence on older hosts. The region F represents combinations in which tissue of the central nervous system is induced with or without associated ear vesicles. Since ear vesicles alone did not form, the ability to produce ears was not measured.

sue, e.g., Triton (Holtfreter, '35). The results of Trampusch ('41) with Amblystoma, and Barbasetti ('48) with Rana indicate that migrant neural crest cells may induce ear formation. If these cells are a part of the normal induction system they may augment activation by the rudiment of the hindbrain itself. Experiments on Acipenser (Ginsberg and Dettlaff, '44) and the chick (Waddington, '37) also indicate that the may become functional (Andres, '45) and their rate of development is characteristic of the donor species (Andres, '49). The results of Woerdeman ('38) show that urodele optic vesicle or fibers arising from its retinal layer can serve as an abnormal inductor for ear formation. Other specific abnormal inductors of the ear may well be found, as is implied by the work of Chuang ('39) and Toivonen ('40).

Further characteristics of induction of the ear have been obtained by replacing ear ectoderm by foreign ectoderm; grafts of prospective gill ectoderm from various stages are placed in the ear region of various stages of Amblystoma (Yntema, '50). The relative responses are represented in a three-dimensional graph (Figs. 150 and 151). Mesodermal activation is found to be greatest in the early neural plate stage and to diminish rapidly during neurulation. Neural activation appears during late neurulation and is greatest at the time of closure of the neural folds. It persists longer than the mesodermal and indications of it are present in motile stages. Periods of maximal response occur in the foreign ectoderm; these precede by short intervals the respective periods of maximal activation. In Amblystoma, foreign ectoderm of the early neurula, competent to respond to mesodermal activation, is not as yet competent to respond to neural activation. This second competence is acquired during neurulation. Both competences, once acquired, are retained for a considerable period in decreasing intensity. The observations that the first competence is qualitatively different from the second and that ectoderm with only the first competence does not respond to the second or neural activation show that the two activations, mesodermal and neural, are also qualitatively different. In anurans, the competence to respond to neural activation is present in prospective ectoderm of gastrular stages (Ponomarewa, '38; Schmidt, '38).

The relative importance of the two types of inductions for normal development varies among different groups of amphibians (Ginsberg, '46, '50). The normality of ears resulting from mesodermal induction only and the increments of response brought about by neural activation can be demonstrated by removing neural plate and fold related to the ear ectoderm before and during neural induction in Amblystoma (Yntema, unpublished). Mesodermal induction alone results in imperfect small ears. By the time the ear plate has formed the rudiment is able to develop into a normal labyrinth without further activation by neural tube or crest.

FORMATION OF CAPSULE OF INNER EAR

Development of a cartilaginous capsule for the membranous labyrinth of the inner ear depends upon the presence of the latter (Lewis, '07), and the normality of the membranous labyrinth depends upon presence of the capsule according to Kaan ('38). This latter relationship has been questioned by Detwiler and Van Dyke ('50). In absence of the auditory vesicle, capsular cartilage does not differentiate in amphibia (Lewis, '07) and in the chick (Reagan, '17; Yntema, '44). In a fish, Acipenser, a solid cartilaginous body forms in the ear region after extirpation of the vesicle (Filatow, '30). In the former cases the vesicle induces the mesenchymal cells to form cartilage. In the latter case the differentiation of cartilage is doubly assured since it occurs in absence of the vesicle and since the vesicle can induce a capsule heterotopically.

The dependence of capsule formation has been further analyzed by heterotopic and heteroplastic transplantations of the vesicles. Following heteroplastic exchange of auditory vesicles, the amount of capsular cartilage formed is influenced by the nature of both the graft and the host, e.g., *Amblystoma punctatum* and *A. tigrinum* (Richardson, '32). In all Amphibia tested a heterotopic vesicle near the ear region will induce a more or less complete capsule (Luther, '24) and the induction is interspecific, since an anuran vesicle will induce capsule from the tissue of a urodele host (Lewis, '07). Reports as to the ability of the ear vesicle to induce capsule formation in the trunk are contradictory. According to most studies on urodeles, no capsular cartilage develops except in some instances in which the vesicle lies next to a developing vertebra and apparently induces hyperplasia of the vertebra (Balinsky, '25; Yntema, '33). In anurans a capsule frequently appears but from no such apparent source (Filatow, '27). In xenoplastic combinations the cartilage about anuran labyrinths in urodele flanks is anuran without contribution from the host (Balinsky, '27; Kaan, '30) and so has arisen from the graft, though care was taken by Kaan to exclude mesectoderm of the neural crest and mesentoderm. Heterotopic vesicles on the head of the urodele have capsules which are derived in part from the host and in part from the grafted ear ectoderm (Yntema, '39). These results indicate the conclusion that the ear rudiment or the ectoderm surrounding it may be a source of mesectoderm for the ear capsule, at least in the heterotopic position. This is contrary to the view generally held that the capsule arises from mesentoderm alone both in the normal position (e.g., Stone, '26) and heterotopically (e.g., Kaan, '30). The mesenchyme which constitutes much if not all of the orthotopic capsule arises from mesentoderm of the ear region and the anterior somites (Stone, '26; Kucherova, '35; Ichikawa, '36; Kaan, '38).

The ear vesicle has the ability to draw mesenchymal cells toward it (Filatow, '27). In the flank these may be from sclerotomes and form capsule, or they may be from other sources and organized into a more or less complete limb. In the orthotopic position cells so attracted form the normal capsule (Kaan, '38). If other structures such as nasal placode, optic cup, or lens placode are substituted for the otic vesicle, no cartilaginous capsule forms (Lewis, '07; Ichikawa, '36; Kaan, '38). Orientation of mesenchymal cells about a celloidin block in the ear region has been reported (Filatow, '27).

FORMATION OF MIDDLE EAR

Effects of absence of the inner ear upon the development of the middle ear in Rana have been observed by Luther ('24) and Violette ('28, '30). The tympanic ring and membrane as well as the middle and external parts of the columella develop independently of the inner ear. The inner end of the columella and the operculum are dependent on the presence of a normal labyrinth for their full development but only the operculum is absent when this factor is removed. In the chick, formation of the stapedial plate depends upon presence of the inner ear: the remainder of the columella forms after extirpation of the otic vesicle (Reagan, '17).

The metamorphic transformation of the frog ear has been described by Witschi ('49). Formation of the tympanic membrane of the frog depends upon the presence of the annular tympanic cartilage (Helff, '40). The quadrate, another visceral cartilage, can also induce formation of the membrane if in contact with the skin. A cartilage of the appendicular skeleton is less effective. The induction is probably brought about by some chemical product of the cartilage, since the tympanic cartilage still retains inductive influences after being killed by various methods.

THE NOSE

DIFFERENTIATION OF THE NASAL PLACODE

Studies on the development of the nasal sac show that it undergoes the typical embryonic process of a gradually increasing differentiation along with a progressive loss by the embryo of the ability to constitute the organ from adjacent tissue.

Early differentiation of the nasal rudiment has occurred by the early neurula stage in Amblystoma (Carpenter, '37) and in Rana (Zwilling, '40); this has been demonstrated by heterotopic transplants. Nasal sacs independent of brain tissue may form from prospective ectoderm of the middle gastrula when transplanted to a blastema (Emerson, '45). This result may indicate a determination on the part of the ectodermal rudiment or may be due to an inductor in the abnormal environment. In any case differentiation of the nasal rudiment does not wait upon formation of the neural plate and folds and its induction may start during gastrulation, as does that of the ear.

During neurulation and later stages the rudiment acquires greater power of self-differentiation (Kawakami, '36; Zwilling, '40). Following extirpation of the nasal rudiment during neurular and head process stages, a new sac develops from the replacing ectoderm (Bell, '06; Luna, '15). This ability is subsequently lost (Burr, '16). Belly ectoderm of the early neurula has the ability to form a normal olfactory sac (Kucherova, '45). The formation of the nasolacrimal duct depends upon the presence of the nasal pit (Ogawa, '29).

INDUCTION OF THE NASAL PLACODE

The problems concerned with the induction of the nasal sac are peculiarly like those of the ear vesicle; they involve the questions of a mesodermal and subsequent neural induction.

Considerable evidence points to the presence of an early mesodermal induction of the nasal sac: (1) the more normal differentiation in explants (Emerson, '45) and heterotopically (Luna, '15; Cooper, '43) in presence of underlying mesoderm; (2) induction of sac by mesoderm with no induced brain (Zwilling, '40; Moore, '46; Kawakami, '43), and induction of sacs which have no connection with brain parts, as in Bufo by Triton (Holtfreter, '36); (3) differentiation in situ of nasal organs after removal of anterior neural plate (Spemann, '12; Raunich, '50); (4) formation of a nasal organ following removal of anterior neural fold and olfactory rudiment, and its absence if underlying mesoderm is included in the extirpate (Siggia, '36); (5) the demonstration of differentiation of the rudiment prior to formation of the neural folds and any intimate relation between nasal and neural rudiments (Carpenter, '37; Zwilling, '40; Schmalhausen, '50).

A second induction by the neural crest and fold adjacent to the nasal rudiment has been indicated by several types of observations: (1) the typical association of the nasal placode with the forebrain in cyclopia (e.g., Adelmann, '37) and in experiments primarily concerned with neural inductions (Raven, '33; Mangold, '33b; Holtfreter, '36); (2) dependence for differentiation upon presence of the underlying neural fold or forebrain rudiment in heterotopic positions (Luna, '15; Siggia, '36; Kawakami, '41) and in explants (Mangold, '33a); (3) induction from prospective gastrular ectoderm by neural tissue (Woerdeman, '38); (4) induction by heterotopic forebrain rudiment from flank ectoderm (Zwilling, '34; Kucherova, '45; Kawakami, '36). Zwilling ('40), however, has carefully repeated this last experiment xenoplastically with negative results and ascribes the positive reports to inclusion of the nasal rudiment with the transplant. It may be noted that regeneration of the nasal organ occurs along with reconstitution of the forebrain in the chick (Waddington and Cohen, '36), and that the regeneration was found by Luna ('15) to be dependent upon presence of adjacent neural rudiments in the frog. The results of Siggia ('36) indicated previously contradict this observation of Luna.

The evidence indicates a series of two inductions of the nasal rudiment, but clarification of the problem is obviously needed.

The normal inductors are not species specific in Amphibia (Holtfreter, '35; Zwilling, '40). As in the case of the ear, abnormal inductors may bring about differentiation of a nasal rudiment without accompanying brain tissue. These include the eye rudiment with or without adjacent neural ectoderm (Ikeda, '37; Woerdeman, '38), heated mouse liver (Holtfreter, '34) and alcohol-treated guinea pig thymus (Toivonen, '40).

FORMATION OF SENSORY EPITHELIUM AND NASAL PASSAGEWAYS

The olfactory ectoderm and its derivative, the olfactory nerve, can differentiate with no central nervous connection in Amphibia (Bell, '06; Siggia, '38; Cooper, '43) and in the chick (Street, '37). Fibers of the olfactory nerve have a proliferative effect on the region of the brain which they may enter in both normal and heterotopic locations (Burr, '24a,

24b; May, '27). Shaping of the ectodermal nasal passageways in heterotopic transplants depends upon presence of the mesectoderm surrounding the nasal pit (Cooper, '43). Moreover, most of the ectodermal nasal structures can form without nearby entoderm. In the chick epithelia and cartilage can differentiate independently but their parts are more normal if they interact (Street, '37).

FORMATION OF NASAL CARTILAGES

The dependence of the nasal cartilages upon the nasal sac in urodeles has been described in contradictory fashion by Burr ('16) and Schmalhausen ('39). According to the earlier work, the cartilages differentiate independently of the sac. In absence of the sac they collapse and join the rudiment of the trabecula, thereby enlarging it. In the latter finding the olfactory cartilages proper, that is, the capsule exclusive of its mediobasal part, form only in presence of the nasal sac and arise in part from mesectoderm derived from the sac itself. The size of the trabecula is not increased following extirpation of the nasal rudiment but varies with the size of the adjacent brain. These findings are contradictory and call for further investigation. The report of Burr recalls the independent formation of the ear cartilage in Acipenser; the report of Schmalhausen indicates an inductive action of the nasal sac on mesenchyme such as the amphibian auditory vesicle exerts.

PROBLEMS

Many of the general problems of embryology can be applied to the ear and nose. The nature of organization can be studied in a system apart from neural induction. Work on the specificity of inductors and the inductive effects of chemical compounds has only been initiated. The factors which produce structural specialization remain unknown; in regard to the ear, the question exists as to why a crista forms in one part, a macula in another. Polarization of ectoderm in relation to intracellular organization has been discussed but a means of analysis is as yet unknown.

An outstanding lack in studies on the ear and nose is work on the structural basis of the origin of function. Some correlation would be desirable between the structure and composition of the sense organs at various stages and the functional derivatives of those states. Some problems on the physiology of the organs have been studied in animals prepared by techniques of experimental embryology.

The amphibians have served for the greater part of the experiments on the sense organs. Further determination of conditions in other groups would broaden understanding and afford a safer basis for generalizations. Contradictions and incomplete observations have been indicated in the discussion. These problems offer good prospect for immediate solutions, and the findings are needed to secure understanding of the conditions involved.

REFERENCES

Adelmann, H. B. 1937 Experimental studies on the development of the eye. IV. The effect of the partial and complete excision of the prechordal substrate on the development of the eyes of *Amblystoma punctatum*. J. Exp. Zool., 75:199–237.

Albaum, H. G., and Nestler, H. A. 1937 Xenoplastic ear induction between *Rana pipiens* and *Amblystoma punctatum*. J. Exp. Zool., 75:1–9.

Andres, G. 1945 Ueber die Entwicklung des Anurenlabyrinths in Urodelen (Xenoplastischer Austausch zwischen Bombinator und *Triton alpestris*). Rev. suisse Zool., 52:400–406.

——— 1949 Untersuchungen an Chimären von Triton und Bombinator. Teil I. Entwicklung xenoplastischer Labyrinthe und Kopfganglien. Genetica, 24:387–534.

Balinsky, B. I. 1925 Transplantation des Ohrbläschens bei Triton. Roux' Arch. Entw.-mech., 105:718–731.

——— 1927 Xenoplastische Ohrbläschentransplantation zur Frage der Induktion einer Extremitätenanlage. Roux' Arch. Entw.-mech., 110:63–70.

Barbasetti, M. A. 1948 Sulle relazioni causali di sviluppo "otocisti-cresta neurale" in trapianti embrionali negli Anfibi. Rend. Acad. naz. Lincei, Ser. 8, 4:489–493.

Bell, E. T. 1906 Experimental studies on the development of the eye and the nasal cavities in frog embryos. Anat. Anz., 29:185–194.

Borghese, E. 1942 Transplantation der Chorda von Neurulen unter die präsumptive Rumpfepidermis mittlerer und später Gastrulen in verschiedener Orientierung bei Triton. Roux' Arch. Entw.-mech., 142:53–82.

Burr, H. S. 1916 The effects of the removal of the nasal pits in Amblystoma embryos. J. Exp. Zool., 20:27–57.

——— 1924a Hyperplasia in the brain of Amblystoma. Proc. Soc. Exp. Biol., N. Y., 21:473–474.

——— 1924b Some experiments of the transplantation of the olfactory placode in Amblystoma. 1. An experimentally produced aberrant cranial nerve. J. Comp. Neurol., 37:455–497.

Carpenter, E. 1937 The head pattern in Amblystoma studied by vital staining and transplantation methods. J. Exp. Zool., 75:103–129.

Choi, M. H. 1931 Determination of the ear and side-specificity of the ear region ectoderm in amphibian embryos. Fol. anat. Japon., 9:315–332.

Chuang, H. H. 1939 Induktionsleistungen von frischen und gekochten Organteilen (Niere, Leber) nach ihrer Verpflanzung in Explantate und verschiedene Wirtsregionen von Triton-Keimen. Roux' Arch. Entw.-mech., 139:556–638.

Cooper, R. S. 1943 An experimental study of the development of the larval olfactory organ of *Rana pipiens* Schreber. J. Exp. Zool., 93:415–451.

Dalcq, A. 1933 La détermination de la vésicule auditive chez le discoglosse. Arch. Anat. micro., 29:389–420.

Detwiler, S. R. 1951 Recent experiments on the differentiation of the labyrinth in Amblystoma. J. Exp. Zool., 118:389–406.

———, and Van Dyke, R. H. 1950 The role of the medulla in the differentiation of the otic vesicle. J. Exp. Zool., 113:179–199.

Domacavalli, A. 1937 Le influenze regionali nello sviluppo dell'otocisti negli anfibi anuri. Riv. Biol., 22:245–248.

Dürken, A. 1951 Die Wirkung von Ultraviolettbestrahlungen auf die Ohranlage von *Triton alpestris*. Roux' Arch. Entw.-mech., 144:521–554.

Emerson, H. S. 1945 The development of late gastrula explants of *Rana pipiens* in salt solution. J. Exp. Zool., 100:497–521.

Evans, H. J. 1943 The independent differentiation of the sensory areas of the avian inner ear. Biol. Bull., 84:252–262.

Filatow, D. 1927 Aktivierung des Mesenchyms durch eine Ohrblase und einen Fremdkörper bei Amphibien. Roux' Arch. Entw.-mech., 110:1–32.

——— 1930 Entwicklungsmechanische Untersuchungen an Embryonen von *Acipenser güldenstädii* und *Acipenser stellatus*. Roux' Arch. Entw.-mech., 122:546–583.

Ginsberg, A. S. 1939 Some data on the determination of the ear in *Triton taeniatus*. Compt. Rend. Acad. Sci. U.R.S.S., 22:370–373.

——— 1946 Specific differences in the determination of the internal ear and other ectodermal organs in certain Urodela. Compt. Rend. Acad. Sci. U.R.S.S., 54:557–560.

——— 1950 Arteigentümlichkeit der Anfangsstadien der Entwicklung des Labyrinths bei Amphibien. Compt. Rend. Acad. Sci. U.R.S.S., 73:229–332.

———, and Dettlaff, T. 1944 Experiments on transplantation and removal of organ rudiments in embryos of *Acipenser stellatus* in early developmental stages. Compt. Rend. Acad. Sci. U.R.S.S., 44:209–212.

Gorbunova, G. P. 1939 Concerning inductive capacity of medulla oblongata in embryos of amphibians. Compt. Rend. Acad. Sci. U.R.S.S., 23:298–301.

Guareschi, C. 1930 Studi sullo sviluppo dell'otocisti degli anfibi anuri. Roux' Arch. Entw.-mech., 122:179–203.

——— 1935 Studi sulla determinazione dell' orecchio interno degli anfibi anuri. Arch. ital. Anat. Embriol., 35:97–129.

Hall, E. K. 1937 The determination of the axes

of the embryonic ear: an experimental study by the method of 90° rotations. J. Exp. Zool., 75:11–39.

Hall, E. K. 1939 On the duration of the polarization process in the ear primordium of embryos of Amblystoma punctatum (Linn.). J. Exp. Zool., 82:173–192.

——— 1941 Reversal of polarization in the ear primordium of Amblystoma punctatum. J. Exp. Zool., 86:141–151.

Harrison, R. G. 1924 Experiments on the development of the internal ear. Science, 59:448.

——— 1935 Factors concerned in the development of the ear in Amblystoma punctatum. Anat. Rec., 64 (suppl. 1):38–39.

——— 1936a Relations of symmetry in the developing ear of Amblystoma punctatum. Proc. Nat. Acad., Wash., 22:238–247.

——— 1936b Relations of symmetry in the developing embryo. Coll. Net, 11:217–226.

——— 1938 Further investigation of the factors concerned in the development of the ear. Anat. Rec. 70 (suppl. 3):35.

——— 1945 Relations of symmetry in the developing embryo. Trans. Conn. Acad. Arts & Sci., 36:277–330.

———, Astbury, W. T., and Rudall, K. M. 1940 An attempt at an x-ray analysis of embryonic processes. J. Exp. Zool., 85:339–363.

Helff, O. M. 1940 Studies on amphibian metamorphosis. XVII. Influence of non-living annular tympanic cartilage on tympanic membrane formation. J. Exp. Biol., 17:45–60.

Holtfreter, J. 1933 Der Einfluss von Wirtsalter und verschiedenen Organbezirken auf die Differenzierung von angelagertem Gastrulaektoderm. Roux' Arch. Entw.-mech., 127:619–775.

——— 1934 Ueber die Verbreitung induzierender Substanzen und ihre Leistungen im Tritonkeim. Roux' Arch. Entw.-mech., 132:307–383.

——— 1935 Ueber das Verhalten von Anurenektoderm in Urodelenkeim. Roux' Arch. Entw.-mech., 133:427–494.

——— 1936 Regionale Induktionen in xenoplastisch zusammengesetzten Explantaten. Roux' Arch. Entw.-mech., 134:466–550.

Ichikawa, M. 1936 Experimental studies on the formation of the auditory capsule of amphibians. Bot. Zool., 4:1211–1223.

Ikeda, Y. 1937 Beiträge zur entwicklungsmechanischen Stütze der Kupfferschen Theorie der Sinnesplakoden. Roux' Arch. Entw.-mech., 136:672–675.

Kaan, H. W. 1926 Experiments on the development of the ear of Amblystoma punctatum. J. Exp. Zool., 46:13–61.

——— 1930 The relation of the developing auditory vesicle to the formation of the cartilage capsule in Amblystoma punctatum. J. Exp. Zool., 55:263–291.

——— 1938 Further studies on the auditory vesicle and cartilaginous capsule of Amblystoma punctatum. J. Exp. Zool., 78:159–183.

Kawakami, I. 1936 Self-differentiation of nose and induction of the same organ by the fore-brain in Triturus pyrrhogaster (Boie). Bot. Zool., 6: 1841–1847, 2006–2012.

——— 1941 Nose-inducing capacity of forebrain of the sense-organs in Triturus pyrrhogaster. Zool. Mag., 53:147–157.

——— 1943 Inductions of the cerebral sensory organs. II. Inductive effect of the archenteron roof. Kagaku, 11:399–402. III. Inductive effects of the uninvaginated portion of the dorsal blastopore lip. Bot. Zool., 11:859–862. (Japanese).

——— 1949 Inductive effects of the heated archenteron roof and uninvaginated portion of the blastoporic lip. Siebutu, 4:41–45.

Kogan, R. 1939 Inductive action of medulla oblongata on the body epithelium of amphibia. Compt. Rend. Acad. Sci. U.R.S.S., 23:307–310.

——— 1944 The chordamesoderm as an inductor of the ear vesicle. Compt. Rend. Acad. Sci. U.R.S.S., 45:39–41.

Kucherova, F. N. 1935 Eksperimentalnoe opredelenie istochnikov mezenkhimy, idushcheĭ na obrazovanie slukhovoĭ kapsuly. Rusk. Arkh. Anat., 14:361–370.

——— 1945 Inductive influence of fore-brain upon body epithelium. Compt. Rend. Acad. Sci. U.R.S.S., 47:307–309.

Levi-Montalcini, R. 1946 Ricerche sperimentali sulla determinazione del placode otico nell'embrione di pollo. Rend. Acad. naz. Lincei, Ser. 8, 1:443–448.

——— 1949 The development of the acousticovestibular centers in the chick embryo in the absence of the afferent root fibers and of descending fiber tracts. J. Comp. Neur., 91:209–242.

Lewis, W. H. 1907 On the origin and differentiation of the otic vesicle in amphibian embryos. Anat. Rec., 1:141–145.

Luna, E. 1915 Ricerche sperimentali sulla morfologia dell'organo dell'olfatto negli anfibi. Arch. ital Anat. Embriol., 14:609–628.

Luther, A. 1924 Entwicklungsmechanische Untersuchungen am Labyrinth einiger Anuren. Comment. biol., Helsingf., 2:1–48.

Mangold, O. 1933a Isolationsversuche zur Analyse der Entwicklung bestimmter Kopforgane. Naturw., 21:394–397.

——— 1933b Ueber die Induktionsfähigkeit der verschiedenen Bezirke der Neurula von Urodelen. Naturw., 21:761–766.

——— 1937 Isolationsversuche zur Analyse der Entwicklung der Gehör-, Kiemen- und Extremitätenregion bei Urodelen. Acta Soc. Fauna Flora fenn., 60:3–44.

May, R. M. 1927 Modifications des centres nerveux dues à la transplantation de l'oeil et de l'organe olfactif chez les embryons d'Anoures. Arch. Biol., Paris, 37:335–396.

Moore, J. A. 1946 Studies in the development of frog hybrids. 1. Embryonic development in the cross Rana pipiens ♀ × Rana sylvatica ♂ . J. Exp. Zool., 101:173–219.

Norris, H. W. 1892 Studies on the development of the ear of Amblystoma. I. Development of the auditory vesicle. J. Morph., 7:23–34.

Ogawa, C. 1921 Experiments on the orientation

of the ear vesicle in amphibian larvae. J. Exp. Zool., *34:*17–43.

Ogawa, C. 1926 Einige Experimente zur Entwicklungsmechanik der Amphibienhörbläschen. Fol. anat. japon., *4:*413–431.

——— 1929 Eliminationsversuch der Nase bei den Amphibienlarven. Fol. anat. japon., *6:*703–710.

Pasteels, J. 1939 Les effets de la centrifugation axiale de l'oeuf fécondé et insegmenté chez les amphibiens anoures. Bull. Acad. Belg. Cl. Sci., *25:*334–345.

Ponomarewa, W. N. 1938 Untersuchungen über die Dauer des induktiven Einflusses in der Bildung der Hörbläschen. Russk. Arkh. Anat., *18:*345–352, 478.

Raunich, L. 1950 Ricerche sperimentali sopra l'induzione dell'organo olfattorio negli Anfibi Urodeli. Arch. Sci. Biol., *34:*309–314.

Raven, C. P. 1933 Zur Entwicklung der Ganglienleiste. III. Die Induktionsfähigkeit des Kopfganglienleistenmaterials von *Rana fusca.* Roux' Arch. Entw.-mech., *130:*517–561.

Reagan, F. P. 1917 The role of the auditory sensory epithelium in the formation of the stapedial plate. J. Exp. Zool., *23:*85–108.

Richardson, D. 1932 Some effects of heteroplastic transplantation of the ear vesicle in Amblystoma. J. Exp. Zool., *63:*413–445.

Röhlich, K. 1929 Experimentelle Untersuchungen über den Zeitpunkt der Determination der Gehörblase bei Amblystoma-Embryonen. Roux' Arch. Entw.-mech., *118:*164–199.

Rudnick, D. 1944 Early history and mechanics of the chick blastoderm. Quart. Rev. Biol., *19:*187–212.

Schmalhausen, O. I. 1939 Rôle of the olfactory sac in the development of the cartilage of the olfactory organ in Urodela. Compt. Rend. Acad. Sci. U.R.S.S., *23:*395–398.

——— 1940 Development of ear vesicles in the absence of medulla oblongata in amphibians. Compt. Rend. Acad. Sci. U.R.S.S., *28:*277–280.

——— 1950 Lokalisation und Entwicklung der Nasenanlage der Wirbeltiere im Zusammenhang mit der Frage ihrer Entstehung. Compt. Rend. Acad. Sci. U.R.S.S., *74:*1045–1048.

Schmidt, G. A. 1938 Die morphogenetische Bedeutung des Nervensystems. I. Die Korrelation in der Entwicklung des Gehörorgans. Russk. Arkh. Anat., *18:*298–344, 475–477.

Sidorov, O. A. 1937 Transplantation in certain Anura of the auditory vesicle in diverse stages of its development in order to discover the moment of its determination and its influence on the mesenchyme. Russk. Arkh. Anat., *16:*25–71, 145–162.

Siggia, S. 1936 Contributi allo studio della determinazione del placode olfattivo in *Discoglossus pictus.* Monit. zool. ital., *47* (suppl.):116–119.

——— 1938 Ulteriori contributi allo studio della determinazione del placode olfattivo in *Discoglossus pictus.* Monit. zool. ital., *48* (suppl.):161–164.

Spemann, H. 1910 Die Entwicklung des invertierten Hörgrübchens zum Labyrinth. Ein kri-

tischer Beitrag zur Strukturlehre der Organanlagen. Roux' Arch. Entw.-mech., *30:*437–458.

——— 1912 Zur Entwicklung des Wirbeltierauges. Zool. Jb., Abt. 3, *32:*1–98.

Stcherbatov, I. I. 1938 Transplantation of auditory vesicle of chick embryo into chorio-allantois. Bull. Biol. Méd. exp., *6:*511–514.

Stone, L. S. 1926 Further experiments on the extirpation and the transplantation of mesectoderm in *Amblystoma punctatum.* J. Exp. Zool., *44:*95–131.

——— 1931 Induction of the ear by the medulla and its relation to experiments on the lateralis system in amphibia. Science, *74:*577.

Street, S. F. 1937 The differentiation of the nasal area of the chick embryo in grafts. J. Exp. Zool., *77:*49–85.

Streeter, G. L. 1907 Some factors in the development of the amphibian ear vesicle and further experiments on equilibration. J. Exp. Zool., *4:*431–445.

——— 1914 Experimental evidence concerning the determination of posture of the membranous labyrinth in amphibian embryos. J. Exp. Zool., *16:*149–176.

——— 1921 Migration of the ear vesicle in the tadpole during normal development. Anat. Rec., *21:*115–126.

Szepsenwol, J. 1933 Recherches sur les centres organisateurs des vésicules auditives chez des embryons de poulets omphalocéphales obtenus expérimentalement. Arch. Anat. micro., *29:*5–94.

Toivonen, S. 1940 Ueber die Leistungsspezifität der abnormen Induktoren im Implantatversuch bei Triton. Ann. Acad. Sci. fenn., *55:*1–150.

Tokura, R. 1924 Zur Frage der Hörbläscheninversion. Fol. anat. japon, *2:*97–106.

——— 1925 Entwicklungsmechanische Untersuchungen über das Hörbläschen und das akustische, sowie faciale Ganglion bei den Anuren. Fol. anat. japon., *3:*173–208.

Trampusch, H. 1941 On ear-induction. Acta neerl. Morph. 4, 195–213.

Violette, H. N. 1928 An experimental study on formation of middle ear in Rana. Proc. Soc. Exp. Biol., N. Y., *25:*684.

——— 1930 Origin of columella auris of Anura. Anat. Rec., *45:*280.

Waddington, C. H. 1937 The determination of the auditory placode in the chick. J. Exp. Biol., *14:*232–239.

———, and Cohen, A. 1936 Experiments on the development of the head of the chick embryo. J. Exp. Biol., *13:*219–236.

Waterman, A. J., and Evans, H. J. 1940 Morphogenesis of the avian ear rudiment in chorioallantoic grafts. J. Exp. Zool., *84:*53–71.

Witschi, E. 1949 The larval ear of the frog and its transformation during metamorphosis. Zeit. Naturf., *4b:*230–242.

Woerdeman, M. W. 1938 Inducing capacity of the embryonic eye. Proc. konink. nederl. Akad. Wetens., *41:*336–343.

——— 1941 On the development of polarity in

the ectoderm of amphibian embryos. Proc. konink. nederl. Akad. Wetens., 44:262–267.

Yntema, C. L.   1933   Experiments on the determination of the ear ectoderm of *Amblystoma
punctatum*. J. Exp. Zool., 65:317–357.

———   1937   An experimental study of the origin
of the cells which constitute the VIIth and VIIIth
ganglia and nerves in the embryo of *Amblystoma
punctatum*. J. Exp. Zool., 75:75–105.

———   1939   Self-differentiation of heterotopic
ear ectoderm in the embryo of *Amblystoma punctatum*. J. Exp. Zool., 80:1–17.

———   1944   Experiments on the origin of the
sensory ganglia of the facial nerve in the chick.
J. Comp. Neurol., 81:147–167.

———   1946   An analysis of the induction of the
ear vesicle in the salamander embryo. Coll. Net,
19:30–31.

———   1948   The symmetry of ears induced from
disharmonic ectoderm. Anat. Rec., 100 (suppl. 1):
95.

———   1950   An analysis of induction of the ear
from foreign ectoderm in the salamander embryo.
J. Exp. Zool., 113:211–244.

Zwilling, E.   1934   Induction of the olfactory
placode by the forebrain in *Rana pipiens*. Proc.
Soc. Exp. Biol., N. Y., 31:933–935.

———   1940   An experimental analysis of the
development of the anuran olfactory organ. J.
Exp. Zool., 84:291–323.

———   1941   The determination of the otic vesicle in *Rana pipiens*. J. Exp. Zool., 86:333–342.

CHAPTER 4

Limb and Girdle

J. S. NICHOLAS

VERTEBRATE APPENDAGES

VERTEBRATE appendages are outgrowths of materials located in the body wall. The localization and determination of the constituent elements occur early in the history of the embryo. Morphologically, there are commonly distinguished two borders, the anterior or preaxial and the posterior or postaxial, and two surfaces, dorsal and ventral, which will later become respectively the extensor and flexor surfaces of the free appendage.

In the embryo, an ectodermal fin fold clearly marks the pre- and postaxial borders. The pectoral and pelvic fins of fishes and the extremities of all tetrapod vertebrates are rotated away from the primitive embryonic position during development.

Frequently, the pre- and postaxial borders are not readily distinguishable in the developing tetrapod limb. This is particularly so in amphibians where there is no ectodermal fold, the limb developing as a cylindrical outgrowth with a rounded tip. In the lizards, an ectodermal fold is present (Mollier, 1895; Peter, '03; Braus, '04a).

The fold when first observed is longitudinal, the preaxial portion being anterior and the postaxial portion being posterior. During the course of development, there is a torsion in the forelimb which brings the preaxial or radial border ventrally while the postaxial or ulnar border becomes dorsal in position. This process is reversed in the hind limb.

Since the ectodermal fold is lacking in Amblystoma the pre- and postaxial borders are first recognizable in the forelimb when they have undergone a partial rotation about halfway between the assumed original rotation and the final degree of limb torsion. The distal portion of the extremity later destined to form the hand serves as an index of the torsion. The plane of flattening of the hand is inclined 45 degrees to the horizontal plane of the embryo. Because of the late appearance of the limb borders, it is impossible to ascertain by observation which radius of the limb disc represents the future radial border. It is indicated, however, in Swett's ('23) work that the material which later is distributed along the proximal border is found in the anteroventral quadrant of the limb disc not far from the center and about a radius which lies from 30 to 45 degrees anterior to the dorsoventral axis. The materials composing the limb bud of Amblystoma are localized much nearer to their definitive location than they are in the lizard. This seems to be the case in even the earliest limb transplantations (Detwiler, '29). This means that as the materials grow into the free extremity they develop without torsion into a limb which is apparently partially twisted. After the digits have formed, further torsion takes place, turning the radial border to a ventral position and the ulnar to a dorsal one.

THE DEVELOPMENT OF THE FORELIMB IN AMBLYSTOMA[*]

In the beginning tail-bud stage (Fig. 152A, stage 25) the pronephric swelling is visible and the somites may be observed through the ectoderm. There is no distinct limb bud present, but the region centered under the fourth segment just ventral to the pronephros contains the material that will give rise to the limb. When the tail bud is more marked (Fig. 152B, stage 29) the somatopleure ventral to the pronephros is thickened. The material is, however, a region rather than a "limb bud" on the surface of the embryo, since the chief cause of the swelling in that region is the pronephric swelling, the somatopleural thickening merely serving to round

---

[*] Modified from Harrison's ('18) description of the course of normal development of the forelimb of the spotted salamander, *A. punctatum*.

it ventrally. After this period the prominence on the side of the embryo becomes distinct (Fig. 152C, stage 33), but it is not until several days later that the extremity itself appears on the surface as a sharper elevation in the region of the fourth somite.

The limb bud at first is a nodule about one and a half somites in diameter, and is being nearest the body. A little later, the first trace of the digitations appears at the extreme tip of the limb, the depression representing the notch between the first two digits (Fig. 152G). The digits elongate rapidly, as does the whole limb, but the joints are at this time not distinct. The dorsal border of the limb becomes distinctly

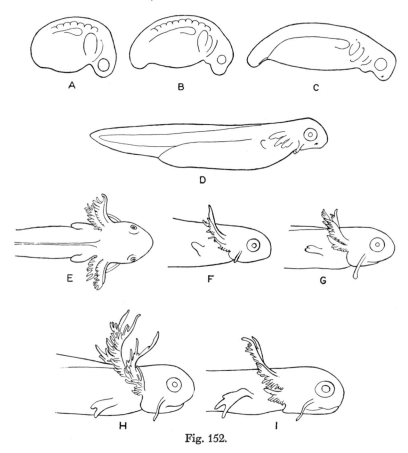

Fig. 152.

almost radially symmetrical. It soon acquires greater convexity on its dorsoposterior border (Fig. 152D), and may be said to point in that direction, though the surface is rounded. From this period growth is rapid. The tip of the bud frees itself from the body wall, the axis of the limb making an angle of 30 to 35 degrees with that of the body when viewed from above, and pointing dorsally at about the same angle to the horizontal. The bud elongates into cylindrical form, being attached to the body wall obliquely at its base. During this process the axis of the limb is more nearly parallel to the median plane (Figs. 152E and F). The distal part of the limb becomes flattened in a plane about 45 degrees to vertical, the dorsal border convex, and at the same time the hand is so twisted as to lie in a vertical instead of an oblique plane. The latter change is in reality partial pronation. The more lateral, which is morphologically the preaxial (radial) border, becomes ventral, the pollex lying on this side. The hand broadens and the forearm becomes somewhat flattened also. The elbow joint is now slightly flexed towards the ventral side (Fig. 152H). The limb is not motile, the changes being due to growth and not to muscular action. The third and fourth digits appear successively on the ulnar (dorsal) border of the hand, first as nodules which slowly elongate, the fourth being considerably behind the third in its development (Fig. 152I). The arm from above is bowed toward the body. The form changes of the limb are concerned largely with the lengthening of the various segments, notably the digits, and the more distinct demarcation of the arm, forearm and manus.

Rotation takes place at the shoulder, the arm is directed more laterally and ventrally, so that the tip of the first digit rests on the substrate. Further rotation at this joint, coupled with flexion at the elbow, brings the manus much further forward beneath the gills, and the animal now rests upon two digits of each limb. The balancers, which serve to support the larva, are lost at stage 46. The first muscular movements take place at the shoulder at stage 44, and later, movement begins at the elbow (stage 45) and wrist joints (stage 46); the limb is then used in crawling, the positions just described being those at rest. These changes are completed just about the time the yolk is entirely gone and the larva begins to feed (Harrison, '18).

BASIC EXPERIMENTAL WORK ON THE LIMB

The limb bud of the anuran larva constitutes a self-differentiating system which develops into a normal limb when transplanted to new and strange surroundings (Braus, '03, '04b, '09; Banchi, '04, '05; Harrison, '07). The various problems which have evolved from this fact of amphibian development have become so numerous and so widespread that they form overlapping sequences in modern experimentation.

The review of only part of the limb problem can be attempted here. This centers about the problems of limb development, limb specificity, limb and girdle relationships and reduplication. These taken together form a combination of studies which have to do with the axial relations, their development, determination and behavior. Chronologically, the first problems to be attacked were problems of the outgrowth of the nerve fibers. Their results yielded the facts which later formed the basis for the modern concepts of nerve outgrowth (Harrison, '15, '24).

We may now attempt to locate more precisely the borders and surfaces of the definitive limb in the disc of tissue out of which it develops. Assuming them to be in the same relative position at the stage at which the operations are done as later, when these features first become visible, an oblique

line crossing the disc through the posterodorsal and the anteroventral quadrants would pass through the ulnar and radial borders and hence divide the flexor from the extensor surface.

The only reliable information bearing on this question is that given in Swett's ('23) paper. The posterodorsal sector forms the whole flexor surface and the distal portion of the extensor; the anterodorsal sector forms the rest of the extensor surface and extends along the radial border almost to the tip. The anteroventral portion forms the shoulder, while the posterior sector does not participate in the formation of the free limb at all but enters only into the shoulder and body wall. If instead of dividing the limb bud vertically and horizontally, as in Swett's experiments, one were to split it obliquely at the proper inclination, the cut would no doubt pass through the growing point of the limb and separate the flexor from the extensor surfaces.

Balfour's (1878) discovery of the composite nature of the elasmobranch fin raised also the question of the possible relationship between the mesodermal somites and the developing limb. That this relationship is variable is shown by the work of Harrison (1895) on teleosts, where a complete series of fin structures either dependent or independent of the mesoderm can be obtained. The limb will develop normally after the damage or complete extirpation of the mesodermal somites. There is no demonstrable contribution of the somites to the musculature of the limb in amphibians (Byrnes, 1898; Lewis, '10; Detwiler, '18, '29).

Byrnes' (1898) analysis of the situation in the frog embryo was obtained by burning the somites in the hind limb region with a hot needle. The defects in the somites produced no defect in the development or musculature of the limb. This experiment was repeated upon the urodele embryo by Lewis ('10), using a more refined technique. He extirpated the somites, cutting out the mesoderm and observing the subsequent defects in the larva. While the ventrolateral musculature was deficient, the limb developed normally, showing no defects in skeleton or musculature. Detwiler ('18, '29), in his study of girdle formation and also in his spinal cord studies, has performed identical experiments with the same results—perfectly independent limb development.

The forelimb region of the urodele embryo is a self-differentiating system. The materials which later form the limb can be located much earlier than they can in anuran forms (Harrison, '17).

The area for forelimb formation has been located in the body wall mesoderm of *Amblystoma punctatum* at stage 25 (Harrison, '15, '17, '18); stage 18, high neural fold (Detwiler, '18); slit blastopore, stage 13 (Detwiler, '29); Vogt ('29) located it in Triton at the beginning of gastrulation.

The time at which a definite structure can be located in the embryo has an important bearing on its usefulness in transplantation. In anuran forms the larvae are quite well developed before the limb bud can be located and removed. In *Amblystoma punctatum* the definitive tissues which later go into the formation of the limb are located before any visible surface indications of the bud can be observed. This location of tissue, consisting of a portion of the somatopleuric mesoderm covered by overlying ectoderm, was originally found in the tail bud stage (Harrison, '17) (stage 29). Since that time, Detwiler ('18), by the use of Nile blue sulfate transplants, was able to locate the limb area in the stage of high neural fold (stage 18), and later traced the definitive material back to the slit blastopore stage (stage 13).

The limb material can then be transplanted before it develops into any sort of structure. Its effect upon the organism upon which it is growing can be tested, as well as its normal and abnormal relationships to it. It affords us, then, a perfect experimental tool for studying various effects and has been used as such to great advantage. The limb disc, at the usual operating stage (29), is localized as a thickening of the somatopleure centered ventral to the fourth myotome and extending ventral to the third and fifth myotomes. The area involved is usually described as a circular area three and one-half somites in diameter (Harrison, '17, '18).

The constant localization of the limb material with reference to other structures which can plainly be observed in the embryo is a very important factor in the ease with which the limb materials can be located. Harrison's experiments in determining the extent of the limb-forming materials furnish an interesting example of the capacity of the limb region to regenerate. The transplantation experiments test its capacity to develop in new and strange surroundings.

The experiments were performed by removing the material (both ectoderm and somatopleuric mesoderm) from a given area. The loose mesoderm left behind after the removal of the majority of the limb-forming tissue was either carefully removed or left in place. When the mesoderm was carefully removed there was less likelihood of regeneration. When the operative area was large the number of regenerating limbs was reduced.

After the removal of tissues from this region, the tissues forming a ring around the outside of the wound tend to migrate toward the center and form a new limb-forming region. This is an area of mesodermal material which under normal conditions would never form a limb but which under the imposed operative conditions moves into the region formerly occupied by limb material. This region Harrison would term as normally possessing a weak potency for limb formation. Under normal conditions it is marginal tissue. It is only under unusual circumstances of limb removal that it possesses the capacity for limb formation.

It is interesting that when a transplant (5 somites in diameter) larger than 3½ somites is removed from the limb region and transplanted to the flank region, and then the central portion of the graft is removed, the behavior of the ring of material around the limb is the same as though it were in normal position. A considerable number of regenerating limbs can be secured after this procedure.

When a wound of 3½ somites in diameter is made in the limb region and the mesoderm carefully cleaned from the floor of the wound, regeneration of a limb seldom occurs. This Harrison ('18) has taken as the region which contains the preponderance of normal limb-forming material. The limb is formed by the rapid multiplication of the cells contained within the limb disc and not by the migration of tissues which lie outside of the disc.

This fact again emphasizes the independence of the limb. The histology of the so-called limb bud shows numerous mitoses while the regions surrounding it show many less karyokinetic figures. This is a histological indication of the limb independence which is proved by transplantation and also by the lack of relationships to the mesodermal somites.

When the limb disc of 3½ somites is removed and the wound is covered by indifferent ectoderm, no limb develops (Harrison, '18). The extirpation of the limb region with the cleaning of mesodermal cells is sufficient to reduce to 14 per cent the chances of regeneration of the limb. When the limb region is removed but the wound not cleaned of mesoderm the amount of regeneration is 82 per cent. When, however, the wound is cleaned and a piece of indifferent ectoderm from any part of the body is healed over the wound, there is no regeneration of the limb. The transplantation of indifferent tissue has blocked the inwandering of the surrounding tissues and prevents reconstitution. If the ectoderm of the normal limb region be thoroughly freed from the closely adherent mesoderm cells, it reacts as indifferent ectoderm taken from other regions of the body and prevents limb growth.

The material which forms the limb constitutes an equipotential system; any part can form the whole; two superimposed limb discs can form a normal limb (Harrison, '18, '21; Schwind, '31). Limb equipotentiality is based upon the results of experiments in which (1) after the extirpation of any half of the limb bud, the remaining half gives rise to a complete normal limb; (2) two superimposed buds form a limb which at first is large but which rapidly regulates to the normal size; (3) a normal limb may develop from two ventral or two dorsal halves if they are properly oriented; (4) after inversion of the limb disc, the radial portion of the limb gives rise to the ulnar portion and vice versa, changing the prospective significance of practically the entire cellular constituency of the bud; (5) the inoculation of mesoderm from the limb region, even though disorganized by the operation, can give rise to a normal limb; (6) a composite limb formed of a half-limb disc of an *Amblystoma tigrinum* embryo transplanted upon an *A. punctatum* embryo in place of a half of the *A. punctatum* limb region gives rise to a perfect composite limb with morphological characteristics of each species recognizable. The evidence seems overwhelming for an equipotential system in Driesch's ('05) sense.

The limb-forming materials are localized in the mesoderm. This is shown by experiments in which the limb ectoderm is transplanted but does not develop a limb; the mesoderm of the limb disc may be removed and the normal limb ectoderm left in its normal location, but no limb develops; the transplantation of mesoderm alone to a strange environment produces limb development (Harrison, '18, '25).

The experimental proof for these statements is so rigorous that one would hardly expect any question to be raised with regard to the truth of the location. However,

Filatow ('28) reports that there is no development of a forelimb in the axolotl after the transplantation of mesoderm alone. "In 20ige Fällen ist das Mesenchymtransplantat nach einigen Tagen verschwunden und dementsprechend hat sich auch die äussere Vorwölbung des das Transplantat bedeckenden Epithels vollständig geglättet." In two other cases, the formation of cartilages unrelated to the extremity was found. In these cases, the transplanted material remained for a longer time. In all others there was no histological trace of the transplant or structures influenced. From these facts, Filatow considers that the materials transplanted have not yet been determined as limb forming. Unfortunately, the exact stage of the animal is not given, but the period of development utilized extends from the tail-bud stage through early motile stages, in which one would expect, on the basis of Harrison's work, that determination would have taken place. Harrison's work receives confirmation from Ruud's ('26) analysis of symmetry relation, but unfortunately this work does not employ the mesoderm alone so that we have no definite experiments which correspond to those of Filatow. Balinsky ('31), working upon *Triturus taeniatus*, finds that the mesenchyme plays an important part in limb differentiation. The results are conflicting and the experiments are not strictly comparable, since the limb and its mesoderm develop much earlier in *A. punctatum* than in either the axolotl or Triturus.

Steiner ('21) has published a short series of experiments in which he has seared the epithelial covering of the hindlimb bud of Rana. His conclusion is that the formative influence of the ectoderm acts upon the mesoderm in the production of a limb and that in this the amphibians studied are similar to the higher vertebrates.

The mass of evidence points to the determination of the limb mesoderm of urodeles as the positive factor of limb formation. The evidence so far amassed for the anuran group, which is scattered and scanty, points to an interaction between the ectoderm and mesoderm. Development of the limb is in all cases taken at later stages than the urodele observations and absolutely no critical experiments have been carried through to show the sequence which is hypothesized as causative. Until clear-cut experiments can give more light upon anuran development, it would seem wiser to continue the concept of mesodermal determination as a working hypothesis; it is a simpler view, it is adequate for describing development, and it keeps one from using the term "organizer" indiscriminately and not in Spemann's sense.

THE GIRDLE

THE PECTORAL GIRDLE

In the amphibian, Harrison ('18) showed that if the limb disc (3½ somites in diameter) were removed the central parts of the scapula would not develop. The peripheral

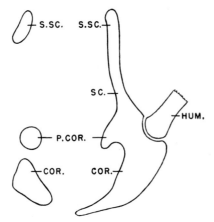

Fig. 153. *S. Sc.*, Suprascapula; *Sc.*, scapula; *P. Cor.*, procoracoid; *Cor.*, coracoid; *Hum.*, humerus (from Harrison, '18).

parts, suprascapula, coracoid and procoracoid, however, were represented by small stubs of cartilage with a shape fairly characteristic of the part which should appear in the specific region occupied by the above structures. (See Fig. 153.)

This finding corroborates Braus' ('09) results and indicates an early localization of the parts of the girdle. If, however, the animals were kept for fairly long periods (ca. 100 days) the rudiments of the outlying girdle parts coalesce into a single cartilaginous mass. This process was studied in detail by Detwiler ('18), who described the steps in restitution of the total structure and who further circumscribed the parts giving rise to the girdle.

From his results, Swett's ('23) work and some unpublished experiments of my own, a diagram can be constructed which shows the localization of parts as we now understand it. These are projected upon the lateral flank of Amblystoma (stage 29) as shown in Figure 154.

The suprascapula develops as a good sized rudiment in the absence of the limb. This

is the most constant of the developing single parts, maintaining its morphology and position with a greater degree of constancy than the other two outlying parts, both of which tend to lie closer than normal to the center of where the limb would have developed.

The procoracoid particularly is affected by limb disc removal and is frequently a much smaller vestige, whereas the coracoid is less affected. The suprascapular rudiment develops from an area that impinges upon the borders of the mesodermal somites; the area indicated by hatching in Figure 154 possesses a greater degree of regional determination than is found in the other two parts and is least affected.

The chondrogenesis of the girdle seems to follow a similar pattern in the Amphibia. Wiedersheim (1889) found the same sequence of formation in Triturus, Siredon and Salamandra that Detwiler finds in Amblystoma. Braus ('09) records just about the same course of events in Bombinator. There are three centers, one for the scapula, one for the coracoid and one for the procoracoid. There is normally no separate center for the suprascapula, but in the absence of the limb this does chondrify separately from the other two outlying elements.

In the normal animal the girdle and its parts are readily recognizable by dissection after a light staining in toto with Ehrlich's haemotoxylin. Before the limb has elongated and while it is still a shelf-like projection from the body wall, the preparations will show an aggregation of heavy mesenchyme which differentiates into characteristic prochondrin before the stage of trifurcation, which indicates the appearance of the first digit. The prochondrin differentiates directly into chondrin, and cartilage is formed about the twentieth day of larval life. At this time the ulnar digit is just beginning to form.

The scapula and the outlying parts which enter into the formation of the glenoid cavity will ossify after metamorphosis, the remaining parts retaining their cartilaginous character.

During development the limb and the girdle present embryonic systems in combination in a most interesting way. Detwiler's ('18) work shows the mosaic character of the girdle; Harrison's ('18) results prove the equipotentiality of the limb. These two systems differentiating in normal contiguity produce a harmonious morphological system, the appendicular skeleton in which the girdle elements, anchored as they are to the body wall, act as the regulators of the posture assumed by the free extremity.

In the diagram (Fig. 154) the nearly central region of the limb area (between 3 and 5) is comparatively free of girdle-forming cells. Gradually the limb posture becomes dominated by the girdle structures at its proximal extremity. This is shown by experiments in which the developing tissues around the limb area are rotated, producing a corresponding rotation of the limb without reversing its laterality. In this process of postural control the outlying rudiments must presumptively be considered as the most effective factors. When the limb is trans-

tated the girdle may, instead of showing its normal morphological components, develop as a plate-like sheet of cartilage.

Since the forelimb mesoderm will grow into a forelimb under various experimental conditions, including the inversion of the mediolateral axis, why is it that a limb disc does not always develop two limbs, as experimentally demonstrated by Nieuwkoop ('46) in embryos deprived of the yolk mass? It is, of course, easy to assume a simple mechanical inhibition caused by the presence of the heavy yolk. When, however, a small bit of head ectoderm is placed

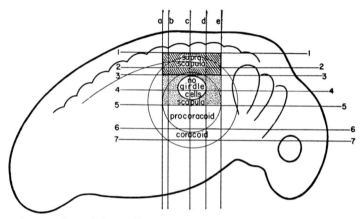

Fig. 154. The various portions of the girdle-forming region have been tested by transplantation experiments for which the parts marked out by the vertical lines (*a* to *e*) and the horizontal lines (*1* to *7*) were employed singly or in combination (from Detwiler, '18; Swett, '23; and Nicholas, unpublished).

planted heterotopically with but a small part of the scapula, the imparted rotation is not corrected in later stages.

The relation between the girdle and the free extremity is important also in reduplication, reversal of symmetry and inversion. The work of Swett ('32, '45) throws some light on these problems but much remains to be explained. Usually the girdle is abnormal when the limb is duplicated after operations involving rotations of various degrees. Usually after orthotopic inverted limb disc transplantations the limb is reversed in its asymmetry and so is its girdle, i.e., a right limb disc upside down on the right side of the embryo becomes a left limb with a left-sided girdle. This speaks strongly for a change in the mosaic structure of the girdle parts, for their localized developmental potencies cannot be irreversibly fixed or determined. When areas as large as 5 somites in diameter are used for transplantation there is seldom formed a reduplicating limb, whether orthotopically or heterotopically transplanted. If this graft is ro-

over the limb mesoderm, replacing its normal covering ectoderm, a similar result is obtained, and here the mechanical effect cannot be assumed to be perceptibly greater than in the normal ectoderm. Yet there is inhibition of differentiation. The presence of the developing girdle might also be thought of as a possible factor that causes the extremity to develop outside the flank instead of inside the coelom, but it lacks the ability to make the mesoderm form a free extremity when covered with head ectoderm. There are still many problems of morphogenesis to which the limb-girdle combination may contribute solutions.

THE PELVIC GIRDLE

Stultz ('36) has performed a series of experiments which yield information regarding the development of the hindlimb and girdle of Amblystoma. The same course of events is followed as in the forelimb but the mosaic constitution of the girdle is not so striking as in the forelimb. In his analysis

Stultz is dealing with a structure which is developing relatively and actually later than the forelimb and therefore will show variants from its pattern. It is remarkable that the course of events is so similar when the differentiation time is so widely separated.

THE LIMB AND GIRDLE IN REPTILES

The amphibian embryos have served as the tool for most of the experimental analy-

ses. A critical morphological study of the development of the forelimbs and hindlimbs and their girdles in Lacerta has been completed by Romer ('42, '44). The first stage which he treats shows the development of the limb-girdle mass in an embryo of 5 to 6 mm. crown-rump length. It is more advanced in development than is the case in Amblystoma, for the mesenchyme composing the limb bud is perceptibly thicker and consists of three layers ar-

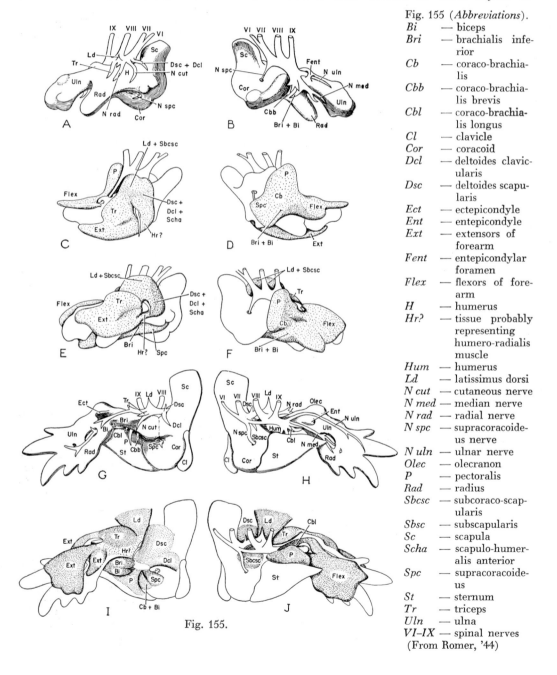

Fig. 155.

Fig. 155 (*Abbreviations*).

Bi	— biceps
Bri	— brachialis inferior
Cb	— coraco-brachialis
Cbb	— coraco-brachialis brevis
Cbl	— coraco-brachialis longus
Cl	— clavicle
Cor	— coracoid
Dcl	— deltoides clavicularis
Dsc	— deltoides scapularis
Ect	— ectepicondyle
Ent	— entepicondyle
Ext	— extensors of forearm
Fent	— entepicondylar foramen
Flex	— flexors of forearm
H	— humerus
Hr?	— tissue probably representing humero-radialis muscle
Hum	— humerus
Ld	— latissimus dorsi
N cut	— cutaneous nerve
N med	— median nerve
N rad	— radial nerve
N spc	— supracoracoideus nerve
N uln	— ulnar nerve
Olec	— olecranon
P	— pectoralis
Rad	— radius
Sbcsc	— subcoraco-scapularis
Sbsc	— subscapularis
Sc	— scapula
Scha	— scapulo-humeralis anterior
Spc	— supracoracoideus
St	— sternum
Tr	— triceps
Uln	— ulna
VI–IX	— spinal nerves

(From Romer, '44)

ranged dorsoventrally. Mollier (1895) interpreted these layers as derivatives of the myotomes, but Romer finds that they are completely separated from the myotomes at this stage and he is certain that their subsequent history is independent of the myotomes.

In his stage II (Figs. 155A–F) Romer shows the rapid differentiation which has occurred in the limb and girdle with a slight increase (1 mm.) in length of the

polarized at different times in development. In Lacerta with the very rapid differentiation one might expect that the axes are not separable by time.

LIMB AND GIRDLE DEVELOPMENT IN BIRDS AND MAMMALS

Normal development of the limbs and girdles is well described in detail in birds and mammals (Hamilton, '52; Patten, '51;

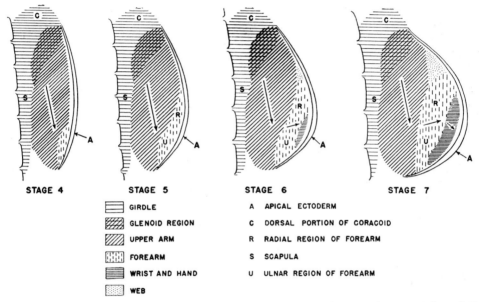

GIRDLE	A	APICAL ECTODERM
GLENOID REGION	C	DORSAL PORTION OF CORACOID
UPPER ARM	R	RADIAL REGION OF FOREARM
FOREARM	S	SCAPULA
WRIST AND HAND	U	ULNAR REGION OF FOREARM
WEB		

Fig. 156. Maps showing the approximate areas for tissues of the future wing parts in stages 4 through 7. The arrows indicate the direction of the future long axes of the wing parts designated. (From Saunders, '48.)

embryo. There is a regional blocking out of the heavy condensing mesenchyme. The halves of the girdle are remote from each other and no dermal elements are present.

When the embryo has reached stage III (Figs. 155 G–J), the girdle and the limb parts are plainly in evidence. The rapidity of limb growth and of its differentiation are both much greater than one would find in a similar stage in Amblystoma.

Lacerta raises interesting problems; first, because of the simultaneity of development of the girdle and the limb; second, because of the three layered composition of the mesenchyme which gives rise to these structures; and third, because of the speed with which differentiation in the whole appendicular skeleton occurs. One would expect results quite different from those obtained in Amblystoma, particularly with reference to the polarization of the limb axes. In Amblystoma the three axes are

Bardeen and Lewis, '01; Broman, '11). There are, however, some experimental findings which demand attention. Hamburger's ('38) implants of the wing primordium into the coelom (cf. Rudnick, '45) showed its capacity for complete self-differentiation. By marking with carbon particles Saunders ('48) has determined the sequential order of the development of the tissues of the wing and their relation to its future parts.

Almost all of the wing bud, at stage 4, consists of the materials which will form the proximal parts of the wing and its girdle. On the basis of his experiments in which the outgrowth has been carefully observed and described, Saunders concludes that development of the limb parts is in proximodistal order and that this is controlled by the ectodermal cap of the wing primordium. The results of the carbon marking experiments are confirmed by the removal of the ectodermal cap in successive developmental stages, which results in suppressing the apical growth zone. The earlier the removal of the ectodermal cap, the greater the deficiency in wing parts.

Saunders rightly interprets his findings in stating that the apical ectoderm is essential. He draws, however, too great a contrast with the results obtained in Amblystoma. His statement that previous workers have assumed a completely passive role for the ectoderm is not justified, since in no case was the role of the ectoderm important to the problems under consideration. Harrison ('18) first showed that when the limb mesoderm was removed and the ectoderm which before formed the cover to the limb mesoderm was used as a cover for the wound, no limb development occurred, although if the wound was left uncovered limb development frequently took place. In the light of this experiment in which mesoderm which possessed the potentiality to form limb was covered by ectoderm which would have formed the covering of the limb, it hardly seems possible that the same conditions prevail in the essentiality of the ectoderm. This is likewise shown in transplantation of limb mesoderm to the flank with a covering of flank ectoderm, for the limb develops with its normal asymmetry if the mesoderm is dorsodorsal in orientation and has reversed asymmetry if oriented dorsoventrally.

The flank ectoderm has dorsodorsal orientation and, if directive, should give the result which Saunders obtained in transplanting the wing primordium with inverted orientation to the hindlimb region. The initial asymmetry was maintained. As Saunders himself states, more evidence is needed on this point, and he has outlined the experimentation which would give the added information.

Just where the mammalian limb is going to fit is problematic but there are already some leads to future work. Rothfels, in a preliminary unpublished study, has removed the limb primordium of the rat embryo at stage 29 and has grown the limb rudiments in tissue culture. Her results in a small group of experiments showed the development of recognizable cartilages representative of complete limbs with deficiencies, in the main, confined to the digits. The deficiencies were about the same whether the ectoderm was present or had been removed from the primordium before culture.

More recently, Moscona ('51) performed dissociation experiments using trypsin to separate the cells of chick limb buds after removal of the dorsal and ventral ectoderm. The dissociated cells were then cultured. Chondrogenic and myogenic cells tended to aggregate, forming an inner nodule of cartilage around which the layer of myoblasts was formed. This is, of course, a far different experiment from that of Saunders, with the chick in place upon its substrate of the yolk mass, but the conditions of the experiment seem to throw some light on the capacity of the dissociated cells to attempt to complete their potential destiny without the ectoderm acting in an essential manner.

The problems of the limb, regarded as solved by all too many, are still with us. The present paradoxical results will be reconciled by those who will complete the thoughtful analysis of future experimentation.

REFERENCES

Balfour, F. M.   1878   A Monograph on the Development of Elasmobranch Fishes. Macmillan and Co., London.

Balinsky, B. I.   1931   Zur Dynamik der Extremitätenknospenbildung. Roux' Arch. Entw.-mech., *123:*565–632.

Banchi, Arturo   1904   Sviluppo degli arti addominali del *Bufo vulgaris* innestati in sede anomala. Monitore Zool. Ital., *15:*396–399.

——— 1905   Sviluppo degli arti pelvici del *Bufo vulgaris* innestati in sede anomala. Arch. Anat. Embriol., *4:*671–693.

Bardeen, C. R., and Lewis, W. H.   1901   Development of the limbs, body wall, and back in man. Am. J. Anat., *1:*1–36.

Braus, H.   1903   Versuch einer experimentellen Morphologie. Münch. mediz. Wochenschrift, *47:*1–5.

——— 1904a   Die Entwickelung der Form der Extremitäten und des Extremitätenskeletts; in Hertwig's Handbuch der Entwickelungslehre der Wirbelthiere, Bd. 3, T. 2, pp. 167–338. Gustav Fischer, Jena.

——— 1904b   Einige Ergebnisse der Transplantation von Organanlagen bei Bombinatorlarven. Verhand. der Anat. Gesellschaft, Jena, pp. 53–65.

——— 1909   Gliedmassenpfropfung und Grundfragen der Skelettbildung. I. Die Skelettanlage vor Auftreten des Vorknorpels und ihre Beziehung zu den späteren Differenzierungen. Morphol. Jahrb., *39:*155–301; also in Exp. Beitr. Morphol., *1:*284–430.

Broman, I.   1911   Normale und abnorme Entwicklung des Menschen. J. F. Bergmann, Wiesbaden.

Byrnes, Esther F.   1898   Experimental studies on the development of limb-muscles in Amphibia. J. Morph., *14:*105–140.

Detwiler, S. R.   1918   Experiments on the development of the shoulder-girdle and the anterior limb of *Amblystoma punctatum*. J. Exp. Zool., 25:499–538.

Detwiler, S. R. 1929 Transplantation of anterior-limb mesoderm from Amblystoma embryos in the slit-blastopore stage. J. Exp. Zool., 52:315–324.

Driesch, H. 1905 Die Entwickelungsphysiologie von 1902–1905. Ergeb. Anat. Entwick., 14:603–807.

Filatow, D. 1928 Ueber die Verpflanzung des Epithels und des Mesenchymes einer vorderen Extremitätenknospe bei Embryonen von Axolotl. Roux' Arch. Entw.-mech., 113:240–244.

Hamburger, V. 1938 Morphogenetic and axial self-differentiation of transplanted limb primordia of two-day chick embryos. J. Exp. Zool., 77:379–400.

Hamilton, H. L. 1952 Lillie's Embryology of the Chick. Henry Holt and Co., Inc., New York.

Harrison, R. G. 1895 Die Entwicklung der unpaaren und paarigen Flossen der Teleostier. Arch. mikr. Anat., 46:500–578.

——— 1907 Experiments in transplanting limbs and their bearing upon the problems of the development of nerves. J. Exp. Zool., 4:239–282.

——— 1915 Experiments on the development of the limbs in Amphibia. Proc. Nat. Acad. Sci., 1:539–544.

——— 1917 Transplantation of limbs. Proc. Nat. Acad. Sci., 3:245–250.

——— 1918 Experiments on the development of the forelimb of Amblystoma, a self-differentiating, equipotential system. J. Exp. Zool., 25:413–462.

——— 1921 On relations of symmetry in transplanted limbs. J. Exp. Zool., 32:1–136.

——— 1924 Some unexpected results of the heteroplastic transplantation of limbs. Proc. Nat. Acad. Sci., 10:69–74.

——— 1925 The effect of reversing the medio-lateral or transverse axis of the fore-limb bud in the salamander embryo. Roux' Arch. Entw.-mech., 106:469–502.

Lewis, W. 1910 The relation of the myotomes to the ventro-lateral musculature and to the anterior limbs in Amblystoma. Anat. Rec., 4:183–190.

Mollier, S. 1895 Die paarigen Extremitäten der Wirbeltiere. II. Das Cheiropterygium. Anat. Hefte, 5: T. 31–38, S. 435–529.

Moscona, A. 1951 Cell suspensions from organ rudiments of chick embryos. Exp. Cell. Res., 3:535–539.

Nieuwkoop, P. D. 1946 Experimental investiga-tions on the origin and determination of the germ cells, and on the development of the lateral plates and germ ridges in urodeles. Arch. Néerl. Zool., 8:1–205.

Patten, B. M. 1951 Early Embryology of the Chick. Blakiston Co., Philadelphia.

Peter, K. 1903 Mitteilungen zur Entwicklungs-geschichte der Eidechse. IV und V. Die Extrem-itätenscheitelleiste der Amnioten und die Anlage der Mitteldarmdrüsen. Arch. Mikr. Anat., 61:509–536.

Romer, A. S. 1942 The development of tetrapod limb musculature—the thigh of Lacerta. J. Morph., 71:251–298.

——— 1944 The development of tetrapod limb musculature—the shoulder region of Lacerta. J. Morph., 74:1–41.

Rudnick, D. 1945 Differentiation of prospective limb material from Creeper chick embryos in coelomic grafts. J. Exp. Zool., 100:1–17.

Ruud, G. 1926 The symmetry relations of transplanted limbs in *Amblystoma tigrinum*. J. Exp. Zool., 46:121–142.

Saunders, J. W. Jr. 1948 The proximo-distal sequence of origin of the parts of the chick wing and the role of the ectoderm. J. Exp. Zool., 108:363–403.

Schwind, J. L. 1931 Heteroplastic experiments on the limb and shoulder girdle of Amblystoma. J. Exp. Zool., 59:265–295.

Steiner, H. 1921 Hand und Fuss der Amphibien, ein Beitrag zur Extremitätenfrage. Anat. Anz., 53:513–542.

Stultz, W. A. 1936 Relations of symmetry in the hind limb of *Amblystoma punctatum*. J. Exp. Zool., 72:317–367.

Swett, F. H. 1923 The prospective significance of the cells contained in the four quadrants of the primitive limb disc of Amblystoma. J. Exp. Zool., 37:207–218.

——— 1932 Reduplications in heteroplastic limb grafts. J. Exp. Zool., 61:129–148.

——— 1945 The role of the peribrachial area in the control of reduplication in Amblystoma. J. Exp. Zool., 100:67–77.

Vogt, W. 1929 Gestaltungsanalyse am Amphibi-enkeim mit örtlicher Vitalfärbung. II. Gastrula-tion und Mesodermbildung bei Urodelen und Anuren. Roux' Arch. Entw.-mech., 120:384–706.

Wiedersheim, R. 1889 Über die Entwicklung des Schulter- und Beckengürtels. Anat. Anz., 4:428–441.

CHAPTER 5

Heart, Blood Vessels, Blood, and Entodermal Derivatives

W. M. COPENHAVER

HEART AND BLOOD VESSELS

THE CARDIOVASCULAR SYSTEM attains functional importance relatively early in the life of an embryo and consequently the prefunctional phase of cardiovascular development is completed rapidly. Furthermore, there is generally a close correlation of morphogenesis and functional differentiation in the later stages of development. For example, as the heart chambers differentiate morphologically in a cephalocaudal direction (from conus toward sinus venosus) there is a corresponding shift in the location of the pacemaker and an acceleration in pulsation rate. On the other hand, experimental studies show a lack of correlation between functional and morphological development in the earlier stages. Presumptive heart mesoderm grown either as an explant or as a heterotopic transplant can develop pulsations without regard to the shape of the developing heart, and the pattern of the main blood vessels (aorta, gill vessels, etc.) can develop to a considerable extent in embryos experimentally deprived of circulation. These are a few of the points which require consideration under their respective headings below.

Localization of the Presumptive Heart Rudiment. By using either vital dyes or surgical procedures, presumptive heart material can be located before there is any observable morphological differentiation of a heart rudiment. In amphibian embryos, the position of the presumptive material has been identified as early as the gastrula stage by tracing the fate of vitally stained regions (Vogt, '29) and by isolation and extirpation procedures. The approximate locations of heart-potency material in urodele amphibians at successive stages are shown in Figure 157.

The boundaries of the presumptive heart material have not been studied so precisely for amphibians as they have been for the chick by Rawles ('43). This stems from the fact that the studies bearing on heart localization in early amphibians have not been devised primarily for ascertaining either the exact boundaries of, or the degree of potency of subdivisions of, the heart-forming area. For example, isolation experiments related to localization have been concerned primarily either with the over-all distribution of organ potency areas in gastrula and neurula stages (Holtfreter, '38; Mangold, '37) or with specific problems of heart self-differentiation (Ekman, '21, '27; Stöhr, '24a; Goerttler, '28; Bacon, '45).

The first visible indications of heart primordia in urodele amphibians are found in early tail-bud stage embryos (Harrison's stage 25). Figure 158 shows the amount of differentiation at stage 27. In anuran amphibians, the heart primordia develop earlier than in urodeles. For example, the presumptive heart material of Bombinator embryos completes the migration shown for urodeles in Figures 157 and 158 when the neural groove has just closed (Ekman, '24). These differences should be remembered when one compares results of experiments on different forms.

In birds and mammals, where considerable cardiac morphogenesis occurs before the lateral rudiments unite, the heart primordia are observable earlier than in amphibians. In man, a cardiogenic plate appears in the presomite stage (Davis, '27). In the chick, the pericardial coelom appears at the one or two somite stage (Rawles, '43). The localization of presumptive heart material in chick embryos before the primordia are observable has been studied by transplanting small pieces of blastoderm either to tissue culture media (Olivo, '28; Rudnick, '38; Spratt, '42) or to the chorioallantoic membrane (Willier and Rawles, '31; Hunt, '32; Butler, '35; Rawles, '43). Figure 159, after Rawles ('43),

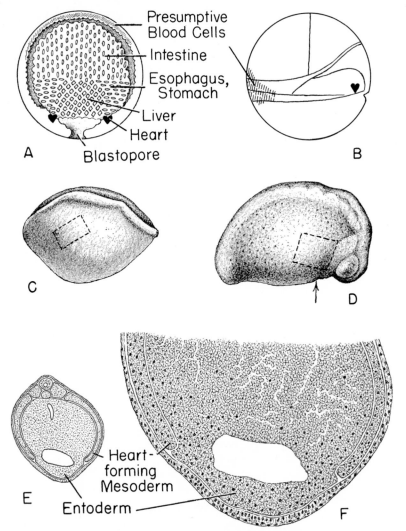

Fig. 157. Location of presumptive heart material in Amblystoma. *A*, Organ-forming areas mapped on the ventral portion of an opened gastrula, dorsal view; *B*, gastrula, lateral view; *C*, neurula, stage 15, right lateral view; *D*, stage 22. Heart-forming areas on *C* and *D* are outlined by broken line. *E*, transverse section at level of arrow in *D*; *F*, enlargement of ventral portion of same section. (*A* and *B*, redrawn after Holtfreter, '38; *C*, redrawn after Bacon, '45.)

shows the location of bilateral areas of an early chick blastoderm which have the potency for differentiating into typical cardiac muscle when divided into small pieces and transplanted to the chorioallantoic membrane of older host embryos. The grafts which contained parts of the areas shown by the darkest shading in Figure 159 produced heart muscle with the greatest frequency.

Heart-Forming Field and Induction. From the experiments cited above and from others which we will consider now it is evident that the heart resembles other organs in the sense that its field is more extensive than its presumptive material. It has been shown for both anurans (Ekman, '21) and urodeles (Copenhaver, '26) that a normal heart can develop after the complete extirpation of a visibly demarcated heart primordium (Fig. 158). In Amblystoma, the heart-forming potency of the neighboring mesoderm is lost in late tail-bud stage embryos (after Harrison's stage 29); in Bombinator, it is lost earlier in correlation with the relatively earlier heart differentiation in anurans.

The extent of mesoderm with heart-forming potency at the stage when the heart primordia are first visibly indicated has been studied by Ekman ('25). He found the mesoderm from the gill region can be induced to take part in heart formation when it is transplanted into the mid-ventral area between the bilateral heart primordia, but mesoderm from a more caudal region can not. Ekman considered this an example of true induction. His experiments pointed to

tiation was not a factor in the results. The evidence indicates the existence of a heart inductor in the entoderm of the definitive heart region. In further support of this view, Bacon found that indifferent presumptive mesoderm from a beginning gastrula is in-

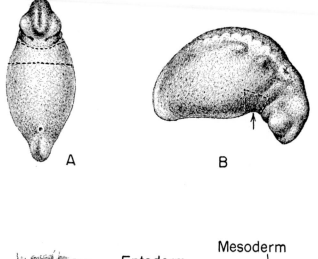

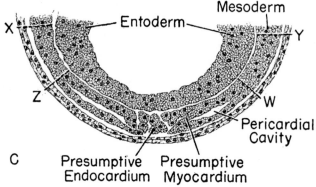

Fig. 158. Heart localization in a tail-bud, stage 27, *Amblystoma punctatum* embryo. *A* and *B*, ventral and lateral views respectively; *C*, ventral portion of a transverse section at level indicated on *B*. Extirpation of all mesodermal tissue over areas outlined on *A* and *B*, extending from *X* to *Y* in section *C*, prevents heart formation. Extirpation of presumptive heart material, extending from *Z* to *W* in section *C*, prevents heart development only when the wound is filled with foreign tissue. Otherwise, mesoderm in *XZ* and *YW* areas migrates ventrad and exhibits heart potency.

the existence of an inductor in the heart primordium, but other experiments have shown that the inducing activity is not limited to the heart itself. It has been shown by Bacon ('45) that a normally structured heart can be organized when the heart rudiment of tail-bud stage Amblystoma is replaced with indifferent presumptive mesoderm from the marginal zone of a beginning gastrula (stage 10). The substituted tissue did not include any presumptive heart material (it did not contain the *lateral* quadrants of the marginal zone) and therefore heart self-differen-

duced to form cardiac tissue when it is grown in cultures with archenteron floor from a late neurula. The organizing power of the heart region is unable to overcome the determination present in most of the mesoderm after gastrulation—at least, it is unable to induce heart from presumptive somite mesoderm from neurula stages (Bacon, '45). On the other hand, mesoderm immediately adjacent to the heart region is still competent to form heart in tail-bud stage Amblystoma embryos, as indicated in Figure 158.

Is the presumptive heart mesoderm itself

dependent upon a secondary entodermal inductor for its differentiation? Nieuwkoop ('46) found an absence of the heart in Triton embryos which developed after complete removal of the entoderm from early neurula. Bacon (personal communication) has obtained similar results for Amblystoma operated upon at Harrison's stages 15-18, and Balinsky ('39) has reported similar findings for neurula stage Tritons. One finds it difficult to explain the lack of heart development in entodermless embryos in view of other evidence favoring ability of very early stages for cardiac self-differentiation.

Heart Determination and Self-Differentiation. The first experimental evidence indicating the stage from which the presumptive heart-field can self-differentiate into an organized heart was obtained by Ekman ('21). Using Bombinator embryos at the stage when the heart is first visibly indicated, he explanted the heart primordium in an ectodermal covering. Using similar methods and materials, Stöhr ('24a) concluded that the heart differentiation in the explants was correlated with the presence of neighboring entodermal and mesodermal cells removed with the heart. Further evidence on the problem has been obtained from both explantations (Ekman, '24, '27, '29; Bacon, '45) and heterotopic transplantations (Stöhr, '24b; Copenhaver, '26). The former method permits a study of heart formation free of confinement and association with other tissues; the latter method permits a study of the organ freed only from the structures with which it is normally associated but it gives more differentiation than the isolation method and enables one to identify the different heart chambers with more assurance. Stöhr's results with this method reemphasized his belief in the importance of "Endomesodermzellen" which were always present in successful transplants. On the other hand, heterotopic transplants on tail-bud stage Amblystoma embryos (Copenhaver, '26) showed that well formed pulsating hearts can develop from presumptive heart mesoderm without the normally associated entomesodermal structures. Particularly strong evidence for the self-differentiating capacity of the heart has been obtained with the explantation method by Bacon ('45), as shown in Figure 160.

The explantation method has been employed in studying the time of heart determination in both anurans (Ekman, '27, '29) and urodeles (Bacon, '45). Bacon's results indicate that the presumptive heart material

of Amblystoma is determined and capable of self-differentiation into typical parts in the crescent blastopore stage (stage 11). But the explants at this stage consisted of a piece of gastrula wall which may have included neighboring entomesodermal cells. The evidence for self-differentiation is unequivocal in the experiments done on medullary plate stages (stages 13–15) since only mesoderm was explanted. Thus the heart primordium is self-differentiating for a con-

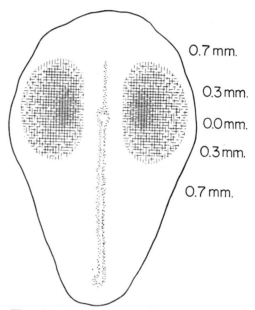

Fig. 159. Map of heart-specific areas on a head-process stage chick blastoderm. Numerals at right show distances in millimeters from the level of the primitive pit. (After Rawles, '43.)

siderable time before the environment of the cardiac region loses its ability to induce heart formation in indifferent mesoderm, as cited earlier.

The heart primordium appears to have a "labile determination" for curvature at an early stage. Some studies have suggested that the heart possesses merely a tendency for curvature since the particular form observed under experimental conditions is variable and obviously influenced by the environment (Spemann, '06; Pressler, '11; Ekman, '24; Stöhr, '24a, '25; Copenhaver, '26). But the results obtained by Bacon ('45) for hearts explanted without confinement show a determination for the characteristic S-type of curvature. This does not deny the view that the S-shape is suited to the environment in which the heart normally develops nor does it contradict other evidence that the curvature can be influenced by the shape of the pericardial cavity and by other mechanical factors.

In birds, the cardiac primordia have greater potentialities for histological than for morphological self-differentiation. Small pieces of chick blastoderm will develop typical cardiac muscle with rhythmical pulsations in culture (Olivo, '28), but they do not

amount of morphological self-differentiation for the rat heart, but it must be noted that neither in mammals nor in birds has morphological differentiation been demonstrated for cardiac primordia completely isolated from other embryonic tissues.

An abundance of evidence could be cited to show that structure and function are not dependent upon each other during the early

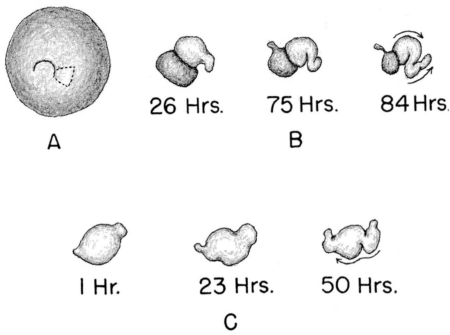

26 Hrs.   75 Hrs.   84 Hrs.

A   B

1 Hr.   23 Hrs.   50 Hrs.

C

Fig. 160. Self-differentiation of presumptive heart material cultured in modified Holtfreter's solution. A, *Amblystoma punctatum*, stage 11. Explant of gastrula wall from outlined area lateral to the blastopore differentiates as shown in B. Arrows show direction of contraction wave at 84 hours after explantation. C, differentiation of presumptive mesoderm explanted from an embryo of stage 15, late medullary plate stage. (Redrawn after Bacon, '45.)

show morphologically differentiated hearts comparable to those formed by amphibian explants. Chorioallantoic grafting of heart-forming areas of the chick blastoderm gives more cardiac morphogenesis than in vitro cultivation does, but morphogenesis is still inferior to histogenesis (Kumé, '35; Rawles, '43). Rawles suggests that the atypical morphogenesis may be the result of abnormal mechanical conditions rather than a restriction of the determination process.

In mammals, as in birds, the tendency for cardiac self-differentiation is greater physiologically than morphologically, as shown by the behavior of whole blastocysts cultivated in vitro (Waddington and Waterman, '33; Nicholas and Rudnick, '34; Goss, '35). The studies by Goss have shown a considerable

development of the heart. Bacon ('45) finds explanted amphibian hearts may differentiate morphologically without developing pulsations, whereas contractions may occur in explanted rudiments lacking morphological differentiation. Numerous studies already cited on self-differentiation have shown that a lack of blood circulation does not prevent the heart from developing well beyond the stage which it normally attains at the beginning of circulation. On the other hand, there is evidence that the blood stream has an influence on the later stages of heart differentiation in both amphibians and birds (Stöhr, '25; Bremer, '31). In the chick heart, a valvelike action occurs at the a-v junction through an "endocardial mound" of cardiac jelly before the establishment of the primordia for the leaflets of the valve (Patten, Kramer and Barry, '48). The authors suggest that the moulding effect of the spiral streams of blood, as described by Bremer, may act particularly on the cardiac jelly and thus "set the pattern followed by the endocardial cushion tissue."

Polarity. The determination of polarity in the heart rudiment has been studied for several species of amphibians with somewhat different results. It is reported that 180 degree rotation of the anteroposterior axis of the heart rudiment in Bombinator does not interfere with normal development when the operation is made in embryos with a just-closed medullary tube, or earlier (Ekman, '21; Stöhr, '25). A similar operation at the tail-bud stage produces a reversed heart, indicating axial determination (Stöhr, '25). In *Rana fusca,* the anteroposterior cardiac axis appears to be determined somewhat earlier than in Bombinator (Ekman, '29). On the other hand, it is reported that the heart of *R. nigromaculata* still lacks anteroposterior axial determination when it is approaching a tubular stage (Ota, '30). However, since Ota reports only three positive cases out of 783 experiments one may well question whether the hearts of the positive cases developed from the rotated rudiments or whether they formed by regeneration from nonrotated neighboring tissue.

In Amblystoma, the anteroposterior axis has been rotated 180 degrees either by a single operation at tail-bud stages or by a bilateral operation at stage 22, shortly after closure of the neural tube (Copenhaver, '26). Both types of operations produced atypical, reversed hearts. When one recalls that the heart of a stage 25 tail-bud Amblystoma is differentiated only to a degree comparable to that of a neural fold Bombinator, it appears that the anteroposterior axis of the heart is determined much earlier in the former species than in the latter. It is suggested that the determination of the anteroposterior cardiac axis should be restudied to learn whether the differences described for Bombinator and Amblystoma are well founded and whether they exist for anurans and urodeles generally.

Determination occurs later for the dorsoventral and transverse axes than for the anteroposterior axis. When the ventral half of the heart rudiment of Bombinator is rotated dorsoventrally, up to beginning tail-bud stages, the parts unite to build a functioning heart (Ekman, '29). Likewise when a right half of the heart rudiment of a tail-bud Amblystoma is replaced with a left half, thus changing the mediolateral axis of a half, the parts combine to form a functioning heart (Copenhaver, '26).

Totipotency of the Heart Rudiment. There is considerable evidence that an entire heart can develop from a part of its rudiment and that each part is therefore equipotential in its early developmental stages. One line of evidence comes from duplications occurring in nature. A most remarkable case of this type was reported by Verocay ('05), of a hen which had seven hearts of approximately equal size. It also became evident from some of the earliest studies in the field of experimental embryology that the heart rudiment is plastic and not a fixed mosaic. It was shown in chick embryos that the bilateral rudiments for one heart can develop into two hearts when they are prevented from uniting (Gräper, '07). In frogs, it was found that the rudiments for two hearts exhibit various degrees of fusion when embryos are joined along the ventral region (Born, '97).

Extensive experimental studies showing totipotency in the amphibian heart rudiment have been made by Ekman ('21) on embryos of Bombinator. He found that a functioning heart will develop after removal of a lateral half and that two hearts, each with circulation, can develop from one rudiment split lengthwise. These studies were confirmed on tail-bud stage Amblystoma embryos (Copenhaver, '26). They were also extended to show that a functioning heart can develop after removal of an anterior half rudiment or from combinations of two anterior or two posterior halves. On the other hand, Stöhr ('27) concluded from studies on Bombinator and Amblystoma that the heart does not fulfill the requirements of an equipotential system. He found that a heart developing from a lateral half rudiment generally has an atypical shape for one or more of its chambers but some of the illustrated cases approximate the normal to such degree that one may question whether they argue against equipotentiality of a half rudiment or whether they indicate merely a labile determination of form. Remarkably normal hearts from lateral half rudiments in Amblystoma have been described by Fales ('46).

Evidence for equipotentiality of anterior and posterior halves may be more questionable than that for lateral halves. In the latter case, the four embryonic divisions are represented in each half rudiment whereas in the former case a presumptive ventricle must form atrium or vice versa. It has been noted previously that the technique is more difficult for combinations of posterior halves than for lateral halves. In order to eliminate the possibility that a transplanted half is resorbed and superseded by host mesoderm, the transplantations should be made heteroplastically on species with pigment differ-

a normal asymmetry whereas the right one frequently develops as a mirror image of the normal. This is seen particularly well in amphibians where experimentally produced double hearts undergo complete functional differentiation, with circulation through each heart. Factors responsible for the situs inversus of the right member of a double heart are not clearly understood. Further questions on cardiac asymmetry will

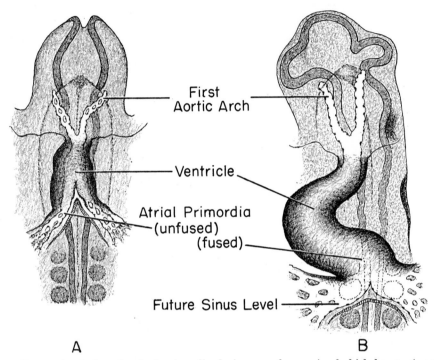

First Aortic Arch

Ventricle

Atrial Primordia (unfused) (fused)

Future Sinus Level

A   B

Fig. 161. Progressive fusion of paired primordia during morphogenesis of chick heart. *A*, at 9-somite (± 29 hour) stage, when first contractions appear; *B*, at 16-somite (± 38 hour) stage, when blood circulation begins. (Redrawn after Patten and Kramer, '33.)

ences in the embryonic tissues (e.g., *Triturus taeniatus* and *T. cristatus*).

Experiments by Goss ('35) show that some totipotency exists in the primordium of the mammalian heart. He found that double hearts develop in 9-day-old rat embryos in hanging drop cultures when the lateral primordia are prevented from uniting. The lateral rudiments self-differentiate beyond the stage when they unite in normal development. Available experimental methods do not maintain the growth of separated mammalian heart primordia for sufficient time to show whether a half can develop a fully differentiated mammalian heart with two atria and two ventricles.

When double hearts develop from separate bilateral primordia, the left heart has

be considered in relation to asymmetry of entodermal derivatives.

Formation of the "Tubular" Heart and Functional Differentiation. Fusion of the bilateral heart primordia occurs in a cephalocaudal sequence, with formation of the bulboventricular region first and the sinus venosus last. Space does not permit reference to all of the studies which have established this point for amphibians, birds and mammals, including man (Davis, '27). Likewise, it has been demonstrated that functional differentiation progresses in a cephalocaudal direction. Sabin ('20) and Johnstone ('25) appear to have been the first to note that the earliest contractions in the chick heart begin in the ventricle. Using a cinematographic method, Patten and Kramer ('33) have extended these studies to give us a detailed account of the series of changes by which the sinus venosus is eventually established as the pacemaker. An excellent review of this work has been presented by

birds, mammals exhibit less fusion and amphibians more. In urodele amphibians, the so-called "tubular" heart of the beat initiation stage contains the future conus, ventricle and cephalic portion of the atrium

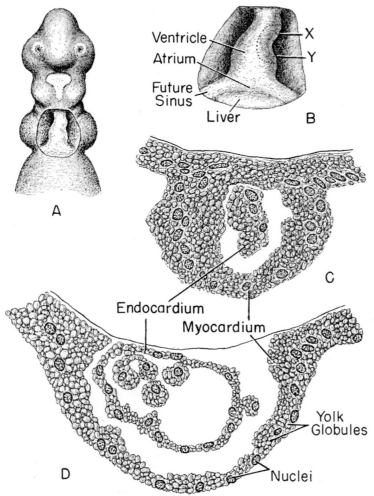

Fig. 162. Heart differentiation in *Amblystoma punctatum* at stage 34, when first contractions appear. *A*, heart in situ after removal of ectoderm and ventral portion of parietal pericardium. *B*, enlargement of a portion of *A*. The outlined area on the bulboventricular region shows extent of contractions observed before fixation. *X* and *Y* indicate levels of sections illustrated in *C* and *D*, respectively. Note abundance of yolk droplets and lack of striations in myocardium.

Patten ('49). Figure 161 shows some of the morphological stages in the cephalocaudal differentiation.

Studies on the genesis of cardiac contractions in mammals (Goss, '38; Dwinnel, '39) and in amphibians (Copenhaver, '39a) have given results which differ in only a few respects from those described for the chick. The degree of fusion of the bilateral primordia at the time of beat initiation varies for different animals; in comparison with

(Fig. 162B). At this time, only the cephalic portion of the heart is invested completely by primordial myocardium. When dealing with amphibian development, some embryologists retain the mistaken impression that a "tubular" heart of four regions is formed all at once. It can be seen that this view is incorrect when Nile blue–stained areas of the early heart are identified in later development (Copenhaver, '39a).

Although the initiation of cardiac function

in the different classes of vertebrates appears to be timed appropriately to the needs of the embryo, it must be emphasized that the initial contractions are not dependent upon conditions within the embryo or upon the development of heart form. This has been shown by explantation, transplantation and tissue culture methods. Furthermore, the initial contractions do not appear to be dependent upon the presence of striations. Goss ('38, '40, '42) has observed cardiac contractions in rat embryos before striations can be seen in the myocardial cells. Similar conclusions have been given for Amblystoma (Copenhaver, '39a). In the chick heart, contractions have been observed at the 9-somite stage (Patten and Kramer, '33), whereas striations have not been observed before the 10 somite stage (Lewis, '19). In this connection, it should be noted that studies with the electron microscope (Schmitt, '45) have shown that the absence of histological signs of striations need not imply the absence of molecular or micellar striations.

In the preceding discussion, reference has been made to the fact that different parts of the embryonic heart have inherently different rhythms. As early as 1890, Fano and Badano cut chick embryo hearts with reference to definite anatomical levels and recorded higher pulsation rates for the atrium than for the ventricle. These early observations have been amply confirmed and extended by later workers. Similar findings have been made for embryonic mammalian hearts (Hall, '51). That the part with the highest rate dominates the other regions was demonstrated clearly by Paff ('36). He grew reversed parts of the chick heart in proximity to each other in culture media and observed the sinoatrial region imposing its rate on the slower beating anterior part when the two pieces became united by a bridge of myocardial tissue. Further evidence for sinus dominance is seen when parts of the embryonic heart are transplanted between different species of amphibians—a transplanted sinus venosus dominates the remainder of the heart of another species to the point of maintaining the donor species rate (Copenhaver, '45).

Figures 163 and 164 summarize quantitative studies on the intrinsic rhythms of each of the cardiac regions at successive developmental stages in Amblystoma punctatum (Copenhaver, '39a) and in the chick (Barry, '42). The rhythm of each part passes through a phase of rate acceleration which is generally followed by a period of decelera-

tion. Eventually, some of the parts enter a phase in which they lack the ability for spontaneous contraction. The conus of the chick heart enters the latter phase very early and its rate is omitted from the figure; the conus of the Amblystoma heart exhibits spontaneous contractions intermittently for a much longer time than in the chick. Another difference between the two species is found in the behavior of the sinus venosus which enters the deceleration phase earlier in Amblystoma. In the chick, there is a question whether the rhythm of the intact heart (and the rate of its sinus) shows any deceleration phase. At most, there is only a slight decrease in rate after about 17 days of incubation (Cohn and Wile, '25) or merely a plateau in the rate curve at that time (Bogue, '33).

Numerous studies have shown that the embryonic heart rate exhibits a progressive acceleration which is most pronounced in the early stages of cardiac function. This appears to be true in fish, amphibians, birds and mammals. Among the studies on chick heart rates, those by Cohn and Wile ('25), Bogue ('32) and Barry ('40) are particularly significant. In both the chick (Fig. 164) and Amblystoma (Fig. 163), one notes a particularly obvious acceleration in heart rate just after the establishment of atrial function, and again just after the initiation of sinus function. The available evidence supports the statement by Barry ('42) that the progressive acceleration in heart rate in the early stages of cardiac function is "due in great measure to the successive addition of new segments of myocardium of increasingly higher inherent automaticity." The progressive acceleration in the chick heart rate in later stages has been correlated with (1) an increase in blood pressure (Barry, '41), or (2) a reduction in cardiac distention following the deflection of blood into newly formed arteries (Alexander and Glaser, '41.) These contradictory views are based on contradictory results obtained with exsanguination experiments on chick embryos—bleeding decreases the heart rate according to Barry, and increases it according to Alexander and Glaser. It seems that the effects of hemorrhage on embryonic heart rate could be profitably reexamined.

The most significant studies correlating stages of heart development and changes in the electrocardiogram have been made on chick hearts by Hoff, Kramer, DuBois and Patten ('39). In the earliest electrocardiogram that can be obtained, there is a sinusoidal pattern produced by a simple deflection of the galvanometer. A deflection resembling the QRS ventricular complex is not obtained until about 38 hours incubation. At this time, the contraction is still primarily ventricular and only the cephalic

ward at first; later it becomes reversed. An approximately adult type of electrocardiogram is established during the fourth day of incubation.

Nervous Control of the Embryonic Heart. Since the work of His and Romberg (1890),

Fig. 163.

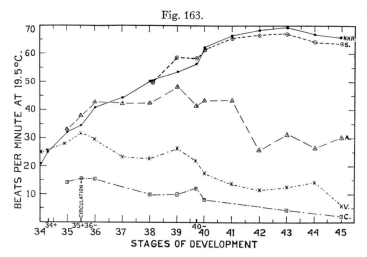

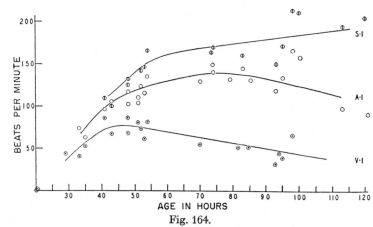

Fig. 164.

Figs. 163 and 164. Inherent rhythms of different regions of transected hearts in Amblystoma (Fig. 163) and in the chick (Fig. 164). The stages shown for Amblystoma cover a 12-day period extending from the time of beat initiation until the embryos begin to feed. *S, A, V,* and *C,* show rates for sinus, atrium, ventricle and conus, respectively. Each point on the Amblystoma curves represents a mean for all cases studied, and the difference shown for the sinus and the intact, normal heart (*N.H.R.*) is statistically insignificant. (Fig. 163 after Copenhaver, '39; Fig. 164 after Barry, '42.)

portion of the atrium is functioning. According to Olivo et al. ('46), the establishment of a QRS pattern is correlated with the differentiation of myofibrillae and may occur at a somewhat earlier stage than that just cited. The P wave (atrial) appears first at 42 hours incubation, soon after the beat becomes established in the caudal part of the atrium. The P deflection is down-

it has been known that the embryonic heart functions preceding innervation. This indicates that the first heart beats are myogenic in origin. Furthermore, Hooker ('11) observed rhythmical cardiac contractions in denervated amphibian embryos reared beyond the stage when the heart of normal embryos becomes innervated. Further evidence for a myogenic origin of heart beat is found in tissue culture experiments (Burrows, '11) and in some of the embryonic heart experiments cited in the earlier part of this discussion. The latter include the development of pulsating hearts from presumptive heart mesoderm after explantation to cultures (Ekman, '21; Stöhr, '24a; Bacon, '45); after transplantation to heterotopic positions on the embryo (Ekman, '21; Stöhr, '29; Copenhaver, '26); and after transplantation to the chorioallantoic membrane (Kumé, '35; Rawles, '43). Neither extrinsic nor intrinsic cardiac nerves were present in the experiments cited above but it may be argued that the evidence does not apply to the adult heart. Among the experiments supporting a myogenic origin of heart beat in the adult, the work reviewed by Haberlandt ('27) has particular significance. He used freezing and chemical agents for separating the neural from the muscular components in adult hearts.

The embryonic heart does not become innervated until some time after the sinus venosus has become established as the pacemaker. Vagus ingrowth (parasympathetic innervation) generally precedes sympathetic innervation, and morphological innervation precedes functional control by a variable period in different species. Vagus ingrowth occurs: (1) in *A. punctatum* at Harrison's stages 44–46 (about 10 to 12 days after beat initiation (Copenhaver, '39b); (2) in the chick at 120 hours incubation according to Abel ('12); (3) in man, at the beginning of the fifth week (His and Romberg, 1890). In *Fundulus heteroclitus* embryos, Armstrong ('35) found that cardiac innervation can be demonstrated by vital staining with methylene blue on the eighth day, about 5 days after the onset of heart beat. He also found that acetylcholine in small amounts induces auricular diastolic arrest on the eighth day whereas the same drug in large amounts does not inhibit contractility preceding innervation. Responses cannot be elicited by reflex vagus stimulation on the eighth day; apparently the reflex arc is not complete until about 36 hours after the vagus ingrowth. Brinley ('35) obtained adrenaline effects on *F. heteroclitus* embryos, indicating the presence of a sympathetic innervation in teleosts; earlier workers failed to find a cardiac sympathetic innervation in this class of vertebrates.

Functional changes correlated with vagus ingrowth have been studied most completely in Fundulus embryos (Armstrong, '31). Several physiological stages can be identified covering the period from the initial reflex vagus response on the ninth day until an adult type of response is attained on about day 12–13. The type of response elicited by vagus stimulation at each successive stage appears to be correlated with the progressive innervation of different parts of the embryonic heart.

The amount of cardiac control normally exerted by the vagi (vagal tone) varies for different species (see review by Clark, '27). In most amphibians, there is very little vagal tone. In this connection, it is interesting to note that embryonic hearts transplanted heteroplastically between *A. tigrinum* and *A. punctatum* maintain their donor species rhythms although they become morphologically and functionally innervated by the host nerves (Copenhaver, '30, '39b). In these cases, the basic heart rate characteristic for the species is apparently myogenic.

EMBRYOGENESIS OF BLOOD VESSELS

The development of blood vascular endothelium falls into two stages: (1) differentiation in situ from mesenchymal cells; (2) formation by vascular sprouts from previously formed vessels. An overlapping in the time of the two stages was noted by Sabin ('17) when she observed that sprouting begins before in situ formation is everywhere complete. Once the embryonic vascular system is fully established, the endothelium of new vessels arises only as an outgrowth from pre-existing vessels. Clark and Clark ('39) have summarized and extended earlier studies on this point.

The mesenchymal cells which form endothelium are usually designated as angioblasts or vasoformative cells. Further studies are needed to show when the earliest vasoformative cells are determined and when their formation from indifferent mesenchyme ceases. Lewis ('31) suggested that endothelium and mesenchyme may be differentiated in the chick at the time when they leave the primitive streak. On the other hand, Sabin ('20) described the formation of new angioblasts from mesoderm throughout the first two days of incubation. Since Sabin's conclusions were based on cytological differences between angioblasts and mesoderm, they do not eliminate the probability that some of the mesodermal cells are determined as angioblasts before they can be identified as such by available technical methods. Since the vasoformative cells arise in diverse embryonic regions, it is difficult to devise experiments to test the time of their determination. However, it is not improbable that some mesodermal cells are determined for endothelium by the end of gastrulation (at a time when other mesodermal cells are determined for other primordia such as heart, limbs, et cetera). If this view of an early determination is correct, it becomes easier to harmonize angiogenesis in the lower vertebrates with that in mammals. In macaque and human chorions, endothelium and mesoderm differentiate simultaneously from cytotrophoblast, according to Hertig ('35). Although the early differentiation of vascular endothelium in man and other mammals is well established, Hertig's interpretation that endothelium arises directly from cytotrophoblast is not universally accepted (Bloom and Bartelmez, '40).

There is no experimental evidence for a view that the early intraembryonic endothelium arises by ingrowth from the extraembryonic endothelium of the yolk region. Explants and heterotopic transplants of cardiac and other organ primordia develop endothelium in situ. Neither is there any evidence for the unusual view that endothelium of the branchial and head vessels arises by outgrowth from the heart. The chief embryonic vessels develop when heart formation is prevented by extirpation of presumptive heart mesoderm in amphibians. Experimental evidence for in situ formation in mammals is seen in the development of blood vessels from mesenchyme in explants of the allantoic bud from rat embryos (Jolly, '40).

The earliest vessels in union with the heart—the truncus arteriosus and the cephalic portions of the vitelline veins—arise in a manner resembling the formation of endocardium. Cells of mesodermal origin aggregate in the pathways of the future vessels and differentiate into primitive endothelium. As the vessels are traced progressively from the heart, the strands of vasoformative cells become progressively more irregular in their pattern and form elaborate capillary networks. The arteries and veins arise by enlargement and differentiation of pathways through the network. This mode of development is found even in parts of the aortae and cardinal veins (Evans, '08; Sabin, '17). An exception to the

formation of vessels from a primitive network is found in the opossum brain (Wislocki, '39). In this species, the cerebral arteries are non-anastomotic "end-vessels," and from the time of their first appearance these arteries and their corresponding veins show their characteristic adult plan.

The pattern of the vascular system is dependent upon several factors. Hereditary factors supposedly play an important part in the formation of the earliest vessels (aorta and large veins) which develop before circulation begins. Many vessels will undergo a fairly extensive development when circulation is prevented—for example, after cardiac extirpation (Knower, '07; Clark, '18; and others). It is obvious that the mechanical effects of circulation cannot apply to vascular development under these conditions. On the other hand, the inherent pattern of the earliest vessels may be dependent upon mechanical and chemical effects from other embryonic tissues.

Chemical and mechanical factors associated with blood flow (function) affect the further development of the vascular system after the embryonic circulation becomes established. Clark ('18) suggested that the formation of new vascular sprouts is influenced by the amount of interchange through the walls of the vessels—interchange between blood and surrounding tissues. Thus the growth and metabolism of outside tissues may control the outgrowth of new vessels. Streeter ('18, '27) also stressed the importance of the endothelial environment and stated that the embryonic vessels do not have a ground plan of their own. In this connection, some observations by Scharrer ('39) are of particular interest. He found that the end-vessel pattern characteristic of the opossum brain will develop in dead brain tissue and he interpreted this finding as evidence for a factor inherent to the cerebral vessels themselves. On the other hand, Wislocki ('39) believes the result can be explained by an environmental factor present even in the dead tissue.

The amount of blood flow through a capillary, rather than the rate of flow, determines whether a given capillary within a meshwork atrophies, remains a capillary, or enlarges to form an arteriole or venule (see Clark's '18 analysis of Thoma's laws). Clark and Clark ('40) find that the differentiation of adventitial cells into smooth muscle is influenced by blood pressure and thus they confirm the histomechanical principle of

Thoma that the thickness of the vessel wall is dependent upon blood pressure.

BLOOD

Experimental studies on amphibians have shown that the blood islands form the sole source of the primitive erythrocytes (see Fig. 165). Following extirpation of this region, as first performed on anurans by Federici ('26) and on urodeles by Goss ('28), "the blood cells were always reduced in number and in some instances were entirely absent." The maximum survival reported by Goss for an embryo lacking blood cells was 32 days. An unanswered question is whether definitive erythrocytes would develop in an embryo lacking the primitive blood cells provided the animal could be maintained until the formation of other hematopoietic regions—liver, spleen, etc.

The progenitors of the red corpuscles are determined considerably in advance of their morphological differentiation in the blood island (considerably before they can be identified by the benzidine technique for hemoglobin as applied by Slonimski, '31). This is evident from the fact that the presumptive blood cells of amphibians can self-differentiate following explantation from neurulae (Slonimski, '31) and from gastrulae (Fernald, '47). Furthermore, presumptive erythrocytes of an amphibian gastrula are localized to a relatively small zone opposite the blastoporal groove, as shown in Figure 158 (Holtfreter, '38; Fernald, '47). The presumptive blood cells of the chick, as in amphibians, are determined in advance of their differentiation but they are dispersed over a relatively large region of the early blastoderm. Erythrocytes will differentiate in chorioallantoic grafts taken from all parts of the blastoderm posterior to the level of the anterior quarter of the primitive streak (Murray, '32).

Goss ('28) has noted that blood cells and endothelial cells differ in their origin because extirpation of the blood island has relatively little effect on the development of the vascular system whereas it eliminates blood formation. Cameron ('41) has observed that the red cell progenitors differ from the endothelial precursors in their susceptibility to x-rays in Amblystoma.

Considerable disagreement exists concerning the capacity of endothelium for erythropoiesis. It is held generally that the endothelium in the blood island region of the yolk sac retains erythrogenic potency for a short time after the development of the earliest blood vessels. An exceptional view attributes hemogenic potency to all endothelium in amphibians until the stage of metamorphosis (Storti, '31). Experimental evidence has been presented to show that the lining of intersinusoidal "capillaries" of avian and mammalian bone marrow is erythrogenic even in the adult (Sabin, '22; and others) but the lining of these channels is probably not a true endothelium (see sum-

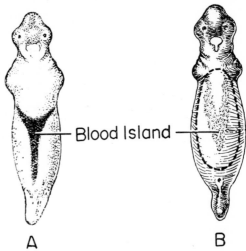

Fig. 165. *A*, Ventral view of an axolotl, stage 31, showing blood island (dark) stained by benzidine. *B*, *Amblystoma punctatum*, stage 32, showing blood island (stippled) and area excised in experimental production of bloodless embryos. (*A*, after Slonimski, '31; *B*, after Goss, '28).

marization by McDonald, '39). On the basis of their defect experiments on amphibians, Federici ('26), Goss ('28), Slonimski ('31) and Fernald ('47) do not attribute any erythrogenic potency to endothelium. Their extirpations of blood-forming cells undoubtedly included endothelium-forming cells of the yolk region but approximately normal vessels developed within this region, presumably from cells migrating from the edge of the wound. Neither the endothelium of the regenerated vessels of the operated field nor that of any other region produced erythrocytes.

Two views exist concerning the nature of the first free blood cells which develop in the blood islands: (1) the primitive cell is a hemocytoblast with potency to form primitive erythroblasts and leukocytes; or (2) the earliest free cell is a primitive erythroblast (megaloblast). The controversy results chiefly from the difficulty of distinguishing morphologically between hemocytoblasts and primitive erythroblasts. The dry imprint technique indicates that the first circulating cells are megaloblasts (Kirschbaum and Downey, '37). An experimental analysis by Block ('46) indicates that the earliest cells are hemocytoblasts. He finds that when the rat yolk sac is transplanted into the anterior chamber of the eye, the primitive cells produce granulocytes as well as erythroblasts. This is interpreted as evidence that the primitive cell itself is not an erythroblast. Regardless of whether the primitive cell is an erythroblast or a hemocytoblast which later develops into an erythroblast, there is general agreement that the primitive erythroblasts and erythrocytes formed in the yolk sac represent a megaloblastic strain differing from the definitive erythrocytes (normoblastic series) characteristic of older embryos and adults.

Environment apparently plays a part in determining whether a primitive stem cell forms an erythrocyte or a leukocyte. Evidence for this includes Dantschakoff's ('24) experiments showing that when the chick yolk sac is transplanted to the chorioallantoic membrane, the stem cells develop mainly into granular leukocytes whereas in their normal location they develop chiefly into primitive erythroblasts. Jordan and Speidel ('23) suggested that the fundamental stimulus for erythropoiesis is "some product of cellular metabolism, probably carbon dioxide."

There is considerable evidence that a decrease in oxygen stimulates the rate of regeneration of erythrocytes in adults. Studies by Grant and Root ('47) on bone marrow blood following hemorrhage in dogs indicate that oxygen content and capacity, rather than oxygen tension and saturation, affect erythropoiesis. Their studies are particularly interesting in relation to the commonly held view that erythropoiesis in marrow is related to a sluggish blood flow and a localized anoxia. They found that stagnant anoxia, following hemorrhage, does not persist any longer in marrow blood than in jugular vein blood.

A discussion of the factors necessary for the maturation of the erythrocyte is beyond the scope of the present review. It is particularly interesting to note that vitamin B_{12}, obtained from liver extract, appears to have the same effects as liver extract in pernicious anemia therapy (West, '48). For a review of the nutritive factors and mechanisms in the regeneration of erythrocytes, reference may be made to Wintrobe ('50).

ENTODERMAL DERIVATIVES

The localization of presumptive organ rudiments within the entoderm has been studied by the vital dye marking method (Vogt, '29; Balinsky, '47a) and by numerous experiments employing the methods of extirpation and transplantation. In amphibians, the different regions of the entoderm appear to be capable of self-differentiation in the gastrula stage as evidenced by the behavior of transplants in the coelomic cavity and by explants in modified Ringer's solution (Holtfreter, '25, '38). On the other hand, evidence for alteration of the prospective fate of amphibian entoderm is seen in the occasional development of muscle from entodermal cells transplanted from gastrulae into the eye chamber of older larvae (Kusche, '29). Histological regulation in amphibian entoderm has been described for neurula stages also (Balinsky, '38). However, studies on the tree frog by Kemp ('46) are more in conformity with Holtfreter's views and indicate that the entoderm in the neurula is unable to regulate histologically although it is capable of considerable morphological regulation.

Extending the studies on amphibian entoderm to earlier stages than those used by Holtfreter, Nicholas ('48) found that the entoderm already possesses some determination in the late blastula stage. When the entire cover of an early gastrula is removed, the entoderm differentiates stomodeal and proctodeal pits. The factors for the formation of these two structures are apparently intrinsic to the yolk entoderm at an early stage.

An understanding of the formation of entodermal structures in the chick has been aided particularly by the method of chorioallantoic grafting. Early blastoderms can be split into two layers: epiblast and entoderm. Grafts have been made of entire layers, of parts of layers, and of small areas of total thickness blastoderms. The experiments indicate that: (1) the gut-forming potency is limited to the epiblast in prestreak and early streak blastoderms (Hunt, '37a); (2) the definitive entoderm does not become determined until just prior to the head-process stage (Hunt, '37a; Rudnick and Rawles, '37); (3) for a time there is an overlapping of gut potentialities in the epiblast and entodermal layers; (4) there is a progressive localization of primordia within the entoderm, occurring at different times for different organs (Rudnick, '35). By means of vital dyes, a cellular migration from ectoderm to entoderm has been demonstrated in correlation with the shift of gut potency from ectoderm to entoderm in the early blastoderm (Hunt, '37b), but there is "no evidence that the localization process itself is to be explained on the basis of a cellular migration" (Rudnick and Rawles, '37).

Mouth Formation. Experiments on the stomodeal region of *A. punctatum* by Adams ('24, '31) showed that mouth invagination is dependent upon contact of the ectoderm with the underlying entoderm. Experiments by Balinsky ('47b) confirmed and extended the view that the entoderm acts as an inductor on the stomodeal ectoderm. Most of Balinsky's experiments were done on *T. taeniatus* embryos in late gastrula and early

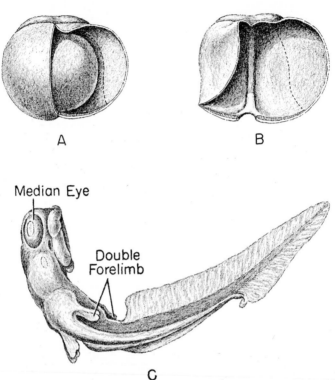

Fig. 166. *A* and *B*, sketch of operation for removal of whole entoderm at neurula stage. *C*, entoderm-free larva of *Triturus alpestris* 20 days after operation. (Redrawn after Nieuwkoop, '46.)

The prospective potencies of the different digestive tract primordia are greater than their individual prospective fates. This is shown by an overlapping of ectodermal and entodermal gut-potency stages (cited above) and by the extent of gut-potency tissue on the early blastoderm (Butler, '35; Rudnick and Rawles, '37).

Complete extirpation of the entoderm from neurula stage amphibian embryos indicates that the entoderm has striking effects on the development of other tissues (Nieuwkoop, '46). Entoderm-free embryos frequently develop two pairs of forelimbs (Fig. 166), they show various degrees of microcephaly and cyclopia, they lack gills and, as described in a previous section, there is a failure of heart development.

neurula stages. He found that ectodermal mouth invagination usually failed after complete removal of mouth entoderm, and that presumptive mouth ectoderm transplanted to abnormal locations produced a mouth invagination only when underlying mouth entoderm was transplanted along with the presumptive ectoderm. A regional factor in the stomodeal ectoderm was indicated by the following experiments: (1) mouth entoderm transplanted to foreign positions did not induce mouth invagination in the overlying foreign ectoderm; (2) mouth invagination failed when mouth ectoderm was completely replaced by foreign ectoderm. In the latter result, the experiments on Triton appear to differ from those on Amblystoma by Adams ('24), where mouth parts were found to develop from foreign ectoderm transplanted into the stomodeal region. Balinsky concludes that there is a regional factor in the presumptive mouth ectoderm but that determination occurs gradually. At the neurula stage, the presumptive mouth ectoderm has only a labile determination and it will not differentiate without an inductive action from the underlying entoderm.

Tooth development in some amphibians differs from that in mammals in regard to the origin of the enamel organs. Experiments by Adams ('24, '31) showed that in *A. punctatum* the enamel organs of some tooth germs arise from ectoderm, others from entoderm. On the other hand, Woerdeman failed to find proof for the formation of teeth from entoderm in xenoplastic grafts between *T. taeniatus* and the axolotl (Woerdeman and Raven, '46).

Studies on Amblystoma by Adams ('24, '31) supported the view that the pulp of the tooth germ is mesectodermal (neural crest) in origin. Her experiments also raised the question whether the entoderm or mesectoderm initiates tooth formation. Among those who have studied this question further, Woerdeman and Raven ('46) concluded that there is a reciprocal inductive influence—that the papilla "induces the epithelium to form a tooth-germ, whilst the size of the papilla depends on the enamel-organ." Hörstadius ('50) demonstrated the reciprocal relationships more specifically by experiments in which tissues from the head were grafted in different combinations into the trunk. He found a failure of tooth development in the following grafts: oral entoderm plus oral ectoderm, oral entoderm plus neural crest, and oral ectoderm plus neural crest. Teeth developed in grafts of oral entoderm plus neural crest plus oral ectoderm. Studies on the mandibular arch by Levy and Detwiler ('51, and personal communication) are essentially in agreement with the views of Hörstadius. Likewise, in vitro studies by Wilde ('51) show that it is necessary to explant cranial neuroepithelium along with stomodeal ectoderm and foregut entoderm for teeth to develop.

Role of Entoderm in Gill Formation. Harrison ('21) studied the respective roles of branchial ectoderm and mesoderm in gill formation by extirpation and transplantation experiments. He established the following facts: (1) the branchial ectoderm of *A. punctatum* is specifically gill forming but an ectodermal region surrounding the gills also has the potency to form gills in a diminishing intensity as the distance from the gills increases; (2) the specific gill pattern is not laid down in the ectoderm; (3) the specific pattern must be determined by the deeper layers. In the absence of experiments on the entoderm, the respective roles of mesoderm and entoderm were not clear but it was suggested that the entoderm did not play merely a passive role. Heteroplastic gill transplantations made by Harrison ('29) showed that gills resembling those of the donor species occurred only when the whole gill complex was transplanted, entoderm included. The importance of the branchial entoderm was demonstrated in experiments on tail-bud stage Amblystoma embryos by Severinghaus ('30) in which it was found that a gill fails to develop after removal of its entoderm.

It is well established that neural crest cells contribute to the formation of the visceral arch skeleton (Landacre, '21; Stone, '22; and others). It has also been shown that the entoderm of the oral region acts as an inductor on the migrating neural crest cells for the formation of cartilage. Following experimentally produced defects in the oral region, Balinsky ('47b) found a correlation between the arrangement, number and size of the visceral cartilages and the presence of entoderm of the pharyngeal pouches. In transplantations of head tissues to the trunk, Hörstadius ('50) found that neural crest transplanted with oral entoderm will produce cartilage whereas neural crest grafted with oral ectoderm alone will not.

Mid-gut Derivatives—Stomach, Intestine, Liver and Pancreas. In amphibians, presumptive entodermal organ rudiments appear to be determined relatively early. The heterotopic transplantation experiments on Bombinator by Holtfreter ('25) showed that the liver and pancreatic primordia are capable of self-differentiation in the late gastrula stage. He found that the liver primordium itself is not a mosaic—it is not regionally determined—and a gallbladder can develop in grafts from either cephalic or caudal portions of the liver rudiment of tail-bud embryos. Whether one presumptive organ rudiment (e.g., stomach) can regulate to form another (eg., liver) is controversial. According to one view (Holtfreter, '25, '38; Kemp, '46, '51; and others) considerable regulation may occur in gross morphology but not in histological structure. According to another view (Kusche, '29; Balinsky, '38, '47b), histological regulation can occur. In xenoplastic grafts between Triturus and the axolotl, Balinsky found that presumptive liver tissue grafted into the stomach region could differentiate into stomach tissue. Likewise, presumptive stomach differentiated into liver cells and pancreatic acini when grafted into the regions of the latter tissues. These experiments suggest that the stomach, liver and pancreas have only a labile type of determination in neurula stage Triturus. In the pancreas, there is an interesting difference between the potencies of the dorsal and ventral primordia in that only the former is capable of differentiating islands of Langerhans (Wolf-Heidegger, '36).

The influence of mesodermal derivatives on the form of the digestive organs has been studied particularly by Kemp ('51). Embryos of R. pipiens at tail-bud stages were transected at different levels and reared in Holtfreter's solution. In other experiments, dorsal and ventral embryonic regions were excised. The following conclusions were drawn: development of a normal pattern of intestinal coiling in anurans is dependent upon the establishment of the vitelline circulation, upon the regulation of hydrostatic pressure within the digestive tract and coelom, and upon the restricted space of the coelomic cavity.

In the chick, chorioallantoic grafts indicate that liver potency tissue exists in both prospective dorsal and prospective ventral embryonic regions until sometime between the pre-somite and third somite stages; after this, the liver is segregated in so far as the potentialities for its development are eliminated from the dorsal region (Rudnick, '35). Segregation of a similar nature occurs at a somewhat later stage for the pancreas.

Liver differentiation in the chick appears to depend upon an inducing action from the heart rudiment, since liver is rarely present in grafts lacking heart tissue whereas the converse occurs quite often (Willier and Rawles, '31). The inducing action occurs particularly in grafts containing prospective liver material; the heart inductor action seems unnecessary when the liver develops from grafted material of some other prospective value, e.g., from prospective dorsal regions (Rudnick, '35). In amphibians, liver differentiation is not dependent upon heart development since liver can differentiate in the absence of the heart in explants from the gastrula stage (Holtfreter, '25).

Embryos survive complete liver extirpation for a longer period than do larvae or adults of the same species. When the operation is done on embryos in the gill-formation stage, survival is about two weeks for anuran amphibians (Yamada, '33) and about four weeks for urodeles (Copenhaver, '43). Developmental defects following embryonic hepatectomy indicate that liver development affects the formation of other embryonic structures through (a) a morphological relationship and (b) a functional relationship. Examples of the first type include modifications in the ventral mesentery and alterations in the course of venous drainage from the intestine. These changes can be seen best when the growth of a hepatectomized embryo is maintained either by parabiosis with a normal embryo (Yamada, '33) or by liver tissue implanted to the tail (Copenhaver, '43). Defects resulting from functional changes following liver extirpation include anemia and retarded growth of the spleen (Copenhaver, '43). The heart may be abnormally small, particularly in anemic animals. Other defects arising either directly or indirectly from functional changes following hepatectomy are distention of the pronephric canals (Holtfreter, '25), hypertrophy of the pronephros (Yamada, '33), and edema (Holtfreter, '25; Yamada, '33).

Numerous studies have established the fact that there is a rapid restoration of liver tissue following partial hepatectomy in mammals. Higgins and Anderson ('31) have shown that the liver of rats can regain its normal size within two to three weeks after a 70 per cent hepatectomy. According to Newman and Grossman ('51), nucleic acid supplements in the diet accelerate the rate of regeneration. Higgins and Anderson noted that restoration of mammalian liver tissue differs from regeneration of the tadpole's tail; in the former, there is no blastema of regenerating tissue at the level of the cut. When a lobe of the liver is removed, there is a proliferation of cells and formation of new lobules throughout the remaining lobes but the extirpated lobe itself is not restored. Considering the fact that most organs have a much greater regenerative capacity in amphibians than in mammals, it is surprising to find that an opposite result has been reported for the liver. Experiments on Bombinator and on R. esculenta by Holtfreter ('25) have confirmed the lack of liver regeneration reported by Banchi ('06) for Bufo. Studies on the salamander, Triturus viridescens, by Jordan and Beams ('30), showed compensatory hypertrophy but no proliferative activity after semihepatectomy. After excision of more than one-half of the liver, the lobular remnants were apparently incapable of effective restoration.

Onset of Liver Function. Functional differentiation of liver tissue has been studied more completely for the chick than for other species. Bile secretion appears on about the sixth day of incubation (Sandstrom, '34). On about the seventh day, appreciable amounts of glycogen are found in the liver although the pancreatic islands do not appear before the eleventh day (Dalton, '37b). From the developmental sequence just cited and from the fact that glycogen is stored by embryonic liver cells cultivated in vitro (Nordmann, '29), it is obvious that the synthesis and storage of glycogen in the embryonic liver is not dependent upon insulin. However, one notes a more adult type of glycogen distribution in the liver after the islands of Langerhans appear. Data on the excretion of uric acid indicate that the liver begins to function in protein metabolism on about the seventh day (Fiske and Boyden, '26). Cholesterol is normally not evident in liver tissue until the eleventh day of incubation, but an earlier capacity for lipid metabolism is indicated by the fact that cholesterol appears on the seventh day in embryonic hepatic cells grafted to the chorioallantois of older embryos (Dalton, '37a). Thus the available evidence indicates that most of the multiple functions of the liver cell appear at about the same time.

Although the hepatic cell is capable of function at an early age, it does not assume its full degree of function until relatively late. In the chick, glycogen storage in the extraembryonic tissues exceeds that in the liver until the seventeenth day of incubation, i.e., until 82 per cent of the incubation period has elapsed (Needham, '31). In mammals, the glycogenic function occurs chiefly in the placenta until relatively late in development. For example, the glycogen content of the rat liver first exceeds that of the placenta after the elapse of 75 per cent of the total gestation period (Corey, '35).

Asymmetry and Situs Inversus. The present discussion will be confined to asymmetry of the heart and viscera; for an analysis of other aspects of symmetry in the developing embryo, reference may be made to Harrison ('45).

Questions related to the development of normal visceral asymmetry and to situs inversus have been studied extensively by the experimental method, particularly in amphibians. Spemann, ('06) showed that a 180 degree rotation of the middle part of the medullary plate and its underlying mesoderm and entoderm frequently produced situs inversus of the gut and heart. Numerous investigators have confirmed and extended this finding. Experiments by von Woellwarth ('50) are particularly significant. In a control series of animals with a part of the medullary plate and its underlying tissue reimplanted with normal orientation, he found visceral situs inversus in about the same frequency as in another series of animals with a similar block of tissue rotated through 180 degrees. Working on the hypothesis that the unexpected results in the nonrotated reimplantations were caused by tissue damage, von Woellwarth made unilateral defects in the different germ layers in gastrula and neurula stage embryos. The following results were obtained from neurula stage operations: defects in the left side of the mesoderm gave weak inversion effects (9 per cent), defects of the right mesoderm gave no inversion effects, defects in entoderm gave strong inversion effects (about equal on the two sides—22 and 21 per cent, respectively, and defects in mesoderm and entoderm gave a strong effect for the left side (41 per cent) and a medium effect for the right (20 per cent). In gastrula stage operations, defects in the presumptive mesoderm of the left side gave strong inversion effects (50 per cent), defects of right mesoderm gave weak effects (8 per cent) and defects of presumptive entoderm of both sides gave weak effects (6 per cent).

The experiments of von Woellwarth show that situs inversus occurs with the greatest frequency after defects to the mesoderm of the left side at the gastrula stage. He believes that the results indicate an asymmetry of the organizer. In this connection, he notes that Goerttler ('28) argued for a physiological asymmetry of the mesoderm. The latter reported that explants of presumptive heart mesoderm from the left side of medullary plate stage urodeles developed pulsations within a few days whereas explants from the right side did not. On the other hand, Holtfreter ('33) found that pulsations began at about the same time in right and left heart anlage explanted from neurula stage axolotls. Nevertheless, there is support for the idea of an asymmetry in the two sides of the heart anlage. Bacon ('45) found that both sides of the bilateral heart rudiment of medullary plate stage Amblystoma are capable of self-differentiation but explants from the left side give a higher percentage of positive cases and an earlier initiation of pulsations. Rawles ('43) obtained essentially similar results for chorioallantoic grafts of heart-forming areas from the early chick blastoderm.

Situs inversus of the heart and gut frequently occur together although either one may appear without the other. This is true both for the cases seen in nature and for those produced experimentally. The most commonly described situs inversus cordis in the absence of situs inversus viscerum is that which occurs in the right member of double hearts produced by prevention of union of the bilateral heart primordia. In these cases, left hearts have normal asymmetry; right hearts frequently show situs inversus. The asymmetry of the right member of double hearts is probably correlated with an environmental influence already discussed by Ekman ('24, '25)—the union of the heart with the blood vessels and the pressure effects within the pericardial cavity favor normal curvature on the left side and situs inversus on the right side when the bilateral heart primordia develop separately. It is not surprising that the right member of double hearts does not develop situs inversus invariably, that both hearts occasionally show the same asymmetry (Fales, '46). Without the environmental effects just cited, normal asymmetry of the right member of double hearts might occur more often than it does. Theoretically, one might expect right heart primordia freed from the influence of the left side to develop with normal asymmetry and with situs inversus in about equal numbers, similar to the results obtained by Ruud and Spemann ('23) for right half blastulae. They found that when blastulae are completely constricted, left halves develop into small animals with normal asymmetry while right halves develop with situs inversus and with normal asymmetry in about equal numbers. For further details on the relation of situs inversus to localized defects in the germ layers and the probable relationship between normal visceral asymmetry and asymmetry in the embryonic "organizer," reference should be made to von Woellwarth ('50).

REFERENCES

Abel, W. 1912 Further observations on the development of the sympathetic nervous system in the chick. J. Anat. and Physiol., *47:*35–72.

Adams, A. E. 1924 An experimental study of the development of the mouth in the amphibian embryo. J. Exp. Zool., *40:*311–379.

——— 1931 Some effects of removal of endoderm from the mouth region of early *Amblystoma punctatum* embryos. J. Exp. Zool., *58:*147–163.

Alexander, R. S. and Glaser, O. 1941 Progressive acceleration in embryonic hearts. J. Exp. Zool., *87:*17–30.

Armstrong, P. B. 1931 Functional changes in the embryonic heart accompanying the ingrowth and development of the vagus innervation. J. Exp. Zool., *58:*43–67.

——— 1935 The role of the nerves in the action of acetylcholine on the embryonic heart. J. Physiol., *84:*20–32.

Bacon, R. L. 1945 Self-differentiation and induction in the heart of Amblystoma. J. Exp. Zool., *98:*87–125.

Balinsky, B. I. 1938 On the determination of entodermal organs in amphibia. Compt. Rend. Acad. Sci. U.R.S.S., *20:*215–217.

——— 1939 Experiments on total extirpation of the whole entoderm in Triton embryos. Compt. Rend. Acad. Sci. U.R.S.S., *23:*196–198.

——— 1947a Kinematik des entodermalen Materials bei der Gestaltung der wichtigsten Teile des Darmkanals bei den Amphibien. Roux' Arch. Entw.-mech., *143:*126–166.

——— 1947b Korrelationen in der Entwicklung der Mund- und Kiemenregion und des Darmkanals bei Amphibien. Roux' Arch. Entw.-mech., *143:*365–395.

Banchi, A. 1906 Sulla rigenerazione degli abozzi del fegato e del pancreas. Arch. ital. di Anat. e di Embriolo., *5:*507–532.

Barry, A. 1940 Age changes in the pulsation frequency of the embryonic chick heart. J. Exp. Zool., *85:*157–170.

——— 1941 The effect of exsanguination on the heart rate of the embryonic chick. J. Exp. Zool., *88:*1–15.

——— 1942 The intrinsic pulsation rates of fragments of the embryonic chick heart. J. Exp. Zool., *91:*119–130.

Block, M. 1946 An experimental analysis of hematopoiesis in the rat yolk sac. Anat. Rec., *96:*289–312.

Bloom, W., and Bartelmez, G. 1940 Hematopoiesis in young human embryos. Am. J. Anat., *67:*21–44.

Bogue, J. Y. 1932 The heart rate of the developing chick. J. Exp. Biol., *9:*351–358.

Born, G. 1897 Über Verwachsungsversuche mit Amphibienlarven. Roux' Arch. Entw.-mech., *4:*349–465.

Bremer, J. L. 1931 The presence and influence of two spiral streams in the heart of the chick embryo. Am. J. Anat., *49:*409–440.

Brinley, F. J. 1935 Evidence of a sympathetic innervation of the teleost heart, with a note on a method of transplanting the heart of Fundulus embryos. Physiol. Zool., *8:*360–373.

Burrows, M. T. 1911 The growth of tissues of the chick embryo outside the animal body, with special reference to the nervous system. J. Exp. Zool., *10:*63–84.

Butler, E. 1935 The developmental capacity of regions of the unincubated chick blastoderm as tested in chorio-allantoic grafts. J. Exp. Zool., 70: 357–395.

Cameron, J. A. 1941 Primitive blood-cell generations in Amblystoma. J. Morph., 68:231–237.

Clark, A. J. 1927 Comparative Physiology of the Heart. Cambridge University Press, Cambridge, England.

Clark, E. R. 1918 Studies on the growth of blood-vessels in the tail of the frog larva—by observation and experiment on the living animal. Am. J. Anat., 23:37–88.

———, and Clark, E. L. 1939 Microscopic observations on the growth of blood capillaries in the living mammal. Am. J. Anat., 64:251–301.

———, and Clark, E. L. 1940 Microscopic observations on the extra-endothelial cells of living mammalian blood vessels. Am. J. Anat., 66:1–49.

Cohn, A. E., and Wile, E. L. 1925 Physiological ontogeny. A. Chicken embryos. V. On the rate of the heart beat during the development of chicken embryos. J. Exp. Med., 42:291–297.

Copenhaver, W. M. 1926 Experiments on the development of the heart of Amblystoma punctatum. J. Exp. Zool., 43:321–371.

——— 1930 Results of heteroplastic transplantation of anterior and posterior parts of the heart rudiment in Amblystoma embryos. J. Exp. Zool., 55:293–318.

——— 1939a Initiation of beat and intrinsic contraction rates in the different parts of the Amblystoma heart. J. Exp. Zool., 80:193–224.

——— 1939b Some observations on the growth and function of heteroplastic heart grafts. J. Exp. Zool., 82:239–271.

——— 1943 Liver extirpation and implantation in Amblystoma embryos with particular reference to blood formation. Am. J. Anat., 73:81–105.

——— 1945 Heteroplastic transplantation of the sinus venosus between two species of Amblystoma. J. Exp. Zool., 100:203–216.

Corey, E. L. 1935 Growth and glycogen content of the fetal liver and placenta. Am. J. Physiol., 112:263–267.

Dalton, A. J. 1937a Cholesterol storage and bile secretion in chorio-allantoic grafts of liver. Anat. Rec., 67:431–439.

——— 1937b The functional differentiation of the hepatic cells of the chick embryo. Anat. Rec., 68:393–409.

Dantschakoff, V. 1924 Wachstum transplantierter embryonaler Gewebe in der Allantois. Zeit. Anat. Entwk., 74:401–431.

Davis, C. L. 1927 Development of the human heart from its first appearance to the stage found in embryos of twenty paired somites. Carnegie Contrib. to Embryol., 19:245–284.

Dwinnell, L. A. 1939 Physiological contraction of double hearts in rabbit embryos. Proc. Soc. Exp. Biol. & Med., 42:264–267.

Ekman, G. 1921 Experimentelle Beiträge zur Entwicklung des Bombinatorherzens. Oversikt av. Finska Vetenskapssocietetens Forhandlingar, 63: 1–37.

——— 1924 Neue experimentelle Beiträge zur frühesten Entwicklung des Amphibienherzens. Soc. Scient. Fenn. Comm. Biol., I.9:1–37.

——— 1925 Experimentelle Beiträge zur Herzentwicklung der Amphibien. Roux' Arch. Entw.-mech., 106:320–352.

——— 1927 Einige experimentelle Beiträge zur frühesten Herzentwicklung bei Rana fusca. Ann. Acad. Scient. Fenn., Ser. A. 27:1–26.

——— 1929 Experimentelle Untersuchungen über die früheste Herzentwicklung bei Rana fusca. Roux' Arch. Entw.-mech., 116:327–347.

Evans, H. M. 1908 On the development of the aortae, cardinal veins and umbilical veins, and the other blood vessels of vertebrate embryos from capillaries. Anat. Rec., 3:498–518.

Fales, D. E. 1946 A study of double hearts produced experimentally in embryos of Amblystoma punctatum. J. Exp. Zool., 101:281–298.

Fano, G., and Badano, F. 1890 Étude physiologique des premiers stades de développment du coeur embryonnaire du poulet. Arch. Ital. Biol., 13:387–422.

Federici, H. 1926 Recherches expérimentales sur les potentialitiés de l'ilot sanguin chez l'embryon de Rana fusca. Arch. de Biol., 36:466–487.

Fernald, R. L. 1947 The origin and development of the blood island of Hyla regilla. Univ. Calif. Publ. Zool., 51:129–147.

Fiske, C. H., and Boyden, E. A. 1926 Nitrogen metabolism of the chick embryo. J. Biol. Chem., 70:535–556.

Goerttler, K. 1928 Die Bedeutung der ventrolateralen Mesodermbezirke für die Herzanlage der Amphibienkeime. Anat. Anzeig. Ergänzungsheft, 66:132–139.

Goss, C. M. 1928 Experimental removal of the blood island of Amblystoma punctatum embryos. J. Exp. Zool., 52:45–61.

——— 1935 Double hearts produced experimentally in rat embryos. J. Exp. Zool., 72:33–49.

——— 1938 The first contractions of the heart in rat embryos. Anat. Rec., 70:505–524.

——— 1940 First contractions of the heart without cytological differentiation. Anat. Rec., 76: 19–27.

——— 1942 The physiology of the embryonic mammalian heart before circulation. Am. J. Physiol., 137:146–152.

Grant, W. C., and Root, W. S. 1947 The relation of O_2 in bone marrow blood to post-hemorrhagic erythropoiesis. Am. J. Physiol., 150:618–627.

Gräper, L. 1907 Untersuchungen über die Herzbildung der Vögel. Roux' Arch. Entw.-mech., 24: 375–410.

Haberlandt, L. 1927 Das Hormon der Herzbewegung. Urban and Schwarzenberg, Berlin.

Hall, E. K. 1951 Intrinsic contractility in the embryonic rat heart. Anat. Rec., 111:381–400.

Harrison, R. G. 1921 Experiments on the development of the gills in the amphibian embryo. Biol. Bull., 41:156–170.

——— 1929 Heteroplastic transplantations in amphibian embryos. Xᵉ Congrès Int. d. Zoologie, Budapest, Part I: 642–650.

——— 1945 Relations of symmetry in the developing embryo. Trans. Conn. Acad. Arts & Sciences, 36:277–330.

Hertig, A. T. 1935 Angiogenesis in the early human chorion and in the primary placenta of the macaque monkey. Carnegie Contrib. to Embryol., 25:37–81.

Higgins, G. M., and Anderson, R. M. 1931 Experimental pathology of the liver. Arch. Path., 12:186–202.

His, W., Jr., and Romberg, E. 1890 Beiträge zur Herzinnervation. Fortschritte der Medizin, 8:374–380.

Hörstadius, S. 1950 The Neural Crest. Oxford University Press, Oxford, England.

Hoff, E. C., Kramer, T. C., DuBois, D., and Patten, B. M. 1939 The development of the electrocardiogram of the embryonic heart. Am. Heart J., 17:470–488.

Holtfreter, J. 1925 Defekt- und Transplantationsversuche an der Anlage von Leber und Pancreas jüngster Amphibienkeime. Roux' Arch. Entw.-mech., 105:330–383.

———— 1933 Die totale Exogastrulation, eine Selbstablösung des Ektoderms vom Entomesoderm. Roux' Arch. Entw.-mech., 129:669–793.

———— 1938 Differenzierungspotenzen isolierter Teile der Urodelengastrula. Roux' Arch. Entw.-mech., 138:522–656.

Hooker, D. 1911 The development and function of voluntary and cardiac muscle in embryos without nerves. J. Exp. Zool., 11:159–186.

Hunt, T. E. 1932 Potencies of transverse levels of the chick blastoderm in the definitive-streak stage. Anat. Rec., 55:41–69.

———— 1937a The development of gut and its derivatives from the mesectoderm and mesentoderm of early chick blastoderms. Anat. Rec., 68:349–369.

———— 1937b The origin of entodermal cells from the primitive streak of the chick embryo. Anat. Rec., 68:449–460.

Johnstone, P. N. 1925 Studies on the physiological anatomy of the embryonic heart. II. An inquiry into the development of the heart beat in chick embryos including the development of irritability to electrical stimulation. Bull. Johns Hopkins Hosp., 36:299–311.

Jolly, J. 1940 Recherches sur la formation du système vasculaire de l'embryo. Arch. d'anat. microscop., 35:295–361.

Jordan, H. E., and Beams, H. W. 1930 Hepatectomy in the salamander with special reference to hemopoiesis and cytology of the liver remnant. Proc. Soc. Exp. Biol. & Med., 28:181–184.

————, and Speidel, C. C. 1923 The fundamental erythrocytopoietic stimulus. Proc. Soc. Exp. Biol. & Med., 21:399–404.

Kemp, N. E. 1946 Regulation in the entoderm of the tree frog Hyla regilla. Univ. Calif. Publ. Zool., 51:159–182.

———— 1951 Development of intestinal coiling in anuran larvae. J. Exp. Zool., 116:259–287.

Kirschbaum, A., and Downey, H. 1937 A comparison of some of the methods used in the studies of hematopoietic tissues. Anat. Rec., 68:227–231.

Knower, H. McE. 1907 Effects of early removal of the heart and arrest of the circulation on the development of frog embryos. Anat. Rec., 1:161–165.

Kumé, M. 1935 The differentiating capacity of various regions of the heart rudiment of the chick as studied in chorio-allantoic grafts. Physiol. Zool., 8:73–90.

Kusche, W. 1929 Interplantation umschriebener Zellbezirke aus der Blastula und der Gastrula von Amphibien. Roux' Arch. Entw.-mech., 120:192–271.

Landacre, F. L. 1921 The fate of the neural crest in the head of urodeles. J. Comp. Neur., 33:1–43.

Levy, B. M., and Detwiler, S. R. 1951 Experimental studies on the development of the mandibular arch in Amblystoma punctatum. J. Dental Research, 30:1–12.

Lewis, M. R. 1919 The development of cross striation in the heart muscle of the chick embryo. Bull. Johns Hopkins Hosp., 30:176–181.

Lewis, W. H. 1931 The outgrowth of endothelium and capillaries in tissue culture. Bull. Johns Hopkins Hosp., 48:242–253.

Mangold, O. 1937 Isolationsversuche zur Analyse der Entwicklung des Gehör-, Kiemen- und Extremitätenregion bei Urodelen. Acta Soc. pro Fauna et Flora Fenn., 60:3–44.

McDonald, J. G. 1939 Avian bone marrow with particular reference to red cell development. Am. J. Anat., 65:291–308.

Murray, P. D. F. 1932 The development in vitro of the blood of the early chick embryo. Proc. Roy. Soc. Lond. B., 111:497–521.

Needham, J. 1931 Chemical Embryology, Vol. II. Cambridge University Press, Cambridge, England.

Newman, E. A., and Grossman, M. I. 1951 Effect of nucleic acid supplements in the diet on rate of regeneration of liver in rats. Am. J. Physiol., 164:251–253.

Nicholas, J. S. 1948 Form changes during pregastrular development. Ann. N.Y. Acad. Sci., 49:801–817.

————, and Rudnick, D. 1934 The development of rat embryos in tissue culture. Proc. Nat. Acad. Sci., 20:656–658.

Nieuwkoop, P. D. 1946 Experimental investigations on the origin and determination of the germ cells, and on the development of the lateral plates and germ ridges in urodeles. Arch. Néerland. Zool., 8:1–205.

Nordmann, M. 1929 Wachstum und Stoffwechsel der Leberzellen in der Gewebskultur. Arch. exp. Zellf., 8:371–414.

Olivo, O. M. 1928 Über die frühzeitige Determinierung der Herzanlage beim Hühnerembryo und deren Differenzierung in vitro. Anat. Anz., Erg. Heft, 66:108–118.

————, Petralia, S., and Ricamo, R. 1946 Elettrocardiogramma e miofibrille nelle colture in vitro di miocardio embrionale. Boll. Soc. Ital. Biol. Sperim., 22/7:911–913.

Ōta, T. 1930 Experimentelle Studien über den Herzbildungsbezirk an den Amphibienlarven. Jap. J. Med. Sci., 2:235–242.

Paff, G. H. 1936 Transplantation of the sinoatrium to the conus in the embryonic heart. Am. J. Physiol., 117:313–317.

Patten, B. M. 1949 Initiation and early changes in the character of the heart beat in vertebrate embryos. Physiol. Rev., 29:31–47.

———, and Kramer, T. C. 1933 The initiation of contraction in the embryonic chick heart. Am. J. Anat., 53:349–375.

———, Kramer, T. C., and Barry, D. A. 1948 Valvular action in the embryonic chick heart by localized apposition of endocardial masses. Anat. Rec., 102:297–312.

Pickering, J. W. 1893 Observations on the physiology of the embryonic heart. J. Physiol., 14:383–466.

Pressler, K. 1911 Beobachtungen und Versuche über den normalen und inversen Situs viscerum et cordis bei Anurenlarven. Roux' Arch. Entw.-mech., 32:1–35.

Rawles, M. E. 1943 The heart-forming areas of the early chick blastoderm. Physiol. Zool., 16:22–45.

Rudnick, D. 1935 Regional restrictions of potencies in the chick during embryogenesis. J. Exp. Zool., 71:83–99.

——— 1938 Differentiation in culture of pieces of the early chick blastoderm. I. The definitive primitive streak and head-process stages. Anat. Rec., 70:351–368.

———, and Rawles, M. E. 1937 Differentiation of the gut in chorio-allantoic grafts from chick blastoderms. Physiol. Zool., 10:381–395.

Ruud, G., and Spemann, H. 1923 Die Entwicklung isolierter dorsaler und lateraler Gastrulahälften von Triton taeniatus und alpestris, ihre Regulation und Postgeneration. Roux' Arch. Entw.-mech., 52:95–166.

Sabin, F. R. 1917 Origin and development of the primitive vessels of the chick and of the pig. Carnegie Contrib. to Embryol., 6:61–124.

——— 1920 Studies on the origin of blood-vessels and of red blood-corpuscles as seen in the living blastoderm of the chick during the second day of incubation. Carnegie Contrib. to Embryol., 9:213–259.

——— 1922 On the origin of the cells of the blood. Physiol. Rev., 2:38–69.

Sandstrom, R. H. 1934 The differentiation of hepatic and pancreatic tissues of the chick embryo in chorio-allantoic grafts. Physiol. Zool., 7:226–246.

Scharrer, E. 1939 The regeneration of end-arteries in the opossum brain. J. Comp. Neur., 70:69–76.

Schmitt, F. O. 1945 Ultrastructure and the problem of cellular organization. The Harvey Lectures, 40:249–268.

Severinghaus, A. E. 1930 Gill development in Amblystoma punctatum. J. Exp. Zool., 56:1–29.

Slonimski, P. 1931 Recherches expérimentales sur la génèse du sang chez les Amphibiens. Arch. Biol., 42:415–477.

Spemann, H. 1906 Über embryonale Transplantation. Verhandl. Ges. deutscher Naturforscher u. Ärzte, 78:189–201.

Spratt, N. T., Jr. 1942 Location of organ-specific regions and their relationship to the development of the primitive-streak in the early chick blastoderm. J. Exp. Zool., 89:69–102.

Stöhr, Ph., Jr. 1924a Experimentelle Studien an embryonalen Amphibienherzen. I. Über Explantation embryonaler Amphibienherzen. Roux' Arch. Entw.-mech., 102:426–451.

——— 1924b Experimentelle Studien an embryonalen Amphibienherzen. II. Über Transplantation embryonaler Amphibienherzen. Roux' Arch. Entw.-mech., 103:555–592.

——— 1925 Experimentelle Studien an embryonalen Amphibienherzen. III. Über die Entstehung der Herzform. Roux' Arch. Entw.-mech., 106:409–455.

——— 1927 Experimentelle Studien an embryonalen Amphibienherzen. IV. Roux' Arch. Entw.-mech., 112:696–738.

Stone, L. S. 1922 Experiments on the development of cranial ganglia and the lateral-line sense organs in Amblystoma. J. Exp. Zool., 35:421–496.

Storti, E. 1931 Sulla capacità ematopoietica dell' endotelio nelle larve degli anfibi. Boll. Soc. Ital. Biol. Sperim., 6:97–99.

Streeter, G. L. 1918 The developmental alterations in the vascular system of the brain of the human embryo. Carnegie Contrib. to Embryol., 8:5–38.

——— 1927 Archetypes and symbolism. Science, 65:405–412.

Verocay 1905 Multiplicitas cordis (Heptocardia) bei einem Huhn. Verhandl. der Deutschen pathol. Ges., Erg. Heft, 16:192–198.

Vogt, W. 1929 Gestaltungsanalyse am Amphibienkeim mit örtlicher Vitalfärbung. Roux' Arch. Entw.-mech., 120:384–706.

Waddington, C. H., and Waterman, A. J. 1933 The development "in vitro" of young rabbit embryos. J. Anat., 67:355–370.

West, R. 1948 Activity of vitamin B_{12} in Addisonian pernicious anemia. Science, 107:398.

Wilde, C. E., Jr. 1951 An in vitro study of the urodele neural crest. Anat. Rec., 111:92.

Willier, B. H., and Rawles, M. E. 1931 Developmental relations of the heart and liver in the chorio-allantoic grafts of whole chick blastoderms. Anat. Rec., 48:277–302.

Wintrobe, M. M. 1950 Factors and mechanisms in the production of red corpuscles. The Harvey Lectures, Ser. 45.

Wislocki, G. B. 1939 The unusual mode of development of the blood vessels of the opossum's brain. Anat. Rec., 74:409–428.

Woellwarth, C. von 1950 Experimentelle Untersuchungen über den Situs Inversus der Eingeweide und der Habenula des Zwischenhirns bei Amphibien. Roux' Arch. Entw.-mech., 144:178–256.

Woerdeman, M. W., and Raven, C. P. 1946 Monographs on the Progress of Research in Holland during the War. Elsevier Publishing Co., New York.

Wolf-Heidegger, G. 1936 Experimentelle Studien zur Genese der Langerhansschen Inseln des Pankreas. Roux' Arch. Entw.-mech., 135:114–134.

Yamada, H. 1933 Über die Elimination der Leber bei den parabiotischen Bufolarven. Folia Anat. Japonica, 11:191–211.

CHAPTER 6

Urinogenital System

R. K. BURNS

THE URINARY and genital systems of vertebrates are related in the adult only in having certain external passages in common; in development, however, most of the internal organs of reproduction are derived from parts of the primitive nephric system. The history of the remarkable transformations involved has long been familiar from comparative morphological studies, but only in recent years have advances in theory and experimental techniques permitted rapid progress in analyzing the mechanisms of control and integration. As the morphological precursor of many genital structures, the nephric system must be given first consideration.

THE NEPHRIC SYSTEM

In many vertebrates the nephric system develops as three distinct entities—pronephros, mesenephros and metanephros—which appear successively in a regular temporospatial order (Fig. 167). However, in certain cyclostomes and primitive amphibians the system is essentially continuous, with little regional specialization (for a recent review see Fraser, '50). The units of the system at all levels develop from the intermediate mesoderm. The pronephric and more anterior mesonephric tubules have a simple metameric disposition, arising from discrete nephrotomes; posteriorly the tubules differentiate within an unsegmented cord of nephric material—secondary and tertiary elements, etc., developing as buds from the primary units, or from residual nephrogenic tissue in association with diverticula from the nephric duct. [For general accounts see Hall ('04); Gray ('32, '36); Hamilton ('52). For the relationship between mesonephros and "definitive kidney" in amphibians see Gray ('32) and Fraser ('50).] The metanephros of amniotes develops entirely in the latter fashion. Its nephrons differentiate within a blastema, more or less continu-

ous with the nephrogenic cord, in relation with the ureteric diverticulum. Thus, the tubules at all levels appear as independent primordia and only secondarily unite with the duct system. The nephric duct is laid down as the duct of the pronephros, serves subsequently as mesonephric duct, and as such gives rise to the ureter. The problems presented are concerned with (1) the history and progressive localization of the nephrogenic materials prior to the appearance of definitive nephric primordia, and (2) the nature of the integrative forces which coordinate the later development of the various parts of the system and relate them to the regional environment.

THE TOPOGRAPHY OF NEPHROGENIC AREAS IN EARLY STAGES OF DEVELOPMENT

The first problem to be considered concerns the *topographic localization* of the prospective nephrogenic materials at successive stages of development, leading up to the appearance of discrete nephric primordia; the related and concurrent problem of the progressive *determination* of these materials is dealt with elsewhere (Holtfreter and Hamburger, see Section VI, Chapter 1). In early development most embryonic organ systems are not precisely localized, and after removal of prospective organ-forming areas extensive reorganizations are possible. Division of the amphibian egg may be followed by essentially normal development of its parts, in which nephric structures show the same regulative capacities as other systems. Bilateral regulation of the nephric system may even occur in dwarf embryos derived from lateral pieces of the early gastrula (Holtfreter, '38). At the beginning of gastrulation, however, there is a definite concentration of the prospective nephrogenic material in the posterior region of the marginal zone, as shown by the consistent results of many vital-staining experiments (for reviews see Pasteels, '42; Nieuwkoop, '47). At this stage a rather sharply defined area representing the pronephros lies somewhat ventrolateral to the dorsal lip of the blastopore (Pasteels, '42). When this area is marked with a vital stain the color is later found to be confined almost entirely to the pronephros and its duct (Fig. 168). The area

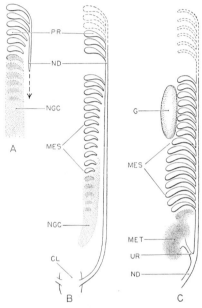

A

B C

Fig. 167. Plan of development of the nephric system of vertebrates. A, Origin and mode of development of the nephric duct; B and C, its relations to the other parts of the system; PR, pronephric units; ND, nephric duct; NGC, nephrogenic cord; G, gonad; MES, mesonephric units; MET, metanephros; UR, ureter; CL, cloaca.

in question lies at the future cephalic end of a band of nephrogenic tissue which, in the course of gastrulation, passes inward around the lateral lip of the blastopore toward its final position in the lateral trunk region.

In salamander embryos final topographic localization of the pronephric material occurs from late gastrula to middle neurula stages. In the early neurula the material has been invaginated and lies in the lateral body wall, anterior to the blastopore and below prospective somites 4 and 5 (Fig. 169, after Yamada, '37; see also Muchmore, '51). After this stage its position relative to adjacent regional structures (somites, limb area, gills, etc.) does not essentially change. By the

middle neurula stage, however, as a result of posterior elongation of the body axis, the location is relatively further forward (Fales, '35; see also Yamada, '37; Nieuwkoop, '47; Muchmore, '51). At this stage transplants of a limited area (Fig. 171) always produce pronephros, and contiguous areas have no pronephric potency (Fales). Nevertheless,

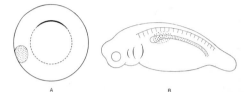

A B

Fig. 168. A, Position of the prospective pronephric area in the early gastrula of the axolotl, according to Pasteels ('42); B, later distribution of the stain.

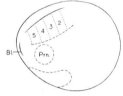

Fig. 169. Position of the pronephric area in the early neurula stage of the salamander, according to Yamada ('37). Prn., Pronephric area; numerals indicate the position of the future somites. Bl., blasto-pore.

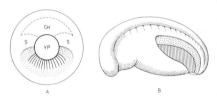

A B

Fig. 170. Position of the mesonephric material (stippled) and the lateral plate material (lined) in a salamander. A, Middle gastrula stage; B, tail-bud stage (after Nieuwkoop, '47). CH, Chorda; S, somite area; YP, yolk plug.

the definitive pronephros-forming area is still not completely autonomous; the character of its final differentiation, as respects the type of tubule produced, and the details of tubule structure, depend on its regional environment—a matter for later consideration (see p. 465).

The topographic localization of the prospective mesonephric tissue has also been established by vital staining. In the middle gastrula stage of a salamander egg it lies ventral and ventrolateral to the blastopore, in the form of an open collar (Fig. 170A, after Nieuwkoop, '47). The sides of the collar are undergoing involution around the lateral lips. (At this stage the pronephric material has for the most part passed in.) Mesonephric potency, however, is not restricted to this band. After extirpation there is extensive reconstitution of the nephrogenic and lateral plate material (Nieuwkoop).

In neural plate stages the mesonephric material is still in process of involution. Two positions have been demonstrated independently (Fig. 171). One lies just lateral to the neural fold, a little anterior to the blastopore (Fales, '35; Nieuwkoop, '47); but at a slightly earlier stage an area within the posterior neural plate also produces mesonephros (see Spofford, '45). The latter area

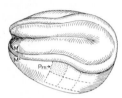

Fig. 171. Position of pronephric and mesonephric areas in the middle neurula stage of Amblystoma, modified from Fales ('35). The pronephric area is stippled; the adjacent areas indicated lack nephric potency. M^1, position of prospective mesonephric material in the hinder part of the medullary plate, according to Spofford ('45). M^2, position of mesonephric material already invaginated and shifted laterally toward its definitive position (Fales, '35; Nieuwkoop, '47).

evidently represents in part the uninvoluted portion of the nephrogenic band; the former consists of material which has been invaginated. After involution is complete, elongation of the body axis shifts the mesonephric material forward to its definitive position (Fig. 170B). At this stage 90 per cent of grafts of the intermediate mesoderm posterior to the ninth somite give rise to well developed mesonephric tubules (Humphrey, '28a).

In chick blastoderms of the head-process stage (comparable to the early neurula of amphibians) mesonephric potency is found in a limited area which includes the anterior part of the primitive streak and the node (Fig. 172A, after Rawles, '36; see also Willier and Rawles, '35). When portions of this area are transplanted to the chorio-allantoic membrane, mesonephros develops (in association with gonad and adrenal cortex). Nephrogenic capacity presumably resides in the mesodermal constituent; however, all three germ layers are included in such transplants. Somewhat earlier, in the definitive streak stage, a prospective nephric area lies

close to the mid-line, a little behind the node (Fig. 172B; for a review and analysis see Rudnick, '44).

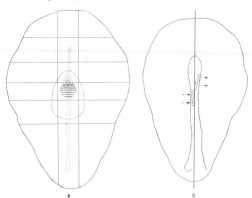

Fig. 172. A, Location of the prospective mesonephros- and gonad-forming areas in the chick blastoderm of the head-process stage, adapted from Rawles; the area within the broken line represents mesonephros, the cross-hatched area gonad and adrenal. B, Location of nephrogenic material (presumably mesonephros) at the stage of the definitive primitive streak, after Rudnick ('44); left side: epiblast—the material is moving toward the primitive groove; right side: mesoblast, showing position of material already involuted and moving laterally.

THE EXISTENCE OF NEPHRIC FIELDS

Although topographically restricted areas representing pronephros or mesonephros can be defined in amphibian eggs as early as gastrula stages, nephrogenic potency is not limited to such areas until much later. In fact, capacity to produce nephric tubules is widely distributed in the gastrula, in keeping with the pluripotency of both ectoderm and mesoderm at this stage (for a discussion see Holtfreter and Hamburger, Section VI, Chapter 1). Almost any part of the ectoderm, epidermal or neural, may produce nephric tubules when transplanted into the pronephric region (Holtfreter, '33; Mangold, '24) or when exposed to the influence of "trunk organizer" (Holtfreter '36); and nephrogenic tissue inserted into the blastocoele may induce nephric tubules in any overlying ectoderm (Holtfreter, '33). Nephric tissue has been obtained also from various regions of the mesoderm which normally give rise to other tissues, for examples, the archenteric roof (Holtfreter, '36) and somite material (Yamada, '37; Muchmore, '51).

The fact that various tissues not normally nephrogenic become so when placed in a nephrogenic region, or brought in contact with nephrogenic tissue, led to the concept of a nephric field (see Holtfreter, '33). Systematic experimentation showed that gastrula ectoderm may produce nephric tubules when implanted into any part of a lateral zone extending from the level of the gills to the cloaca (Fig. 173). However, as with embryonic fields in general, inductive power is not uniform throughout this zone but is strongest near the site of the pronephros. This was shown by the relative frequency of nephric differentiation in grafts placed at various levels in the field. Furthermore, grafts of the prospective pronephric area diminish both in size and in degree of differentiation as they are moved posteriorly from the normal position (Fales, '35).

Evidence of field effects may be adduced with respect to other nephric regions. Gastrula ectoderm implanted in the mesonephric area of the posterior neural plate (Fig. 171) produces mesonephric tubules (Spofford, '48); on the other hand, mesonephric material moved forward into the pronephric area forms pronephric tubules, and its rate of differentiation is correspondingly accelerated (Machemer, '29). Finally, tubules of mesonephric type may be induced to develop precociously in the metanephric blastema of the chick by the action of abnormal inductors (Gruenwald, '42, '43).

From such results it may be concluded that: (1) a variety of foreign tissues, mesodermal and ectodermal, acquire nephrogenic potencies if introduced into a nephrogenic field or exposed to an appropriate inductor; (2) in the differentiation of such materials both the frequency and the special character (pronephric or mesonephric) of the differentiation are modified by the position of the material in the field. It has been suggested (Machemer, Gruenwald, op. cit.) that capacity to produce nonspecific tubular structures is essentially of the same order at all levels of the system, the specific character of the tubule depending on local factors. The appearance of sub-regions within a wider and more generalized nephric field is to be regarded as an aspect of regional differentiation in the embryo as a whole.

It must be recognized, however, that the inductive and integrative activities attributed to the field may function to a remarkable degree in relative isolation. Highly differentiated pronephric structures may be obtained from disorganized cell aggregates* differenti-

* Taken from the dorsolateral lip of the blastopore. The material may possess original pronephric significance in part, or may acquire potency through induction by materials from the organization center.

ating in ectopic situations, or in vitro (Holtfreter, '44). Aggregation and reintegration of cell types on the basis of specific affinities, and assimilation of other types by induction, are postulated. In such tissue complexes it is likely that the essential constituents of the normal field environment are represented.

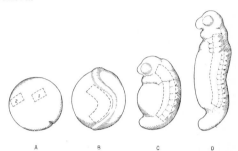

Fig. 173. Influence of the host field in determining the differentiation of pronephros from gastrula ectoderm (Holtfreter, '33). A, Sources of donor ectoderm taken from prospective neural (1) or epidermal (2) areas of the early gastrula; B, C, and D, zones within which pronephric structures may differentiate from such ectoderm, when transplanted into host embryos of different ages.

THE DIFFERENTIATION OF THE PRONEPHROS

With respect to the pronephros it has been shown that during the gastrula stage extensive regulations are possible, and that various non-nephrogenic materials may be assimilated with essentially normal results (p. 464). However, by middle or late neurula stages (corresponding approximately with final restriction of potency; see p. 463) irreversible determinations have occurred. [There has been no analysis of pattern and axiation in the pronephros comparable to the analysis of the limb disc (see Section VII, Chapter 4).] In the frog Discoglossus, the dorsoventral axis is apparently fixed by the middle neurula stage, when inversion of the primordium results in an inverted pronephros (Tung, '35). In the late neurula, division of the pronephric area is followed by development of partial structures which correspond with the plane of section (Holtfreter, '44), and combinations of primordia in middle neurula stages result in mosaic organs with extra parts (Fales, '35). The pronephric primordium is now essentially a mosaic, and problems of a different kind are introduced. To what extent are the individual parts of the complex interdependent in final development; and what is the role of the field in their final differentiation?

The several parts (glomus, nephrostomal canals, tubules, common duct) have distinct origins (see Field, '91; Fales, '35; Cambar, '49). The glomus arises from the coelomic wall and may develop independently after excision of the pronephric primordium (Howland, '21; Miura, '30a; Fales, '35), but an accessory glomus may also develop in heterotopic positions in response to transplanted tubules (Fales). Nephrostomal canals de-

is increasingly impaired (Fales, '35). When older donors are used, however, development is better at all levels. Grafts to the body cavity yield only disorganized tubules, but again the quality of differentiation varies somewhat with the age of the primordium. Apparently two major factors are operative at this period: an organization in the primordium, expressed by capacity for autonomous differentiation, which increases with

EXPERIMENT	AUTHOR		FORM USED	EFFECT ON NEPHRIC DUCT	
Ectopic pronephros _ transplanted or induced	Holtfreter	1934	Triton	Ducts grew out from pronephros	
Excision of entire pronephric primordium	Burns	1938	Amblystoma	Duct absent on operated side	
Excision of pronephric primordium	Waddington	1938	Rana	" " " " "	
Obstruction of duct primordium	O'Connor	1939	Amblystoma Pleurodeles	" " " " " " " " " " "	*
Excision or obstruction of duct primordium	Tung and Ku	1944	Bufo Rana	" " " " " " " " " "	
Obstruction of duct primordium	Van Geertruyden	1946	Rana	" " " " "	*
Excision of entire pronephric primordium	Nieuwkoop	1947	Triton	" " " " "	
Interference with duct primordium by cutting	Holtfreter	1944	Triton Amblystoma	" " posterior to cut " " " " "	*
Staining of primordium of duct (somites 5-7)	O'Connor	1938	Triton Amblystoma	Entire duct contains stain	
Staining prospective mesonephric material	Spofford	1945	Amblystoma	Mesonephros stained — duct clear	
Tip of duct destroyed by cautery	Boyden	1927 1932	Chick	Absent caudal to site of operation	
Tip of duct obstructed by incision	Waddington	1938	"	" " " " " "	
Tip of duct destroyed by cautery	Grünwald	1937	"	" " " " " "	
Tip of duct blocked by graft	Gruenwald	1942	"	" " " " " "	

Fig. 174. Table showing effects of various experimental procedures on the development of the nephric duct, with respect to its origin and manner of formation. Staining experiments (O'Connor, '38) indicate a local origin from a primordium adjacent to and continuous with the pronephros. Asterisks indicate cases in which a short segment of duct was found posteriorly, in communication with the cloaca. According to O'Connor ('39, '40) such pieces are of cloacal origin.

velop from the somatopleure underlying the tubule primordia, and are said to remain after removal of the primordium (Howland, '21); but this is also denied (Dalcq, '42; Cambar, '49). However, primordia developing in ectopic locations, or in the coelom, usually produce tubules without nephrostomes (Fales). In later development there is marked interdependence of parts, probably mediated by functional influences. For example, removal of the glomus, or obliteration of nephrostomal canals, leads to atrophy of the tubules; and reducing the number of tubules results in shrinkage of the common duct (Miura, '30a; Shimasaki, '30a; Fales, '35).

In the middle neurula stage transplantation of the pronephric primordium in the orthotopic position results in normal development, but at posterior levels differentiation

age, and regulative influences essential for normal growth and development, exerted by the regional environment.

ORIGIN AND DEVELOPMENT OF THE NEPHRIC DUCT

The classic view derives the nephric duct from a union of the ends of the anterior pronephric tubules (Fig. 167; for reviews of normal development see Goodrich, '30; Fraser, '50). In many amphibians, however, the tubules do not appear as discrete units but arise from a continuous primordium, the posterior extremity of which represents the duct (e.g., Field, '91). A vital stain applied to the pronephric swelling of a salamander ventral to somites 3 and 4 appears subsequently only in the tubules; but if applied ventral to somites 5-7 the color is later confined to the duct (O'Connor, '38), which presumably has a distinct origin from intermediate mesoderm at this level* (see also Fig. 168; Pasteels, '42). Transections through the pronephric region at the neurula stage indicate approximately the same localization (Holtfreter, '44).

More difficult to determine is the manner in which the duct reaches the cloaca. On this point conflicting views have long existed. The classic theory envisages independent caudal growth of a bud of tissue arising at the pronephric level (Fig. 167), but an alternative view (Field, '91, and others) postulates formation *in situ* by incorporation of local materials at each successive level (hence the term "segmental duct"). The problem has been investigated experimentally by three methods: (1) excision of the pronephric primordium before outgrowth of the duct; (2) interference with the growth of the duct at various levels; (3) the use of vital staining to identify the duct materials. The results are summarized in Fig. 174. In brief, it appears that removal of the primordium, or interference with the tip of the duct, prevents development posterior to the point of intervention (Fig. 175); but if the growing tip is left intact, development continues. Stain applied to the duct rudiment at the point of origin (as noted previously) appears subsequently throughout its length, but not in any adjacent tissue (O'Connor, '38). Conversely, if the prospective mesonephric material is stained prior to the formation of the duct, the latter is subsequently found to be unstained (Spofford, '48). The evidence supports the view that the duct develops by caudal growth of an original primordium rather than by local accretion. An exception must be made with respect to the posterior end of the duct. A short piece—often less than one somite in length—is sometimes found in contact with the cloaca, in the absence of the main part of the duct (Machemer, '29; O'Connor, '39, '40; Holtfreter, '44; Tung and Ku, '44; van Geertruyden, '46). This piece is considered by O'Connor to be of cloacal origin.

However, the territory traversed by the duct is not without influence on its development. In normal development the duct grows backward in a narrow groove between the ventral edges of the somites and the lateral mesoderm, and covered by ectoderm. Obstructions placed across this pathway usually

* In anuran embryos the duct primordium lies at the level of somite 5 according to Dalcq ('42) van Geertruyden ('42), and Cambar ('49).

prevent further development (see Fig. 174); or if the tip of the duct is rotated it usually fails to grow far into strange territory (Tung and Ku, '44). On the other hand, if the pathway is reoriented or dislocated in various ways, the duct may deviate considerable distances in order to reenter and traverse it (Holtfreter, '44; Tung and Ku). The duct is able to traverse the path in either direction, or two ducts may be made to do so in opposite directions (Tung and Ku). When segments of the duct are excised, regeneration

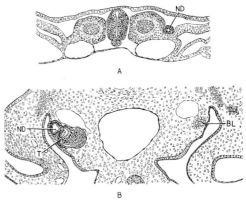

Fig. 175. *A*, Absence of the nephric duct in a chick embryo (left side) after preventing the backward growth of the primordium by transection at the 12-somite stage; *B*, failure of the mesonephric tubule to develop on the operated (right) side in the absence of the nephric duct—only a formless blastema is present (after Waddington, '38); *ND*, nephric duct; *BL*, blastema; *T*, mesonephric tubule.

proceeds along the pathway from either or both ends, (Howland, '26; Tung and Ku). Evidently no irreversible polarizations are involved, either of the pathway or the duct. The properties of the path favoring development of the duct are perhaps in large part mechanical, but the importance of physiological factors has also been stressed (Holtfreter, '44).

In amphibians the nephric ducts terminate in a pair of cloacal diverticula (cloacal horns) which are histologically distinct from the duct (Field, '91; O'Connor, '40); in avian embryos union is with the urodeum. Studies of this relationship have yielded different results. In amphibians cloacal horns develop normally in the absence of the duct, and may even elongate, replacing its hinder end (O'Connor, '39, '40). Elimination of the duct in chick embryos results in reduction and abnormal differentiation of the urodeum (Boyden, '24). The duct readily unites with grafts of cloacal tissue placed along its path

(O'Connor, '40), but may also join other regions of the gut (O'Connor, '39; Holtfreter, '44).

THE DEVELOPMENT OF THE MESONEPHROS

Up to the middle neurula stage at least, while the mesonephric material is still in process of involution, determination within

act as an inductor (for a discussion see Grünwald, '37). Experiments in which development of the duct was prevented in the mesonephric region provide a direct test of this hypothesis (Fig. 176). The results, however, vary greatly and are inconclusive. In most cases only rudiments of tubules, or mere cellular condensations, appear in the absence of the duct (Fig. 175B); and in one species no visible blastema develops. But if the duct is

EXPERIMENT	AUTHOR		FORM USED	STATE OF MESONEPHRIC TUBULES
Grafts of mesonephros — no duct present	Humphrey	1928	Amblystoma	Well-differentiated tubules
Excision of nephric duct	Miura	1930b	Rana, Bufo	No development of tubules
Excision of nephric duct	Shimasaki	1930b	Bufo	Irregular differentiation of tubules
Excision of pronephros and duct	Burns	1938	Amblystoma	Irregular differentiation of tubules
Excision of pronephros and duct	Waddington	1938	Rana	Local condensations of cells
Obstruction of duct primordium	O'Connor	1939	Rana Pleurodeles	Local condensations of cells No condensations present
Obstruction of growing duct	Holtfreter	1944	Triton Amblystoma	Local condensations of cells
Excision or obstruction of duct	Van Geertruyden	1946	Rana	Cellular blastema forms — disappears
Removal of duct after formation Partial removal or displacement of duct	Cambar	1948	Rana Alytes	Local condensations of cells Tubules develop only in close proximity to duct
Tip of duct destroyed by cautery	Boyden	1927, 1932	Chick	Local condensations of cells which later disappear
Tip of duct obstructed by incision	Waddington	1938	Chick	Local condensations of cells
Tip of duct destroyed by cautery	Grünwald	1937	Chick	No tubules caudal to lesion
Tip of duct blocked by graft	Gruenwald	1942	Chick	Irregular differentiation of tubules

Fig. 176. Table showing the effects of absence of the nephric duct on the differentiation of the tubules of the mesonephros. In most cases tubules fail to differentiate, although local cellular condensations may appear; in some species, however, variable development of tubules may occur, subject to later degeneration.

the area is labile to the extent that foreign material is still readily assimilated (Spofford, '48). Subsequently two degrees of autonomy can be demonstrated. In later neurula stages mesonephric tissue placed in ectopic situations (coelom, eye chamber) is capable of producing unspecific tubular structures, but is still plastic to a degree—at the site of the pronephros it precociously forms tubules of pronephric type (Machemer, '29). In this phase, rate of development and final character of morphogenesis are still modified by external forces. After the tail-bud stage determination is fixed. The same material produces typical mesonephros in any location (Humphrey, '28a); and nephrogenic potency is restricted to the prospective mesonephric material (e.g., van Geertruyden, '46; Cambar, '48; cf. also Gruenwald, '42).

The mesonephric tubules originate from nephrotomes or as condensations in the unsegmented nephrogenic cord (p. 462) long after the nephric duct has developed—a fact which long ago suggested that the duct might

removed after brief contact with the nephrogenic tissue, delayed but fairly complete differentiation occurs (O'Connor, '39). Again, if the duct is displaced, tubules develop only where nephrogenic tissue remains in close proximity to the duct (Cambar, '48). In such cases the role of the duct seems clear. In other cases, however, the tubules behave in an irregular fashion, showing considerable autonomy. All stages of differentiation may be realized in the absence of the duct, even in the same species or individual (e.g., Shimasaki, '30b; Humphrey, '28a,b; Burns, '38; Gruenwald, '42; Nieuwkoop, '48). The importance of the duct may well vary in different species, or other inductors may be involved (see Gruenwald, '42, '43; van Geertruyden, '46). Account must be taken also of the fact that all tubule primordia (even in the same region are not of the same morphological order (e.g., Hall, '04; Gray, '32) and may possess different capacities for self-differentiation. These questions require further investigation.

THE DEVELOPMENT OF THE
METANEPHROS

The development of the metanephros presents problems of a similar nature. The embryonic ureter is an outgrowth of the nephric duct, while the kidney tubules differentiate from the adjacent metanephric blastema. Here the analysis rests mainly on experiments with chick embryos. Interference with the growth of the nephric duct at anterior levels results in absence of its hinder part (see Fig. 174) and in consequence the ureter is also lacking. In this case the metanephric tubules fail to differentiate (Boyden, '27; Grünwald, '37) although a blastema appears and may persist for a time. This result is consistent with the generally accepted interpretation of agenesis of the kidney (Boyden, '32; Grünwald, '37, '38; Auer, '47). Congenital absence of a kidney is always accompanied in males by absence of the ductus deferens (nephric duct) and ureter on that side. Furthermore, development of double ureters (a well known anomaly) results in the formation of two kidneys, which may show various degrees of fusion according to propinquity. In an early stage of this anomaly each ureter has its separate blastema (e.g., Wharton, '49).

Evidently the appearance of a blastema and the subsequent differentiation of tubules are distinct phases. The first is independent of the ureter (although if two ureters are present twin blastemas may be formed; cf. the eye-forming area of the neural plate), but the ureter must be present for the differentiation of tubules. This conclusion accords with the fact that metanephric potency has not been demonstrated in parts of the chick blastoderm, but development readily occurs in explants of the metanephric region after the ureter has formed (see Seevers, '32). The ureter is held to be essential.

It is reported that tissues other than the ureter (nephric duct, nervous tissue) may induce differentiation in the metanephric blastema, but the tubules formed are atypical and of mesonephric type (Gruenwald, '42, '43; see p. 465).

THE ORIGIN AND DEVELOPMENT OF
THE OVIDUCT

The embryonic oviduct (Müllerian duct) develops much later than the nephric duct; however, the two structures are closely related in origin and mode of development. In certain fishes and amphibians the ostium is considered to arise from one or more persistent pronephric tubules, or their nephrostomes. The duct reaches the cloaca by the backward growth of a cord of cells from the ostial primordium (for reviews consult Goodrich, '30; Brachet, '35; Willier, '39; Gallien, '44). In amniotes the ostium is said to be formed by invagination of a special area of the coelomic epithelium, near the anterior pole of the mesonephros, and the duct is again formed by backward growth. The resemblances are obvious but in amniotes the role of pre-existing nephric rudiments is not generally admitted. Nevertheless, origin of the ostium from pronephric remains, or from funnel-like structures resembling nephrostomes, has been reported in certain mammals (see von Winiwarter, '10; Brambell, '27; Burns, '41). Recently, also the old problem of the relationship of the developing oviduct to the nephric duct has been re-examined. In both avian and mammalian embryos the growing tip of the duct is almost inseparably applied to the wall of the nephric duct, from which it may derive material (Gruenwald, '41). Altogether, a nephric origin for the Müllerian duct is probable.

The main problems in the development of the oviduct are (1) the origin and nature of the ostial primordium and (2) the mode of extension of the duct to the cloaca. On the first point experimental evidence is limited*; with respect to the second it is clear that development of the oviduct depends on the presence of the nephric duct. In chick embryos in which the posterior part of the nephric duct is lacking as a result of operation at anterior levels (Grünwald, '37) the ostium is present, plus a segment of the oviduct corresponding exactly to the surviving portion of nephric duct. Although development had been initiated it did not proceed beyond the termination of the nephric duct. Further evidence is found again in studies of renal agenesis. Absence or partial development of the nephric duct is accompanied by corresponding deficiencies in the female genital tract (Grünwald, '38, '41; Auer, '47). The nature of the dependence is not established. The nephric duct may be merely a guide—an essential feature of the path along

---

* According to unpublished observations of the author, early extirpation of the pronephros (see Fig. 176), with absence of the nephric duct, is followed long afterward by failure of either oviduct or ostium to appear on the operated side. Formation of the ostium seems to depend in some way on the presence of the pronephros, cf. Gallien ('44).

which the oviduct grows—or it may also contribute material for its formation.

THE GENITAL SYSTEM

Most of the structures which make up the embryonic genital system have been taken over from other systems, and their readaptation to genital functions is a secondary and relatively late phase in their development. The early differentiation of such structures is therefore independent of sexuality. Also, each embryo is at first morphologically bisexual, possessing all necessary structures for the differentiation of either sex. The differentiation of one set of sex primordia and the gradual involution of the other is normally determined by the sex type of the gonad. The initial problems, then, concern the constitution of the gonad primordium and the factors which direct its evolution into an ovary or a testis.

STRUCTURE AND ORGANIZATION OF THE EMBRYONIC GONAD

The sexually undifferentiated gonad is a composite structure. Male and female po-

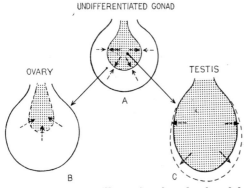

Fig. 177. Diagram illustrating the role of medullary (stippled) and cortical components of the undifferentiated amphibian gonad in the differentiation of ovary and testis. Small arrows indicate the antagonistic inhibitory action exerted by each component against the other until final dominance of one is established.

tentialities are represented by specific histological elements, *medulla* and *cortex*, which have alternative roles in gonadogenesis (Fig. 177). Normal differentiation involves the gradual predominance of one component, while in various types of intersexuality the recessive element persists in varying degree. The extent to which the recessive component develops in the embryo, and the duration of

the bisexual phase, differ widely from group to group and greatly influence reversibility under experimental conditions. In amphibians, in which both components are well developed over a relatively long period, transformation occurs readily; in amniote embryos, however, development is rapid and the recessive component tends to be vestigial and transient. Under such conditions the state of differentiation at the moment of experimental intervention may be a decisive factor in the result.

The medullary and cortical components of the indifferent gonad are laid down through the activities of the somatic or non-germinal constituents of the genital ridge, conveniently called the *structural elements*. In the early testis of an amniote embryo (Fig. 178) the medullary component consists of primary sex cords, the cortical element is represented by the regressing germinal epithelium; however, as long as this epithelium is present, the testis is potentially bisexual. Conversely, in an ovary the male component is represented by more or less rudimentary medullary cords (primary sex cords) and rete elements. All attempts to control sex differentiation experimentally undertake by various means to influence the development of one sex component at the expense of the other.

The *germinal elements* of the gonad are the primordial germ cells, which are often recognizable long before the gonad primordium appears. Nevertheless, as will be shown, they are apparently not essential either for the formation of a genital ridge or for the differentiation of specific histological structure. Eventually their fate as gametes depends upon the differentiation of the structural elements and their role in morphogenesis is secondary.

EARLY TOPOGRAPHIC LOCALIZATION OF THE GONAD CONSTITUENTS

In most vertebrates the germ cells and the structural elements of the gonad have distinct and sometimes widely separated origins. Their history, prior to final localization in the genital ridge, may be for the most part considered separately.

The Structural Elements. In embryos of urodele amphibians, from yolk-plug to middle neurula stages, both structural elements and germ cells are found together in the region of the prospective lateral plate. Heteroplastic exchange of material from this area at the yolk-plug stage (Fig. 170A) results in composite gonads containing both germ cells and structural elements derived from the graft (Nieuwkoop, '47). In tail-bud stages the two elements are still closely associated in the intermediate mesoderm (Humphrey, '28a,b). Transplantation of the gonad-mesonephros complex at this stage shows it to be of the blastoderm (Fig. 172A; see Rawles, '36). (At this stage the germ cells are presumed to be located peripherally, in the "germ cell crescent"; p. 472.) Transplants which include the anterior end of the primitive streak and node produce gonad tissue containing testis cords (in association with

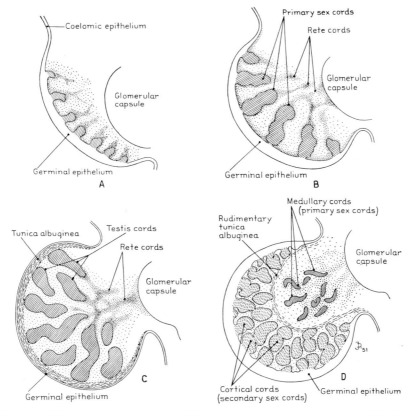

Fig. 178. Diagrams illustrating the origin of medullary and cortical components in the histologically more complex gonads of mammals. A, Genital ridge, with incipient primary sex cords originating from the germinal epithelium. B, Indifferent gonad, in which the medullary component is present as the primary sex cords, while the cortex is potentially represented by the germinal epithelium. C, Development of the testis, with disappearance of the germinal epithelium. D, Development of the ovary, with the production of dominant secondary sex cords and cortex.

capable of autonomous differentiation. Gonads of specific sex are produced, the frequency increasing with age.

In the tail-bud stage of anuran embryos, on the other hand, only the structural elements are found in the mesoderm; the germ cells lie in the "yolk ridge." When the intermediate mesoderm is exchanged between embryos of different sex, the gonads which develop always correspond to the sex of the donor embryo (Humphrey, '33). Thus the capacity to produce a gonad of specific sex resides in the structural elements.

In the chick a localized gonad-forming area exists as early as the head-process stage

mesonephros and adrenal cortex), but such gonads are sterile (Willier, '37, '50). The structural elements of the gonad are thus localized topographically long before the formation of a gonad primordium.

In the embryos of mammals little is known of the localization of the structural elements before the stage of the genital ridge, but close association with the nephrogenic material is assumed.

The Primordial Germ Cells. The history of the primordial germ cells of vertebrates has long been a controversial field. The classic theory of early segregation, as opposed to a later and more local origin, has been supported in many groups and as often denied. For a survey of the general status of the germ cell theory see Heys ('31); for more recent discussions see Willier ('39), Nieuwkoop ('47, '49), Gillman ('48), Witschi ('48) and Johnston ('51). There is as yet no adequate experimental analysis for the early stages of development. But if the ultimate source of the germ cells in most cases remains in doubt, it is generally accepted that they originate outside the gonad-forming area.

Source of the Primordial Germ Cells. In only one case is there significant evidence indicating early segregation of a germinal material in a vertebrate. In the egg of a frog a cytoplasmic substance in the yolk near the vegetal pole has been traced to the "yolk ridge" of the gut (Bounoure, '34), the site where the germ cells are generally identified in anurans. Irradiation of the vegetal pole results in gonads which are sterile (see Bounoure, '50). In urodele eggs, on the other hand, elimination or addition of polar yolk material does not seriously affect the development of germ cells (Nieuwkoop, '47, '50).

In most vertebrates the germ cells as such have first been identified in various parts of the entoderm: the "yolk ridge" of anuran amphibians, the entoderm of the yolk sac in reptiles, the splanchnopleure of the proamnion region of the avian blastoderm, and the hind gut or adjacent yolk sac entoderm in mammalian embryos. Urodele amphibians are a notable exception. In this group most investigators have first identified the germ cells in the "intermediate mesoderm" of the posterior trunk (see Humphrey, '25, '29). A recent experimental analysis (Nieuwkoop, '47, '50) shows that in late yolk-plug and neurula stages they occupy a corresponding position in the prospective lateral mesoderm, ventral and ventrolateral to the blastopore (Fig. 170A). Removal of this area in the early neurula results in sterility. Nevertheless, the entoderm is in some way involved in their differentiation as germ cells. In its absence germ cells fail to appear in the gonad, or are greatly diminished in number. It is concluded that precursor cells in the prospective lateral mesoderm are able to differentiate into germ cells only after contact with the dorsocaudal entoderm (Nieuwkoop).

In avian embryos the germ cells are usually said to lie in the extra-embryonic splanchnopleure, near the germ wall In the chick they tend to be concentrated anteriorly in the "germ cell crescent" (see Swift, '14).

Destruction of the crescent or isolation of the gonad-forming area of the early blastoderm both result in genital ridges or gonads which lack germ cells (for a discussion see Willier, '39, '50). The evidence supports the view that the cells in question are indeed primordial germ cells but it is hardly crucial.

Migration of the Primordial Germ Cells. If the germ cells originate outside the gonad region, sometimes at a considerable distance, there is a problem as to how they reach their destination in the genital ridge. In urodele amphibians the situation is fairly simple. From the earliest known stages, the germ cells lie with the other gonad constituents in the lateral plate mesoderm, and appear to move passively with the lateral plate materials to a point medial to the Wolffian duct (Humphrey, '25; Nieuwkoop, '47). For entry into the genital ridge, independent "amoeboid movement" directed by an influence emanating from the ridge has been suggested. In anurans, according to Bounoure (above), the germinal material is carried from the vegetal pole to the "yolk ridge" by the movements of gastrulation and dorsal closure of the gut. The "yolk ridge" is then separated from the gut by the growth forces which produce the mesentery, after which only a slight lateral shift to the genital ridge is necessary. For this, independent migration and a directive influence from the ridge are again postulated.

In amniote embryos migration from the yolk sac or gut entoderm involves more difficulty. In most cases independent migration through the splanchnopleural mesenchyme is assumed, based on the distribution of germ cells from stage to stage, and the appearance of "pseudopodial" form (e.g., see Witschi, '48). However, passive transport may again be a factor locally, as when germ cells embedded in the coelomic epithelium (prospective germinal epithelium) are shifted around the dorsal angle of the body cavity (see Willier, '39). The most unusual "migration" is described in bird embryos, where the germ cells presumably move from the "germ cell crescent" to the gonad region. According to the classic theory of Swift ('14) they are enveloped by extra-embryonic blood vessels and enter the embryo, some escaping in the gonad region. Definite proof of this hypothesis is lacking. Destruction of the crescent area, or early isolation of the gonad-forming region, both result in sterility, indicating that the germ cells have been eliminated or excluded. However, this result sheds little light on the pathway or manner of migration (for a discussion see Willier, '39).

FORMATION OF THE GENITAL RIDGE

In a strict sense gonadogenesis begins with the formation of the genital ridge. Two problems are presented: (1) the role of extrinsic or regional factors in the origin of the ridge, and (2) the relative importance of the primary gonad constituents: germ cells vs. structural elements. The first problem is inseparable from the larger question of regional organization and has not been completely analyzed. A recent study indicates that general as well as local factors are involved in the production of the ridge (Nieuwkoop, '47, '50). In the urodele, Triton, differentiation depends first on early contact between lateral plate material (future peritoneum) and the entoderm. Later, folds of coelomic epithelium, closely resembling genital ridges, may be induced independently by notochord, Wolffian duct, and probably by mesonephric tissue. In later development gonads may be present in the absence of mesonephros (e.g., Humphrey, '28a,b; Grünwald, '37).

It is well established that the germ cells are not essential for the origin of a gonad. In amphibian embryos sterile genital ridges may develop after removal of the germ cells (e.g., Humphrey, '27, '28a; Nieuwkoop, '47); and elimination of the primordial germ cells of the chick before they reach the gonad region does not prevent the formation of gonads (for a summary see Willier, '39). Furthermore, germ cells in ectopic situations are unable to initiate gonad formation (Humphrey, '28b; Willier, '33; Witschi, '34). These results are opposed to the view that the primordial germ cells act as inductors (Dantschakoff, '32) or are otherwise essential for the origin of a gonad. The evidence indicates that (1) the local appearance of a genital ridge is conditioned by regional influences; (2) primordial germ cells alone cannot induce a genital ridge and are not essential for its origin; and (3) the formation of the ridge is an activity of the structural elements.

THE ROLE OF GERM CELLS VS. STRUCTURAL ELEMENTS IN SEX DIFFERENTIATION

The conclusion last stated may be extended to cover the period of sex differentiation. The characteristic structure of testis or ovary may be developed in the absence of germ cells. Irradiation of the vegetal pole of the frog's egg results later in well differentiated testes and ovaries which are completely sterile (Bounoure, '37, '50), and tadpoles that develop from overripe eggs

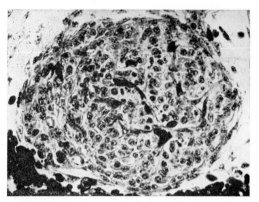

Fig. 179. Sterile gonad, of testicular structure, in a chorio-allantoic graft derived from a small piece of blastoderm containing Hensen's node, taken from an embryo of the head-process stage (from Willier, '39).

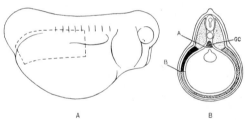

A   B

Fig. 180. Diagram of an experiment demonstrating the role of the structural elements (intermediate mesoderm) in determining the sex-type of the gonad (after Humphrey, '33). *A*, Frog embryo, showing the area of intermediate mesoderm (broken lines) containing the gonad-forming elements. When this area is transplanted to a corresponding position in an embryo of different sex, a situation is set up as in *B*, in which the structural elements of one sex (area *A–B*) are associated with the primordial germ cells (*GC*) of the other. The sex-type of the gonad which develops is always determined by the *structural elements*.

have defective gonads which are typically sterile (Witschi, '51a). When the gonad-forming area of the chick blastoderm is isolated, in the absence of germ cells, sterile testicular structures are produced (Fig. 179; Willier, '37, '50); and gonads of both sexes differentiate after destruction of the germ cells by irradiation (Salzgeber, '50; Dulbecco, '46).

It has been shown further that the structural elements establish the sex-type of the gonad, irrespective of the genetic constitution of the included germ cells. If the intermediate mesoderm of a frog embryo is transplanted orthotopically to an embryo of different sex, the germ cells of one sex are combined with the structural elements of the other (Fig. 180). It is the differentiation of the latter that determines the sex type of the gonad (Humphrey, '33). This principle applies, moreover, in all cases of functional sex transformation, which end in the production of gametes of the opposite sex (pp. 475–476). Even with respect to gamete formation the germ cells are indifferent or bipotential.

APPEARANCE OF SEX-SPECIFIC ORGANIZATION IN THE GONAD

The time at which the gonad primordium becomes organized with respect to its future sex has been determined by testing its capacity for self-differentiation at successive stages of development. In amphibian embryos transplantation of the gonad-forming area shows that sex-specific organization exists long before the appearance of a genital ridge (Humphrey, '28a), but in these experiments mesonephros and other regional elements are also present in the graft. The gonad-forming area of the chick blastoderm (p. 471) likewise shows a degree of sex-specific organization, subject, however, to the same qualification. A certain number of isolates produced gonad-like bodies, with sex cords of male type and the structure of rudimentary testes (Fig. 179). Ovaries were not formed. These experiments are not strict tests of the capacity of the gonad for independent differentiation.

During the formation of the genital ridge, analysis shows that the capacity for specific differentiation appears and increases from stage to stage (see Willier, '39). After a distinct germinal epithelium is present, transplants of the ridge yield gonads of specific sex with much higher frequency than before the germinal epithelium is recognizable; at earlier stages (31 somites or less) only gonads of indeterminate sex are formed. It may be concluded that during formation of the genital ridge in the chick, morphogenetic changes occur which gradually determine the sex-type of the gonad. In the duck embryo, as in the chick, the histologically undifferentiated gonad is strongly organized with respect to sex and, in the

female, to laterality as well. Gonads removed before the beginning of morphological sex differentiation, and cultivated in vitro, produce structurally normal testes, or right and left ovaries. Such gonads are sometimes sterile (Wolff and Haffen, '52).

The organization of the gonad primordium of the rat has also been analyzed by transplantation in various ways. Mesonephric bodies isolated before a genital ridge is present do not produce gonads, but in the ridge stage male organization is well established (Torrey, '50). When sexually undifferentiated primordia are transplanted to the adult kidney (Buyse, '35) there is a striking sex difference in capacity for self-differentiation. (This study was carried out to test the possibility that the differentiation of the grafted gonads might be modified by the hormones of the host. From this standpoint the results were negative.) Testes develop normally but prospective ovaries lack stable organization and give rise to the following types: (1) *retarded ovaries;* (2) *ovotestes,* in which both gonad components are developed but more or less rudimentary; (3) *rudimentary testes,* in which only the medullary component of the ovary has survived; and (4) grafts of indeterminate sex. Evidently, testis organization is strongly fixed in the indifferent primordium (cf. Torrey, '50) but the prospective ovary is extremely labile, the medullary component developing with about the same frequency as the cortical. Similar results were obtained after transplantation to other sites (Moore and Price, '42;[*] Holyoke, '49), with indications that the lability of the ovary is related to its age at transplantation.

Further analysis of the age factor (Torrey, '50) shows that the organization of the testis is fixed as early as the 12-day primordium (early gonadal blastema stage). The critical period for the ovary comes much later, at 15 to 16 days (cf. Moore and Price), when grafts may give rise to ovaries, ovotestes or rudimentary testes. By the seventeenth day (when a cortex is histologically present) all grafts produce typical ovaries. Evidently the sex-specific organization of the gonad primordium is gradually acquired and is realized much earlier in the testis than in the ovary. This fact corresponds with the normal order of development, in which the medullary component (primary sex cords) has priority of origin in both sexes. It is in

* These authors did not describe distinct ovotestes but "transformed" and hypertrophied medullary cords were frequently found.

contrast with conditions in amphibians (Humphrey, '28a) and birds (Willier, '39; Wolff and Haffen, '52), in which the indifferent gonad primordium in both sexes shows sex-specific organization.

THE DIFFERENTIATION OF SEX IN THE GONAD

The lability of gonad organization during the stages when the sex components are being laid down has both a physiological and a structural basis. Development of ovotestes or rudimentary testes from ovaries may be favored by conditions in the graft environment which interfere with cortical differentiation; but the immediate basis for reversal lies in the presence of a differentiated medullary component. Differentiation is essentially a competitive process which may be upset by any condition which effectively inhibits the dominant component—a view which is consistent with the fact that reversal of sex can be induced by various and apparently unrelated experimental procedures.

Effect of Eliminating the Dominant Gonad Component. The simplest test of this concept is direct elimination of the dominant gonad component. In early development this procedure is difficult, but two classic experiments may be cited which are based on survival of a recessive component long beyond the period of sex differentiation. In adult male toads a part of the embryonic cortex survives as the organ of Bidder. After removal of the testes this structure slowly develops into an ovary, capable of producing fertile eggs (Ponse, '24). A parallel case is the removal of the left ovary of the recently hatched female chick. After this operation the rudimentary right gonad, composed chiefly of medullary tissue, frequently develops into a testis which may be fertile (see Domm, '39). In each case a long dormant recessive component retains its capacity to produce a gonad of opposite sex when released from inhibition by removal of the functional gonad.

Sex Reversal Induced by Unspecific or Environmental Agencies. It is well known that in many animals transformation of sex may be induced by various physiological conditions such as nutritional level, the effects of parasitism, disease, or even by factors in the physical environment. A familiar case is the influence of temperature on the differentiation of the gonads in certain amphibians. High temperatures favor differentiation of the medulla, and ovaries are gradually transformed into testes (Witschi,

'29; Piquet, '30). The primary effect, however, seems to be a degenerative change in the cortex, which is followed by medullary differentiation. Low temperatures, on the other hand, promote cortical development by retarding the differentiation of the medulla. Temperature therefore exerts its effects by interference with the dominant component of the gonad, and the result is again consistent with the concept of competitive interaction between medulla and cortex. A comparable effect of temperature on embryonic mammalian gonads has been shown (Torrey, '50).

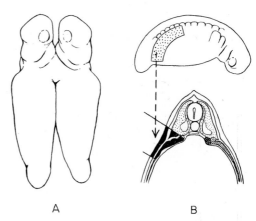

Fig. 181. Methods of inducing sex reversal in amphibians by combining whole embryos or gonads of different sex. *A*, Parabiosis, in which embryos (of the same or of different species) develop with a common circulation; *B*, orthotopic transplantation, bringing together gonads of different sex in the same individual.

Hormonal Control of Gonad Differentiation. If a local interaction between medulla and cortex is the basic mechanism in the differentiation of the gonad,† it is also well known that a gonad is able to influence the differentiation of another at a distance (and to control the development of accessory sex structures as well). From this fact arose the theory of hormones as differentiating agents, which has inspired most of the modern work on sex differentiation. The hormone theory of sex differentiation was first developed with special reference to the freemartin problem by Lillie ('16, '17) and Keller and Tandler ('16). The theory has been tested chiefly by two methods: grafting, during the differen-

† The view that the interactions between medulla and cortex are mediated by special inductor substances, of a different chemical order and with a different mode of action from hormones, will be considered later.

tiation period, of gonads or gonad tissue in various ways (including the union of whole embryos—parabiosis); and treatment of the embryo with hormones. For technical reasons grafting methods have been largely confined to embryos of amphibians and birds.

Grafting Experiments. In amphibians the results of grafting the gonad primordium and of parabiosis (Fig. 181) are essentially the same. In combinations of the same sex, gonad differentiation is normal, but in unlike combinations one sex undergoes inhibition or reversal. Typically the male gonad is dominant, but with marked disparity in size or rate of development (as in certain heteroplastic combinations) the ovary may

hormones in avian development. Gonads, or gonad tissue, grafted to the chorio-allantois failed to modify the sex structures of host embryos, or to be themselves modified (for reviews see Willier, '39, '52). It was eventually shown, however, that grafts to the embryo itself are effective (Wolff, '46). Ovarian grafts induce cortical differentiation on the embryonic testes of the host, but host ovaries are not modified by testis grafts. Evidently in birds the ovary is the dominant gonad.

Administration of Hormones. Reversal of differentiation by treatment with pure hormones follows a similar pattern. Amphibian larvae treated during the differentiation period develop varying degrees of intersexu-

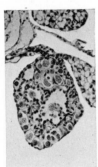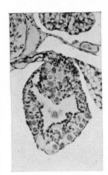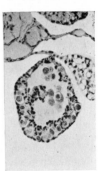

Fig. 182. Sections, in anterior-posterior sequence, through the testis of a salamander, joined in parabiosis with a much larger female of another species. Various stages are shown in the conversion of a testis to an ovary by degeneration of the medulla and development of the cortex. (From Burns, '35.)

predominate. Histologically, reversal involves inhibition and gradual involution of the genetically dominant component, accompanied by differentiation of the recessive (Fig. 182). Reversal may end in complete functional transformation (see Humphrey, '44, '45, '48), or incomplete dominance may lead to prolonged intersexuality. Removal of the graft causing reversal may then permit reversion to the original sex (for reviews see Willier, '39; Witschi, '39; Humphrey, '42). The results depend in detail on various experimental conditions: the relative size and rate of development of the gonads (or grafts), and the time relations of the experiment. In addition to such variables, pronounced species and race differences are known (see Witschi, '34, '39) which are reflected in the composition of the gonads, with respect to the representation of medulla and cortex, or the intensity and timing of humoral activity. These differences evidently have a constitutional basis.

In birds the problem has been studied mainly in the chick embryo. For a long time there was serious doubt as to the role of

ality, according to experimental conditions and species. Two methods have been used: direct injection during the differentiation period, and immersing the subjects in aqueous solutions of the hormone. As in grafting experiments, the histological picture in transforming gonads shows involution of one gonad component and gradual emergence of the other, according to the sex type of the hormone. Early treatment frequently induces complete transformation in either sex (for reviews see Gallien, '44, '50). In some cases, however, large doses may have exactly opposite effects; for example, a female hormone may completely masculinize female gonads (see Padoa, '36, '38, '42; Gallien, '41, '44). Such "paradoxical effects" do not occur, however, at low dosages; and it has been shown further that the same hormone, under the same conditions, may have a feminizing effect at low dosages, produce intersexes at intermediate levels, and have only a masculinizing effect at high dosages (e.g., Padoa, '38, '42; Witschi, '51b). Other examples of paradoxical effects will be found and their significance will be considered later.

In bird embryos, hormones introduced into the egg produce typical reversal effects on the gonads (see Wolff and Ginglinger, '35; Willier, Gallagher, and Koch, '35, '37). Female hormone transforms embryonic testes into ovotestes or ovaries, by reduction of the medullary zone and differentiation of cortex (Fig. 183). Male hormones transform ovaries by repression of the cortex with medullary hypertrophy. The relative value of constitutional vs. hormonal factors is illustrated clearly in consequence of the interesting

have not been regarded as significant. An exception has recently been found in the effects of estrogen on the testes of new-born opossum embryos (Burns, '50). Extensive persistence of the germinal epithelium was found, and in a few cases typical ovotestes were obtained, except that the induced cortex was sterile (Fig. 184). Histological changes followed the usual sequence: repression of testicular development, followed by reactivation of the germinal epithelium to produce a cortex. This result suggests that transformation of

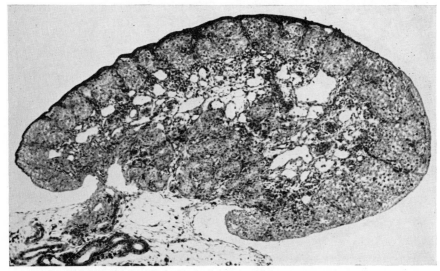

Fig. 183. Ovotestis developed from the left gonad of a genetic male chick by treatment with female hormone. The testicular part of the gonad occupies a central or hilar position; the highly developed cortex is peripheral. (From Willier, '39.)

lateral differences in organization in birds. The left testis (with its incipient cortical element) reacts at much lower dosages than the right, and with increasing doses is more completely transformed (see Willier, '39).

Notwithstanding the fact that the gonads of freemartins are often greatly modified (Willier, '21), exposure of mammalian embryos to relatively large doses of hormones* has usually had but slight effect on the gonads, although accessory genital structures may be completely transformed. In some cases male hormones produce a limited hypertrophy of the medullary cords of the ovary (Jost, '47a; Wells and Van Wagenen, '54); and persistense of localized areas of germinal epithelium on the testis has been reported after the use of either type of hormone (e.g., Raynaud, '42; Jost, '47a). Such changes

---

* Administered to the mother during pregnancy or, in the case of marsupial embryos, directly to the pouch young.

mammalian gonads may prove feasible if proper experimental conditions can be realized. There is substantial evidence that the gonads are potentially bisexual. In addition to the freemartin, the reversals described in rat gonads (p. 474) must be noted, and the anomalous occurrence of *hermaphroditismus verus*, characterized by well differentiated ovotestes, is well known in many mammals.

DIFFERENTIATION OF THE ACCESSORY GENITAL STRUCTURES

On the basis of embryological origin the accessory genital structures of vertebrates comprise three main groups: (1) the sex ducts and associated structures, of nephric origin; (2) derivatives of the cloaca or the urinogenital sinus; and (3) copulatory structures, which develop from the genital tubercle. For a detailed account of the origin and early development of these structures see Willier ('39).

The differentiation of the accessory sex structures has been studied experimentally in various ways. As in the case of the gonads, different forms of grafting were first employed. Eventually grafting was largely

throughout life in the males of many species as complete if somewhat rudimentary structures. An ideal basis for sex reversal is thus provided. In male urodeles elaborate cloacal glands develop, which in females are absent, rudimentary, or (in some species) differently specialized. The dimorphism of these struc-

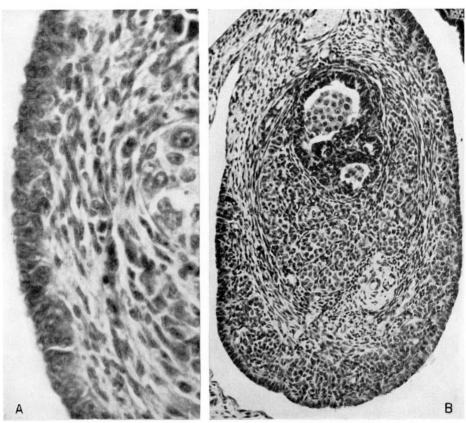

Fig. 184. Stages in the development of ovotestes in opossum embryos after treatment from birth with female hormone. A, Persistence of a thick germinal epithelium on a greatly retarded testis of 14 days (× 500). B, Ovotestis of a male aged 30 days (× 150), in which the medullary zone is separated from a sterile cortex by a thick, fibrous tunica albuginea. (From Burns, '50.)

superseded by administration of pure hormones. The development in recent years of methods of castrating embryos has provided crucial evidence, and tests of the self-differentiating capacities of sex primordia in physiological isolation have lately been utilized.

Results of Grafting Methods. Grafting techniques have been mainly confined to amphibians and birds. The structures to be considered in amphibians are the sex ducts and the glands of the cloaca. In many amphibians both gonaducts are retained indefinitely; the Wolffian ducts function as excretory ducts in both sexes, and Müllerian ducts persist

tures is controlled by the gonads. After castration in larval life both ducts remain in a sexually indifferent condition, and cloacal differentiation does not occur (de Beaumont, '33). Gonads grafted into castrates induce differentiation of the appropriate sex duct, and testis grafts cause development of the cloacal glands. When the gonads are transformed experimentally (p. 476) the subsequent differentiation of gonaducts and cloaca conforms (see Humphrey, '42).

In bird embryos grafting methods long gave negative results, and the role of hormones in sex differentiation was in doubt (see p. 476). It now appears that these failures were due merely to a quantitative insufficiency of hormone, since gonads grafted directly into the embryo are effective. Grafted ovaries induce partial retention of Müllerian ducts in male embryos, while testes stimulate Wolffian ducts and completely inhibit Müllerian ducts in both sexes (Wolff, '46). Similar results have recently been obtained by multiple testis grafts on the chorio-allantois (Huijbers, '51).

consult Colloques Internationaux, Centre National de la Recherche Scientifique (Paris, 1951); La Différenciation Sexuelle chez les Vertébrés.]

It is not possible to consider all findings in detail, but as a basis for discussion the principal results may be summarized as follows:

1. Sex hormones have sex-specific effects on the development of genital structures, either by direct action on the individual primordia,

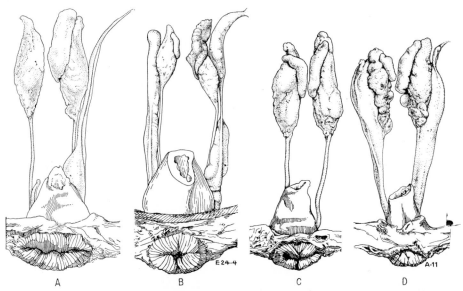

Fig. 185. Development of the sex ducts in chick embryos after treatment with sex hormones (from Willier, '39). *A*, Normal female embryo incubated 18 days; *B*, male embryo treated with female hormone—both oviducts are present and greatly hypertrophied; *C*, normal male embryo of 17 days showing complete absence of oviducts; *D*, female embryo treated with male hormone—the oviducts are absent except for small fragments anteriorly, and the Wolffian ducts are greatly hypertrophied.

Gonad grafting has only recently been utilized in mammalian embryos, chiefly with a view of counteracting the effects of castration. The results are positive, and will be mentioned in that connection.

Administration of Hormones. The production of steroid hormones in pure form enormously accelerated the experimental study of sex differentiation. For the first time it became possible to attack the problem in mammals by administration of effective doses during pregnancy. The different experimental conditions under which hormones have been used, in many different groups and species, have inevitably led to variable and sometimes inconsistent results. [For reviews and analyses of a large literature see Wolff ('38, '47); Willier ('39); Humphrey ('42); Raynaud ('42); Mintz ('47); Moore ('47); Price ('47); Jost ('48); Ponse ('49); Burns ('49). For a recent synopsis of the field

or by acting indirectly, as in release from inhibition, or via other endocrine agencies.

2. In general, male hormones accelerate differentiation of male structures and inhibit certain female structures, in embryos of both sexes; they also induce certain male primordia in females. Conversely, female hormones stimulate the development of female structures and inhibit certain male primordia.

3. In addition to their usual effects, however, both types of hormone in many cases paradoxically stimulate structures of the other sex.

If the effects of hormones as outlined above are in general consistent with theory, the occurrence of so-called "paradoxical effects" is discordant, and has been differently interpreted. It is denied by some that the effects of steroid hormones are in any sense specific, and the validity of the hormone theory in its entirety has been questioned (Moore, '44, '47). It is known, however, that some of the most obvious paradoxical effects either are exerted indirectly, or depend on special experimental conditions. This subject is better discussed after some of the evidence has been presented.

The Effects of Hormones on the Sex Ducts. Although the early differentiation of the gonaducts is independent of sex, they are

regression (such as normally occurs in females) is initiated (e.g., Raynaud, '42; Greene, '42). Paradoxically, it sometimes causes retention of the ducts in females (Greene).

Male hormone induces retention and precocious hypertrophy of the Wolffian ducts in both sexes. In mammalian embryos the epididymis also hypertrophies, and epididymides and seminal vesicles develop in fe-

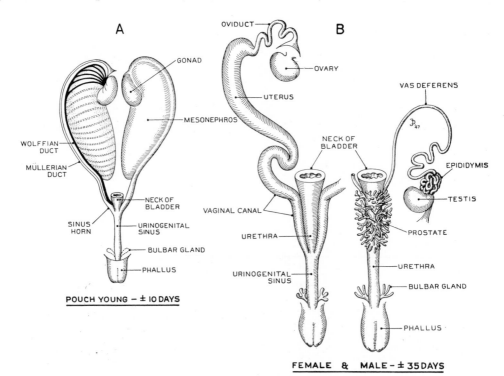

Fig. 186. The normal differentiation of the genital tracts in pouch young of the opossum (from Burns, '49). *A,* Sexually undifferentiated embryo of 10 days, showing male and female sex ducts, urinogenital sinus and phallus; *B,* sexually differentiated genital tracts in young at 35 days, female characterized by vaginal canals and absence of prostate, male showing absence of vaginal structures and numerous prostatic glands.

capable of responding early to adequate doses of sex hormones. *Female hormone* induces hypertrophy of Müllerian ducts in female embryos, and retention with hypertrophy in males. The effects in bird embryos are particularly striking (Fig. 185). In males both oviducts persist and hypertrophy, as does also the right duct of females. However, the period of reactivity is limited; there is a "critical period" for effective action. Retention and development of the ducts in male embryos is secured by injections of female hormone up to the tenth day ("stabilization effect"); later treatment is useless (Wolff, '38). Female hormone typically has no effect on Wolffian ducts, but in some mammals

males (e.g., Greene, '42; Burns, '42; Raynaud, '42; Wells and van Wagenen, '54). The effects of male hormones on the Müllerian ducts are more complex, depending especially on *timing* and *dosage,* and on species differences. In larval amphibians and in chick embryos, treatment during the formative period largely or entirely suppresses the ducts (Fig. 185). [See, e.g., Burns ('39), Foote ('41), Hanaoka ('41) for amphibians; Wolff ('38, '50), Gaarenstroom ('39), Stoll ('48), Huijbers ('51) for the chick.] This effect is also produced by grafts of the embryonic testis (Wolff, '46; Huijbers, '51). For complete suppression the hormone must act early—in chick embryos before the sixth or seventh day; later treatment has no effect (Stoll, '48; cf. the stabilizing effect of female hormone on male Müllerian ducts). Again there is a critical period after which susceptibility is lost.

In larval amphibians the Müllerian ducts develop slowly. Treatment with male hormone during the backward growth of the duct suppresses the unformed portion, but ferentiation of the glands in larvae of either sex (see Burns, '39; Mintz, '47) and a male type of cloaca.

The urinogenital sinus of mammals is derived embryologically from the cloaca. In its primitive condition it receives the sex ducts near the neck of the bladder, and opens externally at the base of the genital tubercle. Differentiation in females is characterized by

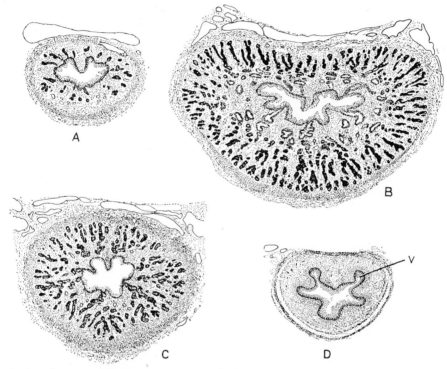

Fig. 187. Development of the sinus region and prostate in young opossums aged 50 days, after treatment from birth with male hormone (from Burns, '49). *A*, Section of normal male sinus showing prostatic glands; *B*, male receiving hormone, showing enormous hypertrophy of the prostate; *C*, female showing great development of the prostate induced by male hormone; *D*, normal female, characterized by vaginal canals and complete absence of prostatic glands; *V*, terminus of vaginal canal.

the part already present persists, and *with large doses* paradoxically hypertrophies (see Mintz, '47). In mammalian embryos complete suppression of the Müllerian ducts is not obtained, but the vaginal region may be inhibited, e.g., in opossums (Burns, '42) and in mice (Raynaud, '42). On the contrary, paradoxical stimulation occurs readily (e.g., Moore, '47; Burns, '49), but is not found with low dosages (Burns, '42, '45a).

Reactions of Cloaca and Urinogenital Sinus to Hormones. The development of cloacal glands in amphibians is conditioned by male hormone; the response of the cloaca to castration and to testis grafts has been noted (p. 478). Male hormones induce precocious dif-

formation of the vagina, while the male ducts retrogress. In the male, regression of the Müllerian ducts and development of the complex of prostatic glands are the chief features (Fig. 186). *Male hormones* produce a male type of sinus in both sexes (for details see Greene, '42; Raynaud, '42, '50; Moore, '47; Burns, '49; Jost, '50; Wells and van Wagenen, '54). The differentiation of males is accelerated; females undergo transformation—vaginal development is partly or entirely suppressed and prostatic glands develop (Fig. 187). Conversely, *female hormone* suppresses prostatic differentiation and produces a sinus of female form, with a vaginal type of epithelium. Permanent suppression of the prostate may be induced by a single dose of hormone administered just before the prostatic buds should appear (Burns, '42); and prostatic glands induced in female embryos continue to develop without further treatment (see Moore, '47). Thus, bud formation represents a critical stage in which development or permanent suppression of the prostate is determined by presence of the proper hormone.

Reactions of the Copulatory Structures to Hormones. In both birds and mammals, hor-

ferentiation is provided by castration of the embryo. The effects of castration in larval amphibians have been mentioned (p. 478), and successful techniques have recently been developed for birds and mammals (Fig. 189). To be decisive the operation must be performed early. After early castration the Müllerian ducts of male embryos, instead of retrogressing, continue to develop (as does also the abortive right oviduct in female chicks). Presumably in normal development regression is conditioned by the testis—in

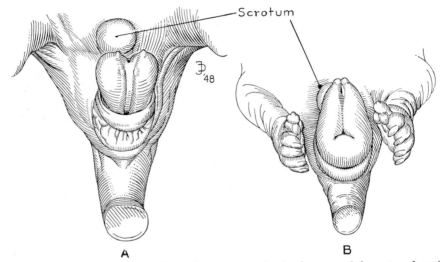

Fig. 188. The effects of male and female sex hormones on the development of the external genital structures in young opossums, treated from birth to an age of 20 days (from Burns, '49). *A*, Precocious development and hypertrophy of the phallus (male type) in a male embryo receiving male hormone; *B*, genital structures of female type produced in another male embryo by female hormone. When both embryos are female the effects are the same.

mones control development of the copulatory structures, producing a complete change in morphology in many species, e.g., the duck (Wolff and Wolff, '48), the opossum, (Moore, '41; Burns, '42, '45b), and various placental mammals (Greene, '42; Raynaud, '42; Jost, '47a; Wells and van Wagenen, '54). The embryological basis for transformation has been studied in the opossum (Burns, '45b). It consists in specific responses of the histological constituents of the embryonic phallus to a given hormone. The erectile tissues, which largely determine the form of the penis, are stimulated by male and virtually suppressed by female hormone, which in turn produces marked hyperplasia of the periurethral and vulvar connective tissues (Fig. 188).

The Effects of Castration or Isolation on the Development of Sex Primordia. The most direct test of the role of hormones in sex dif-

the case of the right oviduct of the chick by the ovaries (Wolff and Wolff, '51). Is development of Müllerian ducts after castration due solely to release from inhibition, or does some positive humoral factor intervene? [In various species of mammals estrogens are known to be present in the placenta and fetal fluids. For a review see Price ('47).] This question has been approached by testing the developmental capacity of the ducts in isolation. After explantation of the embryonic genital tracts in vitro (Jost and Bergerard, '49; Wolff, '50; Jost and Bosic, '51), or transplantation to the chorio-allantois (Wolff, '50), the Müllerian ducts of both sexes persist and continue to differentiate. When explanted after the eighth day of incubation, however, those of male chicks degenerate (Wolff). At this stage regression has been finally determined. The evidence indicates that in the absence of testes the

Müllerian ducts differentiate autonomously. It should be recalled in this connection that the regression of the Müllerian ducts in male embryos is prevented by female hormone (p. 480). Their retention in such case might be due initially to inhibition of the testes, but when there is also marked hypertrophy of the ducts a direct stimulation must be involved.

The effects of castration on the male sex ducts vary in different forms (Fig. 189). In larval amphibians and in chick embryos the Wolffian ducts, which serve as nephric ducts, remain after castration in a sexually undifferentiated condition (de Beaumont, '33;

tance of the time factor. Castration on the twenty-third or twenty-fourth day is followed by almost normal development; if performed somewhat earlier the prostatic buds are arrested and differentiate no further. Castration before the twentieth day suppresses all development—the buds do not appear. The effects of castration are entirely prevented by male hormone or by grafts of the embryonic testis (Jost, '50; Wells, '50).

The copulatory structures are also highly sensitive to castration. Castrated mammalian embryos of both sexes develop external genitalia of female type (see Jost, '47b, '50; Raynaud and Frilley, '47; Raynaud, '50), but

CASTRATION EFFECTS IN EMBRYOS

MAMMALS

	Müllerian Ducts	Wolffian Ducts	U.G. Sinus	Prostate	Ext. Genitalia	Mammary Glands
♂ Castrates	Developed	Absent	♀ type	Absent	♀ type	♀ type
♀ Castrates	Developed	Absent *	♀ type	Absent	♀ type	♀ type

BIRDS

	Müllerian Ducts	Wolffian Ducts		Gen. tubercle	Syrinx
♂ Castrates	Developed	Present		♂ type	♂ type
♀ Castrates	Developed (on both sides)	Present		♂ type	♂ type

Fig. 189. Table summarizing the effects of castration in embryos of birds and mammals, based on the reports of Wolff ('50) and Wolff and Wolff ('51) in the chick and duck; Huijbers ('51) in the chick; Jost ('47b, '50) in the rabbit; Raynaud and Frilley ('47) and Raynaud ('50) in the mouse. Similar but less severe effects have been obtained in the rat (Wells, '50; Wells and Fralick, '51); but Moore ('47) reports little effect in young opossums castrated at the age of 22 days. The asterisk indicates that partial persistence of Wolffian ducts may occur in castrate female mice (see Raynaud, '50).

Wolff, '50). In mammals their retention and sexual differentiation in the male appear to depend upon the testis; they regress in castrate rabbit fetuses, as in the normal female (Jost, 47b, '50). [There is an indication in mice that the Wolffian ducts may persist in part in castrate females, suggesting that the ovary may have a role in the regression of the ducts in normal females (see Raynaud, '50).]

Castration prevents development of the male urinogenital sinus and accessory glands, but female castrates are virtually normal (Fig. 189). In males, development of the vagina (in conjunction with retention of the Müllerian ducts) gives the sinus a female form. Prostatic differentiation is suppressed (Jost, '47b), and in mice coagulating glands are also absent (Raynaud, '50). The effects in the rat embryo are less severe, depending perhaps on time of operation (Wells and Fralick, '51). With respect to the prostate, the results in the rabbit are especially clear (Jost, '47c), illustrating the great impor-

the effects of castration are prevented by male hormones. As in the case of the duct systems and the sinus structures, normal male development evidently depends on the testis, while the female pattern develops without hormonal conditioning, in a somatic or asexual manner. In bird embryos, however, the situation is reversed, the male sex representing the asexual type (Wolff and Wolff, '51).

SOME SPECIAL PROBLEMS AND CONSIDERATIONS

Patterns of Hormonal Control. The hormone theory of sex differentiation was developed by Lillie and his associates with special reference to the case of the freemartin. The dominance of the male twin was explained on the grounds that the testis produces its hormone before the ovary; in fact, no suggestion of endocrine activity in the ovary was seen until late in fetal life. The dominant role of the male hormone was thus emphasized, without positive commitment as to the role of the ovary in female development. (The suggestion was made that in cases of early transfusion the first effect of the male hormone is to inhibit the ovarian cortex, in effect eliminating the fetal ovary as a factor in later development.) The results of castration in mammalian embryos fit into the above picture in a remarkable way. Absence of the testis and its hormone arrests development of all male characters—

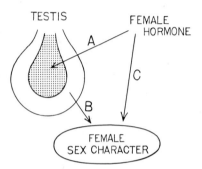

Fig. 190. Diagram illustrating possible modes of hormone action on a sex character. Development of a female structure may result from inhibition of the male component of the gonad (*A*), thus removing an inhibitory influence, as in castration; or after inhibition of the medulla the structure may respond to the differentiating cortex (*B*). Finally, it may be stimulated directly as in *C*. A male character may be adversely affected by any of the above modes of action. Whenever the response of a structure exceeds its normal rate of development, direct stimulation, as in *C*, is indicated.

ducts, sinus derivatives and external genitalia are uniformly affected (see Fig. 189)—while a full complement of female characters appears in castrates of both sexes. It is clear, then, that the male hormone is necessary for development of the male system, and also for inhibition of female development. On the other hand, no essential role for a female hormone is indicated, although the capacity of female primordia to respond to sufficient doses of female hormone is well established (pp. 480–482). The situation conforms closely with Wiesner's "monhormonic theory," based on the results of castration and hormone treatments in early postnatal life (Wiesner, '34, '35).

In amphibians and birds, on the contrary, both gonads participate in the differentiation process. In bird embryos, Müllerian ducts persist and develop after castration in both sexes, as in mammals, regression in the male depending on the testis. But differentiation of the genital tubercle (and syrinx) is con-

ditioned by the ovary, castration producing the male type in both sexes. Administration of hormones produces corresponding effects. Male hormone inhibits Müllerian ducts and produces a genital tubercle of male type, overruling the ovary; female hormone stabilizes the Müllerian ducts in the males and inhibits the tubercle. In larval amphibians, of either sex, both gonaducts are retained after castration in a sexually undifferentiated condition. Grafting of a gonad then induces development of the proper duct and other sexual characters. Sex-reversed gonads have the same effects. Thus both hormones participate in differentiation. It is difficult to escape the impression that the mammalian pattern, in which the male hormone is all important, has evolved in adaptation to the conditions of intra-uterine development.

Mode of Action of Hormones. In the interpretation of hormone action there is always the problem as to how the responses of embryonic primordia are elicited—whether by direct action of a stimulatory or inhibitory nature, or indirectly, by depression or elimination of the normal control mechanism. The ability of various primordia to develop autonomously after castration indicates the importance of the latter alternative.

The situation in an intact embryo is complex. It is possible for an administered hormone to act directly on the individual parts of the genital apparatus, or indirectly, by way of the gonad. Direct action on one gonad component may indirectly influence the other, and through it the accessory structures (Fig. 190). In modified gonads histological appearances suggest that the genetically dominant component is directly inhibited by a heterotypic hormone, allowing development of the recessive component (p. 477, see also Willier, '39). This interpretation is supported by experiments (p. 475) in which removal or depression of the dominant component is followed by recovery and development of the recessive. It is possible, however, that in some cases a hormone may directly stimulate the homotypic gonad component (Vannini, '46).

In interpreting the actions of hormones on accessory sex structures, the status of the individual primordia must be considered. The results of castration show that some (e.g., sex ducts, female sinus derivatives and genitalia) are capable of a high degree of autonomous differentiation; others (e.g., the prostate) are entirely conditioned by hormones. Structures of the first type may develop as a result of indirect action on the gonad, depressing or abolishing an inhibitory mechanism. When, however (as frequently happens under experimental conditions), the parts in question are differentiated precociously, or show marked hypertrophy in comparison with normal structures, direct stimulation by the introduced hormone is indicated (Fig. 190). Direct action is also indicated when castration effects are prevented by hormones (p. 483). The differentiation of structures of the second class probably always involves direct action.

Specificity of Hormone Action. Evidence has been presented showing that, on the whole, the actions of hormones are specific in the sense that a given type of hormone has a stimulatory action on structures of the proper sex, while inhibiting various heterotypic structures. Specificity of action has been denied, however, largely on the basis of paradoxical effects, various examples of which have been cited. [For a summary of the paradoxical effects of various steroid hormones see Wolff, Strudel and Wolff ('48).] To be valid this argument must assume that such effects are the result of direct action of the hormone on heterotypic sex primordia. But in some of the best known cases of paradoxical effects it is probable that the action is mediated indirectly, and in many instances excessive dosage is the determining factor. It must be recalled that under certain conditions gonads also exert paradoxical effects in which the action involves production of the hormone of the other sex (for examples see Ponse, '48; Hill, '50).

The paradoxical effects of high dosages are well known. For example, in opossum embryos receiving large doses of male hormone extreme stimulation of male structures is also accompanied by hypertrophy of Müllerian duct derivatives in both sexes. The latter effect declines rapidly with dosage, and below a certain level disappears completely, although male structures are still stimulated (Burns, '42, '45a). A similar situation appears in many experiments with amphibians. [For paradoxical effects on the gonads see Padoa ('36, '38, '42); Gallien ('41, '44); Vannini ('46); and for the Müllerian ducts, Mintz ('47).] Large doses of female hormone have a strong masculinizing effect on gonads, but low doses are feminizing only. Indeed, the same substance (estradiol), in the same dosage, may have opposite effects depending on the solvent. In aqueous solution there is a masculinizing effect and in oil an orthodox action (Gallien,

'41). The rate of utilization—in effect a difference in dosage—is evidently the determining factor.

The question remains as to how the paradoxical effects of large dosages are exerted. If, for example, female primordia can respond *directly* to a sufficient concentration of male hormone, only a difference in threshold between male and female primordia is involved, and to this extent the hormone is "ambisexual." But when the dose required to elicit a paradoxical response so far exceeds physiological limits, the result has little significance for normal differentiation. There is, however, much evidence suggesting that paradoxical effects are exerted indirectly. Masculinization of gonads by large doses of female hormone is known in some cases to be associated with strong hyperplasia of the interrenal (adrenal cortical) tissue (e.g., Padoa, '38, '42; Witschi, '51b), a potential source of androgen; and in various mammals (see Burrows, '45) treatment with large doses of male hormone is followed by excretion of estrogens, in both intact and castrate individuals. This phenomenon has not as yet been demonstrated in embryos but the possibility must always be considered. On the whole, the evidence provided by paradoxical effects seems at present inconclusive and greatly outweighed by the many unqualified examples of specific action.

Embryonic versus Adult Hormones. The results of parabiosis and various types of gonad grafting in amphibian and bird embryos demonstrate that embryonic gonads produce sex-differentiating substances which are transported and act in the manner of hormones (cf. also the freemartin). The results of embryonic castration confirm this view in the strongest possible manner. A question as to the nature of embryonic hormones, and their relation to adult sex hormones, is naturally posed. The appearance of paradoxical effects, and the fact that steroid hormones do not in all cases produce complete and integrated transformations, have led to the view that embryonic hormones are chemically and physiologically different. But when the responses of sex primordia to steroid hormones are compared with those produced by embryonic gonads in various types of grafting experiments, no essential differences appear. There is in most cases a high degree of specificity in the responses to steroid hormones, and the mechanism of action (stimulation-inhibition) seems identical for many structures. The significance of paradoxical effects has been discussed.

It has been shown further that crystalline sex hormones prevent or repair the effects of embryonic castration (e.g., Jost, '50; Wells, '50) and, conversely, that embryonic gonads are able to repair castration effects in the adult (Jost and Colonge, '49). Moreover, substances have been obtained from embryonic or fetal testes which modify various adult male sex characters (e.g., Leroy, '48; see also Jost, '48). In view of the many other variables which enter into experimental results there seems no necessity at present for assigning embryonic hormones to a different category. There is also no necessity or justification for assuming that they are identical molecularly with any particular steroid hormones.

Embryonic Hormones and Inductor Substances. A similar problem exists with respect to embryonic hormones and the *inductor substances* (corticin, medullarin) which, as mediators of the interactions between cortex and medulla, have been postulated to control differentiation of the gonads (see, e.g., Witschi, '34, '39, '50). The inductor substances may be characterized as follows: (1) as the primary effectors in sex differentiation, they exert their effects early, before embryonic hormones are present; (2) their action is exerted locally, ordinarily within the confines of the gonad; and (3) transport is by diffusion through the tissues rather than by the blood. Thus inductors are humoral in nature but not hormones. It is suggested further that the great variability in the reactions of gonads under experimental conditions, particularly as regards the many race and species differences, presupposes such specificity in organization as to indicate that the inductor substances are probably protein in nature.

The theory of inductor substances has become difficult to maintain in the face of growing evidence that hormones are capable of producing most of the effects ascribed to the inductors. The mechanism of action in the gonad is apparently the same. When gonads undergo transformations (whether by administered hormones or by gonads acting from a distance, as in parabiosis) the histological picture shows a change in the ratio of cortex to medulla. This change is apparently produced by inhibition of the heterotypic gonad component—that is to say, the effect of the hormone is to redirect the mechanism of normal differentiation.

Crystalline hormones, male or female, are also capable of controlling the *primary differentiation* of gonads, so that all embryos from the beginning develop as one sex (see Padoa, '38, '42; Gallien, '44, '50). The dosages required may be minute (see Mintz, '48). If inductors are present their actions are overruled, the hormone assuming the role of the genetically recessive inductor. It may be urged that hormones work by controlling the inductor systems; but, in the absence of direct evidence of the existence of inductor substances, it seems unnecessary to assume two agencies. (For fuller discussions see Willier, '39; Wolff, '47; Jost, '48; Ponse, '49; Burns, '49; Gallien, '50.) The actual evidence seems insufficient to prove that the postulated differences between inductor and hormone effects are more than quantitative, depending on such factors as intensity (concentration) and timing, in conjunction with species differences in the sensitivity of reactor systems.

Under proper conditions the local action of inductors is closely imitated by hormones. Only a few examples may be cited. In amphibians (under normal or experimental conditions) the first responses of the gonaducts to hormones often take place in close proximity to the gonads (normal or grafted); and in chick embryos, gonads and sex ducts both show highly localized reactions to an adjacent graft (Wolff, '46). Finally, the extremely localized action of an embryonic testis in repairing castration atrophy in the adult seminal vesicle (Jost and Colonge, '49) is a case in point.

REFERENCES

Auer, J. 1947 Bilateral renal agenesis. Anat. Rec., *97:*283–292.

Bounoure, L. 1934 Recherches sur la lignée germinale chez la Grenouille rousse aux premiers stades du développement. Ann. Sc. Nat. Zool., *17:* 69–248.

———— 1937 La constitution des glandes génitales chez la Grenouille rousse après destruction étendue de la lignée germinale par l'action des rayons ultra-violets sur l'oeuf. Compt. Rend. Acad. Sc., *204:*1957–1959.

———— 1950 Sur le développement sexuel des glandes génitales de la Grenouille en l'absence de gonocytes. Arch. d'Anat. micr. et de Morph. exp., *39:*247–254.

Boyden, E. A. 1924 An experimental study of the development of the avian cloaca with special reference to a mechanical factor in the growth of the allantois. J. Exp. Zool., *40:*437–471.

———— 1927 Experimental obstruction of the mesonephric ducts. Proc. Soc. Exp. Biol. & Med., *24:*572–576.

———— 1932 Congenital absence of the kidney: an interpretation based on a 10-mm. human embryo exhibiting unilateral renal agenesis. Anat. Rec., 52:325–339.

Brachet, A. 1935 Traité d'Embryologie des Vertébrés. 2d ed. Masson et Cie., Paris.

Brambell, F. W. R. 1927 The development and morphology of the gonads of the mouse. Part II. The development of the Wolffian body and ducts. Proc. Roy. Soc., Series B., 102:206–221.

Burns, R. K. 1935 The process of sex transformation in parabiotic Amblystoma. III. Conversion of testis to ovary in heteroplastic pairs of A. tigrinum and A. punctatum. Anat. Rec., 63:101–129.

———— 1938 Development of the mesonephros in Amblystoma after early extirpation of the duct. Proc. Soc. Exp. Biol. & Med., 39:111–113.

———— 1939 The effects of crystalline sex hormones on sex differentiation in Amblystoma. II. Testosterone propionate. Anat. Rec., 73:73–93.

———— 1941 The origin of the rete apparatus in the opossum. Science, 94:142–144.

———— 1942 Hormones and experimental modification of sex in the opossum. Biological Symposia, 9:125–146.

———— 1945a Bisexual differentiation of the sex ducts in opossums as a result of treatment with androgen. J. Exp. Zool., 100:119–140.

———— 1945b The differentiation of the phallus in the opossum and its reactions to sex hormones. Contr. Embryology, Carnegie Inst. Washington, 31:147–162.

———— 1949 Hormones and the differentiation of sex. Survey of Biological Progress, vol. I. Academic Press, Inc., New York.

———— 1950 Sex transformation in the opossum: some new results and a retrospect. Arch. d'Anat. micr. et de Morph. exp., 39:467–481.

Burrows, H. 1945 Biological Actions of Sex Hormones. Parts III and IV. Cambridge University Press, Cambridge, England.

Buyse, A. 1935 The differentiation of transplanted mammalian gonad primordia. J. Exp. Zool., 70:1–41.

Cambar, R. 1948 Recherches expérimentales sur les facteurs de la morphogénèse du mésonéphros chez les amphibiens anoures. Bull. Biol. France et Belgique, 82:214–285.

———— 1949 Données récentes sur le développement du système pronéphrétique chez les Amphibiens (Anoures en particulier). Ann. Biol., 25:115–130.

Colloques Internationaux du Centre National de la Recherche Scientifique. XXXI: La Différenciation sexuelle chez les Vertébrés. Paris, 1950.

Dalcq, A. 1942 Contribution à l'étude du potential morphogénétique chez les Anoures. III. Opérations visant l'ébauche pronéphrétique au seuil de la gastrulation. Arch. Biol., 53:1–124.

Dantschakoff, W. 1932 Keimzelle und Gonade. Die entodermale Wanderzelle als Stammzelle in der Keimbahn. Experimentelle Beweise. Zeit. Zellforsch. Mikr. Anat., 14:376–384.

de Beaumont, J. 1933 La différenciation sexuelle dans l'appareil uro-génital du Triton et son déterminisme. Roux' Arch. Entw.-mech., 129:120–178.

Domm, L. 1939 Modifications in sex and second-
ary sexual characters in birds; in Sex and Internal Secretions. 2d ed. Williams & Wilkins Co., Baltimore.

Dulbecco, R. 1946 Sviluppo di gonadi in assenza di cellule sessuali nell' embrione di pollo. Sterilizzazione completa mediante esposizione a raggi γ allo stadio di linea primitiva. Rend. Acc. Naz. Lincei, ser. VIII, 1:1211–1213.

Fales, D. E. 1935 Experiments on the development of the pronephros of Amblystoma punctatum. J. Exp. Zool., 72:147–173.

Field, H. H. 1891 The development of the pronephros and segmental duct in amphibia. Bull. Mus. Comp. Zool., Harvard College, 21:201–340.

Foote, C. L. 1941 Modification of sex development in the marbled salamander by administration of synthetic sex hormones. J. Exp. Zool., 86:291–319.

Fraser, E. A. 1950 The development of the vertebrate excretory system. Biol. Rev., 25:159–187.

Gaarenstroom, J. H. 1939 Action of sex hormones on the development of the Müllerian duct of the chick embryo. J. Exp. Zool., 82:31–46.

Gallien, L. 1941 Recherches expérimentales sur l'action amphisexuelle de l'hormone femelle (oestradiol), dans la différenciation du sexe chez Rana temporaria L. Bull. Biol. France et Belgique, 75:369–397.

———— 1944 Recherches expérimentales sur l'organogenèse sexuelle chez les Batraciens Anoures. Bull. Biol. France et Belgique, 78:257–359.

———— 1950 Les hormones sexuelles dans la différenciation du sexe chez les Amphibiens. Arch. d'Anat. micr. et de Morph. exp., 39:337–360.

Gillman, J. 1948 The development of the gonads in man with a consideration of the role of fetal endocrines and the histogenesis of ovarian tumors. Contr. Embryology, Carnegie Inst. Washington, 32:81–131.

Goodrich, E. S. 1930 Studies on the Structure and Development of Vertebrates. The Macmillan Co., London.

Gray, P. 1932 The development of the amphibian kidney. II. The development of the kidney of Triton vulgaris and a comparison of this form with Rana temporaria. Quart. J. Micr. Sci., 75:425–465.

———— 1936 The development of the amphibian kidney. III. The post-metamorphic development of the kidney, and the development of the vasa efferentia and seminal vesicles in Rana temporaria. Quart. J. Micr. Sci., 78:445–473.

Greene, R. R. 1942 Hormonal factors in sex inversion: the effects of sex hormones on embryonic sexual structures of the rat. Biological Symposia, 9:105–123.

Grünwald, P. 1937 Zur Entwickelungsmechanik des Urogenitalsystems beim Huhn. Roux' Arch. Entw.-mech., 136:786–813.

———— 1938 Entwicklungsmechanische Untersuchungen über die Genese einiger Fehlbildungen des Urogenitalsystems. Beitr. z. path. Anat. und z. allg. Path., 100:309–322.

Gruenwald, P. 1941 The relation of the growing tip of the Müllerian duct to the Wolffian duct and its importance for the genesis of malformations. Anat. Rec., *81:*1–19.

Gruenwald, P. 1942 Experiments on distribution and activation of nephrogenic potency in the embryonic mesenchyme. Physiol. Zool., *15:*396–407.

——— 1943 Stimulation of nephrogenic tissue by normal and abnormal inductors. Anat. Rec., *86:*321–339.

Hall, R. W. 1904 The development of the mesonephros and the Müllerian ducts in Amphibia. Bull. Mus. Comp. Zool., Harvard College, *45:*29–125.

Hamilton, H. 1952 Lillie's Development of the Chick. Henry Holt, New York.

Hanaoka, K. 1941 The effect of testosterone-propionate upon the sex differentiation in *Hynobius retardatus*. J. Fac. Sci., Hokkaido Imperial Univ., Series VI, Zool., *7:*413–419.

Heys, F. 1931 The problem of the origin of germ cells. Quart. Rev. Biol., *6:*1–45.

Hill, R. T. 1950 Multiplicity of ovarian functions in the mouse. Arch. d'Anat. micr. et de Morph. exp., *39:*634–642.

Holtfreter, J. 1933 Der Einfluss von Wirtsalter und verschiedenen Organbezirken auf die Differenzierung von angelagertem Gastrulaektoderm. Roux' Arch. Entw.-mech., *127:*619–775.

——— 1934 Über die Verbreitung induzierender Substanzen und ihre Leistungen im Triton-Keim. Roux' Arch. Entw.-mech., *132:*307–383.

——— 1936 Regionale Induktionen in xenoplastische zusammengesetzten Explantaten. Roux' Arch. Entw.-mech., *134:*466–550.

——— 1938 Differenzierungspotenzen isolierter Teile der Urodelengastrula. Roux' Arch. Entw.-mech., *138:*522–656.

——— 1944 Experimental studies on the development of the pronephros. Rev. Canad. de Biol., *3:*220–250.

Holyoke, E. A. 1949 The differentiation of embryonic gonads transplanted to the adult omentum in the albino rat. Anat. Rec., *103:*675–699.

Howland, R. B. 1921 Experiments on the effect of removal of the pronephros of *Amblystoma punctatum*. J. Exp. Zool., *32:*355–395.

——— 1926 Regeneration of the segmental duct and experimental acceleration of growth of the mesonephros in *Amblystoma punctatum*. J. Exp. Zool., *44:*327–353.

Huijbers, M. 1951 The influence of the gonads on the development of the reproductive system in the chick embryo. (Summary of Thesis, Anatomy and Embryology Laboratory, University of Amsterdam.)

Humphrey, R. R. 1925 The primordial germ cells of Hemidactylium and other Amphibia. J. Morph. Physiol., *41:*1–43.

——— 1927 Extirpation of the primordial germ cells of Amblystoma: its effect upon the development of the gonad. J. Exp. Zool., *49:*363–399.

——— 1928a The developmental potencies of the intermediate mesoderm of Amblystoma when transplanted into ventrolateral sites in other embryos: the primordial germ cells of such grafts and their role in the development of a gonad. Anat. Rec., *40:*67–101.

——— 1928b Sex differentiation in the gonads developed from transplants of the intermediate mesoderm of Amblystoma. Biol. Bull., *55:*317–339.

——— 1929 The early position of the primordial germ cells in urodeles: evidence from experimental studies. Anat. Rec., *42:*301–314.

——— 1933 The development and sex differentiation of the gonad in the wood frog (*Rana sylvatica*) following extirpation or orthotopic implantation of the intermediate segment and adjacent mesoderm. J. Exp. Zool., *65:*243–264.

——— 1942 Sex inversion in the Amphibia. Biological Symposia, *9:*81–104.

——— 1944 The functional capacities of heteroplastic gonadal grafts in the Mexican axolotl, and some hybrid offspring of grafted animals. Am. J. Anat., *75:*263–287.

——— 1945 Sex determination in Ambystomid salamanders: a study of the progeny of females experimentally converted to males. Am. J. Anat., *76:*33–66.

——— 1948 Reversal of sex in females of genotype WW in the axolotl (*Siredon* or *Ambystoma mexicanum*) and its bearing upon the role of the Z chromosome in the development of the testis. J. Exp. Zool., 109:171–185.

Johnston, P. M. 1951 The embryonic history of the germ cells of the large-mouth black bass, *Micropterus salmoides* (Lacépède). J. Morph., *88:* 471–542.

Jost, A. 1947a Recherches sur la différenciation de l'embryon de lapin. 2. Action des androgènes synthèse sur l'histogénèse génitale. Arch. d' Anat. micr. et de Morph. exp., 36:242–270.

——— 1947b Recherches sur la différenciation de l'embryon de lapin. 3. Rôle des gonades foetales dans la différenciation sexuelle somatique. Arch. d'Anat. micr. et de Morph. exp., 36:271–315.

——— 1947c The age factor in the castration of male rabbit fetuses. Proc. Soc. Exp. Biol. & Med., *66:*302–303.

——— 1948 Le contrôle hormonal de la différenciation du sexe. Biol. Rev., *23:*201–236.

——— 1950 Sur le contrôle hormonal de la différenciation sexuelle du lapin. Arch. d'Anat. micr. et de Morph. exp., *39:*577–598.

———, and Bergerard, Y. 1949 Culture in vitro d'ébauches du tractus génital du foetus de rat. Compt. Rend. Soc. Biol., *143:*608.

———, and Bosic, B. 1951 Données sur la différenciation des conduits génitaux du foetus de rat étudiée in vitro. Compt. Rend. Soc. Biol., *145:* 647–650.

———, and Colonge, R. A. 1949 Greffe de testicule foetal de Rat sur l'adulte castré et hypophysectomisé. Remarques sur la physiologie du testicule foetal de Rat. Compt. Rend. Soc. Biol., *143:* 140.

Keller, K., and Tandler, J. 1916 Über das Verhalten der Eihäute bei der Zwillingsträchtigkeit des Rindes. Untersuchungen über die Entstehungsursache der geschlechtlichen Unterentwicklung von weiblichen Zwillingskälbern, welche neben einem männlichen Kalbe zur Entwicklung gelangen. Wiener Tierärztl. Wochenschrift, *3:*513.

Leroy, P. 1948 Effet androgène d'extraits embryonnaires de Poulet sur la crête du Chapon. Compt. Rend. Acad. Sci., Paris, *226:*520.

Lillie, F. R. 1916 The theory of the free-martin. Science, 43:611.

——— 1917 The free-martin: a study of the action of sex hormones in the foetal life of cattle. J. Exp. Zool., *23:*371–452.

Machemer, H. 1929 Differenzierungsfähigkeit der Urnierenanlage von *Triton alpestris.* Roux' Arch. Entw.-mech., *118:*200–251.

Mangold, O. 1924 Transplantationsversuche zur Frage der Spezifität und der Bildung der Keimblätter. Arch. mikr. Anat. u. Entw., *100:*198–301.

Mintz, B. 1947 Effects of testosterone propionate on sex development in female Ambystoma larvae. Physiol. Zool., *20:*355–373.

——— 1948 Testosterone propionate minimum for induction of male development in Anurans; comparative data from other vertebrates. Proc. Soc. Exp. Biol. & Med., *69:*358–361.

Miura, K. 1930a Über die Einflüsse der totalen Extirpation des äusseren Glomerulus auf die Vorniere bei Froschlarven. Jap. J. Med. Sci., I: Anat., 2:125–133.

——— 1930b Experimentelle Untersuchungen über die genetische Beziehung zwischen dem Wolffschen Gang und der Urniere bei Froschlarven. Jap. J. Med. Sci., I: Anat., 2:105–124.

Moore, C. R. 1941 On the role of sex hormones in sex differentiation in the opossum (*Didelphys virginiana*). Physiol. Zool., *14:*1–45.

——— 1944 Gonad hormones and sex differentiation. Amer. Nat., *78:*97–130.

——— 1947 Embryonic Sex Hormones and Sexual Differentiation. Charles C Thomas, Springfield, Illinois.

———, and Price, D. 1942 Differentiation of embryonic reproductive tissues of the rat after transplantation into post-natal hosts. J. Exp. Zool., *90:*229–265.

Muchmore, W. B. 1951 Differentiation of the trunk mesoderm in *Amblystoma maculatum.* J. Exp. Zool., *118:*137–180.

Nieuwkoop, P. D. 1947 Experimental investigations on the origin and determination of the germ cells, and on the development of the lateral plates and germ ridges in urodeles. Arch. Néerl. Zool., *8:*1–205.

——— 1948 Some further data concerning the determination of the mesonephros. Experientia, *4:*391–394.

——— 1949 The present state of the problem of the "Keimbahn" in the vertebrates. Experientia, *5:*308–312.

——— 1950 Causal analysis of the early development of the primordial germ cells and the germ ridges in urodeles. Arch. d'Anat. micr. et de Morph. exp., *39:*257–268.

O'Connor, R. J. 1938 Experiments on the development of the pronephric duct. J. Anat., *73:*145–154.

——— 1939 Experiments on the development of the amphibian mesonephros. J. Anat., *74:*34–44.

——— 1940 An experimental study of the development of the amphibian cloaca. J. Anat., *74:*301–308.

Padoa, E. 1936 Effetto paradossale (mascolinizzazione) sulla differenziazione sessuale di girini di *Rana esculenta* trattati con ormone follicolare. Mon. Zool. Ital., *47:*285.

——— 1938 La differenziazione del sesso invertita mediante la somministrazione di ormoni sessuali. Ricerche con follicolina in *Rana esculenta.* Arch. Ital. Anat. e Embr., *40:*122–172.

——— 1942 Il differenziamento del sesso invertita mediante la somministrazione di ormoni sessuali e corticosurrenali. Ricerche con diidrofollicolina, progesterone e acetato di desossicorticosterone, in *Rana esculenta.* Pubbl. Staz. Zool. Napoli, *19:*185–223.

Pasteels, J. 1942 New observations concerning the maps of presumptive areas of the young amphibian gastrula (Amblystoma and Discoglossus). J. Exp. Zool., *89:*255–281.

Piquet, J. 1930 Détermination du sexe chez les Batraciens en fonction de la température. Rev. suisse Zool., *37:*173–281.

Ponse, K. 1924 L'organe de Bidder et le déterminisme des caractères sexuels secondaires du Crapaud (*Bufo vulgaris* L.) Rev. suisse Zool., *31:*177–336.

——— 1948 Actions paradoxales des glandes génitales. Rev. suisse Zool., *55:*477–531.

——— 1949 La différenciation du sexe et l'intersexualité chez les Vertébrés. F. Rouge, Lausanne.

Price, D. 1947 An analysis of the factors influencing growth and development of the mammalian reproductive tract. Physiol. Zool., *20:*213–247.

Rawles, M. E. 1936 A study in the localization of organ-forming areas in the chick blastoderm of the head-process stage. J. Exp. Zool., *72:*271–315.

Raynaud, A. 1942 Modification expérimentale de la différenciation sexuelle des embryons de souris, par action des hormones androgènes et oestrogènes. Actual. Scient. et Indus., nos. 925 and 926, Hermann, édit., Paris.

——— 1950 Recherches expérimentales sur le développement de l'appareil génital et le fonctionnement des glandes endocrines des foetus de souris et de mulot. Arch. d'Anat. micr. et de Morph. exp., *39:*518–569.

———, and Frilley, M. 1947 Destruction des glandes génitales de l'embryon de souris par une irradiation au moyen des rayons x, a l'âge de 13 jours. Ann. d'Endocrinol., *8:*400–419.

Rudnick, D. 1944 Early history and mechanics of the chick blastoderm. Quart. Rev. Biol., *19:*187–212.

Salzgeber, B. 1950 Sterilisation et intersexualité obtenues chez l'embryon de poulet par irradiation aux rayons x. Bull. Biol. France et Belgique, *84:*225–233.

Seevers, C. H. 1932 Potencies of the end bud and other caudal levels of the early chick embryo, with special reference to the origin of the metanephros. Anat. Rec., *54:*217–246.

Shimasaki, Y. 1930a Über die Resektion des Nephrostomalkanälchens der Vorniere bei Bufolarven. Jap. J. Med. Sci., I: Anat., 2:277–289.

———— 1930b Entwicklungsmechanische Untersuchungen über die Urniere des Bufo. Jap. J. Med. Sci., I: Anat., 2:291–319.

Spofford, W. R. 1945 Observations on the posterior part of the neural plate in Amblystoma. I. The prospective significance of posterior neural plate mesoderm. J. Exp. Zool., 99:35–52.

———— 1948 Observations on the posterior part of the neural plate in Amblystoma. II. The inductive effect of the intact part of the chordamesodermal axis on competent prospective ectoderm. J. Exp. Zool., 107:123–159.

Stoll, R. 1948 Actions de quelques hormones sexuelles sur le développement des canaux de Müller de l'embryon de poulet. Arch. d'Anat. micr. et de Morph. exp., 37:118–135.

Swift, C. H. 1914 The origin and early history of the primordial germ cells in the chick. Am. J. Anat., 15:483–516.

Torrey, T. 1950 Intraocular grafts of embryonic gonads of the rat. J. Exp. Zool., 115:37–58.

Tung, T.-C. 1935 On the time of determination of the dorso-ventral axis of the pronephros in Discoglossus. Peking Nat. Hist. Bull., 10:115.

————, and Ku, S.-H. 1944 Experimental studies on the development of the pronephric duct in anuran embryos. J. Anat., 78:52–57.

Van Geertruyden, J. 1942 Quelques précisions sur le développement du pronéphros et de l'uretère primaire chez les Amphibiens Anoures. Ann. Soc. Roy. Belgique, 73:180–195.

———— 1946 Recherches expérimentales sur la formation du mésonéphros chez les Amphibiens Anoures. Arch. Biol., 57:145–181.

Vannini, E. 1946 Sex differentiation in Amphibia. Nature, 157:812.

von Winiwarter, H. 1910 La constitution et l'involution du corps de Wolff, et le développement du canal de Müller dans l'espèce humaine. Arch. Biol., 25:169–268.

Waddington, C. H. 1938 The morphogenetic function of a vestigial organ in the chick. J. Exp. Biol., 15:371–376.

Wells, L. J. 1950 Hormones and sexual differentiation in placental mammals. Arch. d'Anat. micr. et de Morph. exp., 39:499–514.

————, and Fralick, R. 1951 Production of androgen by the testes of fetal rats. Am. J. Anat., 89:63–107.

————, and van Wagenen, G. 1954 Androgeninduced female pseudohermaphroditism in the monkey (Macaca mulatta): anatomy of the reproductive organs. Contr. Embryology, Carnegie Inst. Washington, 35:93–106.

Wharton, L. R. 1949 Double ureters and associated renal anomalies in early human embryos. Contr. Embryology, Carnegie Inst. Washington, 33:103–112.

Wiesner, B. P. 1934 The postnatal development of the genital organs in the albino rat, with a discussion of a new theory of sexual differentiation. J. Obst. Gyn. British Empire, 41:867–922.

———— 1935 The postnatal development of the genital organs in the albino rat, with a discussion of a new theory of sexual differentiation. Jour. Obst. Gyn. British Empire, 42:8–78.

Willier, B. H. 1921 Structures and homologies of free-martin gonads. J. Exp. Zool., 33:63–127.

———— 1933 Potencies of the gonad-forming area in the chick as tested in chorio-allantoic grafts. Roux' Arch. Entw.-mech., 130:616–649.

———— 1937 Experimentally produced sterile gonads and the problem of the origin of germ cells in the chick embryo. Anat. Rec., 70:89–112.

———— 1939 The embryonic development of sex; in Sex and Internal Secretions. 2d ed. Williams & Wilkins Co., Baltimore.

———— 1950 Sterile gonads and the problem of the origin of germ cells in the chick embryo. Arch. d'Anat. micr. et de Morph. exp., 39:267–270.

———— 1952 Development of sex-hormone activity of the avian gonad. Ann. New York Acad. Sci., 55:159–171.

————, Gallagher, T. F., and Koch, F. C. 1935 Sex-modification in the chick embryo resulting from injections of male and female hormones. Proc. Nat. Acad. Sci., 21:625–631.

————, Gallagher, T. F., and Koch, F. C. 1937 The modification of sex development in the chick embryo by male and female sex hormones. Physiol. Zool., 10:101–122.

————, and Rawles, M. E. 1935 Organ-forming areas in the early chick blastoderm. Proc. Soc. Exp. Biol. & Med., 32:1293–1296.

Witschi, E. 1929 Studies on sex differentiation and sex determination in amphibians. II. Sex reversal in female tadpoles of Rana sylvatica following the application of high temperature. J. Exp. Zool., 52:267–291.

———— 1934 Genes and inductors of sex differentiation in amphibians. Biol. Rev., 9:460–488.

———— 1939 Modification of the development of sex in lower vertebrates and in mammals: in Sex and Internal Secretions. 2d ed. Williams & Wilkins Co., Baltimore.

———— 1948 Migration of the germ cells of human embryos from the yolk sac to the primitive gonadal folds. Contr. Embryology, Carnegie Inst. Washington, 32:67–80.

———— 1950 Génétique et physiologie de la différenciation du sexe. Arch. d'Anat. micr. et de Morph. exp., 39:215–240.

———— 1951a Embryogenesis of the adrenal and reproductive glands. Recent Progress in Hormone Research, 6:1–23. (Proceedings, Laurentian Hormone Conference.)

———— 1951b Adrenal hyperplasia in larval frogs treated with natural estrogens. Anat. Rec., 111:35–36.

Wolff, E. 1938 L'action des hormones sexuelles sur les voies génitales femelles des embryons de poulet. Trav. Stat. Zool. Wimereux, 13:825–840.

———— 1946 Recherches sur l'intersexualité expérimentale produite par la méthode des greffes de gonades à l'embryon de poulet. Arch. d'Anat. micr. et de Morph. exp., 36:69–91.

———— 1947 Essai d'interprétation des résultats

obtenus récemment chez les Vertébrés sur l'intersexualité hormonale. Experientia, *3:*272–276, 301–304.

Wolff, E. 1950 Le rôle des hormones embryonnaires dans la différenciation sexuelle des oiseaux. Arch. d'Anat. micr. et de Morph. exp., *39:*426–444.

———, and Ginglinger, A. 1935 Sur la transformation des poulets mâles en intersexués par injection d'hormone femelle (folliculine) aux embryons. Arch. d'Anat., d'Hist. et d'Embry., *20:*219–278.

———, and Haffen, K. 1952 Sur le développement et la différenciation sexuelle des gonades embryonnaires d'oiseau en culture *in vitro*. J. Exp. Zool., *119:*381–403.

———, and Wolff, E. 1948 Sur le déterminisme

de la différenciation du pénis chez le Canard. Arch. d'Anat. micr. et de Morph. exp., *37:*155–167.

———, and Wolff, E. 1951 The effects of castration on bird embryos. J. Exp. Zool., *116:*59–97.

———, Strudel, G., and Wolff, E. 1948 L'action des hormones androgènes sur la différenciation sexuelle des embryons de poulets. Arch. d'Anat., d'Hist. et d'Embry., *31:*237–310.

Yamada, T. 1937 Der Determinationszustand des Rumpfmesoderms im Molchkeim nach der Gastrulation. Roux' Arch. Entw.-mech., *137:*151–270.

——— 1950 Dorsalization of the ventral marginal zone of the Triturus gastrula. I. Ammonia-treatment of the medio-ventral marginal zone. Biol. Bull., *98:*98–121.

CHAPTER 7

Teeth

ISAAC SCHOUR

INTRODUCTION

THE ontogenetic history of the tooth is an interesting and fruitful chapter in developmental histophysiology. The tooth does not belong to the osseous system. It is a highly specialized appendage and passes through many developmental stages. These permit an analysis of different types of growth and are governed by definite principles the integration of which makes for orderliness in the elaboration of the form, size and function of the tooth.

The continuously growing incisors are especially useful for the quantitative and qualitative analysis of developmental processes. Thus the rodent incisor may be regarded as nature's gift to research in tooth development (Schour and Massler, '49).

The component dental structures when growing are highly sensitive to physiological and metabolic processes which become permanently recorded in the completed and calcified enamel and dentin. The tooth is an organ of mastication, but it can also be utilized as a permanent biological kymograph of the life history of the growing individual (Massler, Schour and Poncher, '41).

The tooth proper consists of the calcified enamel, dentin and cementum and the soft internal pulp. However, function calls for a close organic integration with the surrounding gingiva, periodontal membrane and alveolar bone, and topographical correlation with the adjacent and opposing teeth. This section will be confined largely to a consideration of the growth of enamel and dentin.

The progressive development of the teeth consists of the following stages (Noyes, Schour and Noyes, '48) (Fig. 191):

I. Growth
1. Initiation (chemodifferentiation of Huxley)
2. Proliferation
3. Histodifferentiation
4. Morphodifferentiation
5. Apposition
II. Calcification
III. Eruption
IV. Attrition.

Table 15 outlines the morphologic sequence of events and the corresponding physiological processes. These overlap considerably and many of them may occur at the same time in different parts of the tooth. Table 15 also summarizes the developmental physiology of the tooth.

GROWTH

INITIATION

Specific basal cells at definite sites on the dental lamina of the oral epithelium become

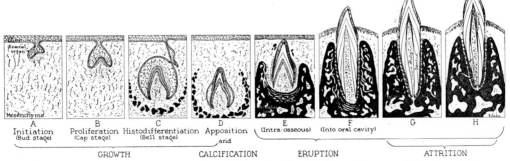

Fig. 191. Diagrammatic representation of life cycle of tooth (from Schour and Massler, '40).

TABLE 15. *Developmental Physiology of the Tooth, Enamel and Dentin (Adapted from Schour and Massler, '40)*

DEVELOPMENTAL STAGES	HUXLEY'S TERMINOLOGY	MORPHOLOGIC STAGES	MAJOR INFLUENCE ON:	HISTOPHYSIOLOGIC CHARACTERISTICS AND EVENTS	QUANTITATIVE AND QUALITATIVE METHODS OF STUDY	ABERRATIONS IN DEVELOPMENT RESULT IN:	SENSITIVITY TO EXPERIMENTAL INTERFERENCES	EXPERIMENTAL CONDITIONS SHOWING SPECIFIC DISTURBANCES
Growth								
1. Initiation	Chemodifferentiation	Dental lamina	Number of teeth	Origin of growth at: 1. Predetermined size 2. Definite time		Disturbances of all subsequent phases of growth	Low	Colchicine and lead poisoning (deficient proliferative growth). Hypovitaminosis A (uninhibited proliferation of enamel epithelium and invasion into pulp)
2. Proliferation		Bud and cap stages		Rapid cell multiplication resulting in: 1. Increase in size 2. Change in form 3. Elaboration of formative organ	Number of mitotic figures			
3. Histodifferentiation	Histodifferentiation		Quality of structure	Specific cells become tall columnar, and acquire growth potential to form enamel and dentin. Their functional life span and rate of activity are established. Proliferative capacity is given up	Cytologic analysis	Atypical structure	Low	Hypovitaminosis A: atypical dentin formation and form of pulp. Vitamin C deficiency
4. Morphodifferentiation		Cap and bell stages	Form and size	Morphologic pattern is assumed. Outlining of dentino-enamel and dentino-cemental junction	Arrangement of cells	Irregular form and size	Medium	
5. Apposition	Auxanodifferentiation	Crown and root formation	Amount of structure	Deposition of matrix at given rates and gradients; sites (growth centers and growth pattern); time (chronology); and duration (functional life span). Result: an incremental pattern which consists of timed gnomonic curves superposed on a morphogenetic pattern	Vital staining (alizarin red S, sodium fluoride, or strontium)	Hypoplasia (deficient amount of matrix formation)	High	Hypovitaminosis A; markedly disturbed gradient of growth; enamel hypoplasia and vascular inclusion of dentin
Calcification			Degree of hardness	Precipitation of mineral salts in protein matrix. Enamel and dentin, unlike bone, not subject to physiologic resorption	X-ray densiometer; histologic staining reaction; degree of fusion of calcospherites; x-ray diffraction	Enamel immature and acid-resistant, chalky and fragile. Dentin showing nonfusion of calcospherites (interglobular and fragile dentin), wide pre-dentin. Cementum and bone with wide osteoid and pre-cementum borders	Most sensitive phase in development; sensitive to even normal variations in body metabolism; reflects constitutional status of individual (neonatal adjustment, weaning, infancy, etc.)	Hypovitaminosis D: wide pre-dentin and interglobular dentin. Parathyroidectomy; interglobular dentin. Fluorosis; chalky-white opacity of enamel
Eruption			Occlusal positioning	Migration of formed tooth to meet opposing and adjacent teeth in occlusal function	Marking of tooth	Deficient eruption, submersion. Excessive eruption, elongation (supra-occlusion). Malocclusion	Very easily affected by local conditions; less readily affected by systemic factors	Local: traumatic occlusion causing decreased rate of eruption; removal or fracture of antagonists allowing for increased rate of eruption
Attrition			Reduction in height of crown	Degrowth process resulting from functional wear. Compensated by eruption	Marking of tooth	Deficient attrition, elongation (supra-occlusion). Excessive attrition, abnormal wearing of crown		Local: deficient wear due to removal of antagonist; abnormal wear due to excessive muscular function. Systemic: deficient calcification of enamel (fluorosis), resulting in abnormal attrition

odontogenic. Experiments on the induction of tooth development have been conducted in amphibians. Holtfreter ('35) transplanted indifferent ectoderm of the tree-frog, Hyla, to the ventral head region of the newt, Triton. Horny teeth developed which were typical of the donor species, but did not occur in the host species.

Sellman ('46), on the basis of extirpation and transplantation experiments in the urodeles which are equipped with dentin teeth even as larvae, concluded that tooth formation requires three components: (1) neural crest, (2) presumptive mouth ectoderm and (3) oral entoderm (the oral plate of the foregut).

Andres ('46) transplanted undetermined ventral ectoderm of a gastrula of a toad to the lateral head region of a salamander neurula. Though this ectoderm is induced by the host to form a variety of tissues, such as cartilage, teeth did not develop.

PROLIFERATION

The odontogenic cells undergo rapid mitotic multiplication leading to changes in the form and size of the enamel organ (the bud, cap, and bell stages, Fig. 191). Adjacent connective tissue cells also proliferate to form the dental papilla (the pulpal organ) and the dental follicle (the periodontal organ). The enamel organ, the dental papilla, and the dental follicle together form the tooth germ.

The enamel organ does much more than its name implies. In addition to supplying the inner enamel epithelium which gives rise to the ameloblasts it exerts an organizing influence on the adjacent mesenchymal cells and outlines the future dentino-enamel and dentino-cemental junctions. It would, therefore, be more appropriate to call it the odontogenic organ.

It appears that even at this early stage the tooth germ contains the entire growth potential of the future tooth. Explants of this stage of development continue to develop in tissue culture through the subsequent stages of histodifferentiation and appositional growth (Glasstone, '36).

Proliferation of a given cell normally ceases with the assumption of the next stage of histodifferentiation. The inverse relation between proliferation and differentiation and specific activity is well illustrated in the ameloblasts. If they do not attain differentiation they continue to proliferate excessively with resulting cyst or tumor formation

(ameloblastoma) (Thoma and Goldman, '46).

HISTODIFFERENTIATION

The formative cells undergo structural as well as chemical changes. They give up their proliferative activity. The cells of the inner enamel epithelium differentiate into tall columnar ameloblasts and exert an organizing influence upon the subjacent mesenchymal cells of the dental papilla, which then differentiate into odontoblasts.

Chemical Interaction and Interdependence of Epithelium and Odontoblasts; Transplantation Experiments. Von Brunn (1887) and others have shown that the presence of the inner epithelium is essential to the differentiation of the odontoblasts and the initiation of dentin formation. However, once differentiation has reached a certain stage, the odontoblasts can proceed with dentin formation without the further presence of the epithelium.

Transplantation experiments with tooth germs of higher vertebrates beginning with those of Legros and Magitot (1874) have yielded further evidence on the interdependencies in tooth development. Huggins et al. ('34) observed dentin formation in 14 days following transplantation of odontoblasts to the abdominal wall. Enamel, on the other hand, will not form in the absence of odontoblasts or dentin (Huggins et al., '34; Glasstone, '36). Transplanted ameloblasts lose their cylindrical character, change to stratified squamous epithelium and fail to form enamel unless the odontoblasts accompany the transplant (Hahn, '41). Dentin formation, therefore, precedes and is essential to enamel formation, although the presence of the epithelial cells and their chemical interaction precede and are essential to the differentiation of the dentin-forming cells and the initiation of dentin formation.

The influence of dentin on enamel formation may be indirect by reversing the stream of tissue fluid (Wassermann, '44). The chemical influence of epithelial cells upon adjacent mesenchymal cells is not only evidenced in the tooth but also has been demonstrated in bone growth. Transplantation of epithelium of the gallbladder or of the urinary tract distal to the kidney causes the differentiation of the adjacent mesenchymal cells into osteoblasts and initiates the formation of bone (Huggins, '31).

Concomitant with their morphological differentiation, the cells acquire their functional assignment and their appositional growth potential to form enamel or dentin. This potentiality may be defined in terms of the amount of work capacity of the cell and is expressed in an orderly sequence of events and processes which occur during the stage of apposition.

The growth energy released at the initiation of development is unorganized and must be distributed according to a definite growth pattern. The process of differentiation is like the direction of a stage play. It occurs in that period in development at which "roles are assigned, cues fixed, appearances timed, and the stage set" (Weiss, '39). The orderliness of the actual performance (apposition) which follows is entirely dependent on the proper differentiation of the cells and their proper environmental condition.

MORPHODIFFERENTIATION

This stage marks the assumption of the morphological pattern of the tooth. The cells of the inner layer of enamel organ arrange themselves to outline the dentino-enamel junction, which serves as a blueprint pattern of the future form and size of the tooth. This junction must be established before any enamel or dentin is deposited, since these structures become calcified soon after they are formed and cannot change thereafter. Both histo- and morphodifferentiation first occur at the tip of the tooth and then proceed toward the apex.

Hertwig's Epithelial Sheath. At the margins of the bell-shaped enamel organ, the inner and outer layers of the enamel epithelium proliferate and give rise to Hertwig's epithelial root sheath. This epithelial sheath outlines the dentino-cemental junction and acts as the blueprint pattern for the shape, size and length of the future root or roots, just as the inner enamel epithelium outlines the shape and size of the crown. In addition, the epithelial sheath initiates the differentiation of the radical odontoblasts just as the ameloblasts initiate the differentiation of the coronal odontoblasts. The cementoblasts probably owe their differentiation to the chemical stimulus of calcified dentin. As soon as the formation of the dentin and cementum of the root is begun, the sheath disintegrates and vestiges can be found later as epithelial rests in the periodontium.

A disturbance in morphodifferentiation and also in proliferation results in a disturbance in the form and size of the dentino-enamel junction. This leads to abnormal forms and sizes such as the peg tooth or Hutchinson's incisor (screwdriver-shaped incisor).

The field concept of development has been applied by Butler ('39) to phylogenetic problems of tooth morphology. He pointed out that certain tooth characters are manifested in groups of teeth to a maximum degree in particular key teeth in each of the incisor, canine, and molar groups. Dahlberg ('45) suggested that tooth anomalies are related specifically to the tooth districts rather than to the dentitions as a whole. Thus, certain points in the human dentition are more susceptible to change than are others.

APPOSITION

In contrast to the rapid, multiplicative, mitotic and cellular type of proliferative growth, appositional growth is slow, additive, incremental and extracellular (Huxley, '32). Apposition of enamel constitutes the fulfillment and full expression of the growth potential acquired by the ameloblasts during histodifferentiation.

Appositional activity of the ameloblasts begins at specific sites, *the growth centers*, and proceeds at a definite time and *chronology*, at definite *rates and gradients* and for a definite number of days, the functional *life span* of the formative cells. The end result is the *incremental pattern* (Schour and Massler, '40).

Physiological Characteristics of Enamel and Dentin. An analysis of the incremental pattern is facilitated by three unique physiological characteristics of the enamel and dentin:

1. *The Rhythmic Manner of Appositional Growth and Calcification.* The hard structures of the tooth, like the trunks of trees, grow by the regular and rhythmic formation of concentric layers or rings.

2. *The High Sensitivity of the Growing and Calcifying Tissues to Fluctuations of Metabolic Processes (Particularly Mineral Metabolism).* The growing tooth depends for its raw materials upon the substances elaborated by the body. Fluctuations in the metabolism of the individual are, therefore, reflected in the layers or rings of the tooth forming at that time. The normal incremental rings are accurate records of the ontogenetic development of the tooth and the normal physiological fluctuations in the metabolism of the individual.

Accentuations of these rings may occur at any given time as a result of severe metabolic fluctuations or disturbances. They are seen as the striae of Retzius in the enamel and Owen's lines of contour in the dentin and may be of physiological or pathological origin. The neonatal ring, for example, reflects the physiological readjustments coincident to birth and is the result of the brief neonatal arrest in growth (Schour, '36). An analysis of various experimental endocrine and vitamin disturbances shows that each particular dysfunction produces characteristically disturbed incremental rings which are superposed on the basic formative pattern. The annual rings of the tree similarly reflect the variations and vicissitudes in climate that the tree had experienced during its growth period.

3. *The Permanence of the Tissues.* Enamel once completely formed and calcified can be destroyed by oral environmental factors but not by systemic alterations. Although completed, the dentin of deciduous teeth undergoes physiological resorption. Enamel, in fact, has lost its formative organ and has not even the power of repair. All available evidence shows that the dentin, as well as the enamel, is not subject to calcium withdrawal. These tissues serve, therefore, as permanent records of physiological or pathological disturbances of metabolism that may occur within the individual during their formative and calcifying stages. This permanence of structure is not found in bone although it also grows in an appositional manner and registers within its structure the effects of disturbances in body metabolism. The records in bone are erased by constant resorptions and reconstructions. Bone thus possesses two of these physiological characteristics of the tooth but lacks the third—its permanence.

The Growth Centers. The dentino-enamel junction is characterized by definite high points which correspond to the number of cusps (in the posterior teeth) or lobes (in the anterior teeth). Amelogenesis and dentinogenesis, just as proliferation and histodifferentiation, begin at these individual points and proceed at a specific rate and gradient of growth. Each summit on the dentino-enamel junction thus acts as an individual growth center from which the growth begins and radiates outward in a definite growth plan.

The Incremental Cones. Beginning at each growth center, successively adjacent ameloblasts begin their formation at successively later intervals, possibly a day apart. The cellular activity spreads peripherally along the dentino-enamel junction like a ripple will spread from a pebble dropped into calm water. Each ameloblast proceeds outwardly away from the dentino-enamel junction at its own characteristic rate and gradient of growth until the required length of the enamel rod is reached. Similarly each odontoblast recedes inwardly away from the dentino-enamel junction. Any given incremental layer of enamel or dentin assumes in three dimensions a conical form. Its apex is directed occlusally and its base rests upon the dentino-enamel junction. These incremental layers are apposed at each growth center, one over the other in the enamel and one within the other in the dentin. The resultant incremental growth pattern consists of a series of gnomonic curves whose form is determined by the dentino-enamel junction.

When the incremental layers of adjacent growth centers meet, as in the molar teeth, the subsequent incremental layers are deposited as fusions of individual cones.

Rates and Gradients of Appositional Growth. Vital staining with sodium fluoride (Schour and Poncher, '37) and alizarine red S (Schour et al., '41) offer a ready method for measuring the rate of apposition. Each injection produces a distinct ring in the enamel or dentin formed at the time. The distance between two successive experimental rings represents the amount of deposition during the time interval that elapsed between the injections.

In human teeth, the average rate of apposition of enamel and dentin is approximately 4 micra per day. This rate, however, decreases as one proceeds from the incisal or cuspal tip toward the gingival level (*locus gradient*); from the anterior incisors to the posterior molar teeth (*anteroposterior gradient*); and within the same cell, from the beginning of functional activity toward its termination (*age gradient*). As Thompson ('17) has pointed out, the method of appositional growth combined with growth gradients may result in a spiral form which is especially evident in the rodent incisor.

Appositional Growth Potential and Formative Life Span. In the tooth it is possible to measure the growth potential of the ameloblast and to assess its functional life span (Massler and Schour, '46). Since only one ameloblast is responsible for a given enamel rod, its length may be taken as a measure of the growth potential and the growth work done by the cell. The formative life span in days may then be obtained by dividing the length of the enamel rod by the daily rate of formation. Thus, L (length of enamel rod) = $G. P.$ (growth potential) = (Daily) rate × life span, = $R × T$ = Time of cellular activity (functional life span).

In the dentin the length of the dentinal tubule represents the growth potential or growth work of the odontoblasts. Such quantitative studies permit a detailed analysis of the growth pattern and size and form of different classes and types of teeth.

It is of interest to note that these rates and gradients of growth are not readily altered by environmental factors. Characteristic gradients in different regions of the same tooth and in different classes and types of teeth appear to correspond with their particular form and contour. This conforms with the statement of D'Arcy Thompson ('17): "A very large part of the specific morphology of the organism depends upon the fact that there is not only an average rate of growth common to the whole, but also a variation of rate in different parts of the organism. The smallest change in the relative magnitudes of these partial or localized velocities of growth will soon be manifested in more and more striking differences of form."

The functional life span of the ameloblasts shows wide gradients, with a maximal life span for the cells over the growth center and a minimal one for those near the cemento-enamel junction. While the odontoblasts, in contrast to the ameloblasts, persist and function throughout life, that period of their activity which is responsible for the formation of the primary dentin tends to be constant (in man, about 350 days for deciduous and about 700 days for the permanent teeth). Thus the presence and morphology of the pulp can be explained on the basis of the limited and decelerating rate of appositional activity of the odontoblasts.

CALCIFICATION

Calcification consists of the deposition of mineral salts and their crystallization. It is a process which does not involve a change in size, but a reorientation of molecular structure and content of the deposited matrix leading to increased polymerization of the ground substance and the precipitation of minerals.

The enamel and dentin in most species show a common basic incremental calcifica-

tion rhythm which recurs at intervals of approximately 16 micra. The common basis of this 16 micron calcification unit is possibly associated with the physicochemical factors concerned in calcospherite formation and the Liesegang ring phenomenon. Striae of Retzius in the enamel and Owen's lines of contour in the dentin constitute physiological or pathological accentuations of the normal incremental rings (Schour and Hoffman, '39).

In the dentin, calcification follows apposition in close succession (one day interval in the rat). In the enamel, the matrix first consists of organic substance (and water) and mineral salts in the ratio of two to one. During the secondary or final calcification the organic substance becomes increasingly impregnated by mineral salts until the mature enamel consists of 96 to 98 per cent inorganic material.

ERUPTION

Eruption is the process by which the tooth migrates from its intraosseous position within the jaw into the oral cavity in order to reach and maintain articulation. The piercing of the tooth through the oral mucosa is only a momentary and transitory event. Eruption continues throughout the life of the tooth.

In the rat, the rate of eruption is about 2 mm. per week in the upper incisors, and about 3 mm. in the lower. Studies in the rabbit show that most of the eruption occurs when the animal is at rest and the incisors are out of occlusion (Rink, '29). Experimental removal of the opposing incisor releases the eruption potential and results in the doubling of the rate of eruption.

ATTRITION

Attrition may be defined as the normal wearing of the teeth due to functional activity. Attrition is a degrowth process and provides an exception to the rule that tooth development proceeds without influence of function (note the development of teeth in dermoid cysts). The charting of the rate of attrition results in a straight line, suggesting that it is a mechanical process which is independent of growth (Hoffman and Schour, '40). The continuous process of attrition is compensated by eruption and serves to regulate articulation. In some species, as in the herbivora and rodentia, the teeth are made functional by attrition.

In the rodent incisor, the rate of eruption

and of attrition is readily measured by notching the exposed enamel surface at the gingival margin. The decrease in distance between the notch and the incisal edge is a measure of the rate of attrition. The increase in distance between the notch and the gingival margin is a measure of the rate of eruption.

REFERENCES

Andres, G. 1946 Über Induktion und Entwicklung von Kopforganen aus Unkenektoderm im Molch (Epidermis, Plakoden und Derivate der Neuralleiste). Revue suisse Zool., 53:502–510.

Brunn, A. v. 1887 Ueber die Ausdehnung des Schmelzorgans und seine Bedeutung für die Zahnbildung. Arch. f. mikr. Anat., 29:367–383.

Butler, P. M. 1939 Studies of mammalian dentition. Differentiation of postcanine dentition. Proc. Zool. Soc., London, 109:1–36.

Dahlberg, A. A. 1945 The changing dentition of man. J. Am. Dent. Assoc., 32:676–690.

Glasstone, S. 1936 Development of tooth germs in vitro. J. Anat., 70:260–266.

Hahn, William E. 1941 The capacity of developing tooth germ elements for self-differentiation when transplanted. J. Dent. Res., 20:5–19.

Hoffman, M. M., and Schour, I. 1940 Quantitative studies in the development of the rat molar. II. Alveolar bone, cementum and eruption (from birth to 500 days). Am. J. Orthodont., 26:854–874.

Holtfreter, J. 1935 Experimentell erzeugte Chimären aus den Organanlagen von Frosch- und Molchkeimen. Sitzber. Ges. Morphol. Physiol. München, 44:24–32.

Huggins, C. B. 1931 The formation of bone under the influence of eptihelium of the urinary tract. Arch. Surg., 22:377–408.

———, McCarroll, H. R., and Dahlberg, A. A. 1934 Transplantation of tooth germ elements and the experimental heterotopic formation of dentin and enamel. J. Exp. Med., 60:199–210.

Huxley, Julian S. 1932 Problems of Relative Growth. Lincoln MacVeagh, The Dial Press, New York.

Legros, Ch., and Magitot, E. 1874 Physiologie Experimentale—Greffes de follicules dentaires et de leurs organes constitutifs isolement. Compt. rend. Séances de l'Academie, 78:357–360.

Massler, M., and Schour, I. 1946 The appositional life span of the enamel and dentin-forming cells. J. Dent. Res., 25:145–150.

———, Schour, I., and Poncher, H. G. 1941 Development pattern of the child as reflected in the calcification pattern of the teeth. J. Dis. Child., 62:33–67.

Noyes, F. B., Schour, I., and Noyes, H. 1948 Oral Histology and Embryology, 6th ed. Lea & Febiger, Philadelphia.

Rink, Karl 1929 Rules of growth in rabbits. Viertelj.-schr. f. Zahnh., 45:543–561.

Schour, I. 1936 The neonatal line in the enamel and dentin of the human deciduous teeth and first permanent molar. J. Am. Dent. Assoc., 23:1946–1955.

———, and Hoffman, M. M. 1939 Studies in tooth development. I. The 16 microns calcification rhythm in the enamel and dentin from fish to man. J. Dent. Res., 18:91–102.

——— Hoffman, M. M., Sarnat, B. G., and Engel, M. B. 1941 Vital staining of growing bones and teeth with Alizarine Red S. J. Dent. Res., 20:411–418.

———, and Massler, M. 1940 Studies in tooth development: The growth pattern of human teeth. J. Am. Dent. Assoc., 27:1778–1793, 1918–1931.

———, and Massler, M. 1949 The teeth; in The Rat in Laboratory Investigation, by Griffith and Farris, 2nd ed., Chapter 6. J. B. Lippincott Co., Philadelphia.

———, and Poncher, H. G. 1937 Rate of apposition of enamel and dentin as measured by the effect of acute fluorosis. Am. J. Dis. Child., 54:757–776.

Sellman, Sven 1946 Some experiments on the determination of the larval teeth in Ambystoma mexicanum. Odontologisk Tidskrift, 54:1–128.

Thoma, Kurt K., and Goldman, Henry M. 1946 Odontogenic tumors: A classification based on observations of the epithelial, mesenchymal, and mixed varieties. Am. J. Path., 22:433–471.

Thompson, D'Arcy W. 1917 Growth and Form. Cambridge University Press, Cambridge, England.

Wassermann, F. 1944 Analysis of enamel formation in the continuously growing teeth of normal and vitamin C deficient guinea pigs. J. Dent. Res., 23:463–509.

Weiss, Paul 1939 Principles of Development. Henry Holt & Co., New York.

CHAPTER 8

Skin and Its Derivatives*

MARY E. RAWLES

INTRODUCTION

ALTHOUGH much information is available on the detailed histological and physiological characteristics of the adult skin and its numerous derivatives in the vertebrates, comparatively little attention has been given to the embryological origin of these characteristics. The purpose of this account is, therefore, to analyze the interrelationship and interaction of the ectoderm and mesoderm, the two primordial tissue components which unite in early development to form the composite structure, the skin and its diverse types of derivatives. Special attention will be given to (1) the causal relations and interactions involved in the differentiation of the dermal and epidermal components, (2) regional specialization of the skin with particular reference to the role of the mesoderm in epidermal specialization, and (3) integumentary patterns, structural and pigmentary.

ORIGIN OF THE SKIN

Early Beginnings of an Integrated System. Embryologically the skin of all vertebrates is a composite structure formed by the joining of two main contributions from separate sources, the ectoderm and the mesoderm. As a result of the formative movements of cells in gastrulation, prospective mesoderm is brought in contact with the inner surface of the epidermal portion of the prospective skin ectoderm. During this process the mesoderm appears to acquire a positive "affinity" for ectoderm, for prior to gastrulation prospective mesoderm resists fusion with ectoderm (Holtfreter, '39). This union between the two is probably the resultant of progressive changes in both ectoderm and mesoderm and is not to be regarded simply

* The writer is indebted to her husband, Mr. John S. Spurbeck, for the preparation of the illustrations.

as an operation of chance. The embryonic layers are presumably held together at first by complementary forces residing directly in the naked contact surfaces of their constituent cells. Sooner or later these primary affinities are superseded by more permanent unions in the form of "cementing tissues" or basement membranes (see Weiss, '47). Thus the embryonic components enter into an intimate union at the surface of the body and behave afterwards as an integrated system.

Source Material of the Epidermis and Dermis. The entire surface ectoderm between the union of the neural folds in the median dorsal line and the median ventral line of the embryo may be regarded roughly as prospective skin epidermis. By means of vital staining and other techniques its origin has been traced to a surface area in the early gastrula in the amphibians and in equivalent stages in the chick (Vogt, '25, '29; Pasteels, '37). Through growth and movements of the skin ectoderm and the accompanying gastrulation processes, the entire embryo is covered by ectoderm at the late gastrula stage (amphibian) or later stages (chick). Strictly speaking, the prospective fate of the skin ectoderm is not entirely epidermal, for in certain loci its development is modified by induction in specific directions, as for instance into lens and conjunctiva over the primordium of the eyecup, oral epithelium and parts of teeth in the mouth, inner ear in the region of the myelencephalon, etc. Nevertheless, the ectoderm in such loci is capable of forming epidermis when grafted to atypical positions, e.g., mouth ectoderm grafted to trunk forms epidermis (Ströer, '33). In a balanced physiological salt solution explanted ectodermal cells merely undergo proliferation and form only epidermis (Holtfreter, '31); and the ectoderm of exo-gastrulae remains a wrinkled mass of epidermal cells (Holtfreter, '33a, b). Furthermore, it is well known that prospective conjunctival ectoderm in the absence of contact with the optic vesicle remains pigmented and opaque like the surrounding true epidermis. The ectoderm thus appears to have a primordial capacity to form epidermis.

Inasmuch as the mesoderm is a relatively thick layer, the upper surface of which is in contact with skin ectoderm while its lower surface is in close union with gut entoderm and is the source of a variety of organs and tissues, the question arises as to what portion of the mesoderm contributes to the formation of the dermis. Does the

(the unsegmented mesoderm lateral to the somites, within which the body cavity arises) plus the closely united ectoderm and entoderm will also produce normal skin and skin derivatives (feathers or hair, as the case may be) when grafted to the embryonic chick coelom as seen in Figure 192 (Rawles, '47; Straus and Rawles, '53) or to the chorioallantoic membrane (Murray, '28).

In view of the fact that it is assumed frequently on the basis of morphological studies (Engert, '00, and others) that the dermis, not only of the dorsal and dorsolateral regions but of the other body regions as well,

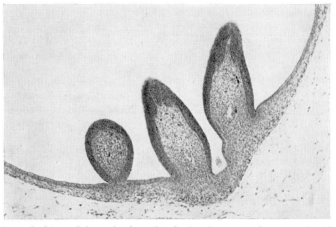

Fig. 192. Section through skin and down feathers developing in intracoelomic graft of lateral plate isolated from right side of 28-somite chick embryo at level of somites 22–25. Total age 10½ days. Compare with skin and feather germs of normal, Fig. 193 C. Iron hematoxylin, 8μ × 75.

dermis arise directly from mesodermal cells which are everywhere in contact with and subjacent to the skin ectoderm, or is its origin restricted to the so-called "dermatome," one of the three arbitrary divisions of the somite? An unequivocal answer to this old and controversial problem has been furnished for the chick and the mouse by the use of experimental techniques. Isolates of early limb buds, taken prior to the entrance of cells from the neural crest, and consisting of somatic mesoderm covered by skin ectoderm, will produce structurally normal skin and skin derivatives, feathers and hair, respectively, when grown in the coelom of a chick embryo host (Hamburger, '39; Rawles, '47). In the case of the chick, the skin from such intracoelomic wing grafts has even been transplanted to the back of newly hatched host chicks, in which case it has continued to grow normally and produce typical wing plumage in normal succession throughout the life span of the bird (Rawles, '44). Moreover, isolates of the lateral plate

is derived from the dermatome, the above experimental results are of considerable interest, for, under the conditions of the experiments, the dermis found in the grafts could not have been derived from dermatome material. Inasmuch as the neural crest was also excluded from the grafted tissue, it too may be ruled out as a contributing factor in the formation of the dermis of the grafted regions, contrary to the suggestion of Raven ('31, '36) for the urodele amphibians. It would appear from the experimental evidence, then, that the dermis of the limbs, flank, and ventral surface of the body is a derivative of the mesoderm of the somatopleure. There is no doubt that the dermatome of the somite contributes to the formation of the dermis of the dorsal and dorsolateral body regions. Grafts of somites, including ectoderm and entoderm, without the adjacent lateral plate bear this out (Straus and Rawles, '53). Furthermore, results obtained from marking, with finely powdered blood carbon, the mesoderm of various portions of the somites between the limb regions of 2½ day chick embryos, have shown clearly that in normal development the somite material does not migrate into the ventrolateral and ventral regions of the body wall. These corroborative results strengthen the conclusion that the dermis arises from mesoderm in contact with and subjacent to the skin ectoderm. It is highly probable that the development of the dermis is a result of contact relationships between ectodermal and mesodermal cells.

The origin of the dermis in the amphibian has not been so clearly established. Again, the problem centers on whether the mesenchymal cells subjacent to the skin ectoderm have a localized source, such as the dermatome or neural crest, or whether their source is more generalized. That the dermatome is not the source of the dermis of lateral and ventral regions is indicated by the results of Detwiler ('37a). When four successive brachial somites were excised on one side of Amblystoma embryos, and replaced by unsegmented, lateral mesoderm and overlying ectoderm, the dermis of the skin on the operated side appeared to be as completely developed as that on the normal side. The dermatome was thus eliminated as a source of the dermis of the lateral and ventral regions at least. Among the amphibians, two possible interpretations are evident. The dermis arises either directly from the external layer of the somatic mesoderm of the lateral somatopleure (or ventral myotomic growth) or from the neural crest cells as Raven ('31, '36) first suggested. According to Raven the greater portion if not all of the dermis of the trunk arises from neural crest cells. His interpretation was based on the interchange of prospective neural crest of the trunk region between embryos of different species of urodeles (Amblystoma mexicanum and Triturus taeniatus or T. alpestris). Owing to species differences in nuclear size and quantity of yolk granules he was able to follow the migration of neural crest cells into the dermis, i.e., into a position between the myotomes and skin ectoderm. Detwiler ('37b) followed neural crest cells which had been stained with Nile blue sulfate to similar positions suggesting their contribution to the dermis or corium. Holtfreter ('35) and Stearner ('46) have presented further evidence in support of this hypothesis. Although these and other experiments leave little doubt that some of the neural crest cells migrate laterally between the somite or myotome and the skin

ectoderm, it is not altogether clear whether these are precursor pigment cells or mesenchymal cells of the dermis or a mixture of both. The problem needs reinvestigation in view of the demonstration for the chick and mouse that trunk and limb dermis arises independently of any contribution from the neural crest. At present the most plausible view appears to be that the mesenchyme just beneath the skin ectoderm of the trunk is not restricted to any one site of origin. The mesenchyme of the head is largely if not entirely of neural crest origin; therefore, it is quite probable that cells derived from the latter give rise to the dermis of the head skin. It is now known that the neural crest exhibits marked regional differences in its potentialities (Hörstadius and Sellman, '46; Niu, '47).

Time of Localization or Specialization of the Ectoderm. It has been clearly shown by the methods of experimental embryology that the parts of a developing system possess greater developmental potentialities at an early stage than at any later period. The ectodermal cells of an amphibian gastrula, for instance, are potentially capable of differentiating into almost any cell type. At this stage their prospective fate has not become irrevocably established and the course which they follow in differentiation depends upon their reactions to inductive stimuli received from the region in which they happen to be placed. During the process of gastrulation, however, the skin ectoderm acquires a certain amount of autonomy or capacity to self-differentiate which enables it to differentiate in a particular direction independent of stimuli from the surrounding tissues. In other words, specialized properties have now been acquired which govern its further histological differentiation (see Section VI, Chap. 1 for the evidence on change in potency during gastrulation). By the end of the gastrulation stage the ectoderm has become more or less a mosaic of areas or fields with differences in intrinsic organization. Although regional specialization has begun it is not yet final—changes are still possible. The time when the prospective fate of the areas becomes definitely established varies among the different organ-specific areas, and there are also time differences among species.

Polar Organizaton of the Skin Ectoderm. The existence of a polarity in the skin ectoderm of early amphibian embryos is evidenced by the orderly beat of the cilia in a predominantly anteroposterior direction.

Experimentation has shown that the time in development when this polarity becomes established varies somewhat among the different species. In many of the anurans and in the axolotl, polarization appears to be acquired during gastrulation, shortly after the round yolk-plug stage and thus considerably in advance of the actual appearance of the cilia (Woerdeman, '25; Tung and Tung, '40). If a rectangular piece of skin ectoderm is excised from a blastula or young gastrula and reimplanted after a rotation of 180 degrees, the cilia arising from this area beat in the normal anteroposterior direction. But if the same rotation operation is performed later in gastrulation, i.e., at the circular blastopore stage and afterwards, the ciliary beat of the particular area is reversed, indicating that polarization had occurred prior to rotation. In *Amblystoma punctatum* similar experiments by Twitty ('28) have shown that polarity is established in the ectoderm somewhat later in development, during the closure of the neural folds, hence about the time that the cilia would normally appear. Cilia developing on areas rotated after the closure of the neural folds were found to beat in opposition to those of the surrounding epidermis. About the time that the direction of the effective stroke of the cilia is established in Amblystoma other changes involving polarity are also taking place, such, for example, as the outgrowth of the placodes of the lateral-line system (Stone, '33) and the anteroposterior polarization of the ear rudiment (Harrison, '36). At this time the ectoderm can no longer be turned inside out and develop into normal skin (Luther, '34). All of these changes are indicative of some fundamental transformation within the cells of the ectoderm. That polarization is imposed upon the skin ectoderm by the underlying entomesodermal tissue is evidenced by the fact that whenever ectodermic vesicles are formed, e.g., as a result of faulty healing-in of the transplant, the ciliary beat of such areas is uncoordinated (Luther, '34). The partial exo-gastrulae obtained by Holtfreter ('33a, b) afford an even more beautiful demonstration of this point. He found that the ciliary beat was regular and polarized in the portions of the ectoderm underlaid by entomesoderm, but was irregular and chaotic in regions not underlaid by this "organizing" tissue. Once ciliary polarity has been induced in the skin ectoderm, it in turn becomes capable of inducing polarity in younger, unpolarized ectoderm if brought into direct contact

(Tung, Tung and Chang, '48). These investigators have also presented evidence that the induction of polarity in the ectoderm involves a chemical interaction.

Surface-interior differences in cells of the skin ectoderm have been demonstrated in the chick embryo by implanting small isolates of head skin ectoderm into the mesoderm of a wing bud (Willier and Rawles, '40). If the isolate becomes completely embedded in the surrounding limb mesoderm, the epithelial character of the ectoderm disappears and its constituent cells intermingle with and become indistinguishable from mesodermal cells of the wing bud. If, as sometimes happens, the isolate rolls up to form a vesicle with its original outer surface facing the cavity and the inner surface contiguous with wing mesoderm, the ectoderm will maintain its epithelial character and differentiate into epidermis. In order to develop normally the original outer surface of the skin ectoderm must be free of cellular contact. The free or outer surface of the ectodermal cells appears to be incompatible with and to resist fusion with mesodermal cells.

Source of the Pigment Cells of the Skin. Pigment cells variously designated as melanophores, chromatophores, pigmentophores, dendritic cells, et cetera, are common and distinctive components of the skin of all vertebrates, including man. They are found in both epidermal and dermal layers and, also, particularly in the lower vertebrates, in perineural and perivascular layers and in the peritoneal lining of the coelomic wall. Controversy over the site of origin of these highly specialized, branched cells has existed for nearly a century. Although many hypotheses have been advanced, the most generally accepted view up until 1934 held that the pigment cells were modified connective tissue cells, or at least originated from the mesoderm. The first suggestion that the neural crest might be the source of these cells is traceable to the observations of Borcea ('09) in teleosts and Weidenreich ('12) in amphibians. Within this same period Harrison ('10) in his studies on nerve regeneration in vitro found pigment cells in cultures of frog spinal cord and clearly predicted their origin from the neural crest. Many years elapsed before this problem received serious attention and was systematically investigated by experimental methods (DuShane, '35). The proof now firmly established by numerous workers for many species of amphibians (see reviews by DuShane,

'43; Rawles, '48; Hörstadius, '50) is based principally upon the following evidence: (1) extirpation of the neural folds (including the primordia of the crest) of neurulae results in a total absence of pigment cells from the operated trunk region; (2) isolated neural folds produce numerous pigment cells when cultured in vitro or (3) when transplanted to the flank of another embryo of the same or of a different species. In the latter case, the pigment cells which develop in the foreign host are always of the donor type. While the entire neural crest is potentially capable of producing all of the various types of pigment cells—melanophores, xanthophores, guanophores—found in the body of an amphibian, it nevertheless does exhibit regional differences as regards the number of these cells produced. The great majority appear to come from the crest of the trunk region (Niu, '47; Twitty, '49).

In birds, as in amphibians, the neural crest origin of the pigment cells (melanophores) has been unequivocally established by a variety of experimental results. The evidence briefly summarized is as follows: (1) explants including the neural crest produce typical melanophores when cultured in vitro (Dorris, '38); (2) melanophores differentiate from isolates containing the crest, or any of its migratory cells, when grafted to the embryonic coelom (Eastlick, '39; Ris, '41) or to the early limb bud (Dorris, '39; Willier and Rawles, '40). Similar isolates without the crest never produce pigment; (3) neural crest cells grafted between embryos of different species of fowl, or even between wild birds and fowl, invariably produce melanophores of the donor type whose activity in the feathers of the host is recorded in the form of a typical donor coloration or pattern.

Among mammals, the mouse embryo has so far been the only representative in which the origin of the pigment-forming cells has been tested experimentally. The results are clear cut, however, in showing that only those tissues containing prospective neural crest, histologically recognizable neural crest or cells migrating from the neural crest, can produce pigment in grafts (Rawles, '47).

Thus the evidence has clearly established the origin of pigment cells of amphibians, birds, and mammals from the neural crest. A similar origin is indicated also for the lamprey (Newth, '51) and for the bony fishes (Borcea, '09; Lopashov, '44; Orton, '53). It is highly probable that the neural crest or its equivalent, the dorsal neural border, is the source of pigment cells in all of the vertebrates. Further proof would be welcome for some of the lower forms.

Migration of Pigment-forming Cells (Melanoblasts) into the Skin. From their locus of origin in the neural crest, prospective pigment cells migrate gradually to all regions of the body of the embryo. During this period of dispersal they cannot be distinguished with certainty either morphologically or histologically from the other embryonic cells with which they are associated. Yet, by means of appropriate transplantation experiments, it has been demonstrated clearly that they have reached all body regions of a chick embryo by the fourth day of incubation and all body regions of a mouse embryo by the twelfth day of gestation— long before there is any visible sign of pigmentation. As development proceeds and biochemical conditions become suitable for the synthesis of melanin, these "colorless" cells begin their characteristic differentiation and henceforth are readily distinguishable from surrounding cells. Observed differences in the distribution patterns of these cells after the differentiation of melanin pigment granules are not, however, necessarily a reflection of corresponding differences in their original dispersal from the neural crest. Recent evidence indicates that the characteristic longitudinal stripes of certain larval amphibians are formed by a secondary rearrangement of pigment cells originally more widely scattered over the lateral surfaces of the somites (Rosin, '43; Twitty, '45). Many prospective pigment cells remain undifferentiated (colorless) for long periods— until after metamorphosis in amphibians— and some undoubtedly become located in positions unfavorable for the synthesis of pigment. Both the reactivity of the pigment cells and the biochemical properties of the skin vary not only with the species, but even regionally within one individual.

The mechanism by which precursor pigment cells (melanoblasts) reach the skin and other locations is by no means completely understood. While it is evident from in vitro and other studies that these cells are capable of independent movements, much of their migratory activity is unquestionably dependent upon contact relationship with certain other strains of cells and tissues. The fact that pigment cells are found primarily along surface membranes (basal layer of the epidermis, parietal membranes, etc.) is significant. The possibility also that their final distribution may be affected somewhat by morphogenetic movements and by growth movements of their tissue substrate should not be overlooked.

The direction and paths of movement of the melanoblasts concerned with skin pigmentation do not appear to be at random. Experimental evidence indicates that they follow more or less predetermined routes, proceeding dorsoventrally in the mesenchymal tissues subjacent to the skin ectoderm. This would seem to imply that their movement is somehow directed by properties intrinsic to the skin and also by the interface between the ectoderm and the prospective dermis. The association of cells and tissues of distinctly different types presupposes some kind of surface compatibility or "affinity." The migratory movement of the precursor pigment cells, therefore, could be dependent upon their specific interaction or contact relationship with cells of the dermis. On this supposition, movement would continue until the contact relationship between the combining elements reaches some sort of equilibrium (Holtfreter, '39; Tyler, '47; Weiss, '47).

Interesting experimental evidence in favor of selective association of cells and tissues of specific types has been obtained recently by Weiss and Andres ('52). They injected dissociated embryonic cells of the chick, including melanoblasts which served as markers, into the blood stream of host chick embryos. Since these injected cells became scattered at random throughout the body of the host, it was possible to determine whether or not any "selectivity" governed the definitive locations of the pigment cells. The results demonstrated conclusively that donor melanoblasts proliferate profusely and synthesize melanin granules of the color and shape characteristic of their genotype, only in locations in the host identical to those in which they would normally have developed pigment in the donor individual. Never were they found in unusual cell and tissue associations.

Certain results obtained from grafting skin in fowl indicate that the invasion of melanoblasts is controlled by the skin and feather germs. When, for example, an area of skin, experimentally deprived of its normal source of pigment cells, is grafted at hatching to a chick host of similar age, melanoblasts from the surrounding regions of the host skin migrate freely into the graft and establish themselves permanently (Rawles, '44). Such an invasion of melanoblasts does not take place when an area

of normal skin containing its full complement of melanoblasts is grafted similarly (Danforth and Foster, '29). It would appear, then, that invasion does not take place if a state of equilibrium has already been attained between the tissues of the skin and the melanoblasts. This phenomenon has been interpreted by Willier ('48) to mean that a constant ratio has been established between the number of melanoblasts and the cells of the skin. The number of melanoblasts, according to this view, is limited not by a self-limitation of their capacity for multiplication, but rather by the cell community (skin). Such a constant ratio may be temporarily thrown off balance by an active regenerating feather papilla in which special conditions are set up favoring the invasion of some of the melanoblasts from the dermis or its specialized unit, the dermal papilla, into the epidermal region (collar) which gives rise to the feather parts. As this invasion of melanoblasts into the regenerating feather parts takes place, other melanoblasts of the dermal regions multiply to restore again the constant ratio. Thus a mechanism is provided for maintaining this constant relationship between the pigment cells and the feather cells throughout the life span of a bird (Willier, '52).

REGIONAL SPECIALIZATION OF THE SKIN

In the higher vertebrates the epidermis enters into a closer and more intimate relationship with the dermis or corium than in the lower vertebrates. The early smooth contour between the two, such as exists permanently in the lower forms, is lost owing principally to the formation of folds or papillae which project into the epidermis and alternate with similar downward projections from the epidermis. The extent of development of the papillae varies greatly in the different body regions. On the palms and soles they reach their greatest height.

Structural Differences. Studies on the development of the skin in the various types of vertebrates show that it is the ectodermal portion which undergoes characteristic structural modifications to fit it for the carrying out of special functions. Increase in epidermal surface is brought about by both evaginations and invaginations which develop in many different ways. Arising as external processes are the so-called epidermal appendages, scales, feathers, hairs, nails, and teeth; arising as invaginations are a variety of glands—mucous, cement, and poison glands of the lower vertebrates; sebaceous, sweat, and milk glands of the higher vertebrates.

A cursory examination of the hair coat of a mammal or the feathers of a bird reveals in various regions of the body—head, breast, back, tail, et cetera—a striking difference in the size, shape, and structure of the epidermal outgrowths. Even one single region, the head of a bird for example, may display various adaptive modifications of the contour feathers to form ornamental plumes, ear coverts, facial bristles, and eyelashes. Among feathers the variety of form is almost limitless, yet each is a modification of the same fundamental structure. Of interest also is the fact that one and the same hair or feather papilla of a particular region may produce a succession of hairs or feathers which display morphological and color differences pertaining to definite stages of the life history.

Not only are there marked regional differences in the epidermal outgrowths, but also variations in the skin proper. Quantitative histological studies of mammalian skin have demonstrated regional differences in growth of the epidermis (Loeb and Haven, '29). Straus's study ('50) of the microscopic anatomy of the skin from ten selected regions of a female gorilla reveals significant differences in structure at all of the various regions examined. The skin is thickest over the back and thinnest over the chest. The epidermis reaches its greatest thickness on the palms and soles, the corium its greatest thickness on the back. In general the total thickness of the skin is a reflection of the thickness of the corium. The above findings hold for mammals in general, including man.

Spectrophotometric analysis of living human skin (Edwards and Duntley, '39) has shown significant differences in the distribution of the pigments (melanin, hemoglobin, carotene) responsible for differences in the color of the skin in the various body regions. Oxyhemoglobin is especially abundant in regions of the skin where the arterial blood supply is rich and where for the most part the dermal papillae are high. Carotene is more abundant in regions where the stratum corneum is thickest. Female skin contains less hemoglobin and melanin but more carotene than male skin. Minor sex differences in distribution of the pigments also occur.

Functional Differences. Differences in structure in the various body regions may be correlated often with integumental differences in function, but there are also intrinsic physiological differences among cells which are revealed only by their method of response to certain stimuli such as hormones, vitamins, light, and temperature. In man, regional differences in photosensitivity of the skin are believed to be dependent to a great extent on variations in thickness of the horny cell layer and upon the development of the skin capillaries. The horny layer functions as a superficial filter absorbing some of the light waves before they reach the living layers of the epidermis. But it is known that the quantity of pigment, the age and sex of the individual, and the season of the year are important factors, also, in determining the regional and individual differences in skin photosensitivity (Ellinger, '41).

A striking demonstration of the existence of intrinsic, qualitative differences among cells of the skin of different body regions is afforded by amphibians at metamorphosis. Under the influence of thyroid hormone, the skin of the tail of a frog tadpole, for instance, responds by undergoing degenerative changes while the response of the adjoining skin of the trunk is one of proliferation. Histologically the two areas of skin response are sharply defined and show no transition. The specific response of these tissues is not altered by heterotopic transplantation (Lindeman, '29). The dependence of certain sexual plumage types upon gonadal hormones in fowl is equally striking. Extensive studies of morphological and color changes in the feathers of the Brown Leghorn have shown that regional differences in the threshold of response to female sex hormone and to thyroxin are dependent on local differences in the growth rate of cells of the individual feather germ (Lillie and Juhn, '32). In many animals melanin pigment is produced by melanophores in certain localized regions of the integument in response to male hormone stimulation. Among cases described are the bill of the sparrow (Keck, '34); the lores, roof and floor of the mouth of the night heron (Noble and Wurm, '40): the dorsolumbar spots of the hamster (Kupperman, '44); the scrotum of the 13-lined ground squirrel (Wells, '45); the sternal spot of the Australian opossum (Bollinger and Hardy, '45). In the human female excess melanin is deposited by melanophores in the skin of certain localized areas (eyelids, nipples, areolae, linea nigra) in response to increased amounts of estrogenic substances present in the body during pregnancy (Davis, Boynton, Ferguson, and Rothman, '45).

There is much evidence that male hormone affects the vascularization of certain localized areas of skin. The highly vascular comb of fowl has long been used as a trustworthy and measurable indicator of the presence of male hormone. The reddening of the sex skin in certain primates and the skin of the legs of the night heron are similar examples of the response of local cutaneous blood vessels to sex hormone stimulation. Hamilton ('48) emphasizes the important role of the sex hormones in regulating the vascularization of the human skin (complexion); and spectrophotometric analysis has shown that the pallor of the white eunuch is mainly the result of lack of hemoglobin in the cutaneous blood vessels.

Regional Differences of the Skin Established Early in Ontogeny. Very little is known about the time of origin of regional specificity in the skin ectoderm, and this point has not been systematically tested. In a series of studies on the development of the dorsal fin in Amblystoma embryos Bodenstein ('52) found some evidence of regional differentials in the response of the ectoderm of young tail-bud stages. If flank ectoderm, for example, is transplanted to the dorsal median region, no fin is produced; but if dorsal median ectoderm is transplanted to the flank, over the somites, a fin is produced. In the absence of more pertinent data, however, it can only be assumed that at some time during the latter part of embryogenesis regional specificity of the skin, which is clearly demonstrable in the early larvae, becomes established. Experiments with a wide variety of larval amphibians have demonstrated that skin from various regions of the body—tail, back, flank, limb buds—transplanted to different locations on the body of the same individual or of another individual of the same or of a different species, retains its individual characteristics. The transplant, moreover, metamorphoses in the manner typical of the region of the animal from which it came, even with regard to individual details of spotting pattern (Uhlenhuth, '17; Weigl, '13; Cole, '22; Reis, '30; and others). Recent experiments have shown that the specific central reflex relations of sensory nerve fibers entering heterotopically located grafts of cornea (Weiss, '42) and skin (Miner, '51) depend upon the sites of origin of the innervated tissues and not upon the origins of the sensory nerves themselves. Thus, in larval newts, tactile stimulation of cornea transplanted to the site of the ear or nasal organ will elicit the typical lid-closure reflex that is obtained by touching the cornea of a normal eye. The intrinsic capacity of the skin tissue for the differentiation of specific sensory nerve endings has been strikingly illustrated by exchanging areas of skin between the bill and leg of the duck (Dijkstra, '33). The skin of the duck's bill normally contains highly specialized sensory nerve endings, the corpuscles of Grandry and Herbst, found nowhere else on the body. When an area of bill skin is transplanted to the leg it becomes invaded by leg nerve fibers and the characteristic corpuscles appear. If leg skin is grafted to the bill, however, no such sensory endings develop, despite its innervation by normal bill nerves.

That the capacity of the skin to respond to hormones is acquired early is evidenced by the fact that skin from young amphibian larvae transplanted to much older larvae attains adult characteristics synchronously with the host, i.e., metamorphoses earlier than it normally would have done if left undisturbed (Uhlenhuth, '17; Weigl, '13); and metamorphic changes in local areas of larval anuran skin can be initiated much earlier than they would normally occur by implanting pellets containing thyroxin under the skin (Kollros and Kaltenbach, '52). During metamorphosis Woronzowa ('32) found that different regions of the skin of Amblystoma tadpoles clearly showed differences in their threshold of response to a given quantity of injected hypophyseal hormone.

In fowl the marked regional differences in the morphology and pigmentation pattern of the adult plumage are directly related to the order of origin of the feather papillae early in embryonic life. Holmes ('35) found that the feather papillae composing the individual plumage tracts arise in a definite time and space order. In a breast tract, for instance, the first longitudinal row of papillae arises parallel to the anteroposterior axis of the body at a position off-center in relation to the prospective tract as a whole, becoming the sixth row in mediolateral order when the tract is completed. After the formation of the papillae composing the primary row, other rows arise in sequence to the right and left of the first, and always definitely oriented with reference to it, until nine parallel rows are formed.

The relation of this definite time and

space order to asymmetry in the adult plumage of the Brown Leghorn has been clearly shown by Juhn and Fraps ('34a, b). These investigators found that the symmetry relations along transverse rows of feathers of the breast tracts follow an orderly distribution with respect to a secondary axis lying approximately at the sixth row, counting

when the characteristics of the humeral tract are becoming established has come from 180 degree rotation of small areas of ectoderm and underlying mesoderm of the dorsal surface of the wing buds of 3- to 4-day chick embryos (Saunders, '50). While the resulting wing plumage was normal in some cases, showing complete regulation of the area,

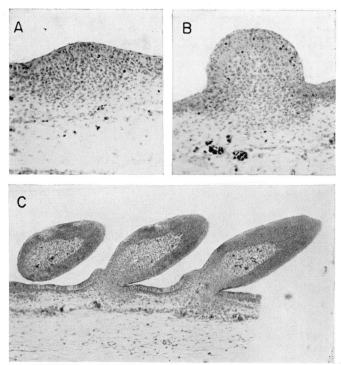

Fig. 193. Sections showing stages in development of down feather. Iron hematoxylin, 8μ. *A*, Early stage in feather formation, breast tract, 9-day embryo. Note aggregation of mesodermal cells (primordium of the dermal papilla) beneath two-layered ectoderm (epidermis). $\times$ 157. *B*, Later developmental stage from same feather tract. Note increased proliferation of mesodermal cells causing ectoderm to protrude beyond the skin level, forming the characteristic feather buds. $\times$ 157. *C*, Feather buds of breast tract of 11-day embryo. Note increase in length of feather bud and the thickening of ectoderm to form barb-ridges. $\times$ 75.

laterally from the mid-line of the bird. The increasing degree of asymmetry with reference to this secondary axis is in accord with observations that pigmentation patterns, normal or hormone-induced, limited to one vane-half of feathers of the breast tract show the relation of mirror images within each tract. Furthermore, the degree of asymmetry in such feather patterns increases as the lateral margins of the tract are approached. Thus the degree of asymmetry of the adult plumage is found to increase with distance from row number 6 (the first row to arise) and to correspond with the time of origin of the various rows of feather papillae composing the tract.

Some indication of the time in ontogeny

there were a sufficient number of cases in which abnormalities occurred in the distribution and orientation of the feathers to indicate that the tract characteristics of the rotated area were partially established.

Role of the Mesoderm in Epidermal Specialization. It would be of considerable interest to know whether the highly specialized epidermal outgrowths, feathers and hairs, arise in situ through some localizing factor in the ectoderm itself or whether they are produced by reaction with the underlying mesodermal tissue mass. In other words, are these specialized skin derivatives the products of embryonic induction? Experimental embryology has demonstrated that, in addition to the central nervous system, inner ear and lens, many other ectodermal organs, such as gills, balancers, fins, teeth, hypophysis, etc., are dependent upon influences exerted by other tissues for their differentiation. Inductive influences, as Weiss ('35) has pointed out, were originally thought of

strating embryonic induction are extirpation and transplantation. To a certain extent both have been applied towards testing the inductive faculties of the tissues comprising the feather germs. Before considering the experimental evidence, a few facts regarding

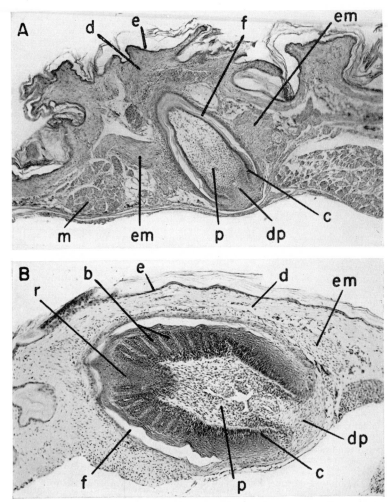

Fig. 194. Sections through the skin of saddle region of a normal Lakenvelder pullet, 3 weeks after hatching, showing the structure of the fully differentiated skin and definitive feathers developing in situ. Delafield's hematoxylin, 10μ. A, × 75; B, × 100. b, Cells of the barb system; c, collar (thick ring of embryonic feather-forming cells); d, dermis or corium; dp, dermal papilla of feather; e, epidermis; em, erector muscles of feather; f, follicle cavity; m, striated muscles; p, pulp of feather; r, rachis.

as being much more specific than they are considered to be at the present time. The term induction has now been extended to include a variety of "organizing" influences from unspecific activation to the very specific organization of typical patterns in space and time. Inductive phenomena are by no means physiologically uniform.

The Feather. The two classic methods that have been employed in general for demon-

the origin of feather germs should be recalled. The first indication of the site of a prospective feather is seen in the mesodermal portion of the dermis or corium, at approximately the fifth day of incubation, in the form of an aggregation or condensation of cells immediately beneath the thin, two-layered epidermis. This condensation is the primordium of the dermal papilla and precedes any visible epidermal response, as indicated by the lack of alteration in the epithelial cells. Rapid growth and proliferation of the dermal cells soon cause the overlying epidermis to protrude, forming the characteristic protuberances or feather germs comprising the various feather tracts (see Fig. 193*A*, *B*, *C*). Before hatching, each dermal papilla sinks beneath the surface of the skin in a tube-like follicle lined with epidermis. Later proliferation of the epidermal cells overlying the dermal papilla gives rise to the embryonic region from which the parts of the definitive feather arise. For information concerning the structure of the definitive or permanent types of feather and its relationship to the fully differentiated skin, see Figure 194*A* and *B*.

The effect of removing the ectoderm, from the upper surface of a 3-day wing bud, on the origin of feather germs of the chick has been tested by Saunders and Weiss ('50). In the absence of ectoderm the prospective dermis is found to be incapable of organizing either a typical corium or dermal papillae. A causal interaction of the inductor type between the ectoderm and subjacent mesoderm in feather germ formation is suggested by these experiments. Evidence of a more crucial nature has come from some recent transplantation experiments of Cairns ('51), in which he was able to induce feather germs in a region of the wing skin ectoderm which normally produces no feather germs by implanting mesoderm from the leg bud of 4-day embryos.

The most conclusive evidence that inductive principles are operative in feather development has come from the beautiful and systematically executed experiments of Lillie and Wang ('41, '44) and Wang ('43) on the papillae of regenerating feathers of the adult fowl. When a feather is shed naturally through the process of molting, or when it is plucked, the dermal papilla, covered by a thin layer of epidermal ("regeneration") cells, is left behind in the base of the tubular follicle. From this epidermal component is formed a thick ring of embryonic cells, the "collar" (Lillie and Juhn, '32), which gives rise to all of the epidermal parts of the regenerating feather. If the dermal papilla is removed, a feather is never formed from the epidermal cells of the follicle wall which grow over the site of extirpation.

The dermal papilla is, therefore, essential for a feather-forming epidermal response. By means of a variety of skillful transplantations, Lillie and Wang succeeded in demonstrating clearly that the mesodermal or dermal portion of the feather papilla functions as a feather "inductor" and determines the symmetry and orientation of the resulting feather. The specificity of epidermal response, i.e., the specific type of feather induced, whether breast or saddle, was found to be dependent upon the tract origin of the overlying epidermis. For example, a saddle feather papilla from which the epidermal cells have been entirely removed, transplanted into an "empty" breast feather follicle, induces a feather of the breast type from the epidermal cells of the breast follicle wall which grow over it, and vice versa. Breast or saddle papillae from which the epidermal cells have not been removed retain their specificity when transplanted into empty follicles of either tract.

The Hair. Hairs, like feathers, are highly keratinized epidermal outgrowths which arise also in a definite time-space sequence. The first series of primordia are uniformly spaced. As noted previously for feather primordia, so here, a second series arises to each side of the first and definitely oriented in relation to it, and so on in transverse rows until the number characteristic of the species is laid down. All of the hair papillae are formed during embryonic life or shortly after birth; hence the number and arrangement are the same in the adult as in the embryo. Growth of the connective tissue of the dermis later on, however, does tend to disrupt the earlier more orderly arrangement and to make the linear order somewhat more difficult to discern.

The first primordia to appear are those of the sensory hairs or vibrissae on the face around the nose and mouth. These arise very early in gestation, long before there is any indication of hair primordia elsewhere on the body surface. In their early developmental stages the sensory hairs differ in certain respects from the general body hairs. The future site of a sensory hair is foreshadowed by a sub-epidermal condensation of the mesodermal cells of the prospective corium, the primordium of the dermal papilla. This precedes any appreciable change in the overlying epithelium. Rapid proliferation of the mesodermal cells raises the epidermis, forming rows of papilla-like elevations easily observable in surface view (Fig. 195*A*). These elevations (Höckerchen) have been described by many of the early investigators for various mammals—cat, sheep, pig, rabbit. In sections they are strikingly similar to down feathers (cf. Figs. 193*A* and 195A). This initial stage is of short duration. Soon tongue-like thickenings of the basal cells of the epidermis grow downward into the underlying corium, forming the follicle with the dermal papilla situated in its base. Other hairs of the face, head, and trunk which arise later do not

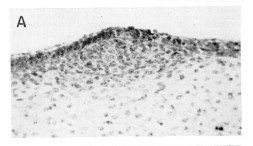

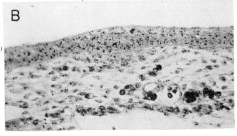

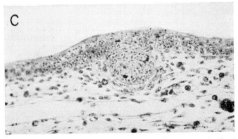

Fig. 195. Sections illustrating early stages in hair formation. Iron hematoxylin, 8μ. × 210. *A*, Beginning of a sensory hair (vibrissa), 22 mm. pig embryo, lower jaw. Note aggregation of mesodermal cells (primordium of dermal papilla) and elevation of two-layered, overlying ectoderm. *B*, Beginning of a body hair, 17-day mouse embryo. Note increase in ectodermal cells, to form the hair primordium, and aggregation of underlying mesodermal cells to form primordium of dermal papilla. *C*, Further down growth of ectodermal cells in the formation of the hair primordium. Same embryo as *B*.

show such pronounced surface elevations of the corium and overlying epidermis. (A striking exception is the European hedgehog, whose spines develop quite like the sensory hairs of other mammals; Davies, '89.) Each body hair begins as a minute epidermal nodule which forms by local proliferation of cells of the germinal or basal layer (Fig. 195*A*). Simultaneous with, or immediately follow-

ing, the initial changes in the epidermis, a condensation of cells in the underlying mesenchyme takes place to form the primordium of the dermal papilla. By continued growth downward of the epidermal tongue of cells (Fig. 195*C*), the follicle is established with the dermal papilla located in its base (Fig. 196*A* and *B*). The hair proper develops from epidermal cells covering the dermal papilla.

Although the ectodermal and mesodermal components of the hair papilla have not been submitted to experimental analysis comparable to that of the feather, the great similarities in the formation of hairs and feathers suggest strongly that the inductive mechanisms involved are similar in these two groups of skin derivatives. In fact, evidence in support of this view is forthcoming from Hardy's ('49) work on culturing mouse skin in vitro. She noted that no epidermal thickenings or "plugs" formed in the absence of mesoderm, and, furthermore, no dermal papillae could be found in areas from which the epidermis had been removed. Normal hair differentiation was obtained from cultures in which the epidermis and dermis were not separated. Such results suggest strongly that an interaction of ectoderm and subjacent mesoderm is necessary for initiating hair formation. It would seem, then, highly probable that hairs, like feathers, are products of embryonic induction.

Epidermal Ridges. Since the initiation of development of both feather and hair primordia appears to be dependent upon an interaction between the ectoderm and the subjacent mesoderm, one is prompted to consider the possibility of the existence of similar inductive relationships in the formation of other specializations of the epidermis, such, for example, as the epidermal ridge systems found on the under surface of the hands and feet. In all of the primates the skin of these regions is characteristically marked with fine, parallel ridges presenting a corrugated appearance. Hairs and sebaceous glands are absent, but sweat glands are abundant and large. The minute details of the ridges and the very definite patterns—loops, whorls, arches—formed by them on the tips of the digits and in consistent sites on the palms and soles show regional as well as individual variation. Even the skin of a small area will show ridge details not found elsewhere on the same or any other individual. This, together with the fact that the ridge pattern in all of its detail remains unchanged throughout life, is the basis for the use of epidermal ridge patterns (dermatoglyphics) in personal identification.

The development of the epidermal ridges is intimately associated with the development of the touch balls or volar pads. These embryonic structures are definitely localized swellings or bulges found on the terminal but in the deep germinal portion in contact with the mesoderm or corium, and is very likely a response to inductive stimuli from the mesoderm. The lower germinal layer begins to increase and form folds which grow downwards into the corium. Simul-

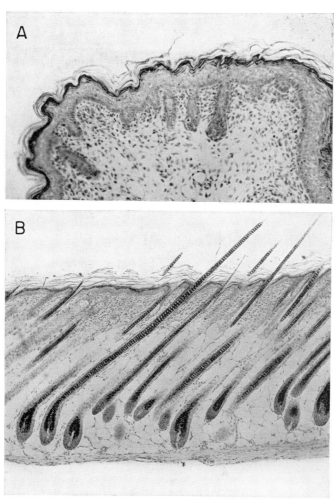

Fig. 196. *A*, Section through head skin of newborn black mouse (C57) showing various stages in the formation of hairs. Delafield's hematoxylin, 10μ. × 157. *B*, Section through dorsal skin of black mouse (C57), 7 days after birth. Note fully differentiated, emerged, pigmented hairs. Lightly stained with Delafield's hematoxylin, 10μ. × 75.

segments of the digits and on the palms and soles. In the human, the volar pads of the hand are evident early in fetal life (sixth week) when the hand is still paddle-like. They become quite prominent about the twelfth to thirteenth week. Soon afterwards they regress and become relatively inconspicuous.

Ridge formation begins when the volar pads are at their peak. The first indication is seen, not on the surface of the epidermis, taneously, the surface of the corium in contact with the epidermis develops elevations or folds (papillae) which project upwards into the epidermis and alternate with the similar downward projections from that layer. Later the outer surface of the epidermis, which has up until now remained smooth, becomes raised into ridges, one corresponding to each of those formed earlier on the lower surface.

Like feathers and hairs, the epidermal

ridges form in a definite time-space order. On the fingertips, the first regions to show ridge differentiation, folding of the epidermis begins in the central portion of the apical pad. Subsequently other foci arise in the distal, lateral, and proximal regions. From these foci, ridge differentiation progresses in orderly sequence until the systems meet and the final pattern configuration is established. Less frequently differentiation of the ridges into the definitive pattern is completed by extension from a single focal center on the apical pad (Bonnevie, '27, '29; Cummins and Midlo, '43). That there is some relationship between pattern type and the degree of elevation and the contour of the volar pad is generally agreed upon. By the nineteenth week the pattern is permanently established in the human fetus in all of its minute detail. Ridges broaden and lengthen to keep pace with the growth of the hands and feet, but no new formations occur (Hale, '49). In the absence of experimental evidence there is no actual proof that the epidermal ridge patterns are the products of embryonic induction, but the fact that the mesodermal substratum is necessary for the regeneration of normal ridge patterns would appear to strengthen this point of view.

Mesodermal Substrate Essential for Regeneration of Epidermis and Cornea. The importance of the mesodermal substrate in the regeneration of normal skin epithelium in the adult human has been nicely demonstrated by Bishop ('45). By removing skin from the forearm to various depths it was found that a portion of the papillary layer must remain to insure the regeneration of normal epidermis. Scar formation resulted when removal was sufficiently deep to include the reticular layer and the bases of the hair follicles.

It has also been pointed out by Cummins and Midlo ('43) that wounds, burns, etc., produce no permanent effect on the epidermal ridge patterns of the volar surfaces unless the injury is deep enough to destroy the dermal papillae, in which case scar tissue is then formed. Since the epidermis of the palms and palmar surface of the fingers reaches a thickness of about 0.8 mm., it follows that tissue damage to a depth of about 1 mm. would be necessary to prevent normal regeneration of the characteristic ridges of the fingers and palm. It is generally known that skin grafted from one region to another of the same individual retains its original characteristics. In this respect the ridged skin of the volar surfaces offers no exception. When it is considered that a skin graft normally includes the papillary layer of the dermis, the retention of specificity of the graft is readily understandable.

Further evidence of a necessary interaction between dermal and epithelial factors in regeneration is shown by the studies of Maumenee and Scholz ('48) on the mammalian cornea. Epithelial cells from the conjunctiva, which migrate over areas denuded of cornea, do not become transformed into typical corneal epithelium unless the underlying stroma is normal.

INTEGUMENTARY PATTERNS

Morphological Patterns. The origin of specific skin patterns, as exemplified by hair and feather direction and by the arrangement of epidermal ridges, presents many interesting developmental problems which are by no means fully understood. As pointed out by Wright ('49a), the formulation of principles of gene action in relation to morphological pattern is of the greatest importance in relating genetics to the physiology of development. While certain broad generalizations have long been apparent, there is a definite need for a systematic study of the action and interaction of genes in the formation of specific patterns.

It is well known that skin patterns are established in their permanent form early in ontogeny. The direction or slope of the hair, for instance, is recognizable immediately after the first indication of the hair primordia. Causal factors, therefore, must be looked for early in embryonic life. In order to identify such factors and to analyze their role in the origin, growth, and differentiation of the definitive pattern, direct experimental evidence is essential. Although numerous experiments have been done to analyze the factors concerned with hair direction in a variety of mammals, the majority have been carried out after the hair primordia were established and have given negative or inconclusive results. Some recent experiments of Kiil ('49) on newborn rats, at a time when the hair primordia are in the processes of development, appear to be the most decisive. By observing tattoo marks that penetrated the upper and lower layers of the skin of the tail and by excising pieces of skin from various regions including the ventral side of the neck where two natural whorls occur, data were obtained which indicate that the pattern of organization of the skin is primarily a phenomenon of differential growth within the layers of the skin itself, and that divergent whorls and rosettes are controlled from their centers by excess growth in the outer layer of skin. In lieu of experimental data, the study of the development of epidermal ridge patterns of anomalous hands and feet of human embryos has led Cummins ('26) to a similar explanation. In many respects hair arrangement is similar to dermatoglyphic configurations. Regions in which hairs slant uniformly in one direction are comparable to open fields of ridge pattern, while irregularities of hair direction localized at the points of juncture of several different hair slants correspond to triradii.

The genetic investigations of Wright ('49a, b; '50) on the guinea pig have contributed importantly towards an interpretation of the relation of genes to the development of pattern. By means of extensive breeding experiments he has shown that three genes, R, M, and St, exert major effects on hair direction in the guinea pig. A schema of the general physiological processes leading to local alterations in skin growth which are due to these genes and their interactions has been presented (Wright, '50, p. 59). Wright's studies of the genetics of normal and abnormal growth patterns of the guinea pig have led to the view that the specificity of gene action is always a chemical specificity—the production of enzymes which guide metabolic processes along particular channels. The development of any morphological pattern is, according to this view, a chain of reactions in which each gene reacts only in the presence of certain conditions, in part environmentally relative to the cell lineage in question, in part the result of the action of genes previously called into action (Wright, '34a, b).

Pigmentation Patterns. Experimental studies in recent years have contributed much towards an understanding of the numerous factors involved in the development of color patterns, especially those in which the important and widely distributed melanins or granular pigments are involved. As the investigations have broadened it has become more and more evident that the principles underlying pigmentary pattern formation are remarkably similar among the vertebrates in general. In analyzing the development of specific pigmentation patterns, attempt has been made to determine to what extent the migration, differentiation, and orientation of the melanin pigment-forming cells (melanophores) into distinctive pat-

terns are dependent on their intrinsic properties imparted to them by their genetic constitution, and to what extent upon extrinsic, environmental factors, i.e., the tissue substrates with which they become associated ultimately.

The Pigment Cell and Pattern Formation. Owing to the well-established fact that prospective pigment cells (melanoblasts) arise from a transitory embryonic structure, the neural crest, and reach the tissues with which they become associated later on through their migratory activities, it has been possible to employ a wide variety of appropriate transplantation, explantation, and deficiency experiments towards clarifying their role in pattern formation.

In fowl and other birds melanoblasts from individuals of varieties exhibiting a specific type of color and pattern have been introduced into feather primordia of individuals exhibiting an entirely different color and pattern. Such combinations have been accomplished by means of various grafting methods (see Rawles, '48). The large body of results obtained has been consistent in showing that melanophores retain their specific characteristics (shape and color of the pigment granules) and react with the foreign feather germs into which they have been introduced, to produce a typical donor color and pattern. In other words, the genetic constitution of the pigment cell governs the type of response which it manifests in a developing feather. Further proof that the color and pattern manifested in feathers is controlled by the particular assemblage of genes with which the pigment cell is endowed has come from grafting melanoblasts from male and female embryos of varieties of fowl showing sex-linked differences in plumage pattern, such as the Barred Plymouth Rock and F_1 hybrids from crosses between Rhode Island Red males and Barred Plymouth Rock females. Without exception, melanoblasts from prospective males reacted with foreign host feather germs to produce a male plumage pattern; those from prospective females, a female plumage pattern, regardless of the sex of the host (Willier and Rawles, '44a, b). With reference to the lack of any influence from the sex hormones of the host, it should be mentioned that among fowl, pigment cells show a differential sensitivity in their response to sex hormones. Melanoblasts of the Barred Plymouth Rock and the cross referred to above are representative of a type which may be classified as "insensitive," their phenotypic manifestation being independent of sex hormones. This is in contrast to melanoblasts of breeds like the Brown Leghorn which are "sensitive" to sex hormones and dependent upon them for expressing their phenotype (see Willier, '50).

In amphibians it has been possible, also, to introduce precursor pigment cells of species exhibiting one characteristic type of pigmentation pattern into individuals exhibiting a different type, by exchanging segments of neural folds (including the neural crest). Results agree in showing that the specific patterns of pigment cell distribution and orientation are dependent primarily upon intrinsic genetic differences in the pigment cells themselves (Twitty, '49).

Numerous histological studies of melanin granules deposited by melanophores in the epidermal cells of feathers and hairs have revealed that within any one genotype the size, shape, and color of the granules exhibit a remarkable specificity. In the numerous cases in which melanoblasts have been transplanted to foreign feather germs, they have always deposited in the feather cells granules characteristic of their own particular genotype.

Tissue Environment and Pattern Formation. While it has been clearly demonstrated in birds and amphibians that the genotypic constitution of the pigment cells is a controlling factor in phenotypic expression of color and pattern, it is equally clear that the surrounding tissues exert a definite influence on the realization of their potentialities. A number of workers with amphibians have shown the influence of the epidermis, somites, and neural tube upon the melanin-forming capacity and the orientation of these specialized cells into patterns (DuShane, '43; Twitty, '49; Dalton, '50).

Evidence of the influence of the tissue substrate on melanophore pattern formation is strikingly brought out by grafting neural crest between widely unrelated individuals such as anurans and urodeles (Baltzer, '41, '43; Leuenberger, '42). Under such conditions the orientation and the distribution of the grafted melanophores are quite definitely altered. The morphology of the individual melanophores, however, is not changed. They retain their specific characteristic size, color, type of branching, etc., and can be easily distinguished from those of the host. In general the results of neural crest exchanges among amphibians have shown that alterations in the normal pigmentation pattern produced by melanophores of a given genotype are progressively more pronounced as the donor and host become farther apart phylogenetically. This would appear to indicate that the arrangement of melanophores into a distinctive pattern is largely a particular kind of response drawn forth by a particular set of physiological conditions existing in their tissue substrates. Changes in one bring about changes in the other; in other words, there is interplay or interaction between intrinsic and extrinsic factors.

In fowl the position of the feather germ on the body—its tract location—determines the specific type of pigmentary response given by melanophores potentially capable of a range of responses, such as black and red or black and white barring, etc. This has been demonstrated convincingly by grafting such melanoblasts to feather germs of various regions of the body. The final pattern obtained is always typical of the region—wing, breast, saddle, etc.—showing that the locus of differentiation, i.e., the particular feather germ or portion of the feather germ in which the melanophore differentiates, determines which of its potencies is realized. It should be emphasized that there is no correlation between the locus of origin of the melanophores of any one genotype and their differential response to feather germs of various body regions. In fact, melanoblasts from the parietal lining of the coelom which would ordinarily never enter feathers will, upon being introduced into the epidermis of developing feathers of various regions, produce all of the intricacies of pattern characteristic of homologous feathers of their genotype (Rawles, '45). Experimental evidence indicates that, in their undifferentiated or melanoblast stages, pigment cells of any one genotype are all alike. This appears to be true, also, for some if not all of the amphibians (Stearner, '46).

The importance of the tissue environment, the feather papilla, in governing the color pattern response of melanophores of the Brown Leghorn to sex hormones has been fully demonstrated experimentally. It has been known for a long time that a variety of female colored, reddish bands, can be produced in the normally black breast feathers of a caponized Brown Leghorn by injecting a known quantity of female sex hormone at definite time intervals after plucking (Lillie and Juhn, '32). In the light of later information regarding the developmental potentialities of the pigment-forming cells, it would appear that in the breast papillae these cells respond to female sex hormone by depositing red melanin granules into the feather-forming epidermal cells. This particular response to estrogen does not occur in vitro, and does not occur in vivo until the epidermis of the feather germ has attained a certain developmental stage (Trinkaus, '48). Willier ('50) has interpreted the response of the estrogen-sensitive melanoblasts, in the zone of differentiation of the feather papilla, in terms of the physiological reaction gradients established by Lillie and Juhn ('32). Since feather papillae of the various tracts and even within the same tract show distinct differences in reaction gradients, the melanophore response as recorded in the finished feather pattern varies in a conformable manner. According to Willier, the feather papilla is to be regarded as an endocrine receptor endowed with special properties for responding to sex hormones. Differences in the responsiveness of the feather papilla appear to be genetically controlled. Danforth ('43) finds that a simple alteration in genotype, e.g., a mutational change of a single H gene in fowl, suffices to change the response of the feather germ from one of sensitivity to estrone and indifference to testosterone, to one in which the tissues respond equally to both, i.e., appear to be insensitive to the difference between these two hormones.

Reactions Between Pigment Cells in Pattern Formation. In the formation of melanin pigmentation patterns there is not only a constant reaction between melanophores and their tissue environments, but also reactions between the individual melanophores themselves. The importance of such reactions in the formation of rhythmic, barred patterns has been emphasized by Nickerson ('44) in his study of the Barred Plymouth Rock and the Silver Campine, two varieties of fowl with distinctly different types of black and white barring patterns. Having established that periodicity is intrinsic to the melanophore and, further, that melanophores of the white bands are able to produce pigment under suitable conditions, Nickerson concluded that the barring rhythm is controlled primarily through the medium of diffusible substances produced by the active melanophores within the black band which inhibit pigment formation by precursor melanophores in their immediate neighborhood (subjacent white band). As growth proceeds and the black band becomes removed from the zone of differentiation of the feather germ, this region will lie beyond the inhibiting influence and a new black band may now be formed. Certain properties of the

feather germ, such as growth rate, size of the barb ridges, etc., are necessarily involved.

It should be mentioned that, although Nickerson for good reasons favored the diffusion hypothesis, he did not lose sight of the theoretical possibility that, in the synthesis of melanin by the active melanophores, some substance essential for melanin production might be removed from the epidermal substratum of the developing barbs of the white region. In either case the barring rhythm would be associated with melanin production by certain groups of active melanophores.

To what extent the pigmentary patterns in the hair coat of mammals are influenced by interactions between pigment cells (melanophores) awaits investigation. For more than fifty years it has been known that the skin epithelium of a white area of a spotted guinea pig gradually becomes black when in contact with an area of black skin transplanted from another region of the same individual. Recently in an attempt to explain this well-known phenomenon Billingham and Medawar ('48, '50) have assumed the passage of a hypothetical, cytoplasmic "ingredient" from the contiguous black pigment cells into the supposedly "white" pigment cells of the skin epithelium of the white area. A "white" pigment cell so transformed in turn transforms other contiguous "white" cells. According to this conception the process of pigmentation proceeds in a manner formally equivalent to a virus infection. In the light of well-established facts regarding the migration of precursor pigment-forming cells in amphibians, birds and other mammals, further and more crucial evidence is imperative to substantiate this view of "infective" transformation of pigment cells.

In larval salamanders, the process of pigmentation appears to be profoundly affected by interactions between developing pigment cells. Certain experimental studies have shown that pigment cells which have an advantage in age or in rate of development are able to inhibit or suppress the differentiation of younger or less rapidly differentiating precursor pigment cells (Twitty, '49; Lehman, '50). In fact, Twitty, on the basis of his extensive experimentation with Triturus, is of the opinion that influences exerted mutually by the pigment cells are of primary importance in their migrations and their arrangement into specific pigmentary patterns.

CONCLUSION

From the foregoing it is evident that the skin of vertebrates is a complex organ composed of a variety of tissue elements and, like other organs and organ systems, progressively increases in diversity during ontogeny. Tissue interrelationships appear to play a vital role in its organization and differentiation. Within recent years information has been obtained concerning the temporal and spatial restriction of developmental potencies of the skin ectoderm and cellular reactions between it and the underlying mesodermal layer in bringing about regional specialization in the skin and its various derivatives. At the present time little is known about intrinsic, qualitative differences among integumentary cells that are revealed only by their particular methods of response to various types of stimuli, both internal and external. It is highly probable, however, that through continued and concerted experimental attack and the use of new and sensitive biophysical and biochemical methods it may yet be possible to obtain definite knowledge of the nature of these intrinsic qualities and thus increase our understanding of how they fit into the pattern of developmental organization of the skin and its diverse derivatives.

REFERENCES

Baltzer, F. 1941 Untersuchungen an Chimären von Urodelen und Hyla. Rev. suisse Zool., 48: 413–482.
———— 1943 Weitere Beobachtungen an Pigmentchimären von Amphibien. Archiv. Julius Klaus-Stiftung, 18:664–670.
Billingham, R. E., and Medawar, P. B. 1948 Pigment spread and cell heredity in guinea pigs' skin. Heredity, 2:29–47.
————, and Medawar, P. B. 1950 Pigment spread in mammalian skin: serial propagation and immunity reactions. Heredity, 4:141–164.
Bishop, G. H. 1945 Regeneration after experimental removal of skin in man. Amer. J. Anat., 76:153–181.
Bodenstein, D. 1952 Studies on the development of the dorsal fin in amphibians. J. Exp. Zool., 120: 213–245.
Bollinger, A., and Hardy, M. H. 1945 The sternal integument of Trichosurus vulpecula. J. & Proc. Roy. Soc. N. S. Wales, 78:122–133.
Bonnevie, K. 1927 Die ersten Entwicklungsstadien der Papillarmuster der menschlichen Fingerballen. Nyt. Mag. f. Naturv., 65:19–56.
———— 1929 Zur Mechanik der Papillarmusterbildung. I. Die Epidermis als formativer Faktor in der Entwicklung der Fingerbeeren und der Papillarmusterbildung. Roux' Arch. Entw.-mech., 117:384–420.

Borcea, M. I. 1909 Sur l'origine du coeur, des cellules vasculaires migratrices et des cellules pigmentaires chez les Téléostéens. Compt. Rend. Acad. Sci. Paris, 149:688–689.
Cairns, J. M. 1951 Induction of regional specificity in feather structure. Anat. Rec., 111:36–37.
Cole, W. H. 1922 The transplantation of skin in frog tadpoles, with special reference to the adjustment of grafts over eyes, and to the local specificity of integument. J. Exp. Zool., 35:353–419.
Cummins, H. 1926 Epidermal-ridge configurations in developmental defects, with particular reference to the ontogenetic factors which condition ridge direction. Amer. J. Anat., 38:89–151.
————, and Midlo, C. 1943 Finger Prints, Palms and Soles. The Blakiston Co., Philadelphia.
Dalton, H. C. 1950 Inhibition of chromatoblast migration as a factor in the development of genetic differences in pigmentation in white and black axolotls. J. Exp. Zool., 115:151–174.
Danforth, C. H. 1943 Gene H and testosterone in the fowl; in Essays in Biology, pp. 159–165. University of California Press, Berkeley, California.
————, and Foster, F. 1929 Skin transplantation as a means of studying genetic and endocrine factors in the fowl. J. Exp. Zool., 52:443–470.
Davies, H. R. 1889 Die Entwicklung der Feder und ihre Beziehungen zu anderen Integumentgebilden. Morph. Jahrb., 15:560–645.
Davis, M., Boynton, M., Ferguson, J., and Rothman, S. 1945 Studies on pigmentation of endocrine origin. J. Clin. Endocrinol., 5:138–146.
Detwiler, S. R. 1937a Substitution of lateral for axial mesoderm in relation to the development and segmentation of spinal ganglia. J. Exp. Zool., 76:35–45.
———— 1937b Observations upon the migration of neural crest cells, and upon the development of the spinal ganglia and vertebral arches in Amblystoma. Am. J. Anat., 61:63–94.
Dijkstra, C. 1933 Die De-und Regeneration der sensiblen Endkörperchen des Entenschnabels (Grandry- und Herbst-Körperchen) nach Durchschneidung des Nerven, nach Fortnahme der ganzen Haut und nach Transplantation des Hautstückchens. Zeit. f. mikro.-anat. Forsch., 34:75–158.
Dorris, F. 1938 The production of pigment in vitro by chick neural crest. Roux' Arch. Entw.-mech., 138:323–334.
———— 1939 The production of pigment by chick neural crest in grafts to the 3-day limb bud. J. Exp. Zool., 80:315–345.
DuShane, G. P. 1935 An experimental study of the origin of pigment cells in Amphibia. J. Exp. Zool., 72:1–31.
————1943 The embryology of vertebrate pigment cells. Part I. Amphibia. Quart. Rev. Biol., 18:109–127.
Eastlick, H. L. 1939 The point of origin of the melanophores in chick embryos as shown by means of limb bud transplants. J. Exp. Zool., 82: 131–157.
Edwards, E. A., and Duntley, S. Q. 1939 Pig-

ments and color of living human skin. Amer. J. Anat., 65:1–33.

Ellinger, F. 1941 The Biologic Fundamentals of Radiation Therapy. Elsevier Publishing Co., Inc., New York.

Engert, H. 1900 Die Entwicklung der ventralen Rumpfmuskulatur bei Vögeln. Morph. Jahrb., 29:169–186.

Hale, A. R. 1949 Breadth of epidermal ridges in the human fetus and its relation to the growth of the hand and foot. Anat. Rec., 105:763–776.

Hamburger, V. 1939 The development and innervation of transplanted limb primordia of chick embryos. J. Exp. Zool., 80:347–389.

Hamilton, J. B. 1948 Influence of the endocrine status upon pigmentation in man and in mammals. Spec. Pub. N. Y. Acad. Sci., 4:341–357.

Hardy, M. H. 1949 The development of mouse hair in vitro with some observations on pigmentation. J. Anat., 83:364–384.

Harrison, R. G. 1910 The outgrowth of the nerve fiber as a mode of protoplasmic movement. J. Exp. Zool., 9:787–848.

——— 1936 Relations of symmetry in the developing ear of Amblystoma punctatum. Proc. Nat. Acad. Sci., 22:238–247.

Hörstadius, S. 1950 The Neural Crest. Oxford University Press, Oxford, England.

———, and Sellman, S. 1946 Experimentelle Untersuchungen über die Determination des knorpeligen Kopfskelettes bei Urodelen. Nova Acta Reg. Soc. Sci. Upsaliensis, Series 4, No. 8, 13:1–170.

Holmes, A. 1935 The pattern and symmetry of adult plumage units in relation to the order and locus of origin of the embryonic feather papillae. Amer. J. Anat., 56:513–537.

Holtfreter, J. 1931 Über die Aufzucht isolierter Teile des Amphibienkeimes. II. Züchtung von Keimen und Keimteilen in Salzlösung. Roux' Arch. Entw.-mech., 124:404–466.

——— 1933a Die totale Exogastrulation, eine Selbstablösung des Ektoderms vom Entomesoderm. Entwicklung und funktionelles Verhalten nervenloser Organe. Roux' Arch. Entw.-mech., 129:669–693.

——— 1933b Organisierungsstufen nach regionaler Kombination von Entomesoderm mit Ektoderm. Biol. Zentralbl., 53:404–431.

——— 1935 Morphologische Beeinflussung von Urodelenektoderm bei xenoplastischer Transplantation. Roux' Arch. Entw.-mech., 133:367–419.

——— 1939 Gewebeaffinität, ein Mittel der embryonalen Formbildung. Arch. exp. Zellforsch., 23:169–209.

Juhn, M., and Fraps, R. M. 1934a Pattern analysis in plumage. I. Curve of barb growth. Proc. Soc. Exp. Biol. & Med., 31:1181–1183.

———, and Fraps., R. M. 1934b Pattern analysis in plumage. III. Action of thyroxin in high concentrations. Proc. Soc. Exp. Biol. & Med., 31:1185–1187.

Keck, W. N. 1934 The control of the secondary sex characters in the English sparrow, Passer domesticus (Linnaeus). J. Exp. Zool., 67:315–347.

Kiil, V. 1949 Experiments on the hair slope and hair pattern in rats. J. Exp. Zool., 110:397–439.

Kollros, J., and Kaltenbach, J. C. 1952 Local metamorphosis of larval skin in Rana pipiens. Physiol. Zool., 25:163–170.

Kupperman, H. S. 1944 Hormone control of a dimorphic pigmentation area in the golden hamster (Cricetus auratus). Anat. Rec., 88:26.

Lehman, H. E. 1950 The suppression of melanophore differentiation in salamander larvae following orthotopic exchanges of neural folds between species of Amblystoma and Triturus. J. Exp. Zool., 114:435–464.

Leuenberger, T. 1942 Das Verhalten der Farbzellen von Triton in Larven der Unke (Bombinator pachypus) bis zur Metamorphose. Rev. suisse Zool., 49:236–241.

Lillie, F. R., and Juhn, Mary 1932 The physiology of development of feathers. I. Growth-rate and pattern in the individual feather. Physiol. Zool., 5:124–184.

———, and Wang, H. 1941 Physiology of development of the feather. V. Experimental morphogenesis. Physiol. Zool., 14:103–133.

———, and Wang, H. 1944 Physiology of development of the feather. VII. An experimental study of induction. Physiol. Zool., 17:1–31.

Lindeman, V. F. 1929 Integumentary pigmentation in the frog, Rana pipiens, during metamorphosis, with especial reference to tail-skin histolysis. Physiol. Zool., 2:255–268.

Loeb, L., and Haven, F. L. 1929 Quantitative studies on the growth of the epidermis. Anat. Rec., 42:217–241.

Lopashov, G. V. 1944 Origin of pigment cells and visceral cartilage in teleosts. Compt. Rend. Acad. Sci. U.R.S.S., 44:169–172.

Luther, W. 1934 Untersuchungen über die Umkehrbarkeit der Polarität zwischen Aussen- und Innenseite des Ektoderms von Amphibienkeimen. Roux' Arch. Entw.-mech., 131:532–539.

Maumenee, A. E., and Scholz, R. O. 1948 III. The histopathology of the ocular lesions produced by the sulfur and nitrogen mustards. Johns Hopkins Hosp. Bull., 82:121–147.

Miner, N. 1951 Cutaneous localization following 180° rotation of skin grafts. Anat. Rec., 109:66–67.

Murray, P. D. F. 1928 Chorio-allantoic grafts of fragments of the two-day chick, with special reference to the development of the limbs, intestine and skin. Australian J. Exp. Biol. & Med. Sci., 5:237–256.

Newth, D. R. 1951 Experiments on the neural crest of the lamprey embryo. J. Exp. Biol., 28:247–260.

Nickerson, M. 1944 An experimental analysis of barred pattern formation in feathers. J. Exp. Zool., 95:361–397.

Niu, M. C. 1947 The axial organization of the neural crest, studied with particular reference to its pigmentary component. J. Exp. Zool., 105:79–113.

Noble, G., and Wurm, M. 1940 The effect of testosterone propionate on the black-crowned night heron. Endocrinology, 26:837–850.

Orton, G. L. 1953 Development and migration of pigment cells in some teleost fishes. J. Morph., 93:69–100.

Pasteels, J. 1937 Études sur la gastrulation des vertébrés méroblastiques. III. Oiseaux. Arch. de Biol., 48:381–488.

Raven, C. P. 1931 Zur Entwicklung der Ganglienleiste. I. Die Kinematik der Ganglienleistenentwicklung bei den Urodelen. Roux' Arch. Entw.-mech., 125:210–292.

———— 1936 Zur Entwicklung der Ganglienleiste. V. Über die Differenzierung des Rumpfganglienleistenmaterials. Roux' Arch. Entw.-mech., 134:122–146.

Rawles, Mary E. 1944 The migration of melanoblasts after hatching into pigment-free skin grafts of the common fowl. Physiol. Zool., 17:167–183.

———— 1945 Behavior of melanoblasts derived from the coelomic lining in interbreed grafts of wing skin. Physiol. Zool. 18:1–16.

———— 1947 Origin of pigment cells from the neural crest in the mouse embryo. Physiol. Zool., 20:248–266.

———— 1948 Origin of melanophores and their role in development of color patterns in vertebrates. Physiol. Rev., 28:383–408.

Reis, K. 1930 Untersuchungen über das Verhalten der Transplantate larvaler Amphibienhaut auf Larven und auf erwachsenen Amphibien, mit besonderer Berücksichtigung der Metamorphose. Roux' Arch. Entw.-mech., 122:494–545.

Ris, H. 1941 An experimental study on the origin of melanophores in birds. Physiol. Zool., 14:48–66.

Rosin, S. 1943 Experimente zur Entwicklungsphysiologie der Pigmentierung bei Amphibien. Rev. suisse Zool., 50:485–578.

Saunders, J. W. 1950 An analysis of the spatial distribution, tract specificity and orientation of feather germs in the humeral tract of the chick wing. Anat. Rec., 108:32–33.

————, and Weiss, P. 1950 Effects of removal on the origin and distribution of feather germs in the wing of the chick embryo. Anat. Rec., 108:93.

Stearner, S. P. 1946 Pigmentation studies in salamanders, with especial reference to the changes at metamorphosis. Physiol. Zool., 19:375–404.

Stone, L. S. 1933 The development of lateral-line sense organs in amphibians observed in living and vital-stained preparations. J. Comp. Neur., 57:507–540.

Straus, W. L., Jr. 1950 The microscopic anatomy of the skin of the gorilla; in The Anatomy of the Gorilla, edited by W. K. Gregory, pp. 213–226. Columbia University Press, New York.

————, and Rawles, Mary E. 1953 An experimental study of the origin of the trunk musculature and ribs in the chick. Am. J. Anat., 92:471–509.

Ströer, W. F. H. 1933 Experimentelle Untersuchungen über die Mundentwicklung bei den Urodelen. Roux' Arch. Entw.-mech., 130:131–186.

Trinkaus, J. P. 1948 Factors concerned in the response of melanoblasts to estrogen in the Brown Leghorn fowl. J. Exp. Zool., 109:135–170.

Tung, T. C., and Tung, Y. F. Y. 1940 Experimental studies on the determination of polarity of ciliary action of anuran embryos. Arch. de Biol., 51:203–218.

————, Tung, Y. F. Y., and Chang, C. Y. 1948 Studies on the induction of ciliary polarity in Amphibia. Proc. Zool. Soc. London, 118:1134–1179.

Twitty, V. C. 1928 Experimental studies on the ciliary action of amphibian embryos. J. Exp. Zool., 50:319–344.

———— 1945 The developmental analysis of specific pigment patterns. J. Exp. Zool., 100:141–178.

———— 1949 Developmental analysis of amphibian pigmentation. Growth Symp., 9:133–161.

Tyler, A. 1947 An auto-antibody concept of cell structure, growth and differentiation. Growth Symp., 6:7–19.

Uhlenhuth, E. 1917 A further contribution to the metamorphosis of amphibian organs. J. Exp. Zool., 24:237–301.

Vogt, W. 1925 Gestaltungsanalyse am Amphibienkeim mit örtlicher Vitalfärbung. I. Methodik. Roux' Arch. Entw.-mech., 106:542–610.

———— 1929 Gestaltungsanalyse am Amphibienkeim mit örtlicher Vitalfärbung. II. Gastrulation und Mesodermbildung bei Urodelen und Anuren. Roux' Arch. Entw.-mech., 120:384–706.

Wang, H. 1943 The morphogenetic functions of the epidermal and dermal components of the papilla in feather regeneration. Physiol. Zool., 16:325–350.

Weidenreich, F. 1912 Die Lokalization des Pigmentes und ihre Bedeutung in Ontogenie und Phylogenie der Wirbeltiere. Zeit. f. Morphol. u. Anthropol., Sonderhft., 2:59–140.

Weigl, R. 1913 Über homöoplastische und heteroplastische Hauttransplantationen bei Amphibien, mit besonderer Berücksichtigung der Metamorphose. Roux' Arch. Entw.-mech., 36:595–625.

Weiss, P. 1935 The so-called organizer and the problem of organization in amphibian development. Physiol. Rev., 15:639–674.

———— 1942 Lid-closure reflex from eyes transplanted to atypical locations in Triturus torosus. J. Comp. Neur., 77:131–169.

———— 1947 The problem of specificity in growth and development. Yale J. Biol. Med., 19:235–278.

————, and Andres, G. 1952 Experiments on the fate of embryonic cells (chick) disseminated by the vascular route. J. Exp. Zool., 121:449–487.

Wells, L. J. 1945 Pigmentation of the scrotum as a sensitive indicator for androgen. Anat. Rec., 91:43–44.

Willier, B. H. 1948 Hormonal regulation of feather pigmentation in the fowl. Spec. Pub. N. Y. Acad. Sci., 4:321–340.

———— 1950 Specializations in the response of pigment cells to sex hormones as exemplified in the fowl. Arch. Anat. micros. Morph. expér., 39:451–466.

Willier, B. H. 1952 Cells, feathers, and colors. Bios, *23:*109–125.

———, and Rawles, Mary E. 1940 The control of feather color pattern by melanophores grafted from one embryo to another of a different breed of fowl. Physiol. Zool., *13:*177–199.

———, and Rawles, Mary E. 1944a Genotypic control of feather color pattern as demonstrated by the effects of a sex-linked gene upon the melanophores. Genetics, *29:*309–330.

———, and Rawles, Mary E. 1944b Melanophore control of the sexual dimorphism of feather pigmentation pattern in the Barred Plymouth Rock fowl. Yale J. Biol. Med., *17:*319–340.

Woerdeman, M. W. 1925 Entwicklungsmechanische Untersuchungen über die Wimperbewegung des Ektoderms von Amphibienlarven. Roux' Arch. Entw.-mech., *106:*41–61.

Woronzowa, M. A. 1932 Analyse der weissen Fleckung bei Amblystomen. Biol. Zentralbl., *52:*676–684.

Wright, S. 1934a Physiological and evolutionary theories of dominance. Amer. Nat., *68:*24–53.

——— 1934b Genetics of abnormal growth in the guinea pig. Symp. Quant. Biol. Cold Spring Harbor, *2:*137–147.

——— 1949a On the genetics of hair direction in the guinea pig. I. Variations in the patterns found in combinations of the R and M loci. J. Exp. Zool., *112:*303–324.

——— 1949b On the genetics of hair direction in the guinea pig. II. Evidence for a new dominant gene, Star, and tests for linkage with eleven other loci. J. Exp. Zool., *112:*325–340.

——— 1950 On the genetics of hair direction in the guinea pig. III. Interactions between the processes due to the loci R and St. J. Exp. Zool., *113:*33–63.

ENERGY EXCHANGE AND ENZYME DEVELOPMENT DURING EMBRYOGENESIS*

E. J. BOELL

INTRODUCTION: ENERGY REQUIREMENTS OF THE EMBRYO

ENERGY is required by the developing organism to sustain four major groups of processes: *maintenance, growth, differentiation,* and *specific functional activities*. Maintenance processes continue throughout life, but, to a certain extent, the others occur in sequence during development. Normally, they are not completely independent of each other, and, although they can to some extent be separated conceptually,† they are not easily dissociable even by experimental means (Needham, '42).

Maintenance metabolism may be defined as the sum total of energy-yielding or energy-requiring processes concerned with the preservation of the living system as an organized entity in its environment. It is at the bottom of the steady state equilibria through which, at least in part, integrity of the organism is preserved; it operates in processes of so-called "active transport," and it is essential for replacement of parts of the living machinery that have been subject to metabolic wear and tear through what Pollister ('54) has termed "maintenance protein synthesis." For the embryo, as for all living beings, maintenance metabolism represents the basic cost of living. During development, maintenance metabolism

* This paper was completed during the tenure of a Fulbright Award for research at the Carlsberg Laboratories in Copenhagen. The author wishes to express his gratitude to Dr. Heinz Holter, Chairman of the Division of Cytochemistry, and to Dr. Søren Løvtrup for their critical reading of parts of the manuscript.

† One of the major limitations in conceptual separation of the fundamental processes in ontogeny is that the embryo's response to a given set of experimental conditions is usually the same no matter whether the investigator is thinking more about maintenance than growth and differentiation at the time, or vice versa.

would be expected to increase, not because maintenance becomes progressively more difficult as the embryo increases in organizational complexity, but simply because there is more embryo to be maintained.

Growth can best be defined in terms of protein synthesis.‡ It is obvious that such

‡ Although the concept of embryonic growth has been under consideration for a long time, there is still no measure of its magnitude that is completely adequate or free from objection. If growth is defined as increase in mass, it is apparent that the process may be independent of synthesis of new materials and may simply involve increase in size by imbibition or deposition of inorganic materials. To measure growth in terms of increase in solids, that is, as dry weight, is satisfactory in the case of embryos whose cells do not contain appreciable quantities of the raw materials for development, but it is completely inapplicable to highly lecithal eggs. In the eggs of amphibians, for example, dry weight decreases during development as yolk is consumed. The use of protein nitrogen as a measure of growth has the same limited applicability. Increase in number of cells or of nuclei may be used to assess growth in certain instances, but in a number of embryos cell number increases while the size of the organism remains essentially unchanged. The use of DNA, suggested by Berenblum, Chain, and Heatley ('39) and recently emphasized by Davidson and Leslie ('50) may be an adequate measure of growth within certain limits. It is clear the DNA content of the individual cells of a given species is constant (Boivin, Vendrely, and Vendrely, '48; Vendrely and Vendrely, '49; Mirsky and Ris, '49). Accordingly, increase in DNA should presumably indicate relative increase in cell number. But it is also equally clear that the karyoplasmic ratio is not constant—at least, not in early development. Therefore, DNA content, while in some cases giving an indication of the relative changes in numbers of nuclei, is not an effective measure of cytoplasmic mass. Furthermore, it may be noted that the use of DNA as a nuclear measure may be questioned. Hoff-Jørgensen and Zeuthen ('52) have reported that the frog egg contains a store of DNA enough for several thousands of new nuclei, and Lindahl ('53) has demonstrated recently that micromeres

an arbitrary definition has certain shortcomings, one of the most important being that a great deal of what is commonly regarded as differentiation is also embraced by it. However, this may be just as well, for, in normal development, growth and differentiation usually proceed apace. Little is known directly about the energetics of protein synthesis in the embryo. The recent studies on the incorporation of labeled amino acids into the microsomes of tissue homogenates and the association of this process with oxidative phosphorylation, through synergistic action between microsomes and mitochondria, are, therefore, of fundamental importance to embryologists (see Pollister, '54, for a review of the literature). Energy is required for peptide bond synthesis, and it may reasonably be expected that embryonic growth, involving as it does the synthesis of protein, will require energy expenditure on the part of the embryo.

Differentiation involves the progressive specialization of cells both structurally and functionally. Its visible manifestations are the form changes associated with cyto- and histogenesis, but, in addition to these important macroscopic or microscopic changes, there are events of equal significance at a molecular or macromolecular level of organization (Porter, '54). The chemical changes in the ontogeny of mitochondria or the elaboration of specific chemical substances, for example Nissl substance, actomyosin, or phosphatase, represent differentiation just as surely as do changes in cell shape or the development of pigment or secretion granules. This may appear obvious, but it is mentioned to emphasize the fact that differentiation involves synthesis of specific materials, as does growth, and such syntheses require energy.

Much confusion and controversy have attended consideration of the energetics of differentiation (Needham, '31, '42; Tyler, '42; Brachet, '50). One of the reasons for this state of affairs stems from a number of overly enthusiastic attempts to assess the cost of differentiation in precise quantitative terms from the results of experiments which

were not designed to yield such information. Another difficulty arises from confusing what may legitimately be considered as energy for differentiation, i.e., energy for the synthesis of specialized materials, with the so-called "Organizational Energy," or OE, of Needham's ('31) terminology. OE refers to a hypothetical quota of energy which is intimately tied up with the organization of the embryo and which should be released as a measurable quantity when the embryo is *disorganized* by cytolysis. If OE really exists, it follows that the energy expenditure during development, as measured directly by heat production, should be significantly less than that calculated from data on respiratory exchange and the foodstuffs consumed during development. Comparison of the results of direct and indirect calorimetry has failed to reveal such a quota of energy (Bohr and Hasselbalch, '03), as have attempts to determine calorimetrically the evolution of heat during cytolysis (Needham, '31). A later study of the bee moth, *Galleria mellonella* (Crescitelli, '35; Taylor and Crescitelli, '37), indicates that energy expenditure during pupation is higher when measured indirectly from respiratory data than when determined calorimetrically. But definite conclusions from these observations cannot be drawn in the absence of chemical data on the sources of energy used during pupation. Smith's ('46, '52) investigations of energetics during the development of the rainbow trout show conclusively that loss in total fuel value of the embryo plus yolk is exactly equivalent to the heat produced.

Failure to find a definite quantity of energy that could be ascribed to OE has been interpreted by some as indicating that differentiation occurs without cost, but such a conclusion is as unwarranted as is the view that differentiation processes require a large proportion of the embryo's total energy expenditure. Butler ('46) has commented on this as follows: "If an organism can synthesize peptide bonds, it appears that it will have no great difficulty putting together protein molecules of any degree of complication. The free energy must come from the metabolic processes going on in the organism. The complete oxidation of a glucose molecule to carbon dioxide and liquid water yields approximately 700,000 cal. of free energy per mol. This is of the order of magnitude sufficient for the building up into proteins of about a hundred amino-acid residues. Thus there is no outstanding difficulty in accounting for the synthesis of living

---

in the sea urchin egg are haploid. RNA, since it is so intimately linked with protein synthesis (Caspersson, '47; Brachet, '47) has also been suggested, particularly as a measure of cytoplasmic growth. Here too, difficulties are encountered, for not all of the RNA is located in the cytoplasm. Moreover, Herrman and Nicholas ('49) and Flexner and Flexner ('51) have reported lack of correlation between RNA content and cell volume.

structures with a fairly modest expenditure of food."

Activity metabolism refers to the energy required to sustain the specific activities of embryonic structures whose functional capacities have been realized. Most organs do not become functional as soon as they appear in the embryo. Nevertheless, when function does commence, the energy expenditure of the organ increases. As an example, the heart may be mentioned. The respiratory rate (mμl. oxygen consumed per μg. per hour) of the beating rat heart, at the earliest stage that it can be removed from the embryo, is 40; it is only 6 for the heart at rest (Boell and Nicholas, unpublished). The difference in metabolic rate in this instance clearly represents the energy used for muscular contraction. It is of interest to note that total oxygen consumption of an embryo from which the heart has been removed is indistinguishable from that of an embryo with its heart *in situ*. This means simply that the heart is so small in relation to the total embryo that its absence produces no noticeable effect on total metabolism.

Another example of activity metabolism is seen in the development of the grasshopper. The smooth course of respiratory increase, which characterizes postdiapause development, is punctuated, between the third and fifth days, by a significant decline in respiratory rate. "At precisely this time the lateral walls of the embryo beat more slowly than they do immediately before or afterward; moreover, blastokinesis (revolution of the embryo around the yolk) has just been completed on the third day. Since Slifer ('32) showed that blastokinesis 'is accomplished by vigorous movements on the part of the embryo itself' the decreased respiration may be attributed to lessened embryonic activity" (Boell, '35).*

It may be concluded that the processes associated with development—maintenance, growth, differentiation, and functional activity—require energy. In the long run, these energy requirements are met through oxidative processes. The embryo is not required to pay a premium for the large synthetic job

* Tuft ('53) apparently has misunderstood this description, for, in referring to the experimental observation in support of his contention that "phases (of development) during which the cells of the embryo spread over the yolky parts of the egg are accompanied by a decrease in O_2 uptake," he states that "a similar phenomenon seems to occur at the same stage in the eggs of *Melanoplus differentialis* (Boell, '35), but this author attributes it to a temporary decrease in the frequency of the heart beat."

it has to do other than that necessitated by its own inefficiency as an energy transformer, but this is a characteristic shared by all living organisms. Neither is the embryo exempt from the construction cost of protein synthesis. "Developmental phenomena," as Weiss ('53) has recently pointed out, "do not violate the laws of thermodynamics . . . the old problem of 'energy of shape' is still with us, presumably because of the fact that the energy requirements in growth and differentiation may be greatly overshadowed by the energy requirements for the continuous anabolic renewal of the protoplasmic system. . . ."

ENERGY RELEASE DURING PERIODS OF REDUCED OXYGEN SUPPLY OR ANAEROBIOSIS

The eggs and embryos of most species will develop continuously and normally only in the presence of oxygen, but no very close correlation exists between the oxygen tension of the environment and that required to sustain normal development. The sea urchin egg will respire and develop normally under oxygen tensions as low as 40 mm. Hg (Amberson, '28); normal development and respiration in the grasshopper egg are possible in a gas mixture containing 10 per cent of oxygen (Bodine and Boell, '34a), and even an egg as large as that of the frog can withstand some variation in oxygen tension without developmental retardation (Parnas and Krasinka, '21). On the other hand, numerous investigators have shown that respiration of the mammalian embryo in vitro requires an atmosphere of pure oxygen, and Philips ('41) has suggested that the normal oxygen tension in air may not be sufficient to sustain an optimal level of respiration in the chick embryo during the period before circulation commences.

Oxygen supply seems to be indispensable for continued development, but most embryos can safely withstand the effects of oxygen lack or reduced respiration for some time. But the embryos of different species vary considerably with respect to resistance to anoxia, and, by implication, with respect to their ability to derive energy from anaerobic reactions or to accumulate an oxygen debt. In the sea urchin, *Arbacia punctulata*, the activation of the egg and the initial cortical changes associated with the process can occur in the complete absence of oxygen (Kitching and Moser, '40), but cell division is immediately blocked as soon as oxygen is withdrawn. Indeed, Amberson ('28) has shown that cleavage is retarded when the oxygen tension falls to 11 mm. Hg, and below 4 mm. mitotic activity is completely blocked. Hultin ('53) has concluded that oxygen is necessary from the beginning to assure development in the sea urchin.

Ascaris eggs are likewise very dependent upon oxygen supply in order to cleave (Brachet, '50, p. 165). It is of interest, therefore, that mitosis continues in Ascaris eggs after centrifugation at 400,000 ×g (Beams and King, '36) although this treatment reduces the rate of oxygen consumption to 25 per cent of normal (Huff and Boell, '36).

The eggs of Fundulus, on the other hand, are remarkably resistant to complete removal of oxygen. Loeb (1895) maintained Fundulus eggs under vacuum for four days and noted that cleavage could occur. In the presence of cyanide, which exerts a strong depressing effect on respiration, development appears to proceed qualitatively normally but at a slower rate than in controls. By contrast, the mitotic process is blocked by cyanide in the eggs of the mackerel, cunner, and scup (Philips, '40).

Frog eggs have been shown to develop through the cleavage stages in the absence of oxygen and in the presence of cyanide when respiration is only 10 per cent of normal (Brachet, '34; Barnes, '44; Spiegelman and Moog, '45). Brachet believes that energy is supplied, during short periods of anaerobiosis, through the utilization of an oxidative reserve, typified by but not necessarily identical with glutathione, rather than through processes leading to the formation of lactic acid. During recovery from anaerobiosis, the respiratory quotient of frog eggs is not unity, as one would expect if accumulated lactic acid were being burned, but ranges between 0.27 and 0.52. During longer periods of anaerobiosis lactic acid is produced, however (Lennerstrand, '33; Brachet, '34; Barth, '46).

That avian and mammalian embryos can derive energy through anaerobic processes is a well established fact (Needham, '31, '42). However, most of the studies on these embryos have been concerned with the analysis of glycolytic mechanisms (see p. 541 ff.) rather than with the ability of the embryo to survive under conditions of reduced oxygen supply. A comparative study of the rate of anaerobic glycolysis and respiration in presomite and early somite rat embryos has revealed the interesting fact that the embryo can derive more energy from anaerobic

breakdown of glucose than from oxidation (Boell and Nicholas, unpublished). This may have considerable significance for the embryo, for a condition of "Everest in utero" probably exists during the period before placentation as well as at birth.

Examples could be multiplied, but those enumerated show that many embryos have the ability to derive energy, and in some cases to develop, under conditions where oxygen is lacking. Survival, during the exigencies of anaerobiosis, seems to be associated with the ability of the embryo to contract an oxygen debt. Sooner or later, however, this must be redeemed aerobically. For the vast majority of embryos, development depends upon an adequate oxygen supply and release of energy through respiratory processes.

RESPIRATION

Oxygen Consumption During Development. With minor variations, the curve shown in

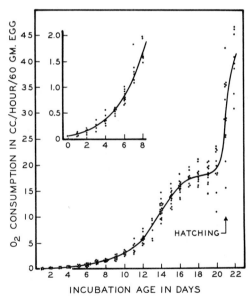

Fig. 197. Oxygen consumption during development of the chick (from Romanoff, '41).

Figure 197 describes the course of respiration during development of a wide variety of animals, both invertebrate and vertebrate. The chief characteristics of the curve are an initial period in which there is a constant percentage increase in oxygen consumption during equal intervals of time, then a period in which the rate of increase gradually lessens, and finally one, near the end of development or of a particular phase of development, in which respiration increases only slightly, if at all.

In the sea urchin, the course of respiratory increase during development can best be represented, as shown in Figure 198, by two

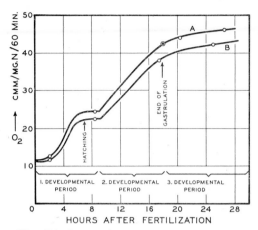

Fig. 198. Course of oxygen consumption during development of the sea urchin. Curves *A* and *B* were obtained from two different lots of eggs. (After Lindahl, '39.)

connecting curves (Lindahl, '39; Borei, '48). The sigmoid part of the curve represents respiration of the embryo from fertilization to the hatching of the blastula; the ascending limb of the second curve coincides with gastrulation, and the terminal portion covers the period in which differentiation is the predominant developmental event.

Metabolic Rate. It may be asked whether the curves shown in Figures 197 and 198 indicate that the rate of metabolism per unit of embryonic material is constantly increasing during development. This is not an easy question to answer owing to the difficulties involved in determining accurately the actual amount of metabolically active embryonic material as distinct from the non-metabolizing components in the developing system (see footnote ‡ on p. 520). However, in some cases, it is possible to separate the embryo from its yolk supply pretty completely, and the study of respiratory rate in these embryos provides a negative answer to the question raised above. This is illustrated in Figure 199, representing a composite graph of data from various sources on the metabolic rate (oxygen consumed per milligram dry weight per hour) of the chick embryo. The points for the first six days of development represent in vitro measurements on the isolated embryo; the terminal points

were taken from Romanoff's ('41) study of the respiration of the intact hen's egg during incubation and have been corrected for the respiratory activity of the extraembryonic membranes through the use of percentage figures from Needham ('32a).

The graph shows that metabolic rate is essentially constant, at an average of 10.1 (range 7.9 to 12.3) between 16 and 288 hours of development. It should not be concluded that Q_{O_2} remains at this level during the remainder of the period to hatching, for Romanoff has shown that it declines to 8 on the thirteenth day of development, and by the nineteenth day it is only slightly more than 5. The decline in respiratory rate undoubtedly reflects the fact that such metabolically sluggish components as feathers, cartilage, and connective tissue now make up an appreciable portion of the total embryonic mass. But from the twelfth day of development, the decline is also brought about in part by a decrease in the respiratory activity of a number of tissues, particularly muscle and liver (Romanoff, '43). Slow decline of basal metabolism during the life span of the individual seems to be the general rule (Needham, '31, '42), but the process may not begin as early in embryonic life as was previously thought.

The chief factor responsible for the increase in rate of oxygen utilization during the first 16 hours may be regarded as the opposite of that which later contributes to its decline. Philips ('42), who has made the most complete study of the metabolism of

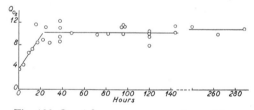

Fig. 199. Q_{O_2} (μl. oxygen per mg. dry weight per hour) of chick embryo. Values for first 144 hours represent measurements of respiration of chick embryos in vitro by Philips ('41, '42), Romanoff ('41, '43), Needham and Nowinski ('37), Dickens and Greville ('33b), Dickens and Simer ('30, '31), and Warburg, Posener, and Negelein ('24). Final three points represent respiratory rate of chick embryos in vivo from Romanoff ('41).

the very young chick embryo, has suggested that the early increase in rate of respiration is correlated with the conversion of intracellular yolk materials into active cellular constituents.

Essential constancy of respiratory rate,

during a substantial part of embryonic life, may be seen in a number of other cases. This was clearly shown by Gray ('26) for the trout embryo, and more recently Hayes, Wilmot, and Livingstone ('51) reported that the respiratory rate of the Atlantic salmon embryo remains unchanged throughout the entire period during which weight data could be obtained. The actively developing grasshopper embryo, which at certain stages can be completely separated from yolk, also has a constant respiratory rate over a considerable period of development (Bodine and Boell, '36a, '37). Of course, during diapause respiratory rate falls, but this special situation will be discussed later. In the rat embryo, the Qo_2 is approximately 30 during the cleavage stages, but it soon falls to a value of about 12 (Boell and Nicholas, '48) which is maintained until around the fifteenth day of development (Dickens and Greville, '33a; Negelein, '25).

Respiratory Increase and Growth. It seems in those cases in which the yolk content of the embryo is relatively small, or where the yolky parts of the egg can be successfully separated from the embryonic materials, the respiratory rate of the embryo is uniform throughout a major part of the total period of development. In other words, as pointed out by Gray ('27), the total respiratory exchange at a given stage of development is proportional to the amount of metabolically active embryonic material. It is, therefore, perhaps more than mere coincidence that respiratory data during development should follow a sigmoid curve (Gray, '29a, b; Brody, '45; Thompson, '42).

During its early phases, growth appears to be an exponential process—that is, approximately the same percentage increase occurs during successive equal intervals of time. The equation $x = a.e^{kt}$ has been found empirically to fit growth data in a great many cases, and a plot of the logarithm of the magnitude of the growing entity against time thus yields a straight line.* When

* It is not intended to attach any strict biological significance to the values of a or k in the equation $x = a.e^{kt}$. The semilogarithmic plots of growth and respiratory data are intended as purely descriptive; the chief justification for their use lies in the fact that a convenient method is thereby provided for comparing and contrasting curves. In arithmetic plots, the similarities and differences between such curves are not always readily apparent. The reader is referred to Sholl's ('54) paper in which is contained a thoughtful analysis of the utility and limitations of empirical curve fitting (see also Levy, '52).

growth rate changes abruptly during development, a series of intersecting straight lines will result. If respiratory increase parallels growth of metabolically active embryonic mass, and the evidence reviewed above strongly suggests such a relationship, the data shown in Figure 197 should yield a linear curve when log respiration is plotted against time (Fig. 200). The points do not

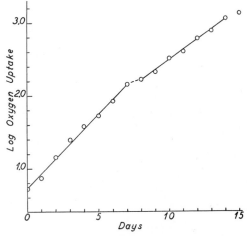

Fig. 200. Semilogarithmic plot of oxygen consumption during development of the chick (data from Table 1 of Romanoff, '41).

fall on a single straight line, however, for between the seventh and eighth days of development an inflection appears, and from then on respiratory increase proceeds at a lower rate than earlier. A similar inflection in the semilogarithmic plots of dry weight or wet weight also occurs on the eighth day. What is responsible for the inflection in the respiratory curve is not known. It is interesting to point out that it occurs at about the time that the embryo shifts from predominantly carbohydrate catabolism to protein (see p. 533), and that the rate of protein absorption for growth is minimal on the eighth day (Needham, '31, Table 111, column 13). Novikoff and Potter ('48) have obtained data on increase in PNA and DNA in the chick embryo, and similar results have been described by Reddy, Lombardo, and Cerecedo ('52). A semilogarithmic plot of Novikoff and Potter's PNA figures yields a pair of intersecting curves almost identical in slope with those for respiration, and with a break on the eighth day. Thus a number of lines of evidence suggest that the period around the eighth day of development is one of transition in the chemical growth of the chick embryo.

It will be noted that the points for the second, third, and fourth days deviate from the straight line drawn in Figure 200. These may represent biologically significant variations since they are all in the same direction, but it may be remarked that Romanoff has shown that the deviations coincide with periods of high variability among embryos

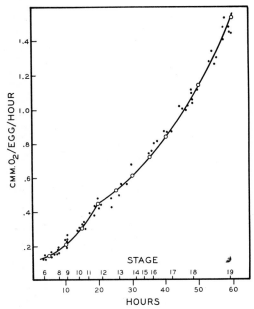

Fig. 201. Oxygen consumption during development of *Rana pipiens*. Small points represent experimental determinations. Large circles represent calculated values from equations $x = 0.095e^{0.077t}$ and $x = 0.45e^{0.031t}$. (From Moog, '44a.)

due to differences in morphological age or mortality during early development.

Respiration of Amphibian Embryos. Typical data for the respiratory exchange of the developing frog embryo are shown in Figure 201 (Moog, '44a). Similar curves have been obtained for a large number of amphibian species, both urodeles and anurans, and in all cases where careful attention has been paid to assure normal development and to avoid injury to the embryos during respiratory measurements, the curves are qualitatively identical to that shown in Figure 201. It has been claimed that respiratory increase does not occur during cleavage in the amphibian embryo, but this may be due to the use of insufficiently sensitive techniques for measuring the very low rates of gaseous exchange in early stages.

As first indicated by Atlas ('38) and subsequently confirmed by Moog ('44a) and a number of others (Barnes, '44; Spiegelman

and Steinbach, '45; Boell, '45; Barth, '46; Ten Cate, '53), respiratory data for the amphibian embryo can be closely approximated by the equation $x = a.e^{kt}$, providing the value of k is changed at an appropriate point in development. On a semilogarithmic plot a *break* in the curve thus appears similar to that in Figure 200. In addition to the papers already cited, semilogarithmic plots of the results obtained by Bialascewicz and Bledovski ('15), Wills ('36), Fischer and Hartwig ('38), and Hopkins and Handford ('43) reveal that the break in the course of respiratory increase is a regularly occurring phenomenon in amphibian development. There are a few exceptions, but in most anurans the break is found approximately at gastrulation; in most urodeles it seems to occur during the tail-bud stages—in *Amblystoma punctatum* at Harrison's stage 32 to 34. The cause of the break is unknown and it is difficult to assess its developmental significance, especially since it does not appear at the same developmental stage in the embryos of different species. There is some indication that it may be correlated with the development of "total respiratory surface" (Moog, '44a; Boell, '45, '48). If this be the case one might expect that the break would occur somewhat later in embryos reared at low temperatures because of the increased solubility of oxygen and decreased respiration of the embryo. A comparison of the work of Atlas, Barth, and Moog, on *Rana pipiens*, shows that this may be the case.* However, Ten Cate ('53) has followed the respiration of a number of different amphibians over a temperature range from 8 to 26°, and there seems to be no systematic variation in the position of the break with temperature. Unfortunately, some of Ten Cate's experimental points show such wide scatter that it is difficult to distinguish so-called breaks from aberrations due probably to technical errors or abnormal development.

It seems reasonable to suggest that the chief reason for the increase in respiratory rate in the amphibian embryo is the same as in the fish, chick or mammal, and this appears to be that the oxygen consumed at

---

* In experiments conducted at the Carlsberg Laboratory, I have found that a break in the respiratory curve occurs at stage 16 in *Xenopus laevis*. Before and after the break the respiratory curves are perfectly linear when plotted semilogarithmically against time. These experiments were done at 15° on individual embryos, and the same embryos were used throughout the entire period of development.

a particular stage of development is related to the amount of embryonic material.* Such a view is consonant with results of respiratory measurements on gastrula explants (Barth, '42; Boell, '42) in which it appears that oxygen uptake is inversely related to yolk content. It is well known that yolk, separated from the protoplasmic matrix in which it is held, has a negligible oxygen consumption. Synthesis of more embryonic material at the expense of the raw materials stored in the egg would thus be expected to result in increased oxygen consumption.

Unfortunately, practically nothing is known about the transformation of yolk into active protoplasm or the rate at which the process occurs, because so far it has proven impossible to separate effectively "active" and "inactive" materials and to measure them with any degree of precision. The term "yolk" has various meanings to different investigators. To some it refers to distinct cytological entities—the yolk platelets or lipochondria. Yolk may also have a broader connotation and may be used to refer to any stored substances in the egg which are used by the embryo for energy and for growth. Yolk platelets clearly do not contain all of the reserve materials for development. This is particularly true of lipoidal substances. When homogenates of amphibian eggs are strongly centrifuged, the lipoidal material is driven to the centripetal pole and can be seen to consist of a whitish layer, probably lipochondria and a droplet of clear oil (Boell, '42). In the intact egg the oil is most likely dispersed as an emulsion in the cytoplasm. This interpretation agrees with Løvtrup's ('53a) calculation that 30 to 50 per cent of the fat in the amphibian egg is outside the yolk platelets. The yolk platelets also do not contain reducing carbohydrate (Gregg and Løvtrup, '50).

If evidence of visible change in the yolk platelets or lipochondria is taken as an index of yolk utilization, one would be forced to believe that the embryo does not call upon its yolk supply for growth or as a source of energy until late in development (Bragg, '39; Daniel and Yarwood, '39; Holtfreter, '46). But visible change in size or pattern of yolk platelets is not a very precise indicator of the beginning or course of yolk consumption. Kutsky ('50) has shown, through the use of P^{32}, that turnover of phosphoprotein in yolk occurs from the very

beginning of development in *R. pipiens* and continues at a low rate throughout. Barth and Jaeger ('47b) found that the enzymes associated with phosphate transfer from yolk are active before gastrulation. Additional evidence for the involvement of yolk in early development has been provided by Friedberg and Eakin ('49). These workers exposed eggs of *Hyla regilla* to glycine, containing C^{14}, and found that the amino acid is taken up by yolk in the early embryo.

Although these studies show that yolk enters the "metabolic pool" much earlier than has generally been supposed, they give no indication of the rate of yolk utilization for growth. But, if it may be concluded that increase in rate of oxygen consumption is related to increase in magnitude of metabolically active components, it may be possible to use respiratory activity, in the absence of better and more orthodox measures, as an index of the transformation of yolk into protoplasm.

It is clear from Figure 201 and from the work of others (Atlas, Barth, Boell, Fischer and Hartwig, Hopkins and Handford, Spiegelman and Steinbach, and Wills) that abrupt changes or cyclic variations in respiration do not occur during amphibian development. Nor is there evidence of increased energy expenditure for such processes as gastrulation, differentiation of the primary germ layers, or their further elaboration into the definitive tissues and organs of the embryo. Any energy expenditure specifically required for these processes, since they occur gradually, is merely represented as part of the general rise in oxygen consumption that occurs during development.

In an earlier study of amphibian respiration, Parnas and Krasinka ('21) claimed that sudden increases in respiratory rate occurred at distinct stages of development, with plateaus of constant oxygen uptake between. The first of these abrupt changes was presumed to occur at the time of gastrulation; another, during closure of the neural folds; and a third, at the time the external gills made their appearance. From these observations, Parnas and Krasinka were led to conclude that major morphogenetic events were associated with increased energy expenditure. There can be no objection to such a conclusion, but it is apparently not validated by the experimental findings of the majority of more recent workers.

Tuft ('53) has reported, however, that the course of respiration in *Xenopus laevis* shows a period, interpreted as coinciding with gas-

---

* It should be unnecessary to mention that this does not mean that rate of development is controlled by respiratory rate.

trulation, during which respiratory increase does not occur, and he has cited the work of Barnes ('44) as showing a similar phenomenon. Løvtrup ('53a, b) and Ten Cate ('53) have also emphasized that periods of relatively constant oxygen consumption have been noted in their experiments. It should be mentioned that, in a number of instances, the period immediately following the break in the rate of respiratory increase seems to be one in which respiration remains constant, but such plateaus, if they may be so designated, are generally of short duration. Extremely long periods of essentially constant respiration, similar to those shown by Tuft or Barnes, are not the rule. It is likely that these plateaus have little fundamental significance, for they are not found consistently, even by the same investigator. Moreover, when they are found, they do not occur uniformly at gastrulation, as stated by Tuft. In this connection, it may be noted that the amphibian embryo is particularly sensitive to injury during gastrulation, and Smith ('46) has found the same to be true for the trout. It seems possible, therefore, that long respiratory plateaus during gastrulation may be an indication of damage to the embryo. The possibility of injury cannot be eliminated from Barnes' experiments, for the eggs used were shaken at the rate of 120 cycles per minute over an amplitude of 8 cm. for 6 to 8 hours during a manometric run, and she has reported that a careful census of the eggs was made routinely after each experiment "to check on the number living." It is also possible that plateaus of respiration represent intervals of developmental retardation due to handling of the eggs or other unfavorable conditions. Under such circumstances chronological time and developmental time would not be equivalent. Time is an adequate base line for development only when it is certain that development is normal. That acceleration of developmental rate occurs after embryos have been depressed by adverse conditions is clear from the work of Buchanan ('38, '40). The heightened respiratory activity after a plateau may reflect a regulatory phenomenon of this kind.

Energy for Maintenance vs. Energy for Development. *Respiratory Metabolism and Cell Division.* Calculations of the amount of energy necessary for cytoplasmic cleavage or for the production of "new surfaces" during mitosis have generally yielded figures so small as to suggest that the energy cost of cell division is negligible. The problem can-

not be dismissed in this way, however, for the cell may not be completely efficient as an energy transformer during division, just as muscle is unable to channel all of the energy released during contraction into mechanical work.

Apparently, respiratory increase does not necessarily follow the increase in number of cells. This was clearly shown in the work of Gray ('27), and more recently Tuft ('53) and Zeuthen ('53) have indicated that increase in number of nuclei bears only a casual relationship to increase in respiration.

A number of indirect approaches to the question of the energetics of cell division have been made through measurements of respiration when cell division is depressed. The difficulties of interpreting the results of such experiments are illustrated by the fact that hypertonic sea water and phenyl urethane inhibit cleavage without appreciably affecting oxygen consumption (Warburg, '08, '10), cyanide depresses respiration without affecting cleavage (see p. 523), and the substituted phenols block cleavage reversibly and at the same time bring about a tremendous increase in oxygen utilization (Clowes and Krahl, '34, '36; Tyler and Horowitz, '38a).

Brachet ('38) studied the respiration of Chaetopterus eggs that had been artificially activated by potassium chloride. Such eggs will develop into ciliated objects resembling trochophores through a process of "differentiation without cleavage." Brachet observed that the oxygen consumption of KCl-activated eggs increased less than in normal eggs. One might be tempted to consider such a difference in respiration as representing the energy cost of cleavage, but Brachet went on to show that the rate of development of the KCl-activated eggs was much slower than normal. This was indicated by the fact that their DNA content was only 30 per cent of that in normally activated eggs. Similarly, Tyler and Horowitz ('38b) investigated respiration of cleaving and non-cleaving parthenogenetic Urechis eggs and found that the respiration of cleaving eggs increased at a faster rate than it did in non-cleaving activated eggs or in fertilized eggs whose cleavage had been blocked by phenyl urethane. Just as in Brachet's experiments, the absence of cleavage was not the only difference between the lots of eggs. To conclude from such experiments that the difference in respiration between normal and nondividing eggs represents the energy cost of cleavage would, as Holter ('49) has pointed out, be completely unwarranted. Indeed, Andresen, Holter, and Zeuthen ('44) have shown that respiration in the absence of cleavage in the egg of the ascidian *Ciona intestinalis* is probably not significantly less than in eggs in which cleavage is occurring. These workers believe that the difference in respiration is altogether due to difference in developmental rate.

A systematic study of the relation between oxidative metabolism and cell division, as revealed by the use of inhibitory

confirmed this observation, but the period of enhanced carbon dioxide output during the mitotic cycle did not agree with that reported by Lyon. It should be noted that the carbon dioxide measured in these experiments may not have had a respiratory origin at all; it may have represented nothing more than carbon dioxide released from sea water by acids liberated from the egg (see p. 534). In contrast with the findings of Lyon and Vles, Meyerhof ('11) reported that calorimetric determinations of energy exchange

TABLE 16. *The Effect of Various Chemical Agents on Cell Division and Respiration in the Sea Urchin Egg* (Arbacia punctulata)*

AGENT	EFFECT ON CLEAVAGE	RESIDUAL RESPIRATION AS PERCENTAGE OF NORMAL
Oxygen lack	Complete block	20–30
KCN	Complete block	20–35
Carbon monoxide	Complete block	30
Sodium azide	Complete block	50
Sodium sulfide	50% block	90
Sodium sulfide	Complete block †	50
Diethyldithiocarbamate	Complete block †	100
Substituted phenols	Complete block	>100 ‡
Phenyl urethane	Complete block	70
Iodoacetate	90% block	54
Barbiturates	Complete block	20

* Data for this table abstracted from Krahl ('50).

† Cleavage block irreversible.

‡ At a concentration slightly less than that required to produce complete reversible block to cell division, various substituted phenols increase respiration from 20 to 260% above normal.

and stimulatory substances, has been conducted during the past two decades by Clowes and Krahl and their collaborators. Table 16 summarizes results for the sea urchin egg abstracted from the comprehensive review of Krahl ('50). From the data summarized in the table, and from what is known about the specific action of a number of the agents listed, it is possible to conclude that energy release during cleavage involves the participation of the cytochrome oxidase system and a system of enzymes concerned with oxidative phosphorylation (see p. 540). It is clearly impossible to state what the relative amount of respiration necessary to support cell division might be.

A number of direct observations of respiratory changes during mitosis have been made. As early as the turn of the century, interest was focused on this problem through the pioneer work of Lyon ('04) when he found that carbon dioxide production after cleavage of the sea urchin egg was considerably greater than before. Vles ('22)

during development of *Strongylocentrotus lividus* eggs failed to reveal any evidence of rhythmic variations that could be correlated with cell division. Gray ('25) then investigated the problem by making respiratory measurements during cleavage in the eggs of *Echinus miliaris*, but he concluded that rhythmic changes specifically associated with cell division were not superimposed on the over-all course of oxygen consumption. Runnström ('34) pointed out, however, that lack of synchrony in cleavage in the large numbers of eggs used by Gray may have obscured an intrinsic respiratory rhythm. In a repetition of Gray's experiments Runnström found that oxygen consumption was higher during the early phases of the mitotic cycle than later in the process.

The above observations were all made on the eggs of sea urchins, but similar experiments have been performed on amphibian eggs. Trurnit (cited by Brachet, '50) measured heat production of Triton eggs by actually inserting one of a delicate pair of thermocouples into the egg, and he observed a peak of heat production during the metaphase of mitosis. Similar results were obtained in suspensions of sea urchin eggs. Stefanelli ('37) determined respiration of single frog eggs in a capillary respirometer, and, although oxygen consumption showed some erratic fluctuations with time, there was some indication of a peak in respiration just before the appearance of the cleavage furrow. A second minor peak is also evident in his curve, and this occurs a few minutes after the cells have separated. In *Rana fusca* eggs, respiratory peaks were noted at the time of cleavage furrow formation by Brachet ('50), and secondary peaks were also seen between the major oscillations.

The most systematic and thorough study of respiratory rhythms during cleavage has been made by Zeuthen ('46, '50a,b, '51, '53; see also the theoretical paper dealing with Zeuthen's results by Linderstrøm-Lang, '46). In the frog egg, only the difference between oxygen taken up and carbon dioxide liberated was measured; the results obtained indicated that divisions one to four were accompanied by rhythmic waves in respiratory rate, the amplitude of the wave being 4 to 5 per cent of the basal rate. Similar phenomena were found in the eggs of Urechis and four species of sea urchin, but in these experiments the total oxygen consumption was measured, not the difference between oxygen and carbon dioxide. Zeuthen noted some variation in the time relations of respiratory rhythms and various phases of the mitotic cycle, but in most cases it appeared that the cytoplasm divided during the period of decreasing respiratory rate, and Zeuthen believes, therefore, that the respiratory rhythms are more intimately related to nuclear events than to cytoplasmic cleavage.

It would appear from the foregoing account that the association of rhythmic variations in respiration with cleavage had been well established, but recently Scholander et al. ('52) have expressed doubt on the occurrence of fluctuations in oxygen consumption during cell division. Working with single sea urchin eggs in a diver of ingenious design, Scholander et al. observed cycles of respiration in some cases, but they failed to find them in others although nuclear and cytoplasmic division were proceeding. When cycling was found, the period of enhanced oxygen utilization seemed to coincide with cytoplasmic cleavage rather than with nuclear division as reported by Zeuthen, and they reported in addition that cycling tended to become strongly damped after the first

cleavage and to disappear altogether after two or three divisions.

Zeuthen ('53) has calculated that the standard error of his measurements on the Urechis egg is only 0.66 per cent, much smaller than the error in Scholander's work, and he has suggested that the spread of experimental points in the observations by Scholander et al. would make it impossible to detect respiratory rhythms consistently in single eggs.

Metabolism During Developmental Block. A number of cases are known in which a period of development is followed by one of complete developmental block. The examples to be discussed are of interest because they represent situations in which complete disengagement of growth and differentiation from maintenance is brought about without experimental interference. In amphibian hybrids (*R. pipiens* eggs × *R. sylvatica* sperm) development proceeds normally through the beginning of gastrulation, but then, although the hybrid embryos remain healthy and viable, further development ceases (Moore, '41, '46). Barth ('46) has been able to show that both hybrid and normal embryos consume oxygen at the same rate during cleavage and blastula stages. At gastrulation, when developmental block sets in, respiration fails to increase in the hybrids as it normally does. Lactic acid production is also decreased in hybrid embryos, but not quite so drastically as respiration. Apparently, however, metabolism is qualitatively identical in the two types of embryos, for the respiratory quotients were found to be the same.

A somewhat analogous situation exists in *Drosophila melanogaster* eggs with chromosomal abnormalities. Absence of the X-chromosome leads to developmental failure at about the time of gastrulation. Just as in the case of the amphibian hybrids, "no-X" eggs respire normally so long as development continues, but respiration ceases to increase when development fails (Boell and Poulson, '39). The embryos are viable and continue to respire for many hours, but the rate of respiration, in the absence of development, remains unaltered at a very low level. By contrast, "attached-X" eggs (those with an extra chromosome) respire and develop normally.

The diapause in insects represents a situation where a reversible block to development is interposed between two periods of active growth and differentiation. During diapause in the grasshopper *Melanoplus differentialis*, cell division, growth, and differentiation occur so slowly, if they occur at all, that one may consider the diapause period as one in which development is completely suspended.* Respiration of the egg, or of the embryo isolated from it, is much lower during diapause than when development is going on even though blocked and developing embryos are of identical size and morphologically indistinguishable (Bodine, '29; Bodine and Boell, '34a,b, '36b, '37; Boell, '35). Quantitative respiratory data for the two types of embryos are summarized in Table 17. During diapause, the embryo, as far as can be ascertained, is simply maintaining itself, and it is reasonable to suppose that the total energy expenditure, as indicated by the oxygen consumed, is channeled into maintenance processes. The same can be said for the amphibian hybrid and the "no-X" Drosophila embryo.

Are Different Respiratory Mechanisms Involved in Maintenance and Development? Fisher and his co-workers have attempted to determine the relative proportions of the total respiratory activity concerned respectively with maintenance and with activity (Fisher, '41; Fisher and Henry, '40, '44; Fisher, Henry and Low, '44; Fisher and Stern, '42; Henry and Henry, '45). Working with yeast, luminous bacteria, and sea urchin eggs, they have produced evidence that a fraction of respiration that is relatively sensitive to urethane or chloral hydrate is concerned with such cell activities as division or luminescence, and that another fraction, much more resistant to these narcotics, is concerned with maintenance. The mass law relation has been applied to their data through the equation

$$\frac{U}{I} \times [N]^a = K$$

U is the fraction of respiration not inhibited by narcotic and is proportional to the free or active enzyme in the cell; I represents the fraction of respiration that can be inhibited by narcotic and is proportional to the amount of inactivated enzyme, and $[N]^a$, for practical purposes, may be regarded as concentration of narcotic. Such a relation assumes, and reasonably so in the case of most narcotics, a reversible combination of narcotic and enzyme. When Fisher plotted $\log \dfrac{U}{I}$ against the log of narcotic concentration, not one straight line resulted, but two, and these in-

* Fitzgerald ('49) has shown, however, that alkaline phosphatase increases late in the diapause period.

tersected at a narcotic concentration about the same as that required to block cleavage completely. At this concentration respiration was inhibited about 70 per cent. Fisher and his co-workers have thus been led to conclude that two respiratory mechanisms operate in the cell: one, accounting for about 70 per cent of the total oxygen consumption, is concerned with cellular activities; the other, corresponding to approximately 30 per cent of the total respiration and more difficult to inhibit with narcotic, is regarded as involved in maintenance metabolism.

TABLE 17. *Respiratory Rates of Diapause and Developing Eggs and Embryos*

EGGS	O_2 UPTAKE PER 100 EGGS PER HOUR
Prediapause	40
Diapause	18
Postdiapause	43

EMBRYOS*	Q_{O_2} (μl. O_2 PER MG. DRY WT. PER HOUR)
Prediapause	1.52
Diapause	0.59
Postdiapause	1.47

* The embryos were dissected free of yolk.

A similar attack on the problem of energy for maintenance and energy for development has been made by Moog ('44a) through the inhibition of respiration and development of the frog egg with Chloretone. Moog suggests that "from the neurula on, normal development requires almost all of the normal oxygen consumption, and that development cannot proceed at all unless at least 50% of the normal oxygen consumption is operating." In Chloretone solution capable of suppressing development completely without killing the embryo, she finds that respiration persists at a value between 40 and 50 per cent of normal, and she interprets these results as suggesting the presence of two systems of respiration concerned respectively with maintenance and growth-differentiation. These conclusions are supported in part by application of the mass law in the same manner as done by Fisher.

The action of lithium on respiration and development in the sea urchin egg may be appropriately mentioned at this time. Lithium, it will be recalled, exerts a vegetalizing influence on the sea urchin embryo. In an attempt to discover biochemical correlates with this phenomenon, Lindahl ('39) was led to study the effects of lithium on respiration. In brief, he found that exposure of sea urchin eggs to lithium soon after fertilization largely prevents the rapid increase which occurs normally between fertilization and hatching of the blastula (see Fig. 198). He thus concluded that respiration in the sea urchin egg consisted of two fractions. One remained constant, or essentially so, throughout development; the second, the lithium-sensitive fraction, rose continuously from fertilization and was largely responsible for the exponential increase in respiration. Presumably normal development depends upon the proper operation of both fractions; if the lithium-sensitive portion of respiration is depressed, vegetalization of the embryo results.

Studies of the effects of carbon monoxide and cyanide on the respiration of yeast, sea urchin eggs, and grasshopper embryos present analogous situations. Here too, carbon monoxide- and cyanide-sensitive and -insensitive fractions have been demonstrated. But some question seems now to exist as to whether there is complete cyanide-insensitivity in any case. Robbie, Boell, and Bodine ('38) showed that approximately 20 per cent of the respiration of the diapause egg, formerly regarded as completely insensitive to cyanide, could be depressed by 0.001 M potassium cyanide when care was taken to avoid loss of cyanide from the medium surrounding the eggs. And Robbie ('46) went on to show that the unfertilized sea urchin egg, long regarded as the classic example of cyanide insensitivity, also had reduced respiratory activity in the presence of this reagent.

Critique and Evaluation. From the account given above, it is apparent that it is difficult, if not impossible, to assess the energy requirements of particular events in the developmental process by a study of the overall gaseous metabolism of the embryo. One can never be certain that minor ripples on the total curve of respiratory increase are significantly correlated with the developmental phenomena with which they appear to coincide temporally. They may represent nothing more than random and fortuitous fluctuations brought about by developmental conditions. Furthermore, it should be emphasized that a period of increased oxygen utilization is not necessarily contemporaneous with an energy-requiring developmental event. The energy needed at the time the event is occurring might be supplied by breakdown of high-energy phosphate compounds such as adenosinetriphosphate (ATP).

Thus a period of enhanced oxygen consumption would occur after the event and would be concerned only with regeneration of the energy stores. This would be identical to the situation in muscle, where oxidative recovery follows contraction.

Nevertheless, when all the observations reviewed above are taken together, they strongly suggest that a certain fraction of the total respiratory exchange is used by the embryo for purposes of maintenance while another fraction is used to support developmental processes.

The question may now be asked whether the energy requirements for these processes can be fixed quantitatively or even relatively. (For various points of view on this question, the reader may consult Needham, '42; Tyler, '42; Brachet, '50; Tuft, '53.) One may be tempted to conclude that the amount of energy needed to maintain a developing embryo is the same as the total energy released by a blocked embryo, so that the difference in metabolic level between embryos in the two states might be regarded as representing the cost of developmental work. Similarly, it might be thought that the energy requirements for development could be derived by subtracting the total metabolism of the unfertilized egg from that of the fertilized egg. Such considerations lead into difficulties, however, for in some cases fertilization is not associated with change in respiratory rate, and in others it actually decreases (Whitaker, '33). Before firm conclusions could be drawn from data on blocked and developing embryos, or fertilized and unfertilized eggs, it would have to be demonstrated that a unit of oxygen consumed had the same calorific value for the two kinds of eggs or embryos. To obtain information on this would require very precise knowledge not only of the amount but also of the kind of foodstuffs being oxidized as energy sources. Although it might be possible to demonstrate by chemical analysis that a decrease in a potential energy source occurs during development, it may be pointed out that it does not follow that such disappearance is brought about exclusively by oxidative or other energy-yielding processes. The substance in question may be synthesized into some other compound, or it may be lost from the egg without participating in energy-yielding processes. There seems to be evidence that considerable quantities of metabolites may disappear from the egg by processes which do not involve the simultaneous utilization of oxygen (Løvtrup, '53b).

There is an additional reason for questioning the validity of considering the maintenance requirements of a developing embryo as identical with those of a blocked embryo. It is entirely conceivable that the cost of maintenance for a developing system would be significantly greater than for a non-developing one. The rate of chemical turnover in the unblocked embryo is certainly more extensive, the deterioration, through activity, of various enzymes is probably greater, and "maintenance protein synthesis," as well as other synthetic processes, is undoubtedly going on at a faster rate. It seems premature, therefore, to attempt to fix either the absolute or relative costs of maintenance and development, either as a total process or in terms of its subdivisions, from the kind of data available at the present time.

On the question of the existence of different respiratory mechanisms concerned with maintenance and development, it can be said that there appears to be little doubt that X-sensitive and X-insensitive fractions of respiration are found in the developing system. But the relationship of such systems to development on the one hand and to maintenance on the other is more obscure. One fundamental difficulty in using data derived from studies with inhibitors, in attempting to assess the relative amounts of energy exchange concerned with maintenance or with development, lies in the fact that the magnitude of the inhibitor-insensitive fraction of respiration, supposedly concerned with maintenance, varies widely and seems to depend upon the particular inhibitor used. Thus, Fisher and Henry ('44) found that sulfanilamides inhibit cell division at concentrations that reduce respiration by no more than 45 per cent, and the concentration of penicillin required to block cleavage completely was found to have absolutely no effect on respiration (Henry and Henry, '45). The very multiplicity of the agents represented by X, and the fact that in certain cases X-sensitive and X-insensitive fractions can both be inhibited by the same substance, permit certain reservations as to the validity of considering the various fractions of respiration as proceeding through different mechanisms.

ENERGY SOURCES DURING DEVELOPMENT

The Ontogenetic Sequence: Carbohydrate, Protein, Fat. Needham ('31, '42) has gathered together an impressive body of data to es-tablish the fact that the chick embryo uses the primary energy sources during development in the order—carbohydrate, protein, fat. Evidence for this has been derived from three sources: (1) chemical analysis of the egg contents and embryo at various stages of development, (2) respiratory quotient data for the egg and isolated embryo, and (3) estimations of the amount and nature of nitrogenous wastes produced by the embryo and extra-embryonic structures.

The results of in vitro studies are in harmony with the concept that carbohydrate is the energy source of major importance for the early chick embryo (Dickens and Greville, 33a,b; Philips, '41, '42). The more recent work of Spratt ('48, '50) points in the same direction, for he found that differentiation of chick blastoderms, when cultivated in synthetic media, would not occur unless glucose was present. Essentially similar results have been obtained by Taylor and Schechtman ('49).

Protein metabolism occurs throughout development, with most of the protein absorbed by the embryo being used for growth. Protein utilization for catabolic purposes begins to be significant on about the fifth or sixth day and is maximal on the eighth or ninth day. Conversely, anabolic protein utilization is high during the first few days of development and minimal on the eighth or ninth day. Subsequently, the rate of absorption of protein for growth rises gradually to a new peak reached on the fifteenth day. Novikoff and Potter ('48) have shown that the pentose nucleic acid content of the embryo fluctuates in phase with the processes outlined above.[*]

Fat is the predominant energy source in avian development. About 60 per cent of the total fatty acid present in the egg at the beginning is combusted, and from this the embryo derives over 90 per cent of its caloric yield. Fat uptake, leading to combustion, begins at about the fourth or fifth day, and continues to increase in intensity, paralleling the increase in size of the embryo, throughout the remainder of the incubation period.

In some few other embryos, the ontogenetic sequence shown for the chick seems to

[*] Novikoff and Potter compare their curve for PNA with data from Needham ('31) showing protein content of the embryo in milligrams per cent dry weight. Had they used instead the intensity of protein absorption by the embryo (which is perhaps a better measure of protein metabolism) the parallelism of their results with those summarized by Needham would have been even more striking.

hold, but much of the evidence is derived from respiratory quotient data. Fiske and Boyden ('26) showed long ago that respiratory quotients can be misleading as indicators of the kinds of metabolites burned, for the combustion of protein will yield respiratory quotients of approximately 1, 0.8, or 0.7, depending upon whether the nitrogenous end product is ammonia, urea, or uric acid. Moreover, with some methods of respiratory quotient determination, three different samples of living material are required, and, unless due consideration be given to assure uniformity of the eggs or embryos used, distorted values will result.

In the grasshopper embryo, the sequence of energy source utilization seems to be the same as in the chick (Slifer, '30; Boell, '35; Hill, '45). The phase characterized by predominant carbohydrate metabolism is very short, however, lasting not more than a day or two. It also appears that protein occupies a relatively insignificant role as an energy source, but that some protein is broken down is indicated by the accumulation of urates in the embryo (Bodine, '46). Approximately 75 per cent of the total oxygen consumption can be accounted for as fat oxidation. However, during the first two weeks of development, fat combustion accounts for no more than a third of the embryo's respiration, while during the post-diapause period almost 90 per cent of the total oxygen consumption is at the expense of fat. Fat has also been shown to be the major energy source in a number of other insects (references in Boell, '35; Crescitelli, '35; Needham, '42; Ludwig, '50a, b), and in the silkworm the utilization of energy sources occurs in the same sequence as in the chick and grasshopper (Needham, '42).

A progressive change in respiratory quotient, with high values initially and lower ones, characteristic of fat oxidation, predominating in later development, has been reported for Fundulus (Amberson and Armstrong, '33), Carcinus (Needham, '33), Urechis (Horowitz, '40), and Trichurus (Nolf, '32). Thus the ontogenetic sequence—carbohydrate, protein, fat—may operate in these embryos also, but, as was pointed out above, respiratory quotient data alone are not adequate proof.

The Fish Embryo. Both in 1931 and 1942, Needham noted that the ontogenetic sequence—carbohydrate, protein, fat—apparently did not hold in certain cases. Echinoderms and amphibians represented outstanding exceptions. Smith's ('46, '52) thorough studies of the energetics of the rainbow trout, Salmo irideus, indicate that this form also represents an exception. Smith has shown that the amount of carbohydrate present at any one time and consumed during particular periods of development is so small in proportion to the total protein and fat combustion that carbohydrate as an energy source can be ignored. Carbohydrate combustion is limited to three short periods of development: (1) immediately after gastrulation, (2) at the time of hatching, and (3) at the onset of starvation after exhaustion of the yolk supplies. In the Atlantic salmon also, carbohydrate metabolism seems to be relatively unimportant, for, according to Hayes and Hollett ('40), glycogen is absent in early development and the amount of glucose present is exceedingly small. It may be remarked that the failure of Hayes and Hollett to find glycogen in the early embryo has been attributed to faulty technique. In Salmo salar, Daniel ('47) reports that glycogen is present at the beginning of development, but he agrees with Smith and Hayes and Hollett that the quantity is small.

In the rainbow trout, protein and fat are used simultaneously and account for 99 per cent of the total caloric yield during development. There is some indication that the percentage of protein burned is higher during early development (39 to 42 per cent) than later on (27 to 30 per cent), and it seems clear that consumption of water-soluble phosphatide fat precedes that of glyceride fat. During early development, Smith's analyses show that ammonia may account for as much as 95 per cent of the total nitrogen excreted. Possibly the initial high respiratory quotients reported for Fundulus (Amberson and Armstrong, '33) may have been due to protein combustion with ammonia as the end product.

The Sea Urchin Embryo. Although respiratory quotients of unity were found for the sea urchin egg immediately after fertilization by some of the earlier workers, it appears now that these values were abnormally high and were biased by the inclusion of non-respiratory carbon dioxide. Runnström ('33) showed that an acid is liberated from sea urchin eggs at fertilization of sufficient strength to release carbon dioxide from bicarbonates in sea water. Accordingly, Runnström ('34) obtained "respiratory quotients" of 2, or even higher, during the first 15 minutes after fertilization.

The origin of the acid is of interest although it is only peripherally related to the question of energy sources. It is probably derived from carbohydrate, for Lindberg ('43) was able to account for it quantitatively by the amount of glycogen lost at fertilization. Moreover, Rothschild ('39) was able to inhibit the production of acid in cytolyzing eggs with phlorizin, but it should be noted that the production of acid under these circumstances may not be the same as in intact eggs. The acid is not lactic acid (Runnström, '33; Rothschild, '39), and there is little likelihood that it is fatty acid, as suggested by Hayes ('38). Lindberg believes that the acid is not a single substance, but a mixture of intermediates of carbohydrate breakdown.

More recent studies by Öhman ('40) indicate that in *Paracentrotus lividus* the respiratory quotient is 0.73 after fertilization; it rises during subsequent development to a value of 0.85. Laser and Rothschild ('39) also noted that the respiratory quotient was low immediately after fertilization. In *Arbacia punctulata*, the respiratory quotient rises after fertilization, but the initial value (0.85) is not as low as that reported by Öhman nor is the increase so marked (Hutchens, Keltch, Krahl, and Clowes, '42). It may be significant that the rise in respiratory quotient is temporally correlated with the development of lithium sensitivity, for Lindahl ('39) has suggested that this fraction of respiration involves carbohydrate catabolism. The low initial respiratory quotient is consonant with the finding by Hutchens, Keltch, Krahl, and Clowes ('42) that, during the first few hours after fertilization, the small quantities of glucose lost from the egg of Arbacia cannot account for the oxygen uptake. It also agrees with Lindberg's ('43) observation that glycogen loss, after an initial rapid breakdown associated with acid formation, proceeds at a low and fairly constant rate. It is also in harmony with the report by Hayes ('38) that fat is lost from the egg throughout development (45 hours) but that the rate of disappearance is most rapid during the three or four hours immediately after fertilization.

Gustafson and Hasselberg ('51) have reported that Kjeldahl nitrogen is constant from fertilization to the pluteus stage in *Paracentrotus lividus* (see the discussion on p. 520). Nevertheless, some protein must be burned, for Hutchens, Keltch, Krahl, and Clowes ('42) have shown that protein combustion leading to ammonia as the end product can account for a portion of the oxygen consumption after fertilization. These collective findings thus suggest that fat is probably the major energy source for a short time after fertilization and that during the period of exponential increase in respiration metabolism is mixed but with carbohydrate becoming increasingly important as development proceeds. It is of interest in passing to note that almost 90 per cent of the respiration of sea urchin spermatozoa can be accounted for by oxidation of phospholipid (Rothschild and Cleland, '52).

The Amphibian Embryo. The sequence of energy sources in Amphibia was recognized by Needham ('42) as being different from that in the chick. Carbohydrate loss during early stages has not been demonstrated, but that it begins at gastrulation has been shown

TABLE 18. *Respiratory Quotients of* Rana pipiens *Embryos*

STAGE	NUMBER OF DETERMINATIONS	R.Q.*
9+	4	0.92
10	2	0.90
11	4	1.01
12	10	0.98
13–14	6	0.88
15	1	0.85

* The first method of Dickens and Simer was used in making these determinations (Dixon, '51).

by histochemical tests (Woerdeman, '33; Raven, '35) and chemical analyses (Brachet and Needham, '35; Heatley and Lindahl, '37; Jaeger, '45; Gregg, '48). The claim of Gregg and Pomerat ('42) that glycogen disappears during cleavage has been withdrawn by Gregg. Loss of glycogen determined by chemical analysis, during development of *Amblystoma mexicanum* has been reported by Løvtrup ('53a), but his analyses were confined to the beginning and end of development and hence do not show when consumption begins.

That disappearance of glycogen is due to combustion rather than storage in the form of some other carbohydrate has been suggested by Gregg, since he found that the total free carbohydrate remains constant at a very low level until late in development. This seems reasonable, but it does not eliminate the possibility that glycogen may be synthesized into some non-carbohydrate product.

Brachet's ('34) study of the respiratory quotient during development in *Rana fusca* is in harmony with the chemical analyses in showing that carbohydrate utilization begins at gastrulation. The values obtained were 0.66 for early cleavage stages, 0.70 for advanced blastulas, and 1.03 for gastrulas. During subsequent development, the respiratory quotient fell slightly. A series of respiratory quotient values for R. pipiens embryos, during and after gastrulation, are shown in Table 18 (Boell, unpublished). The data in the table confirm the findings of Brachet for respiratory quotients of approximately unity during gastrulation. Unfortunately, determinations were not made during cleavage stages. However, additional evidence that low values are characteristic

inally present in the egg. That protein is burned during development is indicated by the fact that ammonia and urea are excreted by the embryo (Brachet, '39, see columns 1 and 2 of Table 19). Boell, Needham, and Rogers ('39) reported that ammonia was produced anaerobically by explants of Rana temporaria gastrulas, but this result may be in error in view of Gregg and Ornstein's ('52) inability to find ammonia production by explanted tissue of R. pipiens. Column 7 of Table 19 suggests that a not inconsiderable portion of the total oxygen consumption can be accounted for as protein combustion,

TABLE 19. *Utilization of Protein as Energy Source by* Rana fusca*

STAGE	NITROGEN EXCRETED BY 100 EMBRYOS PER DAY			PROTEIN EQUIV. TO COL. 3	O_2 NEEDED TO BURN PROTEIN IN COL. 4	O_2 UPTAKE OBSERVED †	% O_2 UPTAKE AS PROTEIN COMBUSTION
	NH_3	UREA	TOTAL N				
	1	2	3	4	5	6	7
Morula-blastula	33	24	38.4	240	228	292	78
Gastrula	32	25	38.1	238	225	520	43
Neurula	31	22	25.9	224	212	800	27

* Figures in columns 1, 2, 3, and 4 represent µg., in columns 5 and 6, µl.
† Data for oxygen consumption in column 6 from Brachet ('34); for columns 1 and 2, from Brachet ('39).

of the period before gastrulation may be seen in the observation that explants from the blastula of A. mexicanum have a respiratory quotient of 0.75 (Boell, Koch, and Needham, '39). Barth ('46) has also obtained high values for the respiratory quotient during gastrulation and later development, although the average is somewhat lower than in the experiments already mentioned. This may possibly be due to the fact that oxygen consumption and carbon dioxide output were not determined on the same sample of eggs. Barth measured the respiratory quotients of cleavage stages but found that they were only slightly lower than during gastrulation. However, Barth apparently feels that the absolute value of the respiratory quotient for early cleavage must be regarded as unknown from his work, for his figures varied from 0.7 to 1.05, depending somewhat on the method used.

The question of protein as an energy source is highly confused. Most of the data summarized by Needham ('31) showed combustion of protein before hatching and somewhat enhanced utilization afterward. There was, however, little agreement as to the amount lost in relation to the amount orig-

and that relatively more energy may be derived from protein combustion during early development than later. These calculations, taken with the observations on carbohydrate catabolism, suggest that protein utilization precedes that of carbohydrate, and it probably continues throughout all of development.

The question of energy source utilization in A. mexicanum has been investigated by Løvtrup ('53a) in a study combining respiratory and reduced weight measurements. His calculations apparently show that carbohydrate is used exclusively as an energy source during cleavage stages. But reduced weight data are of limited utility in establishing this convincingly, and Løvtrup states that "the chemical analyses must of course be decisive on this point." He has also calculated that protein may serve as an energy source and that the amount of protein so used corresponds to 16 per cent of that initially in the egg. Since his observations were continued into the feeding period, Løvtrup has concluded that some of the protein lost, perhaps a major portion, might have been spared had his animals been permitted to feed. It is not possible to determine in his experiments how much protein was used before the animals were capable of feeding, or the extent to which the animals were forced by starvation to call upon their tissue reserves. It seems reasonable to conclude, however, that the degree of inanition was not very great at the time his observations were terminated, for the respiratory rate had not yet begun to decline as it does during starvation.

The results of chemical analyses of the changes in total nitrogen during development *apparently* do not support the view that protein serves as an energy source. In contrast with the earlier findings which

but the changes observed were very slight and did not exceed in magnitude the variation between different samples of eggs or embryos.*

The amphibian egg consists of a large amount of protein in relation to the total dry weight; Needham ('31, p. 1105) gives a figure of 61 per cent. Most of this protein is stored as yolk and serves as a reserve on which the embryo draws for the elaboration of new materials during growth and differentiation. In view of the great quantity of protein in the egg at the beginning, any decrease, as by combustion, is bound to be relatively small. Hence what appears to be

TABLE 20. *Total Nitrogen in Amphibian Embryos†*

SPECIES	μG. N INITIAL	μG. N FINAL	% DIFFERENCE
Amblystoma punctatum	430	430	0
Amblystoma tigrinum	290	280	−3.5
Triturus torosus	260	230	−12
Rana pipiens	160	190	+13

† Data from Wills ('36). In computing the average figures shown above, the first determinations at the beginning of development and the last determinations before the feeding stages were used. The number of determinations represented in the averages are as follows: for *Amblystoma punctatum* and *Triturus torosus*, the first five and the last five; for *A. tigrinum*, the first two and the last two; for *Rana pipiens*, the first nine and the last nine.

showed some loss of protein by combustion, Wills ('36) reported that total nitrogen was essentially constant throughout the prefeeding period of development in four species of amphibia: *Amblystoma punctatum, A. tigrinum, Triturus torosus*, and *Rana pipiens*. A portion of Wills' analyses have been abstracted and are shown in Table 20. Wills included the egg jelly in the material analyzed, but he claimed that its presence did not materially affect the quantity of nitrogen measured. This view is contested by Gregg and Ballentine ('46), who found that jelly nitrogen averages 16 micrograms per embryo, that is about 10 per cent of the total nitrogen in egg plus jelly, and that the vitelline membrane contains about two micrograms. They did, however, confirm Wills, as did also Løvtrup ('53a), by stating that total nitrogen remains nearly constant throughout development. A minor decrease noted at stage 16+ (Shumway) was attributed to loss of the vitelline membrane and the fluid contained in the vitelline space. Some change in the distribution of nitrogen in various constituents of the embryo was found, indicating that protein metabolism was going on even though it did not eventuate in combustion,

constancy of protein may simply mean that changes in total nitrogen are obscured by variability in the samples of eggs and embryos used for analysis. That this factor may not have been adequately taken into account is illustrated both in the data of Gregg and Ballentine and in those of Wills. Gregg and Ballentine obtained an average figure of 162 μg. total nitrogen per egg at the beginning of development from a series of nine samples which ranged from 141 to 202 μg. The standard deviation for their array of figures is 17.2 μg., or 10.6 per cent and this corresponds to 107 μg. of protein. For the combustion of this amount 102 μl. of oxygen would be required. This could mean, using Atlas' ('38) figure of 250 μl. for the total oxygen consumption of one *Rana pipiens* embryo throughout development, that as

* They found also that the quantity of ultracentrifugable nitrogen, presumably representing granular material, is constant throughout development. This is interesting in view of the fact that much of the RNA of the cell is located in such granules and that Bodenstein and Kondritzer ('48), Kutsky ('50), and Krugelis, Nicholas, and Vosgian ('52) showed that RNA increases between ten- and twenty-fold.

much as 40 per cent of the total respiration of the embryo is absorbed by the standard deviation. Wills' data for *R. pipiens* (Table 20) actually indicate more nitrogen present at the end of development than at the beginning, and it can be shown that the difference is *statistically* significant!

The yolk of amphibian eggs contains a relatively high proportion of phosphoprotein. The phosphate linkages are present in the form of high-energy bonds, and Harris ('46) discovered a special phosphoproteinphosphatase capable of releasing phosphate without prior action of protease. The mechanism of phosphate transfer from yolk is complex and involves ATP, other proteins, and several enzymes (Barth and Jaeger, '47a,b; '50a,b; Barth and Barth, '51). The high-energy bonds of phosphoprotein apparently represent a relatively insignificant store of energy, however, for it has been calculated that the net amount available is only 0.15 per cent of the total energy consumption during development (Løvtrup, '53a).

Relatively little work has been done on fat metabolism during amphibian embryogenesis. That some fat is burned is evident from the analytical data of Bialascewicz and Bledovski, Barthelmy and Bonnét, and Parnas and Krasinka (cited from Needham, '31). Furthermore, Atlas ('38) has concluded, from a comparison of the loss in dry weight and oxygen consumption of *R. pipiens,* that some fat is used as an energy source. Løvtrup's findings also point in the same direction. The majority of these workers agree that fat utilization takes place predominantly during the latter part of development, although there may be some indication that it begins earlier than was formerly believed (Løvtrup, '53a).

In conclusion, then, it may be stated that the exact order in which energy sources are used during amphibian ontogeny is unknown. There actually may be no sequence at all in the sense that it can be demonstrated in the chick, but there is some indication that protein combustion precedes that of carbohydrate in early development, and that after gastrulation oxidation of all three foodstuffs occurs.

Factors Responsible for Changes in Energy Source Utilization. A problem of considerable interest concerns the mechanism by which the embryo shifts from one class of foodstuffs to another during development. It might appear reasonable to assume that one energy source would be used preferentially until its concentration in the egg became so reduced that it could no longer be mobilized in adequate amounts; then a second energy source would be called upon. However, most of the information available at present from experimental studies suggests that the change to a second energy source is not brought about by the exhaustion of the one previously used. It has been shown that the chick embryo will enter upon the "protein phase" of metabolism even though carbohydrate is still present or when the carbohydrate supplies are artificially increased by injection of glucose into the egg. There is also evidence that failure to use an energy source is not the result of lack of necessary enzymatic machinery. Dickens and Greville ('33b) have found that chick embryos, in vitro, can burn protein leading to ammonia production during the period of development when the normal fuel is carbohydrate. Likewise, Needham ('32b) has shown that early chick embryos will burn protein when treated with fluoride. The grasshopper embryo, during the stage when 90 per cent of its energy yield is derived from fat oxidation, will burn glucose when it is supplied (Bodine and Boell, '36b), and the embryo can be induced to burn protein by treatment with dinitrophenol (Bodine and Boell, '38). It thus appears that the sequence of energy source utilization depends upon conditions in the embryo itself, but what these are is at present unknown.

The question as to whether various developmental processes may require special or unique sources of energy, different from those used for maintenance, cannot be definitely answered. But it may be suggested, on the following grounds, that they do not. It is becoming increasingly clear that high-energy phosphate bonds in such compounds as ATP represent the immediate energetic source for development, and it seems likely that the oxidative processes required to generate phosphate bond energy would be the same no matter what the ultimate destiny of the energy stored in them may be. The real problem for the student of development is not how high-energy bonds are synthesized, but rather how the energy released from them is directed to bring about specific end results in the embryo. On this question ignorance is complete.

RESPIRATORY MECHANISMS

The Embden-Meyerhof, Citric Acid Cycle, Warburg-Keilin System. In the breakdown of carbohydrate to carbon dioxide and water, in the systems that have been most thoroughly investigated—yeast and skeletal muscle—the initial changes occur equally well in the absence or presence of oxygen. The so-called processes of anaerobic glycolysis are mediated by what is commonly called the Embden-Meyerhof scheme of phosphorylating glycolysis, and the end result of the breakdown of glycogen or glucose is pyruvic acid. In the absence of oxygen, pyruvic acid is reduced to lactic acid by hydrogen transferred from reduced diphosphopyridine nucleotide (DPN). During the anaerobic reactions, some energy is released, and this is stored in high-energy phosphate bonds such as those in ATP. Pyruvic acid is broken down to carbon dioxide and water by a series of oxidative steps involving the tricarboxylic or citric acid cycle. Pyruvate is first oxidatively decarboxylated, by processes involving the participation of coenzyme A, and the two-carbon fragment remaining combines with oxaloacetate to enter the cycle as citrate. Electrons and hydrogen derived from the degradation of citrate back to oxaloacetate are transferred to DPN or to triphosphopyridine nucleotide (TPN) and thence to oxygen via the Warburg-Keilin system of the cytochromes and cytochrome oxidase. During the operation of the citric acid cycle, more high-energy phosphate bonds are generated.

It has been shown during the past few years that the citric acid cycle also plays a role in the oxidation of fatty acids and amino acids. Fatty acids are first broken down by β-oxidation to two-carbon fragments, and these, through coenzyme A, may enter the citric acid cycle. Many amino acids, after deamination, also enter the cycle—in some cases through coenzyme A, in others more directly. These processes and the relationships of the Embden-Meyerhof scheme, the citric acid cycle, and the Warburg-Keilin system are shown diagrammatically in Figure 202.

A conservative estimate shows that some 20 or 30 different enzymes are required to operate the complete scheme, and, in addition, several coenzymes, "factors," and other chemical agents are needed. It does not follow that the scheme outlined above operates in every living cell, but it has been shown to be widely applicable, not only in the case of various vertebrate tissues but also in yeasts and other microorganisms, and one is perhaps not far wrong to conclude that the basic theme, with minor variations, probably applies to most aerobic organisms.

Our problem now is to determine to what extent this complex array of biochemical machinery is present and operative in the embryo. It will be apparent in what follows

that many of the enzymic mechanisms which operate in cellular respiration in the adult organism are present, and functional, during early development, and the egg, far from being a mass of protoplasm with simple enzyme equipment, is provided with or soon synthesizes an impressive battery of enzymes.

Respiratory Mechanisms in Echinoderm Eggs. The sea urchin egg and embryo have

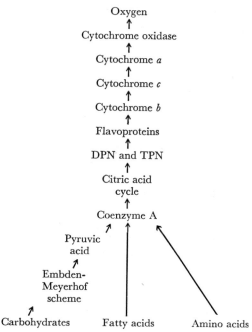

Fig. 202. Schematic representation of mechanisms concerned with oxidation of foodstuffs to carbon dioxide and water.

been more thoroughly investigated, with respect to their oxidative enzyme equipment, than those of any other form. The systematic investigation of respiratory mechanisms during echinoderm development had its beginnings in the thorough studies of Runnström more than twenty years ago. Following Warburg ('10), Runnström ('30) showed that cyanide strongly depressed respiration of the fertilized sea urchin egg but that the unfertilized egg was completely resistant to this inhibitor. In addition, he found that carbon monoxide, also effective as a depressant of respiration of fertilized eggs, stimulated oxygen consumption before fertilization.

Next, Runnström ('30, '32) investigated the ability of eggs to oxidize dimethyl-p-phenylenediamine, the substrate used to test for *Atmungsferment* (cytochrome oxidase), and found that the *potential* activity of the enzyme was the same before fertilization as afterward. Therefore, he concluded that the increased respiration and sensitivity to cyanide after fertilization were not due to synthesis of new enzyme but were brought about by enhancement of the activity of enzyme previously present. In some way, fertilization had accomplished a change in the relationship of the enzyme with other links in the respiratory chain.

Later work by Krahl et al. ('41) confirmed these observations. Cytochrome oxidase activity, measured in the presence of cytochrome c, was the same in unfertilized and fertilized eggs, and the enzyme seemed to have the properties usually associated with cytochrome oxidase from other sources. It is of interest to note that cytochrome oxidase is not localized in mitochondria but rather is associated with non-mitochondrial particulates in the supernatant solution of centrifuged egg homogenates (Hutchens, Kopac, and Krahl, '42).* Gustafson ('52) has assumed that cytochrome oxidase is gradually built into the mitochondria at the time when the mitochondrial population increases after the mesenchyme blastula stage (Gustafson and Hasselberg, '51; Deutsch and Gustafson, '52; Gustafson and Lenicque, '52).

Cytochrome c is abundant in sea urchin sperm (Ball and Meyerhof, '40; Rothschild, '48), but so far it has not been detected in the egg. However, both Ball and Meyerhof and Borei ('50) observed absorption bands of iron porphyrins related to the cytochromes, and Borei believes that sub-detectable amounts of cytochrome may nevertheless be present and functionally significant.

That sea urchin eggs contain dehydrogenases was first demonstrated by Runnström, and this was confirmed by Ballentine ('38, '40), who showed in addition that the total dehydrogenase activity after fertilization was approximately three times greater than before. However, attempts to discover the various specific dehydrogenases concerned with the operation of the citric acid cycle were unsuccessful. The absence of succinic dehydrogenase has been frequently reported (Ball and Meyerhof, '40; Ballentine, '40; Krahl et al., '41), but recently Gustafson

* Weber (personal communication) has obtained results which are at variance with those previously reported. He has found that approximately 90 per cent of the cytochrome oxidase of homogenates of unfertilized eggs of *Paracentrotus lividus* can be recovered in the particulate fraction sedimenting at 600 to 12,000 × g.

and Hasselberg ('51) claimed to have found the enzyme in egg homogenates from two species of sea urchin. It should be noted, however, that Bodine, Lu, and West ('52) showed that reduction of triphenyltetrazolium chloride, used by Gustafson and Hasselberg to measure succinic dehydrogenase activity, is not a specific test for the enzyme. DPN was found to be present in Arbacia eggs by Jandorf and Krahl ('42), and Barron and his co-workers were able to show that the eggs could oxidize pyruvic acid (Goldinger and Barron, '46). This was also shown to be true for the eggs of *Echinus esculentus* by Cleland and Rothschild ('52b).

It seems, therefore, that the dehydrogenases of the citric acid cycle must be present but that something in crude egg homogenates interferes with their activity. A possible explanation of the failure of others to observe active specific dehydrogenases was offered by Keltch et al. ('50) when they showed that echinochrome inactivates a number of dehydrogenases by oxidizing their sulfhydryl groups. Indeed, they found that cell-free, non-mitochondrial particulate systems of unfertilized eggs could oxidize α-ketoglutarate, oxaloacetate, and succinate, and they demonstrated that generation of high-energy phosphate bonds accompanied these oxidations. Thus, they confirmed the earlier observation of Lindberg and Ernster ('48) of oxidative phosphorylation by homogenates of *Strongylocentrotus droebachiensis* eggs. Clowes, Keltch, Strittmatter, and Walters ('50) went on to show that oxidative phosphorylation could be inhibited by nitro- or halo-phenols, and it was concluded that generation of high-energy phosphate bonds occurs, as it does in muscle or kidney, through the citric acid cycle.

That the citric acid cycle operates in the egg of *Echinus esculentus* has been convincingly demonstrated by Cleland and Rothschild ('52b). Evidence for the presence of the enzymes in the cycle rests upon (1) demonstration that malonate, long known to act as an inhibitor of succinic dehydrogenase, blocks the endogenous respiration of egg homogenates, (2) finding that oxygen consumption of egg homogenates can be stimulated by all of the intermediates in the citric acid cycle (see Table 21), and (3) demonstration of the complete oxidation of pyruvic acid.

Evidence for the operation in sea urchin eggs of a typical Embden-Meyerhof glycolytic cycle has also been provided. Gustafson and Hasselberg ('51) demonstrated the presence of aldolase in the eggs of *Paracentrotus lividus*, and Cleland and Rothschild ('52a) showed that lactic and pyruvic acids could be produced from the following intermediates in the Embden-Meyerhof scheme: glycogen, glucose, glucose-1-phosphate, glucose-6-phosphate, fructose-6-phosphate, hexosediphosphate, and phosphoglycerate. Furthermore, they found that glycolysis was greatly depressed by phenylmercuric nitrate, phlorizin, fluoride, and iodoacetate.

Respiratory Mechanisms in Embryos Other than Echinoderms. Respiratory mechanisms in the embryos of other species have not been so thoroughly investigated as in the sea urchin. However, the functional significance of cytochrome oxidase is indicated for most embryos by their sensitivity to cyanide. In a number of cases, cytochrome oxidase has been assayed histochemically (Moog,'43) or manometrically, and the results of the quantitative measurements show that the enzyme is present in sufficient amounts to account for the total respiratory activity of the intact embryo. This is true for the grasshopper (Bodine and Boell, '36a; Allen, '40), various amphibians (Brachet, '34; Spiegelman and Steinbach, '45; Boell, '45), the chick (Albaum and Worley, '42; Albaum, Novikoff, and Ogur, '46; Levy and Young, '48), and the mammalian cerebral cortex (Flexner, Flexner, and Straus, '41).

Attempts to demonstrate the presence of cytochrome *c* in early embryos have been no more successful than in the sea urchin already mentioned. In Amphibia, the presence of pigment, of course, makes direct spectroscopic examination impossible. Yaoi ('28-'29) was unable to find cytochrome *c* in the chick embryo, and he stated that if it was present at all between the fourth and eleventh day its concentration was so low as to be negligible. Likewise, Potter and Dubois ('42) were unable to find cytochrome *c* in the chick embryo until the tenth day. In the cerebral cortex of the pig fetus, the bands of reduced cytochrome *c* were only faintly visible after the middle of gestation (Flexner, Flexner, and Straus, '41). Stotz ('39) stated that cytochrome *c* is present in the early rat embryo (age not specified) in a concentration of 0.3 mg. per gram of tissue (dry weight); in the late rat embryo, he found 0.18 mg. per gram.

It has been claimed that succinic dehydrogenase and other dehydrogenases in the citric acid cycle are absent from the early chick embryo (Banga, '37; Elliott and Greig, '38; Greig, Munro, and Elliott, '39). But

Booth ('35) showed that succinic, lactic, hexosediphosphate, α-glycerophosphate, and glucose dehydrogenases were present on the eighth day. More recent work has shown the presence of an active succinoxidase system as early as the twenty-fifth hour of incubation (Albaum, Novikoff, and Ogur, '46), and Spratt ('52) has found succinic dehydrogenase in the early blastoderm. Potter, Schneider, and Liebl ('45) made measurements of the succinoxidase system in rat liver and brain from the seventeenth day of gestation through the thirtieth day after birth and showed that the activity increased

TABLE 21. *Effect of Citric Acid Cycle Intermediates on Oxygen Consumption of Sea Urchin Egg Homogenates**

SUBSTRATE 10^{-2}M	OXYGEN CONSUMPTION AS PERCENTAGE OF CONTROL
Citrate	135
α-Ketoglutarate	145
Succinate	142
Fumarate	115
Malate	121
Glutamate	110
Pyruvate	120

* Data from Cleland and Rothschild ('52b).

during this period. Flexner and Flexner ('46) believe that the succinoxidase system of the cerebral cortex of the fetal pig is inactive until after the middle of gestation owing to insufficiency of cytochrome *c*. Nothing is known about the presence of succinoxidase in the early stages of amphibian development, but in *Amblystoma punctatum* the enzyme has considerable activity at the first stage tested (Harrison stage 20), and it may reasonably be assumed that it is present even earlier (Boell, '48).

As will be shown below, there is good evidence that the Embden-Meyerhof system of phosphorylating glycolysis exists in the chick embryo (Novikoff, Potter, and Le Page, '48), and Barth and Jaeger's series of studies ('47a,b, '50a,b) give strong evidence of the presence of a mechanism in the amphibian embryo, from early cleavage on, for oxidative production of high-energy phosphate bonds.

Alternate Pathways of Energy Release. *Cyanide-insensitive Respiration.* Cyanide does not inhibit completely the oxygen uptake of most embryos, and in some few cases respiration is almost completely resistant to this reagent. These facts have been mainly responsible for the suggestion that a portion of the total respiratory exchange does not go through the usual Warburg-Keilin system but proceeds instead through a system of "non-ferrous" catalysts. Although, as was mentioned previously, so-called cyanide insensitivity is sometimes the result of inadequate care to insure that cyanide concentration remains constant during an experiment, it is nevertheless true that a very substantial portion of the total respiration of the unfertilized sea urchin egg and of the grasshopper embryo in diapause cannot be depressed by cyanide or carbon monoxide. Both Lindahl ('40) and Robbie ('46) have suggested that residual respiration in the presence of cyanide may be of a special kind that does not normally occur. That inhibitors may induce extraordinary respiratory processes has been shown through the use of fluoride on the chick embryo, of dinitrophenol on the grasshopper embryo, and of azide on paramecium (Boell, '46). Notwithstanding, there remains the possibility that a small but definite fraction of respiratory exchange is mediated by a system of enzymes different from those that operate in the citric acid cycle and the Warburg-Keilin system.* The nature of such a possible pathway is unknown, nor is it known whether it operates normally as a collateral to the main system of respiratory catalysts or whether it becomes functional only when the Warburg-Keilin system has been inhibited.

The Phosphogluconic Acid Shunt. Lindberg has adduced evidence to support the view that respiration in the sea urchin egg, during the period of exponential rise, proceeds by a pathway other than the Embden-Meyerhof scheme (Lindberg, '43; Lindberg and Ernster, '48). He has suggested that glucose breakdown is an oxidative process which bypasses the usual glycolytic cycle through what has been termed the phosphogluconic acid shunt or the Warburg-Dickens scheme. In this, glucose-6-phosphate is oxidized to 6-phosphogluconic acid, and then, through several intermediate steps, to pyruvic acid. The reaction is catalyzed by a specific enzyme, glucose-6-phosphate dehydrogenase, and TPN is an obligatory cofactor (see

Fruton and Simmonds, '53, p. 459 ff.). Evidence for the operation of the scheme in the sea urchin egg stems from the observation that the oxygen consumption of egg homogenates can be stimulated by glucose or hexosemonophosphate, but hexosediphosphate has a negligible effect. Furthermore, Lindberg and Ernster have shown that iodoacetate, which blocks the Embden-Meyerhof system by inhibiting phosphoglyceraldehyde dehydrogenase, does not affect respiration. Additional support of rather indirect nature has been provided by Hultin ('53) and rests upon the demonstration that carbon dioxide fixation by sea urchin eggs, as measured by the uptake of $C^{14}O_2$, is maximal during the period when respiration rises exponentially. The pertinence of this observation will be apparent when it is recalled that the mechanism of carbon dioxide fixation by pyruvic acid, in the formation of malic acid, is coupled through TPN with the oxidation of glucose-6-phosphate to 6-phosphogluconic acid (see Fruton and Simmonds, '53, p. 474 ff.). Additional evidence, of still more peripheral nature, has been furnished by Hörstadius and Gustafson ('47, cited by Hörstadius, '49) that phosphogluconic acid exerts a marked animalizing influence on sea urchin eggs. Finally, although Cleland and Rothschild ('52b) presented cogent arguments for the operation of the Embden-Meyerhof scheme in the sea urchin egg, they showed also that phosphogluconic acid increased the oxygen consumption of egg homogenates and have concluded that the enzymes for the phosphogluconic shunt are present. Perhaps a fraction of respiration proceeds normally through this pathway; on the other hand, as suggested by Hultin ('53), the pathway may have functional significance only when the enzymes concerned with the glycolytic cycle have been inhibited by sulfhydryl reagents. The phosphogluconic acid shunt may thus be analogous to the cyanide-insensitive fraction of respiration.

Non-phosphorylating Glycolysis. Much attention has been given to the elucidation of the mechanism of carbohydrate breakdown in the early chick embryo, and the claim has been made that glycolysis does not proceed through the usual steps of the Embden-Meyerhof scheme, i.e., through a series of phosphorylated intermediates, but occurs through a non-phosphorylating mechanism (see Needham, '42, pp. 610-615, for a review of the literature and summary of the evidence). Needham and his co-workers

---

* One need but recall the reported absence of cytochrome *c* in sea urchin eggs, the early chick embryo, and the cerebral cortex, or the observation of Sanborn and Williams ('50) that cytochrome *x* (which combines certain properties of cytochromes *b* and *c* and succinic dehydrogenase) is destroyed during pupation in Cecropia.

found that the chick embryo was deficient in four essential components of the Embden-Meyerhof system: (1) the embryo could not attack glycogen or a number of hexosephosphates, although glucose could be broken down readily, and it was concluded that phosphorylase, the enzyme esterifying glycogen, was absent or present in too low concentration to be effective; (2) since triosephosphate could not be broken down, it was concluded that triosephosphate dehydrogenase was absent; (3) ATP was present, but in quantities too small to be effective; and (4) DPN was absent. It was postulated, therefore, "that in the chick embryo there are two separate routes of carbohydrate breakdown: (1) a non-phosphorylating glucolysis mechanism, very active and closely bound to the cell structure, and (2) a phosphorylating system closely similar to that in muscle, dealing with glycogen and hexosediphosphate, but of very low activity" because of the deficiencies noted above.

Novikoff, Potter, and Le Page ('48) obtained results which were quite different from those of the Cambridge workers, for they found that embryo homogenates would glycolyze hexosediphosphate, fructose-6-phosphate, and glucose-6-phosphate as well as glucose. Moreover, they extracted from embryos, three to ten days of age, various hexosephosphates and their breakdown products, ATP, and DPN in amounts roughly equivalent to those in adult tissues. They concluded, therefore, that their results did not rule out of consideration a non-phosphorylating pathway for glycolysis but that postulating one was unnecessary since all enzymes and intermediates in the Embden-Meyerhof scheme were present in adequate concentrations.

There can be little doubt, after considering the experimental findings reviewed in the foregoing pages, that in the sea urchin egg and in the chick embryo all of the components necessary for the operation of the scheme shown in Figure 202 are present. Unfortunately, much less is known for most embryos. To suggest that the scheme has general applicability to the other forms commonly used in embryological studies would be no more than to hazard a guess. Such a conclusion may be correct, but it cannot be justified from the experimental evidence available at present. The reconstruction of a complex and intricate mechanism for energy release and energy storage from a few biochemical fragments that have come to hand is not unlike the restoration of a skull from a few chips of brain case, a jawbone, and perhaps a tooth or two. Museums throughout the world give evidence of successes along this line, but the recent disclosures concerning the Piltdown man point up the dangers inherent in such a procedure.

ENZYMES IN ONTOGENESIS

Synthesis of Respiratory Enzymes. It seems reasonable to expect that increased oxygen consumption during development would be accompanied by a corresponding change in the enzymes through which respiratory processes are mediated. Because of its key position in respiration, cytochrome oxidase has been most extensively investigated, and the results obtained in the grasshopper (Bodine and Boell, '36a; Allen, '40), the salamander (Boell, '45), and the chick (Albaum and Worley, '42; Albaum, Novikoff, and Ogur, '46; Levy and Young, '48) agree that increase in respiration is paralleled by increase in the amount of cytochrome oxidase in the embryo.[*] In the sea urchin, Deutsch and Gustafson ('52) have reported that cytochrome oxidase rises during the first four hours after fertilization, but then it falls, during the next twenty hours, to a level equal to or less than the initial value. The homogenates used in these experiments were prepared by subjecting eggs to a freezing mixture and then shaking them vigorously during thawing. It is well known that cytochrome oxidase and certain dehydrogenases as well are inactivated by such treatment; hence the differences in enzyme activity found by Deutsch and Gustafson are probably due largely to variations in

[*] It is impossible to express the quantity of an enzyme by the usual metrical units employed for other chemical entities. In general, what is measured in enzyme studies is the activity of the enzyme under optimal conditions, so that the rate of reaction, during a reasonable period of time, is limited only by the amount of enzyme present in the reaction system. If care is taken to insure such conditions, reaction rate is found to be proportional to the concentration of the enzyme in the system. Measurement of enzyme activity in tissue minces or homogenates gives only an indication of the total *potential* activity of the enzyme. It provides no information on the degree to which the enzyme functions in vivo. This is particularly well illustrated in developing and diapause grasshopper embryos, where it is found that the amounts of cytochrome oxidase are identical. But the enzyme functions to only a slight extent during diapause, as is shown by the lower rate of respiration and the decreased sensitivity to cyanide.

the degree of enzyme inactivation. As will be recalled, Gustafson has claimed that cytochrome oxidase is gradually taken up into mitochondria at the time when they increase in the mesenchyme blastula stage. These results may indicate, therefore, that the sensitivity of the enzyme to freezing and thawing is greater after incorporation into mitochondria than before. In the frog embryo, Spiegelman and Steinbach ('45) failed to find any increase in cytochrome oxidase between stages 6 and 19 (Shumway), although respiration of intact embryos rose approximately 800 per cent during this

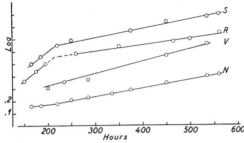

Fig. 203. Developmental changes in total nitrogen (N), volume (V), respiration (R), and succinoxidase (S) in the central nervous system of *Amblystoma punctatum*. Only the dimensions of the log scale are shown on the ordinate. Initial logarithmic values for $N=1.06$; for $V=4.81$; for $R=2.56$; and for $S=2.50$. Abscissa denotes hours of development from fertilization. Volume data from Boell ('48); data for nitrogen, respiration, and succinoxidase from Boell and Shen (unpublished).

period. They have interpreted this result as showing that what changes during development is not the amount of enzyme but the spatial orientation of enzyme and substrate. It will be recalled that the same idea had been expressed earlier for the sea urchin egg by Runnström ('30). The conclusion that a change occurs during development in the relationship of enzyme with its normal substrate is reasonable, but its validity would not be impaired by the demonstration that enzyme synthesis occurs. Brachet ('49) has pointed out that determination of cytochrome oxidase activity is difficult in frog embryos owing to the large endogenous oxygen uptake of egg homogenates, but by means of a spectrophotometric method he has shown a synthesis of cytochrome oxidase similar to that observed in Amblystoma.

In the grasshopper, salamander, and chick embryos, cytochrome oxidase increases relatively more rapidly than respiration. It is clear, therefore, that although most of the respiratory exchange may proceed through cytochrome oxidase, the concentration of enzyme is not the factor that limits the rate of respiration or of respiratory increase. A number of suggestions have been made as to the cause for limitation of respiratory rate, such as the amount of substrate available or the rate at which it is mobilized, affinity between enzyme and substrate, or limiting concentrations of essential intermediates such as cytochrome c or coenzyme. All of these factors are of importance, no doubt, in influencing the rate of respiration, but it would seem that the chief factor responsible for the respiratory rate at a particular time in development is the energy requirement of the embryo.

Changes in succinoxidase activity have been determined in the salamander (Boell, '48) and the chick (Albaum et al., '46). In Amblystoma, the rate of increase during development is probably not significantly different from that of cytochrome oxidase. Shen ('49) has obtained similar results with mitochondrial preparations from developing rat muscle. Cytochrome oxidase and succinoxidase increase exponentially between the fifteenth day of gestation and the second week after birth, and the slopes of the developmental curves are identical. In the chick, however, the two enzymes increase at somewhat different rates between the second and sixth days of development.

It has been suggested that enzymes concerned with general metabolic processes, such as respiration, develop in relation to the growth of the embryo (Boell, '48). In Amblystoma, the developmental curves for respiration, cytochrome oxidase, succinoxidase, and alkaline phosphatase (Krugelis, Nicholis, and Vosgian, '52), as measured in homogenates of the entire embryo, have fairly similar slopes, and the curves seem best interpreted as reflecting the synthesis of metabolically active material from yolk reserves. The relationship between enzyme synthesis and growth in the central nervous system (brain plus spinal cord to the level of the sixth somite) of Amblystoma is shown in Figure 203. Here it can be seen that respiration and succinoxidase increase approximately in parallel with size of the nervous system, as determined by total nitrogen or volume. In the chick embryo, where the relation between enzyme synthesis and growth can also be tested directly, it appears that increase in cytochrome oxidase is proportional to increase in total nitrogen

Ball, E. G., and Meyerhof, B.   1940   On the occurrence of iron-porphyrin compounds and succinic dehydrogenase in marine organisms possessing the copper blood pigment hemocyanin. J. Biol. Chem., *134:*483–493.

Ballentine, R.   1938   Reducing activity of fertilized and unfertilized Arbacia eggs. Biol. Bull., *75:*368.

———   1940   Analysis of the changes in respiratory activity accompanying the fertilization of marine eggs. J. Cell. & Comp. Physiol., *15:*217–232.

Banga, I.   1937   Über den Mechanismus der Milchsäurebildung im Muskel. Zeit. f. Physiol. Chem., *249:*209–210.

Barnes, M. R.   1944   The metabolism of the developing *Rana pipiens* as revealed by specific inhibitors. J. Exp. Zool., *95:*399–417.

Barron, D. H.   1941   The functional development of some mammalian neuromuscular mechanisms. Biol. Rev., *16:*1–33.

Barth, L. G.   1942   Regional differences in oxygen consumption of the amphibian gastrula. Physiol. Zool., *15:*30–46.

———   1946   Studies of the metabolism of development. J. Exp. Zool., *103:*463–486.

———, and Barth, L. J.   1951   The relation of adenosine triphosphate to yolk utilization in the frog's egg. J. Exp. Zool., *116:*99–121.

———, and Jaeger, L.   1947a   Phosphorylation in the frog's egg. Physiol. Zool., *20:*133–146.

———, and Jaeger, L.   1947b   The apyrase activity of various protein fractions of the frog's egg. J. Cell. & Comp. Physiol., *30:*111–130.

———, and Jaeger, L.   1950a   The role of adenosine-triphosphate in phosphate transfer from yolk to other proteins in the developing frog egg. I. General properties of the transfer system as a whole. J. Cell. & Comp. Physiol., *35:*413–436.

———, and Jaeger, L.   1950b   The role of adenosine-triphosphate in phosphate transfer from yolk to other proteins in the developing frog egg. II. Separation of the system into component enzymes, phosphate donor and phosphate acceptor. J. Cell. & Comp. Physiol., *35:*437–460.

Beams, H. W., and King, R. L.   1936   Survival of Ascaris eggs after centrifuging. Science, *84:*138.

Berenblum, I., Chain, E., and Heatley, N. G.   1939   The study of metabolic activities of small amounts of surviving tissue. Bioch. J., *33:*68–74.

Bialascewicz, K., and Bledovski, R.   1915   Cited from Needham, '31.

Bodenstein, D. A., and Kondritzer, A. A.   1948   The effect of nitrogen mustard on nucleic acids during embryonic amphibian development. J. Exp. Zool., *107:*109–121.

Bodine, J. H.   1929   Factors influencing the rate of respiratory metabolism of a developing egg (Orthoptera). Physiol. Zool., *2:*459–482.

———   1946   Uric acid formation in the developing egg of the grasshopper, *Melanoplus differentialis.* Physiol. Zool., *19:*54–57.

———, Allen, T. H., and Boell, E. J.   1937   Enzymes in ontogenesis. III. Activation of naturally occurring enzymes (tyrosinase). Proc. Soc. Exp. Biol. & Med., *37:*450–453.

———, and Boell, E. J.   1934a   Action of carbon monoxide on respiration of normal and blocked embryonic cells. J. Cell. & Comp. Physiol., *4:*475–482.

———, and Boell, E. J.   1934b   Respiratory mechanisms of normally developing and blocked embryonic cells. J. Cell. & Comp. Physiol., *5:*97–113.

———, and Boell, E. J.   1935   Enzymes in ontogenesis. I. Tyrosinase. J. Cell. & Comp. Physiol., *6:*263–275.

———, and Boell, E. J.   1936a   Enzymes in ontogenesis. II. The indophenol oxidase. J. Cell. & Comp. Physiol., *8:*213–230.

———, and Boell, E. J.   1936b   Respiration of embryo versus egg (Orthoptera). J. Cell. & Comp. Physiol., *8:*357–366.

———, and Boell, E. J.   1937   The action of certain stimulating and inhibiting substances on the respiration of active and blocked eggs and isolated embryos. Physiol. Zool., *10:*245–257.

———, and Boell, E. J.   1938   The influence of some dinitrophenols on respiratory metabolism during certain phases of active development. J. Cell. & Comp. Physiol., *11:*41–63.

———, Lu, K-H., and West, W. L.   1952   Reduction of triphenyltetrazolium chloride by mitotically active and blocked embryonic cells. Biol. Bull., *102:*16–21.

Boell, E. J.   1935   Respiratory quotients during embryonic development. J. Cell. & Comp. Physiol., *6:*369–385.

———   1942   Biochemical and physiological analysis of organizer action. Growth (Suppl.), *7:*37–53.

———   1945   Functional differentiation in embryonic development. II. Respiration and cytochrome oxidase activity in Amblystoma punctatum. J. Exp. Zool., *100:*331–352.

———   1946   The effect of sodium azide on *Paramecium calkinsi.* Biol. Bull., *91:*238–239.

———   1948   Biochemical differentiation during amphibian development. Ann. N. Y. Acad. Sci., *49:*773–800.

———, Koch, H., and Needham, J.   1939   Morphogenesis and metabolism. IV. Respiratory quotient of the regions of the amphibian gastrula. Proc. Roy. Soc. London (B) *127:*374–387.

———, Needham, J., and Rogers, V.   1939   Morphogenesis and metabolism. I. Anaerobic glycolysis of the regions of the amphibian gastrula. Proc. Roy. Soc. London (B), *127:*322–356.

———, and Nicholas, J. S.   1948   Respiratory metabolism of the mammalian egg. J. Exp. Zool., *109:*267–282.

———, and Poulson, D. F.   1939   The respiratory metabolism of normal and genetically deficient eggs of *Drosophila melanogaster.* Anat. Rec., 75 (Suppl.): 65–66.

———, and Shen, S. C.   1949   Experimental modification of cholinesterase development in the midbrain of *Amblystoma punctatum.* Anat. Rec., *105:*490.

———, and Shen, S. C.   1950   Development of cholinesterase in the central nervous system of

Amblystoma punctatum. J. Exp. Zool., *113:*583–600.

Bohr, C., and Hasselbalch, K. A. 1903 Cited from Needham, '31.

Boivin, A., Vendrely R., and Vendrely C. 1948 L'acide désoxyribonucléique du noyau cellulaire, dépositaire des caractères héréditaires; arguments d'ordre analytique. Compt. Rend. Acad. Sci. Paris, *226:*1061–1063.

Booth, V. H. 1935 The identity of xanthine oxidase and the Schardinger enzyme. Bioch. J., *29:*1732–1748.

Borei, H. 1948 Respiration of oöcytes, unfertilized eggs and fertilized eggs from Psammechinus and Asterias. Biol. Bull., *95:*124–150.

———— 1950 Cytochrome *c* in sea urchin eggs. Acta Chem. Scand., *4:*1607–1608.

Brachet, J. 1934 Étude du métabolisme de l'oeuf de grenouille (*Rana fusca*) au cours du développement. 1. La respiration et la glycolyse de la segmentation a l'éclosion. Arch. de Biol., *45:*611–727.

———— 1938 The oxygen consumption of artificially activated and fertilized Chaetopterus eggs. Biol. Bull., *74:*93–98.

————1939 Étude du métabolisme de l'oeuf de grenouille (*Rana fusca*) au cours du développement. V. Le métabolisme protéique et hydrocarboné de l'oeuf en relation avec le problème de l'organizateur. Arch. de Biol., *50:*233–267.

———— 1947 Nucleic acids in the cell and embryo. Symp. Soc. Exp. Biol., *1:*207–224.

———— 1949 Discussion of paper by Holter. Publ. Staz. Zool. Napoli, *21* (Suppl.): 73.

———— 1950 Chemical Embryology, translated by L. G. Barth. Interscience Publishers, New York.

————, and Needham, J. 1935 Étude du métabolisme de l'oeuf de grenouille (*Rana fusca*) au cours du développement. IV. La teneur en glycogène de l'oeuf de la ségmentation à l'éclosion. Arch. de Biol., *46:*821–835.

Bragg, A. N. 1939 Observations upon amphibian deutoplasm and its relation to embryonic and early larval development. Biol. Bull., *77:*268–283.

Brody, S. 1945 Bioenergetics and Growth. Reinhold Publishing Corp., New York.

Buchanan, W. J. 1938 Developmental acceleration following inhibition. J. Exp. Zool., *79:*109–127.

———— 1940 Developmental rate and alternating temperature. J. Exp. Zool., *83:*235–248.

Butler, J. A. V. 1946 Life and the second law of thermodynamics. Nature, *158:*153–154.

Caspersson, T. 1947 The relation between nucleic acids and protein synthesis. Symp. Soc. Exp. Biol., *1:*127–151.

Cleland, K. W., and Rothschild, Lord 1952a The metabolism of the sea-urchin egg. Anaerobic breakdown of carbohydrate. J. Exp. Biol., *29:*285–294.

————, and Rothschild, Lord 1952b The metabolism of the sea-urchin egg. Oxidation of carbohydrate. J. Exp. Biol., *29:*416–428.

Clowes, G. H. A., Keltch, A. K., Strittmatter, C. F., and Walters, C. P. 1950 Action of nitro- and

halophenols upon oxygen consumption and phosphorylation by a cell-free particulate system from Arbacia eggs. J. Gen. Physiol., *33:*555–561.

————, and Krahl, M. E. 1934 Action of dinitro compounds on sea urchin eggs. Science, *80:*384–385.

————, and Krahl, M. E. 1936 Studies on cell metabolism and cell division. I. On the relation between molecular structures, chemical properties, and biological activities of the nitrophenols. J. Gen. Physiol., *20:*145–171.

Coghill, G. E. 1929 Anatomy and the Problem of Behavior. Cambridge University Press, Cambridge, England.

Crescitelli, F. 1935 The respiratory metabolism of *Galleria mellonella* (bee moth) during pupal development at different constant temperatures. J. Cell. & Comp. Physiol., *6:*351–368.

Daniel, J. F., and Yarwood, E. A. 1939 The early embryology of *Triturus torosus*. Univ. Calif. Publ. Zool., *43:*321–356.

Daniel, R. L. 1947 Distribution of glycogen in the developing salmon (*Salmo salar* L.). J. Exp. Biol., *24:*123–144.

Davidson, J. N., and Leslie, I. 1950 A new approach in the biochemistry of growth and development. Nature, *165:*49–53.

Detwiler, S. 1946a Experiments upon the midbrain of Amblystoma embryos. Am. J. Anat., *78:*115–138.

———— 1946b A quantitative study of locomotion in larval Amblystoma following either midbrain or forebrain excision. J. Exp. Zool., *102:*321–332.

Deutsch, H. F., and Gustafson, T. 1952 The changes in catalase and cytochrome oxidase in developing sea urchin eggs. Arkiv Kemi, *4:*221–231.

deVillafranca, G. W. 1953 An investigation of the distribution and development of adenosinetriphosphatase activity in developing rat muscle. Doctoral dissertation, Yale University.

Dickens, F., and Greville, G. D. 1933a Metabolism of normal and tumour tissue. VIII. Respiration in sugar-free media. Bioch. J., *27:*832–841.

————, and Greville, G. D. 1933b Metabolism of normal and tumour tissue. IX. Ammonia and urea formation. Bioch. J., *27:*1123–1133.

————, and Šimer, F. 1930 The metabolism of normal and tumour tissue. II. The respiratory quotient, and the relationship of respiration to glycolysis. Bioch. J., *24:*1301–1326.

————, and Šimer, F. 1931 The metabolism of normal and tumour tissue. IV. The respiratory quotient in bicarbonate-media. Bioch. J., *25:*985–993.

Dixon, M. 1951 Manometric Methods, 3d ed. Cambridge University Press, Cambridge, England.

Dumm, M. E., and Levy, M. 1949 Chemistry of the chick embryo. VII. The accumulation of solids, nitrogen, lipids, and peptidase by the gizzard and liver of the chick embryo. J. Cell. & Comp. Physiol., *33:*373–382.

Elliott, K. A. C., and Greig, M. E. 1938 The distribution of the succinic oxidase system in animal tissues. Bioch. J., *32:*1407–1423.

Fischer, F. G., and Hartwig, H. 1938 Vergleichende Messungen der Atmung des Amphibien-Keimes und seiner Teile während der Entwicklung. Biol. Zentralbl., *58:*567–589.

Fisher, K. C. 1941 The fractionation of respiration by the use of narcotics. Biol. Bull., *81:*282.

———, and Henry, R. J. 1940 The use of urethane as an indicator of "activity" metabolism in the sea urchin egg. Biol. Bull., *79:*731–732.

———, and Henry, R. J. 1944 The effects of urethane and chloral hydrate on oxygen consumption and cell division in the egg of the sea urchin, *Arbacia punctulata.* J. Gen. Physiol., *27:*469–481.

———, Henry, R. J., and Low, E. 1944 The effects of sulfanilamide and azide on oxygen consumption and cell division in the egg of the sea urchin, *Arbacia punctulata.* J. Pharmacol. & Exp. Therap., *81:*58–66.

———, and Stern, J. R. 1942 The separation of an "activity" metabolism from the total respiration of yeast by the effects of ethyl carbamate. J. Cell. & Comp. Physiol., *19:*109–122.

Fiske, C. H., and Boyden, E. A. 1926 Nitrogen metabolism in the chick embryo. J. Biol. Chem., *70:*535–556.

Fitzgerald, L. R. 1949 The alkaline phosphatase of the developing grasshopper egg. J. Exp. Zool., *110:*461–487.

Flexner, J. B., and Flexner, L. B. 1948 Biochemical and physiological differentiation during embryonic development. VII. Adenylpyrophosphatase and acid phosphatase activities in the developing cerebral cortex and liver of the fetal guinea pig. J. Cell. & Comp. Physiol., *31:*311–320.

———, and Flexner, L. B. 1951 Biochemical and physiological differentiation during embryonic development. XIV. The nucleic acids of the developing cerebral cortex and liver of the fetal guinea pig. J. Cell. & Comp. Physiol., *38:*1–16.

———, Flexner, L. B., and Straus, W. L., Jr. 1941 The oxygen consumption, cytochrome and cytochrome oxidase activity and histological structure of the developing cerebral cortex of the fetal pig. J. Cell. & Comp. Physiol., *18:*355–368.

Flexner, L. B., and Flexner, J. B. 1946 Biochemical and physiological differentiation during embryonic development. III. Succinic dehydrogenase and succinoxidase in the cerebral cortex of the fetal pig. J. Cell. & Comp. Physiol., *27:*35–42.

Friedberg, F., and Eakin, R. M. 1949 Studies in protein metabolism of the amphibian embryo. I. Uptake of radioactive glycine. J. Exp. Zool., *110:*33–46.

Fruton, J. S., and Simmonds, S. 1953 General Biochemistry. John Wiley & Sons, New York.

Goldinger, J. M., and Barron, E. S. G. 1946 The pyruvate metabolism during the process of cell division. J. Gen. Physiol., *30:*73–82.

Gray, J. 1925 Cited from Needham, '31.

——— 1926 The growth of fish. I. The relation between the embryo and yolk in *Salmo fario.* J. Exp. Biol., *4:*215–225.

——— 1927 The mechanism of cell division. III. The relationship between cell division and growth in segmenting eggs. J. Exp. Biol., *4:*313–321.

——— 1929a The growth of fish. II. The growth-rate of the embryo of *Salmo fario.* J. Exp. Biol., *6:*110–130.

——— 1929b The kinetics of growth. J. Exp. Biol., *6:*248–274.

Gregg, J. R. 1948 Carbohydrate metabolism of normal and hybrid amphibian embryos. J. Exp. Zool., *109:*119–134.

———, and Ballentine, R. 1946 Nitrogen metabolism of *Rana pipiens* during embryonic development. J. Exp. Zool., *103:*143–168.

———, and Løvtrup, S. 1950 Biochemical gradients in the axolotl gastrula, Compt. Rend. Lab. Carlsberg, ser. chim., *27:*307–324.

———, and Ornstein, N. 1952 Anaerobic ammonia production by amphibian gastrulae explants. Biol. Bull., *102:*22–24.

———, and Pomerat, C. M. 1942 The glycogen content of the embryo of *Rana pipiens* during development. Growth, *6:*231–234.

Greig, M. E., Munro, M. P., and Elliott, K. A. C. 1939 The metabolism of lactic and pyruvic acids in normal and tumour tissues. Bioch. J., *33:*443–453.

Gustafson, T. 1952 Nitrogen Metabolism, Enzymic Activity, and Mitochondria Distribution in Relation to Differentiation in the Sea Urchin Egg. Almqvist and Wiksells, Uppsala.

———, and Hasselberg, I. 1951 Studies on enzymes in the developing sea urchin egg. Exp. Cell Res., *2:*642–672.

———, and Lenicque, P. 1952 Studies on mitochondria in the developing sea urchin egg. Exp. Cell Res., *3:*251–274.

Harris, D. L. 1946 Phosphoproteinphosphatase, a new enzyme from the frog egg. J. Biol. Chem., *165:*541–550.

Harrison, R. G. 1935 The origin and development of the nervous system studied by the methods of experimental embryology. Proc. Roy. Soc. London (B), *118:*155–196.

Hayes, F. A. 1938 The relation of the fat changes to the general chemical embryology of the sea urchin. Biol. Bull., *74:*267–277.

———, and Hollett, A. 1940 The carbohydrate metabolism of developing salmon eggs. Canad. J. Res., *18(D):*53–65.

———, Wilmot, I. R., and Livingstone, D. A. 1951 The oxygen consumption of the salmon egg in relation to development and activity. J. Exp. Zool., *116:*377–395.

Heatley, N. G., and Lindahl, P. E. 1937 Studies on the nature of the amphibian organization center. 5. Distribution and nature of glycogen in the amphibian embryo. Proc. Roy. Soc. London (B), *122:*395–402.

Henry, R. J., and Henry, M. D. 1945 The effect of penicillin on eggs of the sea urchin, *Arbacia punctulata.* J. Gen. Physiol., *28:*405–413.

Herrmann, H. 1953 Biochemistry of organogenesis. Arch. Néerl. de Zool., *10* (Suppl.):127–143.

———, and Nicholas, J. S. 1948a Enzymatic liberation of inorganic phosphate from adenosinetriphosphate in developing rat muscle. J. Exp. Zool., *107:*177–181.

———, and Nicholas, J. S. 1948b Quantitative

changes in muscle protein fractions during rat development. J. Exp. Zool., *107*:165–176.

Herrmann, H., and Nicholas, J. S. 1949 Nucleic acid content of whole homogenates and of fractions of developing rat muscle. J. Exp. Zool., *112*: 341–359.

———, Nicholas, J. S., and Vosgian, M. E. 1949 Liberation of inorganic phosphate from adenosinetriphosphate by fractions derived from developing rat muscle. Proc. Soc. Exp. Biol. & Med., *72*:454–457.

Hill, D. L. 1945 Carbohydrate metabolism during embryonic development (Orthoptera). J. Cell. & Comp. Physiol., *25*:205–216.

Hörstadius, S. 1949 Experimental researches on the developmental physiology of the sea urchin. Publ. Staz. Zool. Napoli, *21* (Suppl.): 131–172.

Hoff-Jørgensen, E., and Zeuthen, E. 1952 Evidence of cytoplasmic deoxyribosides in the frog's egg. Nature, *169*:245–246.

Holter, H. 1949 Problems of enzyme localization and development. Publ. Staz. Zool. Napoli, *21* (Suppl.): 60–76.

Holtfreter, J. 1946 Experiments on the formed inclusions of the amphibian egg. I. The effect of pH and electrolytes on yolk and lipochondria. J. Exp. Zool., *101*:355–405.

Hopkins, H. S., and Handford, S. W. 1943 Respiratory metabolism during development in two species of Amblystoma. J. Exp. Zool., *93*:403–414.

Horowitz, N. H. 1940 The respiratory metabolism of the developing eggs of *Urechis caupo*. J. Cell. & Comp. Physiol., *15*:229–308.

Huff, G. C., and Boell, E. J. 1936 Effect of ultracentrifuging on oxygen consumption of the eggs of *Ascaris suum*, Goeze. Proc. Soc. Exp. Biol. & Med., *34*:626–628.

Hultin, T. 1953 Metabolism and determination. Arch. Néerl. de Zool., *10* (Suppl.):76–91.

Hutchens, J. O., Kopac, M. J., and Krahl, M. E. 1942 The cytochrome oxidase content of centrifugally separated fractions of unfertilized Arbacia eggs. J. Cell. & Comp. Physiol., *20*:113–116.

———, Keltch, A., Krahl, M. E., and Clowes, G. H. A. 1942 Studies on cell metabolism and cell division. VI. Observations on the glycogen content, carbohydrate consumption, lactic acid production, and ammonia production of eggs of *Arbacia punctulata*. J. Gen. Physiol., *25*:717–731.

Jaeger, L. 1945 Glycogen utilization by the amphibian gastrula in relation to invagination and induction. J. Cell. & Comp. Physiol., *25*:97–120.

Jandorf, B. J., and Krahl, M. E. 1942 Studies on cell metabolism and cell division. VIII. The diphosphopyridine nucleotide (cozymase) content of eggs of *Arbacia punctulata*. J. Gen. Physiol., *25*:749–754.

Keltch, A. K., Strittmatter, C. F., Walters, C. P., and Clowes, G. H. A. 1950 Oxidative phosphorylation by a cell free particulate system from unfertilized Arbacia eggs. J. Gen. Physiol., *33*: 547–554.

Kielley, W. W., and Meyerhof, O. 1948 Studies on ATPase of muscle. II. A new Mg-activated adenosinetriphosphatase. J. Biol. Chem., *176*:591–601.

Kitching, J. A., and Moser, F. 1940 Studies on a

cortical layer response to stimulating agents in the Arbacia egg. IV. Response to chemical and physical agents in the absence of oxygen and observations of the effects of low oxygen tensions and high hydrostatic pressures upon amoeboid eggs. Biol. Bull., *78*:80–91.

Krahl, M. E. 1950 Metabolic activities and cleavage of eggs of the sea urchin, *Arbacia punctulata*. A review, 1932–1949. Biol. Bull., *98*:175–217.

———, Keltch, A. K., Neubeck, C. E., and Clowes, G. H. A. 1941 Cell metabolism and cell division. V. Cytochrome oxidase activity in the eggs of *Arbacia punctulata*. J. Gen. Physiol., *24*:597–617.

Krugelis, E. J., Nicholas, J. S., and Vosgian, M. E. 1952 Alkaline phosphatase activity and nucleic acids during embryonic development of *Amblystoma punctatum* at different temperatures. J. Exp. Zool., *121*:489–504.

Kutsky, P. B. 1950 Phosphate metabolism in the early development of *Rana pipiens*. J. Exp. Zool., *115*:429–460.

Laser, H., and Rothschild, Lord 1939 The metabolism of the eggs of *Psammechinus miliaris* during the fertilization reaction. Proc. Roy. Soc. London (B), *126*:539–557.

Lennerstrand, Å. 1933 Aerobe und anaerobe Glykolyse bei der Entwicklung des Froscheies (*R. temporaria*). Zeit. vergl. Physiol., *20*:287–290.

Levy, M. 1952 Metabolic patterns in embryonic development. Ann. N. Y. Acad. Sci., *55*:51–56.

———, and Palmer, A. H. 1943 Chemistry of the chick embryo. IV. Aminopeptidase. J. Biol. Chem., *150*:271–279.

———, and Young, N. F. 1948 Chemistry of the chick embryo. V. Accumulation of cytochrome oxidase. J. Biol. Chem., *175*:73–77.

Lindahl, P. E. 1939 Zur Kenntnis der Entwicklungsphysiologie des Seeigeleies. Zeit. vergl. Physiol., *27*:233–250.

——— 1940 Über die CN-resistante Atmung des Seeigeleies. Arkiv för Kemi, Mineral. och Geol., *14A*:1–31.

——— 1953 Somatic reduction division in the development of the sea urchin. Nature, *171*:437.

Lindberg, O. 1943 Studien über das Problem des Kohlehydratabbaus und der Säurebildung bei der Befruchtung des Seeigeleies. Arkiv för Kemi, Mineral. och Geol., *16A*:1–20.

———, and Ernster, L. 1948 On carbohydrate metabolism in homogenized sea urchin eggs. Bioch. Biophys. Acta, *2*:471–477.

Linderstrøm-Lang, K. 1946 Periodic metabolism and diffusion. Compt. Rend. Lab. Carlsberg, ser. chim., *25*:229–272.

Loeb, J. 1895 Untersuchungen über die physiologischen Wirkungen des Sauerstoffmangels. Pflüg. Arch., *62*:249–294.

Løvtrup, S. 1953a Energy sources of amphibian embryogenesis. Compt. Rend. Lab. Carlsberg, ser. chim., *28*:371–399.

——— 1953b Utilization of reserve material during amphibian embryogenesis at different temperatures. Compt. Rend. Lab. Carlsberg, ser. chim., *28*:400–425.

——— 1953c Changes in the content of peptidases during amphibian embryogenesis at different temperatures. Compt. Rend. Lab. Carlsberg, ser. chim., 28:426–443.

Ludwig, D. 1950a The metabolism of starved nymphs of the grasshopper, *Chortophaga viridifasciata*, De Geer. Physiol. Zool., 23:41–47.

———— 1950b Changes in the distribution of nitrogen during starvation in the grasshopper, *Chortophaga viridifasciata*, De Geer. Physiol. Zool., 23:208–213.

Lyon, E. P. 1904 Cited from Needham, '31.

Metzler, C. J., and Humm, D. G. 1951 The determination of cholinesterase activity in the whole brains of developing rats. Science, 113:382–383.

Meyerhof, O. 1911 Untersuchungen über die Wärmetönung der vitalen Oxydationsvorgänge in Eiern. Bioch. Zeit., 35:279–315, 316–328.

Mirsky, A. E., and Ris, H. 1949 Variable and constant components of chromosomes. Nature, 163:666–667.

Moog, F. 1943 Cytochrome oxidase in early chick embryos. J. Cell. & Comp. Physiol., 22:223–231.

———— 1944a The chloretone sensitivity of frogs' eggs in relation to respiration and development. J. Cell. & Comp. Physiol., 23:131–155.

———— 1944b Localizations of alkaline and acid phosphatase in the early embryogenesis of the chick. Biol. Bull., 86:51–80.

———— 1947 Adenyl pyrophosphatase in brain, liver, heart, and skeletal muscle of chick embryos and hatched chicks. J. Exp. Zool., 105:209–220.

———— 1950 The functional differentiation of the small intestine. I. The accumulation of alkaline phosphomonoesterase in the duodenum of the chick. J. Exp. Zool., 115:109–129.

———— 1951 The functional differentiation of the small intestine. II. The differentiation of alkaline phosphomonoesterase in the duodenum of the mouse. J. Exp. Zool., 118:187–208.

———— 1952 The differentiation of enzymes in relation to the functional activities of the developing embryo. Ann. N. Y. Acad. Sci., 55:57–66.

———— 1953 The functional differentiation of the small intestine. III. The influence of the pituitary-adrenal system on the differentiation of phosphatase of the suckling mouse. J. Exp. Zool., 124:329–346.

————, and Steinbach, H. B. 1945 Adenylpyrophosphatase in chick embryos. J. Cell. & Comp. Physiol., 25:133–144.

Moore, J. A. 1941 Developmental rate of hybrid frogs. J. Exp. Zool., 86:405–422.

———— 1946 Studies in the development of frog hybrids. J. Exp. Zool., 101:173–219.

Morgan, E. J. 1930 Xanthine oxidase in the avian embryo. Bioch. J., 24:410–414.

Nachmansohn, D. 1939 Cholinesterase dans le système nerveux central. Boll. Soc. Chim. Biol. (Paris), 21:761–796.

Needham, J. 1931 Chemical Embryology. Cambridge University Press, Cambridge, England.

———— 1932a On the true metabolic rate of the chick embryo and the respiration of its membranes. Proc. Roy. Soc. London (B), 110:46–74.

———— 1932b A manometric analysis of the metabolism in avian ontogenesis. II. The effects of fluoride, iodoacetate, and other reagents on the respiration of blastoderm, embryo, and yolk sac. Proc. Roy. Soc. London (B), 112:114–138.

———— 1933 The energy sources in ontogenesis. VII. The respiratory quotient of developing crustacean embryos. J. Exp. Biol., 10:79–87.

———— 1942 Biochemistry and Morphogenesis. Cambridge University Press, Cambridge, England.

————, and Nowinski, W. W. 1937 Intermediary carbohydrate metabolism in embryonic life. I. General aspects of anaerobic glycolysis. Bioch. J., 31:1165–1184.

Negelein, E. 1925 Über die glykolytische Wirkung des embryonalen Gewebes. Bioch. Zeit., 165:122–134.

Nolf, L. O. 1932 Experimental studies on certain factors influencing the development and viability of the ova of the human Trichurus as compared with those of the human Ascaris. Am. J. Hyg., 16:288–322.

Novikoff, A. B., and Potter, V. R. 1948 Changes in nucleic acid concentration during the development of the chick embryo. J. Biol. Chem., 173:233–238.

————, Potter, V. R., and Le Page, G. A. 1948 Phosphorylating glycolysis in the early chick embryo. J. Biol. Chem., 173:239–252.

Öhman, L. O. 1940 Über die Veränderung des respiratorischen Quotienten während der Frühentwicklung des Seeigeleies. Arkiv för Zool., 32A:1–9.

Parnas, J. K., and Krasinka, Z. 1921 Ueber den Stoffwechsel der Amphibienlarven. Bioch. Zeit., 116:108–137.

Philips, F. S. 1940 Oxygen consumption and its inhibition in the development of Fundulus and various pelagic eggs. Biol. Bull., 78:256–273.

———— 1941 The oxygen consumption of the early chick embryo at various stages of development. J. Exp. Zool., 86:257–289.

———— 1942 Comparison of the respiratory rates of different regions of the chick blastoderm during early stages of development. J. Exp. Zool., 90:83–100.

Pollister, A. W. 1954 Cytochemical aspects of protein synthesis; in Dynamics of Growth Processes, edited by E. J. Boell, pp. 33–67. Princeton University Press, Princeton, New Jersey.

Porter, K. R. 1954 Cell and tissue differentiation in relation to growth; in Dynamics of Growth Processes, edited by E. J. Boell, pp. 95–110. Princeton University Press, Princeton, New Jersey.

Potter, V. R., and DuBois, K. P. 1942 The quantitative determination of cytochrome *c*. J. Biol. Chem., 142:417–426.

————, Schneider, W. C., and Liebl, G. J. 1945 Enzyme changes during growth and differentiation in the tissues of the new born rat. Cancer Res., 5:21–24.

Raven, C. P. 1935 Experimentelle Untersuchungen über den Glykogen-Stoffwechsel des Organizationszentrums in der Amphibiengastrula. Proc. Konin. Akad. Wetensch., 38:1107–1109.

Reddy, D. V. N., Lombardo, M. E., and Cerecedo,

L. R.   1952   Nucleic acid changes during development of the chick embryo. J. Biol. Chem., *198:* 267–270.

Robbie, W. A.   1946   The effect of cyanide on the oxygen consumption and cleavage of the sea urchin egg. J. Cell. & Comp. Physiol., *28:*305–324.

———, Boell, E. J., and Bodine, J. H.   1938   A study of the mechanism of cyanide inhibition. I. Effect of concentration on the egg of *Melanoplus differentialis*. Physiol. Zool., *11:*54–61.

Romanoff, A. L.   1941   The study of the respiratory behavior of individual chicken embryos. J. Cell. & Comp. Physiol., *18:*199–214.

———   1943   Differentiation in respiratory activity of isolated embryonic tissues. J. Exp. Zool., *93:*1–26.

Rothschild, Lord   1939   Effect of phlorizin on the metabolism of cytolyzing sea urchin eggs. J. Exp. Biol., *16:*49–55.

———   1948   The physiology of *Echinus esculentus* spermatozoa. J. Exp. Biol., *25:*15–21.

———, and Cleland, K. W.   1952   The physiology of sea urchin spermatozoa: The nature and localization of the endogenous substrate. J. Exp. Biol., *29:*66–71.

Runnström, J.   1930   Atmungsmechanismus und Entwicklungserregung bei dem Seeigelei. Protoplasma, *10:*106–173.

———   1932   Die Beeinflussung der Atmung und Spaltung im Seeigelei durch Dimethylparaphenylenediamine und Hydrochinon. Protoplasma, *15:*532–565.

———   1933   Zur Kenntnis der Stoffwechselvorgänge bei der Entwicklungserregung des Seeigeleies. Bioch. Zeit, *258:*257–279.

———   1934   Stoffwechselvorgänge während der ersten Mitose des Seeigeleies. Protoplasma, *20:* 1–10.

Sanborn, R. C., and Williams, C. M.   1950   The cytochrome system in the cecropia silkworm, with special reference to the properties of a new component. J. Gen. Physiol., *33:*579–588.

Sawyer, C. H.   1943   Cholinesterase and the behavior problem. I. The relationship between the development of the enzyme and early motility. II. The effects of inhibiting cholinesterase. J. Exp. Zool., *92:*1–29.

Scholander, P. F., Claff, C. L., Sveinson, S. L., and Scholander, S. I.   1952   Respiratory studies on single cells. III. Oxygen consumption during cell division. Biol. Bull., *102:*185–199.

Shen, S. C.   1949   Development of respiratory enzymes in rat muscle. Anat. Rec., *105:*489.

———   1954   Enzyme development as ontogeny of specific proteins (in press).

Sholl, D. A.   1954   Regularities in growth curves, including rhythms and allometry; in Dynamics of Growth Processes, edited by E. J. Boell, pp. 224–241. Princeton University Press, Princeton, New Jersey.

Slifer, E. H.   1930   Insect development. I. Fatty acids in the grasshopper egg. Physiol. Zool., *3:* 503–518.

———   1932   Insect development. III. Blastoki-

nesis in the living grasshopper egg. Biol. Zentralbl., *52:*223–229.

Smith, S.   1946   Studies in the development of the rainbow trout (*Salmo irideus*). I. The heat production and nitrogen excretion. J. Exp. Biol., *23:* 357–378.

———   1952   Studies in the development of the rainbow trout (*Salmo irideus*). II. The metabolism of carbohydrates and fats. J. Exp. Biol., *29:* 650–666.

Spiegelman, S., and Moog, F.   1945   A comparison of the effects of cyanide and azide on the development of frogs' eggs. Biol. Bull., *89:*122–130.

———, and Steinbach, H. B.   1945   Substrate-enzyme orientation during embryonic development. Biol. Bull., *88:*254–268.

Spratt, N. T., Jr.   1948   Development of the early chick blastoderm on synthetic media. J. Exp. Zool., *107:*39–64.

———   1950   Nutritional requirements of the early chick embryo. II. Differential requirements for morphogenesis and differentiation of the heart and brain. J. Exp. Zool., *114:*375–402.

———   1952   Reducing enzyme (dehydrogenase) systems in unincubated and one day old chick embryos. Anat. Rec., *112:*434.

Stefanelli, A. E.   1937   A new form of microrespirometer, with a note on the effect of cleavage on the respiration of the eggs of Rana. J. Exp. Biol., *14:*171–177.

Stotz, E.   1939   The estimation and distribution of cytochrome oxidase and cytochrome *c* in rat tissue. J. Biol. Chem., *131:*555–565.

Taylor, I. R., and Crescitelli, F.   1937   Measurement of heat production of small organisms. J. Cell. & Comp. Physiol., *10:*93–112.

Taylor, K. M., and Schechtman, A. M.   1949   In vitro development of the early chick embryo in the absence of small organic molecules. J. Exp. Zool., *111:*227–253.

Ten Cate, G.   1953   The intrinsic development of amphibian embryos. Doctoral dissertation. North-Holland Publishing Co., Amsterdam.

Thompson, D'Arcy W.   1942   On Growth and Form. Cambridge University Press, Cambridge, England.

Tuft, P.   1953   Energy changes in development. Arch. Néerl. de Zool., *10* (Suppl.): 59–75.

Tyler, A.   1942   Developmental processes and energetics. Quart. Rev. Biol., *17:*197–212, 339–353.

———, and Horowitz, N. H.   1938a   The activities of various substituted phenols in stimulating the respiration of sea urchin eggs. Biol. Bull., *75:* 209–223.

———, and Horowitz, N. H.   1938b   On the energetics of differentiation. VII. Comparison of the respiratory rates of parthenogenetic and fertilized Urechis eggs. Biol. Bull., *74:*99–107.

Vendrely, R., and Vendrely, C.   1949   La teneur de noyau cellulaire en acide désoxyribonucléique à travers les organes, les individus et les espèces animales. Experientia, *5:*327–329.

Vles, F.   1922   Cited from Needham, '31.

Warburg, O.   1908   Beobachtungen über die Oxydations-Prozesse vom Seeigelei. Zeit. Physiol. Chem., *57*:1–16.

Warburg, O. 1910 Über die Oxydationen in lebenden Zellen nach Versuchen am Seeigelei. Zeit. Physiol. Chem., *66*:305–340.

———, Posener, K., and Negelein, E. 1924 Über den Stoffwechsel der Carcinomzelle. Bioch. Zeit., *152*:309–344.

Weiss, P. 1953 Summary comments at the Symposium on the Biochemical and Structural Basis of Morphogenesis. Arch. Néerl. de Zool., *10* (Suppl.):165–176.

Whitaker, D. M. 1933 On the rate of oxygen consumption by fertilized and unfertilized eggs. V. Comparisons and interpretations. J. Gen. Physiol., *16*:497–528.

Wills, I. A. 1936 The respiratory rate of developing amphibia with special reference to sex differentiation. J. Exp. Zool., *73*:481–510.

Woerdeman, M. W. 1933 Über die chemischen Prozesse der embryonalen Induktion. Proc. Konin. Akad. Wetensch., *36*:842–849.

Yaoi, H. 1928–29 Glutathione, cytochrome and hydrogen ion concentration in developing chick embryos. Jap. J. Exp. Med., *7*:135–143.

Youngstrom, K. A. 1938 On the relationship between cholinesterase and the development of behavior in amphibia. J. Neurophysiol., *1*:357–363.

Zeuthen, E. 1946 Oxygen uptake during mitosis. Experiments on the eggs of the frog (*Rana platyrrhina*). Compt. Rend. Lab. Carlsberg, ser. chim., *25*:191–228.

——— 1950a Respiration during cell division in the egg of the sea urchin *Psammechinus miliaris*. Biol. Bull., *98*:144–151.

——— 1950b Respiration and cell division in the egg of *Urechis caupo*. Biol. Bull., *98*:152–160.

——— 1951 Segmentation, nuclear growth and cytoplasmic storage in eggs of echinoderms and amphibians. Publ. Staz. Zool. Napoli, *23*:47–69.

——— 1953 Biochemistry and metabolism of cleavage in the sea urchin egg, as resolved into its mitotic steps. Arch. Néerl. de Zool., *10* (Suppl.): 31–58.

ONTOGENY OF IMMUNOLOGICAL PROPERTIES*

ALBERT TYLER

ANTIGENS IN DEVELOPMENT
SOME GENERAL REMARKS

THE VARIOUS tissues and fluids of an adult organism contain a large assemblage of antigens. Of these the serum proteins and red blood corpuscles of mammals have been most extensively studied immunologically, but a large number of investigations have also been performed with soluble and insoluble constituents of various tissue cells. As a general statement one may say that the diverse antigens exhibit properties of species-specificity and tissue-specificity to various degrees. Certain serum or tissue-proteins show a high degree of species-specificity in that the antisera that are prepared against these materials of one species of animal fail to react or give weaker reactions with similar preparations from other species, depending somewhat on the degree of phylogenetic relationship. Certain antigens termed Forssman or heterogenetic antigens, however, are widely and irregularly distributed in various tissues and species of animals. Similarly, immunization with extracts of one kind of tissue yields antisera that react to various degrees with corresponding preparations from other tissues of the same animal. Where extensive cross-reactions occur specific components of the tissue may nevertheless be demonstrated by absorption of the antiserum with the preparation from the heterologous tissue. This procedure removes the antibodies for such antigens as may be common to various tissues.

It is often supposed that if the chemically different proteins of the different tissues were prepared in pure form no cross-reactions would be obtained. This has, however, not as yet been established experimentally. The difficulties here are due to the ability of

relatively small amounts of antigen to give rise to considerable amounts of antibody, and to the uncertainties involved in specifying the degree of purity of various proteins and other antigenic substances. As an illustration of this, some recent work by Cohn, Wetter and Deutsch ('49) on the proteins of chicken egg-white may be cited. They studied the precipitation of ovalbumin and conalbumin by antibodies produced in rabbits and horses. The ovalbumin was recrystallized six times and found to be of homogeneous molecular size upon sedimentation-velocity and diffusion tests. However, it showed two main components upon electrophoresis. The conalbumin preparation was ultracentrifugally and electrophoretically homogeneous. The electrophoretic patterns (Fig. 205) showed neither conalbumin in the ovalbumin preparation nor the reverse. Nevertheless, the antisera prepared against ovalbumin reacted also with conalbumin. On the other hand, the two ovalbumin components detected electrophoretically were indistinguishable immunologically. From quantitative studies of the various reactions of these preparations these workers conclude that there are antigenically active impurities in these preparations that are not revealed by the various physicochemical tests.

It is, of course, well known that there are no absolute criteria of purity even for simple chemical substances and that crystallizability does not necessarily mean molecular homogeneity. For protein preparations modern methods of determining homogeneity, in regard to different properties, include electrophoresis, sedimentation, diffusion and solubility, and each has certain limits of sensitivity. Experiments of the type cited above tend to show that immunological methods may be more sensitive for the detection of impurities in protein preparations. However, there is some uncertainty that impurities are really being detected by these methods. It would be necessary to show in the first place

* A presentation of the fundamentals of immunology is beyond the scope of this chapter. The uninformed reader should, therefore, consult a recent text such as Boyd's ('47) or Kabat and Mayer's ('48).

that the maximum amount of impurity that might be present in a particular preparation and still be physicochemically undetected is sufficient to induce the formation of the cross-reacting antibodies that are obtained

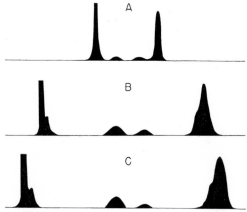

Fig. 205. Electrophoretic patterns of highly purified conalbumin (A) and of six times recrystallized ovalbumin (B and C) (from Cohn, Wetter and Deutsch, '49).

upon immunization. No clear-cut demonstration of this has been made in studies of cross-reactions as far as the present author is aware. For this purpose it would presumably be necessary to run parallel immunizations

portant to test for possible competition of antigens and for adjuvant action. In experiments by Vaughan and Kabat ('53), showing the presence of cross-reacting antibodies after immunization with minimal amounts of highly purified ovalbumin, the quantities of impurities that might be present would not have been presumed to induce antibody formation. However, they interpret their results as due to trace contaminants in their ovalbumin antigen.

Another way of interpreting cross-reactions is on the basis of similar determinant, or combining, groups on chemically different proteins or other antigenic substances. This can best be illustrated by the fundamental experiments of Landsteiner ('17-'46) in which proteins are coupled with small molecular, chemically well defined substances. Thus horse serum protein can be coupled with diazotized arsanilic acid (Atoxyl) as illustrated in Figure 206, the union being presumably with certain amino acids of the protein that have benzene or heterocyclic rings, such as tyrosine, histidine or tryptophane. When this is injected into a rabbit the antiserum that is obtained is found to react not only with the immunizing antigen but also with other proteins, such as chicken serum protein, that have been similarly coupled with diazotized Atoxyl. On the other hand it will not precipitate chicken serum

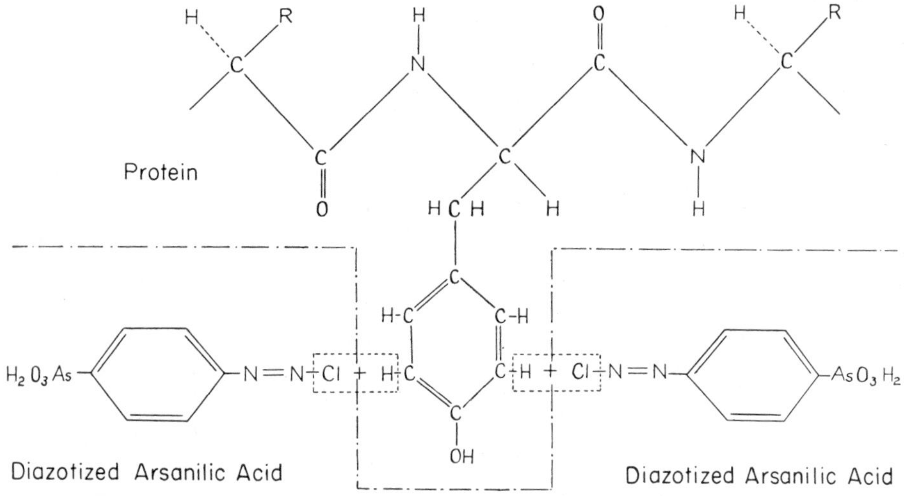

Fig. 206. Illustration of the manner in which a hapten may be coupled with a protein.

with the maximum possible amounts of the suspected impurities and determine whether or not the amounts of antibody produced corresponded to those indicated by the cross-reactions. At the same time it would be im-

protein that has been coupled with other simple substances, such as diazotized sulfanilic acid. The chemically introduced group is, then, a determinant of specificity. It is also termed a hapten. A simple hapten cannot by itself induce antibody formation or precipitate antibodies produced against the conjugated protein.* However, it can combine with the antibodies to form soluble complexes and thereby inhibit the antibodies from precipitating with the conjugated protein. While the specificity of these reactions is so great that stereo-isomers can be distinguished, cross-reactions are also obtained with various haptens. Extensive studies of these have shown that the extent of cross-reaction is dependent upon the degree of similarity in size, shape and constitution of the "working end" of the hapten.

When an azoprotein is used for immunization the antiserum generally contains antibodies directed against the uncoupled protein as well as those against the hapten. It is

may depend upon relatively small determinant groups rather than on the whole structure of the molecule, and that the molecule may contain more than one kind of determinant group. Unfortunately very little is known about the size, number and kind of determinant groups of natural proteins. Experiments by Landsteiner ('42) with hydrolysates of silk protein have shown that peptides of molecular weight of 600 to 1000 can specifically inhibit the precipitation of the intact protein by its antiserum. For the present we can only conclude by analogy with the results of experiments on the coupled proteins that natural proteins may induce the formation of more than one kind of antibody. Some of the antibody molecules would be specific for one determinant group, some

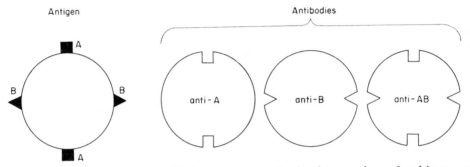

Fig. 207. Diagram illustrating the three kinds of antibody molecules that may be produced in response to immunization with an antigen containing two different kinds of determinant groups.

clear, then, that a single kind of protein can give rise to more than one kind of antibody. This is illustrated further when two different haptens (A and B, see Fig. 207) are coupled with a protein. Thus Haurowitz and Schwerin ('43) obtained distinct anti-A and anti-B antibodies upon injection of such an antigen. They did not find a third possible type, anti-AB. However, Dodd ('52) presents strong evidence for this type of antibody in group O humans immunized with mixed A and B antigens, as well as for its occurrence in normal human group O sera (see also Bird, '53). A less satisfactory interpretation is that some anti-A and anti-B antibodies in group O sera are more cross-reacting than are others.

The work with haptens serves to emphasize that in natural proteins antigenic specificity

* A complex hapten, formed by coupling more than one molecule with a simple substance such as resorcinol, can form a precipitate with the antibodies produced by injection of the azo-protein (see Landsteiner and van der Scheer, '32, '33; Pauling et al., '41).

for another, and some for combinations of determinant groups. If two different proteins possess a common determinant group, then the antiserum induced by one of the proteins will cross-react with the other.

When antisera for two natural proteins of diverse origin cross-react there are, then, at least three possible interpretations. One is that, of the various kinds of determinants of the two proteins, one or more may be identical. Another is that various regions of the two proteins may possess some degree of structural similarity. The third is the possible presence of one of the proteins as a chemically undetected contaminant in preparations of the other. This uncertainty as to interpretation must be taken into account in attempting to analyze investigations on the antigens of adult and embryonic tissues, since cross-reactions are very commonly obtained with such material. In other words, it is important to know what is being detected by the antiserum that is employed. To some extent the difficulties are overcome by the use of the methods of absorption whereby cross-reacting antibodies are removed from an antiserum by precipitation with the heterologous antigen.

It should also be emphasized again that antigens that behave alike serologically are not necessarily identical in over-all chemical constitution. Similarity in serological behavior can be attributed to identity or close structural resemblance of the so-called *determinants* or *combining groups* of the antigens. For convenience in the following discussion the terms *determinants* or *combining groups* will, in general, be omitted, it being understood that when two antigens are designated identical or similar the designation refers primarily to these groups.

RECENT INVESTIGATIONS ON SALINE EXTRACTS OF EMBRYOS

The work of various early investigators gave rather inconsistent results concerning the antigens of embryos and adults. According to some (e.g., Graham-Smith, '04; Braus, '06; Dunbar, '10; Uhlenhuth et al., '10, '39), embryo and adult seemed to possess no antigens in common, whereas others (e.g., Rössle, '05; Kritchewsky, '14, '23; Wilkoewitz and Ziegenspeck, '28) found more or less extensive cross-reactions. The divergent results were evidently not due to species differences but were probably largely due to technical difficulties. Much more consistent results have been obtained by the recent investigators in this field. The work of Burke et al. ('44), Cooper ('46, '48, '50), Schechtman ('47, '48, '52), Nace and Schechtman ('48), Perlmann and Gustafson ('48), Maculla ('48a,b), Ebert ('50, '51, '52), Ten Cate and van Doorenmaalen ('50), Flickinger and Nace ('52), Nace ('53), Spar ('53), Clayton ('53), Perlmann ('53), Telfer and Williams ('53) and Telfer ('54) is in agreement in showing that eggs, embryos and adults possess certain antigens in common. In addition, mainly by means of absorption technique, these workers find antigenic differences and have studied to some extent the changes in antigenicity during development. Some of their results are presented here.

Burke et al. prepared antisera in rabbits against saline extracts of various organs of adult and embryonic chickens. With the exceptions of the lens the extracts of the organs studied (brain, testis, ovary, kidney, liver) showed cross-reactions with the various antisera. The cross reactivity of the antisera could be more or less completely removed by absorption with heterologous extracts (sedimentable constituents obtained after removal of large tissue fragments were used for absorption). When an antiserum against adult brain was thus absorbed and tested with embryo brain extracts, reactions were obtained only with embryos of 300 hours (precipitin test) and 260 hours (complement fixation test) of incubation or older. When an antiserum against 312-hour brain was absorbed with heterologous extracts of other 312-hour organs, it gave reactions (precipitin tests) with brain extract of embryos of 160 hours or older. After absorption of this antiserum with adult brain extract (sediment) it still reacted with the 160-hour extract. According to these experiments, then, antigens of the adult brain first arise at about 260 hours. Earlier embryonic brain seems to possess antigens common to later stages but not to the adult brain. Somewhat similar results were obtained by Burke et al. on the lens (see Table 22). The antiserum against adult lens proved to be rather organ specific and was, therefore, not absorbed. When tested with lens extracts of embryos of various stages, starting with 72 hours, reactions (complement fixation) were obtained only after 160 hours and reached adult intensity at 330 hours. With a 300-hour lens antiserum reactions were obtained at 120 hours. With a 160-hour antiserum reactions were obtained at 96 hours. Thus, again, there is indication of antigens disappearing while new ones arise during the development of an organ. From these and similar tests with other organs Burke et al. specify the approximate time at which adult organ antigens appear as follows: lens, 146 hours; erythrocytes, 100 hours; kidney, 220 hours; brain, testis and ovary, 260 hours. It would appear, then, that adult organ specificity does not arise until a considerable time after the initial morphological differentiation.

This conclusion of Burke et al. is contradicted by the results of Schechtman ('48) and Ebert ('50) indicating the presence of organ (brain, heart, spleen) antigens in the early chick blastoderm, and by the findings of Ten Cate and Van Doorenmaalen ('50), who have detected adult lens antigen in lens vesicles of 60-hour embryos, i.e., before specific morphological differentiation (see Table 23). The latter suggest, also, that the apparent disappearance of a specific embryonic lens antigen during development (Burke et al.) may be attributed to the presence of yolk in the preparations of embryonic antigens. The various experiments seem to be in accord in that the younger the embryo the less organ antigen is detectable, as illustrated in Table 23. It is, however, clear that the complete absence of an antigen cannot be proved by serological methods. So the possibility remains open that "adult" antigens

therefore, absorbed with frog serum. When the absorbed antisera were tested with the saline extracts of brain, liver, kidney and heart, their precipitin titers (dilution of antigen) were found to be greatly reduced. It could be concluded, then, that the presence of serum or of tissue substance with "serum-

TABLE 22. *Reactions of Brain- and Lens-Antisera with Saline Extracts of Brain and of Lens, Respectively, of Chick Embryos of Various Ages (after Burke et al., '44)*

AGE IN HOURS OF EMBRYO SUPPLYING BRAIN EXTRACT	ADULT BRAIN ANTISERUM (ABSORBED WITH TESTIS, OVARY, KIDNEY AND LIVER EXTRACTS)		312-HOUR BRAIN ANTISERUM (SIMILARLY ABSORBED WITH 312-HOUR ORGANS)	AGE IN HOURS OF EMBRYO SUPPLYING LENS EXTRACT	ADULT LENS ANTISERUM	ADULT LENS ANTISERUM	300-HOUR LENS ANTISERUM	160-HOUR LENS ANTISERUM
	Complement fixation	Precipitin test	Precipitin test		Complement fixation	Precipitin test	Complement fixation	Precipitin test
96	0	0	0	72	0	0	0	0
120	0	0	0	96	0	0	0	1+
144	0	0	0	110		0		2+
160	0	0	1+	120	0	0	2+	2+
168	0	0		134		0		4+
184	0	0	1+	144	0		2+	
192	0	0		148		0		4+
208	0	0	1+	160	1+	0	2+	4+
216	0	0		180	1+	0	4+	
232	0	0	2+	200	2+	0	4+	
240	0	0		224	2+	0	4+	
256	0	0	2+	250	2+	1+	4+	
260	1+	0		272	3+	1+	4+	
280	2+	0	2+	300	3+	1+	4+	
300	2+	1+		330	4+	2+	4+	
312	2+	1+	3+	Adult	4+	4+	4+	
312 (unabs.)			4+					
Adult (abs.)	2+	2+						
Adult (unabs.)	4+	4+						

TABLE 23. *Precipitin Reaction of Adult Lens Antiserum with Saline Extracts of Embryonic Chick Lens (after Ten Cate and Van Doorenmaalen, '50)*

Age of embryo, hours	192	168	120	96	74	72	60	54	51	48
Last reactive dilution of extract	6400	3200	1600	800	400	+	+	±	−	−

may be present in the earliest stages of development, or even in the unfertilized egg.

Cooper ('46) demonstrated that antisera against saline extracts of the brain of adult frogs react with extracts of the eggs, embryos and larvae and of adult liver, kidney, heart and serum. Although the brain extract used for immunization, as well as the other organ extracts used in the tests, had been well washed it was suspected that serum might be present in these and be responsible for the cross-reactions. The anti–frog-brain sera were,

like" determinants largely accounted for the cross-reactions. Since some reactivity for the organ extracts remained after the absorption, this indicated that there may also be antigens other than those with serum-protein determinants that are common to brain and the other organs tested. When the absorbed antisera were tested with saline extracts of the eggs, embryos and larvae the titers were also found to be greatly reduced, as is illustrated in Table 24. These results again show that antigens with serum specificity are present in the extracts. For the larval stages this can be interpreted on the basis of the presence of blood at these stages. For the earlier stages the results mean that, even before blood serum develops, antigens are present that have determinants that are similar to at least some of those of constituents of adult serum. Similar results have been obtained by Flickinger and Nace ('52).

In order to obtain further information concerning the nature of these antigens Cooper ('48) prepared antisera against frog serum, egg-brei supernatant and egg-yolk platelets. The antiserum against adult serum cross-reacted with saline extracts of the eggs (unfertilized or fertilized), embryos and larvae of various stages, confirming the above-described results. Also the antisera vs. egg "supernatant" and egg "yolk" cross-reacted with adult serum, thereby demonstrating that the egg substances with serum-like reactivity could act as immunizing antigens. In addition the three kinds of antisera (vs. serum, vs. egg "supernatant" and vs. egg "yolk") all reacted with washed, and subsequently dissolved, yolk platelets as well as with a clear solution prepared by high speed centrifugation of the egg "supernatant." The serum-like determinants are, then, evidently present in both the formed elements and the ground substance of the egg. Tests of the antisera with fractions of the frog serum and of clarified egg "supernatant" prepared by repeated salting out by 34, 50 and 62 per cent saturation with ammonium sulfate gave cross-reactions in all cases. Although these fractions are very likely not completely homogeneous, they may well be sufficiently so to permit the conclusion that determinants of both albumins and globulins of the serum are represented in various substances of the egg. Cooper presents additional evidence, from heat inactivation, that these cross-reactive substances of the egg are proteins and suggests also on the basis of the details of the serological reactions that they are not chemically identical with any of the serum proteins. Tests by the Oudin ('48) technique indicated the presence of five to seven such antigens (Cooper, '50). More recently Clayton ('53) and Spar ('53) report that some antigens appear and others disappear during gastrulation and neurulation in amphibians. Clayton further reports that ectoderm and archenteric roof contain fractions specific to themselves.

In chickens Schechtman ('47) has likewise demonstrated the presence of serum-like antigens in egg yolk and in extracts of embryos

Table 24. *Reaction of Saline Extracts of Eggs, Embryos and Larvae of Rana pipiens with Unabsorbed and Serum-Absorbed Anti-Brain Serum (from Cooper, '46)*

ANTISERUM VS. FROG BRAIN	18–23 MM. LARVAE	11–12 MM. LARVAE	STAGE 17 TAIL BUD	STAGE 13 CLOSED BLASTOPORE	STAGE 12 YOLK PLUG	STAGE 9 LATE CLEAVAGE	STAGE 7 32-CELL STAGE	STAGE 2 UNCLEAVED EGG
TITERS* OBTAINED WITH EXTRACTS OF VARIOUS DEVELOPMENTAL STAGES								
Unabsorbed	1:100	1:200	1:100	1:100	1:100	1:200	1:100	1:100
Absorbed with frog serum	1:50	1:50	0	0	1:10	undiluted	0	1:10 (faint)

* Titer is highest dilution of extract that gives a visible precipitate when layered on antiserum in the ring test (1 hour at room temperature + 3 to 4 hours in cold). Since extracts of different stages may contain different amounts of dissolved material, comparison should not be made between different stages but only between absorbed and unabsorbed antiserum.

at various developmental stages, using antisera against the euglobulin, pseudoglobulin and albumin fractions, as well as against whole serum. The antisera against the serum fractions cross-reacted with the respective fractions and with egg yolk. After absorption with the heterologous fractions the antisera still reacted with the homologous fractions and with egg yolk. After additional absorption with egg yolk the euglobulin antiserum still reacted with the homologous antigen but the pseudoglobulin and albumin antisera failed to do so. Apparently the latter two fractions possess no antigens that are not

of incubation, and more slowly subsequently. These workers suggest that the vitelloid constituent may be a pseudoglobulin possibly identical with livetin, whereas the non-vitelloid constituent may be represented by serum albumin. However, this does not seem to be quite consistent with the previously reported (Schechtman, '47) results showing that when antisera against pseudoglobulin and antisera against albumin are absorbed with yolk they no longer react with the homologous antigen (see above).

In another set of experiments, Schechtman ('48) prepared antisera against a saline ex-

TABLE 25. *Reactions (Ring Tests) of Rabbit Anti–19-day-Chick-Embryo-Brain Sera with Extracts of Blood and Organs of 19-day Embryos and of Early Embryos (from Schechtman, '48)*

ANTI-BRAIN SERA ABSORBED WITH	TESTED WITH SALINE EXTRACTS OF:								
	BLOOD	BRAIN	LIVER	HEART	MUSCLE	YOLK	PRIMITIVE STREAK	EARLY NEURULA	4 TO 5 SOMITES
Unabsorbed	+	+	+	+	+	+	+	+	+
Blood	−	+	+	+	+	+	+	+	+
Brain	−	−	−	−	−	−	−	−	±
Liver	−	±	−	±	−	−	−	−	−
Heart	−	−	−	−	−	−	−	−	−
Muscle	−	±	−	−	−	−			

also present in the heterologous fractions and in yolk.

The tests with embryo extracts were made with anti-whole serum and with anti-euglobulin (absorbed with pseudoglobulin and albumin). Both of these antisera reacted with extracts of embryos (free of visible yolk), from the primitive streak stage to the 15- to 17-somite stage. However, after absorption with yolk the antisera no longer reacted with these extracts, but still reacted with adult serum and with the blood and also the perfused (liver and brain) or washed (heart and muscle) organs of the 19- 20-day embryo. Thus, of the antigens detectable by these antisera, the extracts of the early embryos contain only those that are common to yolk, and that may be termed "yolk-like" or "vitelloid." Although blood is present in the 7- to 8-somite and 15- to 17-somite stages that were tested, the "non-vitelloid" antigens of adult serum were not detectable.

Further detailed tests by Nace and Schechtman ('48), with yolk-absorbed antisera vs. adult serum, showed that "non-vitelloid" antigens are first detectable in the blood of 5-day embryos. These increase rapidly in relative amount up to the ninth day

tract of perfused brain of chicks of 19 to 20 days of incubation. These antisera cross-reacted with extracts of liver, heart, muscle and blood of chicks of the same stage, with yolk and with extracts of yolk-free embryos at the primitive streak, early neurula and 4- to 5-somite stages. Upon absorption with blood the antisera no longer reacted with yolk but still reacted with the various organ and early embryo extracts (see Table 25). It appears, then, that antigens of the brain extract that are not present in blood or yolk are present in the early embryos and the other organs tested. These antigens are evidently not specific for brain, since absorption of the anti-brain sera with either liver or heart removes reactivity for brain and for the early embryos. Ebert ('50) partly confirms these results, but Burke et al. (see above) obtained a brain-specific antiserum after absorption with heterologous organs and found that the absorbed antiserum reacted with extracts of late stages but not of early stages. The basis for this discrepancy is not clear.

In the sea urchin Paracentrotus, Perlmann and Gustafson ('48) find common antigens to be present at stages from the unfertilized eggs to the 48-hour pluteus. From the results of absorption experiments they conclude that there are, in addition, antigens present in the 48-hour embryos that are not detectable in the earlier stages tested (unfertilized eggs, 4-hour and 12-hour embryos). On the other hand, none of the antigens detectable in eggs and early embryos appears to be lost in the later embryo. These workers also examined vegetalized 48-hour embryos, produced as a result of lithium treatment, and found no antigenic difference from the normal plutei. By means of the Ouchterlony ('49, see also Jennings and Malone, '54) technique, of diffusion in agar plates, Perlmann ('53) finds that extracts of the different developmental stages of the sea urchin possess mostly common antigens that are also of similar concentration. Harding et al. ('54), using this method with hybrid embryos, report the appearance of "paternal" antigens at a stage before the morphological traits can be easily detected.

In the Cecropia silkworm Telfer and Williams ('53) describe, in addition to five persistent antigens, one that appears in the blood of fifth instar larvae and disappears during adult development. Telfer ('54) finds an antigen in adult female blood that is undetectable in larvae and almost so in adult males but present in the yolk of unfertilized eggs.

The various investigations described above are more in accord in regard to antigenic resemblances than in regard to differences at various stages in development. They do not rule out the possibility that all antigenic structures are represented in the uncleaved egg and only changes in quantity and location (i.e., distribution to different chemical substances and to different tissues) occur during development. This question will be considered further after presentation of experiments on blood cell antigens.

ANTIGENS OF VERTEBRATE BLOOD CELLS

In humans the A and B isoagglutinogens have been detected in the erythrocytes of the month-old fetus and the M and N agglutinogens at the second month (see Wiener, '43, for references). Presumably these may be present in earlier stages that have not been tested. In rabbits the agglutinogens H_1 and H_2 have been found as early as the 4 mm. stage (Keeler and Castle, '34), at which time the erythrocytes are still nucleated. According to the early work it would seem that all the blood cell antigens appeared on the cells as soon as they were formed. However, there are recent experiments in which some cellular antigens have been found to appear rather late. Briles, McGibbon and Irwin ('48) studied chicken red cell antigens the inheritance of which is determined by two series of multiple allelic genes. The antigens determined by one series were all found in embryos of about 3 days. In the other series one of the antigens was detected in 4-day embryos but the other three antigens did not appear until after hatching. Ycas ('49) studied antigens of sheep red cells, nine of which are detected by use of immune sera and one (R) by means of an isoagglutinin present in the serum of certain sheep (not possessing the R antigen). The former were found to be present at birth, but the latter did not usually appear until two or three weeks later. While the red cells of the newborn R lambs did not possess the antigen, it was found to be present in the serum of the animal at that stage as well as in the adult. This antigen, then, appears in the serum before it can be detected in the red cells of the animals. It would be of further interest to learn whether or not the antigen is detectable in various tissues of the fetus and early embryos. In the chick Witebsky and Szepsenwol ('34) found Forssman antigen to be present in, and equally extractable from, first to twelfth day embryos. In humans fetal hemoglobin is reported to be antigenically different from that of the adult (Darrow et al., '40).

The extensive genetic studies that have been made on the blood groups of man and lower vertebrates have clearly established the fact that these cellular antigens are gene-determined. In fact the antigens seem to be rather direct products of their causative genes, each antigen being produced by the action of a specific gene with no influence, in general, of other genes or of the environment. Since all of the cells of an organism are supposed to contain the full complement of genes, the appearance of these antigens on the surface of particular cells raises the same sorts of questions as are involved in the development of any particular gene-determined character in particular tissues. Certain antigens, such as the A and B characters of humans, are found in most other tissues of the body, whereas others, such as the human M and N antigens, are restricted to the blood cells. Thus, certain genes seem to be active in a variety of tissues in impressing a certain specificity on the tissue substances, while others act to an appreciable extent only in a particular tissue. The work on the development of the blood cell antigens also points to a difference in the time at which various genes may come into action in the same tissue. This work does not rule out the possibility that the differences involve primarily rates of activity in different tissues and concomitant differences in distribution of the antigens in various parts of the cell.

DEVELOPMENT OF NATURAL ANTIBODIES AND OF COMPLEMENT

While in humans the A and B agglutinogens are demonstrable in the early fetus, the corresponding isoagglutinins are usually not found in the serum until some time after birth (see Wiener, '43). In fact it has been shown that when agglutinins are present in the serum of the newborn infant these are derived from the mother by transfer through the placenta. The maternal agglutinins disappear during the first two weeks of postnatal life while new ones characteristic of the infant begin to appear in the serum.

In ruminants transfer of antibodies does not occur across the placenta, which is of the syndesmochorial type with four or five layers of cells separating fetal and maternal bloods instead of the two layers of the hemochorial type of placenta of primates. However, as is well known since the experiments of Orcutt and Howe ('22), antibodies (both immune and natural) are acquired from the mother by newborn ruminants as a result of ingestion of the colostrum. In the recent experiments of Ycas ('49) the normal anti-R antibody could not be detected in the serum of a lamb at birth but was present after ingestion of the colostrum and persisted for a variable period of several weeks. The earliest time of appearance of the lamb's own anti-R was found to be 15 weeks. The transfer of proteins by ingestion of the colostrum has been studied in calves by Hansen and Phillips ('47), who find that gammaglobulin is absorbed only during the first day after birth when the gut wall is apparently permeable to large molecules.

While it has been generally believed that, where transfer of antibodies from mother to fetus occurs, the route is through the placenta, it has been shown recently by Brambell et al. ('49) that this is not necessarily the case. These workers demonstrated in rabbits the presence of maternally derived antibodies in the yolk-sac cavity of embryos at a stage prior to establishment of the embryonic circulation. They have also shown, by ligaturing the yolk-sac stalk of 24-day embryos, that the maternal antibodies do not pass through the placenta, but rather by way of the uterine lumen and yolk sac into the fetal circulation. To what extent these results with rabbits may apply to other mammals remains to be determined, but it seems unlikely that the situation would be the same in species with a very rudimentary yolk sac.

In chickens a naturally occurring hemolysin for sheep erythrocytes is not found until about 5 days after hatching (Pickering and Gladstone, '25). Apparently this antibody is not transferred from the hen to the egg, although other antibodies produced as a result of immunization of the adult hen can evidently accumulate in the egg. For example, such transfer has been shown for diphtheria and tetanus antitoxins (Jukes et al., '34; Fraser et al., '34; Ramon, '28) and for antibodies against Newcastle disease virus (Brandly et al., '46).

Complement (alexin) is apparently formed rather early in mammals. It has been reported (Solling, '37) to be present in low titer in the serum of the 14-week human fetus and to reach full strength at 28 weeks. In chickens, according to one investigation (Sherman, '19), it is present in 17- to 21-day embryos, while according to another (Polk et al., '38) it is not detected until two days after hatching.

DEVELOPMENT OF ANTIBODY-FORMING CAPACITY

It is generally assumed that the ability to form antibodies is lacking or poorly developed in the embryo, the fetus and the newborn (see, for example, Needham, '42; Beveridge and Burnet, '46; Topley and Wilson, '46). Experiments concerning this have been performed with mammals and birds. In mammals the fetus is not readily available for such studies. The problem is also complicated by placental transmission of antibodies and by uncertainties as to whether or not antigens that are introduced into the mother will reach the fetus. However, experiments have been performed on newborn mammals and at various ages after birth. Thus, Freund ('30) injected rabbits with sheep red cells, typhoid bacilli, horse serum and egg white and found that those of one to 20 days of age produced either no antibodies or only very small amounts of antibodies against these antigens. With increasing age the titers of antibody obtained increased.

A detailed study of antibody production in chickens of various ages from hatching to 12 weeks has been made by Wolfe and Dilks ('48). These workers used bovine serum as antigen and obtained very weak, or no, precipitins from the newly hatched chicks. The titers increased up to 5 weeks of age and remained approximately the same to 12 weeks (see Table 26).

That the embryo chick also fails to produce detectable antibodies has been shown by several investigators using a variety of antigens. For example, no antibody response

showed that such grafts begin to regress at the eighteenth day of incubation, and similar results have been subsequently obtained by others (see Waterman, '36). It should be noted, however, that this is the time when the chorioallantois itself starts to regress.

It is also now well known, since the original experiments of Born (1897) and Harrison (1898), that tissue grafting homoplastically or heteroplastically succeeds readily in embryonic stages, whereas it generally fails in the adult. Other chapters of this book deal with the work along this line, and detailed discussion of the greater part of the literature on this subject is presented in

TABLE 26. *Precipitin Titers (Ring Tests) of Antisera vs. Bovine Serum Produced in Chickens Given Three Alternate-Day Injections Starting at Various Ages and Bled 6 and 9 Days after Last Injection (from Wolfe and Dilks, '48)*

Age in weeks	1/7	1	2	3	4	5	6	7	8	9	10	11	12
Av. titers as tube* numbers	1.0	3.0	5.5	6.2	7.7	11.1	11.9	11.1	11.6	11.1	11.4	12.1	12.2
Number of antisera tested	25	26	29	20	31	31	42	59	36	31	18	18	18

* Tube 1 is a 12½ fold dilution and succeeding tubes are serial twofold dilutions.

was obtained with such good antigens as diphtherial and tetanal toxoids (Grasset, '29), *B. sporogenes* and *Vibrio septique* (Weinberg and Guelin, '36) and with a bacteriophage and influenza virus (Beveridge and Burnet, '46). There is a report (Gebauer-Fuelnegg, '32) of antibodies being found in the egg white at 14 days of incubation after injecting the embryos with sheep serum four or five times on alternate days starting at the third day of incubation. This result was obtained in only 5 out of 126 eggs used.

The ability of many viruses and rickettsiae to grow readily on the membranes and tissues of the chick embryo, as first demonstrated by Rous and Murphy ('11) and by Goodpasture and his collaborators ('38-'44), seems to correlate with lack of antibody-forming capacity (see Beveridge and Burnet, '46). For example, Brandly et al. ('46) find that neutralizing antibodies against Newcastle disease virus are not detected in chick embryos earlier than 15 days of incubation. Similarly the ability of various normal and tumor tissues of the same or of other species to grow on the chorioallantois, as shown initially by Murphy ('13), Willier ('24) and Hoadley ('24) appears to depend upon inability of the embryo to form antibody (see Needham, '42; Loeb, '45). Murphy ('14)

the recent book by Loeb ('45). Here we will consider briefly the question of whether or not antibody formation may be responsible for tissue incompatibility.

Loeb and Wright ('27) established the genetic basis of tissue incompatibility in their classic demonstration, with inbred lines of guinea pigs, that the reaction was due to the absence in the host of factors present in the grafted tissue. Kozelka ('33) showed, in chickens, that the factors responsible for the incompatibility of homografts are not represented by the agglutinogens of the blood cells. In rabbits, too, the red cell antigens do not appear to be involved (Medawar, '46b). However, in mice incompatible skin homografts stimulate the formation of antibodies that react with red cells and leukocytes (Amos et al., '54). That an antibody mechanism of some sort is involved in graft-incompatibility is evident from many experiments showing immunity to second transplants. For example, in experiments of Medawar ('46a), inhibitory effects are obtained in rabbit skin that is transplanted to a rabbit that has previously been "immunized" by grafting skin from the same donor or, to a less extent, from another rabbit. Injection of leukocytes also is found to induce this type of immunity to subsequent skin grafting. Skin can grow well in the presence of serum and mesenchymal tissues of an immunized rabbit (Medawar, '48). However, prolonged treatment (Billingham and Sparrow, '54) can prevent dissociated Malpighian cells from forming epithelium upon grafting, thus indicating a specific, in vitro, antibody effect. In tissue culture it has been shown (Harris, '43) that mouse and rat tissues are quite compatible. Even when mouse tissues are taken from animals previously immunized against tissues of the rat, guinea pig or chicken there is no incompatibility exhibited in mixed cultures with each of the latter (Grobstein and Youngner, '49).

It appears, then, that tissues grown in vitro behave much like embryonic tissues in regard to the absence of incompatibility reaction, and this, it seems, should provide a clue to the analysis of the incompatibility problem on the basis of features common to both. One feature common to both is that they are actively growing. Taking this into consideration it would seem reasonable to suppose that any antibodies that might be produced by the tissues of the host embryo or by one of the tissues in culture, in response to the presence of the foreign antigens, would be incorporated into the growing cells. In this location, intimately bound in or on the cells, the antibodies would not be available for action on the foreign tissue. On this basis it is not a necessary conclusion, from the experiments reported in the first part of this section, that the embryo is incapable of antibody formation. Those experiments do not exclude the possibility that any antibodies that are formed may be simply used as part of the building blocks of the tissue. Later, when growth slows down and material is released from the tissue, such antibodies may be liberated and then initiate the incompatibility reaction.

However, there are cases in which cells may survive well into the adult life of a genetically different recipient embryo. This is illustrated by the persistence in the adult chicken of melanoblasts transplanted between embryos (Willier and Rawles, '40, '44) and by the occurrence of erythrocyte mosaicism in adult dizygotic cattle (Owen, '45) and human twins (Dunsford et al., '53), due most likely to reciprocal transfer of the fetal blood through the common placenta. In addition, experiments by Billingham, Brent and Medawar ('53) now show that adult animals may be induced to tolerate foreign skin grafts if they are inoculated during fetal life with cells from the donor strain. Thus mice of

CBA strain injected in utero, at the 15th-16th day, with tissue (isolated cells and clumps from chopped-up adult testis, kidney and spleen) of *A* strain can tolerate *A*-strain skin transplanted in adult life. In chickens transfusion of blood between embryos of different strains renders the recipient, at two weeks after hatching, similarly tolerant to skin grafts received from the donor strain. A somewhat related investigation (Buxton, '54) has shown that the inoculation of chick embryos with killed *Salmonella pullorum* results in a marked decrease in the capacity of the hatched chickens to produce antibodies in their sera when challenged again with the bacterial antigen. Billingham et al. ('53) suggest that the failure of the host's immunological response in their experiments may be related to a specific immunological paralysis provoked by high doses of antigen (see Felton, '49). Another possibility is that "type-transformation" (see below) has been induced in those host cells responsible for the immune response. These highly interesting experiments will undoubtedly stimulate extensive investigation leading to their interpretation, so that one need not speculate further at this time.

THE CONCEPT OF NATURAL AUTO-ANTIBODIES

The results of certain experiments on the interacting substances of eggs and sperm (see Section IV, Chapter 1), along with consideration of various findings of others, reported in immunological literature, led Tyler ('40–'48) to propose a view of cell structure and growth termed an "auto-antibody" concept. This concept states that each of the various macromolecular substances of which cells are constructed bears the same sort of relationship to another of these substances as do antigen and antibody, and that their mode of origin is analogous to that of antibody formation. This view has been applied to the interpretation of certain aspects of the problems of differentiation (Tyler, '47). A brief account of this is presented here along with some of the background of the concept.

The experiments with the fertilizins and the antifertilizins that are derived from the surface layer of eggs and of sperm, respectively, have shown that these substances interact in a manner analogous to that of antigen with antibody (see Section IV, Chapter 1). In the course of this work it was found (Tyler, '40) that upon removal of the gelatinous coat (which is constituted of fertilizin) of the sea-urchin egg an antifertilizin could be extracted from the naked eggs. This antifertilizin, derived from within the egg, was capable of agglutinating intact eggs or of forming a precipitate with the surface coat substance (fertilizin). Thus, from one and the same cell a pair of substances are obtainable that interact in serological manner, and which may be termed complementary substances. Tests with vertebrate blood cells and with bacteria have also yielded such auto-agglutinins, but methods for obtaining them consistently have not as yet been fully worked out. The difficulties here appear to involve interaction and precipitation of the complementary substances in extraction procedures that cause destruction of the cell before surface substance can be sufficiently removed. Also, some may be "univalent" (Tyler, '45, '54) and, thus, not readily detectable by direct testing. There have, however, been a sufficient number of reports in the literature (see Tyler, '47, for references) in which auto-antibodies have been evidently obtained, so that it seems safe to conclude that the situation is a general one for all kinds of cells. Tests have also been made of the possibility that such auto-antibodies might have protective action against toxins, venoms, etc., and evidence for such action has been obtained (Tyler, '46) in the case of a venom. Thus, it has been found that the lethal action on mice of the venom of the Gila monster can be neutralized by serum or by an extract of liver of the same animal.

According to the auto-antibody concept the formation of immune antibodies by an animal, in response to the injection of a foreign antigen, is a special case of the general type of process involved in the synthesis of the macromolecular constituents of cells. The now fairly generally accepted view of the manner of formation of immune antibody is that which was proposed by Breinl and Haurowitz ('30), Alexander ('32), and Mudd ('32) and which has been extended by Pauling ('40). This view proposes that foreign antigen becomes incorporated in the site of synthesis of serum globulin so that, as the polypeptide chains of the new globulin that is being formed fold up, the molecules now bear regional surface configurations that are complementary to certain structures on the antigen. The auto-antibody concept in fact may be inferred from this view, if one considers the situation in the absence of foreign, introduced, antigen. Under such conditions the normal globulin that is formed should bear regional structural configurations that are complementary to chemical structures of the normal site of synthesis. The concept is not, however, restricted to the special case of the formation of serum globulin but applies to any of the macromolecular constituents of cells. Since it is the formation of such substances that is involved in the process of growth, that process, then, may be considered to result from the operation of the same sort of mechanism exemplified in the formation of immune antibodies. Growth also involves an increase in self-duplicating entities, such as genes, and for the formation of these one may assume structures that are both complementary and identical, as Pauling and Delbrück ('40) suggest, or the production of an intermediate template, as Emerson ('45) proposes as an alternative.

RELATION TO SPECIFIC ADHESION OF CELLS

This general point of view has been applied (Tyler, '47) to two aspects of the problem of differentiation. One is the question of the nature of the forces that are responsible for the specific adhesion or nonadhesion of cells and tissues. The other is the phenomenon of induction. In regard to the former Loeb ('22) had early suggested that specific agglutination is the factor involved in binding cells into tissues. That some mechanism analogous to antigen-antibody interaction is involved is suggested by the specificity of the tissue affinities. Thus species specificity is exhibited, for example, in experiments on the reconstitution of a sponge from cells that have been dissociated from one another by forcing the organism through fine bolting cloth (Wilson, '07, '32; Galtsoff, '29). When the dissociated cells of two species are mixed, coalescence is found to occur only between those of the same species. The degree of cell-type specificity that is exhibited in these experiments is not entirely clear, but the evidence is to the effect that the archeocytes are mainly involved and that other cells, such as collar cells, that are on hand may be incorporated. Experiments by Holtfreter ('43–'48) with amphibian embryos offer illustration of the specificity of association of cells within the species. He has shown that isolated cells or clumps of cells from blastulae or early gastrulae will fuse regardless of their prospective significance. While the cells of the same germ layer remain fused, separation later occurs between ectodermal and entodermal cells. At this time, too, initial in vitro combinations of entodermal and ectodermal cells fail to unite. However, mesodermal cells are found to be capable of uniting with either of the others and are thus capable of tying together cells of the other two germ layers. The various interactions occur only as a result of contact and there is no indication of the operation of forces acting at a distance. These and other experiments of Holtfreter and of others serve to emphasize the antigen-antibody analogy. On this basis the specific adhesion or non-adhesion of cells and tissues would depend upon the extent of complementariness of chemical structure of the respective cell surfaces, and the changes that these undergo during development. A similar point of view has been developed in more detail by Weiss ('41, '47).

Through the auto-antibody concept this can be related to genic action. It is known, especially from the work on the antigens of vertebrate blood cells, that the antigenic composition of the cell surface is gene-determined (see reviews by Irwin, '47, '49). The antigens appear to be rather direct products of their causative genes, each of which manifests itself independently of its allele. Cells belonging to different tissues do not, as a rule, possess the same set of surface antigens despite the presumed identity of chromosomal constitution of all the somatic cells of the body. Certain antigens, such as the A and B structures of humans, are found on most other cells and tissue fluids, whereas other antigens, such as M, N, and Rh, are restricted to the red blood cells. According to the auto-antibody concept each gene would serve as a mold or template upon which is formed a complementary structure. This may represent a terminal step or be merely an intermediate step in a series of such syntheses. The antigenic differences between the surface of cells of different tissues can be interpreted in various ways. The simplest, perhaps, would be the assumption that all of the genes are active, but at different rates in different tissues, so that the surface in each case would be composed of a different assortment of the products of activity of the genes. Each antigenic structure on the surface of the cell may, then, be regarded as representing a specific structural aspect of the determining gene or the complement of that structure. The extent to which the cells of one tissue have surface substances that are complementary to those of another tissue

would determine the degree of association of the two tissues. Within one tissue the adhesion of the cells may be regarded as involving combination of surface substance of one cell with complementary subsurface substance of another, in a manner previously suggested (Tyler, '40) for auto-agglutination phenomena.

RELATION TO INDUCTION

For the other aspect of the problem of differentiation that we wish to consider, namely the phenomenon of induction, there is, as yet, only slight indication that the antigen-antibody type of interaction may be involved. One indication is that inductive activity is associated more with protein materials than with other types of extracts of inductor tissue (see Holtfreter, '33, '48b; Barth and Graff, '43). Inductive action requires contact with the inducing tissue and it is evidently not dependent upon special metabolic properties of the latter, since dead tissues possess inductive capacity. This capacity may depend, then, upon the presence of a specific type of protein, or other macromolecular substance, on the surface of the natural inductor. The fact that certain tissues which lack inductive action in the living state acquire this capacity when killed may be attributed to the exposure of inductor substance, previously located in a subsurface position.

For speculation along this line to acquire any significance it would be important to know whether specific morphological changes can be brought about in cells by the action of antibodies. It is, of course, well known that cells of various types can be lysed by treatment with immune antibodies in the presence of complement. This, however, is a lethal effect that would certainly not warrant any consideration unless non-lethal steps in the process were demonstrable. There are two somewhat similar lines of work that bear on this point. One is the work with the so-called reticulo-endothelial immune serum of Bogomolets (see reviews by Pomerat, '45, '46; Straus, '46). This serum is cytotoxic or inhibiting in high concentration. In low doses it has been claimed to stimulate cellular growth and activity. However, careful in vitro tests of this by Pomerat have not revealed any very marked stimulatory action. The other work consists in experiments by Weiss ('47) in which hen's eggs, at 60 hours to 8 days of incubation, were injected with antisera prepared against autolyzed suspensions of liver, kidney or pectoral muscle of adult chickens. Upon examination at 20 days of incubation the total weights of the injected embryos were found to average considerably less than those of the controls. However, the organ corresponding to the antiserum employed showed rather marked relative increase in size. Thus the liver weights averaged 10 per cent above the normal controls and 29 per cent more than the livers of embryos that had been injected with anti-kidney serum. Kidney size in the embryos treated with anti-kidney serum was found to average 28 per cent higher than in the embryos treated with anti-liver serum. Experiments by Ebert ('51, '54) on the enlargement of host-embryo spleen by chorioallantoic grafting of adult spleen can be related to this, as he suggests, on the assumption of a release from the graft of certain of the complementary substances which then become incorporated in the host spleen and serve as templates for the synthesis of further splenic substance.

There is, then, some evidence of a specific stimulating effect of antibodies. This encourages further examination of the possibility that specific morphological alterations may be induced in cells by means of antibodies. In the above cited experiments of Weiss no alteration of cell type seems to be involved, and in no experiments of others does this possibility seem to have been directly tested. Perhaps the nearest approach to this is the work on changes in morphological and antigenic structure in microorganisms. It is well known (see Dubos, '46, for references) that certain transformations, such as the smooth to rough change, can be brought about in many kinds of bacteria by growth in immune serum. Cultures of encapsulated organisms, such as the pneumococci or Friedländer's bacilli, growing in media containing the homologous, specific anticapsular antibody, transform to a nonspecific, non-encapsulated type. The reverse transformation can also be obtained by growth in an antiserum directed against the non-encapsulated organisms. Motile variants of *B. subtilis* can be transformed to nonmotile, and vice versa, by growth in the corresponding antisera. Reversible changes described as phase variation, as for example in the specificity of the flagellar antigens of various Salmonella species, can be induced by means of homologous antisera. Changes in antigenic specificity have been described also in Paramecium (Sonneborn, '48). The manner in which the antibodies act has not,

as yet, been fully elucidated in any of these experiments. The various changes also occur, although generally more slowly, in response to other environmental changes or sometimes spontaneously in the absence of controlled or readily detectable environmental change. In the bacteria it is often uncertain to what extent the antibodies act by selectively inhibiting the types with which they react and thus permit a more rapid growth of the variants in the culture.

Selective action of this type does not appear to be involved in the experiments on directed transformation of pneumococcal types (see McCarty, Taylor and Avery, '46). This tranformation consists in the conversion of a non-encapsulated (R) variant derived from one specific serological type into a serologically different encapsulated (S) type. The conditions for transformation involve several factors, including anti-R serum and desoxyribonucleic acid derived from organisms of the type into which the change is to be directed. The latter is evidently the directive agent in this transformation. The R-antibodies can be replaced by other agents, such as normal serum and agar semisolid medium, that cause a colonial type of growth of the R organisms. The action of the R-antibodies is interpreted as inducing a type of growth in which local conditions surrounding the organisms so modify the cells as to permit absorption or entrance and action of the specific desoxyribonucleic acid.

There is, then, evidence that antibodies can induce changes in cells, but as far as present evidence is concerned, they do not appear to be directive agents. If the antigen-antibody type of reaction is involved in the phenomena of embryonic induction it could conceivably operate in some manner such as is indicated in the experiments on the transformation of pneumococcal types. It is of interest to note, in this connection, that nucleic acids, as Brachet ('47) has emphasized, can act as inductors. This might mean that certain specific nucleic acids are liberated from the surface of living cells having specific inductive action in the embryo. This possibility has not, as yet, been examined, but seems worth investigating. On the other hand, the present status of experimentation along this line does not exclude the possibility that natural auto-antibodies may act rather directly as inductive agents, and various schemes could be devised whereby this would entail inactivation of different sets of genes in cells of different tissues. This becomes similar to the proposals of Sturtevant

('44) and Emerson ('44) for the induction of mutations by means of antisera. The present analysis suggests, then, the desirability of investigation of the occurrence of complementary substances in inductor and reactor tissue and tests of inductive action of such substances as well as of immunologically produced antibodies.

REFERENCES

Alexander, J. 1932 Some intracellular aspects on life and disease. Protoplasma, *14:*296–306.

Amos, D. B., Gorer, P. A., Mikulska, Barbara M., Billingham, R. E., and Sparrow, Elizabeth M. 1954 An antibody response to skin homografts in mice. Brit. J. Exper. Pathol., *35:*203–208.

Barth, L. G., and Graff, S. 1943 Effect of protein extracts of neural plate plus chordamesoderm on presumptive epidermis. Proc. Soc. Exp. Biol. & Med., *54:*118–121.

Beveridge, W. I. B., and Burnet, F. M. 1946 The Cultivation of Viruses and Rickettsiae in the Chick Embryo. Medical Research Council, Special Report Series No. 256, pp. 1–92. His Majesty's Stationery Office, London.

Billingham, R. E., and Sparrow, Elizabeth M. 1954 Studies on the nature of immunity to homologous skin grafts, with special reference to the use of pure epidermal grafts. J. Exp. Biol., *31:*16–39.

———, Brent, L., and Medawar, P. B. 1953 'Actively acquired tolerance' of foreign cells. Nature, *172:*603–606.

Bird, G. W. G. 1953 Observations on haemagglutinin "linkage" in relation to iso-agglutinins and auto-agglutinins. Brit. J. Exper. Pathol., *34:*131–137.

Bogomolets, A. A. 1943 Antireticular cytotoxic serum as a means of pathogenic therapy. Am. Rev. Soviet Med., *1:*101–112.

Born, G. 1897 Über Verwachsungsversuche mit Amphibienlarven. Roux' Arch. Entw.-mech., *4:*349–465.

Boyd, W. C. 1947 Fundamentals of Immunology. Interscience Publishers, New York.

Brachet, J. 1947 Embryologie Chimique. Edit. Desoer, Liege.

Brambell, F. W. R., Hemmings, W. A., Henderson, M., Parry, H. J., and Rowlands, W. T. 1949 The route of antibodies passing from the maternal to the foetal circulation in rabbits. Proc. Roy. Soc., London, Ser. B., *136:*131–144.

Brandly, C. A., Moses, H. E., and Jungherr, E. L. 1946 Transmission of antiviral activity via the egg and the role of congenital passive immunity to Newcastle disease in chickens. Am. J. Veter. Res., *7:*333–342.

Braus, H. 1906 Über das biochemische Verhalten von Amphibienlarven. Roux' Arch. Entw.-mech., *22:*564–580.

Breinl, F., and Haurowitz, F. 1930 Chemische Untersuchungen des Präzipitates aus Hämoglobin und Anti-Hämoglobin-Serum und Bemer-

kungen über die Natur der Antikörper. Z. physiol. Chem., *192:*45–57.

Briles, W. E., McGibbon, W. H., and Irwin, M. R. 1948 Studies of the time of development of cellular antigens in the chicken. Genetics, *33:*97.

Burke, V., Sullivan, N. P., Petersen, H., and Weed, R. 1944 Ontogenetic change in antigenic specificity of the organs of the chick. J. Infect. Diseases, *74:*225–233.

Buxton, A. 1954 Antibody production in avian embryos and young chicks. J. Gen. Microbiol., *10:*398–410.

Clayton, R. M. 1953 Distribution of antigens in the developing newt. J. Embryol. Exp. Morphol., *1:*25–42.

Cohn, M., Wetter, L. R., and Deutsch, H. F. 1949 Immunological studies on egg white proteins. I. Precipitation of chicken-ovalbumin and conalbumin by rabbit- and horse-antisera. J. Immunol., *61:*283–296.

Cooper, Ruth S. 1946 Adult antigens (or specific combining groups) in the egg, embryo and larva of the frog. J. Exp. Zool., *101:*143–172.

——— 1948 A study of frog egg antigens with serum-like reactive groups. J. Exp. Zool., *107:*397–438.

——— 1950 Antigens of frog embryos and of adult frog serum studied by diffusion of antigens into agar columns containing antisera. J. Exp. Zool., *114:*403–420.

Darrow, R. R., Nowakovsky, S., and Austin, M. H. 1940 Specificity of fetal and adult human hemoglobin precipitins. Arch. Pathol., *30:*873–880.

Dodd, Barbara E. 1952 Linked anti-A and anti-B antibodies from group O sera. Brit. J. Exper. Pathol., *33:*1–18.

Dubos, R. J. 1946 The Bacterial Cell. Harvard University Press, Cambridge, Massachusetts.

Dunbar, W. P. 1910 Über das serobiologische Verhalten der Geschlechtszellen. Z. Immunitätsforsch., *7:*454–497.

Dunsford, I., Bowley, C. C., Hutchison, Ann M., Thompson, Joan S., Sanger, Ruth, and Race, R. R. 1953 A human blood group chimera. Brit. Med. J., *2:*81.

Ebert, J. D. 1950 An analysis of the effects of anti-organ sera on the development, in vitro, of the early chick blastoderm. J. Exp. Zool., *115:*351–378.

——— 1951 Ontogenetic change in the antigenic specificity of the chick spleen. Physiol. Zool., *24:*20–41.

——— 1952 Appearance of tissue-specific proteins during development. Ann. N. Y. Acad. Sci., *55:*67–84.

——— 1954 The effects of chorioallantoic transplants of adult chicken tissues on homologous tissues of the host chick embryos. Proc. Nat. Acad. Sci., *40:*337–347.

Emerson, S. 1944 The induction of mutation by antibodies. Proc. Nat. Acad. Sci., *30:*179–183.

——— 1945 Genetics as a tool for studying gene structure. Ann. Missouri Bot. Garden, *32:*243–249.

Felton, Lloyd D. 1949 The significance of antigen in animal tissues. J. Immunol., *61:*107–117.

Flickinger, R. A., and Nace, G. W. 1952 An investigation of proteins during the development of the amphibian embryo. Exper. Cell Research, 3:393–405.

Fraser, D. T., Jukes, T. H., Branion, H. D., and Halpern, K. C. 1934 The inheritance of diphtheria immunity in ducks. J. Immunol., 26:437–446.

Freund, J. 1930 Influence of age upon antibody formation. J. Immunol., 18:315–324.

Galtsoff, P. S. 1929 Heteroagglutination of dissociated sponge cells. Biol. Bull., 57:250–260.

Gebauer-Fuelnegg, E. 1932 Formation of antibodies in fertile hens eggs. Proc. Soc. Exp. Biol. & Med., 29:529–530.

Goodpasture, E. W. 1938 Some uses of the chick embryo for the study of infection and immunity. Amer. J. Hyg., 28:111.

——— 1942 Virus infection of mammalian fetus. Science, 95:391–396.

———, and Anderson, K. 1944 Infection of human skin, grafted on chorioallantois of chick embryos, with virus of herpes zoster. Amer. J. Path., 20:447–455.

———, Douglas, B., and Anderson, K. 1938 A study of human skin grafted on the chorioallantois of chick embryos. J. Exp. Med., 68:891–906.

Graham-Smith, G. S. 1904 [In] Blood Immunity and Blood Relationships, by G. Nuttall. Cambridge University Press, Cambridge, England.

Grasset, E. 1929 Recherches sur la sensibilité du tissu embryonnaire aux antigènes. Essais d'immunisation comparée de l'embryon de poulet et de la poule adulte. Compt. Rend. Soc. de Biol., 101:1102–1104.

Grobstein, C., and Youngner, J. S. 1949 Combination of tissues from different species in flask cultures. Science, 110:501–503.

Hansen, R. G., and Phillips, P. H. 1947 Studies of proteins from bovine colostrum. I. Electrophoretic studies on the blood serum proteins of colostrum-free calves and of calves fed colostrum at various ages. J. Biol. Chem., 171:223–227.

Harding, C. V., Harding, Drusilla, and Perlmann, P. 1954 Antigens in sea urchin hybrid embryos. Exper. Cell Research, 6:202–210.

Harris, Morgan 1943 The compatibility of rat and mouse cells in mixed tissue cultures. Anat. Rec., 87:107–117.

Harrison, R. G. 1898 The growth and regeneration of the tail of the frog larva. Roux' Arch. Entw.-mech., 7:430–485.

Haurowitz, F., and Schwerin, P. 1943 The specificity of antibodies to antigens containing two different determinant groups. J. Immunol., 47:111–119.

Hoadley, L. 1924 The independent differentiation of isolated chick primordia in chorio-allantoic grafts. Biol. Bull., 46:281–315.

Holtfreter, J. 1933 Nachweis der Induktionsfähigkeit abgetöteter Keimteile. Isolations- und Transplantationsversuche. Roux' Arch. Entw.-mech., 128:584–633.

——— 1943 Properties and functions of the surface coat in amphibian embryos. J. Exp. Zool., 93:251–323.

——— 1943 A study of the mechanics of gastrulation, I. J. Exp. Zool., 94:261–318.

——— 1944 A study of the mechanics of gastrulation, II. J. Exp. Zool., 95:171–212.

——— 1948a Significance of the cell membrane in embryonic processes. Ann. N. Y. Acad. Sci., 49:709–760.

——— 1948b Concepts on the mechanism of embryonic induction and their relation to parthenogenesis and malignancy. Growth Symposium, 2:17–49.

Irwin, M. R. 1947 Immunogenetics. Recent Adv. Genet., 1:113–159.

——— 1949 Immunological studies in embryology and genetics. Quart. Rev. Biol., 24:109–123.

Jennings, R. K., and Malone, F. 1954 Rapid double diffusion precipitin analysis. J. Immunol., 72:411–418.

Jukes, T. H., Fraser, D. T., and Orr, M. D. 1934 The transmission of diphtheria antitoxin from hen to egg. J. Immunol., 26:353–360.

Kabat, E. A., and Mayer, M. M. 1948 Experimental Immunochemistry. Charles C Thomas, Springfield, Illinois.

Keeler, C. E., and Castle, W. E. 1934 Blood-group incompatibility in rabbit embryos and in man. Proc. Nat. Acad. Sci., 20:273–276.

Kozelka, A. W. 1933 Serological studies of tissue antagonism in the domestic fowl. Physiol. Zool., 6:159–184.

Kritschewsky, J. L. 1914 Ein Versuch der Anwendung der Immunitätsreaktionen für des Studium des biogenetischen Grundgesetzes. Centralblatt f. Bakt., 72:81–94.

——— 1923 The relation of immunity reactions to the biogenetic law. Investigations of the chemical structure of the protoplasm of animals during embryonic development by means of heterogeneous hemolysins. J. Infect. Dis., 32:192–195.

Landsteiner, K. 1942 Serological reactivity of hydrolytic products from silk. J. Exp. Med., 75:269–276.

——— 1946 The Specificity of Serological Reactions, 2d ed. Harvard University Press, Cambridge, Massachusetts.

———, and Lampl, H. 1917 Über die Antigeneigenschaften von Azoproteinen. XI. Mitteilung über Antigene. Z. Immunitätsforsch., 26:293–304.

———, and Lampl, H. 1918 Über die Abhängigkeit der serologischen Specifität von der chemischen Struktur. Biochem. Z., 86:343–394.

———, and van der Scheer, J. 1932 Serological reactions with simple chemical compounds (precipitin reactions). J. Exp. Med., 56:399–409.

———, and van der Scheer, J. 1933 Anaphylactic shock by azodyes. J. Exp. Med., 57:633–636.

Loeb, L. 1922 On stereotropism as a cause of cell degeneration and death and a means to prolong the life of cells. Science, 55:22–23.

——— 1945 The Biological Basis of Individuality. Charles C Thomas, Springfield, Illinois.

———, and Wright, S. 1927 Transplantation and individuality differentials in inbred families of guinea pigs. Am. J. Pathol., 3:251–283.

Maculla, E. S. 1948a The immunochemistry of

mouse tissue components. I. The comparative antigenic composition of normal mouse tissues. Yale J. Biol. Med., 20:299–314.

Maculla, E. S. 1948b The immunochemistry of mouse tissue components. III. A comparison of the antigenic composition of embryonic mouse organs with that of adult mouse organs and with mouse tumors. Yale J. Biol. Med., 20:465–472.

McCarty, M., Taylor, H. E., and Avery, O. T. 1946 Biochemical studies of environmental factors essential in transformation of pneumococcal types. Cold Spring Harbor Symp. Quant. Biol., 11:177–183.

Medawar, P. B. 1946a Immunity to homologous grafted skin. I. The suppression of cell division in grafts transplanted to immunized animals. Brit. J. Exper. Pathol., 27:9–14.

———— 1946b Immunity to homologous grafted skin. II. The relationship between the antigens of blood and skin. Brit. J. Exper. Pathol., 27:15–24.

———— 1948 Tests by tissue culture methods on the nature of immunity to transplanted skin. Quart. J. Microsc. Sci., 89:239–252.

Mudd, S. 1932 A hypothetical mechanism of antibody formation. J. Immunol., 23:423–427.

Murphy, J. B. 1913 Transplantability of tissues to the embryos of foreign species. Its bearing on questions of tissue specificity and tumor immunity. J. Exp. Med., 17:482–493.

———— 1914 Studies in tissue specificity. II. The ultimate fate of mammalian tissues implanted in the chick embryo. J. Exp. Med., 19:181–186.

Nace, G. W. 1953 Serological studies of the blood of the developing chick embryo. J. Exp. Zool., 122:423–448.

————, and Schechtman, A. M. 1948 Development of non-vitelloid substances in the blood of the chick embryo. J. Exp. Zool., 108:217–234.

Needham, J. 1942 Biochemistry and Morphogenesis. Cambridge University Press, Cambridge, England.

Orcutt, M. L., and Howe, P. E. 1922 The relation between the accumulation of globulins and the appearance of agglutinins in the blood of newborn calves. J. Exp. Med., 36:291–308.

Ouchterlony, Ö. 1949 An in-vitro test of the toxin-producing capacity of Corynebacterium diphtheriae. Lancet, 256:346–348.

Oudin, J. 1948 L'analyse immunochimique qualitative; Méthode par diffusion des antigènes au sein de l'immunsérum précipitant gélosé. Ann. l'Institut Pasteur, 75:30–51, 109–129.

Owen, R. D. 1945 Immunogenetic consequences of vascular anastomoses between bovine twins. Science, 102:400–401.

Pauling, L. 1940 A theory of the structure and process of formation of antibodies. J. Am. Chem. Soc., 62:2643–2651.

————, Campbell, D. H., and Pressman, D. 1941 Serological reactions with simple substances containing two or more haptenic groups. Proc. Nat. Acad. Sci., 27:125–128.

————, and Delbrück, M. 1940 The nature of the intermolecular forces operative in biological processes. Science, 92:77–79.

Perlmann, P. 1953 Soluble antigens in sea urchin gametes and developmental stages. Exper. Cell Research, 5:394–399.

————, and Gustafson, T. 1948 Antigens in the egg and early developmental stages of the sea-urchin. Experientia, 4:481–482.

Pickering, J. W., and Gladstone, R. J. 1925 The development of blood plasma. I. The genesis of the coagulable material in embryo chicks. Proc. Roy. Soc., London, Ser. B., 98:516–522.

Polk, A. D., Buddingh, G. J., and Goodpasture, E. W. 1938 An experimental study of complement and hemolytic amboceptor introduced into chick embryos. Am. J. Pathol., 14:71–86.

Pomerat, C. M. 1945 Reticulo-endothelial immune serum (REIS). III. The effect of strong concentrations on the growth of Walker rat sarcoma 319 in vitro. Cancer Research, 5:724–728.

———— 1946 A review of recent developments on reticulo-endothelial immune serum (REIS). Quarterly of Phi Beta Pi, 42:203–208.

————, and Anigstein, L. 1944 Anti-reticular immune serum: Its action demonstrated by tissue culture technique. Science, 100:456.

————, and Anigstein, L. 1945 Reticulo-endothelial immune serum (REIS). I. Its action on spleen in vitro. Texas Reports on Biol. & Med., 3:122–141.

Ramon, G. 1928 Sur le passage de la toxine et de anti-toxine tétaniques de la poule a l'oeuf et au poussin. Compt. Rend. Soc. Biol., 99:1476–1478.

Roepke, R. R., and Buschnell, L. D. 1936 A serological comparison of the phosphoprotein of the serum of the laying hen and the vitelline of the egg yolk. J. Immunol., 30:109–113.

Rössle, R. 1905 Ueber die chemische Individualität der Embryonalzellen. München. med. Wchnschr., 52:1276.

Rous, P., and Murphy, J. B. 1911 Tumor implantations in the developing embryo; experiments with a transmissable sarcoma of the fowl. J. Am. Med. Assn., 56:741.

Schechtman, A. M. 1947 Antigens of early developmental stages of the chick. J. Exp. Zool., 105:329–348.

———— 1948 Organ antigen in the early chick embryo. Proc. Soc. Exp. Biol. & Med., 68:263–266.

———— 1952 Physical and chemical changes in the circulating blood. Ann. N. Y. Acad. Sci., 55:85–98.

————, and Hoffman, H. 1952 Serological studies of the origin of globulins in the serum of the chick embryo. J. Exp. Zool., 120:375–390.

Sherman, H. W. 1919 Antibodies in the chick. J. Infect. Dis., 25:256–258.

Sölling, P. 1937 Der Komplementgehalt von Seren von Neugeborenen, Säuglingen und Früchten. Z. Immunitätsforsch., 91:15–21.

Sonneborn, T. M. 1948 The determination of hereditary antigenic differences in genically identical Paramecium cells. Proc. Nat. Acad. Sci., 34:413–418.

Spar, I. 1953 Antigenic differences among early developmental stages of Rana pipiens. J. Exp. Zool., 123:467–497.

Straus, R. 1946 Studies on antireticular cytotoxic serum. I. Introduction and review of the literature. J. Immunol., 54:151–154.

Sturtevant, A. H. 1944 Can specific mutations be induced by serological methods? Proc. Nat. Acad. Sci., 30:176–178.

Telfer, W. H. 1954 Immunological studies of insect metamorphosis. II. The role of a sex-limited blood protein in egg formation by the Cecropia silkworm. J. Gen. Physiol., 37:539–558.

———, and Williams, C. M. 1953 Immunological studies of insect metamorphosis. I. Qualitative and quantitative description of the blood antigens of the Cecropia silkworm. J. Gen. Physiol., 36:389–413.

Ten Cate, G., and Van Doorenmaalen, W. J. 1950 Analysis of the development of the eye-lens in chicken and frog embryos by means of the precipitin reaction. Proc. Konink. Nederlandse Akad. van Wetenschappen, 53:3–18.

Topley, W. W. C., and Wilson, G. S. 1946 The Principles of Bacteriology and Immunity, 3d ed. Williams & Wilkins, Baltimore.

Tyler, A. 1940 Sperm agglutination in the keyhole limpet, Megathura crenulata. Biol. Bull., 78: 159–178.

——— 1940 Agglutination of sea-urchin eggs by means of a substance extracted from the eggs. Proc. Nat. Acad. Sci., 26:249–256.

——— 1942 Specific interacting substances of eggs and sperm. Western J. Surg. Obstet. & Gynec., 50:126–138.

——— 1945 Conversion of agglutinins and precipitins into "univalent" (non-agglutinating or non-precipitating) antibodies by photodynamic irradiation of rabbit-antisera vs. pneumococci, sheep-red-cells, and sea urchin sperm. J. Immunol., 51:157–172.

——— 1946 On natural auto-antibodies as evidenced by antivenin in serum and liver extract of the Gila monster. Proc. Nat. Acad. Sci., 32:195–201.

——— 1947 An auto-antibody concept of cell structure, growth and differentiation. Growth (Suppl.) 10:7–19.

——— 1948 Fertilization and immunity. Physiol. Revs., 28:180–219.

———, Fiset, M. L., and Coombs, R. R. A. 1954 The agglutinating and sensitizing capacity of antisera to sheep red cells after varying degrees of photo-oxidation. Proc. Nat. Acad. Sci., 40:736–740.

Uhlenhuth, P., and Haendel, L. 1910 Untersuchungen über die praktische Verwertbarkeit der Anaphylaxie zur Erkennung und Unterscheidung verschiedener Eiweissarten. Z. Immunitätsforsch., 4:761–816.

———, and Wurm, K. 1939 Über Antikörper gegen Froschlaich. Z. Immunitätsforsch., 96: 183–192.

Vaughan, J. H., and Kabat, E. A. 1953 Studies on the antibodies in rabbit antisera responsible for sensitization of human skin. I. The role of impurities in crystalline egg albumin in stimulating the production of skin sensitizing antibody. J. Exp. Med., 97:821–844.

Waterman, A. J. 1936 Heteroplastic transplantation of embryonic tissues of rabbit and rat. Am. J. Anat., 60:1–25.

Weinberg, M., and Guelin, A. 1936 Recherches sur l'immunité active de l'embryon. Compt. Rend. Soc. Biol., 122:1229–1231.

Weiss, P. 1941 Nerve patterns: The mechanics of nerve growth. Growth (Suppl.) 5:163–203.

——— 1947 The problem of specificity in growth and development. Yale J. Biol. & Med., 19:235–278.

Wiener, A. 1943 Blood Groups and Transfusion, 3d ed. Charles C Thomas, Springfield, Ill.

Wilkoewitz, K., and Ziegenspeck, H. 1928 Die verschiedenen Generationen und Jugend- und Altersformen in ihrer Einwirkung auf den Ausfall der Precipitinreaktionen. Botanisch. Arch., 22:227–244.

Willier, B. H. 1924 The endocrine glands and the development of the chick. I. The effects of thyroid grafts. Amer. J. Anat., 33:67–103.

———, and Rawles, M. E. 1940 The control of feather color pattern by melanophores grafted from one embryo to another of a different breed of fowl. Physiol. Zool., 13:177–199.

———, and Rawles, M. E. 1944 Genotypic control of feather color pattern as demonstrated by the effects of a sex-linked gene upon the melanophores. Genetics, 29:309–330.

Wilson, H. V. 1907 On some phenomena of coalescence and regeneration in sponges. J. Exp. Zool., 5:245–258.

——— 1932 Sponges and biology. Amer. Nat., 66:159–170.

Witebsky, E., and Szepsenwol, J. 1934 L'antigène "Forssman" chez les embryos de poulet à différents stades. Compt. Rend. Soc. Biol., 115: 921–923.

Wolfe, H. R., and Dilks, E. 1948 Precipitin production in chickens. III. The variation in the antibody response as correlated with the age of the animal. J. Immunol., 58:245–250.

Woodruff, A. M., and Goodpasture, E. W. 1931. Susceptibility of chorio-allantoic membrane of chick embryos to infection with fowl-pox virus. Am. J. Pathol., 7:209–222.

Ycas, Mary K. W. 1949 Studies of the development of a normal antibody and of cellular antigens in the blood of sheep. J. Immunol., 61:327–348.

Section X

ONTOGENY OF ENDOCRINE CORRELATION

B. H. WILLIER

ONE OF THE ways whereby cells, tissues, and organs of the vertebrate organism are correlated functionally is through hormones *sensu strictu*, i.e., by specific organic chemical substances produced by specialized tissues or glands, which are carried in minute quantities in the blood stream and have as their primary function the exertion of specific physiological effects on other tissues or organs. During the past three decades extensive investigations on the functions of the endocrine glands of embryonic, young, and adult vertebrates have resulted in the establishment of the concept of the integration of the endocrine system, i.e., the interaction and regulation of secretions of two or more endocrine glands. The relations are such that the secretions of one gland act upon another gland, governing its production and liberation of a hormone entirely different in chemical nature. The endocrine gland thus excited may have in turn, through a rise in blood level of the hormone released, a reciprocal effect on the initiating (trophic) gland, depressing its secretion. In such an interrelationship the mechanism is one in which secretion is regulated by a delicate balance between the levels of trophic and "target" gland hormones in the blood. Thus there exists a vast interlocking of functional activity of the endocrine glands. The order and time at which such correlating mechanisms are established in the ontogeny of the individual is the main problem for analysis in this chapter. In treating of the subject attention will be centered on such topics as (1) the course of differentiation of functional activity of endocrine glands, (2) the extent to which their initial activity arises independently of other hormones, and (3) the time of onset of functional interaction between them.

ANTERIOR PITUITARY–THYROID RELATIONS

The functional relationship between the anterior pituitary and the thyroid is one among others to be set up between endocrine glands of the developing embryo. The basic evidence for this relationship comes from a study of the effects of (1) extirpation of primordia of either the anterior pituitary or the thyroid or both at the time of their first visible appearance, in combination with those of (2) grafting of the thyroid or anterior pituitary or administration of extracts or the active principles of these glands.

THYROTROPHIC EFFECTS ON THYROID ACTIVITY

Without doubt the most complete evidence has come from an analysis of the anuran embryo, which is particularly suitable for the type of experimentation required. At early stages (3.5 to 6 mm. in length) removal of the anterior pituitary, an ingrowing primordium from the surface oral ectoderm, results in changes in the thyroid and in the failure of metamorphosis to take place. The thyroid glands are markedly retarded in growth (reduced to one-sixth the normal weight in tadpoles 36 mm. or more in length). The follicles which form are few in number and atrophic, containing little or no colloid, contrasting sharply to a larger number of follicles distended with colloid in the thyroids of normal tadpoles at the time of beginning metamorphosis (Allen, '27; Smith, '20).

The effect of the anterior pituitary in inducing tadpole metamorphosis is indirect rather than direct. Adler ('14) was the first to express the view that the thyroid is dependent upon the anterior pituitary in the anuran larva. He was led to this interpretation by noting in three cases that hypophysectomy (destruction by electric cautery) of 20 mm. Rana tadpoles not only prevents metamorphosis but results in profound changes in the thyroid (marked growth retardation; small amount of abnormal colloid). That the effect of the anterior pituitary is through a trophic action on the thyroid gland is now well established and is based on two principal lines of evidence (see Allen, '29 and '38, for details and citations to literature). (1) The thyroid glands must be present for the anterior pituitary to bring about metamorphosis. Implants or extracts of the anterior pituitary even in excessive amounts fail in the absence of the thyroid. (2) Colloid secretion and accompanying metamorphosis are restored in hypophysectomized tadpoles by implants of the pars anterior of adult frogs or by repeated intraperitoneal injections of extracts of the anterior lobe of bovine pituitary. The anterior pituitary is thus clearly essential for thyroid activity. The effective substance is regarded as a thyrotrophic hormone from the specific nature of the response, i.e., the effect is upon the thyroid gland, enabling it to store thyroglobulin and to release its hormone.

More recent studies likewise indicate for the chick embryo that the anterior pituitary exerts a trophic effect on the thyroid glands (Fugo, '40; Martindale, '41). Following removal of the prosencephalic portion of the head (thereby excluding both primordia of the pituitary) of 33- to 38-hour embryos, thyroid development during the latter half of the incubation period is retarded. The follicles are relatively few in number, small in size, and contain little or no colloid in contrast to normal thyroids of equivalent age where the follicles are numerous, well formed, and contain an abundance of colloid. That such a change can be attributed to the absence of a trophic effect is indicated by the results of grafting the thyroid glands from a pituitaryless embryo of 12 days to the chorio-allantois of 8-day normal and pituitaryless host chicks. After a period of 4 to 10 days of growth on the normal host the thyroid graft shows distinct follicles, which in degree of development and quantity of colloid are characteristic of the host age, whereas on the pituitaryless host the follicles, if formed at all, are very small and colloid is absent or scanty. In either case the thyroid graft is structurally similar to the host thyroid. From this striking difference in response of the thyroids it is inferred that the anterior pituitary of the normal host exerts a trophic effect on the thyroid graft through the extraembryonic circulatory blood vessels.

TIME RELATIONS IN DEVELOPMENT OF SECRETORY ACTIVITY

The foregoing analysis showing that the secretion of thyrotrophic substance by the anterior pituitary is essential for the normal histogenesis and function of the thyroid and operates via the vascular circulation next poses the problem of the time relations in the assumption of secretory activity of these glands. In general, the functional tests for thyroid activity of embryonic glands from various vertebrates (see Table 27) indicate a fairly close correlation between the time of initial colloid accumulation and the capacity to induce metamorphosis in frog tadpoles. During progress toward metamorphosis in anurans the follicles progressively increase in size and in the accumulation of colloid within them. These changes with age are apparently accompanied by an increase of hormonic efficiency. For example, according to Swingle ('23) thyroids, when tested for capacity to induce metamorphic changes in immature host larvae, have a much greater physiological activity at the time of metamorphosis than during earlier larval stages. Prior to the phase of colloid storage the thyroid has little or no capacity to induce metamorphosis.

At what time in thyroid development does iodine or its compounds begin to accumulate? In the frog embryo (10 mm.), the rat fetus (18- to 19-day), the rabbit fetus (20-day), and the chick embryo (7-day), the thyroid has the capacity to accumulate radioactive inorganic iodine as revealed by radioautographs or by Geiger counts (Gorbman and Evans, '41, '43; Jost et al., '49; Wollman and Zwilling, '53). Although probably present earlier, measurable amounts of iodine are first detected by microchemical analysis in bovine fetal thyroids at 60 days of age (Wolff et al., '49) and in the thyroid of pig fetuses of 7 to 8 cm. (46 to 50 days of age) according to Rankin ('41). In all of these cases, iodine is present at least in detectable amounts at a time prior to the onset of formation of follicles. In the calf fetus organic iodine compounds are present in the thyroid before intracellular colloid or follicle formation can be detected histologically (Koneff et al., '49). It is apparent, therefore, that prior to follicle formation the cords or group of epithelial cells of the thyroid already have the capacity to select iodine from the common blood pool of the embryo. The time that the cells of the thyroid acquire a specific selective affinity for iodine is a problem which needs further investigation (see Table 27).

Following the initial accumulation in relatively small amounts, a progressive increase in thyroid iodine ensues. Although, as noted above, inorganic iodine is first detected

TABLE 27. *Onset of Hormonal Activity in Various Developing Vertebrates*

GLAND	SPECIES OF EMBRYO	STAGE OF HISTOGENESIS OF GLAND	STAGE OR TIME OF INITIAL ACTIVITY	METHOD OF ASSAY OR INDEX OF HORMONAL ACTIVITY	INVESTIGATOR AND DATE
Thyroid	Frog (*Hyla regilla*)	Beginning follicle formation, just prior to colloid storage	10 mm. total length	Accumulation of radioactive iodine as sodium salt. Radioautographs of thyroid sections	Gorbman and Evans ('41)
	Chick	Discrete follicles with colloid	11 days	Injection of I^{131} into air chambers of unincubated egg. Radioautographs of thyroid sections	Hansborough and Khan ('51)
		Interlacing epithelial cords with intervening loose mesenchyme. No visible colloid or follicles	7 days	By Geiger counting determined amount of I^{131} concentrated in thyroid 30 or more minutes after injection of radioiodide into allantoic vein of embryo	Wollman and Zwilling ('53)
		Beginning follicles with colloid	10 days	Feeding thyroid to normal frog tadpoles: accelerates metamorphosis	Hopkins ('35)
	Pig	First appearance of follicles with colloid	9 cm.	Intraperitoneal injection of thyroid extracts into hypophysectomized frog tadpoles induces metamorphosis	Rumph and Smith ('26)
		Marked increase in vascularity	7–8 cm. (46–50 days)	Inorganic iodine first detected by microchemical determination	Rankin ('41)
		Follicles with colloid	8–9 cm. (52 days)	Thyroxine and di-iodotyrosine first detected by microchemical determination	
	Calf	Colloid droplets in cytoplasm of thyroid epithelium	60 days	Analytical chemical method of Taurog and Chaikoff. First measurable amounts of thyroxine-like compound	Wolff et al. ('49)
	Rat	Beginning of follicle formation	18–19 days	Accumulation of radioactive iodine. Radioautographs of sections	Gorbman and Evans ('43)

Adrenal medulla	Chick	Not given (see below)	Minute quantity about 7th day, increasing progressively in subsequent days	Extracts of normal and cultured adrenal tested for adrenaline content by (1) blood pressure changes elicited in anesthetized cats recorded by mercury manometer, (2) dilation of frog pupil, and (3) ferric chloride reaction	Lewis and Geiling ('35)
		Partial penetration of strands of medullary cells between groups of cortical cells	6th day (early)	Silver impregnation (protargol method of Bodian). Medullary cells clearly marked by dark brown granules	Dawson ('53)
	Mouse	Sympathoblasts in contact and beginning to penetrate between cortical cords	14.5 days	Cytochemical: chromaffin reaction of Henle. Extracts inhibit rhythmic peristalsis of mouse jejunem (sensitive to 1 in 500,000 or less)	Howard-Miller ('26)
	Pig	Medullary and cortical primordia in juxtaposition. Groups of future medullary cells penetrating cortex	40–45 mm. Chrome reaction gradually becomes definite	Cytochemical: chromaffin reaction of Henle.	Weymann ('22)
	Man	Active immigration of sympathochromaffin masses through cortex	22 weeks	Cytochemical: chromaffin reaction of Henle. (Adrenaline identified as early as 12th week by vasoconstrictor effect of extracts of fresh adrenal)	Keene and Hewer ('27)
Adrenal cortex	Chick	Advanced intermingling of medullary cells and cortical tissue: cortical cells arranged in well-defined cords in some regions	7th day (early). Positive reaction in well-defined cortical cords only	Histochemical reactions for lipid compounds; birefringence	Dawson ('53)
		All cortical cords well-defined and interlaced with strands of medullary cells	Ascorbic acid and sudanophilic lipids already at high levels on 12th day	As indices of cortical function, ascorbic acid quantitatively determined by colorimetric method of Roe and Keuther and lipids histochemically with Sudan black B.	Case ('52)

TABLE 27 (*continued*)

GLAND	SPECIES OF EMBRYO	STAGE OF HISTOGENESIS OF GLAND	STAGE OR TIME OF INITIAL ACTIVITY	METHOD OF ASSAY OR INDEX OF HORMONAL ACTIVITY	INVESTIGATOR AND DATE
Ovary	Chick	Sexually differentiated	8–12 days	Ovarian tissue grafted to coelom of 50-hour embryo in juxtaposition to host testis—formation of ovarian cortex on left testis	Wolff ('47)
Testis	Chick	Sexually differentiated	8–10 days	Testis tissue grafted as above in juxtaposition to left ovary—little or no effect on left ovary; however, suppresses Müllerian ducts	Wolff ('47)
Testis	Rat	Sexually differentiated	15–16 days	Testis tissue grafted upon atrophied seminal vesicles of adult castrated rat causes local activation of seminal epithelium	Jost ('50) (Cf. Moore, '53)
Gonad	Rabbit	Beginning of sex differentiation	About 19 days of gestation	Surgical castration—entire genital tract of both sexes feminine in form.	Jost ('47; '50)
Testis	Calf	About the time that sex differentiation begins	25 mm.	Sex inversion of female ("freemartin") co-twin with male fetus. Interstitial cells appear at beginning of sex differentiation of testis	Lillie ('17) Bascom ('23)
Anterior pituitary (a) Thyrotrophin	*R. pipiens, R. sylvatica*	Primordium (no cell types visible)	Thyrotrophic substance begins not later than 7 days after tail-bud stage	Thyroid or anterior pituitary primordia approximated by grafting either gland before blood circulation begins. Precocious activation of thyroid and consequent initiation of metamorphosis. Differentiated thyroid (few small follicles) implanted in vicinity of hypophysis of tail-bud embryo initiates metamorphic change	Etkin ('39)
	Chick	Differentiation of cell types in progress—mainly acidophiles	11 days	Underdeveloped thyroid from hypophysectomized chick embryo grafted to chorio-allantoic membrane of 8-day normal chick host responds within 2 days and in 4 days resembles normal thyroid of host age	Martindale ('41)

Pig	All cell types present—acidophiles relatively numerous	26–28 cm. (near term)	Intraperitoneal injection of anterior lobe extracts into hypophysectomized tadpoles elicits slight response of thyroid and definite growth of limb buds	Rumph and Smith ('26)
(b) Adrenocorticotrophin				
Mouse	Cf. Francis ('44)	Last 1/3 gestation period	X-irradiation of pituitary of 13-day fetus. Adrenal cortex reduced in volume	Raynaud and Frilley ('50)
Rat	Cf. Tobin ('39)	2–4 days before term	Decapitation of rat fetus before term. Adrenal cortex thinner; cortical cells smaller, fewer mitoses and less osmiophilic granules than normal. Atrophic effects prevented by injected ACTH	Wells ('48) Kitchell and Wells ('52a)
Rabbit	Unknown	Last 1/4 gestation period	Decapitation of 19–22 day fetus. Marked size reduction of adrenal cortex; cortical cells smaller and fewer than normal. Atrophic adrenal restored to normal by ACTH administration	Jost ('48; '51a, b)
(c) Gonadotrophin				
Pig	Marked increase in acidophile population (160–170 mm. stage)	170–180 mm. (small amount, increasing to readily detectable amounts at 250 mm. stage)	Implants of anterior lobe into sexually immature female mouse cause increase in ovarian weight	Smith and Dortzbach ('29)
Rabbit	Unknown	19th day of gestation	Decapitation of male fetus results in reduction of interstitial tissue of testis and underdevelopment of male hormone-dependent receptors. Such effects prevented by gonadotrophin administration	Jost ('48, '51b)
Chick	Basophile-like cells and acidophiles present, the latter becoming dominant type of cell at 18 days	13th day	"Decapitation" of chick embryo (33–38 hours) results in reduction of intertubular tissue of testis and in ovarian cortex beginning on 13th day. Reduction in size of gonads	Fugo ('40)

TABLE 27 (*continued*)

GLAND	SPECIES OF EMBRYO	STAGE OF HISTOGENESIS OF GLAND	STAGE OR TIME OF INITIAL ACTIVITY	METHOD OF ASSAY OR INDEX OF HORMONAL ACTIVITY	INVESTIGATOR AND DATE
(c) Gonadotrophin	Rat	All cell types differentiated (see Tobin, '39)	Present at birth in greater amounts in female than in male	Anterior lobe of infant rat implanted into sexually immature mouse (20–22 day). Index of activity: increase in ovarian weight in host	Clark ('35)
(d) Growth	Frog *R. boylei*	?	Mid-larval period (30–32 mm.)	Removal of primordium of anterior lobe from early anuran embryo results in abrupt and marked drop in growth rate at mid-larval period. Growth rate restored to normal by intraperitoneal injections of bovine A.P. extracts	Smith ('20) Smith and Smith ('23)
	Pig	Population of basophiles exceeds that of acidophiles	110 mm. (Increasing gradually at subsequent stages)	Daily implants of anterior pituitary from pig fetuses (110 mm.) first induce significant increase in bodyweight, length, and skeletal growth in hypophysectomized rats	Smith and Dortzbach ('29)
	Mouse	Pronounced hypoplasia. Typical acidophiles greatly reduced in number	14th day after birth (time of weaning)	Genetically dwarf mouse increases in weight as rapidly as unaffected sibs until end of 2nd week, when growth practically ceases	Smith and McDowell ('30) (Cf. Francis, '44)
	Rat	All cell types differentiated prior to birth (see Tobin, '39)	6th day after birth	Growth rate decreased following ablation of anterior pituitary from infant rats	Walker et al. ('50)
(e) Diabetogenic factor	Calf	Unknown	4-month fetus	Elevation of blood glucose in depancreatized and hypophysectomized toad after injection of extracts of anterior lobe of fetus	Houssay ('48)
Pancreatic Islets	Rat	Beta cells Alpha cells	18-day fetus 2nd day after birth	Sequence of differentiation of cell types of islets determined by Bensley technique.	Hard ('44)

	Cell/structure	Stage	Observation / Method	Reference
Chick	Beta cells Alpha cells D cells	12th day 8th day 14th day	Sequence of differentiation of cell types of islets determined by the Mallory-Azan method (Heidenhain modification)	Villamil ('42)
Calf	Unknown	Fetus under 5 months (growth of hair not commenced)	Insulin content in extracts of pancreas determined quantitatively by mouse convulsion test	Fischer and Scott ('34)
Parathyroid Man	Anastomosing cords of chief cells with intervening blood sinusoids	100–150 mm.	Histological: period of most active development of vascularity, followed by marked increase in number of chief cells.	Norris ('37)

in pig fetuses of 46 to 50 days of age, thyroxine and di-iodotyrosine are first detected a little later, i.e., in 52-day-old fetuses (Rankin, '41). The stage at which the amount of organic iodine compounds becomes prominent is apparently correlated with the appearance of acini and colloid. Moreover, the first appearance of organic iodine is accom-

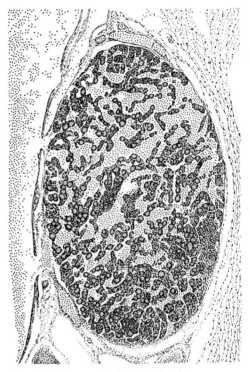

Fig. 208. Section of thyroid of a normal 11-day chick embryo showing marked sinusoidal vascularity at time of rapid formation of discrete follicles with colloid. Carotid artery to the left. Initial ×135.

panied by marked increase in vascularity of the gland (cf. Fig. 208). In the bovine fetus from 53 days to term there is a progressive increase in thyroxine-like compounds of iodine and non-thyroxine iodine. These iodine fractions increase proportionately with increasing fetal size and age (Wolff et al., '49). The rate at which each of these substances accumulates in the fetal thyroid shows an exponential relationship to body weight and length as well as to age of the fetus. Moreover, the increase in their accumulation cannot be accounted for solely on the basis of increase in thyroid growth, since the percentage growth rate of the thyroid declines steadily with increasing age. Apparently as the growth rate declines with age there is a progressive increase in the capacity of the fetal thyroid gland to store iodine and its compounds.

The question next arises as to the time when the thyroid primordium in the course of its development is responsive to the thyrotrophic hormone. Shortly before and at the time of follicle formation the thyroid is known to be responsive to anterior lobe stimulation. That it behaves as an effector organ long before colloid storage begins is brought out in frog embryos by grafting the primordium of either the thyroid or the anterior pituitary so that the two are in closer proximity than in their normal sites (Etkin, '39). Irrespective of whether one or the other gland is shifted or an extra gland grafted, such proximity leads to a precocious activation of the thyroid with consequent precocious metamorphosis. There is no precocity if either gland is grafted to a site outside the neighborhood of the other, i.e., apparently when the thyroid is beyond the range of influence of the anterior lobe (see p. 583). Furthermore, an extra thyroid grafted near the pituitary is activated, whereas the host thyroid at its normal site is not. The activation of the thyroid is first visibly evident at approximately seven days after the operation, at which time the follicles are greatly enlarged and contain abundant colloid, contrasting with the control thyroid where these processes are much less advanced. The activated gland shows a marked increase in size (volume), reaching at 19 days a size over twenty times that of the normal thyroid. It is evident, therefore, that the thyroid primordium is in a responsive state for a considerable length of time prior to its normal histological differentiation and is apparently as responsive as the gland in which follicle formation is about to begin or has begun.

At what time in the course of development of the anterior lobe does the secretion of thyrotrophic substance begin? Is its time of onset prior to or coincident with the histological differentiation of cell types? The early responsiveness of the thyroid analyzed above indicates that the anterior pituitary is concurrently active in producing a thyrotrophic substance. Since the activation of a thyroid in proximity to an anterior lobe is similar in nature to activation by the thyrotrophic hormone known to be produced at later stages, it is inferred that the production of the hormone begins very early in pituitary development of anurans. It apparently begins not later than seven days after the tailbud stage, which is long before it is functionally effective in normal anuran meta-

morphosis (Etkin, '39). Surely at the tailbud stage the cells of the hypophyseal primordium, which has just invaginated to a position below the infundibulum, are not visibly differentiated into cell types (so reported for *R. pipiens* by Kleinholz, '40). The cell types apparently differentiate considerably later. According to Kerr ('39), whose study of histogenesis of the anterior lobe in relation to the thyroid in the anurans (*R. temporaria* and *Bufo bufo*) is the most detailed and complete, the acidophiles appear prior to metamorphosis, i.e., at the stage when the larvae are first completely freeswimming (11 to 13 mm. in length), whereas the basophiles first appear during the most active period of metamorphosis, i.e., of rapid growth of hind legs, appearance of fore-legs, and tail absorption. Furthermore, the histological differentiation of acidophiles and the first occurrence of minute droplets of colloid in the thyroid coincide in time. This, coupled with a steady increase in the number of acidophiles and in the amount of colloid during the early stages up to the beginning of rapid hind-leg growth and with the absence of basophiles, shows a close correspondence between acidophiles and thyroid activity. Thus Kerr was led to infer that thyrotrophic function and general body growth as well are associated with the acidophiles.

In the amniotes but few attempts have been made to correlate the initiation of thyrotrophic activity with the histogenesis of the anterior lobe. Of interest here is the pioneer work of Rumph and Smith ('26). These investigators reported that intraperitoneal injections of extracts of the anterior pituitary from fetal pigs of 140 mm. and 160 mm. stages fail to call forth a response in hypophysectomized frog tadpoles. However, at 260 to 280 mm. stages (near time of birth) a definite although slight response is elicited as indicated by a clear-cut stimulation of hind-limb growth and some activation of the thyroid. This capacity to evoke metamorphic changes appeared to be correlated with the time (260 mm. stage) in histogenesis of the cell types that the acidophiles became nearly as numerous as in the adult pig gland. (See Table 27.)

However, that the acidophiles have a specific functional significance must be questioned in the light of later detailed studies on the cytological differentiation of the anterior pituitary in the fetal pig. Nelson ('33) reports that, although acidophiles are present at the 70 to 100 mm. stages, the population of basophiles greatly predominates. During successively later stages the acidophile population gradually increases until the 160 to 170 mm. stage, at which time a marked rise in their number is exhibited. Although at this time the acidophile population is markedly increased, the functional test as noted above does not indicate thyrotrophic activity. It is possible that although the thyrotrophic substance is produced by the anterior lobe it is not present in sufficient quantity in the extracts thereof to elicit a positive response in hypophysectomized tadpoles. By this method of bio-assay the hormone appears to be present in sufficient quantities only near the time of birth. Nevertheless, its presence as early as 90 mm. is indicated, since at that stage but not earlier (1) minute droplets of colloid appear within follicles of the thyroid and (2) thyroid extracts stimulate metamorphosis in the hypophysectomized tadpole (Rumph and Smith, '26). It must be recognized, however, that (a) the thyroid may attain an initial functional state independently of thyrotrophic secretions, (b) the bioassay method is not sufficiently sensitive for detecting minute quantities of thyrotrophic hormone, and (c) the hormone may be supplied to the fetus by the mother. The evidence is inadequate for deciding whether one type of cell or the other is related to the production of thyrotrophin in the pig fetus.

In the chick embryo a fairly close correlation exists between the time of differentiation of the thyroid and of the cell types of the anterior pituitary. The thyroid begins to store colloid in follicles on the tenth day (Hopkins, '35), at which time the acidophiles are first apparent in the anterior lobe. The acidophiles gradually increase in number with advance in age, becoming the dominant type of cell by the eighteenth day (Rahn, '39) or by the third day after hatching (Payne, '46). Although relatively few basophile-like cells appear to be present as early as the twelfth day, they do not attain a fully differentiated state until about ten days or more after hatching. In the chick the presence of acidophiles and basophile-like cells seems to precede by one day the onset of thyrotrophic secretion, as is revealed by grafting thyroid glands from hypophysectomized donors to the chorio-allantois of normal and hypophysectomized chick hosts. From the differences in thyroid response given it may be inferred that the thyrotrophic hormone is produced in small yet significant amounts as early as the eleventh day and in still greater amounts from the

twelfth to the eighteenth day of incubation (Martindale, '41).

To summarize, it becomes apparent on the basis of functional tests that the anterior pituitary during embryonic development produces a thyrotrophic hormone. Regardless of whether basophiles or acidophiles arise first, a predominance of acidophiles usually occurs according to the majority of investigators during some phase of pituitary development of the growing embryo. Although it is difficult to relate the specific cells to specific secretions, the body of evidence suggests that the acidophiles may be associated with the production of the thyrotrophic hormone and, as will be seen below, of the growth hormone as well.

Since it is evident that a thyrotrophic substance is produced sooner or later by the developing anterior pituitary, it is important to know whether the hormone content increases quantitatively with developmental age. This appears to be the case, as several lines of evidence indicate. From a study of the effects of approximating the primordia of the anterior pituitary and thyroid in anuran embryos, Etkin ('39) concluded that a "field of thyrotrophic substance" surrounds the normal pituitary in quite early stages of development. The activation effect on the thyroid is limited in its range. As noted above, an extra thyroid grafted near the pituitary of a host is activated, whereas the thyroid of the host is not. This suggests that the manner of dispersal of the thyrotrophic substance is by diffusion through the tissues rather than through the blood stream.* Furthermore, it is probable that the anterior pituitary at the stages tested is producing

---

* The concept of a direct and local action of hormones in actuating the expression of the intrinsic potentialities of endocrine receptor glands and tissues is well substantiated by three recent discoveries. (1) Sex hormones of an embryonic gonad in contact with another one of opposite sex constitution or with a terminal sex receptor elicit specific responses of the tissue components in accordance with their pre-existing reaction capacities (for a more extensive treatment of the subject see p. 594). (2) Hormones from a thyroid graft act locally by direct contact in accelerating metamorphic events in the neuronal elements of the hindbrain of the anuran tadpole (Weiss and Rossetti, '51). (3) Hormones from fragments of the anterior pituitary (3½-month cockerel) cultivated for 9 days in vitro in close contact with a thyroid gland of the pre-follicular stage (8½-day chick embryo) greatly stimulate the formation of intracellular colloid droplets in the parenchymal tissue of the thyroid; follicles, however, fail to form (Gaillard, '53).

the hormone in amounts insufficient to have an activation effect via the vascular circulation.

Grafts of the anterior lobe from anuran tadpoles of different ages vary in their effectiveness in bringing about precocious metamorphosis in host tadpoles of immature stages. Anterior pituitaries from animals in metamorphic climax are highly potent as grafts in stimulating metamorphosis, whereas those from donors before the onset of metamorphosis are impotent (Allen, '38). These results may be interpreted as indicating that the normal anterior pituitary undergoes a sudden increase in the production of thyrotrophic substance at the time of metamorphosis (Etkin, '38). This marked change in activity appears to be the primary stimulus at metamorphosis, since it is known that the receptor gland is responsive to the pituitary long before the normal time of metamorphosis. This peak is soon followed by a decline in thyrotrophic activity, since grafts of glands from tadpoles in stages beyond the more active phases of metamorphosis give a retarded response in premetamorphic tadpole hosts. During the subsequent growth of the young or juvenile frog no information is available as to the time that thyrotrophic activity of the anterior lobe again attains a high level. It is highly potent in adult frogs as measured by its capacity to induce precocious metamorphosis.

Since the quantity of thyrotrophic substances is apparently low at first, it should be expected that an excess number of anterior pituitary grafts would produce a precocious metamorphosis. In *Rana sylvatica* this appears to be the case (Etkin, '35). As grafts, a single anterior pituitary primordium is insufficient; but three extra primordia (total of four acting) are sufficient to induce metamorphosis in 7.8 ± 1.4 days as compared with 17.7 ± 0.6 days required for the unoperated controls. Furthermore, the animals with four primordia are significantly smaller than the controls at the time of metamorphosis. Thus the difference in time required for and maximum size attained at metamorphosis give a rough measure of the quantity of hormone produced. The results support the interpretation that the anterior pituitary primordium produces the hormone in small quantities in the anuran embryo.

Little or no information is available as to whether the thyrotrophic substance is produced in increasing amounts during the ontogeny of amniotes. As previously noted, the presence of thyrotrophic activity of the anterior lobe of the fetal pig is indicated near the time of birth but not earlier. The experiments were designed to ascertain the time of onset of secretory activity and not the quantity of hormone produced. More refined quantitative methods of extracting and of bio-assay of the thyrotrophic hormone from the anterior lobe from fetal and postfetal stages are needed in order to ascertain the quantity necessary for thyroid activation and consequent effects on the metabolism of growth.

Finally, the question is raised as to whether the thyroid has a reciprocal action on the anterior pituitary during ontogeny. Does the thyroid hormone released into the blood by the activated thyroid regulate or depress the quantity of thyrotrophic substance produced or released by the anterior pituitary, the trophic gland? Is the secretory output of trophic and effector glands regulated by a balance between the quantities of thyrotrophic and thyroid hormone in the blood circulation? That the thyroid has an effect on the development of the anterior pituitary is brought out by the study of thyroidectomized anuran embryos (Hoskins and Hoskins, '19; Smith, '20). By removing the thyroid primordium from embryos at an early stage (*R. sylvatica* embryos 5 to 8 mm. in length) thyroidless larvae are obtained. At the expected time of metamorphosis of such tadpoles, the anterior lobe is definitely larger and the number of acidophiles greater than in control tadpoles of the same size and age. The validity and significance of these findings must await further investigation. The increase in number of acidophiles is puzzling, in view of the fact that thyroid removal in certain species of mammals during postnatal life commonly leads to a decrease in number or complete loss of acidophiles and an increase of basophiles in the anterior lobe (Severinghaus, '37).

A large body of evidence indicates in general that thyrotrophic potency of the anterior pituitary varies in different species and within the same species at different ages (or phases of reproductive activity). Such potency changes, particularly those following thyroidectomy, lend support to the commonly accepted theory that a high level of thyroid hormone suppresses the production and release of the thyrotrophic substance and, conversely, a low level of the thyroid hormone stimulates the production and release of thyrotrophic substances by the pituitary (for a review of the evidence see Adams, '46). In keeping with this theory is the significant discovery of Courrier ('51) that radioactive thyroxine, when injected intravenously into normal male rabbits, is concentrated selectively in the posterior pituitary.

ANTERIOR PITUITARY–ADRENAL RELATIONS

Another functional relationship established during the course of development of the embryo is that between the anterior pituitary and the adrenal glands. In the main the evidence for this relationship is derived from a study of the effects of (a) extirpation or destruction of the primordia of the anterior lobe or of the adrenal gland and (b) grafting of the anterior pituitary or administration of its extracts from adult animals.

ADRENOCORTICOTROPHIC EFFECTS ON DEVELOPMENT OF ADRENAL CORTEX

That the development of the adrenal glands is altered after removal of the ingrowing primordium of the anterior pituitary in the anuran embryo was first demonstrated by Smith ('20). The cortical or interrenal tissue (in the form of profusely branched cords of cells) is greatly diminished in quantity as compared with that of the normal or thyroidectomized tadpole of the same age (in the thyroidectomized larvae the cortical tissue is hypertrophied). The lipid granules of the cortical cells show a change in reaction to osmic acid, being less intensely blackened as compared to the normal or to the thyroidless tadpole. The diminution in the cortical elements and alteration of the lipid granules may be attributed to the absence of some essential trophic substance, since injection of an extract of fresh bovine anterior lobe into hypophysectomized tadpoles restores the scanty adrenal cortex to normal (Smith and Smith, '23).

That the anterior pituitary exerts a trophic action on the adrenal cortex of the mammalian fetus and the chick embryo is likewise clearly indicated. Destruction of the hypophysis of the 13-day mouse fetus by x-irradiation (Raynaud and Frilley, '50) or decapitation of the rabbit fetus at 19 to 22 days (Jost, '48, '51a), of the rat fetus 2-4 days before term (Wells, '48) and of the chick embryo at 40 to 50 hours (Case, '52), usually leads to a marked diminution in volume of the adrenal cortex, and according to Jost equally so in both sexes. Histologically the cortex is atypical. The cortical cells are not only smaller and fewer in number as compared with the normal but also show a diminution in lipid granules and of ascorbic acid as well in the chick. Similarly, a reduction in size of the adrenal cortex occurs in the human fetus in cases of spontaneous anencephaly and cyclopia, but only when the anterior lobe is distinctly smaller than normal or completely absent (see Edmunds, '50).

From the above observations it is clear that the effects of removing the pituitary, irrespective of the means employed, lead to retrogressive changes in the adrenal cortex of the embryo or fetus. These changes may be attributed to the absence of a specific pituitary hormone, since administration of adrenocorticotrophin (ACTH) to the hypophysectomized embryo or fetus restores the adrenal cortex more or less completely to its normal volume and histology (Jost, '51a,b; Kitchell and Wells, '52a; Case, '52). The results not only indicate that the anterior pituitary of the mammalian fetus and chick embryo at least during the later stages of development produces a hormone comparable in action to ACTH, but also suggest that this specific hormone is essential for the normal histogenesis and growth of the cortical component of the adrenal gland.

EFFECTS OF ADRENAL CORTEX ON ANTERIOR PITUITARY

Does the adrenal cortex in turn have a reciprocal action upon the anterior pituitary of the developing embryo? According to Tobin ('39) total or partial destruction of the adrenal glands of the rat fetus (17 days and older) by electric cautery results in cellular changes in the pituitary. In comparison with normal controls, the number of acidophiles is decreased, the basophile cells show degranulation, and the number of chromophobe cells appears to be increased. These results, although suggestive of a reverse influence, need confirmation and extension. That the anterior pituitary is reactive to secretions of the adrenal cortex during late fetal stages of the rat is indicated by the recent investigations of Kitchell and Wells ('52b). After unilateral adrenalectomy of the rat fetus on the twentieth day, the intact adrenal undergoes a compensatory hypertrophy that can be prevented by subcutaneous implants of cortisone. Implants of cortisone to the normal fetus of the same age fail to produce any significant change in the volume of the adrenal or the histology of the cortex. These results seem to indicate that the liberation of ACTH, which appears to be essential for compensatory hypertrophy of the adrenal, is suppressed by the administered cortisone.

INTERRELATIONS IN TIME OF ONSET OF FUNCTIONAL ACTIVITY

As to the time of onset of functional activity in the anterior pituitary and adrenal cortex during the course of their development no precise information is available. However, certain inferences may be drawn from the data at hand (see Table 27). The preceding analysis indicates that the primordium of the adrenal gland is responsive to ACTH in the rat and mouse during the last third and in the rabbit during the last fourth of the period of gestation. Apparently the period before term is one in which the constituent cortical and medullary cells are assuming step by step an orderly arrangement or oriented cell pattern simulating that characteristic of the adult gland. It is a period of active morphogenesis and to some extent histogenesis. Using the mouse fetus as an example, it is seen according to Waring ('35) that on about the thirteenth day the cortical and medullary primordia are both constituted and closely adpressed. By the fourteenth day the sympathochromaffin elements have begun to migrate into the cortical component, the immigration continuing gradually until the day of birth, when they are concentrated at the center of the gland. The cells of the cortex at 14 days are all more or less alike (finely granular and highly eosinophilic cytoplasm), and their arrangement is haphazard. Between the sixteenth day and term an oriented pattern of cortical cells arises. The cells at the periphery of the cortex become less eosinophilic between the sixteenth and eighteenth days, and at birth have an arrangement which merely foreshadows that characteristic of the glomerular and fasciculate zones of the permanent cortex. Internal to this apparent forerunner of the permanent cortex and interlocking with the medullary cells is a zone of more highly eosinophilic cortical cells, the beginning of the so-called "fetal cortex," "x-zone" of Miller, or "androgenic zone."

It may be inferred, therefore, that at the time of experimental removal of the pituitary in the mammalian fetus the adrenal cortex is clearly responsive to adrenocorticotrophic hormone after the cortical and medullary primordia are already constituted and combined, and especially so during the subsequent critical stages of morphogenesis and histogenesis of the two component tissues. The nature of the effect appears to be that of retarded or arrested morphogenesis, rather than degeneration. No evidence is available as to whether the adrenal at still earlier stages can respond to ACTH. This problem might be resolved by growing the primordia of anterior pituitary and adrenal in juxtaposition, either by grafting or by in vitro cultures, since activation by local diffusion of hormones appears to be a more sensitive test than activation by hormones that pass through the regular blood vessels of the embryo (see p. 583). Also, since ACTH definitely stimulates adrenocortical growth in the rat as early as the fourth day after birth (Moon, '40), the time and degree to which adrenocortical growth is stimulated might be ascertained by injection of ACTH into fetuses at successively earlier stages.

Whether the growth of the primordia of the permanent cortex or the "fetal cortex" is equally or differentially affected by the absence of anterior pituitary is a problem of much significance. An inhibition of the growth of the permanent cortex is to be expected, since in the dwarf mouse, which has an endocrine-deficient anterior pituitary, the characteristic zoning of the cortex is absent or indistinct (Smith and McDowell, '30). Possible effects on the growth of the fetal cortex are of special interest in many mammals (such as mouse, rabbit, cat, human, certain carnivores and ungulates), since it is proportionally very large, constituting the main bulk of the cortex. In some species its growth is relatively enormous, taking place during either fetal or early postnatal life. This hypertrophy apparently is responsible for the relatively large size of the adrenal gland at birth (Hill, '30). In man at birth, for instance, the adrenals constitute 0.2 per cent of the entire body weight, contrasting with 0.1 per cent for the adult (Scammon, '30). The only clues that pituitary secretions possibly regulate the growth of the fetal component have been reported by Elliot and Armour ('11), who attributed the small size of the adrenal of an anencephalous human infant (at birth) to an almost complete absence of the fetal cortex, and by Deanesley ('38), who demonstrated that in pituitary-deficient dwarf mice the x-zone is absent in spite of normal reproductive activity. Moreover, in early postnatal life the fetal cortex often shows a distinct sex difference, persisting longer and attaining a larger size in females than in males. Although often regarded as having possible androgenic functions in sex development, this has not been substantiated for the mouse (Howard-Miller, '27, '39; Howard, '46). According to Gersh and Grollman ('39a,b), the function of the x-zone and the more peripheral fascicular and glomerular zones is identical; both respond to stimulation but not equally, the x-zone being less responsive. Furthermore, the wide-meshed capillary plexus of the x-zone is altered by excessive activity so as to resemble more closely the capillaries of the fasciculate zone (Gersh and Grollman, '41). (For a thor-ough analysis of the relation of the adrenal cortex to the reproductive system in fetal and young postnatal rats, see Moore, '53.)

The changes in vascular pattern of the growing cortex offer a possible index of the onset of functional activity (see Figs. 209*A*, *B*, and *C*). During the early stages of adrenal growth in the embryo the arrangement of the cortical cells is haphazard, at which time the capillaries of the cortex are in the form of a loosely woven and irregular plexus. \t later stages with the growth of the cortex,

portion of the cortical cells becomes ar-ranged into parallel cords or columns of the fascicular zone, the commonly supposed secretory zone of the adrenal of juvenile and adult mammals. With this change in cellular arrangement the earlier unoriented type of capillary circulation is gradually recon-structed into a more or less longitudinally oriented pattern of vessels, i.e., in rather sim-ple lines the plan of the adult circulation (Flint, '00; Whitehead, '33). The significance of the changes in vascular pattern may be interpreted in terms of function (Gersh and Grollman, '41). The change is from a type which permits a slow rate of blood flow to one which favors a much more efficient flow of blood, thus assuring a richer supply of blood to the cortex. The fact that the more efficient mode of blood transportation arises as the cortical cells assume an organization with distinctive properties seems to imply a beginning functional relation and one which, furthermore, may reflect the need of the growing organism for the cortical hor-mone in its metabolism. At least, such a view is in keeping with findings on postnatal mammals that in response to increased needs of the organism for cortical hormone the cortex hypertrophies and the vascular pattern of a hyperactive cortex is altered so as to increase blood flow.

The question next arises as to when in the course of adrenal development the ori-ented type of circulation arises. According to Flint ('00) the beginning of an orderly

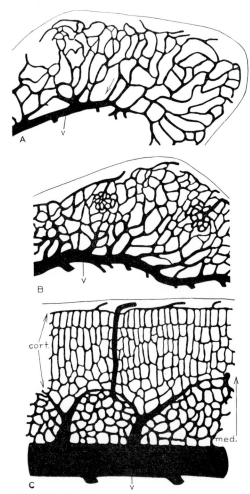

Fig. 209. Three stages in development of the vas-cular pattern of the adrenal of the pig embryo (adapted from Flint, '00).

A, Stage of 3 cm. showing the simple irregular plexus of capillaries of the cortex, which at this stage is comprised of irregular cords of cortical cells. Arrow indicates direction of blood flow from the fibrous capsule (uppermost surface of figure) to the central venule (*v*). Precursor medullary cells ap-parently lie between cortex and capsule.

B, Stage of 8 cm. showing the capillary plexus of two groups of medullary cells (note resemblance to glomeruli), which have invaded the cortex. Each is separately vascularized by an arterial capillary from the capsule. Capillary plexus of cortex is still irregular.

C, Stage of 22 cm. (near birth) showing the ori-ented pattern of the capillary plexus of the cortex, thus reflecting the initial zonation of the cortical tis-sue. The definitive topographical relation of cortex (*cort.*) and medulla (*med.*) is initially established at about the 12 cm. stage, when the invading groups of medullary cells reach their terminal position adjacent to the central vein (*v*).

arrangement of the capillaries is first noted in the pig fetus (12 to 15 cm.) at a stage when the definitive topographical relations of cortex and medulla are first established. During subsequent stages the capillary plexus assumes gradually a more orderly arrangement, and at a stage just before birth (22 cm. fetus) it has a distinct longitudinal orientation, although still of a much simpler pattern than in the adult (see Fig. 209C).

Species variations in the time of origin of an oriented pattern of circulation are expected. In the mouse, for example, the permanent cortex is much less well organized than it is in the pig at birth. Subsequent to birth in the mouse the cortical cells (peripheral to x-zone) gradually assume the form of parallel cords in the fasciculate zone, only becoming distinct at about 25 days after birth. On the assumption that column formation and orientation of circulation are causally related, the capillary plexus should gradually change to a longitudinal orientation. By the fourth week, at any rate, the pattern of circulation is clearly an oriented one (Gersh and Grollman, '41).

A further criterion of beginning functional activity is the time of appearance, rate of accumulation, and identification of the kinds of lipids of the cortex during development. It has commonly been inferred that the lipids of the cortical cells may be the vehicle for cortical hormones, since they are obtained primarily from the lipid fraction of extracts of adult adrenal glands. In the human embryo lipids in the form of fine droplets are already present in the cortical cells at the stage (14 mm.) of initial penetration of the future medullary cells into the cortical primordium. Generally speaking, during subsequent stages in adrenal development the amount of sudanophilic lipids seems to increase in the permanent cortex and to diminish in the fetal cortex. In the latter the lipids gradually diminish during the later weeks of intra-uterine life, disappearing altogether at full term (in the postnatal mouse the homologous x-zone prior to onset of its degeneration is likewise free of sudanophilic lipids according to Howard-Miller, '27). Concomitantly with the active growth and organization of the layers of the permanent cortex the amount of lipid increases. An increase in lipids over earlier stages is indicated at birth when the cortical cells show a beginning arrangement into columns, a further increase at 3 weeks after birth when the fascicular zone is better defined, and a well-marked increase in the glomer-

ular and fascicular zones of a 3-month-old infant (see Keene and Hewer, '27; Uotila, '40).

Although highly suggestive, this increase in sudanophilic lipid, which apparently attains its highest concentration at about the time the permanent cortex acquires a well-defined zonal organization, cannot be regarded by itself as a reliable indicator of cortical hormone production. Sudan III does not discriminate among the various kinds of lipids. Neither does osmic acid, another commonly used reagent for detecting lipid substances in tissues. Nevertheless such histochemical tests, although not useful alone for a differential discrimination of lipids, may be valuable indicators when applied to the adrenal in which changes in cortical activity have been induced experimentally. For example, in the postnatal rat a definite correlation exists between cortical activity and reduction of osmic acid. The reduction of osmic acid is increased by stimulation (induced by unilateral adrenalectomy, cold, etc.) and decreased by depression (induced by injection of variable amounts of cortical hormone) of cortical activity (Flexner and Grollman, '39). Furthermore, the same type of dynamic change in sudanophilic lipids (possibly cholesterol esters) occurs in the adrenal cortex of rats following administration of ACTH or subjection to stress. These changes parallel the alterations in cholesterol content (Sayers et al., '44).

Still another possible key to the onset of adrenal cortical activity in the fetus is the time and rate of accumulation of the vitamin, ascorbic acid, which along with cholesterol esters occurs in high concentration in the functionally active adrenal of juvenile and adult mammals. Only a few attempts have been made to determine the presence of ascorbic acid in the developing adrenal of any vertebrate. By means of a colorimetric method Case ('52) found that the quantity of ascorbic acid rapidly increases in the chick adrenals from the twelfth to the nineteenth day of incubation, rising from a value of 0.95 to 1.67 μg. per milligram of adrenal tissue during this period. The further observation that the total amount of ascorbic acid increases relatively more rapidly than does the net weight suggests that with advancing age the adrenals acquire an increasing capacity to accumulate ascorbic acid. Unfortunately the initial time and rate of accumulation have not yet been determined for adrenals of embryos earlier than the twelfth day (cf. Dawson, '53). The changes in ascorbic acid content during the period under consideration apparently constitute a reliable indicator of functional activity, since in pituitaryless embryos the quantity of ascorbic acid does not rise but remains at a level characteristic of the adrenals of the normal 12-day embryo. Treatment of such pituitaryless embryos with ACTH brings about an apparent increase in sudanophilic lipids of cortical tissue, but whether ascorbic acid is likewise increased has not been determined.

The lack of information on the possible occurrence of ascorbic acid in the adrenal of the mammalian fetus is a challenge. In juvenile and adult mammals the concentration of ascorbic acid (as well as of cholesterol) is regulated by the anterior pituitary. The administration of ACTH and stress (several varieties) both bring about a marked reduction or depletion of ascorbic acid (for a recent consideration and references see Sayers and Sayers, '49, and Long, '49). In all probability ascorbic acid accumulates along with sudanophilic lipids which, as noted above, occur in the developing adrenal cortex. Microchemical and histochemical tests for the presence of ascorbic acid, especially if correlated with alterations in its content under conditions of increased activation, should prove to be valuable methods for the evaluation of the degree of cortical activity, if any, in the fetus or during early postnatal life. Progressive changes in the mechanism of response are indicated in infant rats of increasing age. According to Jailer ('50) the ascorbic acid content of the adrenal declines (24 to 37 per cent) in response to the administration of ACTH to animals 4 to 6 days of age, but no decline occurs upon exposure of the animals to a temperature of 5°C. (stress) until the sixteenth day; also, the administration of adrenaline (epinephrine) causes no increase in ascorbic acid until the eighth day. Further, using fall in ascorbic acid content as an index of activation, no ACTH activity in the anterior pituitary of infant rats is detectable until the eighteenth day of age post partum (Jailer, '51).

Such combined methods of attack now seem feasible for determining cortical activity in the fetus, since at least for a short period prior to birth the adrenal cortex is responsive to adrenocorticotrophic hormone as noted above. In a similar way the changes in birefringent substances may furnish additional clues (Yoffey and Baxter, '47). Special attention should be directed to the histochemical detection of cholesterol esters, cortical sterones, and ascorbic acid, substances known to be present in the functionally active cortex of the adult mammalian adrenal (Yoffey and Baxter, '49). Whether the cortex of the mammalian embryo at any stage contains these substances or chemically related ones has not yet been established. Tests for the occurrence of these substances would have a twofold purpose: (1) to ascertain the period when the growing cortex acquires the capacity to select steroid mother substances from the blood and synthesize them into cortical sterones or allied compounds, and (2) to determine whether such capacity is a key to the approximate time when adrenocorticotrophic substance is released by the anterior lobe in quantities sufficient for cortical activation. Progress along these lines has been made by Dawson ('53) in a study of the time course in histochemical differentiation of the adrenal gland of the chick embryo. As judged by their reactions to given chemical agents or by birefringent properties, several kinds of lipid compounds appear in some cords of the gland as early as the seventh day but are not common to all cords until the eleventh or twelfth day; on the basis of the silver reaction, ascorbic acid, although first detectable on about the tenth day, is not present in appreciable quantities until the twelfth day.

Turning next to the functional activity of the anterior pituitary, very little is known concerning the time when adrenocorticotrophic substance begins to form, the rate of its increase, or whether its production is correlated with the differentiation of cell types (see Table 27). That the anterior pituitary is active in producing and releasing ACTH during the last third or quarter of fetal life in the rat and rabbit and of the last third of the embryonic period of the chick is clearly indicated, since within that period the growth of the adrenal cortex is definitely arrested in the absence of the pituitary and can be restored to normal or partially so by administration of adrenocorticotrophin. Apparently, then, for a short period prior to birth or hatching the trophic hormone in question is present in sufficient concentration to be physiologically effective. This may mark the peak production during embryonic life of the species under consideration.

It is of interest to note parenthetically that at about this time signs of thyroid activity are first noted in the rat fetus. In this species the thyroid does not begin to form follicles and store colloid until 3 to 4 days prior to birth, becoming more marked immediately before term (Kull, '26). It is within this period, i.e., at 18 to 19 days of gestation, that the thyroid first acquires the capacity to concentrate radioactive iodine; the capacity is considerably stronger at birth (Gorbman and Evans, '43). Also, between the 19½ day and term, the thyroid of normal and pituitaryless rat fetuses is reactive to subcutaneous injections of thyrotrophin (Sethre and Wells, '51). From the presumptive evidence at hand, it would appear that in the rat fetus the endocrine functions of the thyroid, anterior lobe, and adrenal cortex begin relatively late, i.e., at a time when nearly 90 per cent of the intra-uterine life is completed.

Whether the anterior pituitary at early stages has ACTH activity is not known but might be tested in the manner suggested on pp. 582 and 583. Likewise, no information is available on whether the production of ACTH increases quantitatively with developmental age. It probably increases rapidly after birth, judging from the marked changes that take place in the growth and vascularity of the adrenal cortex in the rat, mouse, and man.

No systematic attempt has been made to correlate the onset of adrenocorticotrophic activity with the time course of differentiation of the cell types in the anterior pituitary. Of those species in which trophic activity is indicated, only in the anuran, chick, and rat embryos has the occurrence of cell types been reported. In the anuran no relationship is ascertainable since the anterior lobe is removed at a very early stage, long before the histogenesis of cell types begins. Although in the rat, acidophiles, basophiles, and chromophobe cells are already differentiated in fetuses of 18 to 23 days (Tobin, '39), the time order of their differentiation and numerical frequency have not been investigated. In the chick a close correspondence is seen between the indicated period of adrenocorticotrophic activity and active histogenesis of the cell types. Subsequent to the tenth day, when they are first apparent, the acidophiles rapidly increase in number, becoming the predominating type of cell by the eighteenth day (Rahn, '39) or at most by the third day after hatching (Payne, '46). Although basophile-like cells seem to be present from the twelfth day on, typical basophiles are not found until after hatching (cf. Wilson, '52).

That the cellular source of the hormone in the embryonic development of the pituitary is by no means clear is not surprising, since even in postnatal mammals at various ages it has been difficult to assign a specific hormonal secretion to any particular cell type. Reports as to the cellular source of ACTH are diverse and often contradictory, as the following selected examples show. Presumptive evidence that at least one cell type plays a role in the secretion of adrenocorticotrophin is found in the hereditary dwarf mouse (homozygous for a recessive dwarfing gene), in which adrenal cortical aplasia is associated with the complete absence of typical acidophiles in the anterior pituitary (Smith and McDowell, '30). Although these authors were uncertain as to the identification of the other cell types, later studies by Francis ('44) on the fully grown dwarf show that the basophiles are likewise absent and the number of typical chromophobes is markedly reduced (small pyknotic acidophiles and chromophobes comprise the predominating types of cell). More recently, Finerty and Briseno-Castrejon ('49) suggested that the acidophiles secrete ACTH since a marked increase in the percentage of these cells occurs in the anterior pituitary, following unilateral adrenalectomy in the immature male rat. Still more recently, Marshall ('51) was able to show by means of a fluorescent antibody technique adapted to the localization of antigens in cells and tissues that a solution of fluorescent antibody (to pig ACTH) stains selectively the cytoplasm of basophile cells of the pig pituitary. The reaction is highly specific, since cells of the sheep or bovine pituitary do not stain.

In any investigation of the problem of the cellular source of the hormone in pituitary development special attention should be given to the time order of differentiation of the cell types as well as to their progressive changes in numerical frequency and in cytological characteristics. Such an approach, when combined with experimental procedures designed to bring about an imbalance in the normal functional interaction of the adrenal cortex (and other receptor glands) and anterior pituitary, should prove of value in elucidating the problem. For the specific localization of ACTH in cells during the histogenesis of the anterior pituitary the fluorescent antibody technique is undoubtedly the most promising of all.

ON THE ROLE OF ADRENALINE AS A CORRELATING HORMONE IN THE PITUITARY-ADRENAL SYSTEM

As may be seen from an inspection of Table 27, the substance adrenaline* arises

* According to Shepherd and West ('51), in fetal (near term) and early postnatal stages of various

as a rule very early in embryonic life. Both the chromaffin reaction of Henle and the intestinal strip method agree in showing that adrenaline is first detectable at a time when small groups of future medullary cells begin islands of cells proceeds progressively through the cortex toward their definitive topographical position, the quantity of adrenaline gradually increases. In some species the relative quantity present in late fetal

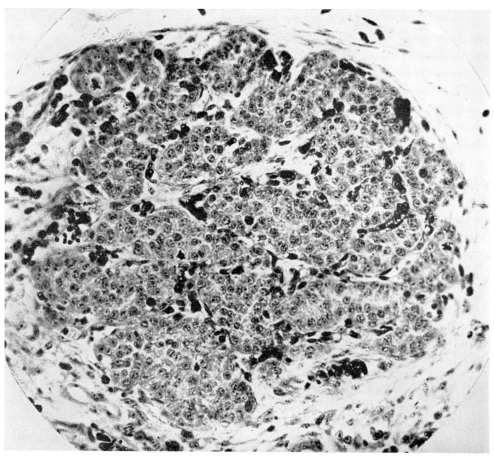

Fig. 210. Portion of adrenal cortex with interlacing cords free of intervening medullary tissue. Developed in a chorio-allantoic graft from a small isolate just back of the primitive pit of a chick blastoderm of the early head-process stage. Initial × 450.

to enter the cortex from the contiguous sympatho-chromaffin primordium (cf. Figs. 209*B*, 210, and 211). As the migration of these mammals (cat, guinea pig, and rabbit) the adrenal glands contain a high proportion of noradrenaline and a small quantity of adrenaline, and, further, the relative amounts of these two substances change with advancing developmental age. The observation that the large amounts of noradrenaline present in the adrenals of fetal and young postnatal mammals generally diminish as the adrenaline content increases in still older animals led to the suggestion that the amine noradrenaline is not only a precursor of adrenaline but indeed may be the hormone of the adrenal gland "in the early days of life."

life may be distinctly greater than in the adult adrenal (McCord, '15; Fenger, '12). This is in keeping with the observation that in many species of mammals the relative volume of the medulla to the whole adrenal is high at birth, rapidly decreasing shortly thereafter until puberty, when a stationary condition is reached (Donaldson, '19).

What is the significance of such an early appearance and quantitative increase in adrenaline? Could they possibly reflect the "needs" of the growing embryo for adrenaline in the operation of mechanisms, especially of those dependent on or controlled by hormonal substances? Paralleling this appearance and increase of adrenaline is a peculiar and striking vascular change associated with the differentiation and migration of the future medullary cells. As shown in Figure 209B, the migrating spherical islands of chromaffin cells in the cortex are provided with a distinctive arrangement of the capil-

gradually increases, a relationship of a functional nature.

Nothing is definitely known as to the function of adrenaline during fetal life. It is significant to note, however, that almost from the beginning the development of the adrenal medulla and of the sympathetic

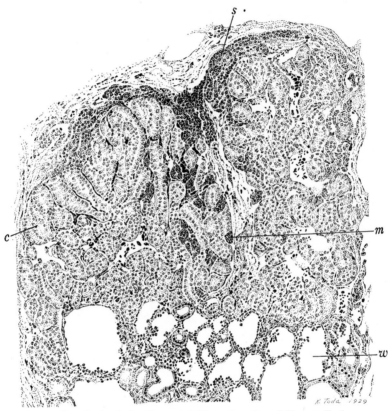

Fig. 211. Section of an adrenal gland showing partial invasion of medullary cells from a mass of sympathoblasts (s). Differentiated from an isolate of the mesonephros-gonad-adrenal complex taken from a 4-day chick embryo and grown for 9 days on the chorio-allantoic membrane of a male host embryo. c, Group of cortical cords free of intervening medullary cells; m, medullary cord; w, portion of mesonephros. Initial × 200. (From Willier, '30.)

laries, which, although continuous with those of the cortex, have a smaller meshwork. In both instances the blood is derived from the arterioles in the capsule. As the islands increase in size and move inward toward the central vein the capillary network of each of them is provided with a separate arteriole. For a short time the capillaries of the cortex act as venules from the capillaries of the island (Flint, '00). These changes in vascular pattern are of a kind that permit a more efficient flow of blood to the islands of chromaffin cells. Apparently as the mode of blood transportation becomes more efficient the adrenaline content of the adrenal gland

nervous system is interlocked. In the course of their functional development the former becomes in effect an integral part of the latter (constituting the so-called "sympathoadrenal system"). It would be of much significance to determine at the time of first appearance of adrenaline, as well as during its increase in the fetal adrenal, whether splanchnic nerve fibers (preganglionic) already terminate around the individual chromaffin cells, as they do in the adult. The possibility, however, that the chromaffin cells may form and store adrenaline as chromophile granules before innervation is established must be recognized, since these processes can continue for a while in the denervated adrenal of the adult. On the other hand, the rate of formation and release of adrenaline into the blood in the adult are partly regulated by the nervous system. The approximate time of release including quantity present in the blood stream of the embryo or fetus could be readily determined, since bio-assay methods sensitive to concentrations of adrenaline of 1 in 500,000, or less, are available.

Once adrenaline is liberated into the blood stream, which seems likely to occur toward the end of embryonic life, the question arises as to its interrelations with other substances within the embryo. (See p. 609.) It is well known that, as a hormone, adrenaline has a highly selective action on effectors innervated by the sympathetic nervous system. Of particular interest here, however, is that on the basis of recent investigations (see Long, '49, for evidence and theoretical considerations) it plays a role in the endocrine activity of the adrenal cortex. The administration of adrenaline as well as its liberation following stimulation of the sympathetic nervous system causes an increase in adrenal cortical activity. Although adrenaline acts as a potent stimulus to adrenal cortical activity, its mechanism of action is unknown. According to the theory of Long its action is indirect, involving the correlation and interplay of anterior pituitary, adrenal cortex, and medulla. The particular merit of this theory is that it combines in one comprehensive picture a variety of factors or conditions, such as activity of the sympathetic nervous system (adrenaline release), adrenocorticotrophic hormone, and stress, all of which are known to call forth secretion by the cortex. Their interaction constitutes an adaptive mechanism enabling the organism to adjust itself to stresses which may arise within or without it. It is conceivable, therefore, that such an interplay of anterior pituitary–adrenal functions as they become established in the embryo creates an internal milieu essential for maintaining a normal state of balance, and in preparing the organism for exigencies appertaining to birth and early postnatal life.

ANTERIOR PITUITARY–GONAD RELATIONS

The gonad is the third component of the endocrine system with which the anterior pituitary becomes interrelated during the course of ontogeny. The concept of anterior pituitary–gonad relations is based almost entirely on extensive researches on immature and adult vertebrates. Experimental procedures designed to determine the effects of removal of one gland upon the other and/or in combination with implantation of either gland or the administration of their active principles as well as the effects of anterior lobe implants on sexually immature animals have yielded evidence which clearly established for many species that specific gonadotrophic secretions of the anterior lobe are essential to the maintenance of structure and function of the gonads, which in turn by secreting sex hormones affect receptor sex structures such as the gonoducts and accessory glands. Moreover, sex hormones released by the gonads have a reciprocal effect on the anterior pituitary, regulating release of gonadotrophic hormones. (For supporting evidence and citations see Engle, '39; Fevold, '39; Moore and Price, '32; Smith, '39.)

The main problem for consideration here is the sequence of events in the establishment of functional relations between anterior pituitary and gonad. Particular attention will be given to such specific problems as (a) the time and degree to which the entire course of gonad development is dependent upon gonadotrophic secretions, and (b) whether the onset of production of sex hormones and their effects on receptor sex structures precedes or coincides with beginning anterior lobe activity.

ONSET OF SEX-HORMONE ACTIVITY OF THE GONAD

As a basis of approach to the over-all problem of the development of functional interaction between the gonad and the anterior pituitary, the time course in the differentiation of functional activity of the gonad will be examined first. At what period are sex hormones initially produced? When are they released into the blood circulation in quantities sufficient to act on such terminal receptors as the seminal vesicle, gonoduct, and phallus, sex structures which react selectively to sex hormones? These questions can be best answered by a consideration of the following several lines of evidence (also refer to Table 27).

1. As is known from the work of Lillie ('17), the vascular connections of the fetal membranes of twin embryos in cattle usually become suitable for the intermingling of the blood of the co-twins either prior to or at about the time that structural sex differentiation of the gonad sets in (25-mm.

stage). If the embryos are of opposite sex and vascular connections are established between them, the female partner is modified in the male direction, forming the freemartin. Since the structural changes are limited to the production of male sex characters in the female co-twin, it has been inferred that the gonads of the male co-twin not only produce but release male sex hormones into the common blood stream at a very early stage. (For certain shortcomings in the purely hormonal interpretation of the freemartin condition see Owen et al., '46; Moore, '47; and Anderson et al., '51.)

2. In the chick, by implanting fragments of a sexually differentiated gonad (6- to 11-day embryo) into the coelom of a host embryo of 50 hours (preceding by about two days the time of origin of the gonad primordia), Wolff ('47) succeeded in bringing about an approximation of grafted tissue and host gonads. If of opposite sex, the grafted tissue modifies the direction of sex development of the reproductive organs of the host. Ovarian tissue causes the formation of ovarian cortex on the left testis; testis tissue has little effect on the left ovary but inhibits or completely suppresses the Müllerian ducts. The degree of sex transformation is dependent upon the volume of the graft and the distance between graft and host gonads. In general, the closer the graft, the greater is the degree of effect. Similar results are obtained by cultivating in vitro duck gonads of sexually indifferent stages in juxtaposition. If left gonads of opposite sex constitution are in more or less intimate contact, the testis is modified into an ovotestis by the ovary (Wolff and Haffen, '52). Since the effects produced in hosts by grafts of embryonic testicular or ovarian tissue and in explants of associated left gonads of opposite sex are identical in character with effects produced by the injection of synthetic sex hormones, it is apparent that the embryonic differentiated gonads produce sex hormones (for further details and argument see Willier, '39, '52).

3. In the rat, according to Jost ('50), a fetal testis (15 to 16 days old) grafted upon the atrophied seminal vesicles of an adult castrate produces within five days an intense but local activation of the seminal epithelium identical in character to the effects of injecting testosterone. Tissues other than testis fail to produce the effect. Although androgenic activity of the fetal testis is shown, the activity seems to depend upon gonadotrophic stimulation, particularly since an embryonic testis graft has little or no effect on the seminal epithelium in hypophysectomized and castrated adult rats.

4. Castration by localized x-irradiation of a duck or chick embryo during the sexually indifferent stage indicates that hormone secretions of the early differentiated gonad are essential in determining the direction of differentiation of other sex structures. An asexual or neutral type is obtained following such precocious castration (Wolff and Wolff, '51). In both males and females the genital tubercle and syrinx (duck only) assume the male shape and oviducts persist. These results imply that in the normal embryo (a) the female form of the genital tubercle and syrinx is conditioned by the presence of ovarian hormone and (b) the retrogression of the oviducts is dependent upon the presence of testicular hormone. These findings are in agreement with the results of injecting sex hormones, male hormones suppressing oviducts in genetic females and female hormones stimulating oviducts in genetic males. (For a more complete analysis of the time and manner of release of sex hormones in bird embryos, see Willier, '52.)

Similarly, the effects of surgical castration of the rabbit fetus indicate that the direction of differentiation of gonoducts and accessory sex structures is influenced by hormonal secretions of the embryonic gonads (Jost, '47, '50). If the gonads are removed from fetuses of either sex before the initiation of structural sexual differentiation (18 to 19 days of gestation) the entire genital tract is feminine in form. In males the development of the Wolffian ducts and prostatic buds is entirely suppressed, the oviducts persist, and the external genitalia are feminine in form. The Wolffian body retrogresses as in normal females. However, castration of male fetuses at successively later stages (20 to 24 days of gestation) brings out the additional point that sex structures, already acted upon by testicular hormones, retain the male type although usually in an undeveloped state. Synthetic androgens administered to castrates have a reparative influence on sex structures which simulates that of the embryonic testis hormones. In castrated females, on the other hand, the genital tract retains a feminine form essentially like that of control females of the same age. Apparently, then, the embryonic testis produces male sex hormones which control the development of the male form of the external genitalia and Wolffian bodies, the formation of the prostate, the persistence of the Wolffian ducts, and the retrogression of the oviducts. In genetic females the further development of the oviducts is conditioned by ovarian sex hormones.

More recently Wells and Fralick ('51) have shown for the fetal rat that surgical removal of the testes on the twentieth day of gestation selectively retards the growth of the seminal vesicles and bulbo-urethral glands and, further, that such specific castration effects are prevented by the administration of testosterone propionate. From the growth responses thus given by the accessory sex organs it is at once clear that for at least a few days prior to birth the testes are active in the production and release of androgenic hormone.

In summary, the embryonic gonads from the time of onset of morphological sex differentiation are active in the production and/or release of specific sex hormones. The hormones are liberated in quantities at least sufficient for effective action through the vascular circulation as judged from the nature of the responses, especially those of the terminal sex receptors. (For a further treatment of the subject see Burns, '49; Jost, '50; Moore, '50.)

ONSET OF GONADOTROPHIC ACTIVITY OF ANTERIOR PITUITARY

The evidence just presented for the existence and action of sex hormones early in embryonic development naturally poses a two-fold problem of (1) the extent to which their production and release are dependent upon gonadotrophic stimulation and (2) the time that the anterior pituitary begins to secrete gonadotrophic substances as well as to release them into the blood circulation of the embryo (see Table 27). Whether functional activity of the gonad during embryonic life is dependent upon gonadotrophic hormones is a problem which is as yet only beginning to be resolved. The most complete and satisfactory analysis yet made is that of Jost ('48, '51b) on the rabbit fetus. If the male fetus is decapitated at the time of initial structural sexual differentiation (about the nineteenth day of gestation) the interstitial tissue of the testis is distinctly reduced as compared with normal controls of the same age. Moreover, testicular hormones are quantitatively deficient, as is indicated by the feminization of the external genitalia and by the arrested development of the prostatic buds as shown in Figure 212. Since

similar effects on the prostate and external genitalia are produced in males castrated at 21 to 22 days, it is inferred that the removal of the hypophysis affects the production of male hormone by the testis. The effects of hypophysectomy are attributed to the absence of specific hormones, since if at the time of decapitation gonadotrophic hormone is administered no signs of insufficient testicular secretions are found. These results are interpreted as indicating that the anterior pituitary of the rabbit fetus is active in producing and releasing gonadotrophic hormones either at the time of or shortly after the onset of testis differentiation. They are apparently released in sufficient quantities to be physiologically effective in maintaining testicular hormone production at a level adequate for regulating the development of such sex characters as the prostate and external genitalia during their initial stages of growth and differentiation.

In other species of vertebrate embryos the evidence thus far available is inconclusive on whether secretions of the anterior lobe are essential for the early development and function of the gonad. In general, so far as results on different species can be compared, removal of the anterior lobe has little or no effect on the early morphological development of the gonads. Two examples suffice to illustrate this point. In the anuran embryo removal of the anterior lobe at the time of its ingrowth has no apparent effect on the growth of the gonads; their development continues a normal course to the stage which is attained in controls at the time of metamorphosis (Smith, '39, p. 942). In the chick embryo after hypophysectomy at 33 to 38 hours primary morphological sex differentiation proceeds in a normal manner until about the thirteenth day, when reductions in intertubular tissue of the testis and in ovarian cortex are first noted; however, the gonoducts in both sexes develop normally both in time and manner (Fugo, '40). On the contrary, Wolff and Stoll ('37) report that the entire course of sex-differentiation of gonads and gonoducts is normal up to the time of hatching in the cyclocephalic chick embryo without hypophysis produced by local x-irradiation at the 12- to 15-somite stage. By the injection of estradiol into such pituitaryless chick embryos intersexual males are produced as readily as in normal male embryos (Wolff, '37). It seems, therefore, that the functional processes concerned in sex-inversion are wholly independent of hypophyseal action. Whether the gonad during early stages of formation could be stimulated by hypophyseal implants or injection of gonadotrophins is conjectural.

Does the production of gonadotrophins increase quantitatively with advance in developmental age? As regards the relative gonadotrophic potency at various embryonic ages the available evidence is not easily assessed, inasmuch as different species of animals and different indices of sexual maturity (i.e., precocious ovulation or open-

elicited in the genital system of the mouse even though the dosage is doubled. Further bio-assay studies are needed at successively later stages in order to ascertain whether the quantity of gonadotrophin continues to increase with fetal age and at what rate of increase.

After birth a gradual increase in gonadotrophin content is clearly evident. Using, for the bio-assay test, the immature female albino mouse at a stage (20 to 22 days of age; 6

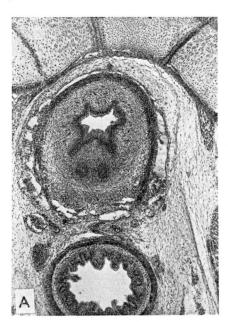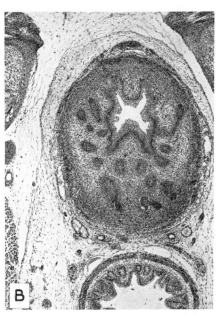

Fig. 212. The prostatic region of two male rabbit fetuses of the same age (28 days). *A*, Decapitated at 19± days; *B*, normal litter male control. Note the arrested development of the two anterior prostatic buds in *A* as contrasted with their ramified stage in *B*. (Courtesy of Jost, '48.)

ing of vagina, increase in gonad weight, etc.) were used for the bio-assay test and, moreover, the unit quantity of implants of anterior pituitary tissue either varied greatly or was not considered. Although the data are inadequate for measuring relative potency, they in general do indicate the presence of gonadotrophins in the anterior pituitary of mammals (including the human) at the more advanced stages prior to birth. The most convincing evidence of their quantitative increase during fetal life has come from a study of the pig fetus. Using the immature mouse as the test animal, Smith and Dortzbach ('29) found that gonad-stimulating hormone is present in readily detectable amounts in anterior pituitaries of pigs of 25 cm., in lesser amounts at the 20- to 21-cm. stage, and none earlier than the 17- to 18-cm. stage. Prior to the last stage no response is

to 8 days prior to the probable time of onset of sexual maturity in the normal) when the genital system is sensitive to small amounts of anterior pituitary, Clark ('35) determined the amount of gonad-stimulating hormone in the anterior lobe of the rat from the day of birth up to and including sexual maturity. Using increase in ovarian weight as the index of activity, the changes in content with increasing age were determined separately for each sex. The activity of the female pituitary increases rather gradually during the first week after birth and then rises sharply between the thirteenth and twentieth days (the probable period of most extensive follicular growth in the normal rat), reaching at that time a level of activity per unit weight of anterior pituitary which is not excelled at subsequent ages even after full sexual maturity is attained. On the other hand, the activity of the male pituitary from the time of birth rises gradually and continuously up to the age of puberty, attaining at that time a high level which is more or less uniformly maintained thereafter. Similarly, in the rabbit the activity of anterior pituitary tissue, as revealed by the rabbit ovulation test, is relatively low at 4 weeks of age but at 3 months is as high as in adult animals (Wolfe and Cleveland, '31).

In sum, so far as the evidence for mammals permits generalization, the gonadotrophic hormones apparently increase quantitatively with advance in developmental age, beginning during the later fetal stages, often attaining a relatively high level at birth, and usually the highest level prior to the onset of sexual maturity. Possible exceptions to this generalization may depend, even when the unit dosage is constant, upon individual and species variables in gonadotrophin content and in the degree of sensitivity of the responding test organ of the recipient animal.

A related problem for consideration is the period in the course of development in which the gonad, as a receptor gland, acquires the capacity to respond to administered hypophyseal hormones. Is gonad responsivity gradually or suddenly attained? In the classic investigations of Smith ('27) and Smith and Engle ('27) it was found that the number of implants of anterior pituitary required to induce precocious sexual maturity in male and female rats and mice is higher in immature than in older animals, the number required being roughly inversely proportional to the postnatal age of the host. Thus, in general, as the recipients approach puberty not only fewer implants but less time is required to obtain the response. These observations clearly suggest that the gonads undergo developmental changes (maturation) which enable them to respond gradually more rapidly to hypophyseal stimulation.

Subsequent investigations have fully established the concept of a gradual increase in responsivity of the gonads after birth to gonadotrophic stimulation. The time course of development of gonad reactivity has been particularly well worked out in the postnatal rat by Price and Ortiz ('44). In the administration of equine gonadotrophin particular care was taken to keep the dosage and length of treatment constant, the main significant variable being the age of the recipient, which ranged from the day of birth to maturity. The degree of response at a given age was ascertained by comparing with normal controls the induced changes in weight and histology of the gonads and accessory reproductive organs, the latter being end organs which reflect changes in amount of sex hormones liberated. Using these criteria, the ovary was found to be only slightly responsive between the day of birth and the sixth day of age; between the fourth and tenth days a definite though small response was indicated; and at succeeding ages the response gradually increased until a maximum was attained at 26 days of age. The response of the testis is definite though relatively small between birth and the sixth day. At successively later ages the reactivity of the testis increases rapidly and reaches a peak at 14 days. Enhanced production of sex hormones by the gonads is indicated by the response of at least some of the accessory organs as early as the sixth day in males and the tenth day in females. In general, the capacity of the gonads and accessory sex structures for precocious structural differentiation develops gradually in response to gonadotrophic stimulation. Thus, in placental mammals (rat and mouse) subsequent to birth a correlation exists between the developmental age of the gonads and their degree of responsivity to gonadotrophins.

Since within a few days after birth of the rat the response is relatively weak, especially in females, it might be expected that during fetal stages the gonads would exhibit little or no response to administered gonadotrophin. Such appears to be the case, since subcutaneous injection of equine gonadotrophin into fetal rats near term fails, during the short time interval allowed for action, to bring about any significant increase in growth of either the ovary or the testis; however, the testis is otherwise stimulated as is shown by a significant increase in the size and number of the interstitial cells. No increase in androgen secretion is indicated, since enhanced development of the prostate and other accessory sex structures is not apparent (Wells, '46).

The effects of treating young opossum in the pouch at different ages (beginning on the eighth day after birth) for short periods of time with equine gonadotrophin reveals the time at which the gonads are responsive to the dosages used (Moore and Morgan, '43). Capacity to respond occurs earlier in males than in females. In males precocious development of the prostate is readily produced subsequent to but usually not earlier than the seventieth day after birth. Since the response of the prostate is a reliable indicator of androgenic activity it is evident that the production and release of male sex hormones by the testis are enhanced by gonadotrophin. In older treated males interstitial cell hypertrophy occurs but spermatogenesis is not hastened. Using the marked response of the uterus as a sign of increased liberation of estrogens by the ovary, there is no apparent stimulation of the ovary by gonadotrophin prior to the hundredth day after birth. However, at the age of 125 days the ovary is definitely stimulated in follicular development and in luteinization and, as is signalized by the accelerated development of the uterus, in the production and release of ovarian hormone.

The gonad of the chick likewise shows an increase in capacity to respond to gonadotrophic hormones with advance in developmental age. According to Domm ('37), in chick embryos examined at 18 days following daily injections of pituitary extracts ("Hebin"), beginning at a time just prior to and continuing through the period of morphological sex differentiation (5 to 9 days of incubation), the gonads in both sexes are hypertrophied, apparently as a result of a marked increase in intertubular tissue of the testis and of medullary tissue in right and left ovaries. There is, however, no significant advance in the differentiation of either the seminiferous cords or the ovarian cortex. Although structural changes are produced, little or no enhancement of sex-hormone activity is indicated, since neither the comb nor the gonoducts in either sex show any significant change from the normal.

The responsiveness of the gonads in newly hatched chicks to daily pituitary injections is still further increased with certain striking sex differences. In contrast to the embryo, a precocious spermatogenesis sets in and sex hormone is actively released by the testis, as is indicated by a precocious onset of male sex behavior, an accelerated growth of the head furnishings, and a hypertrophy of the ductus deferens. In the female, although no increased follicle growth in the ovarian cortex is apparent, the oviduct is hypertrophied, an indication of enhanced production of female sex hormone. Curiously, whereas the right ovary is unmodified, the medulla of the left ovary shows a pronounced hypertrophy. Since medullary hypertrophy is regularly associated with an accelerated growth and masculinization of the head furnishings, it may be assumed that the left ovarian medulla is the source of male hormone under the conditions of the experiment.

Although the time of initial response to administered gonadotrophins has not been ascertained, it is clearly evident from the above data that the gonads, which are already highly reactive by the eighteenth day of incubation, become still more so in newly hatched chicks and probably reach a maximum in still older chicks. Apparently, then, as the gonads undergo developmental changes, their reactivity to hypophyseal stimulation progressively increases.

In the salamander (*Amblystoma tigrinum*) the time sequence in the development of gonad reactivity has been worked out fairly completely by Burns ('34) and Burns and Buyse ('31, '33, '34). The administration of hypophyseal substances to young larvae (30 to 35 mm. long) at the stage of sex differentiation readily stimulates precocious growth and maturation. Gametogenesis sets in precociously in both sexes but to a much greater degree in males than in females, indicating a sex difference in time of attainment of the responsive state. However, soon after metamorphosis at a time when the gonads are still very immature (sexual maturity in the normal is attained many months later), the growth of the testis and of the ovary as well is greatly enhanced by hypophyseal extracts. In males spermatogenesis reaches a peak including the formation of mature spermatozoa; in females many of the ova are practically mature, although falling short of nuclear maturation and ovulation. It is thus apparent that the gonads of post-metamorphic stages have acquired a marked capacity for precocious growth stimulation in sharp contrast to a much more limited yet definite capacity for induced growth during the larval period.

The question next arises as to whether the progressive increase in gonad reactivity is dependent upon the liberation of gonadotrophic hormones during the course of normal development. As many studies show (for background evidence and citations see Smith, '39), in sexually immature stages (from a few days after birth to onset of sexual maturity) of mammals (rat and mouse), ablation of the anterior lobe during the period when the gonad is shown to be responsive to administered gonadotrophin results in either arrested development or a retrogression of the gonad to a more immature state. Structural maturation of the gonad is arrested and functional activity ceases, as is reflected in the atrophic state of sex-hormone dependent structures such as the uterus, prostate, and seminal vesicle. Generally speaking, the extent of retrogressive change appears to be roughly proportional to the state of reactivity of the gonad, being higher in older than in younger stages. Since the structural and functional changes that result from hypophysectomy may be prevented or restored to normal by the administration of gonadotrophins (in the form of either implants or extracts), it is clearly evident that the processes of maturation of the gonad are dependent upon the presence of specific hypophyseal secretions. Such secretions are clearly essential to the maintenance of structural development and function of the gonads, beginning early in postnatal life of the rat and mouse, and even prior to birth in the rabbit, as noted above (p. 595).

The correlation of the time of onset and subsequent increase of gonadotrophic activity with histogenesis of cell types of the anterior pituitary is a difficult problem to resolve. Only a few studies have been oriented toward its solution. The time course of differentiation of the chromophilic cells as related to the initiation of gonadotrophic activity has been worked out most completely for the anterior lobe of the pig fetus (Smith and Dortzbach, '29; Nelson, '33). The basophiles differentiate first (50- to 60-mm. stage), then increase markedly in number, and become the predominate type between the 70- to 100-mm. stages. The acidophiles arise first at the 70- to 80-mm. stage, gradually increase in number during subsequent stages, and at the 160- to 170-mm. stage show a marked rise. This decided increase in number of acidophiles coincides approximately with the time (170- to 180-mm. stage) that the gonad-stimulating hormone is first indicated by functional tests. The activity, although slight at first, increases at the 200- to 221-mm. stage and still more at the 250-mm. stage. Since a significant increase in the acidophile population precedes by a short interval of time the initiation of gonadotrophic activity, it would appear that an age relationship exists between acidophile differentiation and the appearance of the gonad-stimulating principle.

Although such a corresponding relation probably has significance in understanding the ontogeny of functional activity of the hypophysis as an integrated glandular organ, it has little value in assigning a specific physiological secretion to a particular cell type. The shift in proportional numbers of the three kinds of cells and their changes in cell structure under experimental conditions comprise a much more reliable indicator of the cell strain involved. By disturbing experimentally the interfunctional relation of anterior pituitary and gonad (including sex structures dependent upon gonad secretions) during embryonic life, significant new clues may be obtained as to the possible relationship of the time order of differentiation and relative frequency of the cell types at a given stage with the onset and increase of gonadotrophic activity. Specially indicated is a study of the effects, either separately or in combination, of embryonic castration and the injection of sex hormones, each of which during postnatal (or equivalent) stages is known to alter the anterior pituitary both in structure and in gonadotrophic activity (either acceleration or inhibition). Also, in ascertaining the possible secretory significance of the granules of the chromophiles histochemical methods may be useful. For instance, the periodic acid–Schiff reaction indicates that the granules of the basophiles (adult human pituitary) are mucoprotein in nature (Herlant, '49) and therefore allied chemically to gonadotrophic hormones which contain a proportion of polysaccharides and glucosamine (Evans et al., '39).

Such studies as are proposed above might equally well be suitable for ascertaining the time in the course of ontogeny that gonad secretions have a reciprocal action on the anterior pituitary. Although the effects of castration, and especially of the injection of sex hormones, on the differentiation of sex structures of the embryo have been widely explored, little or no attention has been directed in such altered physiological conditions to the possible occurrence of changes in the anterior lobe. As functional tests indicate, both the gonad and anterior pituitary have hormonal activity beginning at least during the later stages of embryonic life and usually attaining gradually a higher value after birth or an equivalent time. So far as can be judged from the available evidence, the interlocking of functional activity is first clearly indicated at about the time the gonads are approaching sexual maturity (Engle, '31). At approximately that time the gonad secretions apparently stimulate the liberation of the gonadotrophic hormones. If correctly determined, does this signify that reciprocal functional relations are established when the gonad attains a level of secretory activity sufficient to cause the release of the previously accumulated gonadotrophins? Or is the relation unidirectional at first, during which time the gonadotrophins are released only in sufficient quantities to maintain gonad growth, maturation, and function? If true, what regulates the gradual release? Answers to these questions await further investigation.

ANTERIOR PITUITARY AND GROWTH

In addition to the production of specific trophic hormones which act selectively on the growth and function of certain "target" endocrine glands, the anterior pituitary produces a growth hormone which plays an essential role in governing the general body growth of the organism. The concept had its origin from observations on human disorders, gigantism and acromegaly, in which overgrowth of the body or its parts is a characteristic feature. Since the overgrowth was usually associated with an adenomatous enlargement of the anterior lobe, the condition was attributed to an overabundance of some growth-promoting principle. Conversely, it gradually became apparent that certain types of arrested growth, i.e., pituitary dwarfism, might be associated with an underactivity of the anterior lobe. Such presumptive evidence initiated, over 40 years ago (1912), an era of experimentation which has continued up to the present time.

Three high lights in the history of the concept may be recognized. (1) The anterior pituitary is essential for growth, since (a) complete hypophysectomy of an immature animal arrests growth and results in dwarfism, and (b) implants and crude extracts can restore growth in hypophysectomized animals and augment growth in normal animals (first clearly established in the rat by Smith, '30). (2) Experimental dwarfism is insufficient proof for the view that a specific hormone exclusively concerned with growth is secreted, since removal of the anterior lobe likewise causes growth regression and diminished function of the gonad, thyroid, and adrenal cortex, secretions of the last two being clearly essential for normal growth. Cessation of growth after hypophysectomy thus appeared to be partly, at least, the result of multiple gland deficiency. As a consequence the principle came to be recognized that the hypophyseal hormones, through an interplay with other hormones and nutritional factors as well as genetic constitution, determine the ultimate size and form of the body and its component organs or parts. (3) Isolation of the growth hormone in chemically purified form by Li, Evans, and Simpson ('45).

In broad terms the objective here is, so far as the data permit, to trace during the course of ontogeny the succession of events in the establishment of the functions of the anterior pituitary as related to the over-all growth of the body. Attention will be centered on such problems as (a) the time and degree to which the anterior pituitary is essential to the promotion of bodily growth, (b) the interplay of hypophyseal growth hormones and hormones of "target" glands in maintaining the metabolic processes of organismic growth, and (c) concomitant dependence upon the genotypic constitution, nutritional factors, etc. of the organism.

That the growth of the body in the anuran tadpole is dependent upon growth-promoting substances of the anterior pituitary is clearly indicated (see Table 27). Ablation of the ingrowing primordium of the anterior lobe from the early anuran embryo results in a diminished growth rate of the body as a whole. At first growth retardation is scarcely noticeable, but at about the mid-larval period (30 to 32 mm.) it is pronounced, at which time "an abrupt change in the direction of the growth curve ensues" (Smith, '20, p. 46). This marked drop in velocity of growth, designated as the "critical point," is followed by a later period of continuous but slow rate of growth. Moreover, the fat-body becomes unusually large, indicating that the utilization of fat is disturbed and contrasting sharply with the minute size of the fat-body of the normal tadpole at the time of completion of metamorphosis. Growth in size of the hypophysectomized tadpole is restored essentially to normal in three ways: by feeding fresh anterior lobe (bovine) or dried residues thereof (Smith, '18, '20), by transplantation of anterior lobe from adult frogs (Allen, '28), and by intraperitoneal injection of extracts of bovine pars anterior (Smith and Smith, '23). By the latter treatment the volume of the hypophysectomized tadpole in a period of three months may be increased to three times that of uninjected normal controls, and the growth of normal tadpoles may be accelerated by an increase of twice the volume of uninjected normal controls. The ultimate attainment of a size notably in excess of the normal in the treated hypophysectomized tadpoles may be attributed in part to the persistence of the larval period and consequent extension of the larval growth span (Smith, '20).

Although the hypophysis is undoubtedly essential to the growth of the tadpole, it is by no means certain that a single growth-promoting principle is concerned. The situation is complicated by the fact that cessation of growth after hypophysectomy is associated with concomitant arrested growth and diminished function of the adrenal cortex and thyroid glands. Likewise, restoration of growth to normal by hypophyseal administration is accompanied by concomitant restoration of the growth and function of the adrenal cortex and thyroid. This thus poses the problem whether tadpole growth is the result of multiple gland activity.

Does thyroid removal affect the growth of the anuran tadpole? If the anterior pituitary alone is essential it might be expected that the thyroidectomized tadpole would continue to grow although metamorphosis would not take place. In contrast to a distinct retardation of growth rate in the pituitaryless tadpole, the thyroidless tadpole, produced by removal of the thyroid primordium shortly after its formation, continues to grow, ultimately attaining a body size much in excess of the normal control (Allen, '18; Hoskins and Hoskins, '19). Concomitantly with the increased growth of the body, the vertebral skeleton continues to increase in size. Calcification proceeds extensively, but little or no ossification takes place. On the contrary, in the hind limb growth of the skeleton practically ceases, and although calcification of the cartilage proceeds the process of ossification is much retarded (Terry, '18). Moreover, growth in body size may be augmented by four times that of thyroidectomized controls by intraperitoneal injections of bovine anterior lobe extracts (Smith and Smith, '23). The degree of growth is sufficiently striking to suggest that the apparent growth-promoting action of the anterior pituitary is independent of thyroid activity. However, the extent to which the increase in body size may be attributed to excess growth stimuli from the hypertrophied anterior pituitary of the thyroidless tadpole or to a supplementary injection of pituitary principles, or to still other factors, is difficult to assess for two main reasons: (1) The rate of growth of thyroidless, pituitaryless, and normal frog larvae on a similar dietary regime may be nearly identical. (2) In thyro-hypophysectomized tadpoles growth of the body, although limited, nevertheless continues, body and hind limb growth keeping pace with one another, indicating that factors other than hypophyseal or thyroid hormones are concerned. Since, however, either thyroid preparations or iodine administered to tadpoles deprived of both glands or of either one alone promptly arrests growth with ensuing metamorphosis, it is clear that the thyroid or its active principle has an antagonistic action to anterior pituitary.

In summary, it appears that the anterior pituitary has a growth-promoting action, whereas the thyroid has an inhibitory action on the processes of growth of the anuran tadpole. This apparent contrasting action on tadpole growth is difficult to interpret, since as yet the evidence is neither adequate nor critical. Moreover, the elucidation of their action on growth is still further complicated by the commonly overlooked fact that hypophysectomy affects not only the thyroid but also the adrenal cortex of the tadpole. It is now well established—for mammals, at least—that the hormones of the adrenal cortex participate in carbohydrate metabolism (influence on the rate of gluconeogenesis from protein). The possibility of a linkage between the anterior pituitary, the thyroid, and the adrenal cortex in regulating growth and differentiation of the anuran tadpole must, therefore, be recognized. Such a functional interaction may in part be resolved by analyzing the effects of purified growth hormone both separately and in all possible combinations with thyroxine, thyrotrophin, ACTH, and adrenocortical hormones on the growth of hypophysectomized, thyrodectomized, and thyro-hypophysectomized tadpoles. Also, the extent to which dietary nutrients play a role in tadpole growth needs to be more precisely ascertained than heretofore.

The role of the anterior pituitary in regulating body growth has been most clearly demonstrated in mammals, especially in the actively growing postnatal rat, for which the evidence is most complete and critical. Complete removal of the anterior lobe from young rats during the period of active growth (usually 26 to 36 days after birth) invariably results in cessation of over-all body growth and leads to permanent dwarfism as a consequence. Save for slight fluctuations among individuals the size, weight, and length remain stationary. Skeletal growth is arrested. The growth stasis thus displayed in pituitaryless rats is readily broken at any time by daily homeo-implants of anterior lobe or injections of growth hormone preparations. Such treatment quickly causes a resumption of growth, which continues more or less normally.

Undergrowth (cretinoid dwarfism) is likewise produced by the removal of the thyroid. In rats dwarfed by thyroidectomy, growth is induced by the administration of growth hormone extracts. On the contrary, thyroid administration to pituitaryless rats fails to stimulate growth. Although these results indicated that the anterior pituitary alone is essential for body growth, it was early shown by Smith ('33) that the hormones of both glands have to some extent a synergistic action in promoting growth. This was brought out by the discovery that the simultaneous administration of growth-hormone extracts and of thyroid (the latter in dosages insufficient to prevent increase in weight) to rats dwarfed by removal of both anterior pituitary and thyroid during active postnatal growth causes a significantly greater skeletal growth and increase in body length and weight than when growth hormone extracts alone are given.

This original concept of synergistic action has been confirmed and broadened by the use of hormones in chemically purified form as they became available. Purified growth hormone restores growth in hypophysectomized rats (also stimulates overgrowth in normal animals), whereas thyroxine has only an insignificant effect on increase in body weight (Marx et al., '42). In combination these hormones are more effective in promoting growth. Thyroxine augments the purified growth hormone in increasing body weight and in reactivating skeletal growth in rats dwarfed by hypophysectomy at 26 to 30 days after birth. The increase in body weight and length of animals, even after a postoperative interval of one year or longer, is significantly greater when both hormones in optimal proportions to each other are administered than when the growth hormone alone is given (Evans, Simpson, and Pencharz, '39; Becks et al., '46). Similarly, the capacity of the growth hormone to stimulate growth in pituitaryless rats is markedly enhanced in combination with thyrotrophic hormone preparations. The thyrotrophic hormone seems to parallel thyroxine in its synergistic effect with growth hormone in promoting the growth of tissues. It seems probable that the thyrotrophic hormone exerts its effect indirectly by increasing the activity of the thyroid gland, but this point has apparently not been clarified. Beyond the apparent stimulation of the synthesis and retention of protein nothing is known concerning the mechanism of the synergistic action of these hormones.

In contrast to thyroxine, partially purified ACTH has a counteracting effect on the action of the growth hormone. In female rats hypophysectomized at 26 to 28 days of age, ACTH in combination with the growth hormone almost completely nullifies the growth-promoting action of the latter. There is little or no gain in body weight or increase in width of the epiphysis (tibia), as opposed to a marked increase in these features obtained with growth hormone alone. ACTH alone is ineffective in eliciting an increase in growth of the body or the epiphysis of the tibia. However, the adrenal glands exhibit a marked increase in weight under the influence of ACTH alone or in combination with growth hormones (Evans et al., '43). The fact that the adrenals are hypertrophied (stimulated by ACTH) furnishes presumptive evidence that adrenal cortical hormones are involved, especially since somatic growth is apparently not inhibited by ACTH in rats deprived of the adrenals and is retarded in normal growing rats by the administration of adrenal cortical hormones.

How can these observations be interpreted in terms of hormonal action on growth processes? On the basis of considerable evidence, the most plausible interpretation is that both the growth and the adrenal cortical hormones alter metabolic processes but in opposite directions. The growth hormone seems to have the property of promoting protein synthesis and retention, and as a consequence promotes bodily growth. The adrenal cortical hormones, on the other hand, owing to their capacity to accelerate the catabolic phases of protein metabolism, have a retarding effect on rats. (For supporting evidence and theory see Long, '42, '43, '49.)

Thus, in rats at the stages of growth under consideration there exists an interlocking of function of the hormones of the anterior pituitary and at least of the thyroid and adrenal cortex in regulating the growth processes. A disturbance in the quantity or rate of hormonal output of any one of these endocrine glands seems to produce a hormonal imbalance, the consequence of which is an arrest, retardation, or distortion of the growth processes. In the normal animal it seems probable that the quantity or rate of output of each of these hormones is regulated by a delicate balance in hormonal level in the blood stream, which in turn is adjusted to the growth potential of the organism. Although this picture is relatively simple and general, it must be recognized that other hormones such as insulin are involved in the unusual complexity of factors that influence growth (see pp. 607–611).

The question next arises as to whether the interlocking of hormonal function operating at 26 to 30 days in regulating growth is likewise found at successively earlier ages, i.e., whether a gradual development of this linkage takes place with increase in age. In contrast to a somewhat abrupt cessation of increase in body weight and length and to a reduction in rate of skeletal growth in rats deprived of the anterior pituitary at 28 days, rats hypophysectomized at 6 days of age continue to gain in body weight and length at a rate of about 50 per cent of normal for approximately three weeks, at which time increase in weight ceases. Increase in skeletal length and differentiation likewise continues at a similar rate (60 per cent) for the same period of time, whereupon it declines abruptly to a still lower rate (20 per cent), at which rate it continues for some time (Walker et al., '50). Similar effects are obtained by removal of the hypophysis from rats at intermediate ages (13 and 21 days). It would appear, therefore, that, irrespective of the age of removal, the pituitaryless rat continues to gain in body weight and length and to advance in skeletal growth and differentiation but only at a subnormal rate and for a limited period. Eventually these processes are arrested. The time of arrest and the developmental age ultimately attained seem to vary in accord with the age of rat at hypophysectomy. In general, the younger the rat the greater is the amount of increase in body weight and length subsequent to hypophysectomy.

At a glance these effects would seem to indicate (*a*) a less complete regulation of growth by the anterior pituitary in the rat at earlier than at later ages subsequent to birth and, as a corollary, (*b*) a rough index of the amount of intrinsic growth capacity that may be independent of the anterior pituitary. However, such interpretations are inadequate, since pituitary removal at early ages disturbs the function of receptor endocrine glands, the secretions of which, as noted above, likewise play a role in regulating metabolic processes of growth. A functional linkage with the thyroid at early postnatal ages is indicated. Rats deprived of the thyroid on the day of birth exhibit for a long period (up to at least 111 days of age) an exceedingly slow rate of increase in body weight and length as well as in size of the skeleton. Skeletal differentiation continues at a greatly retarded rate. The administration of purified growth hormone to such thyroidless rats (beginning 30 days after thyroidectomy and continuing for 30 days) increases body weight (double that of untreated athyroid controls of equivalent ages) and length; skeletal dimensions increase, but skeletal differentiation is no more advanced than in untreated thyroidless rats of equivalent ages. Other features such as the ears, pelage, and genitalia remain immature. Thyroxine alone or in combination with growth hormone stimulates a marked increase in body weight (tripled over that of untreated athyroid rats of the same age) and in skeletal dimensions and differentiation. The rate of gain in body weight and skeletal dimensions appears to be higher with thyroxine alone than with growth hormone alone. Depending upon dosage, thyroxine alone may accelerate differentiation (skeleton) more than growth increment. In combination with growth hormone skeletal differentiation tends to keep pace with growth increment (Ray et al., '50).

It is clear from the above considerations that the growth processes in the postnatal rat from the day of birth onward are greatly altered by ablation of either the anterior pituitary or the thyroid gland, indicating that both glands are involved as essential regulators. However, that normal growth after birth is dependent upon secretions of both glands is best brought out by treatment of the thyroidless rat with thyroxine and purified growth hormone, which in combination have a synergistic action in promoting body growth. However, since the purified hormones were not administered until the athyroid rats had attained an age of 30 days (i.e., after thyroid removal on the day of birth), no indication is furnished as to whether prior to this age these hormones are equally effective in promoting or regulating growth, i.e., whether from the day of birth onward an interlocking of function exists or whether a certain degree of development takes place before the rat is responsive to the hormones. The fact that a significant amount of growth takes place in the absence of either gland poses problems relative to the intrinsic growth potential (independent of hormones) and the degree to which the hormonal regulating mechanisms are established at a given age. The solution to these problems awaits further investigation.

Whether ACTH, which as noted above has a counteracting effect on the action of the growth hormone on somatic growth of older rats, likewise has a similar action on normal rats or on those deprived of the anterior lobe at early postnatal ages is a problem as yet unresolved. The possibility of a linkage of the hormones of the anterior pituitary and the adrenal cortex in regulating growth processes shortly after birth must be recognized, since (1) even prior to birth the adrenal cortex becomes subnormal following hypophysectomy (decapitation) and (2) in normal rats of 4 to 6 days post partum the adrenal cortex is functionally responsive to the administration of ACTH, as indicated by hypertrophy (Moon, '40) and a decline in ascorbic acid content (Jailer, '50). However, whether body growth can be modified in opposite directions by administration of growth hormone and ACTH or ACH to infant rats remains to be analyzed. This early period may be a critical one in which the interlocking of hormonal function is still undergoing progressive changes with age, i.e., not yet fully integrated. This suggestion is partly in keeping with the findings of Jailer, who noted that (1) the administration of adrenaline does not cause an increase in ascorbic acid in the adrenal cortex until the rat has attained an age of 8 days and (2) upon exposure to low temperature (5°C.) there is no decline in adrenal ascorbic acid until the sixteenth day after birth. It is of interest in this connection to note in the dwarf mouse that growth (increase in weight) is as rapid as in unaffected sibs up until the fourteenth day after birth (time of weaning), after which time growth practically ceases, dwarfism becoming manifest thereafter (see pp. 586, 590 and 605).

As to the time of onset of the growth-promoting activity of the anterior pituitary in the course of ontogeny in mammals, information of only a suggestive nature is available (see Table 27). The preceding analysis indicates that, as early as the sixth day after birth of the rat, the anterior pituitary seems to be essential for maintaining a normal growth rate. In a similar manner the thyroid is essential from the day of birth. The question naturally arises next as to the effects of removal of anterior pituitary or thyroid from the fetus. Complete removal of the pituitary by decapitation of a 19- to 22-day fetal rabbit (Jost, '51a) or by destruction by x-irradiation in a 13-day fetal mouse (Raynaud and Frilley, '43, '47) has yielded inadequate but nevertheless suggestive results with respect to effects on body growth. In the case of the rabbit fetus general body development (similar in trunk proportions, size, and fetal movements to normal litter mates) seems to proceed in a more or less normal manner in the absence of the head until nearly term (28 days). Similarly, body growth of a mouse fetus seems to take place in a normal fashion when the thyroid is reduced to an epithelial nodule (without follicles or colloid) by x-irradiation of the buccal-pharyngeal region of a 13-day embryo. These findings may be tentatively interpreted as indicating that these glands are not yet effective as regulators of body growth during the late period in fetal life of a mammal. In contrast to the mammalian fetus, according to Fugo ('40) and Case ('52) the chick embryo when hypophysectomized (removal of all of the forebrain region) at 33 to 38 hours of incubation develops somewhat normally in body proportions and shape, but the size of the body is considerably smaller than in normal controls of the same age (latter third of incubation). Whether such contrasting effects can be attributed to species differences or to a more precocious onset of the growth-promoting activity of the anterior pituitary in birds than in mammals remains problematical.

The hypothesis that the anterior pituitary may be an ineffective regulator of body growth of the mammalian fetus during the later stages of development naturally raises a number of questions. During these stages is growth-promoting activity absent? Or is activity present without being released? If unreleased, when is it first detectable, and does it increase quantitatively with advance in developmental age? So far as is known to the writer, the only experiments designed to answer some of these questions are those of Smith and Dortzbach ('29). Using the hypophysectomized rat as a test animal, these investigators found that daily implants of the anterior pituitary from pig fetuses from about 110 to 260 mm. elicit a definite body-weight increase and skeletal growth of the recipient. Moreover, the growth-promoting effect appears to be specific, since implants of other fetal tissues (muscle, brain, and blood) fail to stimulate growth. Anterior pituitary implants from smaller fetuses (70 to 90 mm.), even though the amount of tissue used may be equivalent to that which is effective from larger fetuses, do not produce a significant change in weight and length. On the basis of the quantity of tissue required it appears that, after activity is first detectable, anterior pituitaries from successively older pig fetuses become progressively more effective in stimulating general body growth of a juvenile rat dwarfed by hypophysectomy. A gradual increase in growth-promoting activity of the pituitary with advance in fetal age is thus indicated.

Is this initial appearance and increase in growth-promoting activity of the anterior pituitary correlated in time with the corresponding development of thyroid activity? In the fetal pig, insofar as the bio-assay methods are reliable sensitive indicators of activity, the thyroid hormone is first detectable by the metamorphosis test in anuran tadpoles (see p. 583) in a fetus of 90 mm. in length, which is approximately the stage when growth-promoting activity of the anterior lobe is first detectable by the rat test. Such a coincidence in the time of onset of hormonal activity may not indicate a causal connection, but merely the initial or preparatory phases in the development of a functional synergism between anterior pituitary and thyroid, a functional relationship of established importance in regulating general body growth of young mammals after birth. Whether in the fetal pig the increase in growth-promoting activity of the pituitary is paralleled by increase in thyroid activity is not known. Such an increase might be expected, however, since in the bovine fetus thyroid iodine increases quantitatively with advance in fetal age.

Since hypophysectomy of the mammalian fetus disturbs the development of the adrenal cortex, the gonad, and probably the thyroid, presumptive evidence is furnished for the view that specific trophic hormones concerned with these receptor glands are released at least during the later stages of fetal development. The apparent absence of changes in over-all body growth of the fetus after hypophysectomy, however, suggests that specific growth-promoting activity is not essential for the maintenance of fetal body growth, a suggestion in keeping with the observation on dwarf mice, where body growth continues normally during fetal and early postnatal life. The validity of these suggestions may be tested by investigating the effects of chemically purified hormones either separately or in combination on the normal fetus as well as on fetuses from which one or more endocrine glands have been removed.

But few attempts have been made to correlate the onset of growth-promoting activity with the temporal course of differentiation of the cell types of the anterior pituitary (see Table 27). In the pig fetus the stage (about 110 mm.) at which growth-promoting activity is first detectable by the rat test is preceded by a pronounced chromatophilic differentiation in which the population of basophiles greatly exceeds that of the acidophiles. In successively older fetuses, however, the acidophile population gradually rises, becoming marked at 160- to 170-mm. stages. This rise seems to parallel an apparent increase in growth-promoting activity of the anterior lobe as noted above. It is obviously difficult to assign to either type of cell a functional role in the elaboration of growth-promoting activity. It might be suspected, however, that the acidophiles are at least associated with the development of such activity, since these cells form adenomatous tumors in such human disorders as acromegaly and related gigantism (Severinghaus, '36) and also since in the dwarf mouse, according to Francis ('44), (a) the number of typical acidophiles (accompanied by an increase of chromophobes) becomes markedly reduced at the time (twelfth day after birth) when the young dwarfs can be singled out from normal mice by length measurement and weight, and (b) the typical acidophiles (only a few chromophobes remain) are completely absent in the adult dwarf. At corresponding ages in normal mice (including those heterozygous for the dwarf gene) the acidophiles and chromophobes comprise the predominating types of cell in the anterior lobe. The basophiles are apparently not involved, since this type of cell does not generally occur in the anterior lobe of normal mice at any age except in those of advanced age or in pregnant females. The problem of relating the functional differentiation of cell types to the production of growth-promoting activity is particularly complex, since, in addition to the growth hormone, trophic hormones may likewise be produced, the latter acting directly on such receptor glands as the thyroid and adrenal cortex, stimulating them to release secretions which play a role in regulating the growth of an organism.

By way of general interpretation, it may be stated that during ontogeny there appears to be a gradual unfolding with time of anterior pituitary and receptor-gland hormones that act in harmony in regulating the ultimate size and form of the body and its component parts or organs. The functional interlocking of these hormones, although initiated in part during the later phases of embryonic or fetal life, does not appear to attain full expression until postembryonic stages of development. The period of elaboration of growth-regulating hormones may be regarded as a second phase in the developmental realization of the specific constitutional growth potential as provided by the genotype of the fertilized egg. During this phase, in contrast to an earlier one in which the growth process is independent of circulating hormones, the growth-regulating hormones gradually take over via the systemic circulation the function of coordinating and regulating in final size and form the expression of the intrinsic growth pattern of the developing organism and its parts. To paraphrase a passage of D'Arcy Thompson ('42, p. 264), hormonal regulation of growth processes is neither simple nor specific, but implies a far-reaching and complicated influence on metabolism of already established growth patterns of the developing body and its parts. The actual growth expression is also dependent upon environmental factors, since nutrients, oxygen supply, temperature, etc. have an effect on the physicochemical background in which the synthetic processes of growth take place.

ISLETS OF LANGERHANS

Concerning the problem of the development of functional activity of the endocrine portion of the pancreas, the islets of Langerhans, little or no precise information is available. Nevertheless, an attempt will be made in this section to direct attention to and to analyze so far as the evidence permits such major problems as (a) the initiation of insulin production and (b) the unfolding of mechanisms of regulation of insulin secretion into the blood circulation. (See Table 27.)

MORPHOGENESIS, CYTOGENESIS, AND INITIATION OF INSULIN PRODUCTION

As a basis for a proper understanding of the functional development of the islets, it is first of all essential to examine the normal course of morphogenesis of the islet tissue and the cytogenesis of the cell types. The sequential steps in these processes have been especially well worked out for the fetal and early postnatal stages of the albino rat by Hard ('44). Generally speaking, the islets originate as cellular outgrowths from the epithelium of the dorsal and ventral pancreatic lobes during their union and transformation into the branching system of ducts and terminal acini, which comprise the exocrine glandular portion of the pancreas. A very few islets are first identified as offsets from the solid dorsal and ventral lobes, respectively, on the thirteenth and fourteenth days of gestation. The majority of embryonic islets, however, are set off from the epithelium of the primitive pancreatic

tubules (formed by a rearrangement of cells of the coalescing pancreatic lobes), which are the progenitors of series of repeated units of exocrine ducts, ductules, and acini. Such islets, which are first apparent on the fifteenth day, increase rapidly in number and in size with advance in fetal age, becoming most marked in an 18-day fetus. During the first week of postnatal life a very active formation of new islets occurs. The majority of these arise from the terminal portions of the ducts at the bases of the acini.* It is of interest to note that the potency for islet formation, although present during the entire course of morphogenesis of the exocrine gland, tends to shift progressively to the more terminal portions of the ducts as they arise.

With respect to the sequence of differentiation of the islet cell types, the beta cell, generally accepted as the source of insulin in adult animals, is the only cell type to arise during fetal life of the rat. The alpha cell does not appear until the second day after birth. The so-called delta cell (interpreted by some as a stem cell) has not been identified during the developmental stages under consideration.

The beta cell is first identified in the

---

* The apparent sequential development of two main groups of islets in the rat seems to be in general agreement with the older findings on several mammalian species (for review, see Bargmann, '39). According to the older investigators the first group of islets, the so-called islets of Laguesse, degenerate and disappear, while the second group is retained as the definitive islets of Langerhans. The validity of this view may be questioned on the basis of the difficulty in distinguishing the islets as to their exact source of origin and in following their subsequent fate. Moreover, in the rat, although there is a sequence in generation of islet tissue, the set of embryonic islets persists into the postnatal period and apparently differs in no essential particular from the second group except as to position of origin. Similarly, in the development of the chick a sequence in the generation of islets has been described by Potvin and Aron ('27), the transitory islets appearing at 8 days of incubation, the definitive islets two days later. A more recent investigation by Villamil ('42), however, indicates that the pattern of islet formation in the chick is actually more complex, in that two types of islets—the so-called "light" and "dark" islets—are simultaneously present on the eighth day. These islets exhibit a differential behavior from the beginning. The dark islets give rise to alpha and delta cells beginning, respectively, on the eighth and fourteenth days, whereas the light islets begin on the twelfth day either to degenerate or to give rise to cells with beta granules. The ultimate fates of these two kinds of islets need to be worked out.

18½-day fetus within a few hours after the vascular capillary network has developed within the larger islets, a relationship of probable functional significance. Only a few beta cells with beginning granule formation occur at this stage. During the succeeding four days two significant changes take place. (1) The number of beta cells in process of differentiation rapidly increases, reaching a peak in 20-day-old fetuses. (2) A concomitant increase in the accumulation of beta granules occurs on the side of the cell toward the capillary, becoming well marked in many cells on the twenty-first day, an orientation suggestive of an actively secreting beta cell. The number of fully mature beta cells packed with secretory granules reaches a peak on the twenty-second day (birth).

On the day of birth the prospective alpha cells may be identified as cords or groups of nongranular cells at the periphery of the islet, i.e., about a core of beta cells. On the second day after birth a few of these outermost cells begin to form secretion granules in the area of cytoplasm adjacent to a capillary. The number of such cells gradually increases, so that by the fifth day the majority of them may be identified as alpha cells, a few of them having attained a fully mature state through a gradual increase in number and size of the secretion granules. The cytological picture is such as to indicate actively secreting alpha cells by the fifth day of postnatal life.

The question next arises as to whether the appearance of beta cells with secretory granules coincides in time with initial insulin production and secretion into the blood of the fetus. As an index of beginning functional activity it is significant to note that in the rat fetus near or at term (1) the islets with differentiating beta cells are highly vascularized, (2) the secretory granules of the beta cells are oriented toward a capillary, and (3) the number of fully mature beta cells packed with secretory granules reaches a peak. The total picture is such as to indicate insulin secretory activity.

However, information concerning the first appearance of insulin in the pancreas and the quantitive changes in content during embryogenesis is meager, owing chiefly to the lack of suitable microchemical or cytochemical methods for its detection. Although the earliest time of appearance has not been determined, insulin is already present in the pancreas of a 5-month fetal calf in proportionally greater quantities than in pancreases of older fetuses, of young calves, and even

of the adult (Banting and Best, '22; Fischer and Scott, '34). (See Table 27.) A progressive decrease in quantity of insulin per gram of pancreatic tissue seems to take place with advance in ontogenetic age of the calf. Such a decline with age may possibly represent a change in balance between rates of production and liberation of insulin, which in turn may be related to the rate of utilization of the hormone in the tissues of the growing organism. It would be of considerable significance in this connection to determine changes not only in the cytological picture of the islets but also in the ratio of islet tissue to acinar tissue with increasing age and body weight (cf. Hess and Root, '38).

Certain indirect evidence presented by Carlson et al. ('11, '14) and by Aron et al. ('23) and Aron ('24) indicates that insulin in both dog and cat fetuses is produced and is liberated during the latter half of the gestation period. If pregnant dogs or cats are pancreatectomized early in the gestation period, the mother develops hyperglycemia resulting in death; if similar operations are performed later in the gestation period, i.e., after the seventh to ninth week of gestation, no signs of hyperglycemia develop until after parturition. Fetal insulin is, therefore, seemingly protecting the mother after pancreatectomy. Whether this can be attributed to (1) passage of fetal insulin into the maternal circulation, (2) oxidation or utilization of excess blood sugar by the fetus, or (3) compensatory adjustment of hormonal mechanisms concerned in regulating carbohydrate metabolism in the mother and placenta remains unsettled. (For a comprehensive review of the subject of carbohydrate and other types of metabolism in the placenta and fetus see Huggett, '41.)

UNFOLDING OF MECHANISMS OF REGULATION OF INSULIN SECRETION

Although in the postnatal mammal a number of regulating mechanisms are probably involved either directly or indirectly, the principal regulator of insulin secretion appears to be the blood sugar level itself. Moreover, the amount of sugar in the blood is governed in the main by an interlocking relationship between liver function (glycogenesis and glycogenolysis) and the rate of secretion of insulin by the islets. It would appear possible, therefore, that a clue as to the period of onset of insulin regulation of sugar in the blood stream might be obtained by an examination of the developmental changes in blood sugar and liver glycogen with the time that insulin secretory activity of the beta cells is cytologically indicated.

Although the causal relations between the accumulation of carbohydrates in the blood and liver and the histogenesis of the cell types of the islets have not been explored on a scale commensurate with the importance of this problem, some suggestive information is available for examination. In the normal chick embryo, Konigsberg ('54) finds by quantitative microchemical methods that the blood sugar rises from 87.1±2.8 mg. per cent on the eighth day to a level of 112±5.5 per cent on the tenth day, remaining somewhat constant at this level until about the fourteenth day. Following this plateau, the blood sugar again rises to an average level of 151.9±6.5 mg. per cent on the sixteenth day. These findings are in general agreement with those of Leibson and Leibson ('43) with respect to the periods of increase and the plateau in blood sugar level, save for the additional point that the blood sugar level apparently reaches a still higher peak after the eighteenth day. Similar parallel changes likewise take place in the amount of liver glycogen. Initially present as traces on the sixth day, the amount of liver glycogen tends to increase gradually until the ninth day, then declines, becoming most marked on the twelfth day (Dalton, '37)— according to Konigsberg changing from 3.90 ±0.62 per cent (dry weight) on the tenth day to 2.32±0.35 per cent on the twelfth day, and to a value of 7.17±0.63 per cent on the fourteenth day. Beginning on the thirteenth day the glycogen content of the liver rises rapidly to its highest value on the nineteenth day and then appears to drop precipitously at about the time of hatching (Dalton, '37; Leibson, '50). It is significant to note that immediately prior to the time of onset of the second rise in carbohydrate accumulation in the blood and liver a few beta cells are first identified on the twelfth day according to Villamil ('42). Whether subsequently the number of beta cells increases concomitantly with the rapid rise in carbohydrates has not been worked out.

In the albino rat fetus at relatively late stages (ca. 16 days to term), according to Corey ('32), the blood sugar increases quantitatively with advance in fetal age, more or less gradually at first, followed by a period of very rapid increase (20± day to term.) This period of rapid increase coincides in time not only with the initiation of beta cell

differentiation and a most rapid increase in their number, but also with a prominent development of the capillary network within the larger islets. A similar pattern of quantitative increase in liver glycogen is exhibited in fetuses between the 16± day and term (Corey, '35).

By way of generalization, both blood sugar and liver glycogen are definitely present in measurable quantities at a time before beta cells can be distinguished cytologically by secretory granules and in the case of blood sugar (probably present from the beginning of vascular circulation) even before the islets are formed. It is clear, therefore, that the early accumulation of carbohydrate in the blood and liver is independent of insulin secretory activity of the islets. At later stages in development, at about the time that the rate of increase in blood sugar and liver glycogen somewhat abruptly become markedly accelerated, beta cell differentiation is initiated. However, whether the striking correspondence in time between these events is a true index of onset of insulin regulation remains problematical.

On the problem of the time in the course of development that hormones of the anterior pituitary and other endocrine glands become interrelated with the functional activity of the islets, the evidence is so scanty as scarcely to permit consideration. Nevertheless, on the basis of considerable evidence bearing on such interrelations in adult mammals, it seems worth while to outline at least briefly some of the specific kinds of problems that challenge the embryologist.

The current view that certain anterior pituitary hormones act directly and/or indirectly in exerting physiological effects which are opposite to that of insulin poses the problem as to when such opposing effects arise in the course of development. In pituitaryless chick embryos (produced by removal of the forebrain region at 33 to 38 hours) profound changes from the normal occur in (1) accumulation of carbohydrates in the blood and liver, (2) the adrenal cortex, and (3) the thyroid. The amount of blood sugar is increased over normal values (see Fig. 213) from the eighth to the thirteenth day, with a drop on the fourteenth day; the amount of liver glycogen increases from the tenth to the fourteenth day (Konigsberg, '54).* Furthermore, pituitary removal leads to subnormal activity of the thyroid and adrenal

---

* Cf. Jost ('51a) for evidence that the quantity of liver glycogen is markedly reduced after pituitary removal (decapitation) in the rabbit fetus.

riety of conditions, chief of which are the function of the parathyroids, the availability of mobilizable calcium, and calcium utilization.

It might be expected on theoretical grounds that the maintenance of calcium and phosphate in the fetal blood in concentrations above those in the mother is in some way related to active deposition of those calcium salts characteristic of developing bone. In the albino rat active bone formation is in progress during the latter third of the gestation period (Strong, '25). Ossification is initiated in a limited number of skeletal elements (first in the clavicle) on the 17± day. During subsequent days the number of such elements with beginning ossification rapidly increases, reaching a peak near term (21 days), when most of the bones of the fetus exhibit ossification centers. Obviously calcium and phosphorus are being utilized in increasing amounts as the number of ossifying bones increases. Although the concentrations of calcium and phosphorus in the blood are known to be high at term, the amounts present at earlier stages have not yet been determined. Whether the concentration of these substances in the blood increases concomitantly with the progressive increases in the calcification of cartilage and of periosteal bone would be of interest.

Although calcium and phosphate occur in fetal blood in concentrations above those actually essential to the process of ossification, the rate of their utilization is apparently determined by the developing skeletal elements. Two main lines of evidence may be cited to show that the individual elements of the vertebrate skeleton differ among themselves in morphogenetic pattern, which among other activities sets the specific site and amount of ossification in a given element. (1) In the rat fetus the time of appearance of bone salts and the specific locus of their deposition varies from one skeletal element to another (Bloom and Bloom, '40). (2) Prospective ("undifferentiated") osteogenic tissue of skeletal elements, such as the jaw (Meckel's cartilage and membrane bone), femur, and palatoquadrate bar, when isolated from the chick embryo (5½- to 6-day) and grown separately as explants in vitro shows a remarkable capacity for independent development of shape and histology. Differences in physiological properties are likewise expressed, since phosphatase activity is found in those elements that in normal development ossify (e.g., femur and palatoquadrate) but not in those that fail to ossify (e.g.,

Meckel's cartilage). Thus, in the absence of both blood and nerve supply each element develops in its own characteristic fashion almost exactly as it does in its appropriate position in the body of the embryo (Fell, '31).

From these considerations it is apparent that the pattern of the skeleton is already mapped out in the early embryo long before the onset of ossification or even chondrification. Each element has acquired its own intrinsic growth pattern and special physiological properties for selecting and utilizing calcium and phosphate from the common blood pool of the fetus. The quantity of uptake would appear to vary from one individual element to another in accordance with the amount of osteogenic tissue (calcifiable tissue) formed or capable of being formed. Furthermore, as the number of skeletal elements with osteogenic tissue increases, the quantity of uptake would be expected to increase progressively until the osteogenic potentialities have reached a peak in their expression.

Although the pattern of osteogenic potency is set early in the development of a given skeletal element, its full expression in normal bone growth is apparently dependent upon a multiplicity of interconnected conditions, chief of which are (1) availability of adequate concentrations of calcium and phosphate in the blood; (2) presence of the parathyroid hormone, which plays an important role in the mobilization and metabolism of calcium; (3) the presence of vitamin D, which apparently facilitates the utilization of calcium and phosphate in ossification; (4) internal secretions of the pituitary (growth hormone), thyroid, and sex glands, which, in influencing the growth process in general, tend as a rule to have a nonspecific regulatory effect on the growth of bone; and (5) mechanical factors (i.e., tension of muscle and ligaments, etc.) that influence the final surface modelling of the bones during the later stages of their development. (For an excellent and comprehensive treatment of the subject see Clark, '52.)

In conclusion, it will be apparent from the foregoing condensed account that the development of parathyroid activity presents problems of an intricate and complex nature. The onset of secretory activity cannot be considered separately from other physiological activities, since all activities are coordinated in maintaining steady states within the fetal body. Future progress in elucidating the physiological role of the fetal parathyroids is dependent mainly upon advances in the understanding of (1) the nature of the properties of the developing skeletal elements that enable them selectively to remove and utilize calcium and phosphate from the blood stream, (2) the mechanisms of deposition of calcium salts in bone, and (3) the time when the parathyroid hormone is produced and released into the fetal blood. A promising approach to the problem of the time of onset of parathyroid activity is that of testing the glands at progressively older developmental stages for capacity to bring about bone resorption when grafted beneath the periosteum of bone in young postnatal host animals. The value of this proposal is obvious from the studies of Chang ('51), who showed for young mice and rats that parathyroid tissue when grafted beneath the periosteum of the parietal bone causes a marked local resorption of bone, indicating the emanation of parathyroid hormone from the graft. The effect is highly specific, since other tissues so grafted cause little or no bone resorption.

REFERENCES

Adams, A. E. 1946 Variations in the potency of thyrotropic hormone of the pituitary in animals. Quart. Rev. Biol., 21:1–32.

Adler, L. 1914 Metamorphosestudien an Batrachierlarven. I. Exstirpation endokriner Drüsen. A. Exstirpation der Hypophyse. Roux' Arch. Entw.-mech., 39:21–45.

Allen, B. M. 1918 The results of thyroid removal in the larvae of Rana pipiens. J. Exp. Zool., 24:499–519.

——— 1927 Influence of the hypophysis upon the thyroid gland in amphibian larvae. Univ. Calif. Pub. Zool., 31:53–78.

——— 1928 The influence of different parts of the hypophysis upon size growth of Rana tadpoles. Physiol. Zool., 1:153–171.

——— 1929 The influence of the thyroid gland and hypophysis upon growth and development of amphibian larvae. Quart. Rev. Biol., 4:325–352.

——— 1938 The endocrine control of amphibian metamorphosis. Biol. Rev., 13:1–19.

Anderson, D., Billingham, R. E., Lampkin, G. H., and Medawar, P. B. 1951 The use of skin grafting to distinguish between monozygotic and dizygotic twins in cattle. Heredity, 5:379–397.

Aron, M. 1924 Le fonctionnement du pancréas et la régulation glycémique chez l'embryon des mammifères. Indications fournies par leur étude au point de vue du fonctionnement du pancréas et de la régulation glycémique chez l'adulte. Arch. Internat. Physiol., 22:273–298.

———, Stulz, E., and Simon, R. 1923 Fonctionnement du pancréas foetal après ablation du pancréas maternel. Compt. Rend. Soc. Biol., 89:571–573.

Banting, F. G., and Best, C. H. 1922 Pancreatic extracts. J. Lab. & Clin. Med., 7:464–472.

Bargmann, W. 1939 Die Langerhansschen Inseln des Pankreas. Handbuch der Microskopischen Anatomie des Menschen, 6 (Part 2): 197–288. Springer, Berlin.

Bascom, K. F. 1923 The interstitial cells of the gonads of cattle, with especial reference to their embryonic development and significance. Am. J. Anat., 31:223–259.

Becks, H. M., Simpson, M. E., Evans, H. M., Ray, R. D., Li, C. H., and Asling, C. W. 1946 Response to pituitary growth hormone and thyroxin of the tibias of hypophysectomized rats after postoperative intervals. Anat. Rec., 94:631–655.

Bloom, W., and Bloom, Margaret A. 1940 Calcification and ossification. Calcification of developing bones in embryonic and newborn rats. Anat. Rec., 78:497–523.

Bodansky, M., and Duff, V. B. 1941a Effects of parathyroid deficiency and calcium and phosphorus of the diet on pregnant rats. J. Nutrition, 21:179–192.

———, and Duff, V. B. 1941b Dependence of fetal growth and storage of calcium and phosphorus of the diet in pregnant rats. J. Nutrition, 22:25–41.

Burns, R. K., Jr. 1934 The transplantation of the adult hypophysis into young salamander larvae. Anat. Rec., 58:415–429.

——— 1949 Hormones and the differentiation of sex; in Survey of Biological Progress, Vol. 1, pp. 233–266. Academic Press, New York.

———, and Buyse, A. 1931 The effects of extracts of the mammalian hypophysis upon immature salamanders. Anat. Rec., 51:155–185.

———, and Buyse, A. 1933 The induction of precocious maturity in the reproductive tract of recently metamorphosed female salamanders by an extract of the mammalian hypophysis. Anat. Rec. 58:37–53.

———, and Buyse, A. 1934 The effect of an extract of the mammalian hypophysis upon the reproductive system of immature male salamanders after metamorphosis. J. Exp. Zool., 67:115–135.

Carlson, A. J., and Drennan, F. M. 1911 The control of pancreatic diabetes in pregnancy by passage of the internal secretion of the pancreas of the fetus to the blood of the mother. Am. J. Physiol., 28:391–395.

———, Orr, J. S., and Jones, W. S. 1914 The absence of sugar in the urine after pancreatectomy in pregnant bitches near term. J. Biol. Chem., 17:19–22.

Case, J. F. 1952 Adrenal cortical-anterior pituitary relationships during embryonic life. Ann. N. Y. Acad. Sci., 55:147–158.

Chang, H. 1951 Grafts of parathyroid and other tissues to bone. Anat. Rec., 111:23–47.

Clark, A. M. 1951 Carbonic anhydrase activity during embryonic development. J. Exp. Biol., 28:332–343.

Clark, Helen M. 1935 A prepubertal reversal of the sex difference in the gonadotropic hormone content of the pituitary gland of the rat. Anat. Rec., *61:*175–192.

Clark, W. E. LeGros 1952 The Tissues of the Body: An Introduction to the Study of Anatomy, 3d ed. Oxford, at the Clarendon Press.

Colowick, S. P., Cori, G. T., and Slein, M. W. 1947 Effect of adrenal cortex and anterior pituitary extracts and insulin on the hexokinase reaction. J. Biol. Chem., *168:*583–596.

Corey, E. L. 1932 Placental permeability to insulin in the albino rat. Physiol. Zool., *5:*36–48.

—— 1935 Growth and glycogen content of the fetal liver and placenta. Am. J. Physiol., *112:* 263–267.

Cori, C. F. 1946 Enzymatic reactions in carbohydrate metabolism. Harvey Lectures, *41:*253–272.

Courrier, R. 1951 Contribution a l'endocrinologie de la thyroïde. Acta endocrinologica, *7:*54–59.

Dalton, A. J. 1937 The functional differentiation of the hepatic cells of the chick embryo. Anat. Rec., *68:*393–409.

Dawson, A. B. 1953 Histochemical evidence of early differentiation of the suprarenal gland of the chick. J. Morph., *92:*579–595.

Deanesley, R. 1938 Adrenal cortex differences in male and female mice. Nature, *141:*79.

Domm, L. V. 1937 Observations concerning anterior pituitary-gonad interrelations in the fowl. Cold Spring Harbor, Symp. Quant. Biol., *5:*241–257.

Donaldson, J. C. 1919 The relative volumes of the cortex and medulla of the adrenal gland in the albino rat. Am. J. Anat., *25:*291–298.

Edmunds, H. W. 1950 Pituitary, adrenal and thyroid in cyclopia. Arch. Path., *50:*727–735.

Elliot, T. R., and Armour, R. G. 1911 The development of the cortex in the human suprarenal gland and its condition in hemicephaly. J. Path. & Bact., *15:*481–488.

Engle, E. T. 1931 The pituitary-gonadal relationship and problem of precocious sexual maturity. Endocrinology, *15:*405–420.

—— 1939 Gonadotropic substances of blood, urine and other body fluids; in Sex and Internal Secretions, edited by Allen, Danforth, and Doisy, chapter XVIII, pp. 1003–1044. Williams & Wilkins Co., Baltimore.

Etkin, W. 1935 Effect of multiple pituitary primordia in the tadpole. Proc. Soc. Exp. Biol. & Med., *32:*1653–1655.

—— 1938 The development of thyrotropic function in pituitary grafts in the tadpole. J. Exp. Zool., *77:*347–377.

—— 1939 A thyrotropic field effect in the tadpole. J. Exp. Zool., *82:*463–495.

Evans, H. M., Fraenkel-Conrat, H. L., Simpson, M. E., and Li, C. H. 1939 Characterization of gonadotropic hormones of the hypophysis by their sugar and glucosamine content. Science, *89:*249–250.

——, Simpson, M. E., and Li, C. H. 1943 Inhibiting effect of adrenocorticotropic hormone on the growth of male rats. Endocrinology, *33:*237–238.

——, Simpson, M. E., and Pencharz, R. I. 1939 Relation between the growth promoting effects of the pituitary and the thyroid hormone. Endocrinology, *25:*175–182.

Fell, H. B. 1931 Osteogenesis in vitro. Arch. exp. Zellforsch., *11:*245–252.

Fenger, F. 1912 On the presence of active principles in the thyroid and suprarenal glands before and after birth. J. Biol. Chem., *11:*489–492; *12:* 55–59.

Fevold, H. L. 1939 The follicle stimulating and luteinizing hormones of the pituitary; in Sex and Internal Secretions, edited by Allen, Danforth, and Doisy, chapter XVII, pp. 966–1002. Williams & Wilkins Co., Baltimore.

Finerty, J. C., and Briseno-Castrejon, B. 1949 Quantitative studies of cell types in the rat hypophysis following unilateral adrenalectomy. Endocrinology, *44:*293–300.

Fischer, A. M., and Scott, D. A. 1934 The insulin content of the pancreas in cattle of various ages. J. Biol. Chem., *106:*305–310.

Flexner, L. B., and Grollman, A. 1939 The reduction of osmic acid as an indicator of adrenal cortical activity in the rat. Anat. Rec., *75:*207–221.

Flint, J. M. 1900 The blood-vessels, angiogenesis, organogenesis, reticulum, and histology of the adrenal. Johns Hopkins Hospital Rept., *9:*153–229.

Francis, T. 1944 Investigations into the development of the pituitary at hereditary anterior pituitary dwarfism in mice. With reference to the pathogenesis of the anterior pituitary dwarfism. Opera ex Domo Biologiae Hereditariae Humanae Universitatis Hafniensis, Vol. 7. Ejnar Munksgaard, Copenhagen.

Fugo, N. W. 1940 Effects of hypophysectomy in the chick embryo. J. Exp. Zool., *85:*271–297.

Gaillard, P. J. 1953 Growth and differentiation of explanted tissues. Internat. Rev. Cytology, *2:* 331–401.

Gersh, I., and Grollman, A. 1939a The relation of the adrenal cortex to the male reproductive system. Am. J. Physiol., *126:*368–374.

——, and Grollman, A. 1939b The nature of the x-zone of the adrenal gland of the mouse. Anat. Rec., *75:*131–153.

——, and Grollman, A. 1941 The vascular pattern of the adrenal gland of the mouse and rat and its physiological response to changes in glandular activity. Contrib. Embryol., Carnegie Inst. Wash., *29:*111–125.

Gorbman, A., and Evans, H. M. 1941 Correlation of histological differentiation with beginning function of developing thyroid gland of frog. Proc. Soc. Exp. Biol. & Med., *47:*103–106.

——, and Evans, H. M. 1943 Beginning of function in the thyroid of the fetal rat. Endocrinology, *32:*113–115.

Greep, R. O. 1948 Physiology and chemistry of the parathyroid hormone; in The Hormones: Physiology, Chemistry and Application, edited by G. Pincus and K. V. Thimann, Vol. 1, pp. 255–300. Academic Press, New York.

Hansborough, L. A., and Khan, M. 1951 The

initial function of the chick thyroid gland with the use of radioiodine (I^{131}). J. Exp. Zool., *116:* 447–453.

Hard, W. 1944 The origin and differentiation of the alpha and beta cells in the pancreatic islets of the rat. Am. J. Anat., *75:*369–398.

Herlant, M. 1949 Study of the pituitary body with periodic acid-Schiff reaction. Nature, *164:* 703–704.

Hess, W. N., and Root, C. W. 1938 Study of the pancreas of the white rat of different age groups. Am. J. Anat., *63:*489–498.

Hill, W. C. O. 1930 Observations on the growth of the suprarenal cortex. J. Anat., *64:*479–502.

Hopkins, Marie L. 1935 Development of the thyroid gland in the chick embryo. J. Morph., *58:* 585–614.

Hoskins, E. R., and Hoskins, M. M. 1919 Growth and development of Amphibia as affected by thyroidectomy. J. Exp. Zool., *29:*1–70.

Hoskins, F. M., and Snyder, F. F. 1933 The placental transmission of parathyroid extract. Am. J. Physiol., *104:*530–536.

Houssay, B. A. 1948 Diabetogenic action of the fetal hypophysis. Compt. Rend. Soc. Biol., *142:* 1160–1161.

Howard, Evelyn 1946 The effect of adrenalectomy on the accessory reproductive glands of mice castrated for short periods. Endocrinology, *38:*156–164.

Howard-Miller, Evelyn 1926 The development of the epinephrin content of the suprarenal medulla in early stages of the mouse. Am. J. Physiol., *75:*267–277.

——— 1927 A transitory zone in the adrenal cortex which shows age and sex relationships. Am. J. Anat., *40:*251–293.

——— 1939 Effects of castration on the seminal vesicles as influenced by age, considered in relation to the degree of development of the adrenal x zone. Am. J. Anat., *65:*105–149.

Huggett, A. St. G. 1941 The nutrition of the fetus. Physiol. Rev., *21:*438–462.

Jailer, J. W. 1950 The maturation of the pituitary-adrenal axis in the newborn rat. Endocrinology, *46:*420–425.

——— 1951 Adrenocorticotropin content of the immature rat pituitary gland. Endocrinology, *49:* 826–827.

Jost, A. 1947 The age factor in the castration of male rabbit fetuses. Proc. Soc. Exp. Biol. & Med., *66:*302–303.

——— 1948 Influence de la décapitation sur le développement du tractus génital et des surrénales de l'embryon de lapin. Compt. Rend. Soc. Biol., *142:*273–275.

——— 1950 Sur le contrôle hormonal de la différenciation sexuelle du lapin. Arch. Anat. micr. et Morph. exp., *39:*577–607.

——— 1951a La physiologie de l'hypophyse foetale. Biol. Méd., *40:*205–229.

——— 1951b Recherches sur la différenciation sexuelle de l'embryon de lapin. IV. Organogenèse sexuelle masculine après décapitation du foetus. Arch. Anat. micr. et Morph. exp., *40:*247–281.

———, Morel, F. F., and Marois, M. 1949 Données préliminaires sur la fixation de radio-iode I^{131} par la thyroïde foetale du lapin. Compt. Rend. Soc. Biol., *143:*142–145.

Keene, M. F. L., and Hewer, E. E. 1927 Observations on the development of the human suprarenal gland. J. Anat., *61:*302–324.

Kerr, T. 1939 On the histology of the developing pituitary in the frog (*Rana t. temporaria*) and in the toad (*Bufo bufo*). Proc. Zool. Soc. London B, *109:*167–180.

Kitchell, R. L., and Wells, L. J. 1952a Functioning of the hypophysis and adrenals in fetal rats: effects of hypophysectomy, adrenalectomy, castration, injected ACTH and implanted sex hormones. Anat. Rec., *112:*561–591.

——— 1952b Reciprocal relation between the hypophysis and adrenals in fetal rats: effects of unilateral adrenalectomy and of implanted cortisone, doca and sex hormones. Endocrinology, *50:*83–93.

Kleinholz, L. H. 1940 The distribution of intermedin: first appearance of the hormone in the early ontogeny of *Rana pipiens*. Biol. Bull., *79:* 432–438.

Koneff, A. A., Nichols, C. W., Jr., Wolff, J., and Chaikoff, I. L. 1949 The fetal bovine thyroid; morphogenesis as related to iodine accumulation. Endocrinology, *45:*242–249.

Konigsberg, I. R. 1954 The effects of early pituitary removal by "decapitation" on carbohydrate metabolism in the chick embryo. J. Exp. Zool., *125:*151–169.

Kull, H. A. 1926 The late embryonic development of the thyroid gland of the albino rat. Anat. Rec., *32:*133–141.

Leibson, L. G. 1950 Glycogen content of the liver in chick embryos in various stages of incubation. (In Russian.) Fiziol. Zhur., *36:*191–202.

———, and Leibson, R. S. 1943 Neural and humoral regulation of the blood-sugar content in ontogenesis. I. Blood-sugar content in the chick embryo and young chicks. Bull. Acad. Sci. U.R.S.S. Ser. Biol., pp. 93–99.

Lewis, M. R., and Geiling, E. M. K. 1935 Survival and increase of epinephrine in tissue cultures of adrenal glands from chick embryos. Am. J. Physiol., *113:*529–533.

Li, C. H., Evans, H. M., and Simpson, M. E. 1945 Isolation and properties of the anterior hypophyseal growth hormone. J. Biol. Chem., *159:* 353–366.

Lillie, F. R. 1917 The free-martin; a study of the action of sex hormones in the foetal life of cattle. J. Exp. Zool., *23:*371–452.

Long, C. N. H. 1942 Pituitary hormones influencing growth in higher animals. Cold Spring Harbor Symp. Quant. Biol., *10:*91–103.

——— 1943 The growth and metabolic hormones of the anterior pituitary. Ann. N. Y. Acad. Sci., *43:*383–426.

——— 1949 The adrenal gland, a regulatory factor; in Chemistry and Physiology of Growth, edited by A. K. Parpart, pp. 266–284. Princeton University Press, Princeton, New Jersey.

Marshall, J. M., Jr. 1951 Localization of adreno-corticotropic hormone by histochemical and immunochemical methods. J. Exp. Med., *94*:21–30.

Martindale, F. M. 1941 Initiation and early development of thyrotropic function in the incubating chick. Anat. Rec., *79*:373–393.

Marx, W., Simpson, M. E., and Evans, H. M. 1942 Synergism between thyrotropic and growth hormones of the pituitary. Body weight increase in hypophysectomized rat. Proc. Soc. Exp. Biol. & Med., *49*:594–597.

McCord, C. P. 1915 The occurrence of pituitrin and epinephrin in fetal pituitary and suprarenal glands. J. Biol. Chem., *23*:435–438.

Moon, H. D. 1940 Effect of adrenocorticotropic hormone in 4-day-old rats. Proc. Soc. Exp. Biol. & Med., *43*:42–44.

Moore, C. R. 1947 Embryonic Sex Hormones and Sexual Differentiation. Charles C Thomas, Springfield, Illinois.

———— 1950 The role of the fetal endocrine glands in development. J. Clin. Endocrinology, *10*:942–985.

———— 1953 Adrenal cortical secretions in relation to the reproductive system of rats. J. Clin. Endocrinology, *13*:330–368.

————, and Morgan, C. F. 1943 First response of developing opossum gonads to equine gonadotropic treatment. Endocrinology, *32*:17–26.

————, and Price, Dorothy 1932 Gonad hormone functions, and the reciprocal influence between gonads and hypophysis with its bearing on the problem of sex-hormone antagonism. Am. J. Anat., *50*:13–71.

Nace, G. W. 1953 Serological studies of the blood of the developing chick embryo. J. Exp. Zool., *122*:423–448.

Needham, J. 1931 Chemical Embryology, Vols. I, II, III. The Macmillan Co., New York.

Nelson, W. O. 1933 Studies on the anterior hypophysis. I. The development of the hypophysis in the pig (*Sus scrofa*). II. The cytological differentiation in the anterior hypophysis of the foetal pig. Am. J. Anat., *52*:307–332.

Nicholas, H. O., Johnson, H. W., and Johnston, R. A. 1934 Diffusible serum calcium in pregnancy. Am. J. Obst. & Gynec., *27*:504:510.

Norris, E. H. 1937 The parathyroid glands and the lateral thyroid in man: their morphogenesis, histogenesis, topographic anatomy and prenatal growth. Contrib. Embryol., Carnegie Inst. Wash., *26*:247–294.

O'Connor, R. J. 1953 Metabolism and glycogen formation in the liver of the chicken embryo. J. Embryol. Exp. Morphol., *1*:105–114.

Owen, R. R., Davis, H. P., and Morgan, R. F. 1946 Quintuplet calves and erythrocyte mosaicism. J. Hered., *37*:291–297.

Payne, F. 1946 The cellular picture of the anterior pituitary of normal fowls from embryo to old age. Anat. Rec., *96*:77–91.

Pickering, J. W., and Gladstone, R. J. 1925 The development of blood plasma. I. The genesis of coagulable material in embryo chicks. Proc. Roy. Soc. London B, *98*:516–522.

Potvin, R., and Aron, M. 1927 Recherches sur l'évolution embryonnaire des îlots pancreatiques endocrines chez le poulet. Compt. Rend. Soc. Biol., *96*:267–269.

Price, Dorothy, and Ortiz, Evelina 1944 The relation of age to reactivity in the reproductive system of the rat. Endocrinology, *34*:215–239.

Rahn, H. 1939 The development of the chick pituitary with special reference to the cellular differentiation of the pars buccalis. J. Morph., *64*:483–517.

Rankin, R. M. 1941 Changes in the content of iodine compounds and in the histological structure of the thyroid gland of the pig during fetal life. Anat. Rec., *80*:123–135.

Ray, R. D., Simpson, M. E., Li, C. H., Asling, C. W., and Evans, H. M. 1950 Effects of the pituitary growth hormone and of thyroxin on growth and differentiation of the skeleton of the rat thyroidectomized at birth. Am J. Anat., *86*:479–516.

Raynaud, A., and Frilley, M. 1943 Effets, sur l'histogenèse de la région bucco-pharyngienne des embryons de souris, d'une application locale de rayons X sur cette région, au 13ᵉ jour de la vie embryonnaire. Compt. Rend. Acad. Sc., *217*:555–557.

————, and Frilley, M. 1947 Destruction du cerveau des embryons de souris au treizième jour de la gestation, par irradiation au moyen des rayons X. Compt. Rend. Soc. Biol., *141*:658–662.

————, and Frilley, M. 1950 Développement intra-utérin des embryons de souris dont les ébauches de l'hypophyse ont été détruites au moyen des rayons X, au 13ᵉ jour de la gestation. II. Développement des capsules surrénales. Compt. Rend. Acad. Sc., *230*:331–333.

Rumph, P., and Smith, P. E. 1926 The first occurrence of secretory products and a specific structural differentiation in the thyroid and anterior pituitary during the development of the pituitary. Anat. Rec., *33*:289–298.

Sayers, G., and Sayers, M. A. 1949 The pituitary-adrenal system. Ann. N. Y. Acad. Sci., *50*: 522–539.

————, Sayers, M. A., Fry, E. G., White, A., and Long, C. N. H. 1944 The effect of the adrenotrophic hormone of the anterior pituitary on the cholesterol content of the adrenal. Yale J. Biol. & Med., *16*:361–392.

Scammon, R. E. 1930 The Measurement of Man, Part IV. University of Minnesota Press, Minneapolis.

Sethre, A. E., and Wells, L. J. 1951 Accelerated growth of the thyroid in normal and "hypophysectomized" fetal rats given thyrotrophin. Endocrinology, *49*:369–373.

Severinghaus, A. E. 1936 The cytology of the pituitary gland. Proc. Assoc. Research in Nervous and Mental Diseases, *17*:69–117.

———— 1937 Cellular changes in the anterior hypophysis with special reference to its secretory activity. Physiol. Rev., *17*:556–588.

Shepherd, D. M., and West, G. B. 1951 Noradrenaline and the suprarenal medulla. Brit. J. Pharm. & Chemotherapy, *6*:665–674.

Sinclair, J. G. 1942 Fetal rat parathyroids as affected by changes in maternal serum calcium and phosphorus through parathyroidectomy. J. Nutrition, 23:141–152.

Smith, P. E. 1918 The growth of normal and hypophysectomized tadpoles as influenced by endocrine diets. Univ. Calif. Pub. Physiol., 5:11–22.

——— 1920 The pigmentary, growth and endocrine disturbances in the anuran tadpole by the early ablation of the pars buccalis of the hypophysis. Am. Anat. Mem. No. 11, pp. 1–151.

——— 1927 The induction of precocious sexual maturity by pituitary homeotransplants. Am. J. Physiol., 80:114–125.

——— 1930 Hypophysectomy and a replacement therapy in the rat. Am. J. Anat., 45:205–273.

——— 1933 Increased skeletal effects in A. P. growth-hormone injections by administration of thyroid in hypophysectomized, thyro-parathyroidectomized rats. Proc. Soc. Exp. Biol. & Med., 30:1252–1254.

——— 1939 The effect on the gonads of the ablation and implantation of the hypophysis and the potency of the hypophysis under various conditions; in Sex and Internal Secretions, edited by Allen, Danforth, and Doisy, Chapter XVI, pp. 931–965. Williams & Wilkins Co., Baltimore.

———, and Dortzbach, C. 1929 The first appearance in the anterior pituitary of the developing pig foetus of detectable amounts of hormones stimulating ovarian maturity and general body growth. Anat. Rec., 43:277–297.

———, and Engle, E. T. 1927 Experimental evidence regarding the rôle of the anterior pituitary in the development and regulation of the genital system. Am. J. Anat., 40:159–217.

———, and McDowell, E. C. 1930 An hereditary anterior-pituitary deficiency in the mouse. Anat. Rec., 46:249–257.

———, and Smith, I. B. 1923 The function of the lobes of the hypophysis as indicated by replacement therapy with different portions of the ox gland. Endocrinology, 7:579–591.

Strong, R. M. 1925 The order, time and rate of ossification of the albino rat (Mus norvegicus albinus) skeleton. Am. J. Anat., 36:313–344.

Swingle, W. W. 1923 Thyroid transplantation and anuran metamorphosis. J. Exp. Zool., 37:219–257.

Terry, G. S. 1918 Effects of the extirpation of the thyroid gland upon ossification in Rana pipiens. J. Exp. Zool., 24:567–587.

Thompson, D'Arcy W. 1942 Growth and Form. 2nd Ed. Cambridge at the University Press, England.

Tobin, C. E. 1939 The influence of adrenal destruction on the prenatal development of the albino rat. Am. J. Anat., 65:151–177.

Uotila, U. U. 1940 The early embryological development of the fetal and permanent adrenal cortex in man. Anat. Rec., 76:183–204.

VanGoor, H. 1940 Die Lokalisation und die Bildung von Kohlensäureanhydrase in Hühner-embryonen. Acta brev. neerl. Physiol., 10:37–39.

Villamil, M. F. 1942 Citogénesis del páncreas exo y endocrino en embriones de pollo. Revista Sociedad Argentina Biologia, 18:416–424.

Walker, D. G., Simpson, M. E., Asling, C. W., and Evans, H. M. 1950 Growth and differentiation in the rat following hypophysectomy at six days of age. Anat. Rec., 106:539–554.

Waring, H. 1935 Development of the adrenal gland in the mouse. Quart. J. Micr. Sci., 78:329–366.

Weiss, Paul, and Rossetti, F. 1951 Growth responses of opposite sign among different neuron types to thyroid hormone. Proc. Nat. Acad. Sci., 37:540–556.

Wells, L. J. 1946 Effects of injections of equine gonadotrophin upon the gonads and adrenals of fetal rats. Proc. Soc. Exp. Biol. & Med. 62:250–254.

——— 1948 Some experimental evidence of production of adrenotrophin by the fetal hypophysis. Proc. Soc. Exp. Biol. & Med., 68:487–488.

———, and Fralick, R. L. 1951 Production of androgen by the testes of fetal rats. Am. J. Anat., 89:63–107.

Weymann, M. R. 1922 The beginning and development of function in the suprarenal medulla of pig embryos. Anat. Rec., 24:299–313.

Whitehead, R. 1933 Growth and mitosis in mouse suprarenal. J. Anat., 67:399–408.

Willier, B. H. 1930 A study of the origin and differentiation of the suprarenal gland in the chick embryo by chorio-allantoic grafting. Physiol. Zool., 3:201–225.

——— 1939 The embryonic development of sex; in Sex and Internal Secretions, edited by Allen, Danforth, and Doisy, Chapter III, pp. 64–144. Williams & Wilkins Co., Baltimore.

——— 1952 Development of sex-hormone activity of the avian gonad. Ann. N. Y. Acad Sci., 55:159–171.

——— 1954 Phases in embryonic development. J. Cell. & Comp. Physiol., 43 (Suppl. 1): 307–317.

———, Gallagher, T. F., and Koch, F. C. 1937 The modification of sex development in the chick embryo by male and female sex hormones. Physiol. Zool., 10:101–122.

Wilson, Margaret E. 1952 The embryological and cytological basis of regional patterns in the definitive epithelial hypophysis of the chick. Am. J. Anat., 91:1–50.

Wolfe, J. M., and Cleveland, R. 1931 Comparison of the capacity of anterior hypophyseal tissue of mature and immature female rabbits to induce ovulation. Anat. Rec., 51:213–218.

Wolff, Et. 1937 L'hypophyse et la thyroïde jouent-elles un rôle dans le déterminisme expérimental de l'intersexualité chez l'embryon de poulet? Compt. Rend. Soc. Biol., 126:1217–1218.

——— 1947 Recherches sur l'intersexualité expérimentale produite par la méthode des greffes de gonades à l'embryon de poulet. Arch. Anat. micr. et Morph. exp., 36:69–90.

————, and Haffen, K. 1952 Sur l'intersexualité expérimentale des gonades embryonnaires de canard cultivées *in vitro*. Arch. Anat. micr. et Morph. exp., *41*:184–207.

————, and Stoll, R. 1937 Le rôle de l'hypophyse dans le développement embryonnaire du poulet, d'après l'étude des cyclocéphales expérimentaux. Compt. Rend. Soc. Biol., *126*:1215–1217.

————, and Wolff, Em. 1951 The effects of castration on bird embryos. J. Exp. Zool., *116*:59–97.

Wolff, J., Chaikoff, I. L., and Nichols, C. W., Jr., 1949 The accumulation of thyroxine-like and other iodine compounds in the fetal bovine thyroid. Endocrinology, *44*:510–519.

Wollman, S. H., and Zwilling, E. 1953 Radio-iodine metabolism in the chick embryo. Endocrinology, *52*:526–535.

Yoffey, J. M., and Baxter, J. S. 1947 The formation of birefringent crystals in the suprarenal cortex. J. Anat., *81*:335–342.

———— 1949 Histochemical changes in the suprarenal gland of the adult male rat. J. Anat., *83*:89–98.

Young, F. G. 1948 The mechanism of action of insulin. Science Progress, *141*:13–37.

Zwilling, E. 1948 Association of hypoglycemia with insulin micromelia in chick embryos. J. Exp. Zool., *109*:197–214.

———— 1951 Carbohydrate metabolism in insulin-treated chick embryos. Arch. Biochem. & Biophysics, *33*:228–242.

THE DETERMINATION OF SIZE

N. J. BERRILL

THE SIZE that any organism finally attains is the result of growth, and the regulation of size is essentially a matter of rate and duration of growth. In most cases the greater part, but not the greatest rate, of growth occurs after the end of the embryonic period proper, during the later phases of the whole developmental cycle when there is comparatively little change of form.

Growth, and therefore size regulation, is associated with all things living, from the sub-microscopical molecular components of a cell to the giant organismal whales and redwoods. Accordingly, any restriction of growth- and size-analysis to certain organisms or organizational levels must be purely arbitrary. The basic phenomenon of growing to a limited size is a general characteristic of organisms and their parts, and above the molecular level at least there seems to be no such thing as a unit of growth. The cell appears to be primarily a metabolic unit and not in any fundamental sense either a growth or an organizational unit. (Berrill, '41; Sinnott, '45).

Specific size, implying regulation of growth, is as characteristic of individual cells and single-celled organisms as it is of multicellular organisms and of populations of all kinds. Protozoa vary in size from the numerous kinds only 2 or 3 micra long, to the relative giants such as certain species of Spirostomum, Stentor, Paramecium and Ameba several millimeters long, that is, a range in linear dimensions of several thousand times. The general problem of cell size is probably best approached with such organisms as these that are comparable to cells but which have an independent existence, so being more amenable to culture and experiment. Within the limits of a single genus, Paramecium appears to offer the greatest range in size, and it has already been subject to extensive genetical investigations. This approach, however, has far outrun the physiological; the modification of size through metabolism control, including temperature effects, is susceptible to a much more intense experimental analysis.

In multicellular organisms the sizes of cells, other than eggs, vary only between certain relatively narrow limits, and while they are by no means everywhere the same, body size is primarily a reflection of cell number rather than cell size. Tissue for tissue, the cells of mouse and elephant vary about 1:2 in linear dimension, cells are of the same size in the 9-foot leaf of the giant water lilies and in the small, while in dwarf and giant species of the slipper-limpet Crepidula, Conklin ('12) found equivalent cell types to be of virtually the same size.

The exceptions to this general condition are significant. Compared with other vertebrates the amphibians have relatively large cells, yet within this group the perennibranchiate urodeles have practically all cell types many times the size of their metamorphosing cousins, erythrocytes for example reaching as much as 70 micra, larger than the eggs of some animals. These forms are also distinguished by a comparatively low rate of metabolism (Smith, '12), a correlation that merits further investigation.

Cells generally have the diploid number of chromosomes, but under certain circumstances may be haploid or polyploid. The cell size varies directly with these nuclear conditions, though not proportionately. Within the limits investigated, organismal and organ sizes in heteroploid amphibian larvae remain unaffected, the cell number in some way becoming adjusted (Fankhauser, '45). In certain insects such as Culex the cells, e.g., intestinal epithelium, become progressively polyploid and enlarge as the larva grows. With the onset of metamorphosis they undergo a series of divisions leading to an imago with a reconstituted gut consisting of relatively small and numerous diploid cells

(Berger, '37). The extent of correlation of larval structure with stability of cell number and organization deserves further study. At the same time there is an implication, in the glandular control of metamorphosis in both insects and amphibians, of a shift or increase in basal metabolic rate, and that the collective changes amounting to metamorphosis may be the differential proliferative response of certain tissues to the new metabolic level.

In contrast to organisms whose size reflects the number of their constituent cells

similar forms under varying conditions are closely related.

The main conclusion from Whitaker's measurements is that, in general, eggs before fertilization or activation are in a state of abnormal metabolism compared with the metabolism of adult tissues or of protozoa; that this unusual condition is in some way the basis of the attainment of large cell size; and that with the restoration of normal metabolism upon activation, cleavages automatically follow until cell sizes associated with normal metabolism are reached. Con-

TABLE 28. *Cell Diameters and Cell Numbers of Some Holoblastic Eggs*

GROUP	GENUS	EGG DIAMETER (MM.)	CELL NUMBER (APPROX. AT END OF COURSE) OF CLEAVAGE
Coelenterata	Aurelia	0.19	2,600
Polycladida	Thyzanozoon	0.12	950
Polychaeta	Serpula	0.07	920
Polychaeta	Lumbrinereis	0.16	4,100
Echinoderma	Toxipneustes	0.11	2,100
Tunicata	Ascidiella	0.16	3,400
Tunicata	Ecteinascidia	0.72	132,000
Cephalochordata	Amphioxus	0.12	9,000
Cyclostomata	Entosphenus	1.00	300,000
Amphibia	Bufo	1.30	450,000
Amphibia	Rana	2.10	700,000
Amphibia	Triturus	2.60	860,000

(the number increasing with growth), are certain small types that maintain a constancy of cell number however much their size may vary. Among these are the rotifers, phylloxerans and Dinophilus (Van Cleave, '32). Inasmuch as there is a limit to the size of individual cells, it may be that these organisms are limited to their peculiar small dimensions simply by some inhibition of cell division.

The outstanding example of cells that attain exceptionally large sizes are eggs of virtually all kinds. Eggs of necessity are cells large enough to yield through successive divisions a number of smaller cells adequate for the formation of some kind of active organism. The problem presented by the unusual extent of growth of oocytes is that of limitation or determination of cell growth in general, and here it may be most susceptible to attack. The most intensive investigations to date have been those of Whitaker ('33) on the changes in respiratory rates of eggs of various marine invertebrates before and after fertilization. Tyler's ('35) investigations of respiration in fertilized eggs of

sequently the curve of cleavage is similar to the curve of growth, and represents the progressive attainment of the new level of equilibrium or cellular steady state.

The size of cells in differentiated tissues varies considerably among different animals, in amphibians relatively large, in Amphioxus small, with the majority of forms between these two extremes. The cell number at the end of embryonic development, that is, at the end of the course of cleavage, is accordingly a product of the initial volume of the egg and the final average size of the constituent cells. Table 28 illustrates this for some holoblastic eggs (after Berrill, '35).

The larval organism produced as the result of cleavage and differentiation of the egg is therefore more or less proportionate in size to the mass of the egg, and in conformity with this, whole larvae derived from half or a quarter of the original egg, as from isolated blastomeres, are proportionately small. After cleavage as such has come to an end and a functional larval organism has been formed, growth proceeds anew as food is obtained and utilized, a growth that continues until sexual maturity is reached. There is a change at the time a larva becomes active, from a condition comparable to a closed system to an open one—from tissues which are differentiating and determinate to tissues that are functionally differentiated and, for the most part, capable of regeneration. The final limit to growth, and

TABLE 29. *Number of Blastomeres and Blastocyst Diameter in Two Races of Rabbits*

HOURS	SMALL RACE	LARGE RACE
	Average Number of Blastomeres	
32¼	4.06	4.41
40	8.29	9.94
41	8.62	11.64
48	14.00	21.75
	Blastocyst Diameter	
144	40.5μ	47.8μ

therefore size, which is reached during this second phase of development, is genetically inherent in the species and in general not subject to experimental modification other than a degree of stunting through some form of malnutrition. There is, however, some indication that growth of the body as a whole proceeds until the gonads attain their functionally differentiated state as tissues. In many forms no further growth occurs after this condition is reached. Even where post-maturity growth is considerable, there is a periodic spawning and a replacement of gonadal tissue, so that the correlation is still present.

In meroblastic eggs the distinction between embryonic development and post-embryonic growth is less clear-cut. The embryo is formed from the blastodisc and the scale of its formation is there determined. The greater part of the egg mass is drawn upon by the developing tissues in a manner comparable with the nourishment of tissues in the adult. The result is that the primary embryo is a rapidly growing system and not one merely undergoing cellular subdivision and differentiation. In many such cases there are three critical sizes in the developmental cycle which are to some extent independent of one another: the size of the embryo when it is more or less differentiated, which is related to the initial scale of organization; the size at hatching or, alternatively, when the yolk has been absorbed; and the size at sexual maturity. In

some instances of diapause in insects, for example, in the grasshopper Melanoplus (Burkholder, '34), the arrest of development takes place approximately at the time of full embryonic differentiation (growth to the hatching size, when the yolk has been fully incorporated), occurring only after diapause has been broken.

In meroblastic vertebrates, however, there does not appear to be any such break in the continuity of growth and the curve of growth does not indicate the place where formation of the embryo yields to growth of formed structures, for growth is continuous throughout the cycle, after the primary divisions of the blastodisc are completed. This holds for mammalian development as well as for other amniotes, and hatching or birth in these forms is little more than a temporary interruption of the growth process associated with the change in the nutritive mechanism.

One of the most significant leads in the analysis of growth and size in amniotes was given by Painter ('28) in connection with the racial size differences between Flemish-giant (5000 gm.) and small Polish (1700 gm.) rabbits. These differences were traced back to early embryonic stages, even though there are no differences in egg size. After 12 days' gestation the embryonic lengths were 23.1 and 18.1 mm., respectively, and he concluded that the larger had correspondingly more cells and therefore was growing and proliferating at a greater rate, equivalent organizational stages varying in size or scale. These investigations were extended by Castle and Gregory ('29), whose results are summarized in Table 29.

TABLE 30. *Weights of Two Races of Chickens at Three Stages of Development*

	WHITE LEGHORN	RHODE ISLAND RED
Adult wt. in gm.	1560	3000
14 days incubation, wt. in gm.	11.37	12.08
72 hrs., wt. in mg.	19.8	20.2

Final size in these animals is accordingly a reflection of early or even initial conditions. It has been correlated with the concentration of glutathione in the foetus at birth (Gregory and Goss, '33; Goss and Gregory, '35; Lerner, Gregory and Goss, '36), greater concentration being associated with the higher growth rate.

The situation in birds appears to be much more obscure. Byerly ('30) could find no consistent weight differences between embryos of the same age of White Leghorns (adult weight, 2010 gm.) and Rhode Island Reds (2770 gm.), although the smaller race embryo was larger up to the tenth day, after which the larger race embryos drew ahead. Blunn and Gregory ('35), however, found consistent but slight differences between the two races (Table 30).

Byerly, Helsel and Quinn ('38), studying hybrids as well, found growth to be practically identical in rate between 2 and 20 days for eggs of the same size, and egg size to be more significant than genetic constitution. Similarly, differences in glutathione concentration at the time of hatching appeared to be too slight to be significant. After hatching, the differential rate of growth becomes more evident, and Gregory, Asmundson, Goss and Landauer ('39) found correlated glutathione differences. Kaufman ('30), comparing hen and pigeon, could not find significant differences in growth rate during the embryonic period, but considered the differences in size of equivalent stages of the two to be due to differences in the size of cells attained immediately before cleavage; for example, liver cells of the 3- and 11-day embryos were markedly larger in the chick.

In contrast to increasing growth rates and larger sizes associated with increase in glutathione concentration are the problems of growth inhibition. These are seen most strikingly in the phenomenon of dwarf males among various groups of animals, including vertebrates. This may be regarded as a matter of sex determination, the male condition often being a consequence of small adult size, particularly among forms normally hermaphrodite. In the gephyrean Bonellia indifferent larvae are produced, those settling in mud growing to a large size as females, those settling on the proboscis of a female remaining minute and becoming male (Herbst, '39). Nowinski ('34) and Baltzer ('40) showed that the effective substance for dwarfing was present in aqueous extracts and was heat-stable. Herbst, however, found that various agents, such as low pH, glycerol, traces of copper, and variations of K^+ and Mg^{++} also induced dwarfing leading to male individuals. Dwarf males are also found among cirripede crustaceans such as Scalpellum, coexisting with large hermaphrodites. Reinhard ('42) is of the opinion that in the Peltogaster, of the same group, previously indifferent larvae settle on the ex-

ternal sac of the parasitic hermaphrodite and become dwarfed males in consequence.

GROWTH RATE

Growth rates are expressed either as mathematical formulae or as a growth curve, the latter method being the more obviously informative and more generally employed. Increase in length, area or mass, plotted against time yields a typical growth curve (Fig. 214a). This is usually a summation or cu-

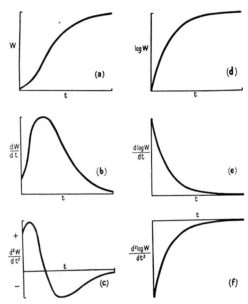

Fig. 214. Curves of growth (from Medawar, '45). (a) The curve of growth; (b) of growth rate; (c) of acceleration; (d) of specific growth; (e) of specific growth rate; (f) of specific acceleration.

mulative curve and it expresses the successive velocities or growth rates as a continuous succession of varying magnitudes. On the other hand, if the differences between the values for successive units of time are plotted against time, a velocity curve or curve of the rate of growth is obtained (Fig. 214b). One is the inverse of the other and each has its value in making clear things which are implicit but inconspicuous.

Growth may be additive or multiplicative. Additive growth is mainly confined to structures such as bone, teeth, scales, otoliths, etc., and above all to the shells of mollusks and Foraminifera. Multiplicative growth is more characteristic of the growing organism and differs in that the increment is itself alive and growing, so that the growth rate is not a fixed increment per unit of time but a percentage of the preceding size per unit of time, and is thus exponential.

A typical growth curve representing the complete period of growth of an organism is generally concave to start with, changing through a relatively straight and steeply ascending phase into an increasing convexity, until it levels off as a straight horizontal line. The so-called point of inflection is where the concavity changes to convexity, and it represents the period at which the absolute growth rate, or increment per unit time, is greatest. At this time the curve for the absolute growth rate normally curves downwards again, rapidly at first but more and more slowly until maximum size and zero rate are reached (cf. Fig. 214b).

A great deal of attention has been given to the significance of the point of inflection— by Brody ('45) for example—but the S-shaped curve is characteristic of many things, equally of the growth of organisms, organs, and populations. Growth of each has its beginning and draws to its natural end, and to quote D'Arcy Thompson, "the motion of a body in a resistant medium . . . for so beginning and so ending the curve must pass through a point of inflection, and it *must be* an S-shaped curve."

The curve of growth, being essentially a generalization, tells nothing about the nature of growth beyond the facts that it has a beginning and an end, attains a certain maximal velocity and has a certain duration. Its value lies primarily in its ability to indicate the presence and operation of restricting factors, cycles of growth, temperature and nutritional influences, etc. It does not express the essence of growth itself nor the nature of the decrement in growth rate. The growth curve indicates that a decrement exists from the beginning and that the duration of growth is determined by the magnitude of the early maximal relative growth rate and the magnitude of the decrement. Accordingly, the size finally attained by any growing unit is a resultant of the quantity of material initially present, the maximum relative growth rate (which is at or close to the initiation of growth and not at a time corresponding to the point of inflection), and the decrement.

Algebraic equations may be made to express the curve of growth, facilitating its analysis and yielding information by mathematical rule of thumb, though there is no such thing as a universal growth equation (Medawar, '45). D'Arcy Thompson worked with the curve of growth and its derivatives,

the curve of growth rate and the curve of acceleration, but the curve of specific growth is generally more amenable to analysis (cf. Fig. 214e, after Medawar), where the logarithm of size (in place of size itself) is plotted against time. The curve of specific growth indicates a progressive decline in the energies of growth, that is, specific acceleration is always negative under actual conditions of development, in contrast to tissue cultures or yeast populations growing in a constant environment (Richards, '28). This is Minot's law, and it follows that the specific growth rate declines more and more slowly as the organism increases in age, or as Minot put it, organisms age fastest when young.

An attempt at an experimental measure of the rate at which the specific growth-rate declines has been made by Medawar ('40). In a later review ('45) on size, shape, and age he concludes, "only one fundamental generalization can be made about the relationship between the size of an organism and its age: that which is represented by the equation

$$\frac{d \log W}{dt} = K.f(t),$$

where $K.f(t)$ is a positive quantity such that $f(t)$ decreases with t, and $df(t)/dt$ increases with t towards a zero bound."

A more biological analysis of growth has been made by Sinnott ('45 and earlier) on cucurbit fruits, with respect to the relation of cell division and cell enlargement to growth rate. During the first part of the growth period, substance (whether measured by wet or dry weight) increases at a constant exponential rate regardless of what the constituent cells are doing. When cell division ceases and rapid vacuolation begins there is no change in this rate. He concludes that the organ rather than its constituent cells is the dominant entity, but that the mechanisms controlling size and form are not known.

In certain slime moulds (Raper, '41; Bonner, '44) the developmental cycle is divided into vegetative (or growth), aggregation, migration, and culmination stages. The last of these corresponds to the late differentiation phase, for example, of the cucurbit fruits in which cell multiplication and differentiation are also separate in time, although it is more purely a morphogenetic movement resulting in change in shape. Bonner and Eldredge ('45) conclude that the motivating force is an internal and not a surface force, and that smaller masses rise up comparatively slowly because cohesive forces are greater in proportion to the internal morphogenetic force, in accordance with the principle of similitude (cf. Thompson, '41).

RELATIVE GROWTH

Studies in relative growth or allometry are essentially studies of changing shape with increase in size, generally in the simplest

growth lies in D'Arcy Thompson's illuminating employment of Cartesian transformations for comparing the shapes of related forms, for these implied the existence of a general gradient-pattern in growth.

The effort to find the simplest relation between two growing dimensions has led generally to the use of a power equation of

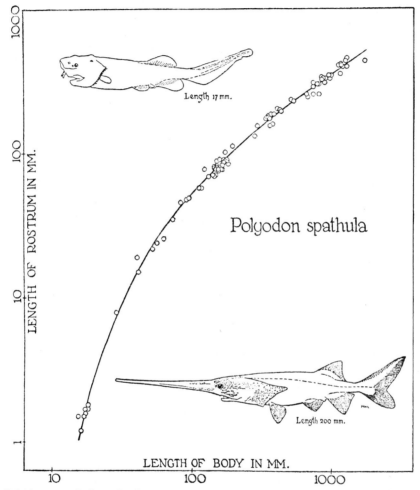

Fig. 215. Relative growth in Polyodon (from D. H. Thompson, '34). Logarithmic plot of rostrum—length/body—length.

form, that is, as exhibited between two varying measurable dimensions, usually linear. The literature is extensive and has become progressively mathematical in a numerical sense. It has also acquired a formidable terminology, and both features have done much to obscure the issues. The terminology is discussed at some length by Needham ('42), Reeve and Huxley ('45), and Richards and Kavanagh ('45).

The inspiration for the work on relative

the form $y=bx^k$ or, in a linear form, log $y=k$ log x + log b (Huxley, '24, '27). The exponent k is the ratio of two specific growth rates and its values are obtained, in a sense, by cancelling out time, so that k becomes a correlation or partition coefficient. The value of b depends on the measuring scales employed and it possesses no unique biological significance. k is a pure number and is not constant, but may be so when specific growth rates change in such a manner as not to affect their ratio. What is important is to know how nearly constant k is, and to what the constancy is due. The value of the allometry equation depends upon this.

allometric organ may shrink to relative insignificance. If $k = 1$, an organ exhibits isometry and grows at the same rate as the body. As a typical example, Huxley ('27)

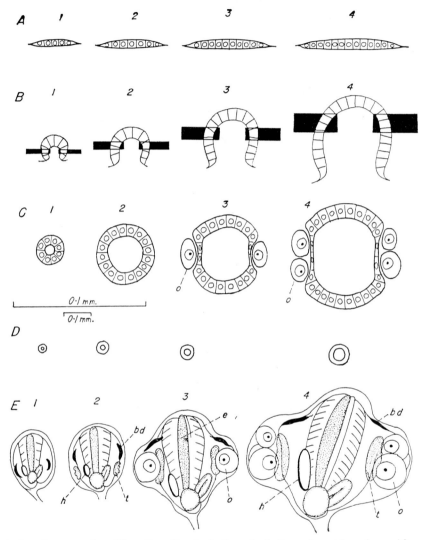

Fig. 216. Development of ascidian Botryllus buds from bud discs of varying size, with reference to final size and extent of gonad development (from Berrill, '41).

A, Discs of maximum sizes *1—4*; B, closing spheres developing from discs *1—4*, with extent of presumptive gonad area indicated in each case by black-out; C, continuation of same series *1—4*, showing failure of ova to segregate in *1* and *2*, single and double segregation in *3* and *4*; D, sphere stage *1—4* reduced to one-fifth previous scale; E, continuation of series *1—4* on reduced scale as far as bud-disc, gill-slit perforation stage, showing the development of the gonads in the four sizes; *bd*, bud disc; *e*, endostyle; *h*, heart; *o*, ovum; *t*, testis.

If k is greater than 1, the organ or dimension grows faster than the body or control dimension; if k is less than 1, it grows more slowly. Given a suitable maximum body-size a positively allometric organ may grow relatively vast, while a negatively

weighed the large chela and claw of 401 male fiddler crabs. He found $y = 0.0073x^{1.62}$ up to a total weight of 1.2 gm. (at which sexual maturity is reached) and $y = 0.083x^{1.255}$ thereafter.

Lumer ('37) discusses the relation between the power equation and the assumption of the sigmoid nature of the growth curves of both x and y, in connection with the autocatalytic and the Gompertz function. He concludes that when the growth of the parts is determinate, the concept of a constant growth-partition coefficient is not valid over the entire growth period. Richards and Kavanagh ('45), on the other hand, believe they may both be sigmoid without invalidating the formula.

There is general agreement that the formula is purely empirical, and various efforts have been made to find some significance for it in simple postulates about growth or in the time laws of growth, but without success. It does make possible a quantitative study of growth gradients by comparing the successive growth ratios of a series of organs, but does not lead to any conclusion concerning the physiological basis of the gradients themselves.

Inasmuch as the primary purpose of the mathematical analysis of biological data is to suggest or develop the significance of the data, the persisting enigma of the relative growth formula indicates possibly an overexpenditure of unrewarded effort, and attempts to understand growth phenomena in other ways may be more successful. Different approaches, more closely bound to the nature of the events, are employed by Medawar ('45), who develops the method of transformations of D'Arcy Thompson by introducing the concepts of time and gradients, utilizing tissue cultures as experimental material, and by Weisz ('46, '47), who has analyzed the growing and changing form of the brine shrimp Artemia in a mathematical manner remote from the standard allometry technique. More recently Bertalanffy ('51) has developed a concept of growth as a counteraction of anabolism and catabolism of building materials, according to the following basic expression:

$$\frac{dy}{dt} = \eta y^m - k y^n$$

The change of body weight y is given by the difference between the processes of building up and breaking down: η and k are constants of anabolism and catabolism, respectively, while the exponents m and n indicate that the latter are proportional to some powers of body weight y.

REGENERATION LIMITS

If an organ or part capable of regeneration is removed, the regenerating organ grows more rapidly than normal, eventually approaching normal size. The allometry equation therefore does not express the growth rate of an organ but only the limit of its relative size. The regenerating part itself grows in the same manner as a whole organism, exhibiting the typical growth curve. In most cases the part regenerated attains its normal size relative to the size of the whole, after which further growth is in unison with the whole.

In some cases a blastema is formed that appears to develop as a unit without evidence of growth gradients, in flatworms and in ascidian buds such as those of Botryllus, etc. (Berrill, '41), and determination of final size is the same as before, a product of initial size, maximum growth rate, and the growth decrement. In others, the growth of the blastema is polarized, at once more complex and yet possibly more susceptible to investigation. In limb regeneration in Amphibia, Litwiller ('39) found a peak of mitotic activity in mesenchyme and epithelium near the base of the young regenerate, but the peak shifts distally in older regenerates as basal regions progressively differentiate.

Similar but more striking phenomena are exhibited by annelids. In the case of both anterior and posterior regeneration a zone of growth maintains a maximum growth rate at its posterior border, while tissue produced by it progressively differentiates anteriorly. Thus in anterior regeneration the oldest tissue is the most anterior and the youngest is in contact with the original anterior cut surface, while in posterior regeneration the oldest tissue is also anterior but is accordingly in contact with the original posterior cut surface. In these cases the quantity of tissue is most readily estimated by number of segments. In many forms the number of segments replaced is approximately, even exactly, the number removed—both anteriorly and posteriorly in syllidean polychaetes (Allen, '21) and posteriorly in earthworms (Moment, '46)—while in others it may be less but is never significantly more. Moment states that the number of segments regenerated posteriorly is a linear function of the distance (as measured by segments and not millimeters) of the cut from the anterior end of the worm. Formation of new segments stops when approximately the species number of segments has been formed, regardless of the size of the segments. He suggests that both in normal growth and in regeneration new cells are added in series until a critical inhibitory voltage is thereby built up, thus stopping proliferation at the growing end. Liebmann ('45), however, attempts to correlate variability in oligochaete regeneration with the state of the chloragogue system.

The problem of size is emphasized even more in the compensatory regeneration in serpulid polychaetes and in certain decapod crustaceans. In serpulids there is a pair of opercula, one of which is large and serves as a tube-stopper, the other being small and rudimentary. If the large operculum is removed, the small one grows to replace it, the stump of the large one regenerating merely a new rudiment (Zeleny, '02, '05). Various experiments show that the functional organ, whichever one it is, holds its mate in check. Okada ('33) found that the growth-inhibitory influence is localized only in the operculum, is not due to a nervous reflex, and is unlikely to be a diffusible chemical substance.

The comparable reversal of large and small claws in crustaceans has been discussed by Zeleny ('05), Przibram ('31), Dawes ('34) and Darby ('35). Dawes attempts to apply the concept of allometry, claiming a higher growth rate on the one side of the animal as compared with the other, bringing about an unequal distribution of substrates for growth and causing one side to develop a snap claw and the other a pinch claw. Darby challenges this interpretation and suggests that a secondary sexual hormone is operating in conjunction with local selectivity.

In neither annelids nor crustaceans has the matter been solved, and it remains the triple problem of arrest of growth, alternative differentiation, and reversal of asymmetry.

Experimental investigations on the control of relative size have been made by Harrison ('29), followed by Twitty and collaborators ('30-'40), employing transplantations of eyes and limbs of Amblystoma, mainly between embryos and larvae of different ages. When such organs are grafted into hosts of the same species but different age from the donor, regulation of size is accomplished by the organ growing slower or faster than the corresponding organ of the host, according to whether the host is the younger or older. The growth rate of a younger eye is accelerated, that of an older one retarded, when grafted to a host of intermediate age.

Twitty suggests that size regulation during development is determined as an equilibrium

between the decreasing specific assimilative capacity of the organ and increasing nutritive conditions in the internal environment. Twitty and Wagtendonk ('40) found evidence of a rise in nutritive level of the blood with age, insofar as it depends upon the amino-acid concentration. They interpret the changes in the eye itself as a general decline in the assimilative capacity of its constitutuent cells. Whether growing cells, and particularly those in progress of successive divisions, undergo aging in this sense seems doubtful. Pomeroy ('41) found that in pigs the eyes and brain continue to grow even under conditions of starvation, so that what may be true for these structures may not hold generally. It appears from these investigations, taken in conjunction with observations of Fankhauser ('45) on the maintenance of normal structure in heteroploid salamanders, that the size and shape of organs and of the whole organism are independent of cell size, and that cell multiplication is subordinated to supra-cellular controls.

A parallel series of experiments involving the transplanting of growing organs to hosts respectively younger and older has been conducted by Bodenstein ('40) with eye and leg discs of Drosophila. His results are similar to those of Twitty—discs transplanted between larvae of the same physiological age grew normally in their heterotropic position, while discs of the same age transplanted simultaneously into younger and older hosts grew better in the older. In any case the growth of the transplant is retarded or accelerated until normal size relationship with the host organ is restored.

A relationship similar to that of the salamander eye and host exists between the lens and eye vesicles of the same animal (Harrison, '29). According to Ballard ('39) the regulatory interaction concerns only the retina and the cells, the mesodermal coats of the eye and cornea having no specific control of eye size.

In general, nutritive level, oxygen tension, etc., however much they may influence the rate of growth and differentiation, have little effect upon the size finally attained. Of greater significance are factors that influence the duration of growth without markedly affecting the developmental rate. This is suggested by experiments of Child ('39) on the effect of time of development on Drosophila wing size. At a constant temperature under pseudo-starvation conditions involving the use of ethyl parahydroxy benzoate, increased wing size was correlated with increase in developmental time, and larvae whose pupation was much delayed developed into small flies with exceptionally large wings. On the other hand, Hersh and Ward ('32) had found the size of the wing to be an exponential function of temperature.

In conclusion, the determination of size of either organisms or their organs remains a problem which is definable but little understood. Fundamentally, size is due to the operation of several factors. The initial size of the growth unit (cf. Berrill, '41), at the moment it ceases to grow at the maximal rate, determines the final size, other things being equal. This is a matter of measurement, but it may be difficult to determine when growth ceases to be maximal. The energy of growth is but vaguely understood but its intensity determines the magnitude of the maximal growth rate. The decrement of growth is widely recognized as basically significant, but its origin remains a mystery. Its value determines the duration of growth. Finally, growth may be polarized and each growth unit, whatever it may actually be, gives rise to a part that continues growth at a maximal rate and a part that exhibits decrement, that is, the establishment of growth and differentiation gradients.

REFERENCES

Allen, E. J. 1921 Regeneration and reproduction of the syllid Procerastea. Phil. Trans. Roy. Soc. London, B, *211:*131–177.

Ballard, W. W. 1939 Mutual size regulation between eyeball and lens, in Amblystoma, studied by means of heteroplastic transplantation. J. Exp. Zool., *81:*261–285.

Baltzer, F. 1940 Über erbliche letale Entwicklung und Austauschbarkeit artverschiedener Kerne bei Bastarden. Naturwiss., *28:*177–187.

Berger, C. A. 1937 Multiplication and reduction of somatic chromosome groups as a regular developmental process in the mosquito, *Culex pipiens.* Contrib. Embryol. Carnegie Inst. Washington, 27:209–232.

Berrill, N. J. 1935 Cell division and differentiation in asexual and sexual differentiation. J. Morph., 57:353–427.

—— 1941 Spatial and temporal growth patterns in colonial organisms. Growth (Suppl.), *5:* 89–111.

Bertalanffy, L. von 1951 Metabolic types and growth types. Am. Nat., *85:*111–117.

Blunn, C. T., and Gregory, P. W. 1935 The embryological basis of size inheritance in the chicken. J. Exp. Zool., *70:*397–414.

Bodenstein, D. 1940 Growth regulation of transplanted eye and leg discs in Drosophila. J. Exp. Zool., *84:*23–37.

Bonner, J. T. 1944 A descriptive study of the development of the slime mold, *Dictyostelium discoideum.* Amer. J. Bot., *31:*175–182.

——, and Eldredge, D. 1945 A note on the rate of morphogenetic movement in the slime mold, *Dictyostelium discoideum.* Growth, 9:287–298.

Brody, S. 1945 Bioenergetics and Growth. Reinhold Publishing Corp., New York.

Burkholder, J. R. 1934 A quantitative study of respiratory metabolism in single developing eggs (Orthoptera). Physiol. Zool., *7:*247–270.

Byerly, T. C. 1930 The effects of breed on the growth of the chick embryo. J. Morph., *50:*341–359.

——, Helsel, W. A., and Quinn, J. P. 1938 Growth in weight and cell number, genetic effects in the chick embryo and chick. J. Exp. Zool., *78:*185–203.

Castle, W. E., and Gregory, P. W. 1929 The embryological basis of size inheritance in the rabbit. J. Morph., *48:*81–104.

Child, G. 1939 The effect of increasing time of development at constant temperature on the wing size of vestigial of *Drosophila melanogaster.* Biol. Bull., *77:*432–442.

Conklin, E. G. 1912 Body size and cell size. J. Morph., *23:*159–188.

Darby, H. 1935 The mechanism of chela differentiation in the crustacea. Publ. No. 452, Carnegie Inst. Washington, pp. 151–170.

Dawes, B. 1934 A study of normal and regenerative growth in the pistol-crab *Alpheus dentipes* Guér.), with special reference to the phenomena of chela reversal. Roux' Arch. Entw.-mech., *131:* 543–574.

Fankhauser, G. 1945 Maintenance of normal structure in heteroploid salamander larvae, through compensation of changes in cell size by adjustment of cell number and cell shape. J. Exp. Zool., *100:*445–455.

Goss, H., and Gregory, P. W. 1935 Glutathione and hereditary size. IV. J. Exp. Zool., *71:*311–316.

Gregory, P. W., Asmundson, V. S., Goss, H., and Landauer, W. 1939 Glutathione values of Cornish lethal and Creeper embryos compared with normal sibs. Growth, *3:*75–84.

——, and Goss, H. 1933 Glutathione concentration and hereditary size. III. J. Exp. Zool., *66:* 335–349.

Harrison, R. G. 1929 Correlation in the development and growth of the eye studied by means of heteroplastic transplantation. Roux' Arch. Entw.-mech., *120:*1–55.

Herbst, C. 1939 Untersuchungen zur Bestimmung des Geschlechts. IX. Der Einfluss des Glycerins auf die Geschlechtsbestimmung bei Bonellia. Roux' Arch. Entw.-mech., *139:*282–302.

Hersh, A. H. 1941 Allometric growth: the ontogenetic and phylogenetic significance of differential rates of growth. Growth (Suppl.), *5:*113–145.

——, and Ward, E. 1932 The effect of temperature on wing size in reciprocal heterozygotes of vestigial in *Drosophila melanogaster.* J. Exp. Zool., *61:*223–244.

Huxley, J. S.   1924   Constant differential growth-ratios and their significance. Nature, *114:*895–896.

——— 1927   The modification of development by means of temperature gradients. Roux' Arch. Entw.-mech., *112:*480–516.

——— 1932   Problems of Relative Growth. Methuen & Co., London.

Kaufman, L.   1930   Innere und äussere Wachstumfaktoren. Untersuchungen an Hühnern und Tauben. Roux' Arch. Entw.-mech., *122:*395–431.

Lerner, I. M., Gregory, W. W., and Goss, H.   1936   Heterogony of the glutathione content of newborn rabbits. Proc. Soc. Exp. Biol. & Med., *35:*283–285.

Liebmann, E.   1945   The correlation between the sexual reproduction and regeneration in a series of oligochaeta. J. Exp. Zool., *91:*373–389.

Litwiller, R.   1939   Mitotic index and size in regenerating amphibian limbs. J. Exp. Zool., *82:*273–286.

Lumer, H.   1937   The consequences of sigmoid growth for relative growth functions. Growth, *1:*140–154.

Medawar, P.   1940   The growth, growth energy, and aging of the chicken's heart. Proc. Roy. Soc. London, B, *129:*332–355.

——— 1945   Size, shape, and age; in Essays on Growth and Form, edited by W. E. Le Gros Clark and P. B. Medawar, pp. 157–187. Oxford University Press, London.

Moment, G.   1946   A study of growth limitation in earthworms. J. Exp. Zool., *103:*487–506.

Needham, J.   1942   Biochemistry and Morphogenesis. The Macmillan Co., London.

Nowinski, W. W.   1934   Die vermännlichende Wirkung fraktionierter Darmextrakte des Weibchens auf die Larven der *Bonellia viridis.* Publ. Staz. Zool. Napoli, *14:*110–145.

Okada, Y. K.   1933   Remarks on the reversible asymmetry in the opercula of the polychaete Hydroides. J. Mar. Biol. Assoc., *18:*655–670.

Painter, T.   1928   Cell size and body size in the rabbit. J. Exp. Zool., *50:*441–453.

Pomeroy, R. W.   1941   The effect of submaintenance diet on the composition of the pig. J. Agric. Soc., *31:*50–67.

Przibram, H.   1931   Connecting Laws in Animal Morphology. London University Press, London.

Raper, K. B.   1941   Developmental patterns in simple slime molds. Growth (Suppl.), *5:*41–76.

Reeve, E. C. R., and Huxley, J. S.   1945   Some problems in the study of allometric growth; in Essays on Growth and Form, edited by W. E. Le

Gros Clark and P. B. Medawar, pp. 121–156. Oxford University Press, London.

Reinhard, E. G.   1942   The reproductive role of the complemental males of Peltogaster. J. Morph., *70:*389–402.

Richards, O. W.   1928   The rate of multiplication of yeast at different temperatures. J. Phys. Chem., *32:*1865–1871.

———, and Kavanagh, A. J.   1945   The analysis of growing form; in Essays on Growth and Form, edited by W. E. Le Gros Clark and P. B. Medawar, pp. 188–230. Oxford University Press, London.

Sinnott, E. W.   1945   The relation of cell division to growth rate in cucurbit fruits. Growth, *9:*189–194.

Smith, B. G.   1912   The embryology of *Cryptobranchus alleghaniensis,* including comparisons with some other vertebrates. II. General embryonic and larval development, with special reference to external features. J. Morph., *23:*455–579.

Thompson, D. H.   1934   Relative growth in Polyodon. Nat. Hist. Survey, Illinois, Biol. Notes, No. 2.

Thompson, D'Arcy W.   1941   On Growth and Form. The Macmillan Co., New York.

Twitty, V. C.   1930   Regulation in the growth of transplanted eyes. J. Exp. Zool., *55:*32–52.

——— 1939   Size regulation and regeneration in salamander larvae under complete starvation. J. Exp. Zool., *81:*399–414.

———, and Wagtendonk, W. J. van   1940   A suggested mechanism for the regulation of proportionate growth, supported by quantitative data on the blood nutrients. Growth, *4:*349–360.

Tyler, A.   1935   On the energetics of differentiation. Biol. Bull., *68:*451–460.

Van Cleave, H. J.   1932   Eutely or cell constancy in its relation to body size. Quart. Rev. Biol., *7:*59–67.

Weisz, P.   1946   The space-time pattern of segment formation in *Artemia salina.* Biol. Bull., *91:*119–140.

——— 1947   The histological pattern of metameric development in artemia Salina. J. Morph. *81:*45–95.

Whitaker, D. M.   1933   On the rate of oxygen consumption by fertilized and unfertilized eggs, V. J. Gen. Physiol., *16:*497–528.

Zeleny, C.   1902   A case of compensatory regulation in the regeneration of *Hydroides dianthus.* Roux' Arch. Entw.-mech., *13:*597–609.

——— 1905   Compensatory regulation. J. Exp. Zool., *2:*1–102.

Section XII

METAMORPHOSIS

WILLIAM ETKIN

POSTEMBRYONIC development in higher animals generally involves extensive changes in form. However, the term "metamorphosis" is not used for such changes unless their occurrence is concentrated in a relatively short period and involves a striking alteration in form. Even then, if the changes are related to sexual development we speak of sexual maturation or puberty rather than of metamorphosis. From a descriptive standpoint, therefore, metamorphosis may be defined as a definitely delimited period in postembryonic development during which marked developmental changes in non-reproductive structures occur. Of course, intergrades between metamorphosis and gradual development occur. Metamorphosis is widespread in the animal kingdom. However, the treatment in this section will be limited to the amphibians and insects, two groups in which experimental analysis has been carried furthest.

The adaptive value of metamorphosis lies in the specialization of the larval form to one mode of life and of the adult to another (Figs. 217 and 220). Metamorphosis effects the transition from one type of specialized body form to the other. For the experimenter it is important to recognize that the evolutionary process producing divergent specialization between larva and adult has occurred repeatedly and independently in different animal groups. There is therefore no *a priori* reason for expecting homology between the mechanisms in the different groups. On the other hand, the numerous independent mechanisms controlling metamorphosis which have been developed in the various animal groups may be expected to display analogous characteristics. In this section we shall examine the different mechanisms regulating metamorphosis with the view of discovering the similarities between them in regard to the nature of the controlling stimulus, the role of specificity of tissue response, the role

of induction, and the role of quantitative variations and other physiological factors.

ENDOCRINE CONTROL OF AMPHIBIAN METAMORPHOSIS

The metamorphosis of the amphibian has been the subject of a large number of investigations. Many of these, however, do not fall within the scope of this discussion since in them metamorphosis has been used merely as an indicator of hormonal activity in an investigation whose primary aim has been the study of the chemistry and pharmacology of various glands. We shall confine our attention to researches which throw some light on the mechanism by which metamorphosis is governed in the normal animal. A number of reviews of the literature from various aspects are available (Allen, '29a; Schulze, '30; Gudernatsch, '33; Allen, '38; Needham, '42).

ROLE OF THE THYROID

The first evidence indicating that amphibian metamorphosis is dependent upon thyroid hormone came from the feeding experiments of Gudernatsch ('12). By feeding dried preparations of various vertebrate glands to tadpoles he found that only the thyroid, of the many substances used, precipitates within a few days a precocious metamorphosis. These observations have been confirmed and extended by numerous workers who have used whole thyroid of various sources on urodele and anuran amphibians (Allen, '29a, '38).

Extracts of the thyroid gland are also effective and may be administered by injection or merely by keeping the animals in solutions of the material. Although considerable information is available on the chemistry and pharmacology of thyroid preparations, it is sufficient here to note that a very active protein fraction, thyroglobulin, can be extracted

631

from the thyroid. This can be fractionated to yield two active iodized derivatives of tyrosine, namely di-iodo-tyrosine and thyroxine. The latter, being far more active than the former in respect to thyroid-like proper-

but fail to show any metamorphic changes even if kept for many times the normal larval period and until they exceed by far the maximum size for control larvae (Allen, '18; Hoskins and Hoskins, '19a). These re-

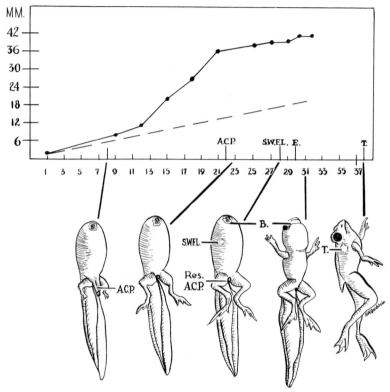

Fig. 217. The pattern of metamorphosis in the frog, *Rana pipiens*. The graph shows the growth of the hind legs (solid line) compared to that of the body (broken line). The scale on the ordinate is for hindleg length; the abscissa scale is given in days, counting the day of emergence of the forelegs as day 30. Metamorphic changes shown in sketches of tadpoles occur at times indicated. Metamorphosis begins with differential acceleration of hind leg growth. When the legs are about half grown the tissue in which the anal canal lies (anal canal piece, *A.C.P.*) begins to be absorbed and completely disappears in two or three days. About this time an area of disintegration in the skin above the gills begins to develop, becoming clearly defined in a few days (skin window for the forelegs, *S.W.F.L.*). When the forelegs emerge the stage of early metamorphosis (prometamorphosis) goes over into metamorphic climax when rapid morphological changes take place. The animal ceases to feed, the horny teeth and beaks (*B*) and the associated fleshy mouth parts are lost and the mouth widens in a few days to that characteristic of the frog. Tail resorption and eye growth proceed rapidly at this time. The last morphological alteration is that of the formation of the tympanum (*T*). (After Etkin, '32; Taylor and Kollros, '46.)

ties on all test animals, is often discussed as though it were "the hormone" of the gland (Means, '48).

In the absence of the thyroid gland, metamorphosis fails to occur. Extirpation of this gland in the frog embryo was first accomplished by Allen ('16) and by Hoskins and Hoskins ('17), who devised a simple technique whereby the primordium of the thyroid is removed at the tail-bud stage (Fig. 218). The operated animals grow normally

sults have been confirmed and extended to other species of Anura by many workers (Allen, '38). So far as is known to the writer no reports on the effects on metamorphosis of removal of the thyroid primordium in urodeles are available; in larvae, however, total thyroidectomy suppresses metamorphosis (Schwartzbach and Uhlenhuth, '28).

The failure of metamorphosis after removal of the primordium of the thyroid gland in the anuran embryo is completely compensated for by reimplantation of the gland at another site. The animals then metamorphose at the same time as the controls (Allen, '29b; Etkin, '39). Such transplanted glands, since they are transplanted as undifferentiated rudiments, must exert their effects by virtue of their functional development rather than by release of any stored hormone they may contain. Thyroids from tadpoles in late metamorphosis induce precocious metamorphosis, whereas the glands of premetamorphic animals are not effective in this way (Swingle, '23; Slowikowska, '23). Presumably these results are produced by the release of stored hormone from the larger glands and are therefore comparable to the results of injection of hormone rather than to transplantation of primordia.

To complete the evidence on the relation of thyroid hormone to metamorphosis it would be desirable to know what the level of thyroid hormone in the blood is during the normal metamorphosis. Unfortunately evidence on this point is meager. Blood plasma from metamorphosing axolotls and tadpoles has been reported to induce metamorphosis in premetamorphic animals (Balthasart, '31), but the data here are not adequate. In the experience of the present author, the feeding or injection of small quantities of blood or tissues from tadpoles in metamorphosis failed to induce metamorphosis in recipient tadpoles.

The lack of evidence on the level of thyroid hormone in the blood of amphibians in relation to metamorphosis is compensated for to some extent by histological studies which show clearly that the secretory activity of the gland correlates closely with the rate of metamorphic change. In the thyroid gland the correlation between the cytological and histological picture and the functional activity of the gland is exceptionally clear. A high level of activity is indicated by columnar epithelium, mild basophilia, vacuolization and loss (release) of the colloid. The criteria of activity have been studied in particular detail by Uhlenhuth ('27) in living and fixed thyroids of salamanders. (For the general literature on microscopic anatomy of the thyroid in relation to function see Means, '48.)

Microscopic studies reveal a histological picture indicating that the thyroid is markedly more active at the time of metamorphosis than before. In urodeles colloid release is a most prominent feature (Uhlenhuth, '27); in anurans increased height of the epithelium is more conspicuous (Etkin, '30). Quantitative studies by Etkin ('36a) and Mazzeschi ('40) show that at the beginning of anuran metamorphosis the thyroid is stimulated to grow much more rapidly than the body as a whole. The cytological picture likewise indicates increasing activity beginning at this time, reaching a maximum at the climax of metamorphosis and quickly dropping back thereafter. These studies suggest that the thyroid releases large quantities of hormone at the time of metamorphosis and is relatively inactive before and after.

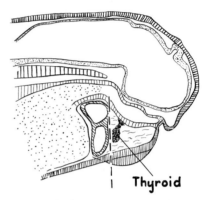

Fig. 218. Sagittal section of frog embryo at late tail-bud stage. The thyroid primordium is removed through slit made along broken line. (After Allen, '18.)

Another source of evidence pointing to the dependence of metamorphosis upon the thyroid hormone is afforded by the action of thiouracil and related compounds. These inhibit the release of thyroid hormone from the gland. When administered to tadpoles they have been found to inhibit metamorphosis (Gordon, Goldsmith and Charipper, '43; Lynn, '48).

Less direct but confirmatory evidence of the essential role of the thyroid in amphibian metamorphosis comes from the study of amphibians with exceptional life histories. In the Jamaican tree toad, *Eleutherodactylus nubicola*, no free-living aquatic larva develops but metamorphosis occurs precociously within the egg membranes. The thyroids likewise show histological evidence of precocious activation correlating well with metamorphosis (Lynn, '36). In a similarly precocious African toad, *Arthroleptella bicolor villiersi*, metamorphosis is closely paralleled by thyroid activation (Brinck, '39).

In permanently neotenous species of amphibians, as will be seen later, the failure to metamorphose is due to lack of tissue sensitivity rather than to failure of glandular activity. But occasional cases of neoteny in species normally metamorphosing have been correlated with pathological thyroid deficiencies (Bolten, '26). In the axolotl, a neotenous form of Amblystoma, Uhlenhuth ('27) found a gland whose structure indicates that the hormone is produced and stored but not released to the circulation.

It can thus be seen that the relation of thyroid to metamorphosis has been approached from many different aspects with concordant results. The evidence shows clearly that the thyroid produces a hormone which serves as the stimulus precipitating metamorphosis.

The thyroid is unique in its relationship to metamorphosis. Many organs, particularly endocrine glands, have been studied in relation to metamorphosis but none, with the exception of the anterior lobe of the hypophysis which will be discussed below, has been found to play any but a subsidiary role. In the initial experiments by which Gudernatsch opened this field of enquiry (Gudernatsch, '12) the results of feeding with thymus, adrenal, testis, ovary, spleen, liver, pancreas and muscle were reported. None of these accelerated metamorphosis. The thymus diet seemed to delay this process, presumably because of its low iodine content (see below). These results on the general ineffectiveness of other organs were confirmed in regard to feeding by Abderhalden ('15) and Hegner ('22). Injection and implantation techniques with non-thyroid substances have likewise yielded negative results. Ovarian and testis implants are without effect (Tutajew and Philippawa, '31), as are insulin (Abderhalden, '24) and adrenal implants when administered by themselves (Woitkewitsch, '37). The pars intermedia and pars nervosa of the hypophysis are likewise without effects on metamorphosis when administered as implants (Swingle, '21; Blount, '32; Etkin, '38). Salamandra has been found to be capable of metamorphosis when deprived of spinal cord and spinal ganglia (Wintrebert, '06).

In an often quoted work, Gutman ('26) claimed to have metamorphosed young specimens of the permanently neotenous urodele, *Necturus maculosus*, by means of injections of both thyroxine and adrenaline. This has not been confirmed. Many observers, on the contrary, have noted that various tissues of larval amphibians may show considerable reduction in volume under unfavorable environmental conditions and yet recover completely on return to normal (Hoskins and Hoskins, '19a; Noble, '24). Gutman's conclusion cannot be accepted, therefore, as being a specific thyroid effect until confirmed by fully controlled experiments. Attempts by the writer to repeat Gutman's experiment failed because the gills of the controls as well as the experimentals showed considerable reduction under the laboratory conditions.

An extensive literature exists on the relation of iodine to the thyroid hormone. Since such work is concerned primarily with the biochemical nature of thyroid secretions, details need not be considered here (Allen, '38; Means, '48). Consideration of certain aspects of the relation of thyroid activity to iodine, however, is essential to an understanding of the relation of thyroid to metamorphosis.

The thyroid hormone contains iodine and therefore cannot be synthesized by the animal body in the absence of this element from the diet. Nearly all iodine that enters the body is normally quickly concentrated in the thyroid. Amphibia raised under iodine-free conditions fail to metamorphose (Uhlenhuth, '19; Lynn and Brambel, '35). Contrariwise, the injection or implantation of iodine can induce metamorphosis of amphibians even in the absence of the thyroid gland (Swingle, '19; Ingram, '29b). We must therefore suppose that, though iodine is normally metabolized through the thyroid gland, the iodization of amino acids or proteins can also take place elsewhere in the body and can lead to the production of effective metamorphic stimulants. This interpretation is made plausible by the fact that proteins can readily be iodized by chemical methods in vitro to yield thyro-active substances (Lerman and Salter, '39).

Figge ('30, '34) found that ligation of the pulmonary aortic arch in Amblystoma larvae inhibits the subsequent metamorphosis of these animals and decreases the effectiveness of thyroid substance on them. This result was attributed by him to the decrease in oxygenation of the blood through the elimination of the pulmonary circulation. He ascribed an important role in the evolution of the metamorphic mechanism to changes in pulmonary circulation. However, Garber ('30), working with Amblystoma, and Helff ('31b) on Rana found that larvae deprived of their lungs metamorphose normally and respond in the usual way to thyroid stimulation. McMullen ('38) made a comparative study of the aortic arches of various urodeles and found no correlation such as Figge postulated between the absence of the pulmonary arch and neoteny. The results may possibly be explained by secondary effects which influence tissue sensitivity.

It may be concluded on the basis of the evidence summarized in this section that the thyroid through its hormone is the primary determinant of metamorphic transformation in amphibians. Except for the hypophysis, which acts through the thyroid as discussed below, no other organ is known to exert significant control over the process. The evidence implies, though it does not definitely prove, that the thyroid hormone acts directly without the mediation of other organs in the initiation of metamorphosis.

ROLE OF HYPOPHYSIS

Hypophysectomy in amphibians prevents metamorphosis. This was first found by Adler ('14), who hypophysectomized tadpoles by cautery. He secured a few survivors of this drastic operation and these showed, among other effects, a failure of metamorphosis. However, the relation of the hypophysis to metamorphosis was not satisfactorily clarified until Allen ('16) and Smith ('16) independently developed the technique of removing the primordium of the pituitary from the frog embryo (Fig. 219). These investigators found that such hypophysectomized tadpoles remain in the larval condition indefinitely. Their rate of growth is retarded but this does not account for the absence of metamorphosis, since the animals may eventually attain or even exceed full size. The development of the hypophysectomized tadpole parallels that of thyroidectomized animals. The hind legs in the two types, for example, develop to the same degree (Allen, '17). These findings have been extensively confirmed (see, for example, Blount, '35; Etkin, '38).

The explanation of the manner of action of the anterior pituitary was soon made apparent by studies of Smith (see summary in Smith, '20) and Allen ('32a). They showed that, in the absence of the anterior pituitary, the thyroid remains very small and poorly developed. It never undergoes the great spurt of growth nor does it give the histological evidence of activation that characterizes the metamorphic period in the normal animal. It is therefore apparent that the anterior pituitary is necessary for the activation of the thyroid and that its influence on metamorphosis is to be accounted for by its control of the thyroid rather than by a direct effect on the tissues.

This control of the thyroid by the anterior pituitary is effected by a thyrotrophic hormone produced in the anterior lobe of the gland. This was demonstrated by experiments with implants, extracts and transplants of the hypophysis in the major groups of vertebrates. Only the evidence relating to the activation of the thyroid in metamorphosis will be considered here.

Transplanted anterior lobes from adult amphibians are effective in inducing metamorphosis in normal and hypophysectomized but not in thyroidectomized larvae. The

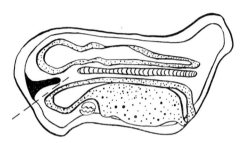

Fig. 219. Sagittal section of frog embryo at early tail-bud stage. Hypophyseal primordium shown in black is removable through slit made along broken line. (After Allen, '29a.)

thyroids of normal and hypophysectomized host animals receiving such implants show clear histological evidence of activation (Allen, '27; Grant, '31). Allen ('31) also found that pituitaries from tadpoles in metamorphosis were effective but those from pre-metamorphic animals were not. Evidence of the development of thyrotrophic function in hypophyses transplanted as rudiments in embryonic stages was found in tadpoles (Atwell, '37; Etkin, '35b) and in Amblystoma (Blount, '35; Atwell and Taft, '40). Etkin ('38) obtained cases in which such transplanted primordia attained full functional activity in hypophysectomized host tadpoles.

Although the first studies with tissue extracts gave conflicting results (see Allen, '38), today it is clear that thyrotrophic preparations derived from the pituitary of various animals are effective in amphibian metamorphosis but only in the presence of the thyroid, which becomes activated by such extracts (Figge and Uhlenhuth, '33; Krichesky, '34; Atwell, '35). Comparative assays of the anterior pituitary of various animals showed the pituitary of the frog to be especially rich in thyrotrophins (Gorb-

man, '46). With regard to the pituitary hormones, no evidence to show a change in
thyrotrophin level in the blood in relation
to metamorphosis is known to the writer.

In the case of the thyroid the lack of
evidence on the level of hormone in the
blood was compensated for to some extent
by extensive and clear-cut cytological evi-

dence showing that the thyroid is activated
at the time of metamorphosis. Unfortunately,
the histological and cytological study of the
pituitary in relation to metamorphosis does
not present unequivocal evidence of any
change in activity at this period (Clements,
'32; Schliefer, '35). In fact, the considerable
variation in the degree of cytological differ-

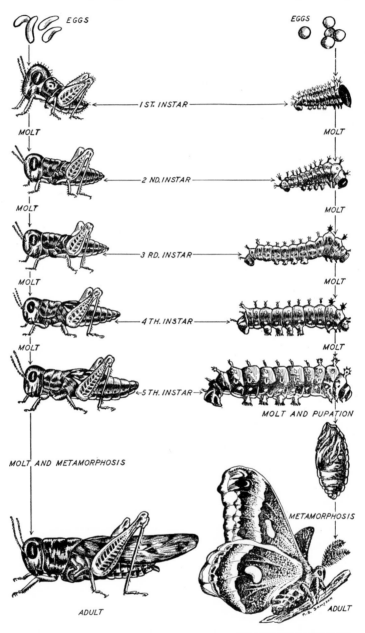

HEMIMETABOLOUS DEVELOPMENT   HOLOMETABOLOUS DEVELOPMENT

Fig. 220. The life history of a hemimetabolous insect, the grasshopper *Melanoplus differentialis*, is
shown at the left. Holometabolous development in the giant silkworm moth, *Platysamia cecropia*, is shown
at the right. (From C. D. Turner, *General Endocrinology*.)

entiation among different species of anurans as reported by these workers suggests that little confidence can be placed in the cytological correlations that have been adduced in specific instances. Unpublished studies by the writer of the growth and histology of the anterior pituitary during the development of the tadpole in *R. pipiens* likewise failed to reveal any change in growth rate or histological picture indicative of a marked change in activity related to metamorphosis.

It may be concluded that, although the activation of the thyroid at the beginning of metamorphosis is clearly dependent upon a thyrotrophic hormone from the pituitary, it cannot be stated whether the initiation of thyroid activity results from an increase in thyrotrophic hormone production or from other factors.

CONTROLLING FACTORS IN INSECT METAMORPHOSIS

The metamorphosis of hemimetabolous insects is commonly described as taking place in stepwise fashion, a small step with each larval* molt. In holometabolous forms, on the other hand, transformation from larva to adult is said to take place in one stage, the pupal stage, at the end of larval development (Fig. 220). However, it must be realized that in all insects there is a process of remodelling taking place at all stages. In hemimetabolous insects noticeable progress toward the adult condition is made with each molt. Nevertheless the last molt, sometimes called the metamorphic molt, usually presents a considerably greater amount of change than any of the earlier ones. In that respect this last molt is similar to the pupal stage of holometabola. Also, although the holometabolous animal does not seem to change toward the adult condition in any obvious way during larval molts, yet the imaginal discs may undergo considerable microscopic change. It is to be expected, therefore, that the basic mechanisms of metamorphosis would be similar in both types of insects.

The earlier experimental work on insect metamorphosis gave only small promise of showing a common basic pattern throughout insects, since many contradictory conclusions were drawn from work on different species.

* The term "larva" will be here used for the young of hemimetabolous insects (nymphs) as well as for those of holometabola in order to emphasize the equivalence, as revealed by experimental analysis, of the early instars in both types of insects.

However, in recent years largely through the comprehensive analyses of Wigglesworth on the bug Rhodnius (Hemiptera, hemimetabola) and Williams on the silkworm Platysamia (Lepidoptera, holometabola) a clarification and simplification of our understanding of the metamorphic process in insects has taken place. It might be best for the sake of clarity to present in outline the interpretation of these experiments and then to proceed to consider the extent to which the work on other forms can be fitted into

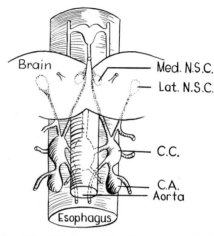

Fig. 221. Relations of head endocrine glands in an insect, generalized type. The brain contains two groups of neurosecretory cells on each side (*Med. N.S.C.* and *Lat. N.S.C.*). These are connected by nerves to the corpora cardiaca (*C.C.*) and corpora allata (*C.A.*). (After Cazal, '48.)

the pattern seen in Rhodnius and Platysamia.

Before doing so, however, it may be well to describe briefly the basic morphology of the organs with which we shall be concerned. Each side of the brain of the insect commonly possesses two groups of large neurons, a medial and a lateral group (Fig. 221). These neurons contain stainable droplets which appear to be secretions. Presumably these secretions are released as hormones, either directly into the blood stream or first being conducted down the axons as in other neurosecretory cells (Cazal, '48; Scharrer, '52a; Thomsen, '52).

Lying more posteriorly in the head, on either side of the anterior end of the aorta, are two pairs of glands. The more anterior pair of these are the corpora cardiaca (C. C.) and behind them the corpora allata (C.A.) (Fig. 221). These are joined to the brain and to each other by nerves. In some insects the C.A. of the two sides are fused to form an unpaired median gland. In the thorax of the insect strands of large cells are found. These are commonly designated as "prothoracic glands."

In the larval and early adult dipteran the arrangement of some of these structures is different (Fig. 222). The cells equivalent

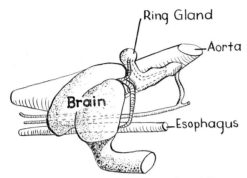

Fig. 222. Head endocrine glands in a larval dipteran, *Eristalis tenax* (after Cazal, '48).

to the C.A. are located dorsal to the aorta, those corresponding to the C.C. are ventral and joined to the C.A. region by lateral lobes presumably equivalent to the prothoracic glands (Possompès, '50a). The entire complex forms the so-called ring gland of Weismann.

RHODNIUS

Rhodnius is a blood-sucking bug which molts at a definite interval (varying from 15 to 28 days depending on the stage) after a single meal of blood. Wigglesworth ('34-'51) in a series of investigations found evidence that the molt is brought on by a hormonal stimulus from the brain. For example, he found that decapitation before a certain stage (the critical period) after the meal prevents the subsequent molt, but decapitation later does not. Brains from post–critical-period animals induce molt in non-activated abdomens. When active animals or parts thereof are joined in parabiosis to non-activated tissues the stimulus to molting is transmitted to the latter, even when the parts are joined by capillary tubing (Fig. 223). By transplantation the active region of the brain was found to be the part of the protocerebrum containing the large neurosecretory cells.

The brain hormone in Rhodnius, acting alone, induces a molt in which larval organs undergo complete transformation to the adult

condition. However, when the corpora allata are active they change the effect of the brain hormone, with the result that the larval tissues lay down structures appropriate for the next nymphal stage, not for the adult condition. During all larval instars except the last in the normal development of the animal both brain and C.A. are active. The molt which ensues is therefore a larval molt from which the animal emerges as the next larval instar. At the last larval stage the C.A. fails to be active in secreting its hormone. Therefore under the unmodified influence of the brain hormone the larval structures undergo complete transformation to the adult condition.

The evidence upon which this interpretation of C.A. function is based is varied and complex. Much of it derives from the remarkable way in which whole insects or body regions from different insects can be joined together in parabiosis (Fig. 223). By joining insect parts, activated and inactivated, with and without brain and corpora allata, the effectiveness of the stimulus in each such part can be tested. In addition to this technique, the brain and corpora allata can be dissected out of larvae and adults and implanted into larvae of various stages. Also, by cutting the head immediately behind the brain, preparations can be secured which have C.A. intact but no brain. The evidence derived from these varied procedures shows that an insect body-part molting under the influence of fifth (last) instar body fluids assumes the adult condition irrespective of its original instar level. Implanted C.A. from younger instars than the fifth change the molt so that nymphal structures are produced. Conversely, fifth instar animals metamorphosing under the influence of stimuli derived parabiotically from earlier instars do not form adults but instead form giant sixth instar nymphs. Curiously, even adults which, of course, do not normally molt at all, can be made to molt when in parabiosis with active nymphal instars. When the metamorphic stimulus comes from an early instar the molt may lead to at least partial reversion to nymphal characters. Wigglesworth ('48) found that the fifth instar larva was more, rather than less, effective in inducing complete transformation in its parabiont when its C.A. was intact than when it was removed. This rather unexpected result was interpreted as showing that not only does the C.A. not secrete any of its hormone in the fifth instar, but it absorbs or otherwise counteracts any such hormone persisting in the tissues from previous stages.

Recently Wigglesworth ('51), following the lead of Williams and other workers on lepidopterans (see below), found that the brain hormone does not act directly upon the tissues but rather activates the prothoracic glands to the production of their hormone. His evidence consists of the fact that transplantation of the strands of gland cells

the diapause when implanted into a non-activated pupa (Fig. 224). Removal or implantation of the corpus allatum, on the other hand, has no effect, showing that activity of this gland plays no role in the adult transformation. That the brain hormone acts by stimulating the prothoracic glands and not directly on the tissues was shown (Williams, '47) by the fact that implantation of an

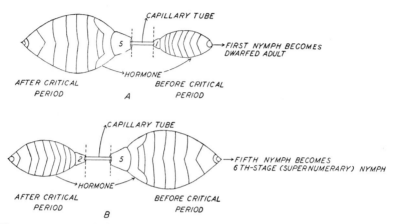

Fig. 223. The union of nymphal instars of Rhodnius by capillary tubes.

A, Fifth nymph, decapitated after the critical period and thus with active glands, is coupled with a first nymph, decapitated before the critical period. Both individuals undergo imaginal molts, the first nymph becoming a diminutive adult. The fifth nymph of Rhodnius, serving as the donor in this instance, furnishes prothoracic hormone with little or no C.A. hormone.

B, Second-stage nymph, decapitated after the critical period, is combined with a fifth nymph that had been decapitated before the critical period. The second nymph, acting as the donor, delivers both C.A. and prothoracic hormones into the body of the fifth nymph. The fifth nymph molts and, under the influence of both hormones, becomes a sixth-stage (supernumerary) nymph. (From C. D. Turner, *General Endocrinology.*)

from the thorax of activated individuals is sufficient in itself to induce molt in non-activated abdomens. Thus the picture of the mechanism of metamorphosis in Rhodnius may be diagrammed as in Figure 225.

PLATYSAMIA

The work of Williams on Platysamia began with an analysis of the mechanism of diapause in this lepidopteran. The animal normally spends the winter as a pupa, and experiment has shown that the freshly collected pupa will not develop into an adult unless it is first exposed to a period of at least two weeks of cold. Williams ('46) was able to show that the influence of cold was exerted through activation of hormone production in the animal's brain. An activated animal induces imaginal development in a non-activated parabiont. The brain from a cold-treated animal is effective in breaking

activated brain into a diapausing abdomen is not effective unless a prothoracic gland is implanted along with it. At first Williams ('49) was of the opinion that the mechanism of post-diapause development involved a different brain hormone from that found by others (see below) to be concerned with larval and pupal molts. Later, however, Williams ('52) was able to show by ligation experiments and transplants of the prothoracic organs and brains from various stages that the same hormonal mechanism is involved in the pupal and larval molt as in the breaking of diapause. Since the role of the C.A. in larval molts was established by others in Lepidoptera (see below), the mechanism of hormonal control of development in Platysamia may be diagrammed as in Figure 225. The correspondence of the mechanism controlling metamorphosis in Rhodnius and Platysamia is seen to be quite complete. In this interpretation diapause

Fig. 224. Parabiotic union in moth pupae. *A,B*, Brainless pupa of *Platysamia cecropia* grafted to a chilled pupa of the same species. The brain of the chilled parabiont provides hormone necessary for the development of both animals. *C,D*, Brainless diapausing pupa of *Telea polyphemus* grafted to a chilled pupa of *P. cecropia*. The successful development of both pupae shows that the brain factor is not species specific. This fact also shown by *E*, which is adult of *P. cecropia* developed from a brainless pupa which had received the brain from a chilled pupa of *T. polyphemus*. (From C. D. Turner, *General Endocrinology*.)

results from a cessation of brain activity in the pupa and the consequent necessity of reactivation of the brain by exposure to cold.

INSECTS IN GENERAL

We may now consider whether the endocrine mechanism discussed above for Rhodnius and Platysamia is applicable to insects in general. Before doing so, however, a note on terminology is necessary. As experimenters have uncovered various factors in insect metamorphosis, names descriptive of their actions have usually been given to these factors. Such names are generally rather unsatisfactory, often being vague, too general, too restricted or sometimes even implying a mode of action later found incorrect. When the source of a factor has been traced to a particular organ it is generally more satisfactory to name it in terms of that organ, and such terminology is favored in this discussion. The term "hormone" will be used for these factors since in general they seem to be hormone-like in their activity. However, as will be seen below, the exact correspondence to a hormone as understood in vertebrate physiology is open to some question. The following terms, their definitions and synonymy are important.

Brain Hormone. An agent produced by the protocerebrum, presumably by the neurosecretory cells contained therein. It acts by

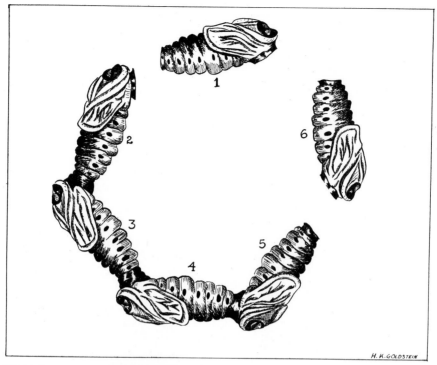

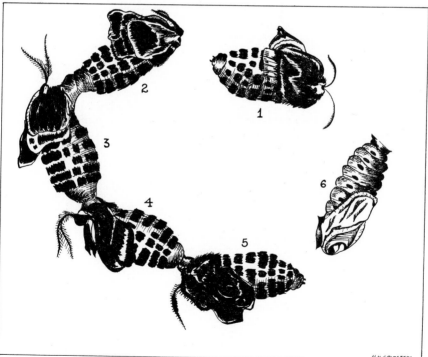

Fig. 226. *Above,* A chain of six brainless diapausing pupae had been established in parabiosis and a single chilled pupal brain implanted under the facial window of the anterior-most individual. When pupae *1* and *2* showed the initiation of development, about 17 days later, pupae *1* and *6* were detached as seen above. *Below,* The same preparation seven weeks later. After detachment of the brain-containing pupa, the activation has continued to spread down the chain of interconnected pupae. The isolated pupa, however, failed to develop. (After Williams, '52.)

mone. However, since the general nutritive values or other positive or negative factors carried in these fluids may play a role in the reaction, they are not of themselves conclusive. In spite of these lacks the concept of a brain hormone and of a prothoracic hormone seem fairly well justified. With respect to the corpus allatum, the evidence for hormone action is less direct and the possibility of some action of the gland upon the metamorphosis hormone other than by secretion of a separate principle has not been excluded. As noted above, Wigglesworth has postulated elimination of the C.A. hormone by this gland in the pre-metamorphic instar. In any case it seems important to realize that the properties of the metamorphic principles in insects may be somewhat different from those we are accustomed to see in vertebrate hormones. A notable instance is the slowness with which the principles may spread from one parabiont to another, as seen in the reports of Wigglesworth ('34) and Williams ('52; Fig. 226). Again the prominence of local effects from C.A., effects that persist through several molts (Piepho, '50) seems hardly consistent with the idea that the viable graft is secreting a hormone. The persistence of C.A. effects for one or two molts after removal of the corpus (Scharrer, '46; Pflugfelder, '37) is also difficult to reconcile with the usual prompt disappearance of hormones from circulation, at least as hormone action is known in vertebrates.

METABOLISM IN RELATION TO METAMORPHOSIS

The well-established effect of the thyroid hormone in raising the rate of metabolism in mammals (Means, '48) raises the problems of whether this hormone has a similar effect in the amphibian larva and whether, if it has, this effect is responsible for metamorphic changes. The possibility that a metabolic effect underlies metamorphosis has provided the basis for numerous speculations on the nature of metamorphic change (e.g., Huxley, '29). Yet the weight of the experimental evidence is against the concept of a rôle of metabolic rate in metamorphosis. In the first place, despite the evidence of earlier studies it is doubtful whether the thyroid does exert a metabolism-increasing effect upon amphibian larvae. The evidence up to 1934 was examined by Etkin ('34), who concluded that the increase in oxygen consumption per unit weight that has been reported during thyroid-induced amphibian meta-

morphosis did not signify an increase in metabolic rate, since it resulted from the loss of body water rather than from an increase in oxygen consumption per individual or per unit dry weight. In studies on the oxygen consumption of tadpoles during normal metamorphosis in the bullfrog, Etkin found no increased oxygen consumption irrespective of the basis of calculation. The rate per individual animal decreased during the metamorphic climax. Furthermore, the analysis of the literature on cold-blooded vertebrates shows that there is no adequate evidence for ascribing a metabolic rate effect to the thyroid hormone in cold-blooded vertebrates generally (Etkin, Root and Mofshin, '40). Though the evidence in this field continues to be conflicting, subsequent reports have in general confirmed the above interpretation (Smith and Everett, '43).

Even the workers who ascribe to thyroid a stimulating effect on metabolism during amphibian metamorphosis do not regard this effect as of causal significance in the process of metamorphosis itself (Helff, '26; Needham, '42). Dinitrophenols, which raise oxygen consumption in mammals and fish (Means, '48; Root and Etkin, '37), do not influence amphibian metamorphosis (Cutting and Tainter, '33).

Cyanides have been reported to inhibit the effect of thyroid on metamorphosis, and this has been taken as supporting the metabolism theory in metamorphosis (Demuth, '33; Hoffman, '35). Borland ('43), however, found a marked accelerating effect of cyanides on metamorphosis. In any case the evidence from cyanides, like that from dinitrophenol, is too indirect to be very helpful on the question of the role of metabolic increase in metamorphosis. Nevertheless, taken as a whole the weight of the evidence negates the idea of a causal role of a metabolism-raising factor in amphibian metamorphosis.

An influence of the corpus allatum on metabolic rate in insects has been reported by Thomsen ('49), who found a 20 per cent decrease after allectomy with almost complete restoration of the rate by replacement therapy. She regarded the activity of the hormone as being primarily on metabolic rate. The numerous influences exerted by the C.A. on the physiology of the adult insect (Pfeiffer, '45b) may also be cited as evidence for a fundamental role of C.A. on basic metabolic processes.

Basal metabolism, being the summation of numerous and varied metabolic pathways, is too general a concept to yield significant data for the analysis of morphogenic factors. Work on individual tissues or enzyme systems holds much greater promise. Enzyme analysis has been most successfully applied to insects. Williams ('51) and his collaborators, who have studied the cytochrome system, find a close correspondence between cytochrome c and the activity of prothoracic gland hormone. The emergence from diapause is correlated with a shift from a cyanide-insensitive flavoprotein oxidation system to a cytochrome system sensitive to cyanide. By inactivating cytochrome oxidase with carbon monoxide and other compounds Williams was able to stop the post-diapause growth processes in the pupa. The cytochrome system in Drosophila (Bodenstein and Sacktor, '52) also parallels the growth activity, although perhaps not the hormone level. Although only preliminary results are available at present it would appear that enzymatic analysis holds great promise of an understanding of hormone activity in morphogenesis. This approach should be extended to the amphibians, where the variations among the tissues in responsiveness to thyroid would seem to provide favorable material for such analysis.

DIRECT AND INDIRECT TISSUE RESPONSE

Amphibians. The demonstration of a hormonal stimulant in the blood raises the question as to whether the responses of the individual tissues are all made directly to this stimulus or whether some at least are not indirect responses induced by neighboring tissues. This question is most conveniently explored by transplanting tissues between animals metamorphosing at different times. If the graft undergoes metamorphosis synchronously with the host tissue, then it may be concluded that it is responding directly to the metamorphic stimulant rather than indirectly through some neighboring organ or by self-differentiation. Such evidence of direct response in amphibians exists for gills (Kornfeld, '14), skin (Uhlenhuth, '17; Helff, '31a), intestine (Sembrat, '24), tail muscle (Helff and Clausen, '29; Fukai, '34), tongue (Helff, '29), and eye (Vrtelowna, '25; Schwind, '33). In some cases the tissue response is one of growth, in others one of histolysis or a combination of the two processes.

A particularly striking type of evidence of direct tissue response was secured by Kollros and collaborators (Kollros, '42; Kalten-

bach, '49). For example, Kollros implanted bits of thyroid directly into the tadpole hindbrain and thereby brought about a localized maturation of the lid-closure reflex mechanisms. By irradiating parts of the tadpole with x-rays Puckett ('37) was able to inhibit the growth-promoting effects of thyroid and thereby separate the growth from the resorption actions of the thyroid hormone, showing that these responses are independent of each other.

On the other hand, Helff and his associates have been able to show that some tissue changes are not direct responses to hormones but are dependent upon stimulation from neighboring structures. The formation of the tympanum in the frog occurs during late stages in the metamorphic climax. The production of this structure involves a modification of the integument and also the formation of a connective tissue sheet, the lamina propria, containing peculiar yellow fibers. Helff ('28) showed that skin from any region transplanted to the ear region was induced to form tympanum. Conversely skin from the ear region transplanted elsewhere failed to form tympanum. By transplanting the annular tympanic cartilage he was able to show that this cartilage was the source of an inductive influence leading to the formation of tympanic membrane in skin overlying it; this inductive effect was present, though weaker, in killed cartilage (Helff, '40). Helff ('34) also found some capacity for tympanum induction in the quadrate and suprascapular cartilages which, because of their positions, can have no influence in the formation of the tympanum in normal metamorphosis. The inductive capacity of the annular cartilage, moreover, persisted for some time after the completion of the membrane in normal metamorphosis. However, the yellow fibers of the lamina propria were shown to form only under influence of contact with the columella (Helff, '31c). Presumably the tympanic and columella cartilages develop under direct thyroid stimulation since on transplantation each continues at least partial development (this point was not directly explored by Helff).

A more complex case in which inductive phenomena play a part is that of the formation of the skin window or opercular perforation, for the foreleg in Anura. This is a definitely circumscribed area of skin of the operculum which undergoes autolysis in the late prometamorphic period (Fig. 217). The forelegs which have meanwhile developed in the opercular cavity are thrust through the

weak spot or opening formed in the autolyzed area. A number of mechanisms were
suggested to explain the formation of the
window. Weber ('25), for example, maintained it is produced by the action of the
poison glands at the base of the leg. The pressure of the developing leg is an obvious possibility. But no experimental analysis was
offered until Helff ('26) showed that skin
from other areas transplanted to the appropriate place would undergo autolysis during
metamorphosis and, conversely, opercular
skin transplanted to the back would not form
the opening. This was interpreted as showing
that the skin is not a self-differentiating
structure nor does it respond directly to the
thyroid hormone but, rather, it is induced to
form the skin window in response to some
local factor.

The identification of any local factors concerned proved quite difficult. Helff was able
to show that it was not the forelimbs, as their
early removal did not prevent the histolysis
in the region of the skin window from taking
place. By pressure the legs accelerate the
actual breaking through of the skin window
but this is secondary to the histolysis. Degenerating gill tissue, when transplanted to
the back, induced histolysis in the overlying
skin. Helff concluded that the autolyzing gill
tissue was the inducing agent responsible for
the formation of the skin window. This interpretation was supported by Van der Jagt
('29), who found that gill tissue increased
in potency for the induction of autolysis in
the overlying skin as metamorphosis pro-
gressed.

However, this conclusion of Helff is not
satisfactory for several reasons. In normal
metamorphosis the opercular histolysis becomes evident before (in *Rana catesbeiana*
as much as a month before) any perceptible
gill reduction occurs. Nor does the gill tissue
make the close contact with the area of histolysis that Helff's experiment indicates to be
necessary for its action to be effective. Furthermore, the capacity for inducing histolysis
in overlying integument seems to be widespread in degenerating tissue, muscle, for example, also showing this effect.

Later investigations by European workers
showed that, at least in the species investigated, different areas of skin have different
potencies for skin window development.
Opercular skin transplanted to the tail underwent histolysis when the tail resorbed,
whereas skin from the back did not. In one
species (*R. ridibunda*) opercular skin formed
a perforation when transplanted to the back

where no degenerating muscle underlay it
(Blacher, Liosner and Woronzowa, '34; Liosner and Woronzowa, '35). In a reinvestigation of this problem Helff ('39) likewise
found that the skin area was not entirely
without determination. He concluded that
induction by degenerating gill tissue, by degenerating skin glands and by self-differentiation (i.e., direct response to hormone)
each plays some part in the formation of the
skin window. However, it would seem that
until the tissue whose histolysis is active in
inducing skin window formation is definitely
identified (as explained above it does not
seem possible that it is gill tissue) the exact
role of self-differentiation cannot be determined because the experimenter cannot be
sure that the skin has not previously been
exposed to some inductive influence when it
is taken for transplantation. Recent work by
Kaltenbach ('49) has shown that a fairly
complete response can be elicited by implantation of thyroxine pellets to the neighborhood of the prospective skin window area,
thereby greatly strengthening the case for
self-differentiation.

Other suggestions of dependent differentiation of tadpole tissues have been made from
time to time, for example, that cutting off
of circulation to the tail by the growth of the
urostyle leads to tail resorption. This crude
concept was disproved by Helff ('30), who
showed that the tail resorbed normally after
extirpation of the urostylar primordium.

Insects. That the hormonal factors in insect metamorphosis operate in many cases
directly on the tissues seems evident. For
example, implanted bits of skin lying in
the haemocoel or in the fat body molt
(Piepho, '38; Bodenstein, '44) and imaginal
discs continue their development (Bodenstein,'43). Most striking is the fact reported
by Williams ('47) that isolated abdomens
which have been largely cleaned out of internal organs except the heart, still are able
to respond to prothoracic gland stimulation.

Although the few insect tissues that have
been studied appear to respond directly to the
metamorphic stimulus, indirect action cannot be excluded. It must be realized that in
amphibians it is with regard to intra-organ
details that Helff found indirect action of
the metamorphic stimuli. Such intra-organ
details have not yet been explored in insects
with respect to metamorphic changes. It is
worth noting, however, that local effects of
one part upon another are well recognized
in the sex organs in this group (Stern, '41).

TISSUE SPECIFICITY AND SENSITIVITY

Amphibians. The responses of the tissues to the thyroid hormone are highly specific. Some tissues (i.e., leg and eye) show growth, others (i.e., tail tissues) show histolysis and resorption, still others (i.e., digestive organs) a combination of the two processes. Furthermore, the response of a given organ varies among the species; the tail is resorbed and the legs are stimulated to growth in anurans but not in urodeles. Even among anurans, the degree of dependence of a given structure upon hormones appears to vary from species to species. Allen ('25) found that in the absence of the thyroid gland the legs of Bufo proceeded relatively further in their development than did those of various Ranidae. Gonadal development is generally independent of the thyroid and metamorphosis (Swingle, '18; Hoskins and Hoskins, '19). But even this varies with the species; Krichel ('31) found accelerated ovogenesis in *Bufo viridis* in normal metamorphosis and as a result of thyroid feeding. Continuance of the development of the brain in the absence of the thyroid from the larval to the adult condition was reported by Hoskins and Hoskins ('19a), but subsequent investigation by Allen ('24) showed that only the superficial form changes but no internal maturation occurs in the absence of the thyroid.

The type of response made by a given group of cells is independent of its histological character. In the tadpole, tail muscle and skin respond by histolysis whereas back muscle or skin do not. In fact, the responsiveness of muscle varies with the region of the tail from which it is taken, anterior muscle degenerating more quickly than posterior and axial more readily than peripheral (Clausen, '30).

Histological examination of metamorphosing tissues shows striking examples of specificity of response that is independent of histological differentiation. Champy ('22) reported a sharp line of separation between the epithelium of the limb and that of the body with respect to their mitotic response to thyroid treatment. Transplantation of the skin shows that the capacity for forming the glands of the dorsal plicae is strictly localized (Helff, '31a), as is the capacity for producing pigment (Lindeman, '29). Another striking case of cell specificity is that of the Mauthner cells, which degenerate under the influence of thyroid whereas neighboring cells may be stimulated to proliferate (Weiss

and Rossetti, '51; Kollros and Pepernik, '52).

The highly specific reactivity of larval structures described above is acquired at a definite and very brief period. The embryonic tissues are not sensitive to thyroid, but they acquire their individual peculiarities of reactivity soon after the larval organs are definitely differentiated (Champy, '22; Etkin, '50). Some experimenters report a relatively slight variation in the time at which different tissues in the same animal become sensitive to the thyroid hormone. The anuran tail is reported to develop sensitivity before the limb buds; the skin, particularly its pigment pattern, is last to become responsive (Alphonse and Bauman, '34; Kuhn, '33; Moser, '50).

A number of workers report progressive sensitization of the tissues to thyroid hormone during development (Allen, '38; Geigy, '41). The writer does not regard the evidence on this point as satisfactory because of the difficulty of controlling the quantitative evaluation of response and the influence of environmental factors. The basic property of thyroid hormone sensitivity is acquired in an all-or-none fashion at the time of operculum formation in *Rana pipiens* larvae (Etkin, '50). Changes in sensitivity, if any, are relatively slight. As compared to the role of tissue specificity, this factor can be of only secondary significance in determining the time and pattern of metamorphic changes.

The problem of the acquisition of sensitivity of the tissues deserves a more sustained experimental analysis, particularly as to its biochemical basis, than has as yet been given to it.

The problems of the evolution of the mechanisms of metamorphosis do not fall within the scope of this chapter, but some comparative observations relating to tissue sensitivity may be made. In permanently neotenous urodeles the tissues are insensitive to the thyroid hormone. Yet the thyroids and pituitary glands of these animals are effective when implanted into organisms capable of showing the metamorphic response (Swingle, '22; Charipper and Corey, '30). Whether the hormone contained in these glands is ever released during the lifetime of these animals is unknown.

In the axolotl, a facultatively neotenous salamander, there is no loss of tissue sensitivity. This is shown most clearly by the fact that axolotl tissues transplanted to Triton hosts at embryonic stages metamorphose with the host (Geigy, '38). Similarly, skin fragments transferred from axolotl to Amblystoma metamorphose with the latter, but in the reverse transplant, i.e., from Amblystoma to axolotl, the transplant remains indefinitely larval (Shtern, '33). The well known artificial induction of metamorphosis in the axolotl by thyroid and pituitary treatments likewise points to the existence of tissue sensitivity, although not indicating the level of sensitivity. It may be inferred that the neoteny of the axolotl results from lack of glandular activity, that of perennibranchs from loss of tissue sensitivity.

Insects. In insects as in amphibians each structure of an animal responds in its own specific way to the common metamorphic stimulus. Also with regard to the early time of acquisition of tissue specificity there is a striking similarity between amphibian tissues and those in insects (except possibly for Diptera, as noted below). Piepho ('38), for example, finds the capacity to pupate appears in caterpillars upon emergence from the egg. Similarly in Rhodnius the ability of early instars to respond to the metamorphic stimulus seems substantially complete (Wigglesworth, '40). Bodenstein ('35) found that the stage from which the thoracic leg transplant was taken made no difference in its responsiveness to host stimuli in Vanessa. Although no quantitative evaluation of the sensitivity of the tissues seems to have been attempted, it can be seen from the facts stated that in these forms, at least, changes in tissue sensitivity do not play a significant role in determining the time or character of molt or metamorphosis. Scharrer ('52a) has interpreted the production of incomplete adults after C.A. removal at early instars in Leucophaea as evidence that the tissues in these animals are not yet fully competent to give the complete hormone response. However, such effects may merely result from the persistence of C.A. hormone as currently understood.

In Drosophila, on the other hand, there is evidence that a progressive increase in responsiveness of the tissues takes place during larval development. Hadorn and Neel ('38) found older larval tissues more sensitive than younger ones to the pupation stimulus from ring gland implants. Bodenstein ('43) reported greater response to transplanted ring glands from older imaginal discs, and similar results were reported by Vogt ('42). It would appear from these results that changes in tissue responsiveness may play a significant role in insect development. On the other hand, the greater response of older discs may come about because they start from a more advanced base line rather than because of any increase in sensitivity. This interpretation seems more consistent with the view, developed above, that larval development in Diptera as in other insects is controlled by a succession of hormonal pulses. Sensitivity in insects, as in amphibians, may be acquired fully at an early stage.

METAMORPHIC PATTERN

Amphibians. The importance in metamorphosis of the time relationships of the changes which take place is illustrated by the abnormality of the metamorphic pattern induced by strong doses of thyroid (Fig. 227). The animals produced by such treatment usually die in the process of metamorphosis in a condition characterized by protruding, overdeveloped lower jaws, with tails largely resorbed but hind legs little more than undifferentiated nubbins. Large open skin windows for the forelegs may form but the legs are not sufficiently developed to protrude. Such distortions were early recognized and descriptively analyzed a number of times (Schreiber, '34a). Many authors speculated on the possibility that the normal pattern of metamorphic change results from differences in the threshold of response of different tissues to thyroid hormone (see, for example, J. Huxley, '22; Schreiber, '34b). To test such theories a number of workers have studied the effects of immersion in different concentrations of thyroid substances upon the progress of metamorphosis in tadpoles (Allen, '32b; Etkin, '35a). Since the results of these studies, consistent among themselves, have repeatedly been misinterpreted as supporting the idea that differential thresholds of response account for the spacing of metamorphic events (for example, see Needham, '42), it is necessary here to examine the idea of thresholds with some care.

The technique used by Blacher and Allen was to observe the tadpoles after a definite period of immersion in solutions of different concentrations of thyroid substance and note which metamorphic changes had occurred. This procedure showed that events characteristic of the early stages of metamorphosis, such as leg growth and intestinal reduction, occurred within the specified period at lower concentrations of the thyroid hormone than did the later metamorphic events, such as mouth changes and forelimb emergence. It is clear, however, that this procedure does not reveal true thresholds, for it is possible that by observing the animals for longer periods even the lowest concentrations might be seen to lead to late metamorphic events. This was clearly recognized by Allen, who stated, "this 'threshold of response' is really a question of time of response."

By following the changes in individual animals continuously for long periods, Etkin found that any effective concentration of thy-

malities in coordination observed by all earlier workers who gave massive thyroid doses.

No single concentration of thyroxine was found effective in inducing a normal "time-table" of metamorphic events. Etkin was partly, though not entirely, successful in inducing a normal timetable in thyroidec-

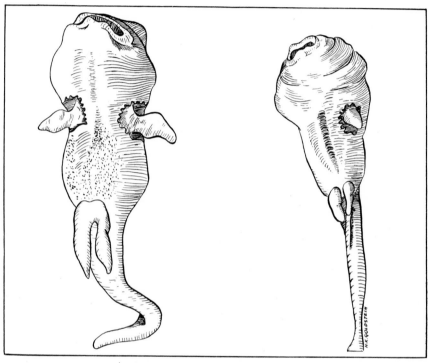

Fig. 227. Abnormal tadpoles metamorphosing under stimulation from strong doses of thyroid (after Schreiber, '34a).

roxine was capable of inducing both early and late metamorphic changes if allowed to operate for a long enough period. The speed of metamorphosis increased with the concentration of thyroxine. In low concentrations the first effect observed was an activation of leg growth, and only after the lapse of considerable time, during which the legs grew to full size, were late metamorphic events initiated. These later events proceeded in an extremely slow and protracted manner. With low concentrations, therefore, early metamorphosis is normal in its time relations but the late events of the metamorphic climax are unduly protracted. In high concentrations the events of the metamorphic climax were precipitated at their normal rates but not enough time was permitted for early events to undergo their appropriate development. This is the explanation of the abnor-

tomized tadpoles by treating them first with low concentrations of thyroxine and subsequently raising the concentration (Fig. 228).

It would appear from the above results that the responses of the tissues show the ordinary stoichiometric relations common to many chemical reactions, i.e., the higher the concentration the faster the reaction proceeds. No true thresholds of response are shown by the tissues. In urodeles the velocity of tissue response is also a function of the concentration of active principle when small doses are used (Zavadovsky, '26).

According to this interpretation the temporal spacing of metamorphic events (Fig. 229) depends upon two factors: (1) inherent differences in the tissues with respect to rate of response, and (2) the patterns of activation of the thyroid gland. The histological evidence discussed above indicates that in Anura the thyroid gland at the beginning of metamorphosis is only slightly active but that through the prometamorphic period becomes more and more active until in the metamorphic climax it reaches a peak of activity accompanied by release of some of

Insects. No direct analysis of the problem of the correlation of metamorphic events is available in insects. Wigglesworth's interpretation is that the same hormone is responsible for the metamorphic molt and for the growth of imaginal structures in Rhodnius. This is

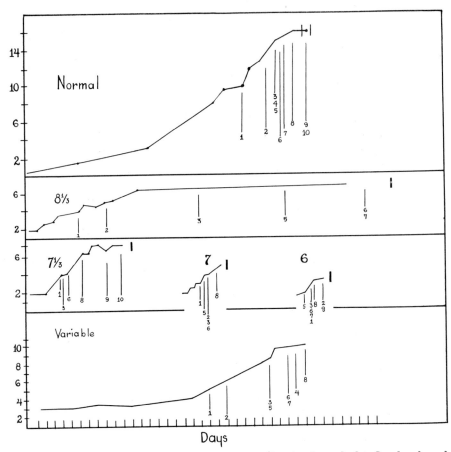

Fig. 228. Metamorphic pattern and thyroxine concentration in the tadpole. Graphs show hind leg growth. The times of occurrence of ten metamorphic events are shown by numbers. The top curve is that of a normal tadpole. The other curves show metamorphic pattern in thyroidectomized tadpoles treated with various thyroxine solutions. The number with each curve expresses the dilution of the solution exponentially, i.e., 6 equals one part thyroxine in 10^6 parts of water. Bottom graph of animal treated with increasing thyroxine concentrations starting from 9 and going to 6–2/3. (After Etkin, '34.)

its stored hormone. The relatively low thyroid hormone concentration in the blood at the beginning of metamorphosis serves to activate the very sensitive leg primordia; the higher concentrations as they are built up in the blood speed the metamorphic process until in the metamorphic climax the flooding of the body with thyroid hormone produces the rapid reaction even in the least sensitive tissues, such as tail and tympanic ring.

also the current interpretation of Williams ('52). Hence it is possible that the temporal relationships of events in pupation and metamorphosis are a function of the interplay of differential tissue sensitivity and changing hormone level as in amphibian metamorphosis. In Platysamia, for example, a pulse of low hormone activity leads to pupation. Then, after diapause a stronger pulse leads to completion of imaginal development.

On the other hand, the difference between

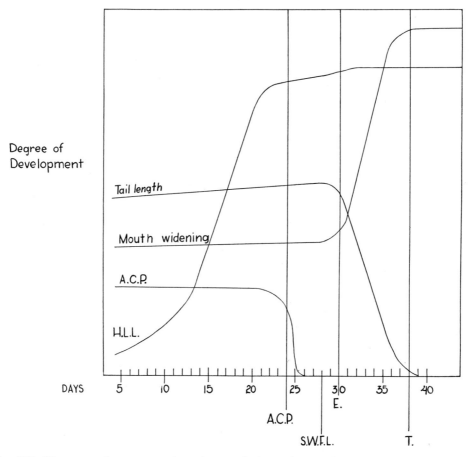

Degree of
Development

Tail length

Mouth widening

A.C.P.

H.L.L.

DAYS   5   10   15   20   25   30   35   40

A.C.P.

E.

S.W.F.L.   T.

Fig. 229. Diagrammatic representation of rate of tissue changes during normal metamorphosis in tadpole. Note that each structure has its own time for beginning and completion of its metamorphic change. *A.C.P.*, Resorption of anal canal piece; *S.W.F.L.*, skin window for the forelegs; *E*, emergence of forelegs, arbitrarily designated as day number 30.

metamorphic and larval molts in insects would appear to depend upon a qualitative difference in the stimulus, the presence or absence of the C.A. factor. In the interpretation of Wigglesworth ('40, '48) this factor serves to activate a different cellular mechanism than does the metamorphic hormone. Because of the more rapid response of the tissues to C.A. hormone the activation of the metamorphic cellular mechanism is forestalled. Hence Wigglesworth's term "juvenile hormone," indicating a positive mode of action, replacing his original "inhibitory hormone" for the C.A. factor. It would appear, however, that the evidence for this mode of action is not clear-cut and an action of the C.A. hormone on the prothoracic gland hormone rather than directly on the tissues has not been excluded. The possibility exists that,

at least for some organs, quantitative differences in the degree of stimulation of the same cellular mechanism may account for the different developmental changes in molting, pupation and metamorphosis.

THE ACTIVATION OF THE METAMORPHIC MECHANISM

In amphibians, metamorphosis depends upon a chain of events precipitated by the action of the thyrotrophic hormone of the anterior pituitary. In insects there is an analogous situation in the action of the brain in stimulating the prothoracic glands. In this section it is proposed to examine what is known of the factors determining the activation of the initiating stimulus from the pituitary or brain.

CONTROL OF PITUITARY ACTIVITY IN AMPHIBIANS

The evidence indicates that the thyroid gland lies ready, so to speak, to respond to pituitary stimulation at all times from the primordial stage onward. One experimental result leading to this conclusion is the fact that when thyroid and pituitary primordia are brought close together in the tail-bud stage of the frog the thyroid is activated within a few days and an extremely precocious metamorphosis is induced (Etkin, '36b, '39). The act of transplantation itself has no influence, since transplants to other localities lead to no precocity (Hoskins and Hoskins, '19a; Etkin, '39). The thyroid activation must therefore be a result of locally concentrated thyrotrophic pituitary hormone. Another indication of the dependence of thyroid activation upon the time of arrival of the pituitary stimulus rather than upon any change in the thyroid itself is shown by the fact that the introduction of additional thyroid primordia (not into the vicinity of the pituitary) does not influence the time of metamorphosis of the host (Allen, '30; Choi, '32).

In contrast to the thyroid the pituitary is independent of any other organ of the body for its activation. This conclusion is based on experiments in the transplantation of the pituitary primordium (Etkin, '38). When the primordium is removed from its normal site and transplanted to another part of the body, the animal undergoes metamorphosis. But this metamorphosis is generally delayed in its onset and protected in its execution. This is interpreted as indicating that the grafted pituitary generally develops its function more slowly than normal. Unlike the thyroid, its function depends upon its developmental rate, which is somewhat inhibited by the experimental interference, rather than upon a hormonal stimulus which would, of course, reach it at the same time wherever it is located.

The precocious activation of the thyroid primordium when placed close to the pituitary primordium, as mentioned above, indicates that the production of thyrotrophic hormone begins very early. That the thyroid-stimulating field existing around the pituitary primordium is due to the same hormone as that which later normally stimulates thyroid development is indicated by the finding that histologically differentiated thyroids respond to the thyrotrophic field. Presumably the amount of hormone produced by the primordium is so small as to be ineffectual when carried by the circulation. Before circulation is established, however, it appears to accumulate around the pituitary primordium in concentration sufficient to produce an effective thyrotrophic field.

As to the pattern of post-primordial development of function in the pituitary, little is known. Using implantation techniques Ingram ('29a) found that it took 15 to 20 pituitaries from tadpoles at the beginning of metamorphosis to equal the effect of three adult frog pituitaries. This indicates, considering the difference in size of the glands concerned (for which exact figures are not available), that the hormone is present in fair quantity in the tadpole pituitary. It must be supposed, therefore, that hormone production begins in the primordium and increases at an unknown rate to reach a high level at the beginning of metamorphosis. Whether the subsequent increase in thyroid activity to the climax of metamorphosis and the eventual cessation of thyroid activity at the close of metamorphosis are paralleled by corresponding changes in the activity of the pituitary is not known.

As seen above, the failure of the axolotl to metamorphose is not due to insensitivity of the tissues to thyroid hormone or of the thyroid to pituitary stimulation. It must therefore rest somehow on the failure of the pituitary to become active. Bytinsky-Salz ('35) explored this problem by exchanging hypophyseal rudiments between the axolotl (*Amblystoma mexicanum*) and a variety of amblystoma (*A. tigrinum*) which metamorphoses normally. He found that the metamorphic response of the host was that characteristic of the host species, not of the pituitary-donor type. This he interpreted (contrary to the conclusion stated above) as indicating that the pituitary is not functionally self-differentiating but is dependent upon some controlling factor elsewhere in the body for its own activation. However, the writer does not find the evidence presented to be convincing. The grafts were made in the orthotopic position, being made to replace the animal's own prospective pituitary area which had been removed. It is therefore impossible to be sure that the pituitary which developed in the animal came from the graft rather than by regeneration of the host's own tissues. This criticism is especially pertinent since hypophysectomies similarly carried out by Blount ('32) yielded a high proportion of regenerated glands.

In this connection it is interesting to note that in the neotenous *Necturus maculosus,* pituitaries of the adult were found potent in thyrotrophic principle when tested by implantation (Charipper and Corey, '30). Presumably in this form the pituitary-thyroid relation remains normal in spite of the loss of the metamorphic response of the tissues to thyroid hormone.

EFFECTS OF ENVIRONMENTAL FACTORS IN AMPHIBIANS

Considerable attention has been given to the influence of environmental factors on amphibian metamorphosis. From the vantage point of our present knowledge of the hormonal mechanisms of metamorphosis the effects of environmental factors must be considered in terms of their possible influences on these mechanisms, particularly on the activation of the pituitary. They may therefore be appropriately   considered at this point.

An external factor may influence the sensitivity or capacity for response of the tissues to thyroid and thus affect metamorphosis. It is clear that Roentgen rays act in this way since Puckett ('37) found it possible to prevent growth processes by x-ray dosage while resorption changes were permitted to continue.

Environmental factors may, on the other hand, influence metamorphosis by their effects on the thyrotrophic activity of the pituitary. Starvation inhibits the onset of metamorphosis in tadpoles when it comes before the beginning of metamorphosis, but accelerates it thereafter (D'Angelo, Gordon and Charipper, '41). The tissues of starved animals retain their sensitivity to thyroxine and their thyroids respond to anterior pituitary injections. It is therefore on the thyroid-activating mechanism of the pituitary that starvation before metamorphosis must act. The functional self-differentiation of the pituitary may be supposed to be brought to a halt in the absence of nourishment. Once the pituitary has been completely activated, on the other hand, the reduced food supply seems to make the released thyroid hormone more effective, perhaps because the cessation of tissue growth permits more active tissue differentiation. Crowding inhibits growth more than it does metamorphosis (Adolph, '31). This would also appear to be due to a differential effect, greater on the growth and development of the pituitary than on that of the body as a whole.

The effects of temperature on metamorphosis appear to operate both on tissue sensitivity and on the endocrine mechanism. A number of workers report that the failure of metamorphosis which occurs in the cold (below 10°C.) is accompanied by loss of tissue sensitivity to thyroid (Huxley, '29; Hartwig, '36). Yet an effect of low temperature also on the endocrine mechanism is indicated by the failure of hibernating tadpoles to continue their metamorphosis when restored to warm conditions (Fosi, '35), and by the fact that manipulation of the temperature can differentially affect metamorphosis and growth (Adler, '16). At 16°C. tadpoles grow larger before metamorphosis than at 24°C. (Etkin, unpublished data).

ACTIVATION OF INSECT MECHANISMS

The release of the hormonal mechanism of molt and metamorphosis in Rhodnius is clearly dependent upon the feeding stimulus, since metamorphosis always follows feeding by a definite number of days, 15 to 20 according to stage (Wigglesworth, '34). If the ventral nerve cord is cut molting is prevented. Presumably feeding provides a stimulus that reaches the brain through the nerve cord. Wigglesworth maintains that the stimulus arises from the stretching of the body wall.

Clearly the mechanism of activation of the brain in Rhodnius cannot apply to insects which do not feed in single huge meals. But we have very little indication of the mechanism governing hormone production or release in other insects. The effects of starvation on insect metamorphosis are similar to those on amphibians. Before a critical period which is near the time of metamorphosis, starvation delays metamorphosis; after the critical period it may have no effect or may even accelerate the process (Bounhiol, '38). As explained above, Williams found that chilling was necessary for the activation of the brain in the diapausing larva of *Platysamia cecropia.*

A comparison of the insect and amphibian reveals a highly suggestive similarity in the relation of the primary endocrine apparatus (i.e., neurosecretory brain cells in insects and pituitary in amphibia) to environmental factors. The vertebrate anterior pituitary is anatomically closely related to the brain both in position and by way of the infundibulum. There appear, however, to be no secretory nerves from the brain to the anterior lobe. However, in recent years the blood supply of the anterior lobe has been shown to consist in part of a portal venous system which brings blood from the hypothalamus to the pituitary (Green, '51). It is believed that through this venous system the neurosecretory apparatus in the hypothalamus is able to exert some controlling influences on the activity of the anterior lobe. It would thus appear that the varied instances where environmental factors influence the metamorphic process in insects and amphibians operate through a basically similar mechanism. The stimuli are received by the nervous system, which transmits them to neurosecretory elements which, in turn, start the endocrine chain mechanism into action. The intimate association of the brain and the primary endocrine apparatus thus permits the development of some degree of control of the endocrine system through environmental factors. In this way the life history of an animal can be brought into synchrony with seasonal change. It would be interesting to explore the influence of cold on the pituitary of such amphibians as hibernate in larval stages, along the lines of the work of Williams on Platysamia.*

In connection with the neurosecretory pathway in insects Scharrer ('52a,b) has suggested that the corpus cardiacum be considered part of the neuroendocrine complex regulating insect development. She has demonstrated that on an anatomical basis the C.C. might be considered as a storage organ for the secretion formed by the neurosecretory cells of the brain [perhaps analogous to the sinus gland of crustacea (Passano, '51)]. Yet experiments with the C.C. have not yielded dramatic results. Pfeiffer ('39) asserted that C.C. removal delays molting in the grasshopper, which is consistent with the above theory. Vogt ('46), on the other hand, found in Drosophila that C.C. implants delay puparium formation. Perhaps clearcut results are not to be expected until both brain and C.C. are treated as a unit.

CESSATION OF METAMORPHIC TRANSFORMATION

Amphibians. As a final step in the regulation of metamorphosis, the processes involved

* The posterior lobe of the pituitary (not involved in metamorphosis) is innervated by neurosecretory fibers from the hypothalamus. The extraordinary morphological parallelism between this and the neurosecretory system of insects has been commented upon by Scharrer and Scharrer ('44). Perhaps this, too, finds its ultimate significance in a linking up of the endocrine gland with environmental factors.

must be brought to a halt. When resorption of the tadpole's tail is complete, for example, no further change is possible. When the tympanic membrane is fully formed no further development seems possible. Yet it is apparent that such considerations do not apply to all metamorphic events. Do the legs of the tadpole cease their rapid growth because they lose their capacity to respond to thyroid or because the hormone itself ceases? It would appear probable that the sensitivity of the leg tissues changes with development, since the legs slow their growth before the metamorphic climax is complete and while the thyroid gland is still very active (Etkin, '32, '36a). On the other hand, skin shedding is a characteristic phenomenon of metamorphosis in Amphibia (Etkin, '32). Plainly the capacity of the skin for responding to thyroid by shedding is not lost at the end of metamorphosis, since it is found in the adult. It must be supposed, therefore, that the cessation of skin shedding late in metamorphosis is a consequence of the reduction in activity of the thyroid which, according to histological studies, takes place at this time (Etkin, '36a).

The inactivation of the thyroid is itself an aspect of metamorphosis that requires explanation. No direct evidence is available to indicate whether this is to be ascribed to a change in sensitivity, as in the case of the tadpole's legs, or to a cessation of pituitary stimulation. From what is known of the general physiology of the thyroid-pituitary relation we might suppose that the second of the above alternatives holds true, since prolonged stimulation of the thyroid gland by pituitary implants is possible. Furthermore, a mechanism for the suppression of thyrotrophic function in the pituitary is suggested by the observation in many animals that thyroid hormone itself, when it reaches a high level in the blood, inhibits the thyrotrophic activity of the pituitary (for a summary of the evidence on this point see Adams, '46).

It can be seen from the above discussion that, though several factors appear to contribute to the mechanism bringing metamorphic change to an end, little direct experimental knowledge in this field is available.

Insects. In insects as in amphibians some metamorphic changes have an inherent end point, as in the resorption of larval organs. This may also apply to constructive changes at metamorphosis when the living cells of the primordium are used up in the metamorphic change, as in the case of the formation of the wings. This situation cannot account entirely for the absence of further development in the adult insect, for experiments reveal that the hypodermis, at least, is potentially capable of further molting and can even revert to the production of larval exoskeleton under appropriate stimulation (Fururkawa, '35; Piepho, '39). The absence of metamorphic change in the adult insect is at least partly due to failure of the hormonal pulses to continue. The disintegration of the prothoracic glands at the end of metamorphosis (Kaiser, '49; Rahm, '52) accounts for the cessation of the hormonal stimulation thereafter. What determines this disintegration or the cessation of C.A. activity at the previous stage in insects is not clear.

In any case it is evident that the morphogenic processes involved in the cessation of metamorphic activity involve both the loss of sensitivity of the tissues and cessation of hormonal activity in both insects and amphibians. It is also noteworthy that the maintenance of the adult morphological structures brought into existence under hormonal stimulation does not require the continued presence of that stimulation for their maintenance. In this respect the morphogenic principles involved in metamorphosis differ from those common, though not universal, in the sex system of vertebrates, where most structures require the continued presence of the hormone under which they developed for their maintenance. This difference correlates, of course, with the cyclic or seasonal nature of sex activity in contrast to the stability of adult characters. A report by Kollros and Pepernik ('52), however, indicates that some metamorphic events in amphibians may also depend for their maintenance upon continued thyroid stimulation. They found that the neurones of the mesencephalic V nucleus regress if thyroid hormone is withdrawn.

SUMMARY

The concept of the metamorphic mechanism operative in amphibian metamorphosis may be stated as follows:

The anterior pituitary begins its thyrotrophic activity early in embryonic development. However, it is not until late in larval life that the rate of hormone production reaches a level high enough to stimulate a pulse of growth and secretion in the thyroid gland. With the activation of the thyroid the concentration of its hormone in the blood rises according to a definite pattern. Each of the larval structures responds to thyroid hormone in its own specific fashion and each at its own rate. As a result of the differences in speed (not in thresholds) of response of the different tissues metamorphic changes occur in a definite sequence of appropriately spaced events. Metamorphic changes are further integrated by inductive effects of one tissue upon others in its immediate neighborhood. The pulse of thyroid activity is brought to an end by inhibition of pituitary activity by the high level of thyroid hormone. Subsequent pulses of thyroid activity during the life of the amphibian produce no metamorphic change because the structures concerned have either completed the possibilities of change or lost their tissue sensitivity.

In insects the first known stimulus to metamorphosis originates in the neurosecretory cells of the brain. These produce a hormone acting upon the prothoracic glands, which in turn produce a hormone acting upon the tissues. Each tissue responds to the hormone of the prothoracic gland by its own characteristic metamorphic transformation. This pulse of hormonal activity is the last of a series of such pulses that occur during larval life. The earlier pulses do not eventuate in metamorphosis because each is accompanied by the secretion of a hormone by the corpus allatum. The response of the tissues to the presence of both prothoracic gland hormone and the hormone of the corpus allatum is to undergo a larval rather than a metamorphic molt.

In both the amphibian and the insect the metamorphic pattern is the product of an interaction of two basic factors, a pulse of hormonal activity and an inherent pattern of tissue sensitivity. In both organisms the hormonal pulse is produced by two glands. The second gland depends for activation upon the first and the first is intimately related to the brain.

The mode of activation of the primary hormonal factor is but little known. Physiological self-differentiation may be predominant in most cases. In others environmental factors or the general body metabolism may play a role by way of the brain. The nature of the tissue response presumably rests on an enzymatic basis, as work on insects is beginning to elucidate.

The remarkable parallelism between the metamorphic mechanism in insect and amphibian can have no basis in homology but must be ascribed to the fundamental similarity of the life processes in all organisms.

There appears to be a limited repertoire of physiological mechanisms by which living things can meet a given problem. Both insects and amphibians were presented by a common evolutionary challenge, to evolve a metamorphic stage transitional between a larva with one mode of life and an adult with another. Both organisms have evolved closely analogous physiological mechanisms to meet this challenge.

REFERENCES

Abderhalden, E. 1915 Studien über die von einzelnen Organen hervorgebrachten Substanzen mit specifischer Wirkung, I. Pflügers Archiv., 162:99–129.

——— 1924 Fortgesetzte Studien über die Beeinflussung der Entwicklung von Kaulquappen durch Verbindungen mit bekannter Struktur. Pflügers Archiv., 206:467–472.

Adams, A. E. 1946 Variations in the potency of thyrotrophic hormone of the pituitary in animals. Quart. Rev. Biol., 21:1–32.

Adler, L. 1914 Metamorphosestudien an Batrachierlarven. I. Roux' Arch. Entw.-mech., 39:21–45.

——— 1916 Untersuchungen über die Entstehung der Amphibienneotenie. Pflügers Archiv., 164:1–101.

Adolph, E. 1931 Body size as a factor in the metamorphosis of tadpoles. Biol. Bull., 61:376–386.

Allen, B. M. 1916 Extirpation experiments in Rana pipiens larvae. Science, 44:755–757.

——— 1917 Effects of the extirpation of the anterior lobe of the hypophysis of Rana pipiens. Biol. Bull., 32:117–130.

——— 1918 The results of thyroid removal in the larvae of Rana pipiens. J. Exp. Zool., 24:499–519.

——— 1924 Brain development in anuran larvae after thyroid or pituitary gland removal. Endocrin., 8:639–651.

——— 1925 The effects of extirpation of the thyroid and pituitary glands upon the limb development of anurans. J. Exp. Zool. 42, 413–430.

——— 1927 Influence of the hypophysis upon the thyroid gland in amphibian larvae. Univ. Calif. Pub. Zool., 31:53–78.

——— 1929a The influence of the thyroid and hypophysis upon growth and development of amphibian larvae. Quart. Rev. Biol., 4:325–352.

——— 1929b Transplants of the thyroid anlagen into anuran tadpoles. Anat. Rec., 44:207.

——— 1930 The early development of organ anlagen in amphibians. Contrib. Marine Biol., Stanford University Press.

——— 1931 Role of hypophysis in the initiation of metamorphosis in Bufo. Proc. Soc. Exper. Biol. & Med., 29:74–75.

——— 1932a The dominant role of the pars anterior of the hypophysis in initiating amphibian metamorphosis. Anat. Rec., 54:65–81.

——— 1932b The response of Bufo larvae to different concentrations of thyroxin. Anat. Rec., 54:45–65.

——— 1938 The endocrine control of amphibian metamorphosis. Biol. Rev., 13:1–19.

Alphonse, P., and Bauman, G. 1934 Indifférence de la peau de jeunes tetards de Bufo vulgaris vis-à-vis de fortes doses de thyroxine. Compt. Rend. Soc. Biol., 117:567.

Atwell, W. J. 1935 Effects of thyreotropic and adrenotropic principles on hypophysectomized Amphibia. Anat. Rec., 62:361–379.

——— 1937 Functional transplants of the primordium of the epithelial hypophysis in amphibia. Anat. Rec., 68:431–447.

———, and Taft, J. 1940 Functional transplants of epithelial hypophysis in three species of Amblystoma. Proc. Soc. Exper. Biol. & Med., 44:53–55.

Baffoni, G. N., and Catte, G. 1950 Il comportamento della cellula di Mauthner di raganella nella metamorfose accelerata con somministrazione di tiroide. Atti della Accad. Naz. dei Lincei, 8 Ser., 9:282–287.

Balthasart, M. 1931 La metamorphose experimentale des amphibiens. Ann. Soc. Roy. Zool. Belg., 62:79–114.

Blacher, L. J., Liosner, D., and Woronzowa, M. 1934 Mechanismus der Perforation der opercularen Membran der schwanzlosen Amphibien. Bull. Acad. Polonaise Sc. et Let., B, 2:325–347.

Bliss, D., and Welsh, J. H. 1952 The neurosecretory system of brachyuran Crustacea. Biol. Bull., 103:157–169.

Blount, R. 1932 Transplantation and extirpation of the pituitary rudiment and the effects upon pigmentation in the urodele embryo. J. Exp. Zool., 63:113–141.

——— 1935 Size relationships as influenced by pituitary rudiment implantation and extirpation in the urodele embryo. J. Exp. Zool., 70:131–185.

Bodenstein, D. 1933 Beintransplantationen an Lepidopterenraupen. I. Roux' Arch. Entw.-mech., 128:564–583.

——— 1935 Beintransplantationen an Lepidopterenraupen. III. Roux' Arch. Entw.-mech., 133:156–192.

——— 1938a Untersuchungen zum Metamorphoseproblem. I. Roux' Arch. Entw.-mech., 137:474–505.

——— 1938b Untersuchungen zum Metamorphoseproblem. II. Roux' Arch. Entw.-mech., 137:636–660.

——— 1939 Investigations on the problem of metamorphosis. VI. J. Exp. Zool., 82:329–356.

——— 1942 Hormone controlled processes in insect development. Cold Spring Harbor Symp. Quant. Biol., 10:17–26.

——— 1943 Hormones and tissue competence in the development of Drosophila. Biol. Bull., 84:34–58.

——— 1944 The induction of larval molts in Drosophila. Biol. Bull., 86:113–124.

———, and Sacktor, B. 1952 Cytochrome c oxidase activity during the metamorphosis of *Drosophila virilis*. Science, n.s. *116:*299–300.

Bolten, M. 1926 Ein Fall von Thyroid-Insuffizienz bei einer Froschlarve. Nederlandsel Tydsch v. Geneesk., *70:*1711–1713.

Borland, J. 1943 The production of experimental goiter in *Rana pipiens* tadpoles by cabbage feeding and methyl cyanide. J. Exp. Zool., *94:*115–140.

Bounhiol, J. 1937 La métamorphose des insectes serait inhibée dans leur jeune age par les corpora allata? Compt. Rend. Soc. Biol., *126:*1189–1191.

—— 1938 Recherches expérimentales sur le déterminisme de la métamorphose chez les Lépidoptères. Bull. Biol. France et Belg. Suppl., *24:* 1–199.

Brinck, H. 1939 A histological and cytological investigation of the thyroids of *Arthroleptella bicolor villiersi* and *Bufo angustriceps* during the normal and experimentally accelerated metamorphosis. Proc. Linn. Soc. London, *151:*120–125.

Buddenbrock, W. von 1931 Untersuchungen über die Häutungshormone der Schmetterlingsraupen, II. Zeit. f. vergl. Physiol., *14:*415–428.

Burtt, E. 1938 On the corpora allata of dipterous insects, II. Proc. Roy. Soc. London B, *126:*210–223.

Bytinsky-Salz, H. 1935 Heteroplastic transplantation of the hypophysis in Amblystoma. J. Exp. Zool., *72:*51–73.

Caspari, E. 1941 The influence of low temperature on the pupation of *Ephestia kuhniella*, Zeller. J. Exp. Zool., *86:*321–331.

——, and Plagge, E. 1935 Versuche zur Physiologie der Verpuppung von Schmetterlingsraupen. Naturwiss., *23:*751–752.

Cazal, P. 1948 Les glandes endocrines rétrocérébrales des insectes. Bull. Biol. France et Belg. Suppl., *32:*1–227.

Champy, C. 1922 L'action de l'extrait thyroidien. Arch. Morph. Gen. Exper., *4:*1–56.

Charipper, H., and Corey, C. 1930 Studies on amphibian endocrines, V. Anat. Rec., *45:*258.

Choi, M. 1932 Homoiotransplantation of the amphibian thyroid anlage. Folio Anat. Jap., *10:*25–27.

Clausen, H. 1930 Rate of histolysis of anuran tail skin and muscle during metamorphosis. Biol. Bull., *59:*199–210.

Clements, D. 1932 Comparative histological studies of the thyroids and pituitaries in frog tadpoles in normal and accelerated metamorphosis. J. Roy. Microsc. Soc., *52:*138–148.

Cutting, C., and Tainter, M. 1933 Comparative effects of dinitrophenol and thyroxine on tadpole metamorphosis. Proc. Soc. Exper. Biol. & Med., *31:*97–100.

D'Angelo, D., Gordon, A., and Charipper, H. 1941 The role of the thyroid and pituitary glands in the anomalous effect of inanition on amphibian metamorphosis. J. Exp. Zool., *87:*259–277.

Demuth, F. 1933 Über die Beziehungen des Energiestoffwechsels zu Wachstum und Differenzierung. Roux' Arch. Entw.-mech., *130:*340–352.

Etkin, W. 1930 Growth of the thyroid gland of *Rana pipiens* in relation to metamorphosis. Biol. Bull., *59:*285–292.

—— 1932 Growth and resorption phenomena in anuran metamorphosis, I. Physiol. Zool., *5:* 275–300.

—— 1934 The phenomena of anuran metamorphosis, II. Physiol. Zool., *7:*129–148.

—— 1935a The mechanisms of anuran metamorphosis, I. J. Exp. Zool., *71:*317–340.

—— 1935b Effects of multiple pituitary primordia in the tadpole. Proc. Soc. Exper. Biol. & Med., *32:*1653–1655.

—— 1936a The phenomena of anuran metamorphosis, III. J. Morph., *59:*69–90.

—— 1936b A thyrotropic field surrounding the immature pituitary of the tadpole. Proc. Soc. Exper. Biol. & Med., *34:*508–512.

—— 1938 The development of thyrotropic function in pituitary grafts in the tadpole. J. Exp. Zool., *77:*347–377.

—— 1939 A thyrotropic field effect in the tadpole, I. J. Exp. Zool., *82:*463–496.

—— 1950 The acquisition of thyroxine-sensitivity by tadpole tissues. Anat. Rec., *108:*541.

——, Root, R., and Mofshin, B. 1940 The effect of thyroid feeding on oxygen consumption of the goldfish. Physiol. Zool., *13:*415–429.

Figge, F. H. 1930 A morphological explanation for failure of Necturus to metamorphose. J. Exp. Zool., *56:*241–254.

—— 1934 The effect of ligation of the pulmonary arch on amphibian metamorphosis. Physiol. Zool., *7:*149–177.

——, and Uhlenhuth, E. 1933 The morphology and physiology of the salamander thyroid gland, VIII. Physiol. Zool., *6:*450–465.

Fosi, V. 1935 Osservzioni sull' influenza della temperatura e degli estratte tiroidei sulla neotenia parziale dei girini di *Rana esculenta*. Monitore Zool. Ital., *46:*249–252.

Fraenkel, G. 1935 A hormone causing pupation in the blowfly *Calliphora erythrocephala*. Proc. Roy. Soc. London. B, *118:*1–12.

Frew, J. 1928 A technique for the cultivation of insect tissues. J. Exp. Biol., *6:*1–11.

Fukai, T. 1934 On the synchronous degeneration of the transplanted tail and the original tail in the metamorphosis of Bufo larva. Folia. Anat. Jap., *12:*159–164.

Fukuda, S. 1939 Acceleration of development of silkworm ovary by transplantation into young pupa. Proc. Imp. Acad. Japan, *15:*19–21.

—— 1940a Induction of pupation in silkworm by transplanting the prothoracic gland. Proc. Imp. Acad. Japan, *16:*414–416.

—— 1940b Hormonal control of molting and pupation in the silkworm. Proc. Imp. Acad. Japan, *16:*417–420.

—— 1941a Induction of metamorphosis in the silkworm by transplanting pupal prothoracic gland. Zool. Mag. (Tokyo), *53:*582–584.

—— 1941b Role of the prothoracic gland in differentiation of the imaginal characters in the silkworm pupa. Annot. Zool. Japon., *20:*9–13.

—— 1944 The hormonal mechanism of larval

molting and metamorphosis in the silkworm. J. Fac. Sci. Imp. Univ. Tokyo, Sect. 4, 6:477–532.

Furukawa, H. 1935 Can the skin of imago be made to molt. Proc. Imp. Acad. Japan, 11:158–160.

Garber, S. T. 1930 Metamorphosis of the axolotl following lung extirpation. Physiol. Zool., 3:373–378.

Geigy, R. 1938 Entwicklungsphysiologische Untersuchungen über die Anuren- und Urodelen-Metamorphose, II. Verh. Schweizer Naturforsch. Ges., 119:1–5.

———— 1941 Thyroxineinwirkung auf verschieden weit entwickelte Froshlarven. Verhandl. Schweiz. Naturforsch. Ges., 121:161–164.

Gorbman, A. 1946 Qualitative variation of the hypophyseal thyrotropic hormone in the vertebrates. Univ. Calif. Pub. Zool., 51:229–244.

Gordon, A., Goldsmith, E., and Charipper, H. 1943 Effect of thiourea on the development of the amphibian. Nature, 152:504–505.

Grant, M. 1931 The release of follicular colloid from the thyroid of Amblystoma jeffersonianum following heteroplastic pituitary implants. Anat. Rec., 49:373–395.

Green, J. D. 1951 The comparative anatomy of the hypophysis with special reference to its blood supply and innervation. Am. J. Anat., 88:225–311.

Gudernatsch, [J.] F. 1912 Feeding experiments on tadpoles, I. Roux' Arch. Entw.-mech., 35:457–483.

———— 1933 Entwicklung und Wachstum; in Handbuch der Inneren Sekretion, edited by M. Hirsch, Vol. 2, pt. 2, pp. 1493–1744. Curt Kabitzsch, Leipzig.

Gutman, A. 1926 Metamorphosis in Necturus maculatus by means of thyroxin-adrenalin treatment. Anat. Rec., 34:133–134.

Hachlow, V. 1931 Zur Entwicklungsmechanik der Schmetterlinge. Roux' Arch. Entw.-mech., 125:26–49.

Hadorn, E. 1937 An accelerating effect of normal "ring-glands" on puparium-formation in lethal larvae of Drosophila melanogaster. Proc. Nat. Acad. Sci., 23:478–484.

————, and Neel, J. 1938 Der hormonale Einfluss der Ringdrüse (corpus allatum) auf die Pupariumbildung bei Fliegen. Roux' Arch. Entw.-mech., 138:281–304.

Hartwig, H. 1936 Über die Beziehungen zwischen Schilddrüse und Entwicklung bei Salamanderlarven unter dem Einfluss verschiedener Temperaturen. Roux' Arch. Entw.-mech., 134:562–587.

Hegner, R. 1922 The effects of prostate substance on the metamorphosis of the intestine of frog tadpoles. Am. J. Physiol., 61:298–299.

Helff, O. M. 1926 Studies on amphibian metamorphosis, I. J. Exp. Zool., 45:1–67.

———— 1928 Studies on amphibian metamorphosis, III. Physiol. Zool., 1:463–495.

———— 1929 Studies on amphibian metamorphosis, IV. Physiol. Zool., 2:334–341.

———— 1930 Studies on amphibian metamorphosis, VIII. Anat. Rec., 47:177–186.

———— 1931a Studies on amphibian metamorphosis, IX. Biol. Bull., 60:11–22.

———— 1931b Studies on amphibian metamorphosis, VI. J. Exp. Zool., 59:167–177.

———— 1931c Studies on amphibian metamorphosis, VII. J. Exp. Zool., 59:179–196.

———— 1934 Studies on amphibian metamorphosis, XII. J. Exp. Zool., 68:305–319.

———— 1939 Studies on amphibian metamorphosis, XVI. J. Exp. Biol., 16:96–117.

———— 1940 Studies on amphibian metamorphosis, XVII. J. Exp. Biol., 17:45–60.

————, and Clausen, H. 1929 Studies on amphibian metamorphosis, V. Physiol. Zool., 2:575–586.

Hoffman, O. 1935 The antagonistic effect of methyl-cyanide on thyroxin-induced metamorphosis. J. Pharm. & Exper. Therap., 54:146.

Hoskins, E., and Hoskins, M. 1917 On thyroidectomy in Amphibia. Anat. Rec., 11:363.

————, and Hoskins, M. 1919a Growth and development of Amphibia as affected by thyroidectomy. J. Exp. Zool., 29:1–69.

————, and Hoskins, M. 1919b Experiments with the thyroid, hypophysis and pineal glands of Rana sylvatica. Anat. Rec., 16:151.

Huxley, J. 1922 Ductless glands and development. J. Hered., 13:349–358.

———— 1929 Thyroid and temperature in cold-blooded vertebrates. Nature, 123:712.

Ingram, W. 1929a Studies of amphibian neoteny, II. J. Exp. Zool., 53:387–410.

———— 1929b Studies in amphibian neoteny, I. Physiol. Zool., 2:149–156.

Joly, P. 1945 Les correlations humorales chez les insectes. Ann. Biol., 21:1–34.

Kaiser, P. 1949 Histologische Untersuchungen über die Corpora allata und Prothoraxdrüsen der Lepidopteren in Bezug auf ihre Funktion. Roux' Arch. Entw.-mech., 144:99–131.

Kaltenbach, J. 1949 Local metamorphosis of Rana pipiens larvae by thyroxin-cholesterol implants. Anat. Rec., 103:544.

Kollros, J. 1942 Localized maturation of lid-closure reflex mechanism by thyroid implants into tadpole hindbrain. Proc. Soc. Exper. Biol. & Med., 49:204–206.

————, and Pepernik, V. 1952 Hormonal control of the size of mesencephalic V nucleus cells in Rana pipiens. Anat. Rec., 113:527.

————, Pepernik, V., Hill, R., and Kaltenbach, J. 1950 The growth of mesencephalic V nucleus cells as a metamorphic event in anurans. Anat. Rec., 108:565.

Kopec, S. 1922 Studies on the necessity of the brain for the inception of insect metamorphosis. Biol. Bull., 42:322–342.

———— 1924 Studies on the influence of inanition on the development and the duration of life in insects. Biol. Bull., 46:1–21.

Kornfeld, W. 1914 Abhängigkeit der metamorphotischen Kiemenrückbildung vom Gesamtor-

tube containing a bubble of oxygen placed over the end of the stem inhibits regeneration (Rose and Rose, '41). This inhibition is not caused by a lack of oxygen, since oxygen is supplied and therefore inhibition must be caused by the accumulation of excretory substances within the glass tube. In the case of the ascidian stolon, either carbon dioxide or urea or uric acid will inhibit zooid formation but allow stolons to grow.

In summary, we may conclude that in some organisms, at any rate, a surface layer prevents free diffusion of substances which inhibit regeneration. When the surface layer is removed by cutting, then carbon dioxide, urea and uric acid escape more readily and the exposed region is able to undergo regeneration.

POTENCIES OF CELLS

During early embryonic development an important question is, In how many ways can the various cells differentiate? Similarly we may ask whether the cells participating in regeneration have wide potencies or limited potencies. This problem is difficult to solve and perhaps we can do little more here than to state the problem.

In the first place we may visualize a number of possibilities as regards the potencies of the regenerating cells.

1. Imagine that all of the cells at the cut surface proliferate and form a mass of undifferentiated cells with wide potencies. Then some inductive influence from adjacent structures must induce differentiation.

2. The cells at the cut surface dedifferentiate morphologically but retain their specificity as regards cell types. Then a muscle cell which dedifferentiates must redifferentiate into a muscle cell. Cells retain their limited potencies.

3. Cells at the cut surface do not proliferate but rather transform directly into the regenerating structures. This process may or may not involve changes in cell type. Some cells must have a number of potencies to supply missing structures.

4. The cells at the cut surface take little part in regeneration and the main source is from undifferentiated cells which migrate to the site of the wound. Missing structures would thus differentiate from reserve cells (embryonic cells, neoblasts, formative cells, eleocytes) which are present throughout adult tissues and have wide potencies.

The whole problem of the origin of the cells which differentiate during regeneration and the very important implications in regard to a possible reversal of biochemical differentiation will be a challenge to investigators for some time. A histological dedifferentiation is clearly shown by Huxley's histological studies on ascidians. How are we going to trace cells during regeneration? Can we trace a nerve cell from the adult ascidian zooid into the stolon during regression and then trace this same cell back into the new zooid which forms from this stolon? Does this nerve cell redifferentiate into a nerve ganglion cell or may it form an intestinal cell? Are cell types immutable? For those who maintain the affirmative to this latter question I would point out that the atom was once considered immutable. As to those who take the negative, I must remind them that conclusive evidence of a major change in cell type is still wanting.

Certain facts are clear and must be considered before reaching a judgment on this question. In forms such as Tubularia the hydranth develops directly from the coenosarc near the cut surface. There is no growth and little cell division. A section of the stem about 2 mm. in length transforms directly and quickly (24 hours) into a hydranth. There can be no question here of reserve cells migrating in from the rest of the stem and differentiating into a hydranth. Indeed, a section of the stem 2 mm. long will transform completely into a bipolar form with a hydranth at each end. Nor is there any proliferation of reserve cells accompanied by a degeneration of cells of the stem. Therefore a cell which is part of the stem is converted directly into a cell forming part of a tentacle.

During the regression of an ascidian zooid into the stolon, the latter becomes packed with cells which dissociate from the tissues of the zooid (Huxley, '26). These cells flow through the circulatory system. They are alive as witnessed by observation of the living stolon and by histological examination. Therefore nerve, heart and intestinal cells pass from the regressing zooid into the stolon. This stolon may then form zooids when cut into short sections. What happens to the nerve, heart and intestinal cells when the new zooid forms? Do they undergo cytolysis or do they take part in the formation of the new zooid? There is no evidence of extensive cytolysis and thus the cells probably enter the new zooid. If they do, will a former nerve cell enter the intestinal tract and become a secretory cell or must it redifferentiate into a nerve cell? This question cannot be answered definitely. Recall, however, that isolated parts of the adult zooid will regress and form a mass of morphologically dedifferentiated cells. This mass can then form a complete zooid of reduced size. In this instance when a region lacking the nerve ganglion is isolated, where does the new nerve ganglion come from? I would like to urge a study of ascidian cell types and their behavior during regression of the zooids, during dedifferentiation of the stolon and during regeneration of the parts of the zooid. This material is relatively easy to handle and changes are relatively rapid, an important consideration where so much exploratory research still remains. Consultation of the papers of Driesch ('06), Spek ('27), Huxley ('26), Deviney ('34), Berrill and Cohen ('36), and Goldin ('48) will be valuable in this connection.

Another form which appears admirable for studies on potencies of cells is the sponge. Here cells may be dissociated and they will aggregate and reconstitute a sponge. The nature of the cells which take part in the formation of the new sponge is still a matter for investigation (Galtsoff, '25; Wilson and Penney, '30; Penney, '33; de Laubenfels, '34). However, since the adult sponge may be broken up into individual cells, there may be a means of separating the various cell types and examining each type for its ability to differentiate. If the various cell types differ by some property such as specific gravity, then centrifuging the dissociated cells in sugar solutions would separate the cells into layers.

CORRELATIVE DIFFERENTIATION

As in embryonic development the differentiation of tissues during regeneration depends on factors located in adjacent tissues. The organizer phenomenon has been investigated in flatworms (Santos, '31; Miller, '38) and in coelenterates (Child, '29; Li and Yao, '45). In Dugesia the head region acts as an organizer inducing changes in the surrounding tissues. A small fragment of the head region transplanted to the body region will induce an outgrowth that develops into a head and in addition induces the host tissue to form a pharynx. What are the similarities between the organizer in Dugesia and the amphibian organizer? 1. A small piece of transplanted tissue induces a large part of the host to differentiate. 2. Dugesia organizer is not species specific and heteroplastic induction occurs. 3. The organ-

izer is localized. In planarians it is restricted to the head region while in an amphibian gastrula only cells from the dorsal and lateral lips of the blastopore will induce.

In flatworms and annelids the nervous system may play a special role in regeneration. The nerve tissue appears to act as an organizer for head structures. However, regeneration of heads will still occur in absence of nerve cord at the cut surface. These observations are in keeping with the properties of the amphibian organizer phenomenon where, although nerve tissue is a good organizer, the chorda-mesoderm is the primary organizer. For a discussion of the role of the nervous system in various invertebrates, see Child ('42, pp. 338–341).

Another expression of correlative differentiation is found in the regeneration of the hydranth in Tubularia. If a piece of stem is isolated, the apical (distal) cut end differentiates into a hydranth while the basal (proximal) cut end forms a stolon. The apical end exercises an inhibition over the regeneration of the basal end, a fact which can easily be demonstrated by preventing the apical end from regenerating with the result that the basal end then regenerates a hydranth instead of a stolon. Thus differentiation of the *basal* end into stolon or hydranth is correlated with the presence or absence of differentiation at the apical end.

The mechanism by which the regenerating apical end influences basal regeneration has been investigated from two points of view, that of electrical differences in potential and that of competition.

1. Correlations have been shown to exist between the *electrical differences in potential* and the behavior of the two cut surfaces of the hydroid stem (see Child, '42, and Lund and others, '47, for literature). If electrodes are placed on the two ends of the stem a P.D. can be measured. If a constant electric current is passed through sea water containing stems, regeneration is inhibited at one pole but normal hydranths regenerate at the opposite pole. Thus an electric current may determine polarity. The question as to whether the electrical potential difference measured between the two ends gives rise to a current *within* the stem of sufficient intensity to account for the inhibition exercised by the distal end over the proximal end is still a matter for investigation. The possibility that P.D.'s are effective in other forms such as the earthworm has been more recently studied by Moment ('46).

The general hypothesis of the E.D.P. as

controlling cellular differentiation is an attractive one but beset with great difficulties which should be a challenge to investigators. The electrical difference in potential must have its origin in concentration differences chemical differences and without significance in regeneration? For a complete discussion of the problem see Lund ('47).

2. Quite a different hypothesis is that of the existence of *competition* among groups

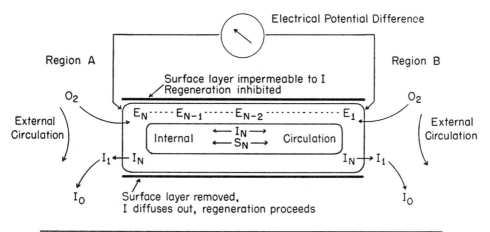

Electrical Potential Difference

Region A   Region B

Surface layer impermeable to I
Regeneration inhibited

O_2 O_2

External   External
Circulation   Circulation

$E_N \cdots E_{N-1} \cdots E_{N-2} \cdots \cdots \cdots E_1$

Internal $\quad \overset{I_N \longrightarrow}{\underset{S_N \longrightarrow}{\longleftarrow}} \quad$ Circulation

$I_1 \leftarrow I_N$ $\qquad\qquad\qquad\qquad$ $I_N \to I_1$

I_0 $\qquad$ Surface layer removed, $\qquad\qquad$ I_0
I diffuses out, regeneration proceeds

ROLE OF INHIBITOR

$[E]_N + [I]_N \rightleftarrows [EI]_{N-1}$

$[Substrates]_N \overset{\downarrow}{\underset{\longleftarrow}{\longrightarrow}}$ Hydranth

Hydranth forms in presence of $[I]_N$ because enzymes are at $[E]_N$.

$[E]_1 + [I_N] \rightleftarrows [EI]_1$

$[Substrates]_N \overset{\downarrow}{\underset{\longrightarrow}{\longleftarrow}}$ Hydranth

Hydranth fails to form in presence of $[I]_N$ because at low concentration $[E]_1$, enzyme is removed.

ROLE OF SUBSTRATES

$[E]_N$

$[Substrates]_N \overset{\downarrow}{\underset{\longleftarrow}{\longrightarrow}}$ Hydranth

Hydranth forms because:
$[E]_N \cdot [Substrates]_N = K_N$ which is above threshold for hydranth regeneration.

$[E]_1$

$[Substrates]_N \overset{\downarrow}{\longleftarrow}$ Hydranth

Hydranth fails to form because:
$[E]_1 \cdot [Substrates]_N = K_1$ which is below threshold for hydranth regeneration.

EFFECT OF BLOCKING INTERNAL CIRCULATION

Rapid utilization of substrates by high concentration of $[E]_N$ lowers concentration to $[S]_{N-1}$. However, $[E]_N \cdot [S]_{N-1} = K_{N-1}$ which is still well above threshold for regeneration.

When Region A is no longer utilizing substrates from Region B, the concentration of S rises to $[S]_{N+1}$. Then $[E]_1 \cdot [S]_{N+1} = K_2$ which is above threshold for regeneration.

Fig. 230.

arising from differences in either the kind of metabolism or the rate of metabolism. What is the primary difference? May not the differences in metabolism themselves be sufficient to account for the polarity phenomena and control of regeneration without any intervention of electrical potentials? Are these potentials merely the consequence of of cells such that some groups more adequately endowed or situated are able to inhibit cells living under less favorable conditions (Barth, '38; Spiegelman, '45). The general assumption is made that differentiating cells require energy for structural changes and need materials for synthesis of chemical constituents. In addition, differ-

entiation results in the formation of excretory products such as carbon dioxide and
nitrogenous compounds and these substances
have inhibitory effects. Therefore any two
groups of cells potentially able to regenerate
may be competing with each other by uti-

ganism or by an environmental difference
imposed from without. The situation is outlined in Figure 230.

Numerous simple experiments are consistent with the competition hypothesis. In
Tubularia it is possible to select pieces of

CONTROL OF REGENERATION BY INHIBITION

By contact

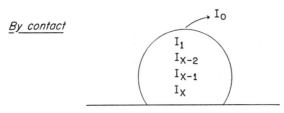

Inhibitor accumulates at surface of contact and hydranth develops
at free surface.

By mutual inhibition

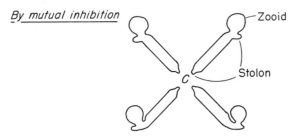

Inhibitor accumulates in center, C, where four sources are in close
proximity.

By CO_2

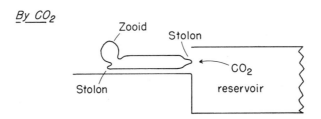

CO_2, urea, uric acid permit stolon growth but inhibit zooid formation.

Fig. 231.

lizing common substrates and by excreting
common inhibitory substances. Now, if the
two groups of cells, A and B, differ initially
by some quantitative factor in their chemical
make-up, then A may be better equipped to
utilize substrates and resist inhibitory compounds as compared with B. Therefore, A
may inhibit the regeneration of B and different structures will result at A and B. The
initial difference between A and B would
be derived from a gradient in the whole or-

stem of such a length and age that regeneration always occurs at the distal (apical)
end but not at the proximal (basal) end.
It is only necessary to make a ligature at
the middle of such stems and then both
ends form hydranths. What are the effects
of tying a ligature? The tissue is constricted
and separated at the ligature so that circulation between the two ends is stopped.
Neither inhibitory substances nor substrates
can pass from the apical end to the basal

end. Of course any electric current flowing through the stem would also be broken by the ligature since there is no connection between the ends save through the non-cellular perisarc. In an effort to see whether the circulation or the cellular connections transmit the inhibition, two kinds of experiments were carried out. 1. Circulation was blocked by means of an oil droplet or an air bubble (Fig. 230). The basal end then was freed of inhibition and regenerated a hydranth. 2. A glass tube was inserted into the coelenteron and the tissue ligatured around this tube. The circulatory fluid would pass through the tube but the cellular connections between the two ends was broken. Under these conditions the basal end was inhibited. Evidently the inhibition is transported through the circulation (Barth, '40; Rose and Rose, '41).

Continuing with the analysis, now using ascidians, it can be shown that excretory products inhibit regeneration of zooids from pieces of the stolon (Barth and Barth, '50). Four to six pieces were placed with one of their ends in close proximity, but not touching, in the manner of spokes in a wheel (Fig. 231). Thus one end of each piece was exposed to the accumulated excretory products of all the others while the opposite end was not so exposed. The ends in close proximity were inhibited and zooids did not form. The opposite free ends developed zooids. Next carbon dioxide was applied in graded concentration to one end of the piece and the end at the highest concentration of carbon dioxide grew out as a stolon while the end at the lowest concentration formed a zooid (Fig. 231). Urea and uric acid also inhibit zooid formation in a like manner.

Analyzing these simple observations we see that substances pass through the circulation between one end, A, of a regenerate to the other end, B, and that the inhibition of end B is released by isolating it from end A. A therefore either (1) takes away from B substances necessary for the regeneration of a particular structure C; or (2) A produces inhibitory products, I, in such amounts that the concentration of I is too high for the regeneration of C at B. Therefore some other structure, D, regenerates at B instead of C. We have advanced no argument for (1). Indeed the arguments for this possibility are as yet too tenuous (Fig. 230) since substrate concentration has not been controlled. However, we have direct evidence that excretory products do inhibit the differentia-

tion of C but permit the differentiation of D.

These observations and experiments make the competition hypothesis attractive for future studies, but it seems only reasonable to investigate the effects of the above experimental treatments on electrical potential differences.

ENVIRONMENTAL FACTORS

For regeneration to proceed the external medium must meet the usual requirements of temperature adjustment, hydrogen ion control, gaseous exchange, salt balance and osmotic pressure. In addition, in marine organisms especially, the rate of circulation of the sea water and the population density are important factors. The presence or absence of a surface for attachment is a factor in sessile animals. In general the requirements for regeneration in regard to environmental factors are more rigid than for simple maintenance. For example, Tubularia stems remain healthy at low oxygen tension, but fail to regenerate a hydranth. In certain ascidians, stolons will maintain themselves in standing sea water at 28° C., but regeneration of a zooid does not occur unless the temperature is reduced to 23° C. (Jaeger and Barth, '48).

Temperature is a very important factor in marine organisms during the summer months when much of the work on regeneration is done. Laboratory temperatures are often too high for regeneration and a lowering of the temperature by a few degrees centigrade is then necessary. Temperature effects are related to rate of circulation of sea water in such a way that regeneration will occur at higher temperatures in running sea water as compared with standing sea water. Certain ascidian stolons will form zooids at 28° C. in running sea water but not in standing sea water. Hydroid stems show a similar behavior. A reasonable interpretation of the above observations is that inhibitory products accumulate in the cells faster in standing sea water, and possibly the oxygen tension within the cell is lower, than in circulating sea water. If this is so then lowering of the temperature will, by lowering the rate of metabolism, decrease the rate of accumulation of excretory products and will also increase the internal oxygen tension.

Population density. The numbers of individual regenerating parts, or perhaps better the total mass of cells per unit volume of external medium, is a factor in regeneration.

A mutual inhibition of regeneration is obtained when many stems or stolons are present as compared with few. Widely separated parts regenerate better than crowded parts. This phenomenon is best explained as a more rapid accumulation of inhibitory substances by many as compared with few regenerates. The optimum number will depend on temperature and rate of circulation of sea water and on proximity of regenerates as discussed above.

Gaseous exchange. It is seen from the foregoing that temperature, circulation and population density are related to gaseous exchange and excretions. Oxygen stimulates regeneration in Tubularia and carbon dioxide inhibits it (Goldin, '42). Increasing hydrogen-ion concentration also inhibits. In ascidians, carbon dioxide, urea and uric acid inhibit. The inhibitory effect on regeneration in Tubularia of accumulated carbon dioxide at high population densities is shown by the use of Warburg manometers. With large numbers of stems of Tubularia in the Warburg flasks and no potassium hydroxide to absorb carbon dioxide, no regeneration occurs. The same number of stems in a flask with potassium hydroxide regenerate completely. Since the respiratory quotient during regeneration is 1.0 it may be that carbon dioxide and ammonia are the chief excretory products.

Salt balance. Calcium salts are particularly necessary for cell aggregation of the dissociated cells of the sponge (Galtsoff, '25). In absence of the Ca^{++} ion, dissociated cells do not aggregate and therefore no regeneration is possible. Ca^{++} no doubt acts on the cell surface to maintain the intercellular matrix as it does in the dividing egg.

Amino acids. The specific quantitative and qualitative effects of various amino acids have been investigated for a number of years by Hammett ('43) and his co-workers on regeneration of hydroids and growth of other forms. The process of regeneration is broken up into a number of individual processes and the papers of this school should be consulted for details.

Radiations often inhibit regeneration without interfering with maintenance of life.

METABOLISM AND REGENERATION

Here is an attractive new field for investigation. The ultramicrochemical and ultramicromanometric methods of the Linderstrøm-Lang and Heinz Holter school plus the methods of Kirk and his co-workers have made possible exact studies on masses of tissue of the order of magnitude provided by regenerates. The cytochemical methods for phosphatases and nucleoproteins offer the opportunity for studying phosphate transfer and the role of nucleic acid during regeneration. Some progress has been made and has been reviewed by Brachet ('50).

The analysis of the problem appears to be as follows: Energy is required for the differentiation of cells. The initial source of this energy comes from cellular oxidations. The free energy of cellular oxidations is transferred and conserved in an energy-rich phosphate bond. Compounds containing the energy-rich phosphate bond transfer phosphate to proteins and the free energy of the splitting of an energy-rich bond is utilized in performing work. The work may be lifting a weight, as in muscular contraction, or the work may consist in change in cell shape and the chemical constitution of the cell. In this analysis the critical linkage between the oxidations and the performance of work appears to be through phosphate compounds and the controlling factors may be the enzymes which split and transfer phosphate.

In this connection Jaeger and Barth ('48) have shown that the undifferentiated stolon cells of ascidians have no water-extractable apyrases while the zooids do. As the stolon differentiates into a zooid the apyrases appear. The initial step in any differentiation may be the formation of a new apyrase which transfers the energy of oxidations to the specific work required for the formation of a specific cell type.

REFERENCES

Barth, L. G. 1938 Quantitative studies of the factors governing the rate of regeneration in Tubularia. Biol. Bull., *74*:155–177.
——— 1940 The process of regeneration in hydroids. Biol. Rev., *15*:405–20.
———, and Barth, Lucena J. 1950 The control of differentiation by external factors. Anat. Rec., *108*:587.
Berrill, N. J. 1951 Regeneration and budding in tunicates. Biol. Rev., *26*:456–475.
———, and Cohen, A. 1936 Regeneration in *Clavellina lepadiformis*. J. Exp. Biol., *13*:352–362.
Brachet, J. 1950 Chemical Embryology. Interscience Publishers, New York.
Child, C. M. 1929 Lateral grafts and incisions as organizers in the hydroid Corymorpha. Physiol. Zool., *2*:342.
——— 1942 Patterns and Problems of Development. University of Chicago Press, Chicago.

structures, the capacity for regeneration again appears. The nervous system which regenerates in the early shield stages fails to regenerate in later formative stages.

AMPHIBIA

Regenerative processes have been studied in amphibians over a very long period. Spallanzani (1768) recorded many definite experiments in the Prodromo, and the literature of the nineteenth century is full of allusions to naturally occurring forms which came to notice because of the abnormality which appeared either during or after the regenerative process. These forms which appear with a fair frequency in nature often are exceedingly difficult to interpret and in some cases impossible to duplicate in the laboratory. Hellmich ('30), for example, figured a salamander with a single but huge limb near the dorsal midline at the general limb level. In this particular location an embryonic transplant would have to be made early in the embryo and probably would resorb in a great proportion of such cases.

It is impossible to interpret the abnormalities found in nature except hypothetically. Bateson (1894) gave a rough classification of abnormalities, as did Przibram ('26) in his later catalogue. Tornier ('06) showed that all the forms produced could be called examples of the multiplicities occurring after regeneration by a single but drastic experiment. With a single cut through a tadpole extending through the forming hind limbs, Tornier secured animals with 6 to 8 multiple limbs.

The situation is considerably clouded in amphibians, owing to the life histories of various forms. Not all amphibians have an equal power for regeneration at all stages in their history; the anurans normally are restricted in regenerative capacity to larval stages. The length of the embryonic and larval stages varies tremendously; in some of the tropical forms metamorphosis is almost part of the embryonic period; in others, as in the bullfrog, two full years may lapse before metamorphosis is complete. These variabilities when correlated with the capacity to regenerate offer little in the way of a constant around which we can collect the varied miscellany of events. Kammerer ('05) discussed an absolute age and claimed that this, rather than the stage, determines regenerative capacity. We find this same general idea in general growth studies when the necessity for evolving a base level has given rise to all sorts of postulated constants.

Embryonic regeneration constitutes dangerous ground, for it is difficult to speak of regeneration in a structure which is going through its formative stages. Nevertheless, the term has been used frequently and the issue was clearly raised when the Roux-Driesch controversy on capacity of the half egg was occupying the center of biological attention. The circumstances of this situation are well known. Suffice it to state that Roux's idea of the egg as a mosaic was founded upon the half embryo developing from a single blastomere. Schultze (1894) turned the egg after killing one blastomere and secured a small but complete embryo. When Roux restudied the question he was faced with a negation of the mosaic idea, but instead of retracting he called the process by which more than a half embryo is formed post-regeneration. Now it is well known that the amphibian egg is capable of a fairly complete internal reorganization; it has been proved most conclusively that its capacity to continue development and ultimately produce a complete and normal embryo can hardly be blocked by any experimental contingency. In the face of these facts, it might be better to assume that the reconstitution is a form of regulation which is possessed to an unusual degree by the embryo.

This is shown clearly in some of the limb experiments (Harrison, '18). In some cases of incomplete duplicity the manus developing after rotation of the embryonic limb disc may be represented only by a small spear of tissue. If this be cut after it has developed to the late embryonic or early larval stages, the regenerating appendage frequently is much more complete than that originally secured and will show sufficient morphological criteria for an accurate diagnosis of the asymmetry. Swett ('24) also used this method in studying the process of reduplication. In both these cases the investigator is using regenerative processes to explain embryonic reactions during the process of reorganization of the limb. These processes differ only in degree from the original formation of the end organ. The embryonic structure is drawn from a wide embryonic field, while the regenerated structure is derived from a much smaller and more localized field. The problem of the field of regenerative organization has been ably discussed by Weiss ('26a) and Guyénot ('29). The essential point which the field concept has added is the postulation of a directive force orienting particles in a field.

In the urodeles the speed of regeneration is sometimes much faster in the larvae than in adults. In older larvae and in neotenous forms there is sometimes a noticeable failure in the capacity of the organism to regenerate after minor operations, e.g., a slight V-shaped piece of tissue may be removed from the dorsal fin extending to the upper surface

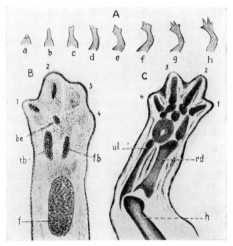

Fig. 234. Regeneration of the salamander extremity (*Triturus taeniatus*). A, a–h, Varying stages in the regeneration of the forelimb; B, differentiation of skeletal parts in the right hind leg; C, further advanced differentiation in the left forelimb. (From Fraisse, 1885.)

of the myotome. The edges heal but the tissue, which is of a rather nondescript and unorganized type, may not be replaced. In fishes when the fibrillae alone are removed from the dorsal fin, there is no reconstitution.

An entirely different situation occurs in the anurans where normally the limbs regenerate only during larval stages. The exceptions will be considered below. Barfurth (1895) worked on the limb problem in *Rana fusca*. When the limb was amputated while still in the condition of a small bud (no real limb), regeneration occurred and was complete in detail. When an amputation was performed upon a paddle-shaped appendage when the digits were just beginning to show, imperfectly formed appendages were secured, the deficiency being marked in the foot. After the stage where digitation is complete and the knee bud is marked, an amputation provokes little or at most imperfect regeneration. These results were

repeated by Byrnes ('04) upon the forelimb with nearly identical results.

Guyénot ('27) studied the decrease in capacity to regenerate. The capacity to regenerate lasts longer in the tail than in the limb. If a limb is heteroplastically grafted from a toad to a salamander it fails to regenerate in its new location. If, however, a tail is similarly grafted, it will regenerate. The failure of the limb is due to something intrinsic in the limb tissue and is not due to the internal medium. The transplanted urodele tail will regenerate even though retrogressing during metamorphosis.

Harrison's ('21) thorough analysis of the problem of asymmetry with the embryonic forelimb has been adequately supplemented by Weiss' ('26b) results with larval and adult limbs. Weiss cut the limb so that he got two definite surfaces, from each of which a complete limb developed. The regenerative blastema is a harmonious equipotential system in the Driesch sense. It is possible, in the light of Holtfreter's ('47) experiments, that the blastema may serve as an organizing center and that the results obtained in some transplantation experiments may be secured from host tissue by induction. This is particularly true in early larval stages.

The active regeneration capacity of newts and salamanders is almost unlimited, particularly with respect to the limb. This will regenerate at any time and at any level (Fritsch, '11). The limb and its girdle can be removed and regeneration of the limb will take place. In other words, no matter how complete the removal, the limb is reconstituted and is a complete functional limb.

Braus ('09) showed the independence of limb formation in the embryo from skeletal parts. Wendelstadt ('04) thought, on the basis of his experiments, that the presence of the skeleton was essential for regeneration. A part of the bone when removed was regenerated, but when the whole structure was carefully disarticulated no regeneration occurred. Strasser (1879), Goette (1879) and later Morrill ('18) had shown that when the limb was sectioned, perichondrium and periostium became very active and made up a substantial part of the blastema. Weiss ('25a) repeated and extended Wendelstadt's experiments and showed that removal of the skeleton did not prevent the appearance of skeleton in the newly regenerating limb, but in confirmation of Wendelstadt there was *no* regeneration of a completely extirpated skeletal element in its old bed. Only if a remnant of a skeletal element is left behind will this regenerate in its own right. Bischler ('26) showed that Wendelstadt's results were faulty, for when repeated in a large variety of experiments, she secured regeneration of both the free extremity and the skeleton.

Milojevic ('24) thought he had determined a polarization of the materials in the blastema. By interchanging the cap of fore and hind limb regenerating blastemas he found that during the first ten days the basal part

nutritional conditions, the interaction of other systems with their effects together with degenerative phenomena and capacities of regrowth. In this chaotic milieu the investigator is always trying to find order and certainly reaches a point when his own observations are coalesced into a subjective unit which appears satisfactory. So far, our ideas of the formation of the blastema can be outlined in much oversimplified form under the following headings:

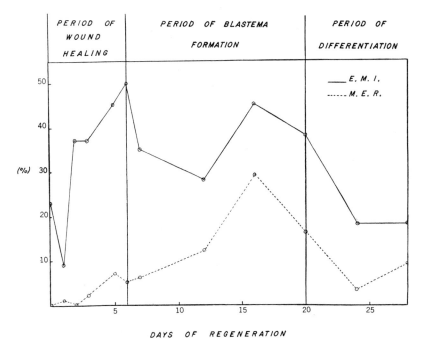

Fig. 235. Changes in the epidermal mitotic index (*E.M.I.*) and mesenchymal epidermal ratio (*M.E.R.*) during a 28-day period of regeneration. (From Manner, '53.)

influenced the distal part no matter what the orientation of the graft. After this indifferent period the distal part develops according to its origin with respect to both its axes and the form of the appendage. This work may be correct but the criteria used are not as reliable as Milojevic thought them to be. In the early regenerates it is very difficult to differentiate the fore from the hind limb and the bones themselves are too similar in form to permit an accurate interpretation.

The origin of the blastema has proved a fascinating enigma. So far there has not been a single absolutely critical experiment. Every worker in the field of limb regeneration has honestly tried to come to grips with this question, which is an exceedingly important one since it involves tissue reactions,

1. **Regeneration by extension,** in which after the healing of the wound and the dedifferentiation of tissues the regeneration blastema is formed and then becomes organized with the parts remaining, each giving rise to like tissues and the structures which grow to normal limits in replacement of the missing parts. This type of regeneration seems to occur in the tail but is not clear-cut in the limb.

2. **Blastema formation,** by the invasion of the wound area by new elements, generally from the blood stream, which act in the organization of the blastema and join with the cells there in the new growth process: hematogenic origin.

3. **The participation of the epidermis,** through dedifferentiation and a direct amalgamation of the epidermal elements into

blastema. This idea will need discussion since it has been revived by Rose's ('48) work.

4. **The origin of the blastema from reserve cells,** similar to the archeocytes of the worms

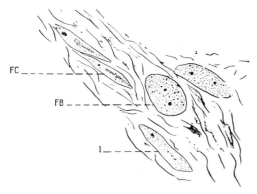

Fig. 236. Transition from fibroblast to fibrocyte. *FB*, Fibroblast; *I*, an intermediate type; *FC*, fibrocyte. Camera lucida drawing. × 450. (From Manner, '53.)

or from cells which retain their embryonal capacities and potentialities.

Unfortunately, most workers in the field usually adopt an intermediate position with regard to the above headings, e.g., Puckett ('34) considers the blastema as a cell mass composed of materials secured by complete dedifferentiation of all the formed elements. This logically means that the parts so generally derived have to undergo a complete sorting-out process to attain their later definite structural relationships. It is a combination of like from like with an intermediary dedifferentiation. The process of this sorting out is of course very difficult to follow and a causative mechanism so far has not been ascertained.

Manner ('53), like many others, has studied in detail the three phases which have to be considered in regeneration of the limb of Triturus, using as indices the changes in mitotic activity of the epidermal and mesenchymal tissues during the 28 days following amputation. (See Fig. 235.)

In securing his figures for the mitotic index he has been most careful to avoid some of the pitfalls of this method, e.g., Litwiller ('39) has shown that the mitotic index varies with the time of day; in recognition of this, Manner has removed the blastemata used for his study at a fixed time for all cases. Since the epidermis is the only tissue which can be counted accurately, he counts the mitotic mesenchymal cells

and compares this figure with the total number of epidermal cells at any given stage. A total count of all cells in the mesenchyme is practically impossible, since the amount of debris resulting from amputation is an obscuring factor which he recognizes. Nevertheless, by this comparison he secures a relative value which can be employed.

Manner draws a rather sharp line in definition between the fibroblast shown by Maximow and Bloom ('52) to possess the capacity for the formation of all connective tissue elements and the fibrocyte which has lost its embryonal capacities.

The evidence from this paper, as well as from others (Nassonov, '30; Thornton, '38b; Needham, '42; Liebman, '49), all points to a fibroblast cell as the effective agent in blastema formation. The possible influences engendered in the degeneration after amputation and the relationship of nerves and muscles are taken up as logical steps in the proximodistal progress of regeneration. It is fairly clear that the like from like principle does not hold here and that the sorting-out process is conditioned by the nerve sup-

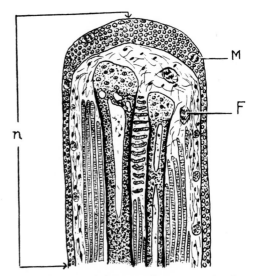

Fig. 237. General diagram of a regenerating forelimb. *M*, Epidermal mitotic cell; *F*, mesenchymal mitotic cell; *n*, the epidermal cells on one side, in a single section, from the level of amputation to the middle of the blastema. (From Manner, '53.)

ply in the presence of muscle. Epidermis certainly is not primarily needed (Weiss, '27); bone may be elimated from the stumps (Weiss, '25b; Thornton, '38b), and still regeneration takes place.

Other evidence such as the regeneration

TABLE 31. *Summary of the Major Histological Changes Occurring in the Adult Urodele Limb During a 28-Day Period of Regeneration (from Manner, '53)*

DAYS OF REGENERATION	MAJOR HISTOLOGICAL OBSERVATIONS
1 Day	The amputation wound is closed over by the migrating epidermal cells.
2 Days	Numerous phagocyte cells are present in the wound area. The disintegration of cartilage begins. The continued migration of the epidermal cells to the distal end of the regenerating limb results in an accumulation of these cells at this point.
5 Days	The disintegration of the striated muscle begins. The epidermal cells continue to accumulate at the distal end of the regenerating limb.
6 Days	The connective tissue, with its component cells, migrates between the cut end of the bone and the overlying epidermis. The disintegration of the cartilage and bone continues, resulting in cartilage and muscle fragments which presumably are incorporated into the blastema.
16 Days	There is a maximal accumulation of the epidermal cells at the tip of the regenerating limb. The disintegration of the cartilage and muscular tissue continues.
20 Days	The first finger makes its appearance. The fibroblasts are beginning to differentiate into chondroblasts. The disintegration of the cartilage and muscle ceases.
28 Days	The second finger makes its appearance. The new cartilage continues to differentiate.

of a haploid chimaeric limb (Hertwig, '27), or Butler's ('35) transplantations of an un-irradiated limb to an irradiated host which had no capacity for regeneration, or the histological studies showing that any or all of the mesodermal tissues can give rise to the formative elements of the blastema—all of these point to mesenchymal components as the essential elements in blastema formation.

A different line of evidence is secured in the work of Heath ('53). He replaced the ectoderm of the embryonic limb buds in two slow-growing species of salamander. When *A. tigrinum* ectoderm (fast-growing) is grafted over *Triturus torosus* limb bud mesoderm there is first a slight retardation in development, later an acceleration resulting in a larger than normal limb. When *T. torosus* ectoderm (slow-growing) is used

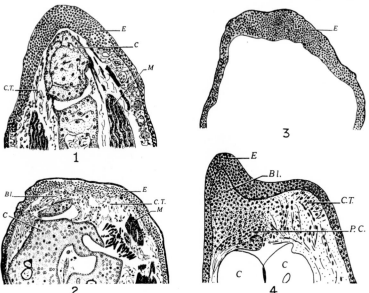

Fig. 238. *1*, 48 hours after amputation. *E*, Epidermis; *C*, cartilage; *M*, muscle; *C.T.*, connective tissue. Camera lucida drawing. × 100.

2, 6 days after amputation. *E*, Epidermis; *C*, cartilage; *M*, muscle; *C.T.*, connective tissue; *Bl*, blastema. Camera lucida drawing. × 100.

3, Epidermis at 16 days after amputation. *E*, Epidermis. Camera lucida drawing. × 100.

4, 20 days after amputation. *E*, Epidermis; *Bl.*, blastema; *C.T.*, connective tissue; *C*, cartilage; *P.C.*, precartilaginous tissue. Camera lucida drawing. × 100. (From Manner, '53.)

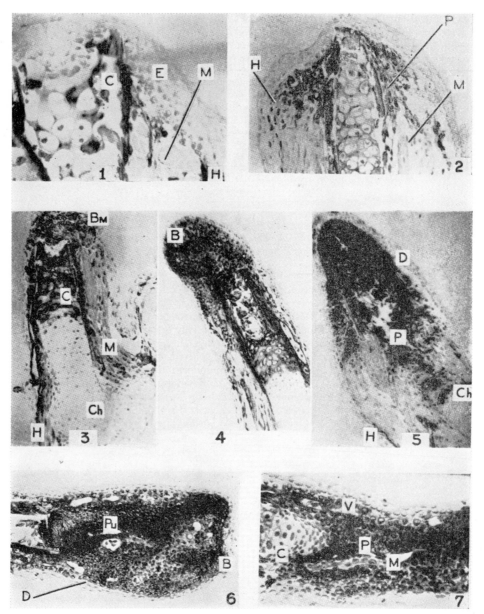

Fig. 239. *Amblystoma punctatum* larvae; 6μ sections of regenerating forelimbs, stained for alkaline phosphatase (from Karczmar and Berg, '51).

1, Normal enzyme distribution. Healing on the first day after amputation. *E,* Epidermal cap, + (single plus); *M,* muscle, + (single plus); *C,* diaphysis and marrow of humerus, + + (double plus); *H,* hypodermis. × 150.

2, Dedifferentiation and first increase in enzyme activity, third day after amputation. Hypodermis (*H*), perichondrium (*P*) and weakly staining muscle (*M*) dedifferentiating distally into + + (double plus) mesenchyme.

3, Accumulation of enzyme-rich mesenchyme: fifth day after amputation. *Bm,* Mesenchyme, staining + + (double plus) to + + + (triple plus); *C,* proximal epiphysis of humerus with + + + (triple plus) matrix; *Ch,* hyaline cartilage of shoulder joint with enzyme-free matrix; *M,* muscle, + (single plus); *H,* hypodermis, + + + (triple plus). × 80.

4, Early blastema with an apical gradient of enzyme activity, 9½ days after amputation. This section was incubated 20 hours beyond the optimum time, to test for the leakage of stain. The reference to cover the limb mesoderm of *A. tigrinum* the result is a smaller than normal limb. When the chimaeric larval limbs are amputated they regenerate according to the growth rate of the original mesodermal components. If the fast- or slow-growing species epidermis was an essential part in the formation of the blastema, it did not register in the size of the regenerate although it did have an effect upon the original limb growth. This indirect evidence suggests strongly that there is no epidermal contribution to the blastema.

Another line of evidence for the importance of mesoderm in the formation of the blastema is found in the work of Karczmar and Berg ('51). They have studied the occurrence of alkaline phosphatase during both embryonic development and regeneration in Amblystoma. Brachet ('46), Krugelis ('50), Lindeman ('49) and Moog ('44) have correlated the alkaline phosphatase content with various steps in differentiation phases of normal ontogeny. The importance of the study is that it tests whether normal ontogenic processes, in which alkaline phosphatase levels are low, are duplicated in the dedifferentiation subsequent to injury.

Histochemical localization of alkaline phosphatase was made (1) on 25 young larvae, 13 to 17 mm. long, (2) on 60 regenerating larvae, 25–47 mm. long, and (3) on adult regenerating limbs. In ontogeny the hind limb primordium (stage 47) shows cells with a high alkaline phosphatase content. As the limb bud (stages 49 and 50) begins to project from the body wall, the phosphatase activity is strongest at its apex. This relation persists and increases as the limb parallels the trunk (stage 50); later (stage 50+) the stain shows a definite concentration at the base of the elongating limb, marking the

site of presumptive limb components. In stages 51 and 52, enzyme activity decreases locally and the differentiating tissues separate regionally into loci of lower and higher enzyme activity.

This brief description is applicable to the regional development of the differentiating limb components. When, however, the specific tissue differentiations occur there is a decrease in the alkaline phosphatase activity during myogenesis and by the time the muscle bundles are formed the phosphatase decreases to the relatively low larval level. A similar condition prevails in cartilage formation, although there is a slight but perceptible rise at the beginning of bone differentiation. Throughout limb development, there is no demonstrable localization of alkaline phosphatase in the epidermis of the body wall.

Karczmar and Berg ('51) (see photomicrographs 1 to 7, Fig. 239) have divided the regeneration process into three overlapping phases: (1) dedifferentiation, (2) growth and (3) differentiation. They have traced the localization of the alkaline phosphatase in each of these stages. There is an increase in level about three days after amputation, rising through the growth period between the fourth and fifth day and becoming regionally localized in the regenerate on the fifteenth day (see photomicrograph 7, Fig. 239). After this the enzyme distribution follows the ontogenetic pattern.

The evidence on the epidermal contribution to the blastema seems clear. The epidermis covers the wound in a few hours, but is phosphatase-negative until six days after amputation, by which time the blastema is well formed and growing. The localization of the enzyme is variable, after this period stronger at the apex of the epidermis over

---

structures still provide an accurate measure of enzyme activity: muscle stains + (single plus); acellular diaphyseal shaft + + (double plus). Blastematic nuclei (*B*) stain + + + (triple plus). × 20.

5, Conical blastema, staining + + + (triple plus), 10 days after amputation. This section through the margin of the perichondrial sheath of the humerus, *P* + + (double plus) demonstrates the enzyme distribution in muscle. *H*, Hypodermis, + + + (triple plus); *D*, enzyme-free distal edge of collagenous derma, + (single plus) marking the level of amputation; *Ch*, hyaline cartilage, with + (single plus) matrix. Note the patches of enzyme activity on the epidermis. × 20.

6, Differentiating blastema with regions of high and low enzyme activity, 13 days after amputation. *D*, Newly secreted matrix of the differentiating derma, + (single plus); *Pu*, presumptive perichondrium, + + + (triple plus) of humerus and ulna—the parallel, + + (double plus) area is the differentiating muscle of upper arm and forearm; *B*, finger-bud blastema, + + + (triple plus). × 80.

7, Detail of a differentiating blastema, 12 days after amputation. *C*, Rudiment of humerus, illustrating from right to left, the primary differentiation of chondrocytes accompanied by a drop in enzyme activity from + + + (triple plus) to + (single plus), and the secondary increase of intra- and extra-cellular enzyme activity in the hypertrophic chondrocytes; *M*, differentiating muscle, staining + + (double plus); *P*, differentiating perichondrium, staining + + + (triple plus); *V*, blood vessel with + + + (triple plus) walls.

the blastema and weaker at the base of the limb. This brief increase in level extends over the fifth and ninth days, after which there is a decrease, and no alkaline phosphatase is demonstrable after the twelfth day.

As is apparent in Figure 240, changes in the phosphatase level occur with or before the first histological criteria of differentiation,

It is essentially a formation from mesenchyme derived from fibroblast cells rich in alkaline phosphatase or by similar cells secured from dedifferentiation of muscle and cartilage.

The possibility of an epidermal contribution to the blastema seems at present most unlikely on the basis of former histological

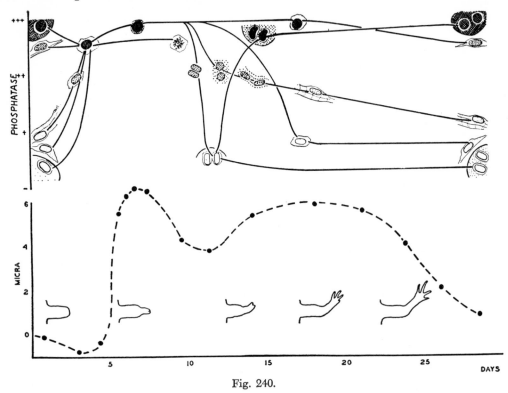

Fig. 240.

both in embryonic limb formation and in larval limb regeneration. The cells composing the regeneration blastema react distinctively to phosphatase stains. Fibroblast and dedifferentiating muscle appear to furnish the chief components contributing to the blastema, a finding in agreement with those of Butler ('33), Thornton ('38a,b, '42) and Forsyth ('46). The contribution of the epidermis to the blastema, as advanced by Godlewski ('28) and Rose ('48), receives no support from the studies on phosphatase localization and level. The phosphatase in the epidermis appears after the preliminary phases of regeneration are complete and it is seldom that the epidermis elements merge with the blastema.

The problem of blastema origin then stands at present on a fairly substantial accumulation of material which clearly supports the older histological observations.

studies which show the non-participation of epidermal structures as well as the later studies of Thornton ('38a,b), Manner ('53), Heath ('53) and Karczmar and Berg ('51). The descriptions of careful observers cannot easily be thrown aside and the indirect evidence on mitotic loci and the abundance of embryonal fibroblasts, combined with chimaeric limb regeneration studies and the alkaline phosphatase correlation, all add to the fund of knowledge which places the burden of proof upon those who claim an epidermal contribution to the blastema. On the basis of the evidence, it is much more likely that the epidermis is either passive or an inhibitor of regeneration.

This idea is supported by Rose's ('44, '45) observations on regeneration of the limb in adult anurans. These forms are recalcitrant to limb regeneration, but limb development can be initiated by preventing wound healing, either by treatment with strong sodium chloride solutions, by stripping the epithelium from the amputation surface, or by causing a temporary vitamin deficiency. He suggests that the dermal layer of the skin prevents the regenerative processes which lead to the formation of a rapidly growing blastema.

Gidge and Rose ('44) suggest again that timing of healing is a factor in the normal failure of regeneration in frogs. The dermis redifferentiates before the blastema cells can grow, and the dedifferentiated elements vicariously become scar tissue which acts further in inhibiting the regenerative growth. A stripped wound is covered by epidermis but not by dermis. The regenerate consists of cartilage only. When, however, the wound is covered with larval skin, a distal blastema develops and a regenerate composed of all limb tissues is formed.

This work forms a promising lead for future work in the puzzling field of anuran limitations for regeneration. In the urodele embryo the ectoderm sometimes inhibits rather than assists in differentiation, but the facts here seem quite different from those needed to explain the regenerative inhibition in anurans.

The one dominant factor in limb regeneration is the import of the nervous system. This has been shown beyond peradventure by Singer ('42–'49) and by Singer and Egloff ('49). There is a basic quantitative minimum of innervation required for limb regeneration. This can come from the motor, sensory or sympathetic nervous system. If this basic minimum is not present limb regeneration will not occur. The limitation of space prevents the discussion which this important work deserves and the reader is referred to the original sources for this material.

Weissfeiler ('24) and Vallette ('26) worked on the regeneration of the amphibian head region. Vallette ('26) found that if the cut is anterior to the nasal capsule, a complete regeneration occurs. If it is posterior to it, the wound heals but regeneration does not occur. This is true also in the embryo, where May ('27) found that in the early stages the nasal capsule can regenerate but that it is one of the first of the organs to become fixed.

Weissfeiler found that the forebrain will regenerate if the nasal capsule is not disturbed, but not if the capsule is removed. This is an interesting corollary to Burr's ('16) experiment in which, when the em-

bryonic olfactory placodes are removed, the forebrain fails to develop to normal size.

Vallette transplanted the jaw to various regions, then cut the jaw and followed the regenerative process. It reconstituted a typical jaw no matter where located.

Hooker ('25) studied the regeneration of the spinal cord after section in various stages. While the time is progressively longer as the anurans approach metamorphosis,

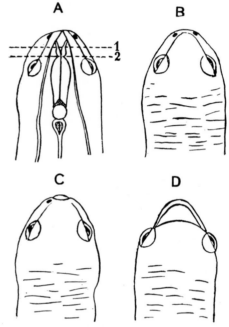

Fig. 241. Triton head regeneration. *A*, The levels of the cuts *1* and *2*; *B*, normal; *C*, regeneration after cut at level *1*; *D*, regeneration after cut at second level. (From A. v. Szüts, '14.)

the process is complete both morphologically and physiologically. These studies and those of Guyénot and Schotté on the influence of the nervous system will be considered in greater detail under that head.

ENDOCRINE EFFECTS

The majority of the workers dealing with the interaction of the endocrine secretions upon the process of regeneration have employed fishes; Grobstein ('42–'48) has contributed papers dealing with regeneration of the gonopod under varying conditions. The gonopodium of the male Platypoecilus has a declining regenerative capacity which is due to the inhibition of regeneration of circulating androgen; testosterone propionate changes the female gonopod to form a regenerate of the male type. A masculinized female has a declining regenerative capacity from which it does not recover after the withdrawal of androgen.

In Gambusia, Turner ('47) has given the results on normal and castrated males. In the castrate the rate of regeneration is the same as for juvenile males or females. Hopper ('49a) has performed the same experiments on both males and females of Lebistes where the castrate females regenerate normally while the castrate males regenerate a female type of fin. When he exposed the fishes to ethynyl testosterone in two concentrations (Hopper, '49b) the females developed and also could regenerate typical anal fins; the males showed no loss of regenerative capacity. These three investiga-

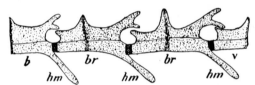

Fig. 242. Vertebral breaking point in the lizard tail (*Lacerta muralis*) (from Slotopolsky, '21–'22).

tors, using similar methods for the study of three different teleost fishes, show how very different the regenerative behavior can be in respect to hormonal activity.

In the urodeles, Schotté and Hall ('52) have tested the effects of hypophysectomies performed at varying times on the formation of the regenerating forelimb. The wound-healing phase was severely affected by the hormonal imbalance, dedifferentiation was affected but not so severely, while blastema and growth phases were hardly affected at all. They propose that the growth factor is not the acting one, but that probably it is the ACTH factor acting through cortisone to regulate the wound epidermis action upon the cut stump tissues. Considerably more information will be needed before this mechanism of action can be confirmed.

Richardson ('45) has studied the effect of the interrelationship of the thyroid and hypophysis upon hind limb regeneration. The hypophysis in the absense of the thyroid has a greater inhibiting effect than thyroid acting alone in the absence of the hypophysis. When Antuitrin-G and thyroxine were supplied as substitutes for the hypophysis and thyroid, respectively, good cartilaginous skeletal regeneration was secured. Regeneration without removal of hypophysis and thyroid is accelerated by Antuitrin-G.

REPTILIAN REGENERATION

Fraisse (1885) listed thirty or forty cases of regeneration observed chiefly on lizards, with a few observations on the serpents. There are also a few scattered observations upon some of the turtles. The double- and triple-tailed lizards, however, held most of the attention, but in the category of abnormality rather than regeneration. These are naturally occurring forms.

Cuvier (1829) commented on the necessity for the study of regeneration in the lizard and remarked concerning his interest in the abnormal development of bone after autotomy. Gachet (1833) found that regeneration was not confined to the lizards *Lacerta agilis* and *L. viridis*, but that it was possessed in varying degrees in others of the reptiles. He examined five lizards with double tails, four with regenerating tails and several with single or double regenerating tails. Of the native forms, *L. muralis*, *L. viridis* and *L. ocellata* were represented, and also *Anolis iguana*. His findings were all verified by dissections and are completely described in Fraisse's (1885) monograph. Gachet gives the literature to his date, together with a description of cases under discussion.

Guyénot and Matthey ('28) and Guyénot and Ponse ('30) traced the regeneration of the limb and repeated Fraisse's work on the formation of the blastema and the regeneration of the tail. Weiss ('23) tested the effect of transplantation on the regenerate as well as the effect of the whole upon the graft and the graft upon the whole. A tail blastema transplanted to the limb region regenerates a miniature tail, not a limb. Occasionally when a small strip of tissue or a small incision is made near the hind limb, a small but imperfect tail results.

Slotopolsky ('21–'22) restudied the mechanism of autotomy in the lizard Lacerta and found the explanation of the evenness of level with which it occurs, for there are two vertebrae behind the pelvic girdle in which the midpoint of the vertebra is an unfused part, giving a rough articular surface which, because of strong muscular contraction, serves as a line of cleavage. While other forms of autotomy occur in the higher vertebrates, this is the only series recorded in which the mechanism is similar to the much more efficient mechanism of the arthropods. Many rodents autotomize the tail but the epidermis is all that is lost. Sumner and Collins ('18) described this process for Peromyscus. Other forms tend to chew parts which are caught in traps, but this is distinctly not an automatic reflex type.

The various tissues regenerated within the tail structure are far different from its original composition. The external form of the tail, including its scaly covering, is fairly tebrae are not segmented but form a continuous tube which, because it is thin walled and little calcified, has the same or greater degree of flexibility as had the segmented structure. The muscle mass regenerates but shows little of the original segmentation and

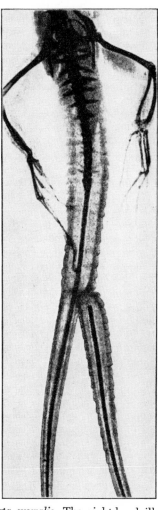

Fig. 243. X-rays of regenerates of the tail in *Lacerta muralis*. The right-hand illustration shows a regenerate replacing the normal. The stimulation in this case was by cutting the ninth tail vertebra, whereas the left figure was cut at the fourteenth with regeneration occurring at the breaking point of the eighteenth tail vertebra. (From Slotopolsky, '21–'22.)

completely reconstituted, but the internal relations are not normal. The spinal cord regenerates incompletely; the membranes extend down a rather amorphous type of tube formed of procartilage, the nervous tissue itself being reduced to a thin strand chiefly glial rather than neuronal. Seldom are spinal ganglia formed, for the nerve trunk gives rise to no nerve roots except at the anterior end of the regenerate. The ver-

the organ has a flaccidity which is quite different from the original state. Woodland ('21) gave an excellent picture of this condition in the gecko (*Hemidactylus flaviviridis*).

Limbs are shown by Egger (1888) and Marcucci ('30) to have the ability to regenerate in part, but here as in the tail region the skeletal elements are imperfect and, because of this, many of the appendages regenerated are tail-like in appearance. The scales are much more like scales which cover the tail than those ordinarily found on the limb. The character of the scales, their size and location, has frequently been used as species diagnostic, and here the form of the regenerate seems to change the scale pattern; e.g., in Weiss' ('30) case where the tail was transplanted heterotopically to the limb region, the tail was later covered by the scutes which formed from the material which originally would have covered a limb, but the scales were definitely tail scales. Noble

an observation by H. Müller (1864) that temperature had a decided effect upon regeneration in lizards. Noble and Clausen found that when the temperature was kept constant the skin of any definite area regenerated the same type of scale. They found no evidence of reversion to a common type. Moreover, the scales of the head and back are regenerated in a form similar to the original. The size of the regenerate has something to do with form, for small areas of epidermis can be removed even on a regenerating tail and will be restored to the original scalation.

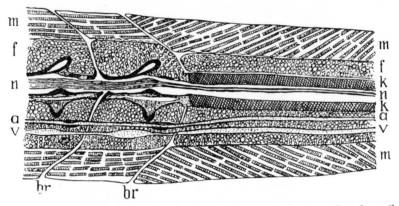

Fig. 244. Tail regenerate in the gecko (*Hemidactylus flaviviridis*). K, Reconstituted cartilaginous tube surrounding central canal with poorly regenerated nervous system. (From Woodland, '21.)

and Bradley ('33), and later Noble and Clausen ('36), ran a series of experiments to determine what the factors might be which are involved in the pattern, form and color of the scales.

While it has been known for a long while that the lizard scales in a regenerate may be quite different in arrangement and form, Boulenger (1888) pointed out that the regenerate might be a much less special or individualized type of scale and that therefore it was closer to the ancestral type. Werner (1896) confirmed this idea and introduced the idea of reversion to the ancestral condition. Tornier ('06) pointed out that this type of reasoning was slightly unsafe, but the idea had caught and was extended by Werber ('05) and carried to its logical *reductio ad absurdum* by Barbour and Stetson ('29), who compared the scale pattern in an extant regenerating form with that of an "undoubted ally of Jurassic age."

Marcucci ('26) and Avel and Verrier ('30) gave data which showed that the shape and size of the regenerate determine the scale form. When Noble and Clausen ('36) decided to repeat this work they made use of

The work of Bovet ('30) and Marcucci ('32) seems to indicate that the factors controlling scale form lie in the mesoderm of the blastema, but this can be changed by temperature effects (Noble and Clausen, '36). Noble and Clausen have studied the formation of the relatively broader ventral scalation—this type of scale can be caused to form on the dorsal side of the tail by implanting muscle from the ventral half of the tail. The converse experiment also holds. The pigment or shade of the scale is determined by the scale location and is not affected by the transplant. Barber ('44) has studied the healing of the wound over the tail and compared this with the healing in the limb region. She concludes that the healing is responsible for the restriction of regeneration in the limb.

PHYSIOLOGICAL REGENERATION

We can now turn from the active or acute type of restorative process to the repetitive or physiological process which is characteristic of both the preceding group and the subsequent group of birds and mammals.

Here it would seem possible to differentiate sharply, but the line is not so clear as one would think, as the subject when analyzed yields a difficult series of interrelations, some of which occur during all the normal states of use and repair, shading to an acute restoration of parts which are badly damaged if not completely ruined by a physiological overload. The step between a normal and a pathological process is so minute that it is hard to determine except by arbitrary rule which one belongs in which category. The same condition exists here, and in the following evaluation of the repetitive processes it is by no means simple to place them under a hard and fast series of definitions.

Epidermal Replacement. The stratum germinativum, or malpighian layer, is constantly giving rise to new elements which are replacing the superficial parts. In reptiles the replacement may be gradual as in the Chelonia and Crocodilia, or in rapid bursts of cornified epithelium as in some lizards and serpents, in which the surface cornification may be a complete cast rigidly mirroring every detail of the underlying parts. Even the corneal layer of the eye is sloughed at an ecdysis. Here again the process has a superficial resemblance to that occurring in arthropods. The glands in association with the cuticle, and the individual scales of which the cuticle are composed, all have their basic levels of regeneration through the activity of the stratum germinativum.

The skin of mammals has a similar constitution and replacement power but the surface epithelium is sloughed slowly, and the replacement is not noticeable unless there is an actual denudation of a large area with subsequent restoration. Bishop ('45), attacking this problem experimentally, finds by biopsies of varying thickness that the limitation of healing and scar formation can be fairly definitely marked out. Complete regeneration results when removal does not go below the reticular layer. Fibrosis is inhibited if the papillary layer is left intact. In the birds the situation is quite different, for they seem to have the attributes of both groups. Feather regeneration occurs after feather removal, and the process of reformation is essentially similar to the embryonic process. Samuel (1870) gave the first nearly complete picture of the process. Lillie and Juhn ('32) showed the complete picture of feather regeneration and the pattern of the regenerating feathers.

In addition to the usual process, birds have a periodic moulting in many cases and this process is similar to the ecdytic phenomena in reptiles. They have, however, little replacement of skin as the keratinization does not seem to reach the same degree as it does in mammals. Moreover, birds possess in the beak an unusual integumentary appendage, with the capacity to regenerate a large proportion of this structure after injury or removal. Scales and spurs also can be replaced.

Hair growth and that of claws, hooves and nails are relatively constant and do not call for special consideration. The growth of horns, however, proceeding as it does in a very definite way in the forms which possess the epidermal types, is really a remarkable case of repetitive restitution. It was studied in detail by William Harvey and John Hunter. The correlation between the testis and the antlers was made very clearly because castrates in which the horns are shed do not regain the increasing branched antler but the rudimentary form.

The glands in connection with the integument—sebaceous, sweat, ceruminous, mucous and the necrobiotics—all have the potentiality for comparatively rapid regeneration. The mammary gland was investigated quite early, and it was found that the nipple does not regenerate, nor will the gland regenerate if the organ is completely removed. If a part is left, however, the work of Gardner and Chamberlin ('40–'41) shows the amount of reorganization which can occur. The tubular ducts and the glandular epithelium both undergo amazing phases of growth and reconstitute an active gland from its involuted condition in a short time.

While considering the general situation in epidermal structures, it might be well to digress for a moment to see what the superficial reactions are during wound healing. Epithelium in general gives rise to both the glandular and the surface types. Occasionally one type may form the other, but they usually run true to rule. Peters (1885) found that after the cornea is scraped the wound is first covered by lymph which forms a clot through which the epithelium becomes active by (1) spreading movement and (2) cell proliferation. Movement by spreading is the initial reaction to the produced defect. In the entire contiguous cell area the cells are amoeboid and spread over the denuded area. Mitosis resulting in cellular proliferation begins about 20 hours after the injury, and here also the reaction extends to cells quite removed from the area of injury. The same process seems nearly universal in epithelial wounds. Barfurth (1891) showed a similar process in frog larvae, and Poynter ('22) in chick embryos; Oppel ('12) traced the movements of corneal epithelium of the cat, but missed completely the amoeboid stage. Matsumoto ('18) repeated Oppel's tissue culture experiments using intra vital stain to trace the reaction and confirmed Peters. Rose ('48) has reinvestigated the role of the epidermis and returns to the older idea of Godlewski that the blastema is formed from differentiated epidermis.

Muscle Tissues. Muscle does regenerate from muscle remaining after injury. The difficulty with reconstitution here seems to be the infiltration of connective tissue which prevents the slower muscle elements from entering. It was formerly thought that myofibrillae had no capacity for regeneration but that the entire replacement was a fibrous connective tissue. This is true for heart damage late in life.

Cartilage and Bone. Cartilage does not regenerate readily in the higher vertebrates, in which it is formed from perichondrium. Bone regeneration is a complex process, depending first upon the formation of cartilage with the appearance of callus, then cartilage and the chondroclasts, osteoblasts and osteoclasts, resulting in the typical bone reconstitution. The time required for complete repair is variable and depends to a large extent on calcium utilization. There is an important line here between the vitamin complex and other internal factors.

The Gut. Desquamation is constantly occurring from the entire alimentary mucosa, probably greater in degree than that occurring in the epidermis. There is a constant and consistent replacement of the glandular content of the salivary, esophageal, gastric and intestinal regions. The proliferation of the mucosa is not of the pronounced cyclic type, but is a continuous process. When a part of the gut is removed, the intestine remaining does not reconstitute the part. The gut remains in its reduced condition. Flint ('10) removed 80 per cent of the intestine in dogs, with viability; in such cases the extent of villation is markedly increased, and physiological readjustment takes place by a compensating hypertrophy of the villi which makes possible an increase in the absorptive area. Grant ('45) has experimentally removed the epithelial cells of the gastric mucosa and finds that the cells are replaced within a few hours, provided that the underlying gland cells are not disturbed.

Glands. There have been many studies on the regeneration of glands. Podwyssozki (1881) studied the regeneration of liver in the rabbit. The bile ducts give rise to liver cells. The salivary glands and kidney have also been studied. The kidney is an example of compensating hypertrophy, but the regenerative phase is in many cases a very active one.

In these three big classes of vertebrates, there is by far more regeneration than one would suspect in a superficial examination of the field. Hyperplasia and compensatory hypertrophy play an important part in these forms. The repetitive type of regeneration is a vital and probably one of the chief survival values of these forms.

GENERAL HISTOLOGY

The early studies on the histology of the regenerative process interpreted it in the light of embryonic development (Goette, 1879; Strasser, 1879). Barfurth (1891) was the first to point out the wandering character of the epithelial cells and their stretching quality which covers the wound before active cell divisions occur. At the same time Peters (1885) showed that this same process occurred after wounds of the cornea. Since then it has been found frequently (Poynter in chick embryos, and numerous individuals working on amphibians).

In the tail, regeneration is brought about by a typical succession, each tissue regenerating its like. Nerve cord gives rise to nerve cord, but the regenerated nerve cord is frequently different from the original, as are also the spinal ganglia and spinal nerves. The situation is entirely different in the limbs, and here we fortunately have excellent studies of Naville ('24), Böhmel ('29) and Hellmich ('30).

THE EYE AND LENS

The experimental attack upon the eye and its regenerative capacity goes back to Bonnet and Blumenbach, who recognized that a large part of the eye could be regenerated provided that a small portion remained after the original operation. Colucci (1891) showed that the lens regenerated from the edge of the iris. This paper is a remarkably well done piece of work which was completely neglected until brought to attention by Emery (1897). The workers during the intervening period, however, were moved by the controversial points which were raised by Gustav Wolff (1895). His paper stressed the origin of the regenerating lens from the iris epithelium instead of the corneal epithelium—a distinct change from its ontogeny. This viewpoint was a rebellion against the Haeckel dominance and was primarily directed against Darwinism as championed by Haeckel. Wolff's findings were immediately in the spotlight; how much so is shown by the attachment of his name instead of Colucci's to this type of regeneration. Since the conclusions were advanced against Darwinism, the cudgels of the scientists were immediately brought to the attack. The results were immediately attacked and experiments repeated. Everyone was sceptical, but the repetition of the work and its confirmation by E. Müller (1896) and others, with the discovery by Emery of Colucci's work, made Fischel's ('00) later confirmation a redundancy.

Wolff showed that the dorsal border of the iris was the formative area in lens regeneration. From his viewpoint this was the most advantageous place for it to form, for as it increased in size it practically fell into place in normal location. He followed also the extrusion of pigment which occurs at the border of the iris during lens formation. Wolff's observation was an important one. He was opposed by Weismann, who took the stand that regeneration was a power acquired by natural selection. Wolff attempted to show (1) that the reaction was purposeful, and (2) that purposefulness is a common property, primitive in nature, which can be explained neither by heredity nor by natural selection.

Fischel took the view that the process had no purpose, citing the many anomalies which occurred in the nature of imperfect lenses or double formations. To him the process was a mechanical one. The limitation of regeneration to the dorsal border of the iris was explained by gravity. He invoked turgor acting from the region of the vitreous as inhibiting regeneration. He did prevent regeneration in one series of experiments by transplanting cornea into the eye, thus increasing the internal pressure. When, however, he introduced foreign bodies such as bread pills and potato, his results were unsuccessful for lens inhibition, but were highly successful in attracting Wolff's ridicule. The controversy grew from the acidulous to the philippic, for Wolff was clever in both argument and experiment. He cut the spinal cord of his animals to inactivate them, then placed them on their backs until regeneration had occurred. Regeneration oc-

curred as before from the original dorsal border of the iris and Fischel's idea of the action of gravity was exploded. In the course of these experiments he found that Triturus completed the process faster than Salamandra; the axolotl was very slow in regeneration if it occurred at all.

Wachs ('14) recalled the problems of the eye. His paper gave an excellent review of the background of the work and laid out clearly many of the problems which could be approached. He worked out the variations of the process in different species and the details of factors, such as the age of the animal at the time of regeneration, the degree of differentiation at the time of constriction from the iris, and its relative size. He gave proof to Fischel's contention that turgor was a controlling factor in regeneration. He supported and extended Wolff's findings. The lens regeneration occurs without injury to the iris, since it occurs if the lens is removed through the roof of the mouth instead of through the cornea. When the iris is injured, regeneration is slowed and the lens may be less perfectly formed than when the iris is intact. Injury is not necessarily a factor, since the lens may be removed and replaced after which no regeneration takes place. If a small lens from a younger animal is placed in a host, regeneration is inhibited. The small lens grows more rapidly (younger tissue) until it reaches the size appropriate for the host eye.

Wolff used grafting experiments to study the effects of the lens upon regeneration. These are partly mechanical and partly chemical, reacting to a stimulating chemical effect from the retina. If the lens is pushed posteriorly into the vitreous, there is an initial reaction all around the border of the iris as though regeneration were about to occur; however, it never is completed. If the lens is removed and minced lens placed in the eyeball, no regeneration occurs until the minced lens is resorbed. The first experiment might be due to a mechanical effect, but the second seems to have removed this completely and indicates the chemical control of the reaction. If the eye receives the grafting of an extra dorsal border of the iris, it will not form a lens until the host lens is removed, but when this is done two lenses regenerate, one from the grafted iris and one from the normal one. If the dorsal border of the iris is transplanted into the vitreous humor after lens removal, it forms a lens more quickly than it would in its original location. Lenses are not formed in head connective tissue, auditory vesicle, or any other region unless the retina is present. If the retina with iris is transplanted and rounds up to form a vesicle, the lens regenerates.

Sato ('30, '33) showed that there is a gradient of material in the iris. Sato divided

lens capsule is left behind. In rabbits (Randolph, '00), complete regeneration may occur after injury, but here the regeneration is from old lens epithelium, not from the border of the iris.

Within recent years studies have appeared (Harrison '29, '33; Twitty, '34; Twitty and

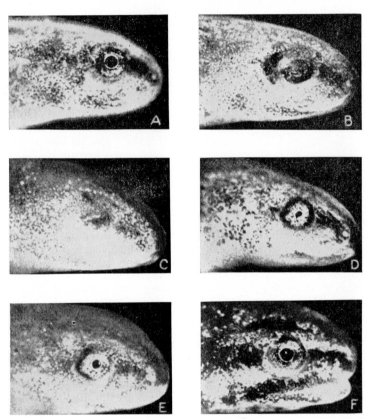

Fig. 245. Reconstitution of the eye in *Triturus taeniatus*. *A*, Before the operation; *B–F*, after 2, 14, 21, 28 and 49 days. (From H. Wachs, '14.)

the iris into six parts with definite localization of potency. Beckwith ('27) had shown that if the eye is rotated early the choroid fissure develops ventrally. Sato turned it in later stages and the choroid fissure retains its rotated position. In this case the lens regenerates from the ventral margin of the iris opposite to the choroid fissure. If the lens is removed early and replaced by indifferent ectoderm, the eye may never have a lens, in which case the vitreous humor may be both incomplete and imperfect.

The majority of these experiments have been performed upon amphibians. The experiments have at one time or another been duplicated on teleosts, lizards and other forms. The removal of an opaque lens is a frequent operation, but in the mammals the

Schwind, '31; Stone, '30) in which, by heteroplastic transplantation, the effects of the graft upon the host and the host upon the graft have been studied. In general these studies give a mass of evidence to show that ultimately the eye tends to regulate to an average condition; a large eye on a small host tends to conform to its surroundings— it is larger than the eye removed to the host but smaller than it would have been upon the donor.

Reports by Schotté ('38) and his coworkers show that lens may be formed from tissues foreign to the eye. The chief outlook of this work has been not the regeneration of the lens but the transformation of other tissues into lens. This links the eye to the problem of determination. It likewise adds another link from a different angle to the chain of circumstances which tie so many ideas with the embryonic nature of the blastema. The eye is being used as a test for the reaction of the new forming tissue. Schotté adopts the thesis that the fate of a regenerate depends upon the inductive action of the organ used which is based on Weiss' ('26a) experiment in which the tail blastema was substituted for a leg (Guyénot and Schotté, '27). Schotté and Hummel ('39) used tissues from larvae throughout one series of experiments, working with the limb blastema. They made four types of transplant: (1) ectodermal cap, (2) cap plus mesenchyme, (3) mesenchyme separated from cap, and (4) regenerating mesenchyme attached to old tissues of the limb. They used regenerates not older than 5 to 6 days in order to have indifferent tissues. The blastemal tissue was placed in the left eye of the host after removal of the lens, while the right eye served as the control after its lens had been removed.

Regeneration may occur from fragments of lens epithelium left behind and here it is exceedingly rapid. In their control series regeneration occurred in one case in two days, in another in three, both of which they attributed to lens epithelium left behind. Regeneration changes as modifications of the transplant occurred in 69 per cent of the xenoplastic cases and in 33 per cent of the homoplastic. Lens formation in the total series was 23 per cent, with 46 per cent occurring in the xenoplastic series. These figures Schotté and Hummel were at a loss to explain and they relied upon a statistical study which was to some extent vitiated by their footnote (4), in which they stated that the errors decreased as experimentation proceeded, which indicates that both criteria and observations of completeness of operative removal were inadequate at the time of the first operation.

The confusing numerical differences between the homoplastic and xenoplastic combinations seem quite significant and can be interpreted in the light of Wachs' ('14) experiments. The xenoplastic graft is much more frequently resorbed and in the case of some anuran species we know definitely that resorption takes place with extreme rapidity. Let us postulate for the sake of argument that the degenerating blastema liberates substances into the eye which may stimulate lens development—the chemical factor. These substances are not liberated while the blastema is intact. Further, xenoplastic

tissue during degeneration sometimes forms epithelial pearls which might easily simulate the histological picture of early lens formation. Schotté and Hummel may be right, but the persistence of qualifying footnotes throughout their discussion indicates that all possible factors have not adequately been weighed.

Their best case does not depend upon the statistical interpretation but upon structural organization—blood and notochordal elements were found in one case (tail blastema) surrounded by capsular fibers. Either the blastema was being transformed, or else the lens capsule was proliferating so fast that it circled the resorbing blastema before complete internal disintegration occurred.

The conclusion of Schotté and Hummel that the regenerating tissues of urodeles and anurans are totipotent, in the sense that they are capable of differentiations which are normally observed only in embryonic tissues, will certainly have to await acceptance subject to a more critical experimental analysis.

The original work on the eye by Colucci (1891) was to determine how much regenerative capacity the eye would show. The whole eye will regenerate provided some of it has been left behind. Regeneration may not occur if only the choroid is left behind. Fuchs ('24) found that tadpoles could regenerate the whole eye from the optic stalk.

Reyer ('48) has brought together all the work upon the embryos and larvae of Triturus, studying carefully the regeneration of the lens from the dorsal iris in five age groups. The process in every case is similar although varying in minor details, and swelling and depigmentation occur in the older animals. The reader is referred to Reyer ('54) for a complete review and discussion of the lens problem and its general relationship to definitive potentiality.

CONCLUSION

The present discussion of regeneration aims merely to point out a few of the high points of what has been done as well as to point to a few of the things which need to be done. Since the work has been centered about the limb, eye and tail these have received the greatest amount of attention. The regenerative capacities of internal organs have been scantily treated, although the recent literature on liver regeneration shows that many of the fundamental potentialities of organ-forming tissues still remain for discovery. The fragmentary work which has been done on many of the other glands is a case in point. These problems are more difficult technically than the relatively simple ones so far studied, but with care and patience they should yield much in the next decade.

It is evident that regeneration is a complex primarily depending upon the two cardinal things peculiar to tissues: differentiation, and proliferation resulting in growth. The determination of these tissues is usually and generally uniformly controlled by position in the total organism. The potentiality of a cell, whether embryonic or blastemal, to differentiate into either a structure harmonious to its region or the replacement of such, is the resultant of many factors such as the compatibility of the tissues, the relationship of the proliferating parts, and the interplay of growth inhibitors and regulators. The solution of this complex still remains to engage our study and attention.

REFERENCES

Avel, M., and Verrier, M. L.   1930   Un cas de régénération hypotypique de la patte chez *Lacerta vivipara*. Bull. Biol. France et Belg., *64:*198–204.

Barber, L. W.   1944   Correlations between wound healing and regeneration in forelimbs and tails of lizards. Anat. Rec., *89:*441–453.

Barbour, T., and Stetson, H. C.   1929.   The squamation of Homoeosaurus. Bull. Mus. Comp. Zool., *69:*99–104.

Barfurth, D.   1891   Zur Regeneration der Gewebe. Arch. mikr. Anat., *37:*406–491.

——— 1895   Die experimentelle Regeneration überschüssiger Gliedmassentheile bei den Amphibien. Roux' Arch. Entw.-mech., *1:*91–116.

——— 1899   Eine Larve von *Petromyzon planeri* mit drei Schwanzspitzen. Roux' Arch. Entw.-mech., *9:*27–31.

Bateson, W.   1894   Materials for the Study of Variation. Macmillan and Co., London.

Beckwith, C. J.   1927   The effect of the extirpation of the lens rudiment on the development of the eye in *Amblystoma punctatum*, with special reference to the choroid fissure. J. Exp. Zool., *29:*217–260.

Beigel, C.   1910   Zur Regeneration des Kiemendeckels und der Flossen der Teleostier. Bull. internat. d.l'Acad. d. Cracovie, Ser. B., Sci. Nat., July, *1910:*655–690.

——— 1912   Regeneration der Barteln bei Siluroiden. Roux' Arch. Entw.-mech., *34:*363–370.

Biberhofer, R.   1906   Über Regeneration bei *Amphioxus lanceolatus*. Roux' Arch. Entw.-mech., *22:*15–17.

Bischler, V.   1926   L'influence du squelette dans la régénération, et les potentialités des divers territoires du membre chez *Triton cristatus*. Rev. suisse Zool., *33:*431–560.

Bishop, G. H.   1945   Regeneration after experimental removal of skin in man. Am. J. Anat., *76:*153–182.

Böhmel, W.   1929   Regeneration nach Entnahme von Skeletteilen beim Axolotl. Roux' Arch. Entw.-mech., *115:*464–509.

Boulenger, G. A.   1888   On the scaling of the reproduced tail in lizards. Proc. Zoöl. Soc., London, *1888:*351–353.

Bovet, D.   1930   Les territoires de régénération; leurs propriétés étudiées par la méthode de déviation du nerf. Rev. suisse Zool., *37:*83–145.

Brachet, J.   1946   Localisation de la phosphatase alcaline pendant le développement des Batraciens. Experientia, *2:*143.

Braus, J.   1909   Gliedmassenpropfung und Grundfragen der Skelettbildung. I. Die Skelettanlage vor Auftreten des Vorknorpels und ihre Beziehung zu späteren Differenzierungen. Morph. Jahr., *39:*284–430.

Broussonet, M.   1786   Observations sur la régénération de quelques parties du corps des Poissons. Hist. l'Acad. Roy. des Science (de Paris), Amsterdam, *1786:*684–688.

Burr, H. S.   1916   The effects of the removal of the nasal pits in Amblystoma embryos. J. Exp. Zool., *20:*27–57.

Butler, E. G.   1933   The effects of X-radiation on the regeneration of the forelimb of Amblystoma larvae. J. Exp. Zool., *65:*271–315.

——— 1935   Studies on limb regeneration in X-rayed Amblystoma larvae. Anat. Rec., *62:*295–307.

Byrnes, E. F.   1904   Regeneration of the anterior limbs in the tadpoles of frogs. Roux' Arch. Entw.-mech., *18:*171–177.

Colucci, V. S.   1891   Sulla regenerazione parziale dell' occhio nei Tritoni. Istogenesi e sviluppo. Mem. della R. Acad. Sc. Ist Bologna, Ser. 5, *1:*593–629.

Cuvier, G.   1829   The Animal Kingdom. Vol. 2. G. B. Whittaker, London.

Duncker, G.   1905   Über Regeneration des Schwanzendes bei Syngnathiden. Roux' Arch. Entw.-mech., *20:*30–37.

——— 1907   Über Regeneration des Schwanzendes bei Syngnathiden. Roux' Arch. Entw.-mech., *24:*656–662.

Egger, E.   1888   Ein Fall von Regeneration einer Extremität bei Reptilien. Arbeiten zool.-zootom. Inst. Würzburg, *8:*201–212.

Emery, C.   1897   Wer hat die Regeneration der Augenlinse aus dem Irisepithel zuerst erkannt und dargestellt? Anat. Anz., *13:*63–64.

Fischel, A.   1900   Ueber die Regeneration der Linse. Anat. Hefte, *14:*1–256.

Flint, J. M.   1910   Compensatory hypertrophy of the small intestine following resection of large portions of the jejunum and ileum. Trans. Conn. State Med. Soc., *1910:*283–335.

Forsyth, J. W.   1946   The histology of anuran limb regeneration. J. Morph., *79:*287–322.

Fraisse, P.   1885   Die Regeneration von Geweben und Organen bei Wirbeltieren. Cassel, Berlin.

Fritsch, C.   1911   Experimentelle Studien über

Regenerationsvorgänge des Gliedmassenskeletts der Amphibien. Zool. Jahrb. (Abt. f. allg. Zool. u. Physiol.), *30:*377–472.

Fuchs, F. 1924 Augenregeneration nach Entfernung des Bulbus bei Alytes und Bufo. Zool. Jahrb. (Abt. f. allg. Zool.), *41:*121–178.

Gachet, M. H. 1833 Mémoire sur la reproduction de la queue des reptiles sauriens. Actes d. l. soc. Linnéenne d. Bordeaux, nr. VI, *1833:*213–259.

Gardner, W. U., and Chamberlin, T. L. 1940–41 Local action of estrone on mammary glands of mice. Yale. J. Biol. & Med., *13:*461–465.

Gidge, N. M., and Rose, S. M. 1944 The role of larval skin in promoting limb regeneration in adult Anura. J. Exp. Zool., *97:*71–85.

Godlewski, E. 1928 Untersuchungen über Auslösung und Hemmung der Regeneration beim Axolotl. Roux' Arch. Entw.-mech., *114:*108–143.

Goette, A. 1879 Ueber Entwickelung und Regeneration des Gliedmassenskeletts der Molche. Leopold Voss, Leipzig.

Grant, E. R. 1945 Rate of replacement of the surface epithelial cells of the gastric mucosa. Anat. Rec., *91:*175–186.

Grobstein, C. 1942 Endocrine and developmental studies of gonopod differentiation in certain poeciliid fishes. II. Effect of testosterone propionate on the normal and regenerating anal fin of adult *Platypoecilus maculatus* females. J. Exp. Zool., *89:*305–328.

—— 1947a Decline in regenerative capacity of the *Platypoecilus maculatus* gonopodium during its morphogenesis. J. Morph., *80:*145–160.

—— 1947b The role of androgen in declining regenerative capacity during morphogenesis of the *Platypoecilus maculatus* gonopodium. J. Exp. Zool., *106:*313–314.

—— 1948 Optimum gonopodial morphogenesis in *Platypoecilus maculatus* with constant dosage of methyl testosterone. J. Exp. Zool., *109:*215–233.

Guyénot, E. 1927 La perte du pouvoir régénérateur des Anoures, studiée par la méthode des heterogreffes, la notion de territoires. Rev. suisse Zool., *34:*1–53.

—— 1929 La notion de territoires en biologie. Actes de la Soc. Helvétique des Sci. Nat., Davos, part II, pp. 81–91.

——, and Matthey, R. 1928 Les processus régénératifs dans la patte postérieure du lézard. Roux' Arch. Entw.-mech., *113:*520–529.

——, and Ponse, K. 1930 Territoires de régénération et transplantations. Bull. Biol. France et Belg., *64:*251–287.

——, and Schotté, O. 1927 Greffe de régénérat et différenciation induite. Compt. Rend. Soc. Phys. et Hist. Nat. Geneve, *44:*21–23.

Harrison, R. G. 1893 Ueber die Entwicklung der nicht knorpelig vorbildeten Skelettheile in den Flossen der Teleostier. Arch. mikr. Anat., *42:*248–278.

—— 1918 Experiments on the development of the forelimb of Amblystoma, a self-differentiating equipotential system. J. Exp. Zool., *25:*413–462.

—— 1921 On relations of symmetry in transplanted limbs. J. Exp. Zool., *32:*1–136.

—— 1929 Correlation in the development and growth of the eye studied by means of heteroplastic transplantation. Roux' Arch. Entw.-mech., *120:*1–55.

—— 1933 Heteroplastic grafting in embryology. Harvey Lectures, 1933–34, Series 29, pp. 116–157.

Heath, H. D. 1953 Regeneration and growth of chimaeric amphibian limbs: limb regeneration and growth. J. Exp. Zool., *122:*339–366.

Hellmich, W. 1930 Untersuchungen über Herkunft und Determination des regenerativen Materials bei Amphibien. Roux' Arch. Entw.-mech., *121:*135–203.

Hertwig, G. 1927 Beiträge zum Determinations- und Regenerationsproblem mittels der Transplantation haploidkerniger Zellen. Roux' Arch. Entw.-mech., *111:*292–316.

Hoadley, L. 1928 On the localization of developmental potencies in the embryo of *Fundulus heteroclitus*. J. Exp. Zool., *52:*7–44.

Holtfreter, J. 1947 Neural induction in explants which have passed through a sublethal cytolysis. J. Exp. Zool., *106:*197–222.

Hooker, D. 1925 Studies on regeneration in the spinal cord. III. Reestablishment of anatomical and physiological continuity after transection in frog tadpoles. J. Comp. Neur., *38:*315–348.

—— 1930 Physiological reactions of goldfish with severed spinal cord. Proc. Soc. Exp. Biol. & Med., *28:*89–90.

—— 1932 Spinal cord regeneration in the young rainbow fish, *Lebistes reticulatus*. J. Comp. Neur., *56:*277–297.

Hopper, A. F. 1949a Development and regeneration of the anal fin of normal and castrate males and females of *Lebistes reticulatus*. J. Exp. Zool., *110:*299–319.

—— 1949b The effect of ethynyl testosterone on the intact and regenerating anal fins of normal and castrated females and normal males of *Lebistes reticulatus*. J. Exp. Zool., *111:*393–413.

Kammerer, P. 1905 Über die Abhängigkeit des Regenerationsvermögens der Amphibienlarven von Alter, Entwicklungsstadium und spezifischer Grösse. Experimentelle Studie. Roux' Arch. Entw.-mech., *19:*148–180.

Karczmar, A. G., and Berg, G. G. 1951 Alkaline phosphatase during limb development and regeneration of *Amblystoma opacum* and *Amblystoma punctatum*. J. Exp. Zool., *117:*139–164.

Krugelis, E. J. 1950 Properties and changes of alkaline phosphatase activity during amphibian development. Compt. Rend. Lab. Carlsberg, Ser. Chim., *27:*273–290.

Lewis, W. H. 1912 Experiments on localization and regeneration in the embryonic shield and germ ring of a teleost fish (*Fundulus heteroclitus*). Anat. Rec., *6:*325–334.

Liebman, E. 1949 The leucocytes in regenerating limbs of *Triturus viridescens*. Growth, *13:*103–118.

Lillie, F. R., and Juhn, M. 1932 The physiology

of development of feathers. I. Growth-rate and pattern in the individual feather. Phys. Zool., 5: 124–184.

Lindeman, V. F. 1949 Alkaline and acid phosphatase activity of the embryonic chick retina. Proc. Soc. Exp. Biol. & Med., 71:435–437.

Litwiller, R. 1939 Mitotic index and size in regenerating amphibian limbs. J. Exp. Zool., 82: 273–286.

Manner, H. W. 1953 The origin of the blastema and of new tissues in regenerating forelimbs of adult Triturus viridescens viridescens (Rafinesque). J. Exp. Zool., 122:229–257.

Marcucci, E. 1926 Rigenerazione degli arti nei Rettili. Boll. Soc. Nat. Napoli, 38:8–19.

——— 1930 Il potere rigenerativo degli arti nei Rettili. Ricerche sperimentali sopra alcune specie de Saurii. Arch. Zool. Ital., 14:227–252.

——— 1932 Trapianti di pelle e rigenerazione in Lacerta muralis. Arch. Zool. Ital., 17:435–447.

Matsumoto, S. 1918 Contribution to the study of epithelial movement. The corneal epithelium of the frog in tissue culture. J. Exp. Zool., 26:545–563.

Maximow, A. A., and Bloom, W., 1952 A Textbook of Histology, 6th ed. W. B. Saunders Co., Philadelphia.

May, R. M. 1927 1re Thèse: Modifications des centres nerveux dues à la transplantation de l'oeil et de l'organe olfactif chez les embryons d'anoures. 2e Thèse: Propositions données par la Faculté. (Thèses presentées à la Faculté des Sciences de Paris.) Arch. de Biol., 37:337–395.

Milojevic, B. D. 1924 Beiträge zur Frage über die Determination der Regenerate. Roux' Arch. Entw.-mech., 103:80–94.

Moog, F. 1944 Localizations of alkaline and acid phosphatases in the early embryogenesis of the chick. Biol. Bull., 86:51–80.

Morgan, T. H. 1900 Regeneration in Teleosts. Roux' Arch. Entw.-mech., 10:120–134.

——— 1902 Further experiments on the regeneration of the tail of fishes. Roux' Arch. Entw.-mech., 14:539–561.

Morrill, C. V. Jr., 1906 Regeneration of certain structures in Fundulus heteroclitus. Biol. Bull., 12:11–20.

——— 1918 Some experiments on regeneration after exarticulation in Diemyctylus viridescens. J. Exp. Zool., 25:107–126.

Müller, E. 1896 Über die Regeneration der Augenlinse nach Exstirpation derselben bei Triton. Arch. f. mikr. Anat., 47:23–33.

Müller, H. 1864 Über die Regeneration der Wirbelsäule und des Rückenmarkes bei Tritonen und Eidechsen. Frankfurt a.M.

Nabrit, M. S. 1938 Regeneration in the tail fins of embryo fishes (Opsanus and Fundulus). J. Exp. Zool., 79:299–308.

Nassonov, N. V. 1930 Die Regeneration der Axolotlextremitäten nach Ligaturanlegung. Roux' Arch. Entw.-mech., 121:639–657.

Naville, A. 1924 Recherches sur l'histogenèse et la régénération chez les Batraciens anoures (Corde dorsale et téguments). Arch. de Biol., 34:235–343.

Needham, J. 1942 Biochemistry and Morphogenesis. Cambridge University Press, London.

Nicholas, J. S. 1927 The application of experimental methods to the study of developing Fundulus embryos. Proc. Nat. Acad. Sci., 13:695–700.

———, and Oppenheimer, J. M. 1942 Regulation and reconstitution in Fundulus. J. Exp. Zool., 90:127–157.

Noble, G. K., and Bradley, H. T. 1933 The relation of thyroid and the hypophysis to the molting process in the lizard (Hemidactylus brookii). Biol. Bull., 64:289–298.

———, and Clausen, H. J. 1936 Factors controlling the form and color of scales on the regenerated tails of lizards. J. Exp. Zool., 73:209–229.

Nusbaum, J., and Sidoriak, S. 1900 Beiträge zur Kenntnis der Regenerationvorgänge nach künstlichen Verletzungen bei älteren Bachforellenembryonen (Salmo fario L.). Roux' Arch. Entw.-mech., 10:645–684.

Nussbaum, M. 1886–1887 Die Teilbarkeit der lebenden Materie. Arch. mikr. Anat., 26 (1886): 485–538; 29 (1887): 265–366.

Oppel, A. 1912 Causalmorphologische Zellenstudien. V. Die aktive Epithelbewegung, ein Faktor beim Gestaltungs- und Erhaltungsgeschehen. Roux' Arch. Entw.-mech., 35:371–456.

Oppenheimer, J. 1936 Processes of localization in developing Fundulus. J. Exp. Zool., 73:405–444.

Peters, A. 1885 Über die Regeneration des Epithels der Cornea. Inaugural Dissertation, Bonn.

Philippeaux, J. M. 1867 Régénération des membres chez l'Axolotl et la Salamandre. Compt. Rend. Acad. Paris, 1867, pp. 1162–1163.

Podwyssozki, W., Jr. 1881 Experimentelle Untersuchungen über die Regeneration der Drüsengewebe. II. Die Regeneration des Nierenepithels, der Meibom'schen Drüsen und der Speicheldrüsen. Beiträge zur path. Anat. u. Physiol., 2:1–28.

Poynter, C. W. M. 1922 The effects of ultraviolet rays on developing mollusks (Limnaeus). Anat. Rec., 23:32.

Przibram, H. 1926 Regeneration und Transplantation bei Tieren; in Handb. der norm. u. pathol. Physiologie, Vol. 14, part I, pp. 1080–1113.

Puckett, W. O. 1934 The effects of X-radiation on limb development in Amblystoma. Anat. Rec., 58:32–33.

——— 1936 The effects of X-radiation on limb development and regeneration in Amblystoma. J. Morph., 59:173–213.

Randolph, R. L. 1900 The regeneration of the crystalline lens. Johns Hopkins Hosp. Rpts. (Contr. to Med. Sci. . . . dedicated to William Henry Welch . . .), 8:237–263.

Reyer, R. W. 1948 An experimental study of lens regeneration in Triturus viridescens viridescens. I. Regeneration of a lens after lens extirpation in embryos and larvae of different ages. J. Exp. Zool., 107:217–268.

——— 1954 Regeneration of the lens in the amphibian eye. Quart. Rev. Biol., 29:1–46.

Richardson, D. 1945 Thyroid and pituitary hormones in relation to regeneration. 2. Regeneration of the hind leg of the newt, *Triturus viridescens*, with different combinations of thyroid and pituitary hormones. J. Exp. Zool., *100:*417–429.

Rose, S. M. 1944 Methods of initiating limb regeneration in adult Anura. J. Exp. Zool., *95:*149–170.

———— 1945 The effect of NaCl in stimulating regeneration of limbs of frogs. J. Morph., *77:*119–140.

———— 1948 Epidermal dedifferentiation during blastema formation in regenerating limbs of *Triturus viridescens*. J. Exp. Zool., *108:*337–361.

Samuel, S. 1870 Die Regeneration. Virchow's Arch. f. pathologische Anat. u. Physiol. u. f. klinische Medicin, *50:*323–354.

Sato, T. 1930 Beiträge zur Analyse der Wolff'schen Linsenregeneration, I. Roux' Arch. Entw.-mech., *122:*451–493.

———— 1933 Beiträge zur Analyse der Wolff'schen Linsenregeneration, II. Roux' Arch. Entw.-mech., *130:*19–78.

Schotté, O. E. 1938 Induction of embryonic organs in regenerates and neoplasms. Collecting Net, *13:*1–6.

————, and Hall, A. B. 1952 Effect of hypophysectomy upon regeneration in progress (*Triturus viridescens*). J. Exp. Zool., *121:*521–556.

————, and Hummel, K. P. 1939 Lens induction at the expense of regenerating tissues of amphibians. J. Exp. Zool., *80:*131–165.

Schultze, D. 1894 Die künstliche Erzeugung von Doppelbildungen bei Froschlarven mit Hilfe abnormal Gravitätswirkung. Roux' Arch. Entw.-mech., *1:*269–305.

Scott, G. G. 1907 Further notes on the regeneration of the fins of *Fundulus heteroclitus*. Biol. Bull., *12:*385–400.

Singer, M. 1942 The nervous system and regeneration of the forelimb of adult Triturus. I. The role of sympathetics. J. Exp. Zool., *90:*377–399.

———— 1945 The nervous system and the regeneration of the forelimb of adult Triturus. III. The role of the motor supply. J. Exp. Zool., *98:*1–21.

———— 1946a The nervous system and regeneration of the forelimb of adult Triturus. IV. The stimulating action of a regenerated motor supply. J. Exp. Zool., *101:*221–239.

———— 1946b The nervous system and regeneration of the forelimb of adult Triturus. V. The influence of number of nerve fibers including a quantitative study of limb innervation. J. Exp. Zool., *101:*299–337.

———— 1947a The nervous system and regeneration of the forelimb of adult Triturus. VI. A further study of the importance of nerve number, including quantitative measurements of limb innervation. J. Exp. Zool., *104:*223–249.

———— 1947b The nervous system and regeneration of the forelimb of adult Triturus. VII. The relation between number of nerve fibers and surface area of amputation. J. Exp. Zool., *104:*251–265.

———— 1949 The invasion of the epidermis of the regenerating forelimb of the urodele, Triturus, by nerve fibers. J. Exp. Zool., *111:*189–209.

————, and Egloff, F. R. L. 1949 The nervous system and regeneration of the forelimb of adult Triturus. VIII. The effect of limited nerve quantities on regeneration. J. Exp. Zool., *111:*295–314.

Slotopolsky, B. 1921–22 Beiträge zur Kenntnis der Verstümmelungs- und Regenerationsvorgänge am Lacertilierschwanze. Zool. Jahrb., *43:*219–322.

Spallanzani, L. 1768 Prodromo di un'opera sopra le riproduzioni animali. Modena. (Math. physikal. Abhandl., Leipzig, 1769).

Stone, L. S. 1930 Heteroplastic transplantation of eyes between the larvae of two species of Amblystoma. J. Exp. Zool., *55:*193–261.

———— 1952 An experimental study of the inhibition and release of lens regeneration in adult eyes of *Triturus viridescens viridescens*. J. Exp. Zool., *121:*181–223.

Strasser, H. 1879 Zur Entwicklung der Extremitätenknorpel bei Salamandern und Tritonen. Morph. Jahrb., *5:*240–315.

Studnicka, F. K. 1912 Über Regenerationserscheinungen im caudalen Ende des Körpers von *Petromyzon fluviatilis*. Roux' Arch. Entw.-mech., *34:*187–238.

Sumner, F. B. 1904 A study of early fish development: experimental and morphological. Roux' Arch. Entw.-mech., *17:*92–149.

————, and Collins, H. H. 1918 Autotomy of the tail in rodents. Biol. Bull., *34:*1–6.

Swett, F. H. 1924 Regeneration after amputation of abnormal limbs in Amblystoma. Anat. Rec., *27:*273–288.

Szüts, A. von 1914 Beiträge zur Kenntnis der Abhängigkeit der Regeneration vom Zentralnervensystem. Roux' Arch. Entw.-mech., *38:*540–545.

Thornton, C. S. 1938a The histogenesis of muscle in the regenerating forelimb of *Amblystoma punctatum*. J. Morph., *62:*17–47.

———— 1938b The histogenesis of the regenerating forelimb of larval Amblystoma after exarticulation of the humerus. J. Morph., *62:*219–241.

———— 1942 Studies on the origin of the regeneration blastema in *Triturus viridescens*. J. Exp. Zool., *89:*375–389.

Tornier, G. 1906 Der Kampf der Gewebe im Regenerat bei Begünstigung der Hautregeneration. Roux' Arch. Entw.-mech., *22:*348–369.

Turner, C. L. 1947 The rate of morphogenesis and regeneration of the gonopodium in normal and castrated males of *Gambusia affinis*. J. Exp. Zool., *106:*125–143.

Twitty, V. C. 1930 Regulation in the growth of transplanted eyes. J. Exp. Zool., *55:*43–53.

———— 1934 Growth correlations in Amphibia studied by the method of transplantation. Cold Spring Harbor Symposia on Quantitative Biology, *2:*148–156.

————, and Schwind, J. L. 1931 The growth of

eyes and limbs transplanted heteroplastically between two species of Amblystoma. J. Exp. Zool.,
59:61–86.

Vallette, M.   1926   Mécanisme de la régénération
du museau chez les Urodèles. Arch. Sci. phys. et.
nat., Génève, *8*:28–32.

Wachs, H.   1914   Neue Versuche zur Wolffschen
Linsenregeneration. Roux' Arch. Entw.-mech.,
39:384–451.

Weiss, P.   1923   Die Transplantation von entwick-
elten Extremitäten bei Amphibien. I. Morphologie der Einheilung. Roux' Arch. Entw.-mech.,
99:150–167.

———   1925a   Unabhängigkeit der Extremitä-
tenregeneration vom Skelett (bei *Triton cristatus*). Roux' Arch. Entw.-mech.,   *104*:359–
394.

———   1925b   Die seitliche Regeneration der
Urodelenextremität. Roux' Arch. Entw.-mech.,
104:395–408.

———   1926a   Physiologie der Formbildung
(Entwicklung und Regeneration). Jahresbericht
ges. Physiologie f. d. Jahr 1926, pp. 77–112.

———   1926b   Ganzregenerate aus halbem Ex-
tremitätenquerschnitt. Roux' Arch. Entw.-mech.,
107:1–53.

———   1927   Die Herkunft der Haut im Ex-

tremitätenregenerat. Roux' Arch. Entw.-mech.,
109:584–610.

———   1930   Potenzprüfung am Regenerations-
blastem. II. Das Verhalten des Schwanzblastems
nach Transplantation an die Stelle der Vorderex-
tremität bei Eidechsen (Lacerta). Roux' Arch.
Entw.-mech., *122*:379–394.

Weissfeiler, J.   1924   Régénération du cerveau et
du nerf olfactif chez les batraciens urodèles. Rev.
suisse Zool., *32*:1–44.

Wendelstadt, H.   1904   Experimentelle Studie
über Regenerationsvorgänge am Knochen und
Knorpel. Arch. mikr. Anat., *63*:766–795.

Werber, I.   1905   Regeneration der Kiefer bei der
Eidechse *Lacerta agilis*. Roux' Arch. Entw.-mech.,
19:248–258.

Werner, F.   1896   Über die Schuppenbekleidung
des regeneration Schwanzes bei Eidechsen. Sitzber. Ak. Wiss. Wien, math.-nat. Kl., *105*:123–146.

Wolff, G.   1895   Entwicklungsphysiologische Studien. I. Die Regeneration der Urodelenlinse.
Roux' Arch. Entw.-mech., *1*:380–390.

Woodland, W. N. F.   1921   Some observations on
caudal autotomy and regeneration in the Gecko
(*Hemidactylus flaviviridis*, Rüpel) with notes on
the tails of Sphenodon and Pygopus. Quart. J.
Micr. Sci., *65*:63–100.

Section XIV

TERATOGENESIS

EDGAR ZWILLING

INTRODUCTION

PREVIOUS chapters in this book have demonstrated that normal development depends on a harmonious sequence of closely interdependent events. Such development is the end product of the expression of the intrinsic potentialities of cells or groups of cells as conditioned and modified by their relationship to each other and to the rest of the embryo. What the student of embryology sees under ordinary circumstances are the visible results of these expressed potencies. Prior to this there are intracellular rearrangements and localization of formative materials. As development progresses masses of tissues migrate from one region of the embryo to another. Having arrived at their destinations they in turn may influence adjacent tissues and initiate definite developmental tendencies. In this manner a pattern of organ-forming regions is laid out. Within each of these regions, then, we have seen how similar dependencies exist in which later parts require the influence of adjacent regions for their normal formation. Subsequent to the elaboration of the basic pattern for a structure there is a period which is characterized by cellular differentiation and growth. All of these events presumably are consequences of prior chemical and physical processes. In a situation where such a vast array of orderly interactions must occur in order that a normal structure be formed it is not surprising that deviations from the normal are frequently encountered. Disturbances in either the spatial or the temporal synchronization of the many developmental interrelationships may lead to abnormal individuals and structures. Many minor deviations which occur are considered to be within the range of normality. Only the more extreme deviants are regarded as aberrant.

Variants from the normal, monstrosities of every sort, have fascinated students of biology and medicine from ancient times to the present. Many superstitions have been built around them and they have occasioned much fantasy and speculation. However, to modern students of embryology these terata (the name given the abnormal individuals) provide further material for the study of development. Not only has the application of principles derived from other experimental procedures been instructive in explaining the nature of terata, but the terata themselves have been utilized in elucidating normal developmental relationships.

Hypotheses concerning the causation of human terata have been numerous and have included such diverse agencies as celestial influences, gods, devils, hybrids (i.e., human × some other animal), maternal impressions and imagination, mechanical pressure (extra-abdominal, intra-abdominal and amniotic), amniotic and umbilical strangulation, disease, faulty implantation, etc. [For an excellent account of the older history the reader is referred to Ballantyne ('04) and Schwalbe ('06-'37).] Recent years have witnessed a revival of interest in these problems in medical circles, partly as the result of an increased attention to inherited anomalies but largely because of the discoveries concerning the possible role of viruses, blood factor antagonisms, nutritional factors and radiations in the etiology of congenital malformations (for recent bibliography see Gruenwald, '47; Morison, '52).

Embryological studies must eventually provide the basis for an analysis of the problems in human teratology. Since most investigations of the experimental production of monsters have been undertaken on invertebrates and lower vertebrates one of the problems has been to what extent the observations and conclusions derived from these studies may be applicable to humans. Increasing evidence indicates that no unique principles apply to mammals—that any observed differences result from differences in the details of development and the mode of nutrition found in placental embryos. We feel, therefore, that until more controlled and reliable data on human material are forthcoming one must accept the generalizations derived from studies of other forms.

What, then, are the major problems in teratology? Briefly they may be separated into two classes: (1) What are the causal agents? and (2) How do these agents produce their effects?

THE CAUSAL AGENTS

In their quest for information about the etiology of congenital malformations many of the teratologists of the past have become strong proponents of either environmental or hereditary factors as the exclusive cause of the abnormalities. Mall ('08), one of the most influential American teratologists of his time, emphasized that all anomalies were the result of external influences on normal ova. These abnormal influences were caused by faulty nutrition, the consequence of poor implantation. Streeter ('30, '31), on the other hand, has placed extreme emphasis on the importance of genetic factors not only for the embryonic phases of development but for all subsequent stages of life; everything depended on one's being a "good egg" to start with. Observations of the past few decades indicate quite strongly that a compromise between the two is more representative of the facts—that not only may anomalies be mediated by both hereditary and environmental factors, but similar kinds of anomalies may be produced by either.

Hereditary Factors. A wide variety of congenital anomalies, in many kinds of animals, has been found to be transmitted from generation to generation in a regular mendelian fashion. There is no doubt about the genetic basis for these conditions [the reader is referred to Grüneberg ('52), Gruenwald ('47), and Landauer ('51) for bibliographies on this subject]. The mode of inheritance is varied. Characters may be transmitted as simple recessives, i.e., the condition is not expressed unless the individual receives a mutant gene for the character from each parent. Other characters may be transmitted as dominants. In this situation a single factor, from one parent, will produce the anomaly. The actual expression of either type of inheritance may vary from relatively minor to severe and often lethal maldevelopment.

Many of the dominant mutations are pe-
culiar in that the presence of two mutant genes (homozygotes) produces effects which are more severe than found in heterozygotes. Heterozygotes of the Creeper mutation in fowl (Dunn and Landauer, '26; Landauer and Dunn, '30; Landauer, '32) produce a characteristic chondrodystrophy. The long bones, especially of the legs, are disproportionately shortened. However, most of the heterozygotes are quite viable. Homozygotes, on the other hand, never survive to hatching. Most of them are retarded and die during the third or fourth day of development. Some survive to later stages and show a typical phokomelic condition—extremely short legs, deformed beaks and eyes and a general dwarfing.

Another example of this sort is the mutation Kinky in the mouse (Caspari and David, '40). In the heterozygotes the only expression is an absence or fusion of tail vertebrae. Gluecksohn-Schoenheimer ('49a) has shown that the homozygotes are, for the most part, lethal and evince, before death, a wide variety of duplication and twinning. That this may be a more severe and possibly early expression of a similar tendency in heterozygotes is indicated by forking of the distal part of the tail and occasional occurrence of duplication of the vagina in the latter.

Lethal effects, however, are not invariable consequences of homozygosity in dominant mutations. In many cases the heterozygous and homozygous conditions are distinguishable only by breeding tests. On the other hand there are mutations like Yellow (Robertson, '42) and the spotting genes in mice (Russell and Fondal, '51) in which there are relatively minor effects on pigment or color pattern in heterozygotes but in which the homozygous condition leads to severe and frequently lethal defects.

Essentially the same syndrome of effects may be produced in a given species by entirely independent recessive or dominant mutations. The type of inheritance cannot be determined from the appearance of the individual animals. Conditions similar to the chondrodystrophy produced by the Creeper factor have been caused by at least five distinct recessive lethals in fowl (Landauer, '35; Asmundson, '39, '42; Landauer, '41; Lamoreux, '42; Hays, '44). Likewise rumplessness may result, in fowl, from the action of two independent mutations—one dominant (Dunn, '25), the other recessive (Landauer, '45a). While the recessive rumpless chickens may have other associated anomalies (accessory ribs, scoliosis, lordosis), frequently they cannot be distinguished from the dominant rumpless by appearance alone.

The genetic situation is further complicated in that both the "penetrance" (i.e., incidence of effected individuals) and the "expressivity" (degree of the effect) may be altered by both genetic and environmental factors. Both of the rumpless mutations (Dunn and Landauer, '34, '36; Landauer, '45a) may be, by proper selection experiments, modified strongly so that there is a high incidence of "normal" tails even though the mutant genes are present. Embryological studies (Zwilling, '45a) demonstrate that minor anomalies, which have no permanent morphological effect, occur early in development of some genetic rumpless chicks. Such altered expression of a mutation is a result of the genetic background upon and with which a given gene must operate. In some instances (Landauer, '33) only a single modifying gene may be responsible, in others it is evident that a complex of modifying factors is involved. Occasionally, as in species or strain crosses, the modifying backgrounds are so diverse that the entire pattern of dominance may be reversed. Reed ('37) has reported a dominant mutation in *Mus musculus* which causes anomalies which vary from fusion of vertebrae to absence of the tail (ribs may be absent or fused). When the Fused gene is introduced into another species, *Mus bactrianus*, it behaves as a recessive. Many other examples of such phenomena could be cited.

Extra-genetic factors may alter the expression of a given mutant. Some of the early experiments with Drosophila (Goldschmidt, '38) have shown that the expression of many mutants may be altered by increased or lowered temperatures at critical stages. The analyses of Wright ('34) indicate that such factors as age of mother and season (which seem to affect the condition of the mother) may influence the expression of mutant genes in mammals. In view of the variable situations produced by both genetic background and extra-genetic factors it is not surprising that there are many cases, especially in human heredity, in which the mode of transmission of a suspected hereditary character is not certain.

Environmental Factors. Virtually every environmental factor has been instrumental in producing anomalies in some organism or other provided that the factor is modified in the proper way and at the proper time. Temperature variations, mechanical disturbances (vibration, pressure), a host of chemicals, irradiations with hard rays (x-rays) and ultraviolet and modification of the gaseous environment have all been shown to produce effects when properly applied. [Gruenwald ('47) has compiled most of the important references to that date.]

During the early part of the present century efforts were made to relate more directly with mammalian terata the results of experiments on anamniotes. For a long time these attempts were equivocal. In most instances it was demonstrated that toxic substances (heavy metals, etc.) increased the abortion rate, but not, at least to any great extent, the rate of production of monsters. Essentially the same conclusions were reached when surveys were made of human alcoholics or of people engaged in occupations involving exposure to toxic compounds. In recent years the unequivocal relation to mammalian terata of at least four factors has been demonstrated:

1. Considerable evidence has accumulated which shows that dietary deficiencies of pregnant mothers may be responsible for anomalous development in their young. Much of these data are in the agricultural literature. One of the most conclusive analyses has been contributed by Warkany and Schraffenberger ('43). These authors produced a syndrome, including micromelia, in rats by means of a riboflavin-deficient diet. All symptoms were eradicated by replacement therapy if the riboflavin-containing diet was fed prior to the thirteenth day of gestation.

2. A number of authors have described the effects of irradiations (mostly x-rays) on the development of mammals. Russell ('50) has published a thorough analysis of the effects on mouse embryos of whole body x-irradiation of the mother. Dose and time after copulation were varied. The data were analyzed in terms of the incidence of various anomalies as related to the time of irradiation. Pre-implantation stages were non-reactive. In implanted embryos the incidence of most abnormalities rose gradually, reached a peak, then fell off abruptly. A somewhat different situation was revealed (Wilson, Brent and Jordan, '53) in a less extensive study with rats. These authors irradiated only the exteriorized embryos. There was an abrupt transition: 8-day embryos were merely retarded in growth while those exposed on the ninth and tenth days showed a number of anomalies (see also p. 715).

3. It has been shown that blood factor incompatibilities between a mother and a fetus may result in abnormal development. The best known case is that involving Rh factors [see Levine ('48) for review of the literature]; in this situation Rh positive blood from a fetus may produce antibodies in an Rh negative mother which may in turn have a deleterious effect on the fetus. In practice it is found that subsequent fetuses are more severely affected and have more severe symptoms of erythroblastosis. (Note that when several such cases occur in one family the records may resemble those for direct inheritance, yet these conditions arise only indirectly through the blood factor incompatibilities.)

4. Considerable evidence has been presented (Gregg, '41; Erickson, '44) which indicates that various congenital anomalies (cataract, microcephaly, heart disease, dental defects, etc.) occur after women contract rubella (German measles) during the early months of pregnancy. It has been assumed by most people that the virus crosses the placenta and attacks the fetal tissues directly. Hamburger and Habel ('47) have shown that some viruses may produce teratological effects when applied directly to a chick embryo. Gillman et al. ('48) have produced a number of congenital anomalies (hydrocephalus, cleft palate, eye and tail defects, etc.) by injecting trypan blue into rats during pregnancy or prior to conception. The dye itself does not reach the embryo; instead, according to these authors, it produces metabolic disturbances in the mother which in turn affect the developing embryos. These authors believe that it is not necessary for viruses or other disease-causing organisms to act directly on the fetus. They may produce their effects indirectly, through an accumulation in the blood of products of disturbed maternal metabolism. This concept has far reaching implications for further studies on the etiology of human congenital malformations.

Two generalizations from these studies of environmental effects should be emphasized at this time. (1) Essentially the same effects may be produced by a variety of seemingly unrelated treatments. (2) In many instances the morphological consequences of environmental interventions are essentially the same as those caused by genetic factors.

Phenocopies. When experimental treatment of a genetically normal embryo modifies its development so that its final appearance duplicates that of a mutant of the same species it is called a phenocopy (Goldschmidt, '38). Goldschmidt was the first to recognize that phenocopies could be of great value in elucidating gene action. His comparison of the effects of temperature variation on wing development with mutant wing conditions in Drosophila is now classic. A high incidence of a particular type of wing defect was obtained when the larvae were subjected to the proper temperature at the proper time (i.e., phenocritical period). It was reasoned that the temperature alteration modified the rate of processes important for wing development, that these were probably the same processes disturbed by mutant genes which produced wing defects, and that the phenocritical period for a given condition was the same as the period when the gene producing a similar condition was operative.

This reasoning is very suggestive, but one must, in order to have valid conclusions of this sort, verify each step. Even in Drosophila Henke, Fink and Ma ('41) have shown that phenocopies may be produced by treating larvae at periods other than the critical one for the mutant copied. An example from vertebrate material may be used to illustrate some of the problems in studies of phenocopies. Tail reduction occurs in different ways in the two rumpless mutations of chickens. Presumptive tail tissue degenerates (Zwilling, '42), in dominant rumpless embryos, prior to its incorporation into the tail (i.e., during the second and third days). The degree of tail reduction is correlated with the amount of degenerate tissue. In recessive rumpless embryos (Zwilling, '45a) degeneration does not occur until after rather abnormal tail structures have formed. Abnormal tail morphogenesis may occur at any stage between the third and sixth days and the degree of tail reduction is correlated with the time when the abnormalities appear. Structures proximal to the involved regions continue to develop normally.* Phenocopies

* Several mutations in mice cause taillessness of one degree or another. Chesley ('35) and Gluecksohn-Schoenheimer ('49b) have described the developmental events leading to tail defects in a number of them. In one case (Brachyury heterozygotes) the tail may develop normally at first and then degenerate distal to a given point. In other genetic combinations (T/t°, T/t¹) the tail may, at first, form normally except that the notochord is missing. After a while the tail in these degenerates completely. Here we see at least two more genetic mechanisms which result in tail loss. At least two groups (Hamburgh, '52; Waddington and Carter, '52) are studying tail defects (phenocopies) which follow injection of trypan blue into pregnant mice.

of rumplessness occur sporadically (Landauer and Dunn, '25), may be produced by mechanical jarring (Landauer and Baumann, '43), by transection of the posterior part of an early embryo's body (Zwilling, '45b), by local irradiation (Wolff, '36) and by topical application of several chemicals (Ancel, '50). After the discovery (Landauer, '45b) that a high incidence of rumplessness is a consistent consequence of injection of insulin into the yolk sac of early embryos (prior to 72 hours) a series of studies was undertaken to establish any relationship between these phenocopies and the mutants.

Moseley ('47) made a very careful study of the morphology of insulin-treated embryos at various stages. Roughly 20 per cent of her rumpless embryos resembled the recessive condition. The majority of the rumpless embryos (2/3), however, achieved the tailless condition in a manner which was unlike that seen in either of the mutant types. Tail defects in this large group followed an abnormal deviation of caudal structures which forced them into the cloaca where, after a variable time, they degenerated. Only an embryological study could reveal these facts, since an examination of advanced embryos or hatched chicks merely indicated that there was a marked resemblance to the mutant types. Evidence (Landauer and Rhodes, '52) indicates that insulin rumplessness is mediated via an interference with anaerobic glycolysis. Pyruvic acid, injected somewhat before or simultaneously with insulin, markedly decreased the incidence of rumplessness. Mortality was lowered. Similar treatment of embryos of both mutant strains (Landauer, '54) had no effect on incidence of rumplessness in either. Embryological study thus reveals that the final adult phenocopy condition may be reached by morphogenesis which is unlike that found in mutant forms. The work by Landauer indicates that even the morphological similarity between some of the insulin-treated embryos and the recessive mutants is probably preceded by different metabolic disturbances. The extent, therefore, to which phenocopies can be used in elucidating the action of genetic factors is limited. It must be borne in mind that no a priori conclusions can be drawn about gene action from the mere production of a phenocopy. One must, without additional evidence, be literal and insist that, by definition, only the appearance of a mutant has been duplicated. These points will be stressed again below in our discussion of micromelia.

HOW AGENTS PRODUCE THEIR EFFECTS

To say that genetic or environmental factors are the causal agents of anomalies does not, however, explain how these agents produce their effects. In the absence of more specific information rather general hypotheses have been advanced to explain the action of agencies which produce terata. One of the oldest of these (Ballantyne credits Harvey's work of 1651 with its foundation) is the concept of arrested development. Initially this hypothesis was utilized to describe the fact that in many anomalies development seems to have stopped at an early stage in the formation of a structure and that primitive features are retained; for example, a cleft palate results from a failure of the two palatal primordia to fuse and, thereby, an early embryonic condition persists. Later authors have extended the implications of this concept to include situations in which one does not necessarily find persistent embryonic conditions. In such instances the anomaly is supposedly preceded by temporary arrest at some stage and this arrest is the prime contributing factor to the subsequent abnormal development. Following the St. Hilaires and Dareste, Stockard ('21) was one of the strongest proponents of this concept. He argued that a slowing or virtual stopping of development (by way of low temperature, oxygen lack or various chemical and physical interventions) was the primary result of the treatment and that the type of deformity depended on the time in development when this occurred. E. Wolff ('48) considers arrests of development of sufficient importance as a first step in production of terata that he postulates this as the first of his laws of teratogenesis.

Attempts to establish the mechanism of action of teratogenic agents, genetic or otherwise, have been very fruitful on the morphological level. Careful embryological studies have provided considerable information which is basic for causal analyses. In some cases unsuspected relationships have been revealed. Grüneberg's ('38) grey lethal mutation in rats is a case in point. Skeletal anomalies, excess of erythrocytes and hemoglobin, heart enlargement, lung emphysema, etc., are all related by means of a "pedigree of causes" to an early anomaly of cartilage. However, just as in normal development, there is a deficiency in our knowledge of the metabolic events (and possibly unknown cellular relationships) which cause the visible morphogenetic interactions. We know little or nothing about the events which lead to the initial cartilage abnormalities in the grey lethal rat, which cause presumptive tail tissue to degenerate in rumpless chicks, etc. Most authors still accept Stockard's ('21) four principles as explanations of causation. These are, in his own words:

Probably the most completely studied teratological condition is that of micromelia (leg shortening) in chickens. It may be profitable to discuss this condition in some detail to evaluate possible causal relations.

Chondrodystrophy-like micromelias occur frequently. They are found in many animals besides chickens (man, cattle, dogs, rabbits,

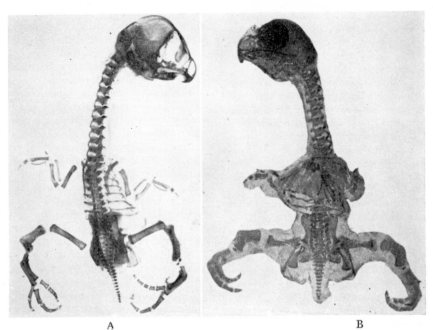

A   B

Fig. 246. *A*, An example of inherited chondrodystrophy in a 21-day chick embryo (courtesy of Dr. W. F. Lamoreux, Cornell University, and the editors of the *Journal of Heredity*).

B, A markedly similar condition in an embryo from a hen which was fed a biotin deficient diet (courtesy of Dr. J. R. Couch and the editors of the *Anatomical Record*).

1. ". . . Every type of developmental monster known in the literature may be produced by one and the same experimental treatment.

2. ". . . The same structural abnormality may be induced in the embryos of various species by a great number of different experimental treatments.

3. ". . . In all cases the initial effect of the experimental treatment is a lowering of the developmental rate, and the resulting deformity is always secondarily due to this slow rate of development.

4. ". . . The type of monster or deformity is determined by the developmental period during which the slowing in rate is experienced."

These principles preclude specificity of action of the agents. They also preclude specific tissue or rudiment requirements which, in the presence of metabolic disturbances, may result in an anomalous structure.

salamanders). The condition is characterized by a disproportionate shortening of the long bones of the extremities, due largely to growth retardation which is a consequence of hypoplasia of epiphyseal cartilages. Frequently the chondrocranium, especially the jaw elements, is also distorted. As mentioned above, there are a number of independent mutations in domestic fowl which are responsible for this type of condition. Similar chondrodystrophy-like syndromes occur sporadically (Landauer, '27) and have been produced experimentally in chickens. Byerly et al. ('35) reported the development of short-legged embryos from eggs of chickens on a deficiency diet which could be mitigated by wheat germ. A similar anomaly was reported by Lyons and Insko ('37); in their case the dietary imbalance was reversed by manganese supplements. Romanoff and Bauernfeind ('42) demonstrated that a riboflavin deficiency caused micromelia. Essentially similar abnormalities were produced by biotin deficiencies by Couch et al. ('48). These were eliminated by injections of biotin into the deficient eggs. Essentially the same syndrome has been produced by sulfanilamide and eserine sulfate (Ancel, '45a), by insulin (Landauer, '47a), thallium (Karnofsky, Ridgeway and Patterson, '50), boric acid (Landauer, '52) and pilocarpine (Landauer, '53). With all of these substances, injected at the proper time, both the extremities and the head are affected and the limbs of both sides are involved symmetrically (there are frequently other associated anomalies but these will not be discussed here). Usually the most severe cases of micromelia are found in embryos which are quite dwarfed.

Even though a similar syndrome is produced by all of these treatments a number of significant facts are revealed by a close inspection of the data. The critical period is different for different substances. Insulin must be injected at 120 hours (Landauer, '47a), sulfanilamide at 48 hours (Zwilling and DeBell, '50) and boric acid at 96 hours (Landauer, '52) for maximum incidence and severity of micromelia. This does not necessarily mean that sulfanilamide and boric acid are inactive until a later stage. Rather the evidence points to their continued activity over a period of time which, for maximum effect, must include the earlier stages.

While the micromelias produced by the various substances are superficially similar, a detailed analysis reveals that there are differences in detail. With insulin (Landauer, '54) and sulfanilamide (Zwilling and DeBell, '50) all of the long bones of the leg are shortened and the tibiotarsus shows the greatest relative reduction. With boric acid (Landauer, '52) and pilocarpine (Landauer, '54) the femur and tibia are relatively normal but the tarsometatarsus is greatly reduced. There are, in addition, differences in digital involvement; insulin and sulfanilamide cause little or no toe reduction while boric acid does result in shortening or absence of the toes. Although differences in incidence may result from injecting these substances at times other than the optimum, the morphological details remain constant for a given chemical.

The various dietary deficiencies which result in micromelia involve substances (biotin, riboflavin) which are generally accepted as components of co-enzymes involved in carbohydrate cycles. It is thus of extreme importance that carbohydrates are involved in

some way in the action of most of the micromelia-inducing chemicals (thallium is exceptional). The teratogenic effects of insulin may be almost completely eliminated by simultaneous injections of nicotinamide (Landauer, '48a). In addition, insulin produces hypoglycemia (Zwilling, '48, '51) and other pronounced carbohydrate disturbances. Both severity and incidence of hypoglycemia correlate well with the degree and incidence of micromelia. In like manner the teratogenic effects of sulfanilamide (Zwilling and DeBell, '50), of eserine sulfate (Landauer, '49) and of pilocarpine (Landauer, '53) may be more or less completely mitigated by injections of nicotinamide (which is a component of co-enzyme I). The effects of boric acid (Landauer, '52) are most convincingly related to its capacity to complex with riboflavin and render the latter metabolically inactive. Nicotinamide is not effective in alleviating boric acid defects. This last point is of great significance, since it might be considered that nicotinamide merely provides an alternate source of energy which may be used to overcome general depressing effects of the chemicals. That it does not do so with boric acid points to a more specific action of the chemicals on one or another link in the carbohydrate chain. It is of great importance that these diverse chemicals have been shown to have some relation to carbohydrate metabolism. This provides the first basis for the elimination of some of the vagueness in previous discussions of etiology of anomalies. The fact that different substances differ in the details of their effects points to rather subtle and specific metabolic requirements of the components of the limb rudiments.

This material also allows us to evaluate the importance of lowered developmental rate as a prime factor in teratogenesis. At least two substances [adrenal cortical extracts (Landauer, '47b; Karnofsky, Ridgeway and Patterson, '51) and para-aminobenzoic acid (Zwilling and DeBell, '50)] cause dwarfing of chick embryos after injection at 5 days. The size reduction is perfectly proportionate, with no special effects on the limbs; it is of the same order of magnitude as that produced by sulfanilamide and insulin and occurs over the same period of time. Moreover, there is no mitigation of the dwarfing when the micromelia produced by sulfanilamide and insulin is eliminated by nicotinamide therapy. These facts indicate that a substance may produce quite general effects (i.e., retardation) as well as specific effects but that the latter need not be causally related to the former. On the basis of results from the more completely analyzed cases, most embryologists have abandoned the idea that retardation per se may be the cause of anomalies.

Finally, the analyses of micromelias in chicks have implications for an interpretation of phenocopies. There are, at present, no indications that the effects of the Creeper mutation are altered by nicotinamide therapy (Landauer, '54). The blood-sugar levels are quite normal in this stock (Zwilling, unpublished). Despite the similarity in appearance of the induced and genetic micromelias, apparently the metabolic derangements leading to the morphological condition are quite different. This is not surprising. The abnormal carbohydrate metabolism probably has its ultimate expression in quantitative or qualitative alterations of protein synthesis. Similar changes in proteins may be produced by the genetic factors by considerably different pathways. In this case, again, the phenocopies have not copied the initial metabolic action of the genes.

A CLASSIFICATION OF TERATA BASED ON EMBRYOLOGY

Rather than repeat the usual teratological classification the writer will present a new type of classification of terata based on knowledge of inductive and morphological relationships. It will be shown how dislocations in normal processes may give rise to various kinds of familiar malformations and, at the same time, by drawing on both for examples, it will be shown that there are no basic differences, at least on the morphological level, between genetic and experimental anomalies. This classification is not final; there are, doubtless, instances of over-simplification or omission. The intent here is to be provocative rather than definitive. Many of the cases have been placed in a given category even though their analyses are not complete from the present point of view. Future studies may very well indicate the proper position of these examples. It must be borne in mind that many cases of teratological development may involve more than one of the categories which we present. Whenever the information is at hand we have included some of the data in regard to the physiological disturbances which precede the morphological ones.

Teratological development may result from:

1. Abnormal initial stimulus.
    a. Initial stimulus absent.
    b. Deficient initial stimulus.
    c. Excessive initial stimulus.
2. Abnormal response of reacting tissues.
    a. Absence of response.
    b. Partial or incomplete response.
    c. Excessive response.
    d. Mechanical interference with response.
3. Abnormality of both initial stimulus and responding tissue.
4. Abnormal differentiation of component tissues.
5. Abnormal growth of structures.
6. Degenerative processes.
    a. Abnormal degeneration.
    b. Excessive "normal" degeneration.
    c. Failure of degeneration to occur.
7. Abnormality of functional activity or regulatory mechanisms.

ABNORMAL INITIAL STIMULUS

Initial Stimulus Absent. In most cases of agenesis it is very difficult to establish whether the initial stimulus is lacking or whether the reacting tissues are unable to respond to the stimulus. Probably cases of anidian development in amniotes (in which cells of the blastoderm may divide and even form blood islands, but in which embryonic tissue never develops) represent instances in which the primary organizing stimuli are absent; but this has never been definitely demonstrated. There are, however, well established cases involving secondary inductors which show that the stimulus for development may be lacking. Boyden ('27) and Gruenwald ('37, '42) have demonstrated by experimental procedures that the elaboration of a metanephric kidney (in chick embryos) depends upon the prior formation of a ureteric bud. Normally this bud grows up from the cloaca to the metanephrogenous blastema and stimulates the latter to elaborate tubules, etc. The blastema does not differentiate if the ureteric bud fails to reach it after a surgical block (see Section VII, Chapter 6). Substantiating evidence for this relationship has been found in the case of the wingless mutation of chicks (Waters and Bywaters, '43; Zwilling, '49). In the homozygous recessives the metanephrogenous tissue does not develop beyond the blastema stage; this is associated with absence of the ureteric bud.

Deficient Initial Stimulus. Probably the best example of this category is microcephaly (reduced head).

Excessive Initial Stimuli. An increase in the

indicate some of the sources of confusion in this type of experimentation.

CONDITION OF GAMETES AND ZYGOTES

One of the most consistent observations made by investigators in the field of experimental teratology is the extreme variability in the reactions of fertilized eggs or embryos to the treatments to which they are subjected. Zygotes from the same set of parents do not all respond equally to a given set of conditions, and the incidence of response differs in offspring from different parents. Variations in reactivity of zygotes and embryos may be due to alterations in their physiological condition or to their genetic constitution.

Physiological Condition. It is quite evident that normal development can be expected only from zygotes that have been produced and raised under normal conditions. Some effects may be produced by factors acting before the onset of embryonic development. The experiments of Witschi ('22, '30, '34) on eggs which were retained in the female's uterus for 3 to 5 days prior to fertilization are familiar examples. Such over-ripe eggs are frequently polyspermic. Among eggs fertilized by one sperm Witschi found axial duplications, supernumerary appendages, pigment changes and a tendency towards the production of neoplasms. According to Witschi such abnormalities result from a lack of "coordination" in the egg and embryo, probably due to alterations in the cortical layer. In chick eggs it has been known for a long time that proper storage conditions are essential for good development (Landauer, '51). Proper temperature and humidity must be maintained. Extended storage, even under optimum conditions, may also result in impaired development. Poor pre-incubation conditions result in poor hatchability, early mortality and anomalies. In experiments in which the effects of some particular treatment of eggs are to be evaluated these conditions must be controlled carefully. The reactions of eggs which have been improperly stored cannot be compared with those which have been handled carefully. It is likely that at least some of the contradictions in the literature are due to these factors. Even under proper conditions of storage one may encounter differences in susceptibility of eggs from the same hens at different times of the year. Landauer and Baumann ('43) found that the incidence of rumplessness resulting from mechanical jarring of eggs was greater during the summer months than in the spring. In another study Landauer ('43) found that there was a greater incidence of micromelia during the fall and early winter than in the late winter and early spring. The reverse was found for eye defects (micro- and anophthalmia). These few illustrations are presented to indicate that one must know the condition of material with which one performs experiments. There is little doubt that similar variations in gametes and zygotes exist in other forms.

The researches of the Hertwigs and others (see Frets, '31, for bibliography) demonstrate that the fertilization of eggs with sperm previously subjected to treatment with various chemicals (methylene blue, chloral hydrate, strychnine, etc.) results in the formation of many terata. Similar results may be obtained after irradiation [it is important to note that after exposure of sperm to increased doses the incidence of abnormalities decreases because of the ability of the otherwise inactivated sperm to initiate parthenogenetic development (Hertwig, '28; Rugh and Exner, '40)]. More clearly related to the practical consideration of physiological conditions are observations on the effects of fertilization of eggs by "stale" sperm. Nalbandov and Card ('43) have obtained data of this sort for chickens. They removed the males from pens of tested hens and collected eggs for as long as 35 days following this separation. They found that eggs fertilized with older sperm had a lower hatchability and greater early embryonic mortality, with embryonic death occurring earliest in those eggs fertilized by the oldest sperm. There was no increase in incidence of terata. Aberrant development was found in a similar experiment (Dharmarajan, '50). Some observations (unpublished) made by the writer at Storrs indicate that embryos from eggs fertilized by stale sperm are much more susceptible to various treatments (both in regard to mortality and incidence of abnormalities) than are more vigorous embryos.

Genetic Constitution. The importance of genetic uniformity in experimental material is well established at the present time. There is still, however, a tendency among some investigators to neglect this factor in comparing their results with teratological agents with those of others. Stockard emphasized this point by indicating the difference between trout and Fundulus embryos in regard to the incidence of twinning. Trout embryos not only yielded a much higher percentage of these abnormalities after similar treatment, but also showed a much greater incidence of spontaneous duplicate embryos. Holtfreter ('45) has demonstrated that a difference in neuralization response between the ectoderm of *Amblystoma punctatum* and *Triturus torosus* is the result of an increased susceptibility of the former to hypertonic salt solutions. This susceptibility is in turn related to differences

is injected into the yolk sacs of unincubated eggs than do embryos of other breeds of chickens. Moreover, it is possible (Landauer and Bliss, '46) to select a "high" and a "low" susceptibility line from amongst the White Leghorns themselves (progeny from hens giving high and low incidences of rumplessness were saved and inbred). After continued selection the susceptibility of the high line

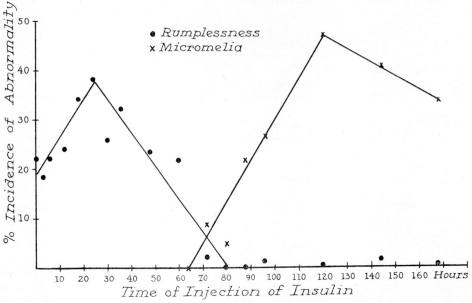

Fig. 247. Effect of time of injection of 2 units of insulin on the incidence of rumplessness and micromelia. All injections into yolk-sac of embryos of ages indicated. The continued small incidence of rumplessness beyond 72 hours is the same as the sporadic occurrence in controls. (Data from Landauer and Bliss, '46; Landauer, '47a.)

in the resistance of the cell membrane of the outer ectodermal cells.

The above examples refer to differences between genera. Similar differences may be found between different strains within a species. Warkany et al. ('42) demonstrated a strain difference between Sprague-Dawley and Wistar rats in regard to the production of skeletal abnormalities as a result of dietary deficiencies (later shown to be riboflavin). The former strain had a higher incidence of abnormalities. However, this was shown to be due to its greater resistance to the deficiency, since the Wistar rats were so affected by this treatment that they failed to produce any young. An even more striking demonstration of genetically conditioned response to experimental conditions has been provided by Landauer ('48b). White Leghorn embryos yield a considerably higher percentage of rumpless embryos after insulin

increased to such an extent that, with 2 units after 4 hours of incubation, the incidence of rumplessness was 51.9 per cent while in the low line it was 18.2 per cent (Landauer, unpublished). This increased susceptibility to injection of insulin at early stages is not retained at later stages. When insulin is administered at 5 days there is a high incidence of micromelia. This incidence is no greater in the high line (i.e., high in regard to production of rumplessness) than in the low line.

STAGE OF TREATMENT

It has been recognized for some time that the stage during which an embryo is subjected to a particular type of treatment is of utmost importance in determining the type of abnormality which the treatment will cause. In general the younger an embryo is when subjected to some foreign environment the more profound will be the alterations produced. This is frequently expressed by a higher incidence of very early mortality or a cessation of development at an early stage. Among the survivors, however, one may find a surprising regularity in the appearance of a particular defect. This has been taken to indicate that the cells

is being most actively elaborated. This may, in general, be true. However, Solberg ('38) has presented material which demonstrates that different structures vary considerably in regard to the relationship between their sensitivity to x-ray treatment and the time of actual elaboration of the organ. As indicated in Fig. 248, some organs in Fundulus react to x-rays both prior and subsequent to

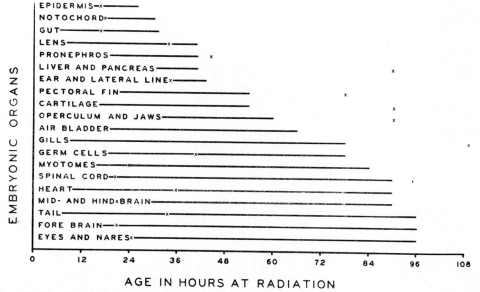

AGE IN HOURS AT RADIATION

Fig. 248. The effects of x-rays on the differentiation of the embryonic organs of *Fundulus heteroclitus*. The *x* indicates the stage in development when the anlage of an organ appears. The line to the right of each organ's name indicates over which period that organ may be affected by the irradiation (see text). (Courtesy of Dr. A. N. Solberg and the editors of the *Journal of Experimental Zoology*.)

which are the precursors of the affected structures are particularly susceptible to the treatments at that stage. Moreover, when the same treatment is administered to embryos at different stages not only will there be a difference in incidence of a particular anomaly but new anomalies may be produced; a new set of structures has become susceptible. The data from Landauer and Bliss ('46) and Landauer ('47a) in regard to injection of insulin into chick embryos illustrate this point (Fig. 247): when these injections are made from 0 to 64 hours of incubation the most frequently encountered anomaly is rumplessness. From 72 to 168 hours, however, the insulin produces a high incidence of micromelia.

There is a widespread belief that the sensitive or critical period in the development of a structure occurs chiefly during its early formative stages, when the cells are as yet undifferentiated or when the structure

their formation, while others are affected only before the structure appears. By drawing a line perpendicular to the time axis one can determine which structure will be affected by the irradiation at any given stage. This does not indicate the degree to which the structures are affected.

In order to obtain good anterior duplications by means of physical or chemical interferences one must treat very early embryonic stages. Only poorly organized or posterior duplications have resulted from centrifugation of amphibian blastulae and gastrulae (Torrey and Breneman, '41; Pasteels, '47). In Stockard's ('21) experiments with Fundulus anterior duplications were obtained most successfully when early cleavage stages were treated. This was confirmed by Hinrichs and Genther ('31), who demonstrated that U-V irradiation 30 minutes prior to first cleavage was most favorable for production of anterior duplications. The pre-cleavage stage is also most sensitive to centri-fugation (Forsthoefel, '51). There may, thus, be a considerable delay before visible effects of some treatments are evident.

Ancel ('45a) concluded that the micro-melic effect of sulfanilamide resulted from its interference with pre-cartilaginous mes-enchyme. He applied the drug at 48 hours. The writer's earlier discussion of the differ-ences in susceptible periods to various micromelia-inducing chemicals (p. 705) in-dicates that stages of active chondrification are also affected. In addition, the application of sulfanilamide at 120 hours (Zwilling and DeBell, '50) will also produce micromelia. Moreover, if sulfanilamide is injected at 48 hours and nicotinamide at 120 hours (exposing the limb to the drug during the pre-cartilage stage) the micromelic effects are entirely abolished. All of this indicates that sulfanilamide acts over a considerable period of time. This probably is true of other teratogenic agents. It is likely that some of them may have relatively little effect until development of a particular structure has proceeded sufficiently for it to reach its sensitive stage. Experiments must be care-fully planned for accurate determination of sensitive periods and not based solely on the results of treating one stage. In like manner, in view of the fact that indistinguishable end results may be mediated through more than one developmental pathway (i.e., limb-lessness or taillessness, either by degeneration of normally formed structure or failure of the structure to be elaborated), only the most limited conclusions about sensitive pe-riods can be obtained from the appearance alone of a fully developed organism.

NATURE OF TERATOGENIC AGENCY

Instances where the same terata have been produced by a variety of treatments have led to the emphasis on stage of treatment and neglect of specific action of the agent (vide supra). However, there is evidence which indicates that the specific nature of the substance used is of considerable impor-tance. Most impressive, in recent years, has been the research of Ancel ('45a, '45b, '50) and his collaborators. These investigators have applied some 90 or more substances to chick embryos of the same age in the same manner. They have found considerable dif-ferences in regard to the terata produced. For instance, eserine sulfate and a number of sulfa compounds produce micromelia (frequently accompanied by parrot beak and occasionally by syndactyly) but no rump-lessness or coelosomy (a condition in which the viscera protrude from and are outside the body cavity). Another group of sub-stances (ricin, trypaflavine, etc.) produced coelosomy but no micromelia or rumpless-ness. Still another group (sodium cacodylate, sodium methyl arsonate, saponin) resulted in rumplessness, which was frequently asso-ciated with coelosomy and ectro- or hemi-melia (a condition in which all or part of a limb is absent), but no micromelia. More-over, these substances retain their specific action even when applied simultaneously (Ancel, '47). Trypaflavine alone resulted in the non-development of the amnion but no rumplessness, while methyl arsonate pro-duced rumplessness and no abnormalities of the amnion. Together they produced, in addi-tion to embryos with either of the two anomalies, some embryos which were both rumpless and anamniotic. Ancel and his group have not overlooked or minimized the im-portance of the stage when these substances are applied. They have demonstrated that the same substance may have different effects on different stages. All specific effects must, therefore, be defined in terms of both the stage treated (or affected) and the nature of the agent.

The investigations of Hamburger and Habel ('47) offer additional evidence for specific action. These authors have shown that two different viruses (influenza-A and mumps), both of which penetrate embryonic tissues and multiply therein, may have dif-ferent teratological effects. Both of the viruses, applied to 48-hour embryos, were toxic but only the influenza-A was terato-genic. It caused a specific syndrome: micro-cephaly, micrencephaly, twisting of the axis and impairment of growth of the amnion. It must be concluded that these differences in effect are due to specific differences in the action of the two viruses.

Along with the specific action of many substances one frequently finds "general toxic effects" or "non-specific mortality." As implied, these effects are noted in those in-dividuals which succumb to the treatment at a relatively early stage and usually show a uniformity regardless of the nature of the treatment. The more specific effects are found in the survivors. In early chick embryos, for example, one encounters a typical syndrome preceding death due to a variety of causes: the extraembryonic blood vessels break down and the entire embryo is retarded, with the head especially showing the retardation.

While the substances which produce such general effects may alter embryo metabolism in a specific manner, the visible effects show no specificities in these moribund embryos. In determining whether a given effect is specific one must very carefully consider the general toxic effects and use adequate controls. The non-specific symptoms of moribundity must be recognized so that they may not be confused with more specific effects.

EFFECTS OF DOSE

In general the greater the dose of a given treatment the greater will be its effect. This may be due to an increase in intensity of action at the time of application or to an increased duration of its action. Both of these points must be borne in mind in any discussion of critical periods. It is possible to subject an embryo to a treatment prior to the critical period for a structure, yet if the effects of the treatment persist long enough, it may include the critical stage for this structure. A more intense treatment may produce anomalies in a stage which does not respond to less intense treatment. Thus Job, Leibold and Fitzmaurice ('35) produced hydrocephalus and defects of the eyes and jaws in rats which had been exposed to x-rays during the ninth, tenth and eleventh days of gestation. Exposure of older embryos to the same dose did not produce any abnormalities. Warkany and Schraffenberger ('47), on the other hand, obtained some anomalies after irradiating with higher doses as late as the sixteenth day of gestation. There was a very high incidence as late as the fourteenth day after the intense treatment.

While it is true that many teratogenic agencies are most effective in doses which are toxic to a fairly high percentage of the treated embryos, one must not confuse the toxic effects with the teratogenic ones. There is ample evidence to show that the two are frequently separable. Ancel ('45c) has shown that the toxicity of some substances may increase without concomitant increase in teratogenicity. On the other hand Landauer and Bliss ('46) have shown that an increase in dose of insulin causes a relatively greater increase in the teratogenic effect than in toxicity. If one injects both sulfanilamide and nicotinamide into an egg, there is a much greater mortality than with the former alone (Zwilling and DeBell, '50). However, the micromelic effects of the sulfanilamide are eliminated.

RECOVERY

One of the factors involved in differences of response to the same treatment in a relatively homogeneous group of embryos is the ability of some of them to recover from the effects of the treatment sufficiently early for the affected structures to resume some semblance of normality. In some types of experiments recovery phenomena may be demonstrated by removing the embryos from the altered environment and placing them in a normal one. In such cases the degree of recovery is usually related to the duration of the treatment. Under certain conditions some of the effects of treatment may be alleviated by slowing down the metabolic rate of the exposed individuals shortly after the treatment. This was done by Cook ('39), who kept Ascaris eggs at low temperatures following a lethal x-ray treatment. On return to higher temperatures the lethal effects of the irradiation were not noted, although other effects (delayed cleavage) were still present. Child ('41) cites numerous instances in which recovery seems to be related to an acclimatization (differential acclimation or tolerance) to a toxic environment. It has been noted (Zwilling, '48) that chick embryos may have quite different patterns of hypoglycemia after treatment with the same dose of insulin. Some remain hypoglycemic for as long as 8 days, while others recover normal blood sugar levels at various intervals prior to this. The recovery is associated with a decrease in the micromelic effect of the insulin; embryos which recover early are less micromelic. Such differences in tolerance and ability to recover are probably related to genetic differences between individuals (see above).

RÉSUMÉ

In this chapter an endeavor has been made to show that aberrant development results from a distortion of normal developmental processes; that both genetic and environmental factors may be responsible for producing anomalies; and that the same developmental principles are involved in both. Terata may follow treatment of embryos with highly toxic foreign substances but also may result from dietary imbalance, blood factor incompatability, irradiations and action of disease-causing agents. The reaction of the embryo may depend not only on the stage at which it is subjected to the abnormal influence, but on the nature of the teratogenic agency, the length of time it is exposed, the physiological condition of the embryo and its resistance or susceptibility as determined by its genetic constitution. Similar anomalies may result from more than one developmental aberration.

Teratology is still at the stage where it is most concerned with the visible effects which are the expression of prior physiological disturbances. The next big step in studies of the etiology of anomalous development must concern itself with the details of these physiological processes.

REFERENCES

Ancel, P. 1945a L'achondroplasie. Sa réalisation expérimentale — sa pathogénie. Ann. d'Endocrinol., 6:1–24.

———— 1945b Sur l'action tératogène élective de certaines substances chimiques. Compt. Rend. Soc. Biol., 139:983–984.

———— 1945c Les variations individuelles dans les expériences de tératogènes. Rev. Sci., 83:99–106.

———— 1947 Sur la mise en évidence de différences individuelles dans la constitution des embryons par l'action associés de deux substances chimiques tératogènes. Compt. Rend. Soc. Biol., 141:208–209.

———— 1950 La chimiotératogenèse chez les Vertébrés. G. Doin et Cie, Paris.

Arey, L. B. 1954 Developmental Anatomy, 6th ed. W. B. Saunders Co., Philadelphia.

Asmundson, V. S. 1939 Some factors affecting hatchability of eggs. Poul. Sci., 18:399.

———— 1942 An inherited micromelia in the domestic fowl. J. Hered., 33:328–330.

Atlas, M. 1935 The effects of temperature on the development of Rana pipiens. Physiol. Zool., 8:290–310.

Bagg, H. J. 1929 Hereditary abnormalities of the limbs, their origin and transmission. II. A morphological study with special reference to the etiology of club-feet, syndactylism, hypodactylism, and congenital amputation in descendants of X-rayed mice. Am. J. Anat., 43:167–219.

Ballantyne, J. W. 1904 Manual of Antenatal Pathology and Hygiene. William Green & Sons, Edinburgh.

Baltzer, F. 1930 Über die Entwicklung des Tritonmerogons Triton taeniatus ♀ × cristatus ♂. Rev. suisse Zool., 37:325–332.

Barth, L. G. 1946 Studies on the metabolism of development. J. Exp. Zool., 103:463–486.

————, and Jaeger, L. 1947 Phosphorylation in the frog's egg. Physiol. Zool., 20:133–146.

Bodenstein, D. 1948 The effect of nitrogen mustard on embryonic amphibian development. II. Effects on eye development. J. Exp. Zool., 108:93–126.

————, and Kondritzer, A. A. 1948 The effect of nitrogen mustard on nucleic acids during embryonic amphibian development. J. Exp. Zool., 107:109–122.

Bonnevie, K. 1934 Embryological analysis of gene manifestation in Little and Bagg's abnormal mouse tribe. J. Exp. Zool., 67:443–520.

———— 1936 Abortive differentiation of the ear vesicles following a hereditary brain-anomaly in the "Short-tailed Waltzing Mice." Genetica, 18:105–125.

———— 1943 Hereditary hydrocephalus in the house mouse. I. Manifestations of the hy-mutation after birth and in embryos 12 days old or more. Skr. norske Vidensk Akad. Oslo, Mat.-Nat. Kl. No. 4, pp. 3–32.

Boyden, E. A. 1922 The development of the cloaca in birds with special reference to the origin of the bursa of Fabricius, the formation of the urodeal sinus, and the regular occurrence of a cloacal fenestra. Am. J. Anat., 30:163–202.

———— 1927 Experimental obstruction of the mesonephric ducts. Proc. Soc. Exp. Biol. & Med., 24:572–576.

Brachet, J. 1947a Embryologie Chimique. Masson et Cie, Paris.

———— 1947b Biochemical and physiological interrelations between nucleus and cytoplasm during early development. Growth, 11:309–324.

Briggs, R. W. 1941 The development of abnormal growths in Rana pipiens embryos following delayed fertilization. Anat. Rec., 81:121–135.

————, and Berrill, N. J. 1941 Transplantation experiments with an ectodermal growth of frog embryos. Growth, 5:273–284.

Byerly, T. C., Titus, H. W., Ellis, N. R., and Landauer, W. 1935 A new nutritional disease of the chick embryo. Proc. Soc. Exp. Biol. & Med., 32:1542–1546.

Caspari, E., and David, P. R. 1940 Inheritance of a tail abnormality in the house mouse. J. Hered., 31:427–431.

Chang, T. K. 1940 Cellular inclusions and phagocytosis in normal development of mouse embryos. Peking Nat. Hist. Bull., 14:159–170.

Chesley. P. 1935 Development of the short-tailed mutant in the house mouse. J. Exp. Zool., 70:429–459.

Child, C. M. 1941 Patterns and Problems of Development. University of Chicago Press, Chicago.

Cohen, A. 1938 Myotome fusion in the embryo of Amblystoma punctatum after treatment with lithium and other agents. J. Exp. Zool., 79:461–473.

Cook, E. V. 1939 Recovery of Ascaris eggs from X-rays. Radiol., 32:289–293.

Couch, J. R., Cravens, W. W., Elvehjem, C. A., and Halpin, J. G. 1948 Relation of biotin to congenital deformities in the chick. Anat Rec., 100:29–48.

Dharmarajan, M. 1950 Effect on the embryo of staleness of the sperm at the time of fertilization in the domestic hen. Nature, 165:398.

Dunn, L. C. 1925 The inheritance of rumplessness in the domestic fowl. J. Hered., 16:127–134.

Reed, S. C. 1937 The inheritance and expression of fused, a new mutation in the house mouse. Genetics, *22*:1–13.

Robertson, G. G. 1942 An analysis of the development of homozygous yellow mouse embryos. J. Exp. Zool., *89*:197–231.

Romanoff, A. L., and Bauernfeind, J. C. 1942 Influence of riboflavin deficiency in eggs on embryonic development (*Gallus domesticus*). Anat. Rec., *82*:11–21.

Rugh, R., and Exner, F. 1940 Developmental effects resulting from exposure to X-rays. II. Development of leopard frog eggs activated by bullfrog sperm. Proc. Am. Phil. Soc., *83*:607–619.

Russell, E. S., and Fondal, E. L. 1951 Quantitative analysis of normal and four alternative degrees of an inherited macrocytic anemia in the house mouse. J. Hematol., *6*:892–905.

Russell, L. B. 1950 X-ray induced developmental abnormalities in the mouse and their use in the analysis of embryological patterns. J. Exp. Zool., *114*:545–602.

Saunders, J. R., Jr. 1948 The proximo-distal sequence of origin of parts of the chick wing and the role of the ectoderm. J. Exp. Zool., *108*:363–404.

Schwalbe, E. 1906–37 Die Morphologie der Missbildungen des Menschen und der Tiere. G. Fischer, Jena.

Solberg, A. N. 1938 The susceptibility of *Fundulus heteroclitus* embryos to X-radiation. J. Exp. Zool., *78*:441–469.

Stockard, C. R. 1921 Developmental rate and structural expression: An experimental study of twins, "double monsters" and single deformities, and the interaction among embryonic organs during their origin and development. Am. J. Anat., *28*:115–277.

Streeter, G. L. 1930 Focal deficiencies in fetal tissues and their relation to intra-uterine amputation. Contributions to Embryology, Carnegie Institution of Washington, *22*:1–44.

———— 1931 Development of the egg as seen by the embryologist. Sci. Mon., *32*:495–506.

Sze, L. C. 1953 Respiration of the parts of the hybrid gastrula *Rana pipiens* × *R. sylvatica*. Science, *117*:479–480.

Torrey, T. W., and Breneman, W. R. 1941 Abnormalities in frog embryos induced by centrifugation. Proc. Ind. Acad. Sci., *50*:213–228.

Waddington, C. H., and Carter, T. C. 1952 Malformations in mouse embryo induced by Trypan blue. Nature, *169*:28–31.

Warkany, J., Nelson, R. C., and Schraffenberger, E. 1942 Congenital malformations induced in rats by maternal nutritional deficiency. II. Use of varied diets and of different strains of rats. Am. J. Dis. Children, *64*:860–866.

————, and Schraffenberger, E. 1943 Congenital malformations induced in rats by maternal nutritional deficiency. V. Effects of a purified diet lacking riboflavin. Proc. Soc. Exp. Biol. & Med., *54*:92–94.

————, and Schraffenberger, E. 1947 Congenital malformations induced in rats by Roentgen rays. Am. J. Roentgenol. & Rad. Ther., *57*:455–463.

Waters, N. F., and Bywaters, J. H. 1943 A lethal embryonic wing mutation in the domestic fowl. J. Hered., *34*:213–217.

Wilson, J. G., Brent, R. L., and Jordan, H. C. 1953 Differentiation as a determinant of the reaction of rat embryos to X-irradiation. Proc. Soc. Exp. Biol. & Med., *82*:67–70.

Witschi, E. 1922 Überreife der Eier als kausaler Faktor bei Entstehung von Mehrfachbildungen und Teratomen. Verh. der Naturforsch. Gesell. Basel, *34*:33–40.

———— 1930 Experimentally produced neoplasms in the frog. Proc. Soc. Exp. Biol. & Med., *27*:475–477.

———— 1934 Appearance of accessory "organizers" in overripe eggs of the frog. Proc. Soc. Exp. Biol. & Med., *31*:419–420.

Wolff, E. 1936 Les bases de la tératogénèse expérimentale, des vertébrés amniotes, d'après les résultats de méthodes directes. Arch. d'Anat., d'Histol. et d'Embryol., *22*:1–382.

———— 1948 La Science des Monstres. Gallimard, France.

Wright, S. 1934 An analysis of variability in number of digits in an inbred strain of guinea pigs. Genetics, *19*:506–536.

Zwilling, E. 1942 The development of dominant rumplessness in chick embryos. Genetics, *27*:641–656.

———— 1945a The embryogeny of a recessive rumpless condition of chickens. J. Exp. Zool., *99*:79–91.

———— 1945b Production of tail abnormalities in chick embryos by transecting the body during the latter part of the second day of incubation. J. Exp. Zool., *98*:237–247.

———— 1948 Association of hypoglycemia and insulin micromelia in chick embryos. J. Exp. Zool., *109*:197–214.

———— 1949 The role of epithelial components in the developmental origin of the "wingless" syndrome of chick embryos. J. Exp. Zool., *111*:175–187.

———— 1951 Carbohydrate metabolism in insulin-treated chick embryos. Arch. Biochem. & Biophys., *33*:228–242.

————, and DeBell, J. T. 1950 Micromelia and growth retardation as independent effects of sulfanilamide in chick embryos. J. Exp. Zool., *115*:59–82.